PEARSON   ALWAYS LEARNING

Engineering Mechanics

Custom Edition for Northwestern University

Taken From:
Engineering Mechanics: Statics & Dynamics, Fifth Edition
by Anthony Bedford and Wallace Fowler

Statics and Mechanics of Materials, Third Edition
by R.C. Hibbeler

Cover Art: *Zakim Bridge 1*, by S. Olsen/K. Mirza

Taken from:

Engineering Mechanics: Statics & Dynamics, Fifth Edition
by Anthony Bedford and Wallace Fowler
Copyright © 2008 by Pearson Education, Inc.
Published by Prentice Hall
Upper Saddle River, New Jersey 07458

Statics and Mechanics of Materials, Third Edition
by R.C. Hibbeler
Copyright © 2011, 2004 by Pearson Education, Inc.
Published by Prentice Hall

This special edition published in cooperation with Pearson Learning Solutions.

All trademarks, service marks, registered trademarks, and registered service marks are the property of their respective owners and are used herein for identification purposes only.

Pearson Learning Solutions, 501 Boylston Street, Suite 900, Boston, MA 02116
A Pearson Education Company
www.pearsoned.com

Printed in the United States of America

1 2 3 4 5 6 7 8 9 10 V0ZN 16 15 14 13 12 11

000200010271275083

SD

ISBN 10: 1-256-45398-6
ISBN 13: 978-1-256-45398-7

Contents

STATICS

Taken from: *Engineering Mechanics: Statics and Dynamics*, Fifth Edition by Anthony Bedford and Wallace Fowler.

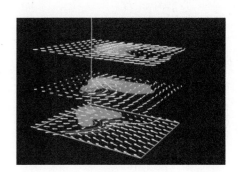

Taken from: *Statics and Mechanics of Materials*, Third Edition by R.C. Hibbeler.

MECHANICS OF MATERIALS

Taken from: *Engineering Mechanics: Statics and Dynamics*, Fifth Edition by Anthony Bedford and Wallace Fowler.

DYNAMICS

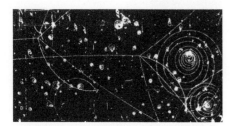

Engineering Mechanics
STATICS

Taken from: *Engineering Mechanics: Statics and Dynamics*, Fifth Edition
by Anthony Bedford and Wallace Fowler.

Introduction

How do engineers design and construct the devices we use, from simple objects such as chairs and pencil sharpeners to complicated ones such as dams, cars, airplanes, and spacecraft? They must have a deep understanding of the physics underlying the design of such devices and must be able to use mathematical models to predict their behavior. Students of engineering begin to learn how to analyze and predict the behaviors of physical systems by studying mechanics.

◀ Engineers are guided by the principles of statics during each step of the design and assembly of a structure. Statics is one of the sciences underlying the art of structural design.

1.1 Engineering and Mechanics

How can engineers design complex systems and predict their characteristics before they are constructed? Engineers have always relied on their knowledge of previous designs, experiments, ingenuity, and creativity to develop new designs. Modern engineers add a powerful technique: They develop mathematical equations based on the physical characteristics of the devices they design. With these mathematical models, engineers predict the behavior of their designs, modify them, and test them prior to their actual construction. Aerospace engineers use mathematical models to predict the paths the space shuttle will follow in flight. Civil engineers use mathematical models to analyze the effects of loads on buildings and foundations.

At its most basic level, mechanics is the study of forces and their effects. Elementary mechanics is divided into *statics*, the study of objects in equilibrium, and *dynamics*, the study of objects in motion. The results obtained in elementary mechanics apply directly to many fields of engineering. Mechanical and civil engineers designing structures use the equilibrium equations derived in statics. Civil engineers analyzing the responses of buildings to earthquakes and aerospace engineers determining the trajectories of satellites use the equations of motion derived in dynamics.

Mechanics was the first analytical science. As a result, fundamental concepts, analytical methods, and analogies from mechanics are found in virtually every field of engineering. Students of chemical and electrical engineering gain a deeper appreciation for basic concepts in their fields, such as equilibrium, energy, and stability, by learning them in their original mechanical contexts. By studying mechanics, they retrace the historical development of these ideas.

Mechanics consists of broad principles that govern the behavior of objects. In this book we describe these principles and provide examples that demonstrate some of their applications. Although it is essential that you practice working problems similar to these examples, and we include many problems of this kind, our objective is to help you understand the principles well enough to apply them to situations that are new to you. Each generation of engineers confronts new problems.

Problem Solving

In the study of mechanics you learn problem-solving procedures that you will use in succeeding courses and throughout your career. Although different types of problems require different approaches, the following steps apply to many of them:

- Identify the information that is given and the information, or answer, you must determine. It's often helpful to restate the problem in your own words. When appropriate, make sure you understand the physical system or model involved.

- Develop a *strategy* for the problem. This means identifying the principles and equations that apply and deciding how you will use them to solve the problem. Whenever possible, draw diagrams to help visualize and solve the problem.

- Whenever you can, try to predict the answer. This will develop your intuition and will often help you recognize an incorrect answer.

- Solve the equations and, whenever possible, interpret your results and compare them with your prediction. This last step is a *reality check*. Is your answer reasonable?

Numbers

Engineering measurements, calculations, and results are expressed in numbers. You need to know how we express numbers in the examples and problems and how to express the results of your own calculations.

Significant Digits   This term refers to the number of meaningful (that is, accurate) digits in a number, counting to the right starting with the first nonzero digit. The two numbers 7.630 and 0.007630 are each stated to four significant digits. If only the first four digits in the number 7,630,000 are known to be accurate, this can be indicated by writing the number in scientific notation as 7.630×10^6.

If a number is the result of a measurement, the significant digits it contains are limited by the accuracy of the measurement. If the result of a measurement is stated to be 2.43, this means that the actual value is believed to be closer to 2.43 than to 2.42 or 2.44.

Numbers may be rounded off to a certain number of significant digits. For example, we can express the value of π to three significant digits, 3.14, or we can express it to six significant digits, 3.14159. When you use a calculator or computer, the number of significant digits is limited by the number of digits the machine is designed to carry.

Use of Numbers in This Book   You should treat numbers given in problems as exact values and not be concerned about how many significant digits they contain. If a problem states that a quantity equals 32.2, you can assume its value is 32.200. ... We generally express intermediate results and answers in the examples and the answers to the problems to at least three significant digits. If you use a calculator, your results should be that accurate. Be sure to avoid round-off errors that occur if you round off intermediate results when making a series of calculations. Instead, carry through your calculations with as much accuracy as you can by retaining values in your calculator.

Space and Time

Space simply refers to the three-dimensional universe in which we live. Our daily experiences give us an intuitive notion of space and the locations, or positions, of points in space. The distance between two points in space is the length of the straight line joining them.

Measuring the distance between points in space requires a unit of length. We use both the International System of units, or SI units, and U.S. Customary units. In SI units, the unit of length is the meter (m). In U.S. Customary units, the unit of length is the foot (ft).

Time is, of course, familiar—our lives are measured by it. The daily cycles of light and darkness and the hours, minutes, and seconds measured by our clocks and watches give us an intuitive notion of time. Time is measured by the intervals between repeatable events, such as the swings of a clock pendulum or the vibrations of a quartz crystal in a watch. In both SI units and U.S. Customary units, the unit of time is the second (s). The minute (min), hour (h), and day are also frequently used.

If the position of a point in space relative to some reference point changes with time, the rate of change of its position is called its *velocity*, and the rate of change of its velocity is called its *acceleration*. In SI units, the velocity is expressed in meters per second (m/s) and the acceleration is expressed in meters per second per second, or meters per second squared (m/s^2). In U.S.

Customary units, the velocity is expressed in feet per second (ft/s) and the acceleration is expressed in feet per second squared (ft/s^2).

Newton's Laws

Elementary mechanics was established on a firm basis with the publication in 1687 of *Philosophiae Naturalis Principia Mathematica*, by Isaac Newton. Although highly original, it built on fundamental concepts developed by many others during a long and difficult struggle toward understanding (Fig. 1.1).

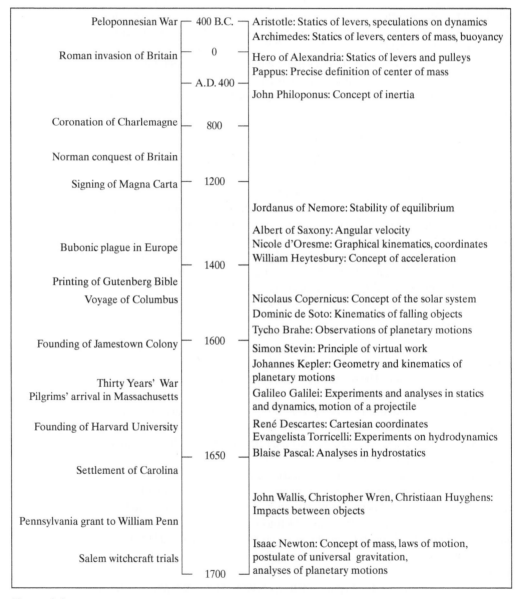

Figure 1.1

Chronology of developments in mechanics up to the publication of Newton's *Principia* in relation to other events in history.

Newton stated three "laws" of motion, which we express in modern terms:

1. *When the sum of the forces acting on a particle is zero, its velocity is constant. In particular, if the particle is initially stationary, it will remain stationary.*

2. *When the sum of the forces acting on a particle is not zero, the sum of the forces is equal to the rate of change of the linear momentum of the particle. If the mass is constant, the sum of the forces is equal to the product of the mass of the particle and its acceleration.*

3. *The forces exerted by two particles on each other are equal in magnitude and opposite in direction.*

Notice that we did not define force and mass before stating Newton's laws. The modern view is that these terms are defined by the second law. To demonstrate, suppose that we choose an arbitrary object and define it to have unit mass. Then we define a unit of force to be the force that gives our unit mass an acceleration of unit magnitude. In principle, we can then determine the mass of any object: We apply a unit force to it, measure the resulting acceleration, and use the second law to determine the mass. We can also determine the magnitude of any force: We apply it to our unit mass, measure the resulting acceleration, and use the second law to determine the force.

Thus Newton's second law gives precise meanings to the terms *mass* and *force*. In SI units, the unit of mass is the kilogram (kg). The unit of force is the newton (N), which is the force required to give a mass of one kilogram an acceleration of one meter per second squared. In U.S. Customary units, the unit of force is the pound (lb). The unit of mass is the slug, which is the amount of mass accelerated at one foot per second squared by a force of one pound.

Although the results we discuss in this book are applicable to many of the problems met in engineering practice, there are limits to the validity of Newton's laws. For example, they don't give accurate results if a problem involves velocities that are not small compared to the velocity of light (3×10^8 m/s). Einstein's special theory of relativity applies to such problems. Elementary mechanics also fails in problems involving dimensions that are not large compared to atomic dimensions. Quantum mechanics must be used to describe phenomena on the atomic scale.

International System of Units

In SI units, length is measured in meters (m) and mass in kilograms (kg). Time is measured in seconds (s), although other familiar measures such as minutes (min), hours (h), and days are also used when convenient. Meters, kilograms, and seconds are called the *base units* of the SI system. Force is measured in newtons (N). Recall that these units are related by Newton's second law: One newton is the force required to give an object of one kilogram mass an acceleration of one meter per second squared:

$$1 \text{ N} = (1 \text{ kg})(1 \text{ m/s}^2) = 1 \text{ kg-m/s}^2.$$

Because the newton can be expressed in terms of the base units, it is called a *derived unit*.

To express quantities by numbers of convenient size, multiples of units are indicated by prefixes. The most common prefixes, their abbreviations, and the multiples they represent are shown in Table 1.1. For example, 1 km is 1 kilometer, which is 1000 m, and 1 Mg is 1 megagram, which is 10^6 g, or 1000 kg. We frequently use kilonewtons (kN).

Table 1.1   The common prefixes used in SI units and the multiples they represent.

Prefix	Abbreviation	Multiple
nano-	n	10^{-9}
micro-	μ	10^{-6}
milli-	m	10^{-3}
kilo-	k	10^3
mega-	M	10^6
giga-	G	10^9

U.S. Customary Units

In U.S. Customary units, length is measured in feet (ft) and force is measured in pounds (lb). Time is measured in seconds (s). These are the base units of the U.S. Customary system. In this system of units, mass is a derived unit. The unit of mass is the slug, which is the mass of material accelerated at one foot per second squared by a force of one pound. Newton's second law states that

$$1 \text{ lb} = (1 \text{ slug})(1 \text{ ft/s}^2).$$

From this expression we obtain

$$1 \text{ slug} = 1 \text{ lb-s}^2/\text{ft}.$$

We use other U.S. Customary units such as the mile (1 mi = 5280 ft) and the inch (1 ft = 12 in). We also use the kilopound (kip), which is 1000 lb.

Angular Units

In both SI and U.S. Customary units, angles are normally expressed in radians (rad). We show the value of an angle θ in radians in Fig. 1.2. It is defined to be the ratio of the part of the circumference subtended by θ to the radius of the circle. Angles are also expressed in degrees. Since there are 360 degrees (360°) in a complete circle, and the complete circumference of the circle is $2\pi R$, 360° equals 2π rad.

Equations containing angles are nearly always derived under the assumption that angles are expressed in radians. Therefore, when you want to substitute the value of an angle expressed in degrees into an equation, you should first convert it into radians. A notable exception to this rule is that many calculators are designed to accept angles expressed in either degrees or radians when you use them to evaluate functions such as sin θ.

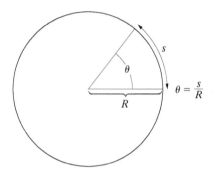

Figure 1.2
Definition of an angle in radians.

Conversion of Units

Many situations arise in engineering practice that require values expressed in one kind of unit to be converted into values in other units. For example, if some of the data to be used in an equation are given in SI units and some are given in U.S. Customary units, they must all be expressed in terms of one system of units before they are substituted into the equation. Converting units is straightforward, although it must be done with care.

Suppose that we want to express 1 mile per hour (mi/h) in terms of feet per second (ft/s). Because 1 mile equals 5280 feet and 1 hour equals 3600 seconds, we can treat the expressions

$$\left(\frac{5280 \text{ ft}}{1 \text{ mi}}\right) \quad \text{and} \quad \left(\frac{1 \text{ h}}{3600 \text{ s}}\right)$$

as ratios whose values are 1. In this way, we obtain

$$1 \text{ mi/h} = (1 \text{ mi/h})\left(\frac{5280 \text{ ft}}{1 \text{ mi}}\right)\left(\frac{1 \text{ h}}{3600 \text{ s}}\right) = 1.47 \text{ ft/s}.$$

Some useful unit conversions are given in Table 1.2.

Table 1.2 Unit conversions.

Time	1 minute	=	60 seconds
	1 hour	=	60 minutes
	1 day	=	24 hours
Length	1 foot	=	12 inches
	1 mile	=	5280 feet
	1 inch	=	25.4 millimeters
	1 foot	=	0.3048 meters
Angle	2π radians	=	360 degrees
Mass	1 slug	=	14.59 kilograms
Force	1 pound	=	4.448 newtons

RESULTS

- Identify the given information and the answer that must be determined.
- Develop a strategy; identify principles and equations that apply and how they will be used.
- Try to predict the answer whenever possible.
- Obtain the answer and, whenever possible, interpret it and compare it with the prediction.

Problem Solving: These steps apply to many types of problems.

SI Units—The *base units* are time in seconds (s), length in meters (m), and mass in kilograms (kg). The unit of force is the newton (N), which is the force required to accelerate a mass of one kilogram at one meter per second squared.

U.S. Customary Units—The base units are time in seconds (s), length in feet (ft), and force in pounds (lb). The unit of mass is the slug, which is the mass accelerated at one foot per second squared by a force of one pound.

Systems of units.

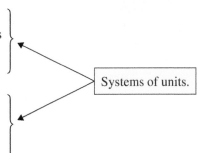

$\theta = \dfrac{s}{R}$

Definition of an angle in radians.

Equivalent quantities, such as 1 hour = 60 minutes, can be written as ratios whose values are 1:

$$\left(\frac{1\text{ h}}{60\text{ min}}\right) = 1,$$

and used to convert units. For example,

$$15\text{ min} = 15\text{ min}\left(\frac{1\text{ h}}{60\text{ min}}\right) = 0.25\text{ h}.$$

Conversion of units.

A comprehensive resource on units has been compiled by Russ Rowlett of the University of North Carolina at Chapel Hill and made available online at www.unc.edu/~rowlett/units.

Active Example 1.1 **Converting Units** (▶ *Related Problem 1.11*)

A man is riding a bicycle at a speed of 6 meters per second (m/s). How fast is he going in kilometers per hour (km/h)?

Strategy
One kilometer is 1000 meters and one hour is 60 minutes × 60 seconds = 3600 seconds. We can use these unit conversions to determine his speed in km/h.

Solution

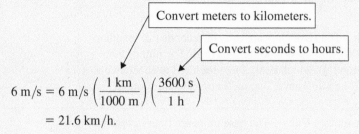

Convert meters to kilometers.

Convert seconds to hours.

$$6 \text{ m/s} = 6 \text{ m/s} \left(\frac{1 \text{ km}}{1000 \text{ m}} \right) \left(\frac{3600 \text{ s}}{1 \text{ h}} \right)$$
$$= 21.6 \text{ km/h}.$$

Practice Problem A man is riding a bicycle at a speed of 10 feet per second (ft/s). How fast is he going in miles per hour (mi/h)?
Answer: 6.82 mi/h.

Example 1.2 **Converting Units of Pressure** (▶ *Related Problem 1.16*)

Deep Submersible Vehicle.

The pressure exerted at a point of the hull of the deep submersible vehicle is 3.00×10^6 Pa (pascals). A pascal is 1 newton per square meter. Determine the pressure in pounds per square foot.

Strategy
From Table 1.2, 1 pound = 4.448 newtons and 1 foot = 0.3048 meters. With these unit conversions we can calculate the pressure in pounds per square foot.

Solution
The pressure (to three significant digits) is

$$3.00 \times 10^6 \text{ N/m}^2 = (3.00 \times 10^6 \text{ N/m}^2) \left(\frac{1 \text{ lb}}{4.448 \text{ N}} \right) \left(\frac{0.3048 \text{ m}}{1 \text{ ft}} \right)^2$$
$$= 62{,}700 \text{ lb/ft}^2.$$

Critical Thinking
How could we have obtained this result in a more direct way? Notice from the table of unit conversions in the inside front cover that 1 Pa = 0.0209 lb/ft². Therefore,

$$3.00 \times 10^6 \text{ N/m}^2 = (3.00 \times 10^6 \text{ N/m}^2) \left(\frac{0.0209 \text{ lb/ft}^2}{1 \text{ N/m}^2} \right)$$
$$= 62{,}700 \text{ lb/ft}^2.$$

Example 1.3   **Determining Units from an Equation** (▶ *Related Problem 1.20*)

Suppose that in Einstein's equation

$$E = mc^2,$$

the mass m is in kilograms and the velocity of light c is in meters per second.

(a) What are the SI units of E?
(b) If the value of E in SI units is 20, what is its value in U.S. Customary base units?

Strategy

(a) Since we know the units of the terms m and c, we can deduce the units of E from the given equation.
(b) We can use the unit conversions for mass and length from Table 1.2 to convert E from SI units to U.S. Customary units.

Solution

(a) From the equation for E,

$$E = (m \text{ kg})(c \text{ m/s})^2,$$

the SI units of E are kg-m^2/s^2.

(b) From Table 1.2, 1 slug = 14.59 kg and 1 ft = 0.3048 m. Therefore,

$$1 \text{ kg-m}^2/\text{s}^2 = (1 \text{ kg-m}^2/\text{s}^2)\left(\frac{1 \text{ slug}}{14.59 \text{ kg}}\right)\left(\frac{1 \text{ ft}}{0.3048 \text{ m}}\right)^2$$

$$= 0.738 \text{ slug-ft}^2/\text{s}^2.$$

The value of E in U.S. Customary units is

$$E = (20)(0.738) = 14.8 \text{ slug-ft}^2/\text{s}^2.$$

Critical Thinking

In part (a), how did we know that we could determine the units of E by determining the units of mc^2? The dimensions, or units, of each term in an equation must be the same. For example, in the equation $a + b = c$, the dimensions of each of the terms a, b, and c must be the same. The equation is said to be *dimensionally homogeneous*. This requirement is expressed by the colloquial phrase "Don't compare apples and oranges."

Problems

1.1 The value of π is 3.14159265.... If C is the circumference of a circle and r is its radius, determine the value of r/C to four significant digits.

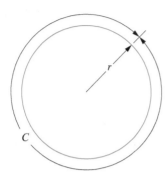

Problem 1.1

1.2 The base of natural logarithms is $e = 2.718281828....$

(a) Express e to five significant digits.

(b) Determine the value of e^2 to five significant digits.

(c) Use the value of e you obtained in part (a) to determine the value of e^2 to five significant digits.

[Part (c) demonstrates the hazard of using rounded-off values in calculations.]

1.3 A machinist drills a circular hole in a panel with a nominal radius $r = 5$ mm. The actual radius of the hole is in the range $r = 5 \pm 0.01$ mm.

(a) To what number of significant digits can you express the radius?

(b) To what number of significant digits can you express the area of the hole?

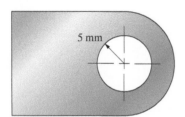

5 mm

Problem 1.3

1.4 The opening in the soccer goal is 24 ft wide and 8 ft high, so its area is 24 ft $\times$ 8 ft = 192 ft^2. What is its area in m^2 to three significant digits?

Problem 1.4

1.5 The Burj Dubai, scheduled for completion in 2008, will be the world's tallest building with a height of 705 m. The area of its ground footprint will be 8000 m^2. Convert its height and footprint area to U.S. Customary units to three significant digits.

Problem 1.5

1.6 Suppose that you have just purchased a Ferrari F355 coupe and you want to know whether you can use your set of SAE (U.S. Customary unit) wrenches to work on it. You have wrenches with widths $w = 1/4$ in, $1/2$ in, $3/4$ in, and 1 in, and the car has nuts with dimensions $n = 5$ mm, 10 mm, 15 mm, 20 mm, and 25 mm. Defining a wrench to fit if w is no more than 2% larger than n, which of your wrenches can you use?

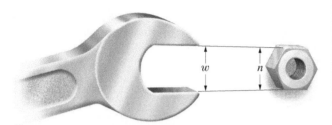

Problem 1.6

1.7 Suppose that the height of Mt. Everest is known to be between 29,032 ft and 29,034 ft. Based on this information, to how many significant digits can you express the height (a) in feet? (b) in meters?

1.8 The maglev (magnetic levitation) train from Shanghai to the airport at Pudong reaches a speed of 430 km/h. Determine its speed (a) in mi/h; (b) in ft/s.

Problem 1.8

1.9 In the 2006 Winter Olympics, the men's 15-km cross-country skiing race was won by Andrus Veerpalu of Estonia in a time of 38 minutes, 1.3 seconds. Determine his average speed (the distance traveled divided by the time required) to three significant digits (a) in km/h; (b) in mi/h.

1.10 The Porsche's engine exerts 229 ft-lb (foot-pounds) of torque at 4600 rpm. Determine the value of the torque in N-m (newton-meters).

Problem 1.10

▶ **1.11** The *kinetic energy* of the man in Active Example 1.1 is defined by $\frac{1}{2}mv^2$, where m is his mass and v is his velocity. The man's mass is 68 kg and he is moving at 6 m/s, so his kinetic energy is $\frac{1}{2}(68 \text{ kg})(6 \text{ m/s})^2 = 1224 \text{ kg-m}^2/\text{s}^2$. What is his kinetic energy in U.S. Customary units?

1.12 The acceleration due to gravity at sea level in SI units is $g = 9.81 \text{ m/s}^2$. By converting units, use this value to determine the acceleration due to gravity at sea level in U.S. Customary units.

1.13 A *furlong per fortnight* is a facetious unit of velocity, perhaps made up by a student as a satirical comment on the bewildering variety of units engineers must deal with. A furlong is 660 ft (1/8 mile). A fortnight is 2 weeks (14 nights). If you walk to class at 2 m/s, what is your speed in furlongs per fortnight to three significant digits?

1.14 Determine the cross-sectional area of the beam (a) in m^2; (b) in in^2.

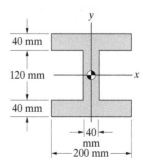

Problem 1.14

1.15 The cross-sectional area of the C12×30 American Standard Channel steel beam is $A = 8.81$ in^2. What is its cross-sectional area in mm^2?

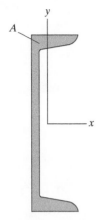

Problem 1.15

▶ **1.16** A pressure transducer measures a value of 300 lb/in^2. Determine the value of the pressure in pascals. A pascal (Pa) is one newton per square meter.

1.17 A horsepower is 550 ft-lb/s. A watt is 1 N-m/s. Determine how many watts are generated by the engines of the passenger jet if they are producing 7000 horsepower.

Problem 1.17

1.18 Chapter 7 discusses distributed loads that are expressed in units of force per unit length. If the value of a distributed load is 400 N/m, what is its value in lb/ft?

1.19 The moment of inertia of the rectangular area about the x axis is given by the equation

$$I = \tfrac{1}{3}bh^3.$$

The dimensions of the area are $b = 200$ mm and $h = 100$ mm. Determine the value of I to four significant digits in terms of (a) mm^4, (b) m^4, and (c) in^4.

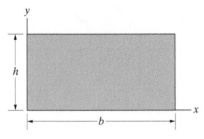

Problem 1.19

▶ **1.20** In Example 1.3, instead of Einstein's equation consider the equation $L = mc$, where the mass m is in kilograms and the velocity of light c is in meters per second. (a) What are the SI units of L? (b) If the value of L in SI units is 12, what is its value in U.S. Customary base units?

1.21 The equation

$$\sigma = \frac{My}{I}$$

is used in the mechanics of materials to determine normal stresses in beams.

(a) When this equation is expressed in terms of SI base units, M is in newton-meters (N-m), y is in meters (m), and I is in meters to the fourth power (m^4). What are the SI units of σ?
(b) If $M = 2000$ N-m, $y = 0.1$ m, and $I = 7 \times 10^{-5}$ m^4, what is the value of σ in U.S. Customary base units?

1.2 Newtonian Gravitation

BACKGROUND

Newton postulated that the gravitational force between two particles of mass m_1 and m_2 that are separated by a distance r (Fig. 1.3) is

$$F = \frac{Gm_1m_2}{r^2},\tag{1.1}$$

where G is called the universal gravitational constant. The value of G in SI units is 6.67×10^{-11} N-m²/kg². Based on this postulate, he calculated the gravitational force between a particle of mass m_1 and a homogeneous sphere of mass m_2 and found that it is also given by Eq. (1.1), with r denoting the distance from the particle to the center of the sphere. Although the earth is not a homogeneous sphere, we can use this result to approximate the weight of an object of mass m due to the gravitational attraction of the earth. We have

$$W = \frac{Gmm_E}{r^2},\tag{1.2}$$

where m_E is the mass of the earth and r is the distance from the center of the earth to the object. Notice that the weight of an object depends on its location relative to the center of the earth, whereas the mass of the object is a measure of the amount of matter it contains and doesn't depend on its position.

When an object's weight is the only force acting on it, the resulting acceleration is called the acceleration due to gravity. In this case, Newton's second law states that $W = ma$, and from Eq. (1.2) we see that the acceleration due to gravity is

$$a = \frac{Gm_E}{r^2}.\tag{1.3}$$

The *acceleration due to gravity at sea level* is denoted by g. Denoting the radius of the earth by R_E, we see from Eq. (1.3) that $Gm_E = gR_E^2$. Substituting this result into Eq. (1.3), we obtain an expression for the acceleration due to gravity at a distance r from the center of the earth in terms of the acceleration due to gravity at sea level:

$$a = g\frac{R_E^2}{r^2}.\tag{1.4}$$

Since the weight of the object $W = ma$, the weight of an object at a distance r from the center of the earth is

$$W = mg\frac{R_E^2}{r^2}.\tag{1.5}$$

At sea level $(r = R_E)$, the weight of an object is given in terms of its mass by the simple relation

$$W = mg.\tag{1.6}$$

The value of g varies from location to location on the surface of the earth. The values we use in examples and problems are $g = 9.81$ m/s² in SI units and $g = 32.2$ ft/s² in U.S. Customary units.

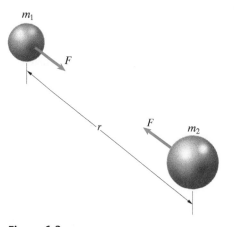

Figure 1.3
The gravitational forces between two particles are equal in magnitude and directed along the line between them.

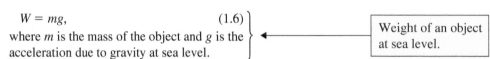
RESULTS

The gravitational force between two particles of mass m_1 and m_2 that are separated by a distance r is

$$F = \frac{Gm_1m_2}{r^2}, \qquad (1.1)$$

where G is the universal gravitational constant. The value of G in SI units is

$$6.67 \times 10^{-11} \text{ N-m}^2/\text{kg}^2.$$

> Newtonian gravitation.

When the earth is modeled as a homogeneous sphere of radius R_E, the acceleration due to gravity at a distance r from the center is

$$a = g\frac{R_E^2}{r^2}, \qquad (1.4)$$

where g is the acceleration due to gravity at sea level.

> Acceleration due to gravity of the earth.

$$W = mg, \qquad (1.6)$$

where m is the mass of the object and g is the acceleration due to gravity at sea level.

> Weight of an object at sea level.

Active Example 1.4 **Weight and Mass** (▶ *Related Problem 1.22*)

The C-clamp weighs 14 oz at sea level. [16 oz (ounces) = 1 lb.] The acceleration due to gravity at sea level is $g = 32.2$ ft/s². What is the mass of the C-clamp in slugs?

Strategy
We must first determine the weight of the C-clamp in pounds. Then we can use Eq. (1.6) to determine the mass in slugs.

Solution

$$14 \text{ oz} = 14 \text{ oz} \left(\frac{1 \text{ lb}}{16 \text{ oz}}\right) = 0.875 \text{ lb.}$$

> Convert the weight from ounces to pounds.

$$m = \frac{W}{g} = \frac{0.875 \text{ lb}}{32.2 \text{ ft/s}^2} = 0.0272 \text{ slug.}$$

> Use Eq. (1.6) to calculate the mass in slugs.

Practice Problem The mass of the C-clamp is 0.397 kg. The acceleration due to gravity at sea level is $g = 9.81$ m/s². What is the weight of the C-clamp at sea level in newtons?

Answer: 3.89 N.

Example 1.5   Determining an Object's Weight (▶ *Related Problem 1.27*)

When the Mars Exploration Rover was fully assembled, its mass was 180 kg. The acceleration due to gravity at the surface of Mars is 3.68 m/s^2 and the radius of Mars is 3390 km.

(a) What was the rover's weight when it was at sea level on Earth?

(b) What is the rover's weight on the surface of Mars?

(c) The entry phase began when the spacecraft reached the Mars atmospheric entry interface point at 3522 km from the center of Mars. What was the rover's weight at that point?

Mars Exploration Rover being assembled.

Strategy

The rover's weight at sea level on Earth is given by Eq. (1.6) with $g = 9.81$ m/s^2.

We can determine the weight on the surface of Mars by using Eq. (1.6) with the acceleration due to gravity equal to 3.68 m/s^2.

To determine the rover's weight as it began the entry phase, we can write an equation for Mars equivalent to Eq. (1.5).

Solution

(a) The weight at sea level on Earth is

$$W = mg$$
$$= (180\text{ kg})(9.81\text{ m/s}^2)$$
$$= 1770\text{ N }(397\text{ lb}).$$

(b) Let $g_M = 3.68$ m/s^2 be the acceleration due to gravity at the surface of Mars. Then the weight of the rover on the surface of Mars is

$$W = mg_M$$
$$= (180\text{ kg})(3.68\text{ m/s}^2)$$
$$= 662\text{ N }(149\text{ lb}).$$

(c) Let $R_M = 3390$ km be the radius of Mars. From Eq. (1.5), the rover's weight when it is 3522 km above the center of Mars is

$$W = mg_M\frac{R_M^2}{r^2}$$
$$= (180\text{ kg})(3.68\text{ m/s}^2)\frac{(3,390,000\text{ m})^2}{(3,522,000\text{ m})^2}$$
$$= 614\text{ N }(138\text{ lb}).$$

Critical Thinking

In part (c), how did we know that we could apply Eq. (1.5) to Mars? Equation (1.5) is applied to Earth based on modeling it as a homogeneous sphere. It can be applied to other celestial objects under the same assumption. The accuracy of the results depends on how aspherical and inhomogeneous the object is.

Problems

▶ **1.22** The acceleration due to gravity on the surface of the moon is 1.62 m/s². (a) What would the mass of the C-clamp in Active Example 1.4 be on the surface of the moon? (b) What would the weight of the C-clamp in newtons be on the surface of the moon?

1.23 The 1 ft × 1 ft × 1 ft cube of iron weighs 490 lb at sea level. Determine the weight in newtons of a 1 m × 1 m × 1 m cube of the same material at sea level.

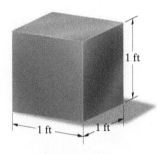

1 ft

1 ft

1 ft

Problem 1.23

1.24 The area of the Pacific Ocean is 64,186,000 square miles and its average depth is 12,925 ft. Assume that the weight per unit volume of ocean water is 64 lb/ft³. Determine the mass of the Pacific Ocean (a) in slugs; (b) in kilograms.

1.25 The acceleration due to gravity at sea level is $g = 9.81$ m/s². The radius of the earth is 6370 km. The universal gravitational constant $G = 6.67 \times 10^{-11}$ N-m²/kg². Use this information to determine the mass of the earth.

1.26 A person weighs 180 lb at sea level. The radius of the earth is 3960 mi. What force is exerted on the person by the gravitational attraction of the earth if he is in a space station in orbit 200 mi above the surface of the earth?

▶ **1.27** The acceleration due to gravity on the surface of the moon is 1.62 m/s². The moon's radius is $R_M = 1738$ km. (See Example 1.5.)

(a) What is the weight in newtons on the surface of the moon of an object that has a mass of 10 kg?

(b) Using the approach described in Example 1.5, determine the force exerted on the object by the gravity of the moon if the object is located 1738 km above the moon's surface.

1.28 If an object is near the surface of the earth, the variation of its weight with distance from the center of the earth can often be neglected. The acceleration due to gravity at sea level is $g = 9.81$ m/s². The radius of the earth is 6370 km. The weight of an object at sea level is mg, where m is its mass. At what height above the surface of the earth does the weight of the object decrease to $0.99mg$?

1.29 The planet Neptune has an equatorial diameter of 49,532 km and its mass is 1.0247×10^{26} kg. If the planet is modeled as a homogeneous sphere, what is the acceleration due to gravity at its surface? (The universal gravitational constant is $G = 6.67 \times 10^{-11}$ N-m²/kg².)

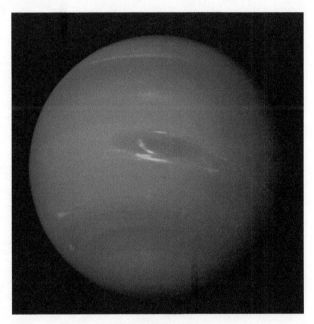

Problem 1.29

1.30 At a point between the earth and the moon, the magnitude of the force exerted on an object by the earth's gravity equals the magnitude of the force exerted on the object by the moon's gravity. What is the distance from the center of the earth to that point to three significant digits? The distance from the center of the earth to the center of the moon is 383,000 km, and the radius of the earth is 6370 km. The radius of the moon is 1738 km, and the acceleration due to gravity at its surface is 1.62 m/s².

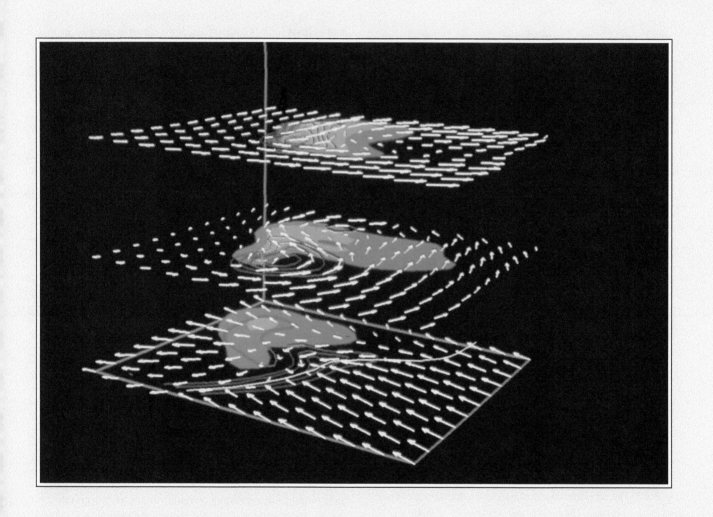

CHAPTER

2

Vectors

If an object is subjected to several forces that have different magnitudes and act in different directions, how can the magnitude and direction of the resulting total force on the object be determined? Forces are vectors and must be added according to the definition of vector addition. In engineering we deal with many quantities that have both magnitude and direction and can be expressed and analyzed as vectors. In this chapter we review vector operations, express vectors in terms of components, and present examples of engineering applications of vectors.

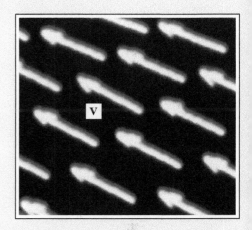

◀ Fields of vectors show the velocities and directions of a gas flow at three vertical positions. Vectors are used to describe and analyze quantities that have magnitude and direction, including positions, forces, moments, velocities, and accelerations.

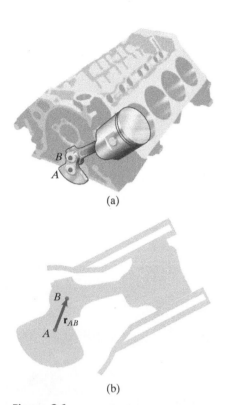

(a)

(b)

Figure 2.1
(**a**) Two points *A* and *B* of a mechanism.
(**b**) The vector $\mathbf{r}_{AB}$ from *A* to *B*.

Figure 2.2
Representing the force cable *AB* exerts on
the tower by a vector **F**.

2.1 Scalars and Vectors

BACKGROUND

A physical quantity that is completely described by a real number is called a *scalar*. Time is a scalar quantity. Mass is also a scalar quantity. For example, you completely describe the mass of a car by saying that its value is 1200 kg.

In contrast, you have to specify both a nonnegative real number, or *magnitude*, and a direction to describe a vector quantity. Two vector quantities are equal only if both their magnitudes and their directions are equal.

The position of a point in space relative to another point is a vector quantity. To describe the location of a city relative to your home, it is not enough to say that it is 100 miles away. You must say that it is 100 miles west of your home. Force is also a vector quantity. When you push a piece of furniture across the floor, you apply a force of magnitude sufficient to move the furniture and you apply it in the direction you want the furniture to move.

We will represent vectors by boldfaced letters, **U**, **V**, **W**, ..., and will denote the magnitude of a vector **U** by $|\mathbf{U}|$. A vector is represented graphically by an arrow. The direction of the arrow indicates the direction of the vector, and the length of the arrow is defined to be proportional to the magnitude. For example, consider the points *A* and *B* of the mechanism in Fig. 2.1a. We can specify the position of point *B* relative to point *A* by the vector $\mathbf{r}_{AB}$ in Fig. 2.1b. The direction of $\mathbf{r}_{AB}$ indicates the direction from point *A* to point *B*. If the distance between the two points is 200 mm, the magnitude $|\mathbf{r}_{AB}| = 200$ mm.

The cable *AB* in Fig. 2.2 helps support the television transmission tower. We can represent the force the cable exerts on the tower by a vector **F** as shown. If the cable exerts an 800-N force on the tower, $|\mathbf{F}| = 800$ N. (A cable suspended in this way will exhibit some sag, or curvature, and the tension will vary along its length. For now, we assume that the curvature in suspended cables and ropes and the variations in their tensions can be neglected. This assumption is approximately valid if the weight of the rope or cable is small in comparison to the tension. We discuss and analyze suspended cables and ropes in more detail in Chapter 10.)

Vectors are a convenient means for representing physical quantities that have magnitude and direction, but that is only the beginning of their usefulness. Just as real numbers are manipulated with the familiar rules for addition, subtraction, multiplication, and so forth, there are rules for manipulating vectors. These rules provide powerful tools for engineering analysis.

Vector Addition

When an object moves from one location in space to another, we say it undergoes a *displacement*. If we move a book (or, speaking more precisely, some point of a book) from one location on a table to another, as shown in Fig. 2.3a, we can represent the displacement by the vector **U**. The direction of **U** indicates the direction of the displacement, and $|\mathbf{U}|$ is the distance the book moves.

Suppose that we give the book a second displacement **V**, as shown in Fig. 2.3b. The two displacements **U** and **V** are equivalent to a single displacement of the book from its initial position to its final position, which we represent by the vector **W** in Fig. 2.3c. Notice that the final position of the book is the same whether we first give it the displacement **U** and then the displacement **V** or we first give it the displacement **V** and then the displacement **U** (Fig. 2.3d). The displacement **W** is defined to be the sum of the displacements **U** and **V**:

$$\mathbf{U} + \mathbf{V} = \mathbf{W}.$$

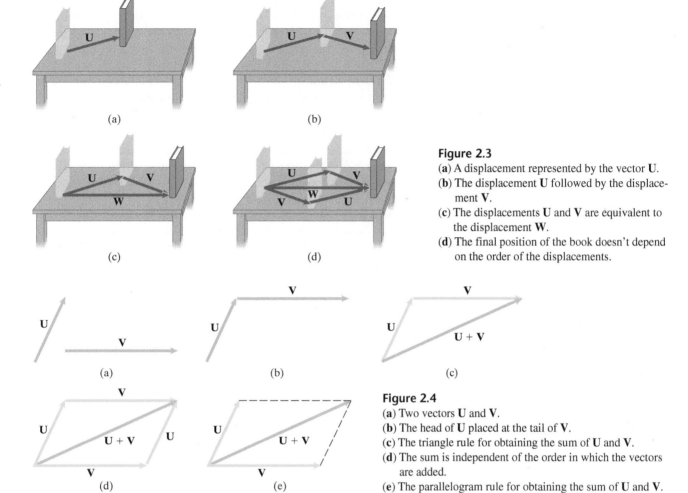

Figure 2.3
(**a**) A displacement represented by the vector **U**.
(**b**) The displacement **U** followed by the displacement **V**.
(**c**) The displacements **U** and **V** are equivalent to the displacement **W**.
(**d**) The final position of the book doesn't depend on the order of the displacements.

Figure 2.4
(**a**) Two vectors **U** and **V**.
(**b**) The head of **U** placed at the tail of **V**.
(**c**) The triangle rule for obtaining the sum of **U** and **V**.
(**d**) The sum is independent of the order in which the vectors are added.
(**e**) The parallelogram rule for obtaining the sum of **U** and **V**.

The definition of vector addition is motivated by the addition of displacements. Consider the two vectors **U** and **V** shown in Fig. 2.4a. If we place them head to tail (Fig. 2.4b), their sum is defined to be the vector from the tail of **U** to the head of **V** (Fig. 2.4c). This is called the *triangle rule* for vector addition. Figure 2.4d demonstrates that the sum is independent of the order in which the vectors are placed head to tail. From this figure we obtain the *parallelogram rule* for vector addition (Fig. 2.4e).

The definition of vector addition implies that

$$\mathbf{U} + \mathbf{V} = \mathbf{V} + \mathbf{U} \quad \text{Vector addition is commutative.} \tag{2.1}$$

and

$$(\mathbf{U} + \mathbf{V}) + \mathbf{W} = \mathbf{U} + (\mathbf{V} + \mathbf{W}) \quad \text{Vector addition is associative.} \tag{2.2}$$

for any vectors **U**, **V**, and **W**. These results mean that when two or more vectors are added, the order in which they are added doesn't matter. The sum can be obtained by placing the vectors head to tail in any order, and the vector from the tail of the first vector to the head of the last one is the sum (Fig. 2.5). If the sum of two or more vectors is zero, they form a closed polygon when they are placed head to tail (Fig. 2.6).

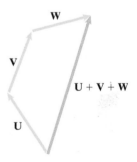

Figure 2.5
Sum of the three vectors **U**, **V**, and **W**.

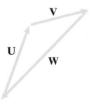

Figure 2.6
Three vectors **U**, **V**, and **W** whose sum is zero.

Figure 2.7
Arrows denoting the relative positions of points are vectors.

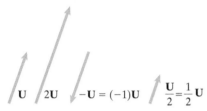

Figure 2.8
A vector **U** and some of its scalar multiples.

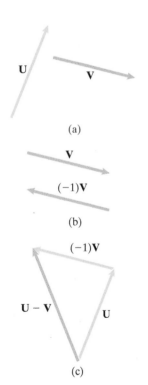

(a)

(b)

(c)

Figure 2.9
(a) Two vectors **U** and **V**.
(b) The vectors **V** and (-1)**V**.
(c) The sum of **U** and (-1)**V** is the vector difference **U** − **V**.

A physical quantity is called a vector if it has magnitude and direction and obeys the definition of vector addition. We have seen that displacement is a vector. The position of a point in space relative to another point is also a vector quantity. In Fig. 2.7, the vector $\mathbf{r}_{AC}$ from A to C is the sum of $\mathbf{r}_{AB}$ and $\mathbf{r}_{BC}$. A force has direction and magnitude, but do forces obey the definition of vector addition? For now we will assume that they do. When we discuss dynamics, we will show that Newton's second law implies that force is a vector.

Product of a Scalar and a Vector

The product of a scalar (real number) a and a vector **U** is a vector written as a**U**. Its magnitude is $|a||\mathbf{U}|$, where $|a|$ is the absolute value of the scalar a. The direction of a**U** is the same as the direction of **U** when a is positive and is opposite to the direction of **U** when a is negative.

The product (-1)**U** is written as $-$**U** and is called "the negative of the vector **U**." It has the same magnitude as **U** but the opposite direction. The division of a vector **U** by a scalar a is defined to be the product

$$\frac{\mathbf{U}}{a} = \left(\frac{1}{a}\right)\mathbf{U}.$$

Figure 2.8 shows a vector **U** and the products of **U** with the scalars 2, -1, and $1/2$.

The definitions of vector addition and the product of a scalar and a vector imply that

$$a(b\mathbf{U}) = (ab)\mathbf{U}, \quad \text{The product is associative with} \tag{2.3}$$
$$\text{respect to scalar multiplication.}$$

$$(a + b)\mathbf{U} = a\mathbf{U} + b\mathbf{U}, \quad \text{The products are distributive} \tag{2.4}$$
$$\text{with respect to scalar addition.}$$

and

$$a(\mathbf{U} + \mathbf{V}) = a\mathbf{U} + a\mathbf{V}, \quad \text{The products are distributive} \tag{2.5}$$
$$\text{with respect to vector addition.}$$

for any scalars a and b and vectors **U** and **V**. We will need these results when we discuss components of vectors.

Vector Subtraction

The difference of two vectors **U** and **V** is obtained by adding **U** to the vector (-1)**V**:

$$\mathbf{U} - \mathbf{V} = \mathbf{U} + (-1)\mathbf{V}. \tag{2.6}$$

Consider the two vectors **U** and **V** shown in Fig. 2.9a. The vector (-1)**V** has the same magnitude as the vector **V** but is in the opposite direction (Fig. 2.9b). In Fig. 2.9c, we add the vector **U** to the vector (-1)**V** to obtain **U** − **V**.

Unit Vectors

A *unit vector* is simply a vector whose magnitude is 1. A unit vector specifies a direction and also provides a convenient way to express a vector that has a particular direction. If a unit vector **e** and a vector **U** have the same direction, we can write **U** as the product of its magnitude $|\mathbf{U}|$ and the unit vector **e** (Fig. 2.10),

$$\mathbf{U} = |\mathbf{U}|\mathbf{e}.$$

Any vector **U** *can be regarded as the product of its magnitude and a unit vector that has the same direction as* **U**. Dividing both sides of this equation by $|\mathbf{U}|$ yields

$$\frac{\mathbf{U}}{|\mathbf{U}|} = \mathbf{e},$$

so *dividing any vector by its magnitude yields a unit vector that has the same direction*.

Figure 2.10
Since **U** and **e** have the same direction, the vector **U** equals the product of its magnitude with **e**.

RESULTS

A physical quantity that is completely described by a real number is called a *scalar*. A *vector* has both magnitude and direction and satisfies a defined rule of addition. A vector is represented graphically by an arrow whose length is defined to be proportional to the magnitude.

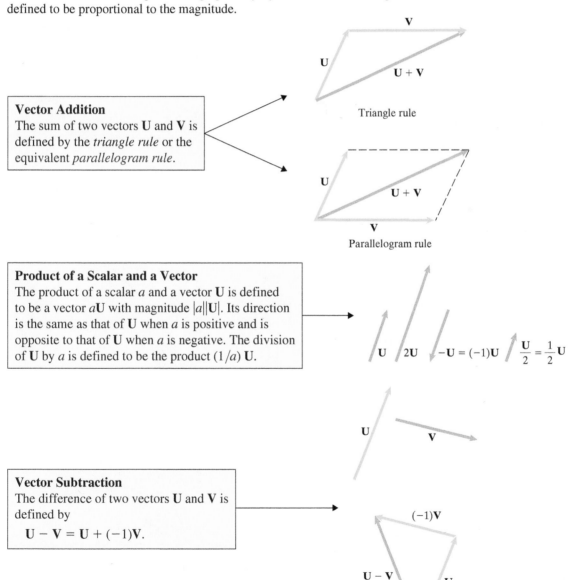

Vector Addition
The sum of two vectors **U** and **V** is defined by the *triangle rule* or the equivalent *parallelogram rule*.

Triangle rule

Parallelogram rule

Product of a Scalar and a Vector
The product of a scalar *a* and a vector **U** is defined to be a vector *a***U** with magnitude $|a||\mathbf{U}|$. Its direction is the same as that of **U** when *a* is positive and is opposite to that of **U** when *a* is negative. The division of **U** by *a* is defined to be the product $(1/a)\,\mathbf{U}$.

Vector Subtraction
The difference of two vectors **U** and **V** is defined by
$$\mathbf{U} - \mathbf{V} = \mathbf{U} + (-1)\mathbf{V}.$$

Unit Vectors
A unit vector is a vector whose magnitude is 1.
Any vector **U** can be expressed as |**U**|**e**, where
e is a unit vector with the same direction as **U**.
Dividing a vector **U** by its magnitude yields a
unit vector with the same direction as **U**.

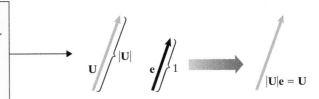

| Active Example 2.1 | Vector Operations (▶ *Related Problem 2.1*) |

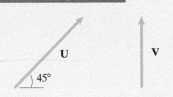

The magnitudes of the vectors shown are |**U**| = 8 and |**V**| = 3. The vector **V** is
vertical. Graphically determine the magnitude of the vector **U** + 2**V**.

Strategy
By drawing the vectors to scale and applying the triangle rule for addition, we
can measure the magnitude of the vector **U** + 2**V**.

Solution

Drawing the vectors **U** and 2**V**
to scale, place them head to tail.

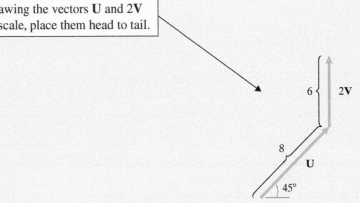

The measured value of
|**U** + 2**V**| is 13.0.

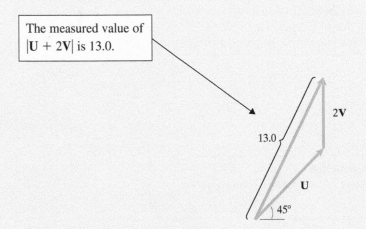

Practice Problem The magnitudes of the vectors shown are |**U**| = 8 and |**V**| = 3.
The vector **V** is vertical. Graphically determine the magnitude of the vector **U** − 2**V**.

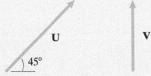

Answer: |**U** − 2**V**| = 5.7.

Example 2.2   Adding Vectors (▶ *Related Problem 2.2*)

Part of the roof of a sports stadium is to be supported by the cables *AB* and *AC*. The forces the cables exert on the pylon to which they are attached are represented by the vectors $\mathbf{F}_{AB}$ and $\mathbf{F}_{AC}$. The magnitudes of the forces are $|\mathbf{F}_{AB}| = 100$ kN and $|\mathbf{F}_{AC}| = 60$ kN. Determine the magnitude and direction of the sum of the forces exerted on the pylon by the cables.

Strategy
By drawing the parallelogram rule for adding the two forces *with the vectors drawn to scale*, we can measure the magnitude and direction of their sum.

Solution
We graphically construct the parallelogram rule for obtaining the sum of the two forces with the lengths of $\mathbf{F}_{AB}$ and $\mathbf{F}_{AC}$ proportional to their magnitudes (Fig. a). By measuring the figure, we estimate the magnitude of the vector $\mathbf{F}_{AB} + \mathbf{F}_{AC}$ to be 155 kN and its direction to be 19° above the horizontal.

(a) Graphical solution.

Critical Thinking
In engineering applications, vector operations are nearly always done analytically. So why is it worthwhile to gain experience with graphical methods? Doing so enhances your intuition about vectors and helps you understand vector operations. Also, sketching out a graphical solution can often help you formulate an analytical solution.

Problems

▶ **2.1** In Active Example 2.1, suppose that the vectors $\mathbf{U}$ and $\mathbf{V}$ are reoriented as shown. The vector $\mathbf{V}$ is vertical. The magnitudes are $|\mathbf{U}| = 8$ and $|\mathbf{V}| = 3$. Graphically determine the magnitude of the vector $\mathbf{U} + 2\mathbf{V}$.

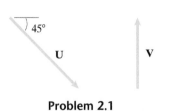

Problem 2.1

▶ **2.2** Suppose that the pylon in Example 2.2 is moved closer to the stadium so that the angle between the forces $\mathbf{F}_{AB}$ and $\mathbf{F}_{AC}$ is 50°. Draw a sketch of the new situation. The magnitudes of the forces are $|\mathbf{F}_{AB}| = 100$ kN and $|\mathbf{F}_{AC}| = 60$ kN. Graphically determine the magnitude and direction of the sum of the forces exerted on the pylon by the cables.

Refer to the following diagram when solving Problems 2.3 through 2.5. The force vectors F_A, F_B, and F_C lie in the same plane.

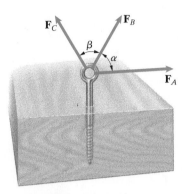

Problems 2.3–2.5

2.3 The magnitude $|\mathbf{F}_A| = 80$ lb and the angle $\alpha = 65°$. The magnitude $|\mathbf{F}_A + \mathbf{F}_B| = 120$ lb. Graphically determine the magnitude of $\mathbf{F}_B$.

2.4 The magnitudes $|\mathbf{F}_A| = 40$ N, $|\mathbf{F}_B| = 50$ N, and $|\mathbf{F}_C| = 40$ N. The angles $\alpha = 50°$ and $\beta = 80°$. Graphically determine the magnitude of $\mathbf{F}_A + \mathbf{F}_B + \mathbf{F}_C$.

2.5 The magnitudes $|\mathbf{F}_A| = |\mathbf{F}_B| = |\mathbf{F}_C| = 100$ lb, and the angle $\alpha = 30°$. Graphically determine the value of the angle β for which the magnitude $|\mathbf{F}_A + \mathbf{F}_B + \mathbf{F}_C|$ is a minimum and the minimum value of $|\mathbf{F}_A + \mathbf{F}_B + \mathbf{F}_C|$.

2.6 The angle $\theta = 50°$. Graphically determine the magnitude of the vector $\mathbf{r}_{AC}$.

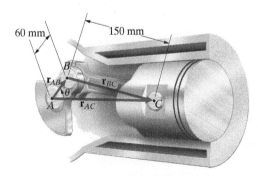

Problem 2.6

2.7 The vectors $\mathbf{F}_A$ and $\mathbf{F}_B$ represent the forces exerted on the pulley by the belt. Their magnitudes are $|\mathbf{F}_A| = 80$ N and $|\mathbf{F}_B| = 60$ N. Graphically determine the magnitude of the total force the belt exerts on the pulley.

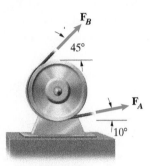

Problem 2.7

2.8 The sum of the forces $\mathbf{F}_A + \mathbf{F}_B + \mathbf{F}_C = \mathbf{0}$. The magnitude $|\mathbf{F}_A| = 100$ N and the angle $\alpha = 60°$. Graphically determine the magnitudes $|\mathbf{F}_B|$ and $|\mathbf{F}_C|$.

2.9 The sum of the forces $\mathbf{F}_A + \mathbf{F}_B + \mathbf{F}_C = \mathbf{0}$. The magnitudes $|\mathbf{F}_A| = 100$ N and $|\mathbf{F}_B| = 80$ N. Graphically determine the magnitude $|\mathbf{F}_C|$ and the angle α.

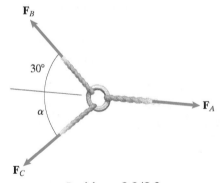

Problems 2.8/2.9

2.10 The forces acting on the sailplane are represented by three vectors. The lift **L** and drag **D** are perpendicular. The magnitude of the weight **W** is 500 lb. The sum of the forces **W** + **L** + **D** = **0**. Graphically determine the magnitudes of the lift and drag.

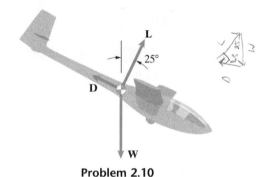

Problem 2.10

2.11 A spherical storage tank is suspended from cables. The tank is subjected to three forces, the forces **F**$_A$ and **F**$_B$ exerted by the cables and its weight **W**. The weight of the tank is $|\mathbf{W}| = 600$ lb. The vector sum of the forces acting on the tank equals zero. Graphically determine the magnitudes of **F**$_A$ and **F**$_B$.

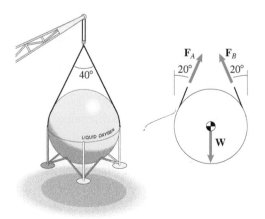

Problem 2.11

2.12 The rope *ABC* exerts forces **F**$_{BA}$ and **F**$_{BC}$ of equal magnitude on the block at *B*. The magnitude of the total force exerted on the block by the two forces is 200 lb. Graphically determine $|\mathbf{F}_{BA}|$.

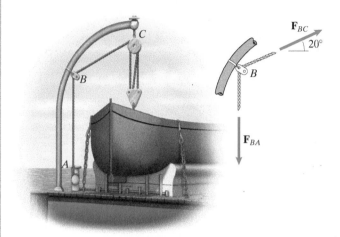

Problem 2.12

2.13 Two snowcats tow an emergency shelter to a new location near McMurdo Station, Antarctica. (The top view is shown. The cables are horizontal.) The total force **F**$_A$ + **F**$_B$ exerted on the shelter is in the direction parallel to the line *L* and its magnitude is 400 lb. Graphically determine the magnitudes of **F**$_A$ and **F**$_B$.

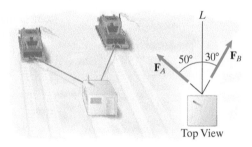

Problem 2.13

2.14 A surveyor determines that the horizontal distance from *A* to *B* is 400 m and the horizontal distance from *A* to *C* is 600 m. Graphically determine the magnitude of the vector **r**$_{BC}$ and the angle α.

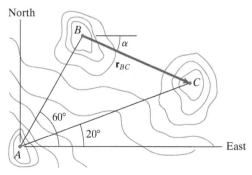

Problem 2.14

2.15 The vector **r** extends from point A to the midpoint between points B and C. Prove that

$$\mathbf{r} = \tfrac{1}{2}(\mathbf{r}_{AB} + \mathbf{r}_{AC}).$$

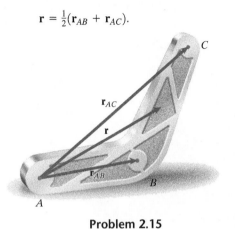

$\mathbf{r}_{AC}$

$\mathbf{r}$

$\mathbf{r}_{AB}$

Problem 2.15

2.16 By drawing sketches of the vectors, explain why

$$\mathbf{U} + (\mathbf{V} + \mathbf{W}) = (\mathbf{U} + \mathbf{V}) + \mathbf{W}.$$

2.2 Components in Two Dimensions

BACKGROUND

Vectors are much easier to work with when they are expressed in terms of mutually perpendicular vector components. Here we explain how to express vectors in cartesian components and give examples of vector manipulations using components.

Consider the vector **U** in Fig. 2.11a. By placing a cartesian coordinate system so that the vector **U** is parallel to the x–y plane, we can write it as the sum of perpendicular *vector components* $\mathbf{U}_x$ and $\mathbf{U}_y$ that are parallel to the x and y axes (Fig. 2.11b):

$$\mathbf{U} = \mathbf{U}_x + \mathbf{U}_y.$$

Then by introducing a unit vector **i** defined to point in the direction of the positive x axis and a unit vector **j** defined to point in the direction of the positive y axis (Fig. 2.11c), we can express the vector **U** in the form

$$\mathbf{U} = U_x\mathbf{i} + U_y\mathbf{j}. \tag{2.7}$$

The scalars U_x and U_y are called *scalar components of* **U**. *When we refer simply to the components of a vector, we will mean its scalar components.* We will refer to U_x and U_y as the x and y components of **U**.

The components of a vector specify both its direction relative to the cartesian coordinate system and its magnitude. From the right triangle formed by the vector **U** and its vector components (Fig. 2.11c), we see that the magnitude of **U** is given in terms of its components by the Pythagorean theorem:

$$|\mathbf{U}| = \sqrt{U_x^2 + U_y^2}. \tag{2.8}$$

With this equation the magnitude of a vector can be determined when its components are known.

Manipulating Vectors in Terms of Components

The sum of two vectors **U** and **V** in terms of their components is

$$\begin{aligned} \mathbf{U} + \mathbf{V} &= (U_x\mathbf{i} + U_y\mathbf{j}) + (V_x\mathbf{i} + V_y\mathbf{j}) \\ &= (U_x + V_x)\mathbf{i} + (U_y + V_y)\mathbf{j}. \end{aligned} \tag{2.9}$$

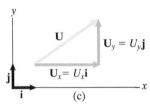

(a)

$\mathbf{U}$

$\mathbf{U}_y$

$\mathbf{U}_x$

(b)

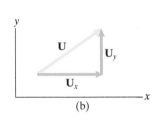

$\mathbf{U}$

$\mathbf{U}_y = U_y\mathbf{j}$

$\mathbf{U}_x = U_x\mathbf{i}$

j

i

(c)

Figure 2.11
(a) A vector **U**.
(b) The vector components $\mathbf{U}_x$ and $\mathbf{U}_y$.
(c) The vector components can be expressed in terms of **i** and **j**.

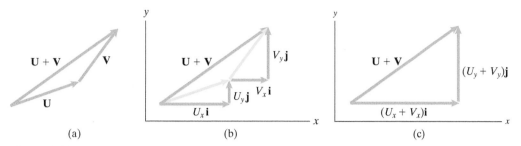

Figure 2.12
(a) The sum of **U** and **V**. (b) The vector components of **U** and **V**. (c) The sum of the components in each coordinate direction equals the component of **U** + **V** in that direction.

The components of **U** + **V** are the sums of the components of the vectors **U** and **V**. Notice that in obtaining this result we used Eqs. (2.2), (2.4), and (2.5).

It is instructive to derive Eq. (2.9) graphically. The summation of **U** and **V** is shown in Fig. 2.12a. In Fig. 2.12b we introduce a coordinate system and show the components **U** and **V**. In Fig. 2.12c we add the x and y components, obtaining Eq. (2.9).

The product of a number a and a vector **U** in terms of the components of **U** is

$$a\mathbf{U} = a(U_x\mathbf{i} + U_y\mathbf{j}) = aU_x\mathbf{i} + aU_y\mathbf{j}.$$

The component of $a\mathbf{U}$ in each coordinate direction equals the product of a and the component of **U** in that direction. We used Eqs. (2.3) and (2.5) to obtain this result.

Position Vectors in Terms of Components

We can express the position vector of a point relative to another point in terms of the cartesian coordinates of the points. Consider point A with coordinates (x_A, y_A) and point B with coordinates (x_B, y_B). Let $\mathbf{r}_{AB}$ be the vector that specifies the position of B relative to A (Fig. 2.13a). That is, we denote the vector *from* a point A *to* a point B by $\mathbf{r}_{AB}$. We see from Fig. 2.13b that $\mathbf{r}_{AB}$ is given in terms of the coordinates of points A and B by

$$\mathbf{r}_{AB} = (x_B - x_A)\mathbf{i} + (y_B - y_A)\mathbf{j}. \tag{2.10}$$

Notice that the x component of the position vector from a point A to a point B is obtained by subtracting the x coordinate of A from the x coordinate of B, and the y component is obtained by subtracting the y coordinate of A from the y coordinate of B.

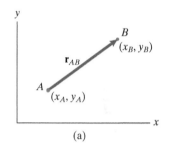

(a)

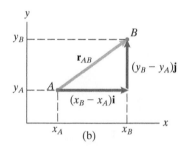

(b)

Figure 2.13
(a) Two points A and B and the position vector $\mathbf{r}_{AB}$ from A to B.
(b) The components of $\mathbf{r}_{AB}$ can be determined from the coordinates of points A and B.

RESULTS

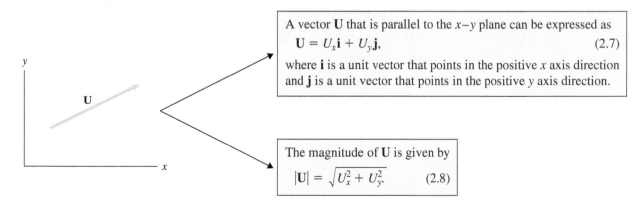

A vector **U** that is parallel to the x–y plane can be expressed as

$$\mathbf{U} = U_x\mathbf{i} + U_y\mathbf{j}, \tag{2.7}$$

where **i** is a unit vector that points in the positive x axis direction and **j** is a unit vector that points in the positive y axis direction.

The magnitude of **U** is given by

$$|\mathbf{U}| = \sqrt{U_x^2 + U_y^2}. \tag{2.8}$$

Manipulating Vectors in Terms of Components

Vector addition (or subtraction) and multiplication of a vector by a number can be carried out in terms of components.

$$\begin{cases} \mathbf{U} + \mathbf{V} = (U_x\mathbf{i} + U_y\mathbf{j}) + (V_x\mathbf{i} + V_y\mathbf{j}) \\ \qquad = (U_x + V_x)\mathbf{i} + (U_y + V_y)\mathbf{j}, \quad (2.9) \\ a\mathbf{U} = a(U_x\mathbf{i} + U_y\mathbf{j}) \\ \qquad = aU_x\mathbf{i} + aU_y\mathbf{j}. \end{cases}$$

Position Vectors in Terms of Components

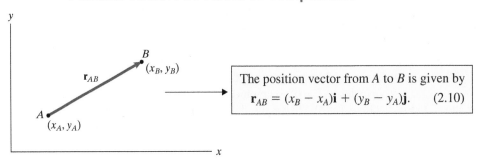

The position vector from A to B is given by

$$\mathbf{r}_{AB} = (x_B - x_A)\mathbf{i} + (y_B - y_A)\mathbf{j}. \quad (2.10)$$

Active Example 2.3   **Determining Components** (▶ *Related Problem 2.31*)

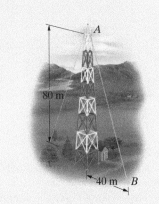

The cable from point A to point B exerts a 900-N force on the top of the television transmission tower that is represented by the vector $\mathbf{F}$. Express $\mathbf{F}$ in terms of components using the coordinate system shown.

Strategy

We will determine the components of the vector $\mathbf{F}$ in two ways. In the first method, we will determine the angle between $\mathbf{F}$ and the y axis and use trigonometry to determine the components. In the second method, we will use the given slope of the cable AB and apply similar triangles to determine the components of $\mathbf{F}$.

Solution

First Method

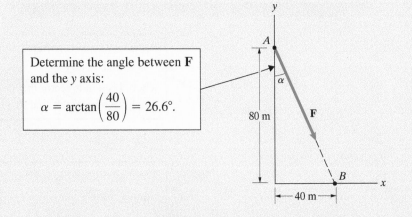

Determine the angle between $\mathbf{F}$ and the y axis:

$$\alpha = \arctan\left(\frac{40}{80}\right) = 26.6°.$$

Use trigonometry to determine **F** in terms of its components:

$$\mathbf{F} = |\mathbf{F}|\sin\alpha\mathbf{i} - |\mathbf{F}|\cos\alpha\mathbf{j}$$
$$= 900\sin 26.6°\,\mathbf{i} - 900\cos 26.6°\,\mathbf{j}\,(\text{N})$$
$$= 402\mathbf{i} - 805\mathbf{j}\,(\text{N}).$$

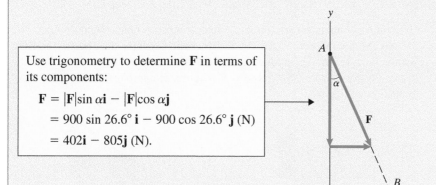

Second Method

Using the given dimensions, calculate the distance from A to B:

$$\sqrt{(40\text{ m})^2 + (80\text{ m})^2} = 89.4\text{ m}.$$

Use similar triangles to determine the components of **F**:

$$\frac{|F_x|}{|\mathbf{F}|} = \frac{40\text{ m}}{89.4\text{ m}} \quad\text{and}\quad \frac{|F_y|}{|\mathbf{F}|} = \frac{80\text{ m}}{89.4\text{ m}},$$

so

$$\mathbf{F} = \frac{40}{89.4}(900\text{ N})\mathbf{i} - \frac{80}{89.4}(900\text{ N})\mathbf{j}$$
$$= 402\mathbf{i} - 805\mathbf{j}\,(\text{N}).$$

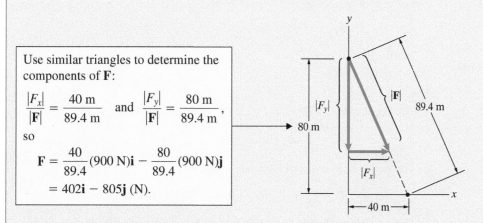

Practice Problem The cable from point A to point B exerts a 900-N force on the top of the television transmission tower that is represented by the vector **F**. Suppose that you change the placement of point B so that the magnitude of the y component of **F** is three times the magnitude of the x component of **F**. Express **F** in terms of its components. How far along the x axis from the origin of the coordinate system should B be placed?

Answer: $\mathbf{F} = 285\mathbf{i} - 854\mathbf{j}$ (N). Place point B at 26.7 m from the origin.

| **Example 2.4** | **Determining Components in Terms of an Angle** (▶ *Related Problem 2.33*) |

Hydraulic cylinders are used to exert forces in many mechanical devices. The force is exerted by pressurized liquid (hydraulic fluid) pushing against a piston within the cylinder. The hydraulic cylinder AB exerts a 4000-lb force $\mathbf{F}$ on the bed of the dump truck at B. Express $\mathbf{F}$ in terms of components using the coordinate system shown.

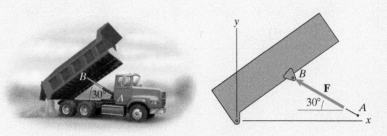

Strategy

When the direction of a vector is specified by an angle, as in this example, we can determine the values of the components from the right triangle formed by the vector and its components.

Solution

We draw the vector $\mathbf{F}$ and its vector components in Fig. a. From the resulting right triangle, we see that the magnitude of $\mathbf{F}_x$ is

$$|\mathbf{F}_x| = |\mathbf{F}|\cos 30° = (4000\ \text{lb})\cos 30° = 3460\ \text{lb}.$$

$\mathbf{F}_x$ points in the negative x direction, so

$$\mathbf{F}_x = -3460\mathbf{i}\ (\text{lb}).$$

The magnitude of $\mathbf{F}_y$ is

$$|\mathbf{F}_y| = |\mathbf{F}|\sin 30° = (4000\ \text{lb})\sin 30° = 2000\ \text{lb}.$$

The vector component $\mathbf{F}_y$ points in the positive y direction, so

$$\mathbf{F}_y = 2000\mathbf{j}\ (\text{lb}).$$

The vector $\mathbf{F}$, in terms of its components, is

$$\mathbf{F} = \mathbf{F}_x + \mathbf{F}_y = -3460\mathbf{i} + 2000\mathbf{j}\ (\text{lb}).$$

The x component of $\mathbf{F}$ is -3460 lb, and the y component is 2000 lb.

Critical Thinking

When you have determined the components of a given vector, you should make sure they appear reasonable. In this example you can see from the vector's direction that the x component should be negative and the y component positive. You can also make sure that the components yield the correct magnitude. In this example,

$$|\mathbf{F}| = \sqrt{(-3460\ \text{lb})^2 + (2000\ \text{lb})^2} = 4000\ \text{lb}.$$

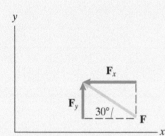

(a) The force $\mathbf{F}$ and its components form a right triangle.

| **Example 2.5** | **Determining an Unknown Vector Magnitude** (▶ *Related Problem 2.47*) |

The cables A and B exert forces $\mathbf{F}_A$ and $\mathbf{F}_B$ on the hook. The magnitude of $\mathbf{F}_A$ is 100 lb. The tension in cable B has been adjusted so that the total force $\mathbf{F}_A + \mathbf{F}_B$ is perpendicular to the wall to which the hook is attached.

(a) What is the magnitude of $\mathbf{F}_B$?
(b) What is the magnitude of the total force exerted on the hook by the two cables?

Strategy

The vector sum of the two forces is perpendicular to the wall, so the sum of the components parallel to the wall equals zero. From this condition we can obtain an equation for the magnitude of $\mathbf{F}_B$.

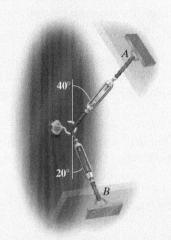

Solution

(a) In terms of the coordinate system shown in Fig. a, the components of $\mathbf{F}_A$ and $\mathbf{F}_B$ are

$$\mathbf{F}_A = |\mathbf{F}_A| \sin 40°\mathbf{i} + |\mathbf{F}_A| \cos 40°\mathbf{j},$$
$$\mathbf{F}_B = |\mathbf{F}_B| \sin 20°\mathbf{i} - |\mathbf{F}_B| \cos 20°\mathbf{j}.$$

The total force is

$$\mathbf{F}_A + \mathbf{F}_B = (|\mathbf{F}_A| \sin 40° + |\mathbf{F}_B| \sin 20°)\mathbf{i}$$
$$+ (|\mathbf{F}_A| \cos 40° - |\mathbf{F}_B| \cos 20°)\mathbf{j}.$$

Now we set the component of the total force parallel to the wall (the y component) equal to zero:

$$|\mathbf{F}_A| \cos 40° - |\mathbf{F}_B| \cos 20° = 0,$$

We thus obtain an equation for the magnitude of $\mathbf{F}_B$:

$$|\mathbf{F}_B| = \frac{|\mathbf{F}_A| \cos 40°}{\cos 20°} = \frac{(100 \text{ lb})\cos 40°}{\cos 20°} = 81.5 \text{ lb.}$$

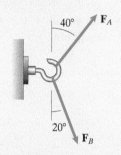

(b) Since we now know the magnitude of $\mathbf{F}_B$, we can determine the total force acting on the hook:

$$\mathbf{F}_A + \mathbf{F}_B = (|\mathbf{F}_A| \sin 40° + |\mathbf{F}_B| \sin 20°)\mathbf{i}$$
$$= [(100 \text{ lb})\sin 40° + (81.5 \text{ lb})\sin 20°]\mathbf{i} = 92.2\mathbf{i} \text{ (lb).}$$

The magnitude of the total force is 92.2 lb.

Critical Thinking

We can obtain the solution to (a) in a less formal way. If the component of the total force parallel to the wall is zero, we see in Fig. a that the magnitude of the vertical component of $\mathbf{F}_A$ must equal the magnitude of the vertical component of $\mathbf{F}_B$:

$$|\mathbf{F}_A| \cos 40° = |\mathbf{F}_B| \cos 20°.$$

Therefore the magnitude of $\mathbf{F}_B$ is

$$|\mathbf{F}_B| = \frac{|\mathbf{F}_A| \cos 40°}{\cos 20°} = \frac{(100 \text{ lb}) \cos 40°}{\cos 20°} = 81.5 \text{ lb.}$$

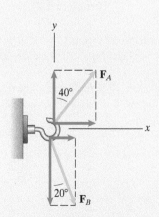

(a) Resolving $\mathbf{F}_A$ and $\mathbf{F}_B$ into components parallel and perpendicular to the wall.

Problems

2.17 A force $\mathbf{F} = 40\mathbf{i} - 20\mathbf{j}$ (N). What is its magnitude $|\mathbf{F}|$?

Strategy: The magnitude of a vector in terms of its components is given by Eq. (2.8).

2.18 An engineer estimating the components of a force $\mathbf{F} = F_x\mathbf{i} + F_y\mathbf{j}$ acting on a bridge abutment has determined that $F_x = 130$ MN, $|\mathbf{F}| = 165$ MN, and F_y is negative. What is F_y?

2.19 A support is subjected to a force $\mathbf{F} = F_x\mathbf{i} + 80\mathbf{j}$ (N). If the support will safely support a force of magnitude 100 N, what is the allowable range of values of the component F_x?

2.20 If $\mathbf{F}_A = 600\mathbf{i} - 800\mathbf{j}$ (kip) and $\mathbf{F}_B = 200\mathbf{i} - 200\mathbf{j}$ (kip), what is the magnitude of the force $\mathbf{F} = \mathbf{F}_A - 2\mathbf{F}_B$?

2.21 The forces acting on the sailplane are its weight $\mathbf{W} = -500\mathbf{j}$ (lb), the drag $\mathbf{D} = -200\mathbf{i} + 100\mathbf{j}$ (lb), and the lift $\mathbf{L}$. The sum of the forces $\mathbf{W} + \mathbf{L} + \mathbf{D} = \mathbf{0}$. Determine the components and the magnitude of $\mathbf{L}$.

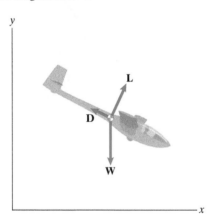

Problem 2.21

2.22 Two perpendicular vectors $\mathbf{U}$ and $\mathbf{V}$ lie in the *x–y* plane. The vector $\mathbf{U} = 6\mathbf{i} - 8\mathbf{j}$ and $|\mathbf{V}| = 20$. What are the components of $\mathbf{V}$?

2.23 A fish exerts a 10-lb force on the line that is represented by the vector $\mathbf{F}$. Express $\mathbf{F}$ in terms of components using the coordinate system shown.

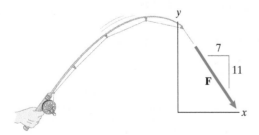

Problem 2.23

2.24 A man exerts a 60-lb force $\mathbf{F}$ to push a crate onto a truck. (a) Express $\mathbf{F}$ in terms of components using the coordinate system shown. (b) The weight of the crate is 100 lb. Determine the magnitude of the sum of the forces exerted by the man and the crate's weight.

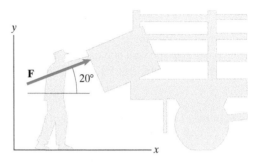

Problem 2.24

2.25 The missile's engine exerts a 260-kN force $\mathbf{F}$. (a) Express $\mathbf{F}$ in terms of components using the coordinate system shown. (b) The mass of the missile is 8800 kg. Determine the magnitude of the sum of the forces exerted by the engine and the missile's weight.

Problem 2.25

2.26 For the truss shown, express the position vector $\mathbf{r}_{AD}$ from point A to point D in terms of components. Use your result to determine the distance from point A to point D.

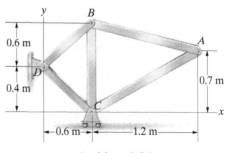

Problem 2.26

2.27 The points $A, B, \ldots$ are the joints of the hexagonal structural element. Let $\mathbf{r}_{AB}$ be the position vector from joint A to joint B, $\mathbf{r}_{AC}$ the position vector from joint A to joint C, and so forth. Determine the components of the vectors $\mathbf{r}_{AC}$ and $\mathbf{r}_{AF}$.

2.28 Determine the components of the vector $\mathbf{r}_{AB} - \mathbf{r}_{BC}$.

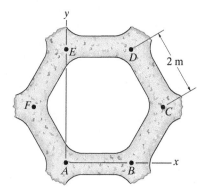

Problems 2.27/2.28

2.29 The coordinates of point A are $(1.8, 3.0)$ ft. The y coordinate of point B is 0.6 ft. The vector $\mathbf{r}_{AB}$ has the same direction as the unit vector $\mathbf{e}_{AB} = 0.616\mathbf{i} - 0.788\mathbf{j}$. What are the components of $\mathbf{r}_{AB}$?

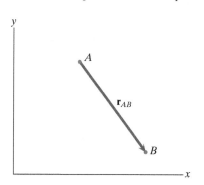

Problem 2.29

2.30 (a) Express the position vector from point A of the front-end loader to point B in terms of components.

(b) Express the position vector from point B to point C in terms of components.

(c) Use the results of (a) and (b) to determine the distance from point A to point C.

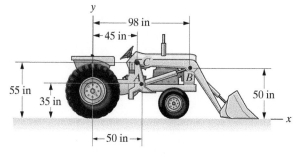

Problem 2.30

▶ **2.31** In Active Example 2.3, the cable AB exerts a 900-N force on the top of the tower. Suppose that the attachment point B is moved in the horizontal direction farther from the tower, and assume that the magnitude of the force $\mathbf{F}$ the cable exerts on the top of the tower is proportional to the length of the cable. (a) What is the distance from the tower to point B if the magnitude of the force is 1000 N? (b) Express the 1000-N force $\mathbf{F}$ in terms of components using the coordinate system shown.

2.32 Determine the position vector $\mathbf{r}_{AB}$ in terms of its components if (a) $\theta = 30°$; (b) $\theta = 225°$.

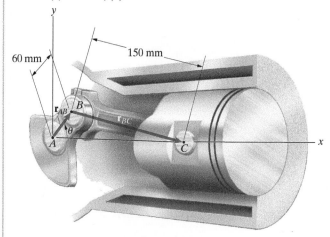

Problem 2.32

▶ **2.33** In Example 2.4, the coordinates of the fixed point A are $(17, 1)$ ft. The driver lowers the bed of the truck into a new position in which the coordinates of point B are $(9, 3)$ ft. The magnitude of the force $\mathbf{F}$ exerted on the bed by the hydraulic cylinder when the bed is in the new position is 4800 lb. Draw a sketch of the new situation. Express $\mathbf{F}$ in terms of components.

2.34 A surveyor measures the location of point A and determines that $\mathbf{r}_{OA} = 400\mathbf{i} + 800\mathbf{j}$ (m). He wants to determine the location of a point B so that $|\mathbf{r}_{AB}| = 400$ m and $|\mathbf{r}_{OA} + \mathbf{r}_{AB}| = 1200$ m. What are the cartesian coordinates of point B?

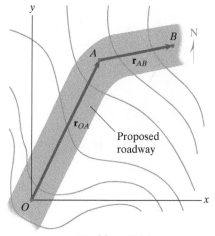

Problem 2.34

2.35 The magnitude of the position vector $\mathbf{r}_{BA}$ from point B to point A is 6 m and the magnitude of the position vector $\mathbf{r}_{CA}$ from point C to point A is 4 m. What are the components of $\mathbf{r}_{BA}$?

2.36 In Problem 2.35, determine the components of a unit vector $\mathbf{e}_{CA}$ that points from point C toward point A.

Strategy: Determine the components of $\mathbf{r}_{CA}$ and then divide the vector $\mathbf{r}_{CA}$ by its magnitude.

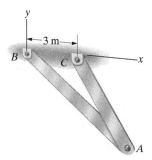

Problems 2.35/2.36

2.37 The x and y coordinates of points A, B, and C of the sailboat are shown.

(a) Determine the components of a unit vector that is parallel to the forestay AB and points from A toward B.

(b) Determine the components of a unit vector that is parallel to the backstay BC and points from C toward B.

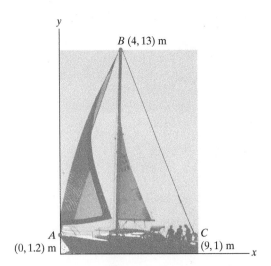

Problem 2.37

2.38 The length of the bar AB is 0.6 m. Determine the components of a unit vector $\mathbf{e}_{AB}$ that points from point A toward point B.

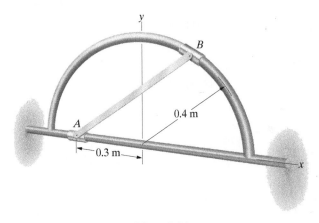

Problem 2.38

2.39 Determine the components of a unit vector that is parallel to the hydraulic actuator BC and points from B toward C.

2.40 The hydraulic actuator BC exerts a 1.2-kN force $\mathbf{F}$ on the joint at C that is parallel to the actuator and points from B toward C. Determine the components of $\mathbf{F}$.

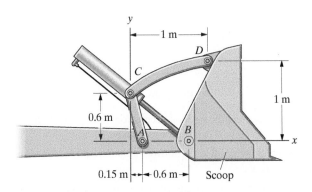

Problems 2.39/2.40

2.41 A surveyor finds that the length of the line *OA* is 1500 m and the length of the line *OB* is 2000 m.

(a) Determine the components of the position vector from point *A* to point *B*.

(b) Determine the components of a unit vector that points from point *A* toward point *B*.

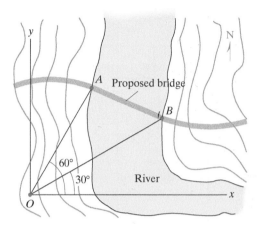

Problem 2.41

2.42 The magnitudes of the forces exerted by the cables are $|\mathbf{T}_1| = 2800$ lb, $|\mathbf{T}_2| = 3200$ lb, $|\mathbf{T}_3| = 4000$ lb, and $|\mathbf{T}_4| = 5000$ lb. What is the magnitude of the total force exerted by the four cables?

2.43 The tensions in the four cables are equal: $|\mathbf{T}_1| = |\mathbf{T}_2| = |\mathbf{T}_3| = |\mathbf{T}_4| = T$. Determine the value of T so that the four cables exert a total force of 12,500-lb magnitude on the support.

Problems 2.42/2.43

2.44 The rope ABC exerts forces $\mathbf{F}_{BA}$ and $\mathbf{F}_{BC}$ on the block at B. Their magnitudes are equal: $|\mathbf{F}_{BA}| = |\mathbf{F}_{BC}|$. The magnitude of the total force exerted on the block at B by the rope is $|\mathbf{F}_{BA} + \mathbf{F}_{BC}| = 920$ N. Determine $|\mathbf{F}_{BA}|$ by expressing the forces $\mathbf{F}_{BA}$ and $\mathbf{F}_{BC}$ in terms of components.

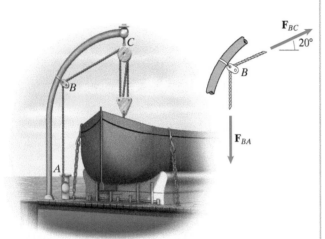

Problem 2.44

2.45 The magnitude of the horizontal force $\mathbf{F}_1$ is 5 kN and $\mathbf{F}_1 + \mathbf{F}_2 + \mathbf{F}_3 = \mathbf{0}$. What are the magnitudes of $\mathbf{F}_2$ and $\mathbf{F}_3$?

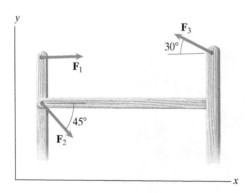

Problem 2.45

2.46 Four groups engage in a tug-of-war. The magnitudes of the forces exerted by groups B, C, and D are $|\mathbf{F}_B| = 800$ lb, $|\mathbf{F}_C| = 1000$ lb, and $|\mathbf{F}_D| = 900$ lb. If the vector sum of the four forces equals zero, what is the magnitude of $\mathbf{F}_A$ and the angle α?

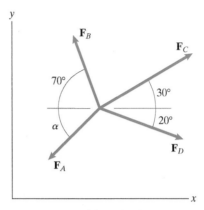

Problem 2.46

▶ **2.47** In Example 2.5, suppose that the attachment point of cable A is moved so that the angle between the cable and the wall increases from 40° to 55°. Draw a sketch showing the forces exerted on the hook by the two cables. If you want the total force $\mathbf{F}_A + \mathbf{F}_B$ to have a magnitude of 200 lb and be in the direction perpendicular to the wall, what are the necessary magnitudes of $\mathbf{F}_A$ and $\mathbf{F}_B$?

2.48 The bracket must support the two forces shown, where $|\mathbf{F}_1| = |\mathbf{F}_2| = 2$ kN. An engineer determines that the bracket will safely support a total force of magnitude 3.5 kN in any direction. Assume that $0 \le \alpha \le 90°$. What is the safe range of the angle α?

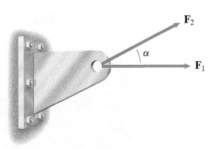

Problem 2.48

2.49 The figure shows three forces acting on a joint of a structure. The magnitude of $\mathbf{F}_C$ is 60 kN, and $\mathbf{F}_A + \mathbf{F}_B + \mathbf{F}_C = \mathbf{0}$. What are the magnitudes of $\mathbf{F}_A$ and $\mathbf{F}_B$?

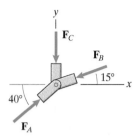

Problem 2.49

2.50 Four coplanar forces act on a beam. The forces $\mathbf{F}_B$ and $\mathbf{F}_C$ are vertical. The vector sum of the forces is zero. The magnitudes $|\mathbf{F}_B| = 10$ kN and $|\mathbf{F}_C| = 5$ kN. Determine the magnitudes of $\mathbf{F}_A$ and $\mathbf{F}_D$.

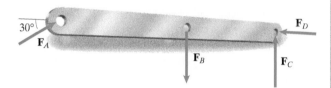

Problem 2.50

2.51 Six forces act on a beam that forms part of a building's frame. The vector sum of the forces is zero. The magnitudes $|\mathbf{F}_B| = |\mathbf{F}_E| = 20$ kN, $|\mathbf{F}_C| = 16$ kN, and $|\mathbf{F}_D| = 9$ kN. Determine the magnitudes of $\mathbf{F}_A$ and $\mathbf{F}_G$.

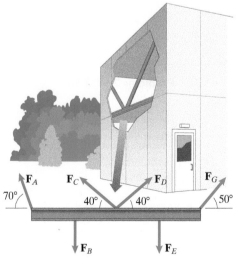

Problem 2.51

2.52 The total weight of the man and parasail is $|\mathbf{W}| = 230$ lb. The drag force $\mathbf{D}$ is perpendicular to the lift force $\mathbf{L}$. If the vector sum of the three forces is zero, what are the magnitudes of $\mathbf{L}$ and $\mathbf{D}$?

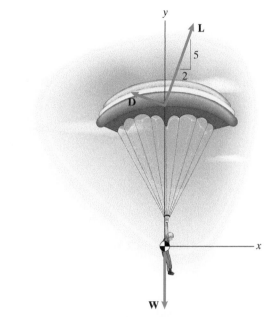

Problem 2.52

2.53 The three forces acting on the car are shown. The force $\mathbf{T}$ is parallel to the x axis and the magnitude of the force $\mathbf{W}$ is 14 kN. If $\mathbf{T} + \mathbf{W} + \mathbf{N} = \mathbf{0}$, what are the magnitudes of the forces $\mathbf{T}$ and $\mathbf{N}$?

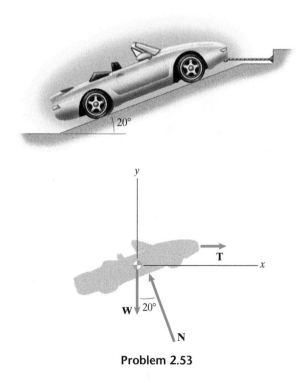

Problem 2.53

2.54 The cables A, B, and C help support a pillar that forms part of the supports of a structure. The magnitudes of the forces exerted by the cables are equal: $|\mathbf{F}_A| = |\mathbf{F}_B| = |\mathbf{F}_C|$. The magnitude of the vector sum of the three forces is 200 kN. What is $|\mathbf{F}_A|$?

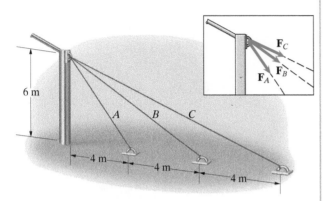

Problem 2.54

2.55 The total force exerted on the top of the mast B by the sailboat's forestay AB and backstay BC is $180\mathbf{i} - 820\mathbf{j}$ (N). What are the magnitudes of the forces exerted at B by the cables AB and BC?

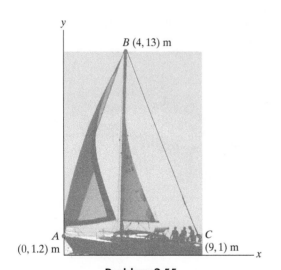

Problem 2.55

2.56 The structure shown forms part of a truss designed by an architectural engineer to support the roof of an orchestra shell. The members AB, AC, and AD exert forces $\mathbf{F}_{AB}$, $\mathbf{F}_{AC}$, and $\mathbf{F}_{AD}$ on the joint A. The magnitude $|\mathbf{F}_{AB}| = 4$ kN. If the vector sum of the three forces equals zero, what are the magnitudes of $\mathbf{F}_{AC}$ and $\mathbf{F}_{AD}$?

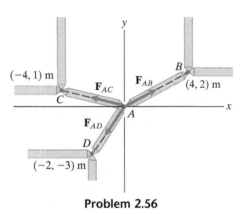

Problem 2.56

2.57 The distance $s = 45$ in.

(a) Determine the unit vector $\mathbf{e}_{BA}$ that points from B toward A.

(b) Use the unit vector you obtained in (a) to determine the coordinates of the collar C.

2.58 Determine the x and y coordinates of the collar C as functions of the distance s.

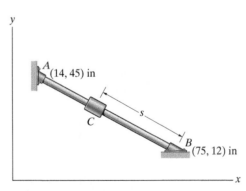

Problems 2.57/2.58

2.59 The position vector **r** goes from point A to a point on the straight line between B and C. Its magnitude is $|\mathbf{r}| = 6$ ft. Express **r** in terms of components.

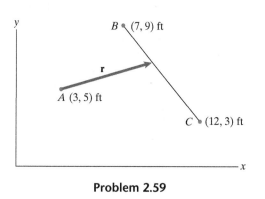

Problem 2.59

2.60 Let **r** be the position vector from point C to the point that is a distance s meters from point A along the straight line between A and B. Express **r** in terms of components. (Your answer will be in terms of s.)

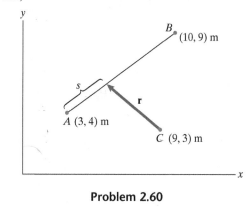

Problem 2.60

2.3 Components in Three Dimensions

BACKGROUND

Many engineering applications require vectors to be expressed in terms of components in a three-dimensional coordinate system. In this section we explain this technique and demonstrate vector operations in three dimensions.

We first review how to draw objects in three dimensions. Consider a three-dimensional object such as a cube. If we draw the cube as it appears when the point of view is perpendicular to one of its faces, we obtain Fig. 2.14a. In this view, the cube appears two dimensional. The dimension perpendicular to the page cannot be seen. To remedy this, we move the point of view upward and to the right, obtaining Fig. 2.14b. In this *oblique* view, the third dimension is visible. The hidden edges of the cube are shown as dashed lines.

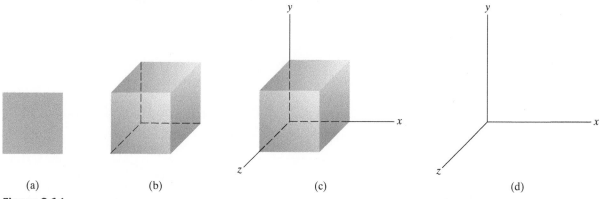

(a) (b) (c) (d)

Figure 2.14
(**a**) A cube viewed with the line of sight perpendicular to a face.
(**b**) An oblique view of the cube.
(**c**) A cartesian coordinate system aligned with the edges of the cube.
(**d**) Three-dimensional representation of the coordinate system.

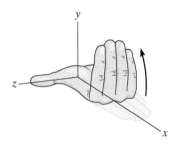

Figure 2.15
Recognizing a right-handed coordinate
system.

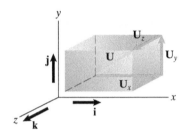

Figure 2.16
A vector **U** and its vector components.

We can use this approach to draw three-dimensional coordinate systems. In Fig. 2.14c we align the x, y, and z axes of a three-dimensional cartesian coordinate system with the edges of the cube. The three-dimensional representation of the coordinate system alone is shown in Fig. 2.14d. The coordinate system shown is said to be *right handed*. If the fingers of the right hand are pointed in the direction of the positive x axis and then bent (as in preparing to make a fist) toward the positive y axis, the thumb points in the direction of the positive z axis (Fig. 2.15). Otherwise, the coordinate system is left handed. Because some equations used in mathematics and engineering do not yield correct results when they are applied using a left-handed coordinate system, we use only right-handed coordinate systems.

We can express a vector **U** in terms of vector components $\mathbf{U}_x$, $\mathbf{U}_y$, and $\mathbf{U}_z$ parallel to the x, y, and z axes, respectively (Fig. 2.16), as

$$\mathbf{U} = \mathbf{U}_x + \mathbf{U}_y + \mathbf{U}_z. \qquad (2.11)$$

(We have drawn a box around the vector to help in visualizing the directions of the vector components.) By introducing unit vectors **i**, **j**, and **k** that point in the positive x, y, and z directions, we can express **U** in terms of scalar components as

$$\mathbf{U} = U_x\mathbf{i} + U_y\mathbf{j} + U_z\mathbf{k}. \qquad (2.12)$$

We will refer to the scalars U_x, U_y, and U_z as the x, y, and z components of **U**.

Magnitude of a Vector in Terms of Components

Consider a vector **U** and its vector components (Fig. 2.17a). From the right triangle formed by the vectors $\mathbf{U}_y$, $\mathbf{U}_z$, and their sum $\mathbf{U}_y + \mathbf{U}_z$ (Fig. 2.17b), we can see that

$$|\mathbf{U}_y + \mathbf{U}_z|^2 = |\mathbf{U}_y|^2 + |\mathbf{U}_z|^2. \qquad (2.13)$$

The vector **U** is the sum of the vectors $\mathbf{U}_x$ and $\mathbf{U}_y + \mathbf{U}_z$. These three vectors form a right triangle (Fig. 2.17c), from which we obtain

$$|\mathbf{U}|^2 = |\mathbf{U}_x|^2 + |\mathbf{U}_y + \mathbf{U}_z|^2.$$

Substituting Eq. (2.13) into this result yields the equation

$$|\mathbf{U}|^2 = |\mathbf{U}_x|^2 + |\mathbf{U}_y|^2 + |\mathbf{U}_z|^2 = U_x^2 + U_y^2 + U_z^2.$$

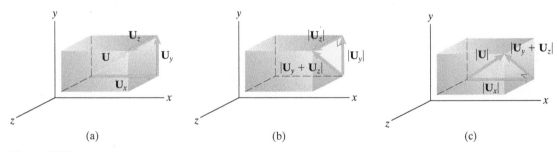

(a)   (b)   (c)

Figure 2.17
(**a**) A vector **U** and its vector components.
(**b**) The right triangle formed by the vectors $\mathbf{U}_y$, $\mathbf{U}_z$, and $\mathbf{U}_y + \mathbf{U}_z$.
(**c**) The right triangle formed by the vectors **U**, $\mathbf{U}_x$, and $\mathbf{U}_y + \mathbf{U}_z$.

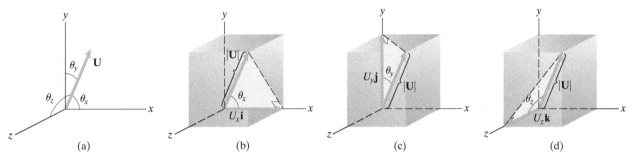

Figure 2.18
(a) A vector **U** and the angles θ_x, θ_y, and θ_z.
(b)–(d) The angles θ_x, θ_y, and θ_z and the vector components of **U**.

Thus, the magnitude of a vector **U** is given in terms of its components in three dimensions by

$$|\mathbf{U}| = \sqrt{U_x^2 + U_y^2 + U_z^2}. \tag{2.14}$$

Direction Cosines

We described the direction of a vector relative to a two-dimensional cartesian coordinate system by specifying the angle between the vector and one of the co-ordinate axes. One of the ways we can describe the direction of a vector in three dimensions is by specifying the angles θ_x, θ_y, and θ_z between the vector and the positive coordinate axes (Fig. 2.18a).

In Figs. 2.18b–d, we demonstrate that the components of the vector **U** are respectively given in terms of the angles θ_x, θ_y, and θ_z, by

$$U_x = |\mathbf{U}| \cos \theta_x, \quad U_y = |\mathbf{U}| \cos \theta_y, \quad U_z = |\mathbf{U}| \cos \theta_z. \tag{2.15}$$

The quantities $\cos \theta_x$, $\cos \theta_y$, and $\cos \theta_z$ are called the *direction cosines* of **U**. The direction cosines of a vector are not independent. If we substitute Eqs. (2.15) into Eq. (2.14), we find that the direction cosines satisfy the relation

$$\cos^2 \theta_x + \cos^2 \theta_y + \cos^2 \theta_z = 1. \tag{2.16}$$

Suppose that **e** is a unit vector with the same direction as **U**, so that

$$\mathbf{U} = |\mathbf{U}|\mathbf{e}.$$

In terms of components, this equation is

$$U_x\mathbf{i} + U_y\mathbf{j} + U_z\mathbf{k} = |\mathbf{U}|(e_x\mathbf{i} + e_y\mathbf{j} + e_z\mathbf{k}).$$

Thus the relations between the components of **U** and **e** are

$$U_x = |\mathbf{U}|e_x, \quad U_y = |\mathbf{U}|e_y, \quad U_z = |\mathbf{U}|e_z.$$

By comparing these equations to Eqs. (2.15), we see that

$$\cos \theta_x = e_x, \quad \cos \theta_y = e_y, \quad \cos \theta_z = e_z.$$

The direction cosines of a vector **U** are the components of a unit vector with the same direction as **U**.

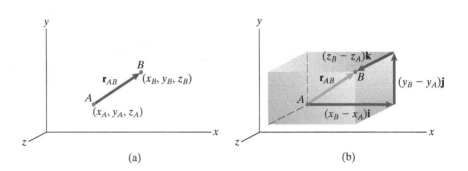

Figure 2.19
(a) The position vector from point A to point B.
(b) The components of $\mathbf{r}_{AB}$ can be determined from the coordinates of points A and B.

Position Vectors in Terms of Components

Generalizing the two-dimensional case, we consider a point A with coordinates (x_A, y_A, z_A) and a point B with coordinates (x_B, y_B, z_B). The position vector $\mathbf{r}_{AB}$ from A to B, shown in Fig. 2.19a, is given in terms of the coordinates of A and B by

$$\mathbf{r}_{AB} = (x_B - x_A)\mathbf{i} + (y_B - y_A)\mathbf{j} + (z_B - z_A)\mathbf{k}. \tag{2.17}$$

The components are obtained by subtracting the coordinates of point A from the coordinates of point B (Fig. 2.19b).

Components of a Vector Parallel to a Given Line

In three-dimensional applications, the direction of a vector is often defined by specifying the coordinates of two points on a line that is parallel to the vector. This information can be used to determine the components of the vector.

Suppose that we know the coordinates of two points A and B on a line parallel to a vector $\mathbf{U}$ (Fig. 2.20a). We can use Eq. (2.17) to determine the

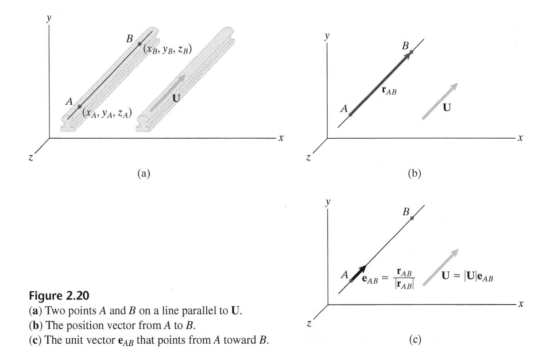

Figure 2.20
(a) Two points A and B on a line parallel to $\mathbf{U}$.
(b) The position vector from A to B.
(c) The unit vector $\mathbf{e}_{AB}$ that points from A toward B.

position vector $\mathbf{r}_{AB}$ from A to B (Fig. 2.20b). We can divide $\mathbf{r}_{AB}$ by its magnitude to obtain a unit vector $\mathbf{e}_{AB}$ that points from A toward B (Fig. 2.20c). Since $\mathbf{e}_{AB}$ has the same direction as $\mathbf{U}$, we can determine $\mathbf{U}$ in terms of its scalar components by expressing it as the product of its magnitude and $\mathbf{e}_{AB}$.

More generally, suppose that we know the magnitude of a vector $\mathbf{U}$ and the components of any vector $\mathbf{V}$ that has the same direction as $\mathbf{U}$. Then $\mathbf{V}/|\mathbf{V}|$ is a unit vector with the same direction as $\mathbf{U}$, and we can determine the components of $\mathbf{U}$ by expressing it as $\mathbf{U} = |\mathbf{U}|(\mathbf{V}/|\mathbf{V}|)$.

RESULTS

Any vector $\mathbf{U}$ can be expressed as

$$\mathbf{U} = U_x\mathbf{i} + U_y\mathbf{j} + U_z\mathbf{k}, \tag{2.12}$$

where $\mathbf{i}$ is a unit vector that points in the positive x axis direction, $\mathbf{j}$ is a unit vector that points in the positive y axis direction, and $\mathbf{k}$ is a unit vector that points in the positive z axis direction.

The magnitude of $\mathbf{U}$ is given by

$$|\mathbf{U}| = \sqrt{U_x^2 + U_y^2 + U_z^2}. \tag{2.14}$$

Direction Cosines

The direction of a vector $\mathbf{U}$ relative to a given coordinate system can be specified by the angles θ_x, θ_y, and θ_z between the vector and the positive coordinate axes.

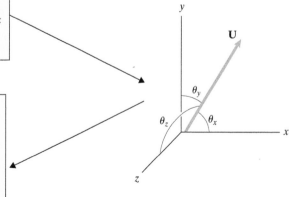

The components of $\mathbf{U}$ are given by

$$U_x = |\mathbf{U}|\cos\theta_x,$$
$$U_y = |\mathbf{U}|\cos\theta_y, \tag{2.15}$$
$$U_z = |\mathbf{U}|\cos\theta_z.$$

The terms $\cos\theta_x$, $\cos\theta_y$, and $\cos\theta_z$ are called the *direction cosines* of $\mathbf{U}$. The direction cosines are the components of a unit vector with the same direction as $\mathbf{U}$.

Position Vectors in Terms of Components

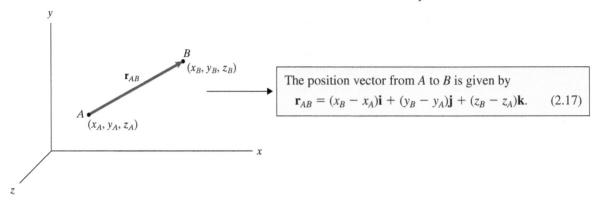

The position vector from A to B is given by

$$\mathbf{r}_{AB} = (x_B - x_A)\mathbf{i} + (y_B - y_A)\mathbf{j} + (z_B - z_A)\mathbf{k}. \qquad (2.17)$$

Components of a Vector Parallel to a Given Line

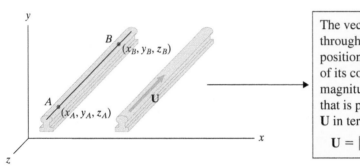

The vector $\mathbf{U}$ is parallel to the line through points A and B. Obtain the position vector $\mathbf{r}_{AB}$ from A to B in terms of its components. Divide $\mathbf{r}_{AB}$ by its magnitude to obtain a unit vector $\mathbf{e}_{AB}$ that is parallel to the line. Then the vector $\mathbf{U}$ in terms of its components is given by

$$\mathbf{U} = |\mathbf{U}|\mathbf{e}_{AB}.$$

Active Example 2.6   **Direction Cosines** (▶ *Related Problem 2.67*)

The coordinates of point C of the truss are $x_C = 4$ m, $y_C = 0$, $z_C = 0$, and the coordinates of point D are $x_D = 2$ m, $y_D = 3$ m, $z_D = 1$ m. What are the direction cosines of the position vector $\mathbf{r}_{CD}$ from point C to point D?

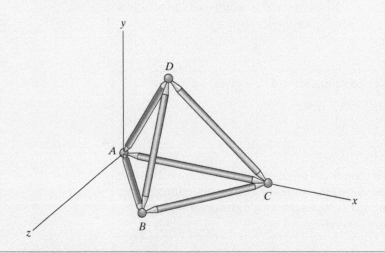

Strategy

Knowing the coordinates of points C and D, we can determine $\mathbf{r}_{CD}$ in terms of its components. Then we can calculate the magnitude of $\mathbf{r}_{CD}$ (the distance from C to D) and use Eqs. (2.15) to obtain the direction cosines.

Solution

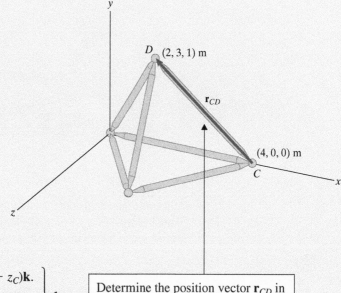

$\mathbf{r}_{CD} = (x_D - x_C)\mathbf{i} + (y_D - y_C)\mathbf{j} + (z_D - z_C)\mathbf{k}.$
$= (2 - 4)\mathbf{i} + (3 - 0)\mathbf{j} + (1 - 0)\mathbf{k} \text{ (m)}$
$= -2\mathbf{i} + 3\mathbf{j} + \mathbf{k} \text{ (m)}.$

Determine the position vector $\mathbf{r}_{CD}$ in terms of its components.

$|\mathbf{r}_{CD}| = \sqrt{r^2_{CDx} + r^2_{CDy} + r^2_{CDz}}$
$= \sqrt{(-2 \text{ m})^2 + (3 \text{ m})^2 + (1 \text{ m})^2}$
$= 3.74 \text{ m}.$

Calculate the magnitude of $\mathbf{r}_{CD}$.

$\cos \theta_x = \dfrac{\mathbf{r}_{CDx}}{|\mathbf{r}_{CD}|} = \dfrac{-2 \text{ m}}{3.74 \text{ m}} = -0.535,$

$\cos \theta_y = \dfrac{\mathbf{r}_{CDy}}{|\mathbf{r}_{CD}|} = \dfrac{3 \text{ m}}{3.74 \text{ m}} = 0.802,$

$\cos \theta_z = \dfrac{\mathbf{r}_{CDz}}{|\mathbf{r}_{CD}|} = \dfrac{1 \text{ m}}{3.74 \text{ m}} = 0.267,$

Determine the direction cosines.

Practice Problem The coordinates of point B of the truss are $x_B = 2.4$ m, $y_B = 0$, $z_B = 3$ m. Determine the components of a unit vector $\mathbf{e}_{BD}$ that points from point B toward point D.

Answer: $\mathbf{e}_{BD} = -0.110\mathbf{i} + 0.827\mathbf{j} - 0.551\mathbf{k}.$

| Example 2.7 | **Determining Components in Three Dimensions** (▶ *Related Problem 2.76*) |

The crane exerts a 600-lb force **F** on the caisson. The angle between **F** and the *x* axis is 54°, and the angle between **F** and the *y* axis is 40°. The *z* component of **F** is positive. Express **F** in terms of components.

Strategy

Only two of the angles between the vector and the positive coordinate axes are given, but we can use Eq. (2.16) to determine the third angle. Then we can determine the components of **F** by using Eqs. (2.15).

Solution

The angles between **F** and the positive coordinate axes are related by

$$\cos^2 \theta_x + \cos^2 \theta_y + \cos^2 \theta_z = (\cos 54°)^2 + (\cos 40°)^2 + \cos^2 \theta_z = 1.$$

Solving this equation for $\cos \theta_z$, we obtain the two solutions $\cos \theta_z = 0.260$ and $\cos \theta_z = -0.260$, which tells us that $\theta_z = 74.9°$ or $\theta_z = 105.1°$. The *z* component of the vector **F** is positive, so the angle between **F** and the positive *z* axis is less than 90°. Therefore $\theta_z = 74.9°$.

The components of **F** are

$$F_x = |\mathbf{F}| \cos \theta_x = 600 \cos 54° = 353 \text{ lb},$$

$$F_y = |\mathbf{F}| \cos \theta_y = 600 \cos 40° = 460 \text{ lb},$$

$$F_z = |\mathbf{F}| \cos \theta_z = 600 \cos 74.9° = 156 \text{ lb}.$$

Critical Thinking

You are aware that knowing the square of a number does not tell you the value of the number uniquely. If $a^2 = 4$, the number a can be either 2 or −2. In this example, knowledge of the angles θ_x and θ_y allowed us to solve Eq. (2.16) for the value of $\cos^2 \theta_z$, which resulted in two possible values of the angle θ_z. There is a simple geometrical explanation for why this happened. The two angles θ_x and θ_y are sufficient to define a line parallel to the vector **F**, *but not the direction of* **F** *along that line*. The two values of θ_z we obtained correspond to the two possible directions of **F** along the line. Additional information is needed to indicate the direction. In this example, the additional information was supplied by stating that the *z* component of **F** is positive.

| **Example 2.8** | Determining Components in Three Dimensions *(▶ Related Problem 2.86)* |

The tether of the balloon exerts an 800-N force **F** on the hook at *O*. The vertical line *AB* intersects the *x*–*z* plane at point *A*. The angle between the *z* axis and the line *OA* is 60°, and the angle between the line *OA* and **F** is 45°. Express **F** in terms of components.

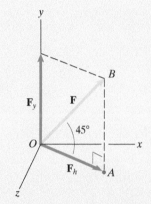

Strategy

We can determine the components of **F** from the given geometric information in two steps. First, we express **F** as the sum of two vector components parallel to the lines *OA* and *AB*. The component parallel to *AB* is the vector component $\mathbf{F}_y$. Then we can use the component parallel to *OA* to determine the vector components $\mathbf{F}_x$ and $\mathbf{F}_z$.

Solution

In Fig. a, we express **F** as the sum of its *y* component $\mathbf{F}_y$ and the component $\mathbf{F}_h$ parallel to *OA*. The magnitude of $\mathbf{F}_y$ is

$$|\mathbf{F}_y| = |\mathbf{F}| \sin 45° = (800 \text{ N}) \sin 45° = 566 \text{ N},$$

and the magnitude of $\mathbf{F}_h$ is

$$|\mathbf{F}_h| = |\mathbf{F}| \cos 45° = (800 \text{ N}) \cos 45° = 566 \text{ N}.$$

In Fig. b, we express $\mathbf{F}_h$ in terms of the vector components $\mathbf{F}_x$ and $\mathbf{F}_z$. The magnitude of $\mathbf{F}_x$ is

$$|\mathbf{F}_x| = |\mathbf{F}_h| \sin 60° = (566 \text{ N}) \sin 60° = 490 \text{ N},$$

and the magnitude of $\mathbf{F}_z$ is

$$|\mathbf{F}_z| = |\mathbf{F}_h| \cos 60° = (566 \text{ N}) \cos 60° = 283 \text{ N}.$$

The vector components $\mathbf{F}_x$, $\mathbf{F}_y$, and $\mathbf{F}_z$ all point in the positive axis directions, so the scalar components of **F** are positive:

$$\mathbf{F} = 490\mathbf{i} + 566\mathbf{j} + 283\mathbf{k} \text{ (N)}.$$

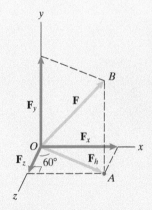

(a) Resolving **F** into vector components parallel to *OA* and *OB*.

(b) Resolving $\mathbf{F}_h$ into vector components parallel to the *x* and *z* axes.

Critical Thinking

As this example demonstrates, two angles are required to specify a vector's direction relative to a three-dimensional coordinate system. The two angles used may not be defined in the same way as in the example, but however they are defined, you can determine the components of the vector in terms of the magnitude and the two specified angles by a procedure similar to the one we used here.

Example 2.9   Determining Components in Three Dimensions   (▶ *Related Problem 2.90*)

The rope extends from point B through a metal loop attached to the wall at A to point C. The rope exerts forces $\mathbf{F}_{AB}$ and $\mathbf{F}_{AC}$ on the loop at A with magnitudes $|\mathbf{F}_{AB}| = |\mathbf{F}_{AC}| = 200$ lb. What is the magnitude of the total force $\mathbf{F} = \mathbf{F}_{AB} + \mathbf{F}_{AC}$ exerted on the loop by the rope?

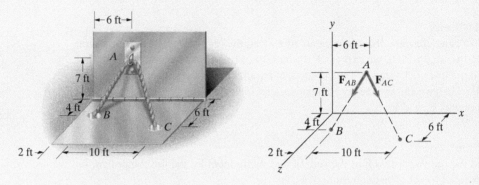

Strategy

The force $\mathbf{F}_{AB}$ is parallel to the line from A to B, and the force $\mathbf{F}_{AC}$ is parallel to the line from A to C. Since we can determine the coordinates of points A, B, and C from the given dimensions, we can determine the components of unit vectors that have the same directions as the two forces and use them to express the forces in terms of scalar components.

Solution

Let $\mathbf{r}_{AB}$ be the position vector from point A to point B and let $\mathbf{r}_{AC}$ be the position vector from point A to point C (Fig. a). From the given dimensions, the coordinates of points A, B, and C are

$$A: (6, 7, 0) \text{ ft,} \qquad B: (2, 0, 4) \text{ ft,} \qquad C: (12, 0, 6) \text{ ft.}$$

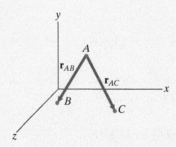

(a) The position vectors $\mathbf{r}_{AB}$ and $\mathbf{r}_{AC}$.

Therefore, the components of $\mathbf{r}_{AB}$ and $\mathbf{r}_{AC}$, with the coordinates in ft, are given by

$$\mathbf{r}_{AB} = (x_B - x_A)\mathbf{i} + (y_B - y_A)\mathbf{j} + (z_B - z_A)\mathbf{k}$$
$$= (2 - 6)\mathbf{i} + (0 - 7)\mathbf{j} + (4 - 0)\mathbf{k}$$
$$= -4\mathbf{i} - 7\mathbf{j} + 4\mathbf{k} \text{ (ft)}$$

and

$$\mathbf{r}_{AC} = (x_C - x_A)\mathbf{i} + (y_C - y_A)\mathbf{j} + (z_C - z_A)\mathbf{k}$$
$$= (12 - 6)\mathbf{i} + (0 - 7)\mathbf{j} + (6 - 0)\mathbf{k}$$
$$= 6\mathbf{i} - 7\mathbf{j} + 6\mathbf{k} \text{ (ft)}.$$

Their magnitudes are $|\mathbf{r}_{AB}| = 9$ ft and $|\mathbf{r}_{AC}| = 11$ ft. By dividing $\mathbf{r}_{AB}$ and $\mathbf{r}_{AC}$ by their magnitudes, we obtain unit vectors $\mathbf{e}_{AB}$ and $\mathbf{e}_{AC}$ that point in the directions of $\mathbf{F}_{AB}$ and $\mathbf{F}_{AC}$ (Fig. b):

$$\mathbf{e}_{AB} = \frac{\mathbf{r}_{AB}}{|\mathbf{r}_{AB}|} = -0.444\mathbf{i} - 0.778\mathbf{j} + 0.444\mathbf{k},$$

$$\mathbf{e}_{AC} = \frac{\mathbf{r}_{AC}}{|\mathbf{r}_{AC}|} = 0.545\mathbf{i} - 0.636\mathbf{j} + 0.545\mathbf{k}.$$

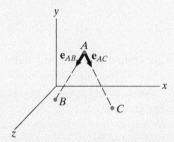

(b) The unit vectors $\mathbf{e}_{AB}$ and $\mathbf{e}_{AC}$.

The forces $\mathbf{F}_{AB}$ and $\mathbf{F}_{AC}$ are

$$\mathbf{F}_{AB} = (200 \text{ lb})\mathbf{e}_{AB} = -88.9\mathbf{i} - 155.6\mathbf{j} + 88.9\mathbf{k} \text{ (lb)},$$
$$\mathbf{F}_{AC} = (200 \text{ lb})\mathbf{e}_{AC} = 109.1\mathbf{i} - 127.3\mathbf{j} + 109.1\mathbf{k} \text{ (lb)}.$$

The total force exerted on the loop by the rope is

$$\mathbf{F} = \mathbf{F}_{AB} + \mathbf{F}_{AC} = 20.2\mathbf{i} - 282.8\mathbf{j} + 198.0\mathbf{k} \text{ (lb)},$$

and its magnitude is

$$|\mathbf{F}| = \sqrt{(20.2)^2 + (-282.8)^2 + (198.0)^2} = 346 \text{ lb}.$$

Critical Thinking

How do you know that the magnitude and direction of the total force exerted on the metal loop at A by the rope is given by the magnitude and direction of the vector $\mathbf{F} = \mathbf{F}_{AB} + \mathbf{F}_{AC}$? At this point in our development of mechanics, we assume that force is a vector, but have provided no proof. In the study of dynamics it is shown that Newton's second law implies that force is a vector.

Example 2.10 | Determining Components of a Force (▶ *Related Problem 2.95*)

The cable AB exerts a 50-N force $\mathbf{T}$ on the collar at A. Express $\mathbf{T}$ in terms of components.

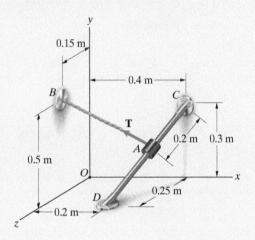

Strategy

Let $\mathbf{r}_{AB}$ be the position vector from A to B. We will divide $\mathbf{r}_{AB}$ by its magnitude to obtain a unit vector $\mathbf{e}_{AB}$ having the same direction as the force $\mathbf{T}$. Then we can obtain $\mathbf{T}$ in terms of scalar components by expressing it as the product of its magnitude and $\mathbf{e}_{AB}$. To begin this procedure, we must first determine the co-ordinates of the collar A. We will do so by obtaining a unit vector $\mathbf{e}_{CD}$ pointing from C toward D and multiplying it by 0.2 m to determine the position of the collar A relative to C.

Solution

Determining the Coordinates of Point A   The position vector from C to D, with the coordinates in meters, is

$$\mathbf{r}_{CD} = (0.2 - 0.4)\mathbf{i} + (0 - 0.3)\mathbf{j} + (0.25 - 0)\mathbf{k}$$
$$= -0.2\mathbf{i} - 0.3\mathbf{j} + 0.25\mathbf{k} \ (\text{m}).$$

Dividing this vector by its magnitude, we obtain the unit vector $\mathbf{e}_{CD}$ (Fig. a):

$$\mathbf{e}_{CD} = \frac{\mathbf{r}_{CD}}{|\mathbf{r}_{CD}|} = \frac{-0.2\mathbf{i} - 0.3\mathbf{j} + 0.25\mathbf{k}}{\sqrt{(-0.2)^2 + (-0.3)^2 + (0.25)^2}}$$
$$= -0.456\mathbf{i} - 0.684\mathbf{j} + 0.570\mathbf{k}.$$

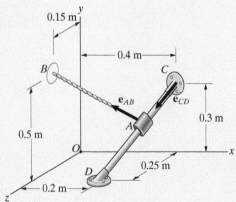

(a) The unit vectors $\mathbf{e}_{AB}$ and $\mathbf{e}_{CD}$.

Using this vector, we obtain the position vector from C to A:

$$\mathbf{r}_{CA} = (0.2 \ \text{m})\mathbf{e}_{CD} = -0.091\mathbf{i} - 0.137\mathbf{j} + 0.114\mathbf{k} \ (\text{m}).$$

The position vector from the origin of the coordinate system to C is $\mathbf{r}_{OC} = 0.4\mathbf{i} + 0.3\mathbf{j}$ (m), so the position vector from the origin to A is

$$\mathbf{r}_{OA} = \mathbf{r}_{OC} + \mathbf{r}_{CA} = (0.4\mathbf{i} + 0.3\mathbf{j}) + (-0.091\mathbf{i} - 0.137\mathbf{j} + 0.114\mathbf{k})$$
$$= 0.309\mathbf{i} + 0.163\mathbf{j} + 0.114\mathbf{k} \ (\text{m}).$$

The coordinates of A are $(0.309, 0.163, 0.114)$ m.

Determining the Components of T Using the coordinates of point A, we find that the position vector from A to B is

$$\mathbf{r}_{AB} = (0 - 0.309)\mathbf{i} + (0.5 - 0.163)\mathbf{j} + (0.15 - 0.114)\mathbf{k}$$

$$= -0.309\mathbf{i} + 0.337\mathbf{j} + 0.036\mathbf{k} \text{ (m)}.$$

Dividing this vector by its magnitude, we obtain the unit vector $\mathbf{e}_{AB}$ (Fig. a).

$$\mathbf{e}_{AB} = \frac{\mathbf{r}_{AB}}{|\mathbf{r}_{AB}|} = \frac{-0.309\mathbf{i} + 0.337\mathbf{j} + 0.036\mathbf{k} \text{ (m)}}{\sqrt{(-0.309 \text{ m})^2 + (0.337 \text{ m})^2 + (0.036 \text{ m})^2}}$$

$$= -0.674\mathbf{i} + 0.735\mathbf{j} + 0.079\mathbf{k}.$$

The force **T** is

$$\mathbf{T} = |\mathbf{T}|\mathbf{e}_{AB} = (50 \text{ N})(-0.674\mathbf{i} + 0.735\mathbf{j} + 0.079\mathbf{k})$$

$$= -33.7\mathbf{i} + 36.7\mathbf{j} + 3.9\mathbf{k} \text{ (N)}.$$

Critical Thinking

Look at the two ways unit vectors were used in this example. The unit vector $\mathbf{e}_{CD}$ was used to obtain the components of the position vector $\mathbf{r}_{CA}$, which made it possible to determine the coordinates of point A. The coordinates of point A were then used to determine the unit vector $\mathbf{e}_{AB}$, which was used to express the force **T** in terms of its components.

Problems

2.61 A vector $\mathbf{U} = 3\mathbf{i} - 4\mathbf{j} - 12\mathbf{k}$. What is its magnitude?

Strategy: The magnitude of a vector is given in terms of its components by Eq. (2.14).

2.62 The vector $\mathbf{e} = \frac{1}{3}\mathbf{i} + \frac{2}{3}\mathbf{j} + e_z\mathbf{k}$ is a unit vector. Determine the component e_z.

2.63 An engineer determines that the attachment point will be subjected to a force $\mathbf{F} = 20\mathbf{i} + F_y\mathbf{j} - 45\mathbf{k}$ (kN). If the attachment point will safely support a force of 80-kN magnitude in any direction, what is the acceptable range of values of F_y?

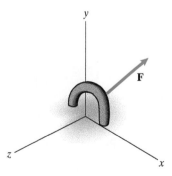

Problem 2.63

2.64 A vector $\mathbf{U} = U_x\mathbf{i} + U_y\mathbf{j} + U_z\mathbf{k}$. Its magnitude $|\mathbf{U}| = 30$. Its components are related by the equations $U_y = -2U_x$ and $U_z = 4U_y$. Determine the components.

2.65 An object is acted upon by two forces $\mathbf{F}_1 = 20\mathbf{i} + 30\mathbf{j} - 24\mathbf{k}$ (kN) and $\mathbf{F}_2 = -60\mathbf{i} + 20\mathbf{j} + 40\mathbf{k}$ (kN). What is the magnitude of the total force acting on the object?

2.66 Two vectors $\mathbf{U} = 3\mathbf{i} - 2\mathbf{j} + 6\mathbf{k}$ and $\mathbf{V} = 4\mathbf{i} + 12\mathbf{j} - 3\mathbf{k}$.

(a) Determine the magnitudes of **U** and **V**.

(b) Determine the magnitude of the vector $3\mathbf{U} + 2\mathbf{V}$.

▶ **2.67** In Active Example 2.6, suppose that you want to redesign the truss, changing the position of point D so that the magnitude of the vector $\mathbf{r}_{CD}$ from point C to point D is 3 m. To accomplish this, let the coordinates of point D be $(2, y_D, 1)$ m, and determine the value of y_D so that $|\mathbf{r}_{CD}| = 3$ m. Draw a sketch of the truss with point D in its new position. What are the new direction cosines of $\mathbf{r}_{CD}$?

2.68 A force vector is given in terms of its components by $\mathbf{F} = 10\mathbf{i} - 20\mathbf{j} - 20\mathbf{k}$ (N).

(a) What are the direction cosines of **F**?

(b) Determine the components of a unit vector **e** that has the same direction as **F**.

2.69 The cable exerts a force **F** on the hook at O whose magnitude is 200 N. The angle between the vector **F** and the x axis is 40°, and the angle between the vector **F** and the y axis is 70°.

(a) What is the angle between the vector **F** and the z axis?

(b) Express **F** in terms of components.

   Strategy: (a) Because you know the angles between the vector **F** and the x and y axes, you can use Eq. (2.16) to determine the angle between **F** and the z axis. (Observe from the figure that the angle between **F** and the z axis is clearly within the range $0 < \theta_z < 180°$.) (b) The components of **F** can be obtained with Eqs. (2.15).

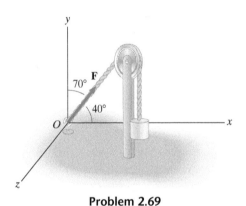

Problem 2.69

2.70 A unit vector has direction cosines $\cos \theta_x = -0.5$ and $\cos \theta_y = 0.2$. Its z component is positive. Express it in terms of components.

2.71 The airplane's engines exert a total thrust force **T** of 200-kN magnitude. The angle between **T** and the x axis is 120°, and the angle between **T** and the y axis is 130°. The z component of **T** is positive.

(a) What is the angle between **T** and the z axis?

(b) Express **T** in terms of components.

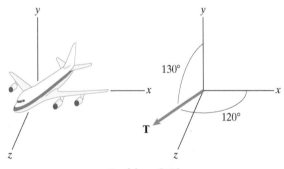

Problem 2.71

Refer to the following diagram when solving Problems 2.72 through 2.75.

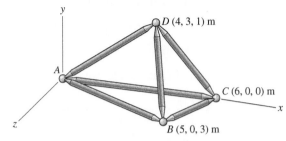

Problems 2.72–2.75

2.72 Determine the components of the position vector $\mathbf{r}_{BD}$ from point B to point D. Use your result to determine the distance from B to D.

2.73 What are the direction cosines of the position vector $\mathbf{r}_{BD}$ from point B to point D?

2.74 Determine the components of the unit vector $\mathbf{e}_{CD}$ that points from point C toward point D.

2.75 What are the direction cosines of the unit vector $\mathbf{e}_{CD}$ that points from point C toward point D?

▶ **2.76** In Example 2.7, suppose that the caisson shifts on the ground to a new position. The magnitude of the force **F** remains 600 lb. In the new position, the angle between the force **F** and the x axis is 60° and the angle between **F** and the z axis is 70°. Express **F** in terms of components.

2.77 Astronauts on the space shuttle use radar to determine the magnitudes and direction cosines of the position vectors of two satellites A and B. The vector $\mathbf{r}_A$ from the shuttle to satellite A has magnitude 2 km and direction cosines $\cos \theta_x = 0.768$, $\cos \theta_y = 0.384$, $\cos \theta_z = 0.512$. The vector $\mathbf{r}_B$ from the shuttle to satellite B has magnitude 4 km and direction cosines $\cos \theta_x = 0.743$, $\cos \theta_y = 0.557$, $\cos \theta_z = -0.371$. What is the distance between the satellites?

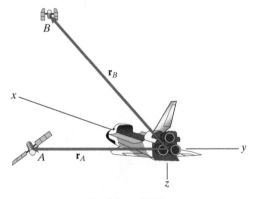

Problem 2.77

2.78 Archaeologists measure a pre-Columbian ceremonial structure and obtain the dimensions shown. Determine (a) the magnitude and (b) the direction cosines of the position vector from point A to point B.

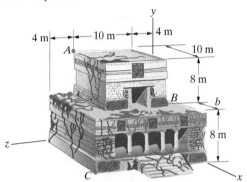

Problem 2.78

2.79 Consider the structure described in Problem 2.78. After returning to the United States, an archaeologist discovers that a graduate student has erased the only data file containing the dimension b. But from recorded GPS data he is able to calculate that the distance from point B to point C is 16.61 m.

(a) What is the distance b?

(b) Determine the direction cosines of the position vector from B to C.

2.80 Observers at A and B use theodolites to measure the direction from their positions to a rocket in flight. If the coordinates of the rocket's position at a given instant are (4, 4, 2) km, determine the direction cosines of the vectors $\mathbf{r}_{AR}$ and $\mathbf{r}_{BR}$ that the observers would measure at that instant.

2.81* Suppose that the coordinates of the rocket's position are unknown. At a given instant, the person at A determines that the direction cosines of $\mathbf{r}_{AR}$ are $\cos \theta_x = 0.535$, $\cos \theta_y = 0.802$, and $\cos \theta_z = 0.267$, and the person at B determines that the direction cosines of $\mathbf{r}_{BR}$ are $\cos \theta_x = -0.576$, $\cos \theta_y = 0.798$, and $\cos \theta_z = -0.177$. What are the coordinates of the rocket's position at that instant?

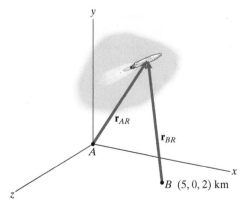

Problems 2.80/2.81

2.82* The height of Mount Everest was originally measured by a surveyor in the following way. He first measured the altitudes of two points and the horizontal distance between them. For example, suppose that the points A and B are 3000 m above sea level and are 10,000 m apart. He then used a theodolite to measure the direction cosines of the vector $\mathbf{r}_{AP}$ from point A to the top of the mountain P and the vector $\mathbf{r}_{BP}$ from point B to P. Suppose that the direction cosines of $\mathbf{r}_{AP}$ are $\cos \theta_x = 0.5179$, $\cos \theta_y = 0.6906$, and $\cos \theta_z = 0.5048$, and the direction cosines of $\mathbf{r}_{BP}$ are $\cos \theta_x = -0.3743$, $\cos \theta_y = 0.7486$, and $\cos \theta_z = 0.5472$. Using this data, determine the height of Mount Everest above sea level.

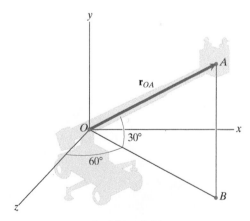

Problem 2.82

2.83 The distance from point O to point A is 20 ft. The straight line AB is parallel to the y axis, and point B is in the x–z plane. Express the vector $\mathbf{r}_{OA}$ in terms of components.

Strategy: You can express $\mathbf{r}_{OA}$ as the sum of a vector from O to B and a vector from B to A. You can then express the vector from O to B as the sum of vector components parallel to the x and z axes. See Example 2.8.

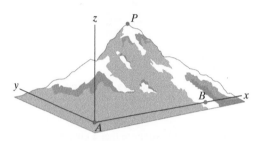

Problem 2.83

2.84 The magnitudes of the two force vectors are $|\mathbf{F}_A| = 140$ lb and $|\mathbf{F}_B| = 100$ lb. Determine the magnitude of the sum of the forces $\mathbf{F}_A + \mathbf{F}_B$.

2.85 Determine the direction cosines of the vectors $\mathbf{F}_A$ and $\mathbf{F}_B$.

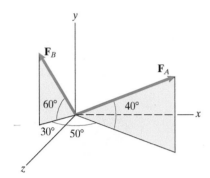

Problems 2.84/2.85

▶**2.86** In Example 2.8, suppose that a change in the wind causes a change in the position of the balloon and increases the magnitude of the force $\mathbf{F}$ exerted on the hook at O to 900 N. In the new position, the angle between the vector component $\mathbf{F}_h$ and $\mathbf{F}$ is 35°, and the angle between the vector components $\mathbf{F}_h$ and $\mathbf{F}_z$ is 40°. Draw a sketch showing the relationship of these angles to the components of $\mathbf{F}$. Express $\mathbf{F}$ in terms of its components.

2.87 An engineer calculates that the magnitude of the axial force in one of the beams of a geodesic dome is $|\mathbf{P}| = 7.65$ kN. The cartesian coordinates of the endpoints A and B of the straight beam are $(-12.4, 22.0, -18.4)$ m and $(-9.2, 24.4, -15.6)$ m, respectively. Express the force $\mathbf{P}$ in terms of components.

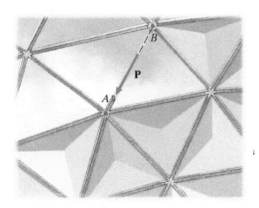

Problem 2.87

2.88 The cable BC exerts an 8-kN force $\mathbf{F}$ on the bar AB at B.
(a) Determine the components of a unit vector that points from point B toward point C.
(b) Express $\mathbf{F}$ in terms of components.

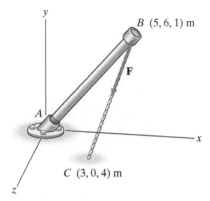

Problem 2.88

2.89 A cable extends from point C to point E. It exerts a 50-lb force $\mathbf{T}$ on the plate at C that is directed along the line from C to E. Express $\mathbf{T}$ in terms of components.

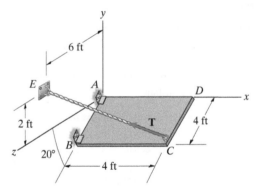

Problem 2.89

▶**2.90** In Example 2.9, suppose that the metal loop at A is moved upward so that the vertical distance to A increases from 7 ft to 8 ft. As a result, the magnitudes of the forces $\mathbf{F}_{AB}$ and $\mathbf{F}_{AC}$ increase to $|\mathbf{F}_{AB}| = |\mathbf{F}_{AC}| = 240$ lb. What is the magnitude of the total force $\mathbf{F} = \mathbf{F}_{AB} + \mathbf{F}_{AC}$ exerted on the loop by the rope?

2.91 The cable AB exerts a 200-lb force $\mathbf{F}_{AB}$ at point A that is directed along the line from A to B. Express $\mathbf{F}_{AB}$ in terms of components.

2.92 Cable AB exerts a 200-lb force $\mathbf{F}_{AB}$ at point A that is directed along the line from A to B. The cable AC exerts a 100-lb force $\mathbf{F}_{AC}$ at point A that is directed along the line from A to C. Determine the magnitude of the total force exerted at point A by the two cables.

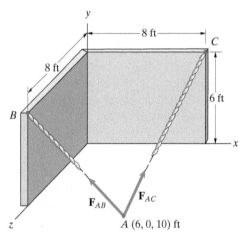

Problems 2.91/2.92

2.93 The 70-m-tall tower is supported by three cables that exert forces $\mathbf{F}_{AB}$, $\mathbf{F}_{AC}$, and $\mathbf{F}_{AD}$ on it. The magnitude of each force is 2 kN. Express the total force exerted on the tower by the three cables in terms of components.

2.94 The magnitude of the force $\mathbf{F}_{AB}$ is 2 kN. The x and z components of the vector sum of the forces exerted on the tower by the three cables are zero. What are the magnitudes of $\mathbf{F}_{AC}$ and $\mathbf{F}_{AD}$?

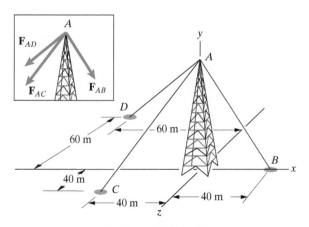

Problems 2.93/2.94

▶ **2.95** In Example 2.10, suppose that the distance from point C to the collar A is increased from 0.2 m to 0.3 m, and the magnitude of the force $\mathbf{T}$ increases to 60 N. Express $\mathbf{T}$ in terms of its components.

2.96 The cable AB exerts a 32-lb force $\mathbf{T}$ on the collar at A. Express $\mathbf{T}$ in terms of components.

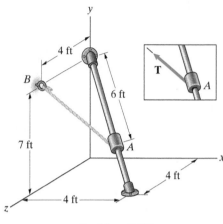

Problem 2.96

2.97 The circular bar has a 4-m radius and lies in the x–y plane. Express the position vector from point B to the collar at A in terms of components.

2.98 The cable AB exerts a 60-N force $\mathbf{T}$ on the collar at A that is directed along the line from A toward B. Express $\mathbf{T}$ in terms of components.

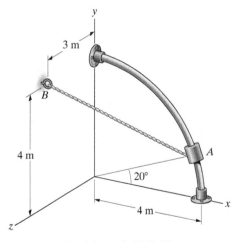

Problems 2.97/2.98

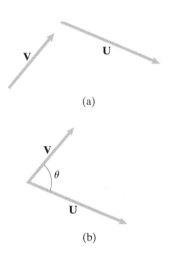

(a)

(b)

Figure 2.21
(**a**) The vectors **U** and **V**.
(**b**) The angle θ between **U** and **V** when the two vectors are placed tail to tail.

2.4 Dot Products

BACKGROUND

Two kinds of products of vectors, the dot and cross products, have been found to have applications in science and engineering, especially in mechanics and electromagnetic field theory. We use both of these products in Chapter 4 to evaluate moments of forces about points and lines.

The dot product of two vectors has many uses, including determining the components of a vector parallel and perpendicular to a given line and determining the angle between two lines in space.

Definition

Consider two vectors **U** and **V** (Fig. 2.21a). The *dot product* of **U** and **V**, denoted by **U** · **V** (hence the name "dot product"), is defined to be the product of the magnitude of **U**, the magnitude of **V**, and the cosine of the angle θ between **U** and **V** when they are placed tail to tail (Fig. 2.21b):

$$\mathbf{U} \cdot \mathbf{V} = |\mathbf{U}||\mathbf{V}| \cos \theta. \tag{2.18}$$

Because the result of the dot product is a scalar, the dot product is sometimes called the scalar product. The units of the dot product are the product of the units of the two vectors. *Notice that the dot product of two nonzero vectors is equal to zero if and only if the vectors are perpendicular.*

The dot product has the properties

$$\mathbf{U} \cdot \mathbf{V} = \mathbf{V} \cdot \mathbf{U}, \quad \text{The dot product is commutative.} \tag{2.19}$$

$$a\,(\mathbf{U} \cdot \mathbf{V}) = (a\mathbf{U}) \cdot \mathbf{V} = \mathbf{U} \cdot (a\mathbf{V}), \quad \begin{array}{l}\text{The dot product is associative}\\\text{with respect to scalar}\\\text{multiplication.}\end{array} \tag{2.20}$$

and

$$\mathbf{U} \cdot (\mathbf{V} + \mathbf{W}) = \mathbf{U} \cdot \mathbf{V} + \mathbf{U} \cdot \mathbf{W}, \quad \begin{array}{l}\text{The dot product is associative}\\\text{with respect to vector addition.}\end{array} \tag{2.21}$$

for any scalar a and vectors **U**, **V**, and **W**.

Dot Products in Terms of Components

In this section we derive an equation that allows you to determine the dot product of two vectors if you know their scalar components. The derivation also results in an equation for the angle between the vectors. The first step is to determine the dot products formed from the unit vectors **i**, **j**, and **k**. Let us evaluate the dot product **i** · **i**. The magnitude $|\mathbf{i}| = 1$, and the angle between two identical vectors placed tail to tail is zero, so we obtain

$$\mathbf{i} \cdot \mathbf{i} = |\mathbf{i}||\mathbf{i}| \cos (0) = (1)(1)(1) = 1.$$

The dot product of **i** and **j** is

$$\mathbf{i} \cdot \mathbf{j} = |\mathbf{i}||\mathbf{j}| \cdot \cos (90°) = (1)(1)(0) = 0.$$

Continuing in this way, we obtain

$$\begin{array}{lll}\mathbf{i} \cdot \mathbf{i} = 1, & \mathbf{i} \cdot \mathbf{j} = 0, & \mathbf{i} \cdot \mathbf{k} = 0,\\\mathbf{j} \cdot \mathbf{i} = 0, & \mathbf{j} \cdot \mathbf{j} = 1, & \mathbf{j} \cdot \mathbf{k} = 0,\\\mathbf{k} \cdot \mathbf{i} = 0, & \mathbf{k} \cdot \mathbf{j} = 0, & \mathbf{k} \cdot \mathbf{k} = 1.\end{array} \tag{2.22}$$

The dot product of two vectors **U** and **V**, expressed in terms of their components, is

$$\mathbf{U} \cdot \mathbf{V} = (U_x\mathbf{i} + U_y\mathbf{j} + U_z\mathbf{k}) \cdot (V_x\mathbf{i} + V_y\mathbf{j} + V_z\mathbf{k})$$
$$= U_xV_x(\mathbf{i} \cdot \mathbf{i}) + U_xV_y(\mathbf{i} \cdot \mathbf{j}) + U_xV_z(\mathbf{i} \cdot \mathbf{k})$$
$$+ U_yV_x(\mathbf{j} \cdot \mathbf{i}) + U_yV_y(\mathbf{j} \cdot \mathbf{j}) + U_yV_z(\mathbf{j} \cdot \mathbf{k})$$
$$+ U_zV_x(\mathbf{k} \cdot \mathbf{i}) + U_zV_y(\mathbf{k} \cdot \mathbf{j}) + U_zV_z(\mathbf{k} \cdot \mathbf{k}).$$

In obtaining this result, we used Eqs. (2.20) and (2.21). Substituting Eqs. (2.22) into this expression, we obtain an equation for the dot product in terms of the scalar components of the two vectors:

$$\mathbf{U} \cdot \mathbf{V} = U_xV_x + U_yV_y + U_zV_z. \tag{2.23}$$

To obtain an equation for the angle θ in terms of the components of the vectors, we equate the expression for the dot product given by Eq. (2.23) to the definition of the dot product, Eq. (2.18), and solve for $\cos\theta$:

$$\cos\theta = \frac{\mathbf{U} \cdot \mathbf{V}}{|\mathbf{U}||\mathbf{V}|} = \frac{U_xV_x + U_yV_y + U_zV_z}{|\mathbf{U}||\mathbf{V}|}. \tag{2.24}$$

Vector Components Parallel and Normal to a Line

In some engineering applications a vector must be expressed in terms of vector components that are parallel and normal (perpendicular) to a given line. The component of a vector parallel to a line is called the *projection* of the vector onto the line. For example, when the vector represents a force, the projection of the force onto a line is the component of the force in the direction of the line.

We can determine the components of a vector parallel and normal to a line by using the dot product. Consider a vector **U** and a straight line L (Fig. 2.22a). We can express **U** as the sum of vector components $\mathbf{U}_p$ and $\mathbf{U}_n$ that are parallel and normal to L (Fig. 2.22b).

The Parallel Component   In terms of the angle θ between **U** and the vector component $\mathbf{U}_p$, the magnitude of $\mathbf{U}_p$ is

$$|\mathbf{U}_p| = |\mathbf{U}| \cos\theta. \tag{2.25}$$

Let **e** be a unit vector parallel to L (Fig. 2.23). The dot product of **e** and **U** is

$$\mathbf{e} \cdot \mathbf{U} = |\mathbf{e}||\mathbf{U}| \cos\theta = |\mathbf{U}| \cos\theta.$$

Comparing this result with Eq. (2.25), we see that the magnitude of $\mathbf{U}_p$ is

$$|\mathbf{U}_p| = \mathbf{e} \cdot \mathbf{U}.$$

Therefore the parallel vector component, or projection of **U** onto L, is

$$\mathbf{U}_p = (\mathbf{e} \cdot \mathbf{U})\mathbf{e}. \tag{2.26}$$

(This equation holds even if **e** doesn't point in the direction of $\mathbf{U}_p$. In that case, the angle $\theta > 90°$ and $\mathbf{e} \cdot \mathbf{U}$ is negative.) When the components of a vector and the components of a unit vector **e** parallel to a line L are known, we can use Eq. (2.26) to determine the component of the vector parallel to L.

The Normal Component   Once the parallel vector component has been determined, we can obtain the normal vector component from the relation $\mathbf{U} = \mathbf{U}_p + \mathbf{U}_n$:

$$\mathbf{U}_n = \mathbf{U} - \mathbf{U}_p. \tag{2.27}$$

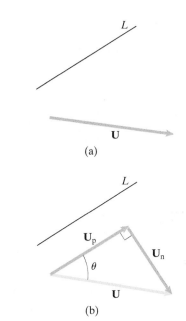

Figure 2.22
(a) A vector **U** and line L.
(b) Resolving **U** into components parallel and normal to L.

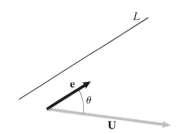

Figure 2.23
The unit vector **e** is parallel to L.

RESULTS

Dot Product

The dot product of two vectors **U** and **V** is defined by

$$\mathbf{U} \cdot \mathbf{V} = |\mathbf{U}||\mathbf{V}|\cos\theta, \tag{2.18}$$

where θ is the angle between the vectors when they are placed tail to tail. Notice that $\mathbf{U} \cdot \mathbf{U} = |\mathbf{U}|^2$. If $|\mathbf{U}| \neq 0$ and $|\mathbf{V}| \neq 0$, $\mathbf{U} \cdot \mathbf{V} = 0$ if and only if **U** and **V** are perpendicular.

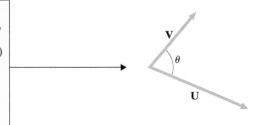

Dot Product in Terms of Components

The dot product of **U** and **V** is given in terms of the components of the vectors by

$$\mathbf{U} \cdot \mathbf{V} = U_x V_x + U_y V_y + U_z V_z. \tag{2.23}$$

Vector Components Parallel and Normal to a Line

A vector **U** can be resolved into a vector component $\mathbf{U}_p$ that is parallel to a given line L and a vector component $\mathbf{U}_n$ that is normal to L. If **e** is a unit vector that is parallel to L, the parallel component of **U** is given by

$$\mathbf{U}_p = (\mathbf{e} \cdot \mathbf{U})\,\mathbf{e}. \tag{2.26}$$

The normal component can be obtained from the relation

$$\mathbf{U}_n = \mathbf{U} - \mathbf{U}_p. \tag{2.27}$$

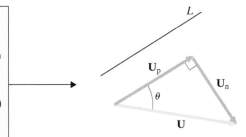

Active Example 2.11 Dot Products (▶ *Related Problem 2.99*)

The components of two vectors **U** and **V** are $\mathbf{U} = 6\mathbf{i} - 5\mathbf{j} - 3\mathbf{k}$ and $\mathbf{V} = 4\mathbf{i} + 2\mathbf{j} + 2\mathbf{k}$. (a) What is the value of $\mathbf{U} \cdot \mathbf{V}$? (b) What is the angle between **U** and **V** when they are placed tail to tail?

Strategy

Knowing the components of **U** and **V**, we can use Eq. (2.23) to determine the value of $\mathbf{U} \cdot \mathbf{V}$. Then we can use the definition of the dot product, Eq. (2.18), to calculate the angle between the vectors.

Solution

$$\begin{aligned}
\mathbf{U} \cdot \mathbf{V} &= U_x V_x + U_y V_y + U_z V_z \\
&= (6)(4) + (-5)(2) + (-3)(2) \\
&= 8.
\end{aligned}$$

Use the components of the vectors to determine the value of $\mathbf{U} \cdot \mathbf{V}$.

$$\mathbf{U} \cdot \mathbf{V} = |\mathbf{U}||\mathbf{V}|\cos\theta,$$

so

$$\begin{aligned}
\cos\theta &= \frac{\mathbf{U} \cdot \mathbf{V}}{|\mathbf{U}||\mathbf{V}|} \\
&= \frac{8}{\sqrt{(6)^2 + (-5)^2 + (-3)^2}\ \sqrt{(4)^2 + (2)^2 + (2)^2}} \\
&= 0.195.
\end{aligned}$$

Use the definition of $\mathbf{U} \cdot \mathbf{V}$ to determine θ.

Therefore $\theta = 78.7°$.

Practice Problem The components of two vectors $\mathbf{U}$ and $\mathbf{V}$ are $\mathbf{U} = 6\mathbf{i} - 5\mathbf{j} - 3\mathbf{k}$ and $\mathbf{V} = V_x\mathbf{i} + 2\mathbf{j} + 2\mathbf{k}$. Determine the value of the component V_x so that the vectors $\mathbf{U}$ and $\mathbf{V}$ are perpendicular.

Answer: $V_x = 2.67$.

Example 2.12   Using the Dot Product to Determine an Angle (▶ Related Problem 2.100)

What is the angle θ between the lines AB and AC?

Strategy
We know the coordinates of the points A, B, and C, so we can determine the components of the vector $\mathbf{r}_{AB}$ from A to B and the vector $\mathbf{r}_{AC}$ from A to C (Fig. a). Then we can use Eq. (2.24) to determine θ.

Solution
The vectors $\mathbf{r}_{AB}$ and $\mathbf{r}_{AC}$, with the coordinates in meters, are

$$\mathbf{r}_{AB} = (6 - 4)\mathbf{i} + (1 - 3)\mathbf{j} + (-2 - 2)\mathbf{k} = 2\mathbf{i} - 2\mathbf{j} - 4\mathbf{k} \ (\mathrm{m}),$$
$$\mathbf{r}_{AC} = (8 - 4)\mathbf{i} + (8 - 3)\mathbf{j} + (4 - 2)\mathbf{k} = 4\mathbf{i} + 5\mathbf{j} + 2\mathbf{k} \ (\mathrm{m}).$$

Their magnitudes are

$$|\mathbf{r}_{AB}| = \sqrt{(2\ \mathrm{m})^2 + (-2\ \mathrm{m})^2 + (-4\ \mathrm{m})^2} = 4.90\ \mathrm{m},$$
$$|\mathbf{r}_{AC}| = \sqrt{(4\ \mathrm{m})^2 + (5\ \mathrm{m})^2 + (2\ \mathrm{m})^2} = 6.71\ \mathrm{m}.$$

The dot product of $\mathbf{r}_{AB}$ and $\mathbf{r}_{AC}$ is

$$\mathbf{r}_{AB} \cdot \mathbf{r}_{AC} = (2\ \mathrm{m})(4\ \mathrm{m}) + (-2\ \mathrm{m})(5\ \mathrm{m}) + (-4\ \mathrm{m})(2\ \mathrm{m}) = -10\ \mathrm{m}^2.$$

Therefore,

$$\cos\theta = \frac{\mathbf{r}_{AB} \cdot \mathbf{r}_{AC}}{|\mathbf{r}_{AB}||\mathbf{r}_{AC}|} = \frac{-10\ \mathrm{m}^2}{(4.90\ \mathrm{m})(6.71\ \mathrm{m})} = -0.304.$$

The angle $\theta = \arccos(-0.304) = 107.7°$.

Critical Thinking
What does it mean if the dot product of two vectors is negative? From Eq. (2.18) and the graph of the cosine (Fig. b), you can see that the dot product is negative, as it is in this example, only if the enclosed angle between the two vectors is greater than $90°$.

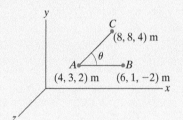

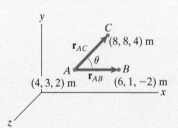

(a) The position vectors $\mathbf{r}_{AB}$ and $\mathbf{r}_{AC}$.

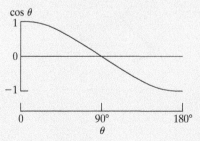

(b) Graph of $\cos\theta$.

Example 2.13   Vector Components Parallel and Normal to a Line (▶ *Related Problem 2.111*)

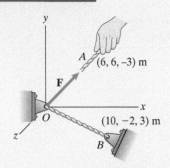

Suppose that you pull on the cable *OA*, exerting a 50-N force **F** at *O*. What are the vector components of **F** parallel and normal to the cable *OB*?

Strategy

Expressing **F** as the sum of vector components parallel and normal to *OB* (Fig. a), we can determine the vector components by using Eqs. (2.26) and (2.27). But to apply them, we must first express **F** in terms of scalar components and determine the scalar components of a unit vector parallel to *OB*. We can obtain the components of **F** by determining the components of the unit vector pointing from *O* toward *A* and multiplying them by $|\mathbf{F}|$.

Solution

The position vectors from *O* to *A* and from *O* to *B* are (Fig. b)

$$\mathbf{r}_{OA} = 6\mathbf{i} + 6\mathbf{j} - 3\mathbf{k} \ (\text{m}),$$

$$\mathbf{r}_{OB} = 10\mathbf{i} - 2\mathbf{j} + 3\mathbf{k} \ (\text{m}).$$

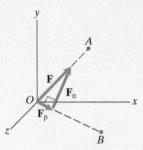

Their magnitudes are $|\mathbf{r}_{OA}| = 9$ m and $|\mathbf{r}_{OB}| = 10.6$ m. Dividing these vectors by their magnitudes, we obtain unit vectors that point from the origin toward *A* and *B* (Fig. c):

(a) The components of **F** parallel and normal to *OB*.

$$\mathbf{e}_{OA} = \frac{\mathbf{r}_{OA}}{|\mathbf{r}_{OA}|} = \frac{6\mathbf{i} + 6\mathbf{j} - 3\mathbf{k} \ (\text{m})}{9 \ \text{m}} = 0.667\mathbf{i} + 0.667\mathbf{j} - 0.333\mathbf{k},$$

$$\mathbf{e}_{OB} = \frac{\mathbf{r}_{OB}}{|\mathbf{r}_{OB}|} = \frac{10\mathbf{i} - 2\mathbf{j} + 3\mathbf{k} \ (\text{m})}{10.6 \ \text{m}} = 0.941\mathbf{i} - 0.188\mathbf{j} + 0.282\mathbf{k}.$$

The force **F** in terms of scalar components is

$$\mathbf{F} = |\mathbf{F}|\mathbf{e}_{OA} = (50 \ \text{N})(0.667\mathbf{i} + 0.667\mathbf{j} - 0.333\mathbf{k})$$

$$= 33.3\mathbf{i} + 33.3\mathbf{j} - 16.7\mathbf{k} \ (\text{N}).$$

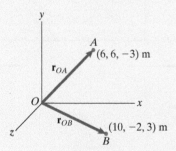

(b) The position vectors $\mathbf{r}_{OA}$ and $\mathbf{r}_{OB}$.

Taking the dot product of $\mathbf{e}_{OB}$ and **F**, we obtain

$$\mathbf{e}_{OB} \cdot \mathbf{F} = (0.941)(33.3 \ \text{N}) + (-0.188)(33.3 \ \text{N}) + (0.282)(-16.7 \ \text{N})$$

$$= 20.4 \ \text{N}.$$

The parallel vector component of **F** is

$$\mathbf{F}_{\text{p}} = (\mathbf{e}_{OB} \cdot \mathbf{F})\mathbf{e}_{OB} = (20.4 \ \text{N})(0.941\mathbf{i} - 0.188\mathbf{j} + 0.282\mathbf{k})$$

$$= 19.2\mathbf{i} - 3.83\mathbf{j} + 5.75\mathbf{k} \ (\text{N}),$$

and the normal vector component is

$$\mathbf{F}_{\text{n}} = \mathbf{F} - \mathbf{F}_{\text{p}} = 14.2\mathbf{i} + 37.2\mathbf{j} - 22.4\mathbf{k} \ (\text{N}).$$

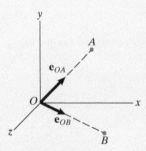

(c) The unit vectors $\mathbf{e}_{OA}$ and $\mathbf{e}_{OB}$.

Critical Thinking

How can you confirm that two vectors are perpendicular? It is clear from Eq. (2.18) that the dot product of two nonzero vectors is zero if and only if the enclosed angle between them is 90°. We can use this diagnostic test to confirm that the components of **F** determined in this example are perpendicular. Evaluating the dot product of $\mathbf{F}_{\text{p}}$ and $\mathbf{F}_{\text{n}}$ in terms of their components in newtons, we obtain

$$\mathbf{F}_{\text{p}} \cdot \mathbf{F}_{\text{n}} = (19.2)(14.2) + (-3.83)(37.2) + (5.75)(-22.4) = 0.$$

Problems

▶ **2.99** In Active Example 2.11, suppose that the vector **V** is changed to **V** = 4**i** − 6**j** − 10**k**.

(a) What is the value of **U** · **V**?

(b) What is the angle between **U** and **V** when they are placed tail to tail?

▶ **2.100** In Example 2.12, suppose that the coordinates of point *B* are changed to (6, 4, 4) m. What is the angle θ between the lines *AB* and *AC*?

2.101 What is the dot product of the position vector **r** = −10**i** + 25**j** (m) and the force vector **F** = 300**i** + 250**j** + 300**k** (N)?

2.102 Suppose that the dot product of two vectors **U** and **V** is **U** · **V** = 0. If $|\mathbf{U}| \neq 0$, what do you know about the vector **V**?

2.103 Two *perpendicular* vectors are given in terms of their components by **U** = U_x**i** − 4**j** + 6**k** and **V** = 3**i** + 2**j** − 3**k**. Use the dot product to determine the component U_x.

2.104 The three vectors

$$\mathbf{U} = U_x\mathbf{i} + 3\mathbf{j} + 2\mathbf{k},$$

$$\mathbf{V} = -3\mathbf{i} + V_y\mathbf{j} + 3\mathbf{k},$$

$$\mathbf{W} = -2\mathbf{i} + 4\mathbf{j} + W_z\mathbf{k}$$

are mutually perpendicular. Use the dot product to determine the components U_x, V_y, and W_z.

2.105 The magnitudes $|\mathbf{U}| = 10$ and $|\mathbf{V}| = 20$.

(a) Use Eq. (2.18) to determine **U** · **V**.

(b) Use Eq. (2.23) to determine **U** · **V**.

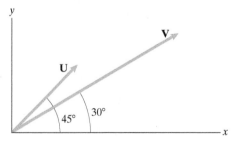

Problem 2.105

2.106 By evaluating the dot product **U** · **V**, prove the identity $\cos(\theta_1 - \theta_2) = \cos\theta_1\cos\theta_2 + \sin\theta_1\sin\theta_2$.

Strategy: Evaluate the dot product both by using Eq. (2.18) and by using Eq. (2.23).

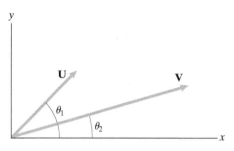

Problem 2.106

2.107 Use the dot product to determine the angle between the forestay (cable *AB*) and the backstay (cable *BC*) of the sailboat.

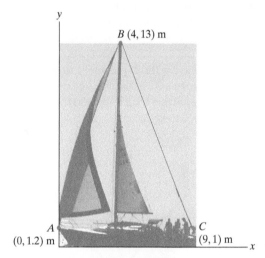

Problem 2.107

2.108 Determine the angle θ between the lines *AB* and *AC*

(a) by using the law of cosines (see Appendix A);

(b) by using the dot product.

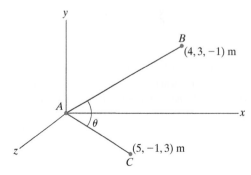

Problem 2.108

2.109 The ship O measures the positions of the ship A and the airplane B and obtains the coordinates shown. What is the angle θ between the lines of sight OA and OB?

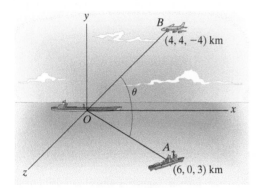

Problem 2.109

2.110 Astronauts on the space shuttle use radar to determine the magnitudes and direction cosines of the position vectors of two satellites A and B. The vector $\mathbf{r}_A$ from the shuttle to satellite A has magnitude 2 km and direction cosines $\cos \theta_x = 0.768$, $\cos \theta_y = 0.384$, $\cos \theta_z = 0.512$. The vector $\mathbf{r}_B$ from the shuttle to satellite B has magnitude 4 km and direction cosines $\cos \theta_x = 0.743$, $\cos \theta_y = 0.557$, $\cos \theta_z = -0.371$. What is the angle θ between the vectors $\mathbf{r}_A$ and $\mathbf{r}_B$?

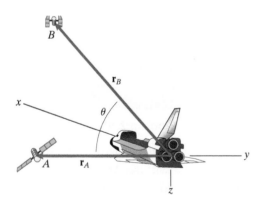

Problem 2.110

▶ **2.111** In Example 2.13, if you shift your position and the coordinates of point A where you apply the 50-N force become $(8, 3, -3)$ m, what is the vector component of $\mathbf{F}$ parallel to the cable OB?

2.112 The person exerts a force $\mathbf{F} = 60\mathbf{i} - 40\mathbf{j}$ (N) on the handle of the exercise machine. Use Eq. (2.26) to determine the vector component of $\mathbf{F}$ that is parallel to the line from the origin O to where the person grips the handle.

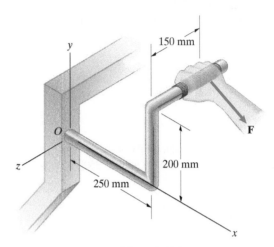

Problem 2.112

2.113 At the instant shown, the Harrier's thrust vector is $\mathbf{T} = 17,000\mathbf{i} + 68,000\mathbf{j} - 8,000\mathbf{k}$ (N) and its velocity vector is $\mathbf{v} = 7.3\mathbf{i} + 1.8\mathbf{j} - 0.6\mathbf{k}$ (m/s). The quantity $P = |\mathbf{T}_p||\mathbf{v}|$, where $\mathbf{T}_p$ is the vector component of $\mathbf{T}$ parallel to $\mathbf{v}$, is the power currently being transferred to the airplane by its engine. Determine the value of P.

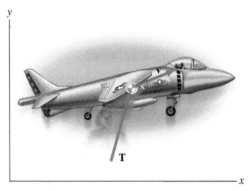

Problem 2.113

2.114 Cables extend from A to B and from A to C. The cable AC exerts a 1000-lb force $\mathbf{F}$ at A.

(a) What is the angle between the cables AB and AC?

(b) Determine the vector component of $\mathbf{F}$ parallel to the cable AB.

2.115 Let $\mathbf{r}_{AB}$ be the position vector from point A to point B. Determine the vector component of $\mathbf{r}_{AB}$ parallel to the cable AC.

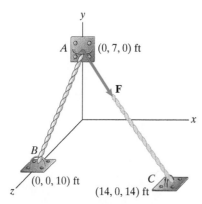

Problems 2.114/2.115

2.116 The force $\mathbf{F} = 10\mathbf{i} + 12\mathbf{j} - 6\mathbf{k}$ (N). Determine the vector components of $\mathbf{F}$ parallel and normal to the line OA.

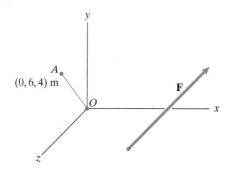

Problem 2.116

2.117 The rope AB exerts a 50-N force $\mathbf{T}$ on collar A. Determine the vector component of $\mathbf{T}$ parallel to the bar CD.

2.118 In Problem 2.117, determine the vector component of $\mathbf{T}$ normal to the bar CD.

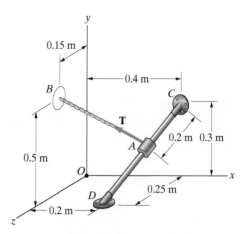

Problems 2.117/2.118

2.119 The disk A is at the midpoint of the sloped surface. The string from A to B exerts a 0.2-lb force $\mathbf{F}$ on the disk. If you express $\mathbf{F}$ in terms of vector components parallel and normal to the sloped surface, what is the component normal to the surface?

2.120 In Problem 2.119, what is the vector component of $\mathbf{F}$ parallel to the surface?

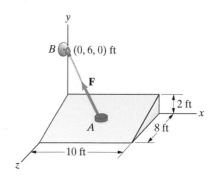

Problems 2.119/2.120

2.121 An astronaut in a maneuvering unit approaches a space station. At the present instant, the station informs him that his position relative to the origin of the station's coordinate system is $r_G = 50i + 80j + 180k$ (m) and his velocity is $v = -2.2j - 3.6k$ (m/s). The position of an airlock is $r_A = -12i + 20k$ (m). Determine the angle between his velocity vector and the line from his position to the airlock's position.

2.122 In Problem 2.121, determine the vector component of the astronaut's velocity parallel to the line from his position to the airlock's position.

Problems 2.121/2.122

2.123 Point P is at longitude 30°W and latitude 45°N on the Atlantic Ocean between Nova Scotia and France. Point Q is at longitude 60°E and latitude 20°N in the Arabian Sea. Use the dot product to determine the shortest distance along the surface of the earth from P to Q in terms of the radius of the earth R_E.

Strategy: Use the dot product to determine the angle between the lines OP and OQ; then use the definition of an angle in radians to determine the distance along the surface of the earth from P to Q.

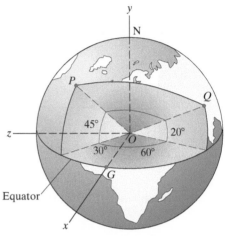

Problem 2.123

2.5 Cross Products

BACKGROUND

Like the dot product, the cross product of two vectors has many applications, including determining the rate of rotation of a fluid particle and calculating the force exerted on a charged particle by a magnetic field. Because of its usefulness for determining moments of forces, the cross product is an indispensable tool in mechanics. In this section we show you how to evaluate cross products and give examples of simple applications.

Definition

Consider two vectors U and V (Fig. 2.24a). The *cross product* of U and V, denoted $U \times V$, is defined by

$$U \times V = |U||V| \sin \theta \, e. \tag{2.28}$$

The angle θ is the angle between U and V when they are placed tail to tail (Fig. 2.24b). The vector e is a unit vector defined to be perpendicular to both U and V. Since this leaves two possibilities for the direction of e, the vectors U, V, and e are defined to be a right-handed system. The *right-hand rule* for determining the direction of e is shown in Fig. 2.24c. If the fingers of the right hand are pointed in the direction of the vector U (the first vector in the cross product) and then bent toward the vector V (the second vector in the cross product), the thumb points in the direction of e.

Because the result of the cross product is a vector, it is sometimes called the vector product. The units of the cross product are the product of the units of the two vectors. Notice that the cross product of two nonzero vectors is equal to zero if and only if the two vectors are parallel.

An interesting property of the cross product is that it is *not* commutative. Eq. (2.28) implies that the magnitude of the vector $\mathbf{U} \times \mathbf{V}$ is equal to the magnitude of the vector $\mathbf{V} \times \mathbf{U}$, but the right-hand rule indicates that they are opposite in direction (Fig. 2.25). That is,

$$\mathbf{U} \times \mathbf{V} = -\mathbf{V} \times \mathbf{U}. \quad \text{The cross product is } \textit{not} \text{ commutative.} \quad (2.29)$$

The cross product also satisfies the relations

$$a\,(\mathbf{U} \times \mathbf{V}) = (a\mathbf{U}) \times \mathbf{V} = \mathbf{U} \times (a\mathbf{V}) \quad \begin{array}{l}\text{The cross product is} \\ \text{associative with} \\ \text{respect to scalar} \\ \text{multiplication.}\end{array} \quad (2.30)$$

and

$$\mathbf{U} \times (\mathbf{V} + \mathbf{W}) = (\mathbf{U} \times \mathbf{V}) + (\mathbf{U} \times \mathbf{W}) \quad \begin{array}{l}\text{The cross product is} \\ \text{distributive with} \\ \text{respect to vector} \\ \text{addition.}\end{array} \quad (2.31)$$

for any scalar a and vectors $\mathbf{U}$, $\mathbf{V}$, and $\mathbf{W}$.

Cross Products in Terms of Components

To obtain an equation for the cross product of two vectors in terms of their components, we must determine the cross products formed from the unit vectors $\mathbf{i}$, $\mathbf{j}$, and $\mathbf{k}$. Since the angle between two identical vectors placed tail to tail is zero, it follows that

$$\mathbf{i} \times \mathbf{i} = |\mathbf{i}||\mathbf{i}| \sin(0)\mathbf{e} = \mathbf{0}.$$

The cross product $\mathbf{i} \times \mathbf{j}$ is

$$\mathbf{i} \times \mathbf{j} = |\mathbf{i}||\mathbf{j}| \sin 90°\mathbf{e} = \mathbf{e},$$

where $\mathbf{e}$ is a unit vector perpendicular to $\mathbf{i}$ and $\mathbf{j}$. Either $\mathbf{e} = \mathbf{k}$ or $\mathbf{e} = -\mathbf{k}$. Applying the right-hand rule, we find that $\mathbf{e} = \mathbf{k}$ (Fig. 2.26). Therefore,

$$\mathbf{i} \times \mathbf{j} = \mathbf{k}.$$

Continuing in this way, we obtain

$$\begin{array}{lll}\mathbf{i} \times \mathbf{i} = \mathbf{0}, & \mathbf{i} \times \mathbf{j} = \mathbf{k}, & \mathbf{i} \times \mathbf{k} = -\mathbf{j}, \\ \mathbf{j} \times \mathbf{i} = -\mathbf{k}, & \mathbf{j} \times \mathbf{j} = \mathbf{0}, & \mathbf{j} \times \mathbf{k} = \mathbf{i}, \\ \mathbf{k} \times \mathbf{i} = \mathbf{j}, & \mathbf{k} \times \mathbf{j} = -\mathbf{i}, & \mathbf{k} \times \mathbf{k} = \mathbf{0}.\end{array} \quad (2.32)$$

These results can be remembered easily by arranging the unit vectors in a circle, as shown in Fig. 2.27a. The cross product of adjacent vectors is equal to the third vector with a positive sign if the order of the vectors in the cross product is the order indicated by the arrows and a negative sign otherwise. For example, in Fig. 2.27b we see that $\mathbf{i} \times \mathbf{j} = \mathbf{k}$, but $\mathbf{i} \times \mathbf{k} = -\mathbf{j}$.

The cross product of two vectors $\mathbf{U}$ and $\mathbf{V}$, expressed in terms of their components, is

$$\begin{aligned}\mathbf{U} \times \mathbf{V} &= (U_x\mathbf{i} + U_y\mathbf{j} + U_z\mathbf{k}) \times (V_x\mathbf{i} + V_y\mathbf{j} + V_z\mathbf{k}) \\ &= U_xV_x(\mathbf{i} \times \mathbf{i}) + U_xV_y(\mathbf{i} \times \mathbf{j}) + U_xV_z(\mathbf{i} \times \mathbf{k}) \\ &\quad + U_yV_x(\mathbf{j} \times \mathbf{i}) + U_yV_y(\mathbf{j} \times \mathbf{j}) + U_yV_z(\mathbf{j} \times \mathbf{k}) \\ &\quad + U_zV_x(\mathbf{k} \times \mathbf{i}) + U_zV_y(\mathbf{k} \times \mathbf{j}) + U_zV_z(\mathbf{k} \times \mathbf{k}).\end{aligned}$$

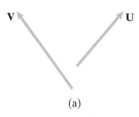

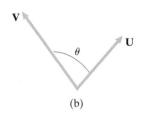

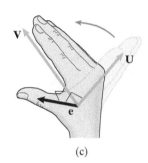

Figure 2.24
(**a**) The vectors $\mathbf{U}$ and $\mathbf{V}$.
(**b**) The angle θ between the vectors when they are placed tail to tail.
(**c**) Determining the direction of $\mathbf{e}$ by the right-hand rule.

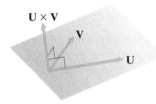

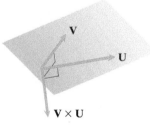

Figure 2.25
Directions of $\mathbf{U} \times \mathbf{V}$ and $\mathbf{V} \times \mathbf{U}$.

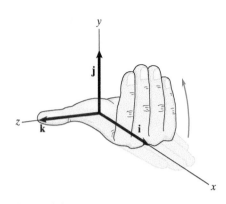

Figure 2.26
The right-hand rule indicates that $\mathbf{i} \times \mathbf{j} = \mathbf{k}$.

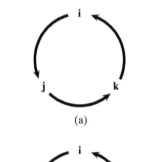

(a)

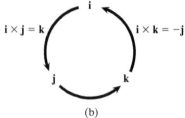

(b)

Figure 2.27
(a) Arrange the unit vectors in a circle with arrows to indicate their order.
(b) You can use the circle to determine their cross products.

By substituting Eqs. (2.32) into this expression, we obtain the equation

$$\mathbf{U} \times \mathbf{V} = (U_y V_z - U_z V_y)\mathbf{i} - (U_x V_z - U_z V_x)\mathbf{j}$$
$$+ (U_x V_y - U_y V_x)\mathbf{k}. \tag{2.33}$$

This result can be compactly written as the determinant

$$\mathbf{U} \times \mathbf{V} = \begin{vmatrix} \mathbf{i} & \mathbf{j} & \mathbf{k} \\ U_x & U_y & U_z \\ V_x & V_y & V_z \end{vmatrix}. \tag{2.34}$$

This equation is based on Eqs. (2.32), which we obtained using a right-handed coordinate system. It gives the correct result for the cross product only if a right-handed coordinate system is used to determine the components of $\mathbf{U}$ and $\mathbf{V}$.

Evaluating a 3 × 3 Determinant

A 3 × 3 determinant can be evaluated by repeating its first two columns and evaluating the products of the terms along the six diagonal lines:

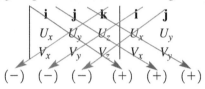

Adding the terms obtained from the diagonals that run downward to the right (blue arrows) and subtracting the terms obtained from the diagonals that run downward to the left (red arrows) gives the value of the determinant:

$$\begin{vmatrix} \mathbf{i} & \mathbf{j} & \mathbf{k} \\ U_x & U_y & U_z \\ V_x & V_y & V_z \end{vmatrix} = \begin{array}{l} U_y V_z \mathbf{i} + U_z V_x \mathbf{j} + U_x V_y \mathbf{k} \\ -U_y V_x \mathbf{k} - U_z V_y \mathbf{i} - U_x V_z \mathbf{j}. \end{array}$$

A 3 × 3 determinant can also be evaluated by expressing it as

$$\begin{vmatrix} \mathbf{i} & \mathbf{j} & \mathbf{k} \\ U_x & U_y & U_z \\ V_x & V_y & V_z \end{vmatrix} = \mathbf{i}\begin{vmatrix} U_y & U_z \\ V_y & V_z \end{vmatrix} - \mathbf{j}\begin{vmatrix} U_x & U_z \\ V_x & V_z \end{vmatrix} + \mathbf{k}\begin{vmatrix} U_x & U_y \\ V_x & V_y \end{vmatrix}.$$

The terms on the right are obtained by multiplying each element of the first row of the 3 × 3 determinant by the 2 × 2 determinant obtained by crossing out that element's row and column. For example, the first element of the first row, $\mathbf{i}$, is multiplied by the 2 × 2 determinant

$$\begin{vmatrix} \mathbf{i} & \mathbf{j} & \mathbf{k} \\ U_x & U_y & U_z \\ V_x & V_y & V_z \end{vmatrix}.$$

Be sure to remember that the second term is subtracted. Expanding the 2 × 2 determinants, we obtain the value of the determinant:

$$\begin{vmatrix} \mathbf{i} & \mathbf{j} & \mathbf{k} \\ U_x & U_y & U_z \\ V_x & V_y & V_z \end{vmatrix} = (U_y V_z - U_z V_y)\mathbf{i} - (U_x V_z - U_z V_x)\mathbf{j} + (U_x V_y - U_y V_x)\mathbf{k}.$$

Mixed Triple Products

In Chapter 4, when we discuss the moment of a force about a line, we will use an operation called the *mixed triple product*, defined by

$$\mathbf{U} \cdot (\mathbf{V} \times \mathbf{W}). \tag{2.35}$$

In terms of the scalar components of the vectors,

$$
\begin{aligned}
\mathbf{U} \cdot (\mathbf{V} \times \mathbf{W}) &= (U_x\mathbf{i} + U_y\mathbf{j} + U_z\mathbf{k}) \cdot \begin{vmatrix} \mathbf{i} & \mathbf{j} & \mathbf{k} \\ V_x & V_y & V_z \\ W_x & W_y & W_z \end{vmatrix} \\
&= (U_x\mathbf{i} + U_y\mathbf{j} + U_z\mathbf{k}) \cdot [(V_yW_z - V_zW_y)\mathbf{i} \\
&\quad - (V_xW_z - V_zW_x)\mathbf{j} + (V_xW_y - V_yW_x)\mathbf{k}] \\
&= U_x(V_yW_z - V_zW_y) - U_y(V_xW_z - V_zW_x) \\
&\quad + U_z(V_xW_y - V_yW_x).
\end{aligned}
$$

This result can be expressed as the determinant

$$
\mathbf{U} \cdot (\mathbf{V} \times \mathbf{W}) = \begin{vmatrix} U_x & U_y & U_z \\ V_x & V_y & V_z \\ W_x & W_y & W_z \end{vmatrix}. \tag{2.36}
$$

Interchanging any two of the vectors in the mixed triple product changes the sign but not the absolute value of the result. For example,

$$
\mathbf{U} \cdot (\mathbf{V} \times \mathbf{W}) = -\mathbf{W} \cdot (\mathbf{V} \times \mathbf{U}).
$$

If the vectors $\mathbf{U}$, $\mathbf{V}$, and $\mathbf{W}$ in Fig. 2.28 form a right-handed system, it can be shown that the volume of the parallelepiped equals $\mathbf{U} \cdot (\mathbf{V} \times \mathbf{W})$.

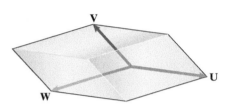

Figure 2.28
Parallelepiped defined by the vectors $\mathbf{U}$, $\mathbf{V}$, and $\mathbf{W}$.

RESULTS

Cross Product
The cross product of two vectors $\mathbf{U}$ and $\mathbf{V}$ is defined by

$$\mathbf{U} \times \mathbf{V} = |\mathbf{U}||\mathbf{V}|\sin\theta\,\mathbf{e}. \tag{2.28}$$

As in the dot product, θ is the angle between the vectors when they are placed tail to tail. The unit vector $\mathbf{e}$ is defined to be perpendicular to $\mathbf{U}$, perpendicular to $\mathbf{V}$, and directed so that $\mathbf{U}$, $\mathbf{V}$, $\mathbf{e}$ form a right-handed system. If $|\mathbf{U}| \neq 0$ and $|\mathbf{V}| \neq 0$, $\mathbf{U} \times \mathbf{V} = \mathbf{0}$ if and only if $\mathbf{U}$ and $\mathbf{V}$ are parallel.

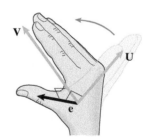

Cross Product in Terms of Components
The cross product of $\mathbf{U}$ and $\mathbf{V}$ is given in terms of the components of the vectors by

$$
\begin{aligned}
\mathbf{U} \times \mathbf{V} &= (U_yV_z - U_zV_y)\mathbf{i} - (U_xV_z - U_zV_x)\mathbf{j} \\
&\quad + (U_xV_y - U_yV_x)\mathbf{k}
\end{aligned} \tag{2.33}
$$

$$
= \begin{vmatrix} \mathbf{i} & \mathbf{j} & \mathbf{k} \\ U_x & U_y & U_z \\ V_x & V_y & V_z \end{vmatrix} \tag{2.34}
$$

Mixed Triple Product
The operation $\mathbf{U} \cdot (\mathbf{V} \times \mathbf{W})$ is called the mixed triple product of the vectors $\mathbf{U}$, $\mathbf{V}$, and $\mathbf{W}$. It can be expressed in terms of the components of the vectors by the determinant

$$\mathbf{U} \cdot (\mathbf{V} \times \mathbf{W}) = \begin{vmatrix} U_x & U_y & U_z \\ V_x & V_y & V_z \\ W_x & W_y & W_z \end{vmatrix}. \qquad (2.36)$$

When $\mathbf{U}$, $\mathbf{V}$, $\mathbf{W}$ form a right-handed system, the volume of the parallelepiped shown equals $\mathbf{U} \cdot (\mathbf{V} \times \mathbf{W})$.

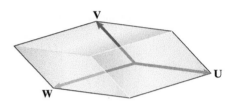

Active Example 2.14 **Cross Products** (▶ *Related Problem 2.124*)

The components of two vectors $\mathbf{U}$ and $\mathbf{V}$ are $\mathbf{U} = 6\mathbf{i} - 5\mathbf{j} - \mathbf{k}$ and $\mathbf{V} = 4\mathbf{i} + 2\mathbf{j} + 2\mathbf{k}$. (a) Determine the cross product $\mathbf{U} \times \mathbf{V}$. (b) Use the dot product to prove that $\mathbf{U} \times \mathbf{V}$ is perpendicular to $\mathbf{U}$.

Strategy
(a) Knowing the components of $\mathbf{U}$ and $\mathbf{V}$, we can use Eq. (2.33) to determine $\mathbf{U} \times \mathbf{V}$. (b) Once we have determined the components of the vector $\mathbf{U} \times \mathbf{V}$, we can prove that it is perpendicular to $\mathbf{U}$ by showing that $(\mathbf{U} \times \mathbf{V}) \cdot \mathbf{U} = 0$.

Solution

$$\mathbf{U} \times \mathbf{V} = (U_y V_z - U_z V_y)\mathbf{i} - (U_x V_z - U_z V_x)\mathbf{j}$$
$$+ (U_x V_y - U_y V_x)\mathbf{k}$$
$$= [(-5)(2) - (-1)(2)]\mathbf{i} - [(6)(2) - (-1)(4)]\mathbf{j}$$
$$+ [(6)(2) - (-5)(4)]\mathbf{k}$$
$$= -8\mathbf{i} - 16\mathbf{j} + 32\mathbf{k}.$$

(a) Use the components of the vectors to determine $\mathbf{U} \times \mathbf{V}$.

$$(\mathbf{U} \times \mathbf{V}) \cdot \mathbf{U} = (\mathbf{U} \times \mathbf{V})_x U_x + (\mathbf{U} \times \mathbf{V})_y U_y + (\mathbf{U} \times \mathbf{V})_z U_z$$
$$= (-8)(6) + (-16)(-5) + (32)(-1)$$
$$= 0.$$

(b) Show that $(\mathbf{U} \times \mathbf{V}) \cdot \mathbf{U} = 0$.

Practice Problem The components of two vectors $\mathbf{U}$ and $\mathbf{V}$ are $\mathbf{U} = 3\mathbf{i} + 2\mathbf{j} - \mathbf{k}$ and $\mathbf{V} = 5\mathbf{i} - 3\mathbf{j} - 4\mathbf{k}$. Determine the components of a unit vector that is perpendicular to $\mathbf{U}$ and perpendicular to $\mathbf{V}$.

Answer: $\mathbf{e} = -0.477\mathbf{i} + 0.304\mathbf{j} - 0.825\mathbf{k}$ or $\mathbf{e} = 0.477\mathbf{i} - 0.304\mathbf{j} + 0.825\mathbf{k}$.

Example 2.15   Minimum Distance from a Point to a Line (▶ *Related Problem 2.133*)

Consider the straight lines *OA* and *OB*.
(a) Determine the components of a unit vector that is perpendicular to both *OA* and *OB*.
(b) What is the minimum distance from point *A* to the line *OB*?

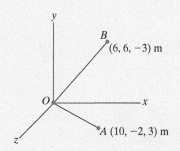

Strategy

(a) Let $\mathbf{r}_{OA}$ and $\mathbf{r}_{OB}$ be the position vectors from *O* to *A* and from *O* to *B* (Fig. a). Since the cross product $\mathbf{r}_{OA} \times \mathbf{r}_{OB}$ is perpendicular to $\mathbf{r}_{OA}$ and $\mathbf{r}_{OB}$, we will determine it and divide it by its magnitude to obtain a unit vector perpendicular to the lines *OA* and *OB*.

(b) The minimum distance from *A* to the line *OB* is the length *d* of the straight line from *A* to *OB* that is perpendicular to *OB* (Fig. b). We can see that $d = |\mathbf{r}_{OA}| \sin \theta$, where θ is the angle between $\mathbf{r}_{OA}$ and $\mathbf{r}_{OB}$. From the definition of the cross product, the magnitude of $\mathbf{r}_{OA} \times \mathbf{r}_{OB}$ is $|\mathbf{r}_{OA}||\mathbf{r}_{OB}| \sin \theta$, so we can determine *d* by dividing the magnitude of $\mathbf{r}_{OA} \times \mathbf{r}_{OB}$ by the magnitude of $\mathbf{r}_{OB}$.

Solution

(a) The components of $\mathbf{r}_{OA}$ and $\mathbf{r}_{OB}$ are

$$\mathbf{r}_{OA} = 10\mathbf{i} - 2\mathbf{j} + 3\mathbf{k} \ (\text{m}),$$

$$\mathbf{r}_{OB} = 6\mathbf{i} + 6\mathbf{j} - 3\mathbf{k} \ (\text{m}).$$

By using Eq. (2.34), we obtain $\mathbf{r}_{OA} \times \mathbf{r}_{OB}$:

$$\mathbf{r}_{OA} \times \mathbf{r}_{OB} = \begin{vmatrix} \mathbf{i} & \mathbf{j} & \mathbf{k} \\ 10 & -2 & 3 \\ 6 & 6 & -3 \end{vmatrix} = -12\mathbf{i} + 48\mathbf{j} + 72\mathbf{k} \ (\text{m}^2).$$

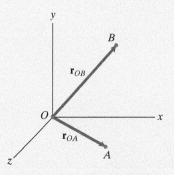

(a) The vectors $\mathbf{r}_{OA}$ and $\mathbf{r}_{OB}$.

This vector is perpendicular to $\mathbf{r}_{OA}$ and $\mathbf{r}_{OB}$. Dividing it by its magnitude, we obtain a unit vector **e** that is perpendicular to the lines *OA* and *OB*:

$$\mathbf{e} = \frac{\mathbf{r}_{OA} \times \mathbf{r}_{OB}}{|\mathbf{r}_{OA} \times \mathbf{r}_{OB}|} = \frac{-12\mathbf{i} + 48\mathbf{j} + 72\mathbf{k} \ (\text{m}^2)}{\sqrt{(-12 \ \text{m}^2)^2 + (48 \ \text{m}^2)^2 + (72 \ \text{m}^2)^2}}$$

$$= -0.137\mathbf{i} + 0.549\mathbf{j} + 0.824\mathbf{k}.$$

(b) From Fig. b, the minimum distance *d* is

$$d = |\mathbf{r}_{OA}| \sin \theta.$$

The magnitude of $\mathbf{r}_{OA} \times \mathbf{r}_{OB}$ is

$$|\mathbf{r}_{OA} \times \mathbf{r}_{OB}| = |\mathbf{r}_{OA}||\mathbf{r}_{OB}| \sin \theta.$$

Solving this equation for $\sin \theta$, we find that the distance *d* is

$$d = |\mathbf{r}_{OA}| \left(\frac{|\mathbf{r}_{OA} \times \mathbf{r}_{OB}|}{|\mathbf{r}_{OA}||\mathbf{r}_{OB}|} \right) = \frac{|\mathbf{r}_{OA} \times \mathbf{r}_{OB}|}{|\mathbf{r}_{OB}|}$$

$$= \frac{\sqrt{(-12 \ \text{m}^2)^2 + (48 \ \text{m}^2)^2 + (72 \ \text{m}^2)^2}}{\sqrt{(6 \ \text{m})^2 + (6 \ \text{m})^2 + (-3 \ \text{m})^2}} = 9.71 \ \text{m}.$$

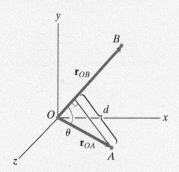

(b) The minimum distance *d* from *A* to the line *OB*.

Critical Thinking

This example is an illustration of the power of vector methods. Determining the minimum distance from point *A* to the line *OB* can be formulated as a minimization problem in differential calculus, but the vector solution we present is far simpler.

Example 2.16 | Component of a Vector Perpendicular to a Plane (► *Related Problem 2.139*)

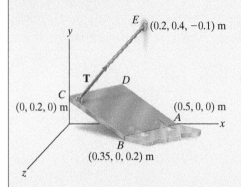

The rope CE exerts a 500-N force $\mathbf{T}$ on the door $ABCD$. What is the magnitude of the component of $\mathbf{T}$ perpendicular to the door?

Strategy

We are given the coordinates of the corners A, B, and C of the door. By taking the cross product of the position vector $\mathbf{r}_{CB}$ from C to B and the position vector $\mathbf{r}_{CA}$ from C to A, we will obtain a vector that is perpendicular to the door. We can divide the resulting vector by its magnitude to obtain a unit vector perpendicular to the door and then apply Eq. (2.26) to determine the component of $\mathbf{T}$ perpendicular to the door.

Solution

The components of $\mathbf{r}_{CB}$ and $\mathbf{r}_{CA}$ are

$$\mathbf{r}_{CB} = 0.35\mathbf{i} - 0.2\mathbf{j} + 0.2\mathbf{k} \ (\text{m}),$$
$$\mathbf{r}_{CA} = 0.5\mathbf{i} - 0.2\mathbf{j} \ (\text{m}).$$

Their cross product is

$$\mathbf{r}_{CB} \times \mathbf{r}_{CA} = \begin{vmatrix} \mathbf{i} & \mathbf{j} & \mathbf{k} \\ 0.35 & -0.2 & 0.2 \\ 0.5 & -0.2 & 0 \end{vmatrix} = 0.04\mathbf{i} + 0.1\mathbf{j} + 0.03\mathbf{k} \ (\text{m}^2).$$

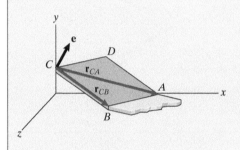

Dividing this vector by its magnitude, we obtain a unit vector $\mathbf{e}$ that is perpendicular to the door (Fig. a):

$$\mathbf{e} = \frac{\mathbf{r}_{CB} \times \mathbf{r}_{CA}}{|\mathbf{r}_{CB} \times \mathbf{r}_{CA}|} = \frac{0.04\mathbf{i} + 0.1\mathbf{j} + 0.03\mathbf{k} \ (\text{m}^2)}{\sqrt{(0.04 \ \text{m}^2)^2 + (0.1 \ \text{m}^2)^2 + (0.03 \ \text{m}^2)^2}}$$
$$= 0.358\mathbf{i} + 0.894\mathbf{j} + 0.268\mathbf{k}.$$

(a) Determining a unit vector perpendicular to the door.

To use Eq. (2.26), we must express $\mathbf{T}$ in terms of its scalar components. The position vector from C to E is

$$\mathbf{r}_{CE} = 0.2\mathbf{i} + 0.2\mathbf{j} - 0.1\mathbf{k} \ (\text{m}),$$

so we can express the force $\mathbf{T}$ as

$$\mathbf{T} = |\mathbf{T}| \frac{\mathbf{r}_{CE}}{|\mathbf{r}_{CE}|} = (500 \ \text{N}) \frac{0.2\mathbf{i} + 0.2\mathbf{j} - 0.1\mathbf{k} \ (\text{m})}{\sqrt{(0.2 \ \text{m})^2 + (0.2 \ \text{m})^2 + (-0.1 \ \text{m})^2}}$$
$$= 333\mathbf{i} + 333\mathbf{j} - 167\mathbf{k} \ (\text{N}).$$

The component of $\mathbf{T}$ parallel to the unit vector $\mathbf{e}$, which is the component of $\mathbf{T}$ perpendicular to the door, is

$$(\mathbf{e} \cdot \mathbf{T})\mathbf{e} = [(0.358)(333 \ \text{N}) + (0.894)(333 \ \text{N}) + (0.268)(-167 \ \text{N})]\mathbf{e}$$
$$= 373\mathbf{e} \ (\text{N}).$$

The magnitude of the component of $\mathbf{T}$ perpendicular to the door is 373 N.

Critical Thinking

Why is it useful to determine the component of the force $\mathbf{T}$ perpendicular to the door? If the y axis is vertical and the rope CE is the only thing preventing the hinged door from falling, you can see intuitively that it is the component of the force perpendicular to the door that holds it in place. We analyze problems of this kind in Chapter 5.

Problems

▶ **2.124** In Active Example 2.14, suppose that the vector **V** is changed to **V** = 4**i** − 6**j** − 10**k**. (a) Determine the cross product **U** × **V**. (b) Use the dot product to prove that **U** × **V** is perpendicular to **V**.

2.125 Two vectors **U** = 3**i** + 2**j** and **V** = 2**i** + 4**j**.
(a) What is the cross product **U** × **V**?
(b) What is the cross product **V** × **U**?

2.126 The two segments of the L-shaped bar are parallel to the x and z axes. The rope AB exerts a force of magnitude $|\mathbf{F}| = 500$ lb on the bar at A. Determine the cross product $\mathbf{r}_{CA} \times \mathbf{F}$, where $\mathbf{r}_{CA}$ is the position vector from point C to point A.

2.127 The two segments of the L-shaped bar are parallel to the x and z axes. The rope AB exerts a force of magnitude $|\mathbf{F}| = 500$ lb on the bar at A. Determine the cross product $\mathbf{r}_{CB} \times \mathbf{F}$, where $\mathbf{r}_{CB}$ is the position vector from point C to point B. Compare your answer to the answer to Problem 2.126.

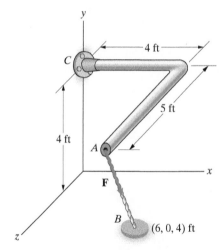

Problems 2.126/2.127

2.128 Suppose that the cross product of two vectors **U** and **V** is **U** × **V** = **0**. If $|\mathbf{U}| \neq 0$, what do you know about the vector **V**?

2.129 The cross product of two vectors **U** and **V** is **U** × **V** = −30**i** + 40**k**. The vector **V** = 4**i** − 2**j** + 3**k**. The vector **U** = 4**i** + U_y**j** + U_z**k**. Determine U_y and U_z.

2.130 The magnitudes $|\mathbf{U}| = 10$ and $|\mathbf{V}| = 20$.
(a) Use the definition of the cross product to determine **U** × **V**.
(b) Use the definition of the cross product to determine **V** × **U**.
(c) Use Eq. (2.34) to determine **U** × **V**.
(d) Use Eq. (2.34) to determine **V** × **U**.

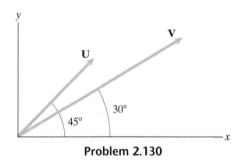

Problem 2.130

2.131 The force **F** = 10**i** − 4**j** (N). Determine the cross product $\mathbf{r}_{AB} \times \mathbf{F}$.

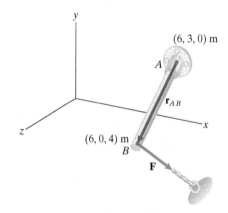

Problem 2.131

2.132 By evaluating the cross product **U** × **V**, prove the identity $\sin(\theta_1 - \theta_2) = \sin\theta_1 \cos\theta_2 - \cos\theta_1 \sin\theta_2$.

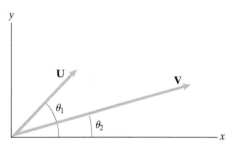

Problem 2.132

▶ **2.133** In Example 2.15, what is the minimum distance from point B to the line OA?

2.134 (a) What is the cross product $\mathbf{r}_{OA} \times \mathbf{r}_{OB}$? (b) Determine a unit vector $\mathbf{e}$ that is perpendicular to $\mathbf{r}_{OA}$ and $\mathbf{r}_{OB}$.

2.135 Use the cross product to determine the length of the shortest straight line from point B to the straight line that passes through points O and A.

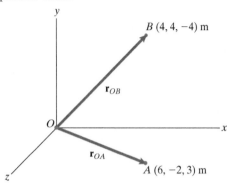

Problems 2.134/2.135

2.136 The cable BC exerts a 1000-lb force $\mathbf{F}$ on the hook at B. Determine $\mathbf{r}_{AB} \times \mathbf{F}$.

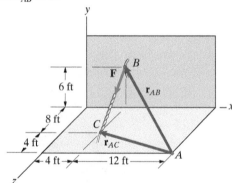

Problem 2.136

2.137 The force vector $\mathbf{F}$ points along the straight line from point A to point B. Its magnitude is $|\mathbf{F}| = 20$ N. The coordinates of points A and B are $x_A = 6$ m, $y_A = 8$ m, $z_A = 4$ m and $x_B = 8$ m, $y_B = 1$ m, $z_B = -2$ m.

(a) Express the vector $\mathbf{F}$ in terms of its components.

(b) Use Eq. (2.34) to determine the cross products $\mathbf{r}_A \times \mathbf{F}$ and $\mathbf{r}_B \times \mathbf{F}$.

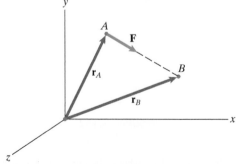

Problem 2.137

2.138 The rope AB exerts a 50-N force $\mathbf{T}$ on the collar at A. Let $\mathbf{r}_{CA}$ be the position vector from point C to point A. Determine the cross product $\mathbf{r}_{CA} \times \mathbf{T}$.

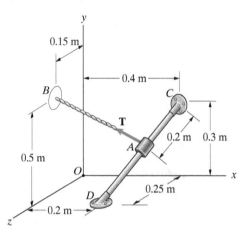

Problem 2.138

▶ **2.139** In Example 2.16, suppose that the attachment point E is moved to the location $(0.3, 0.3, 0)$ m and the magnitude of $\mathbf{T}$ increases to 600 N. What is the magnitude of the component of $\mathbf{T}$ perpendicular to the door?

2.140 The bar AB is 6 m long and is perpendicular to the bars AC and AD. Use the cross product to determine the coordinates x_B, y_B, z_B of point B.

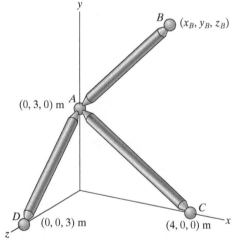

Problem 2.140

2.141* Determine the minimum distance from point P to the plane defined by the three points A, B, and C.

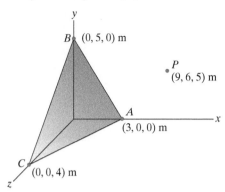

Problem 2.141

2.142* The force vector $\mathbf{F}$ points along the straight line from point A to point B. Use Eqs. (2.28)–(2.31) to prove that

$$\mathbf{r}_B \times \mathbf{F} = \mathbf{r}_A \times \mathbf{F}.$$

Strategy: Let $\mathbf{r}_{AB}$ be the position vector from point A to point B. Express $\mathbf{r}_B$ in terms of $\mathbf{r}_A$ and $\mathbf{r}_{AB}$. Notice that the vectors $\mathbf{r}_{AB}$ and $\mathbf{F}$ are parallel.

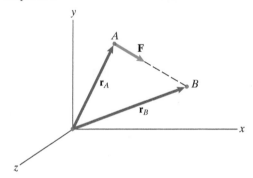

Problem 2.142

2.143 For the vectors $\mathbf{U} = 6\mathbf{i} + 2\mathbf{j} - 4\mathbf{k}$, $\mathbf{V} = 2\mathbf{i} + 7\mathbf{j}$, and $\mathbf{W} = 3\mathbf{i} + 2\mathbf{k}$, evaluate the following mixed triple products:

(a) $\mathbf{U} \cdot (\mathbf{V} \times \mathbf{W})$;

(b) $\mathbf{W} \cdot (\mathbf{V} \times \mathbf{U})$;

(c) $\mathbf{V} \cdot (\mathbf{W} \times \mathbf{U})$.

2.144 Use the mixed triple product to calculate the volume of the parallelepiped.

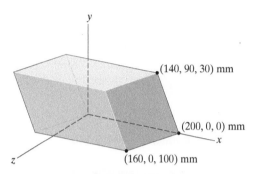

Problem 2.144

2.145 By using Eqs. (2.23) and (2.34), show that

$$\mathbf{U} \cdot (\mathbf{V} \times \mathbf{W}) = \begin{vmatrix} U_x & U_y & U_z \\ V_x & V_y & V_z \\ W_x & W_y & W_z \end{vmatrix}.$$

2.146 The vectors $\mathbf{U} = \mathbf{i} + U_y\mathbf{j} + 4\mathbf{k}$, $\mathbf{V} = 2\mathbf{i} + \mathbf{j} - 2\mathbf{k}$, and $\mathbf{W} = -3\mathbf{i} + \mathbf{j} - 2\mathbf{k}$ are coplanar (they lie in the same plane). What is the component U_y?

Review Problems

2.147 The magnitude of $\mathbf{F}$ is 8 kN. Express $\mathbf{F}$ in terms of scalar components.

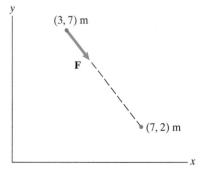

Problem 2.147

2.148 The magnitude of the vertical force $\mathbf{W}$ is 600 lb, and the magnitude of the force $\mathbf{B}$ is 1500 lb. Given that $\mathbf{A} + \mathbf{B} + \mathbf{W} = \mathbf{0}$, determine the magnitude of the force $\mathbf{A}$ and the angle α.

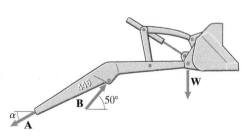

Problem 2.148

2.149 The magnitude of the vertical force vector **A** is 200 lb. If **A** + **B** + **C** = **0**, what are the magnitudes of the force vectors **B** and **C**?

2.150 The magnitude of the horizontal force vector **D** is 280 lb. If **D** + **E** + **F** = **0**, what are the magnitudes of the force vectors **E** and **F**?

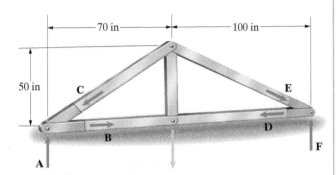

Problems 2.149/2.150

Refer to the following diagram when solving Problems 2.151 through 2.157.

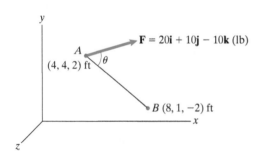

Problems 2.151–2.157

2.151 What are the direction cosines of **F**?

2.152 Determine the components of a unit vector parallel to line *AB* that points from *A* toward *B*.

2.153 What is the angle θ between the line *AB* and the force **F**?

2.154 Determine the vector component of **F** that is parallel to the line *AB*.

2.155 Determine the vector component of **F** that is normal to the line *AB*.

2.156 Determine the vector $\mathbf{r}_{BA} \times \mathbf{F}$, where $\mathbf{r}_{BA}$ is the position vector from *B* to *A*.

2.157 (a) Write the position vector $\mathbf{r}_{AB}$ from point *A* to point *B* in terms of components.

(b) A vector **R** has magnitude $|\mathbf{R}| = 200$ lb and is parallel to the line from *A* to *B*. Write **R** in terms of components.

2.158 The rope exerts a force of magnitude $|\mathbf{F}| = 200$ lb on the top of the pole at *B*.

(a) Determine the vector $\mathbf{r}_{AB} \times \mathbf{F}$, where $\mathbf{r}_{AB}$ is the position vector from *A* to *B*.

(b) Determine the vector $\mathbf{r}_{AC} \times \mathbf{F}$, where $\mathbf{r}_{AC}$ is the position vector from *A* to *C*.

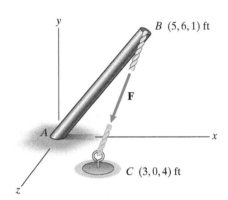

Problem 2.158

2.159 The pole supporting the sign is parallel to the *x* axis and is 6 ft long. Point *A* is contained in the *y–z* plane. (a) Express the vector **r** in terms of components. (b) What are the direction cosines of **r**?

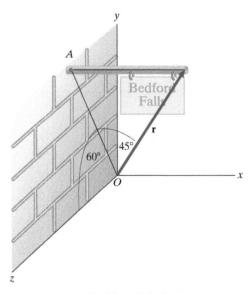

Problem 2.159

2.160 The z component of the force **F** is 80 lb. (a) Express **F** in terms of components. (b) What are the angles θ_x, θ_y, and θ_z between **F** and the positive coordinate axes?

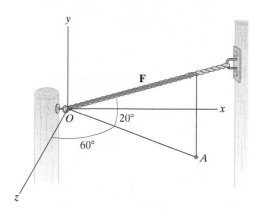

Problem 2.160

2.161 The magnitude of the force vector F_B is 2 kN. Express it in terms of components.

2.162 The magnitude of the vertical force vector **F** is 6 kN. Determine the vector components of **F** parallel and normal to the line from B to D.

2.163 The magnitude of the vertical force vector **F** is 6 kN. Given that $\mathbf{F} + \mathbf{F}_A + \mathbf{F}_B + \mathbf{F}_C = 0$, what are the magnitudes of $\mathbf{F}_A$, $\mathbf{F}_B$, and $\mathbf{F}_C$?

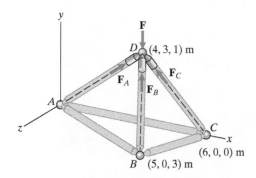

Problems 2.161–2.163

2.164 The magnitude of the vertical force **W** is 160 N. The direction cosines of the position vector from A to B are $\cos \theta_x = 0.500$, $\cos \theta_y = 0.866$, and $\cos \theta_z = 0$, and the direction cosines of the position vector from B to C are $\cos \theta_x = 0.707$, $\cos \theta_y = 0.619$, and $\cos \theta_z = -0.342$. Point G is the midpoint of the line from B to C. Determine the vector $\mathbf{r}_{AG} \times \mathbf{W}$, where $\mathbf{r}_{AG}$ is the position vector from A to G.

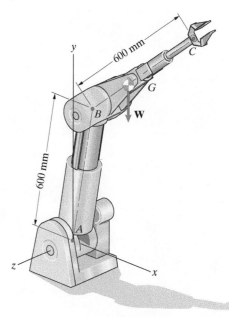

Problem 2.164

2.165 The rope CE exerts a 500-N force **T** on the hinged door.
(a) Express **T** in terms of components.
(b) Determine the vector component of **T** parallel to the line from point A to point B.

2.166 In Problem 2.165, let $\mathbf{r}_{BC}$ be the position vector from point B to point C. Determine the cross product $\mathbf{r}_{BC} \times \mathbf{T}$.

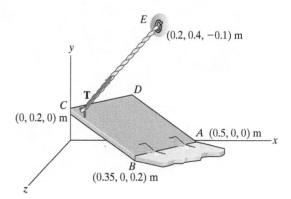

Problems 2.165/2.166

CHAPTER
3

Forces

In Chapter 2 we represented forces by vectors and used vector addition to sum forces. In this chapter we discuss forces in more detail and introduce two of the most important concepts in mechanics, equilibrium and the free-body diagram. We will use free-body diagrams to identify the forces on objects and use equilibrium to determine unknown forces.

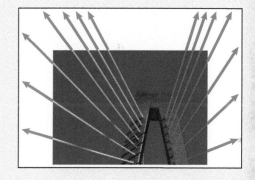

◀ The forces due to the weight of the bridge are transferred to the vertical support towers by cables. In this chapter we use free-body diagrams to analyze the forces acting on objects in equilibrium.

Figure 3.1
A force **F** and its line of action.

3.1 Forces, Equilibrium, and Free-Body Diagrams

BACKGROUND

Force is a familiar concept, as is evident from the words push, pull, and lift used in everyday conversation. In engineering we deal with different types of forces having a large range of magnitudes. In this section we define some terms used to describe forces, discuss particular forces that occur frequently in engineering applications, and introduce the concepts of equilibrium and free-body diagrams.

Terminology

Line of Action   When a force is represented by a vector, the straight line collinear with the vector is called the *line of action* of the force (Fig. 3.1).

Systems of Forces   A *system of forces* is simply a particular set of forces. A system of forces is *coplanar,* or *two dimensional,* if the lines of action of the forces lie in a plane. Otherwise it is *three dimensional*. A system of forces is *concurrent* if the lines of action of the forces intersect at a point (Fig. 3.2a) and *parallel* if the lines of action are parallel (Fig. 3.2b).

External and Internal Forces   We say that a given object is subjected to an *external force* if the force is exerted by a different object. When one part of a given object is subjected to a force by another part of the same object, we say it is subjected to an *internal force*. These definitions require that you clearly define the object you are considering. For example, suppose that you are the object. When you are standing, the floor—a different object—exerts an external force on your feet. If you press your hands together, your left hand exerts an internal force on your right hand. However, if your right hand is the object you are considering, the force exerted by your left hand is an external force.

Body and Surface Forces   A force acting on an object is called a *body force* if it acts on the volume of the object and a *surface force* if it acts on its surface. The gravitational force on an object is a body force. A surface force can be exerted on an object by contact with another object. Both body and surface forces can result from electromagnetic effects.

Gravitational Forces

You are aware of the force exerted on an object by the earth's gravity whenever you pick up something heavy. We can represent the gravitational force, or weight, of an object by a vector (Fig. 3.3).

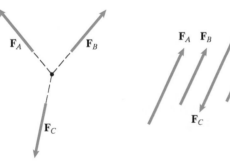

Figure 3.2
(a) Concurrent forces.
(b) Parallel forces.

(a)

(b)

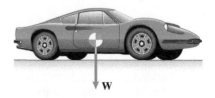

Figure 3.3
Representing an object's weight by a vector.

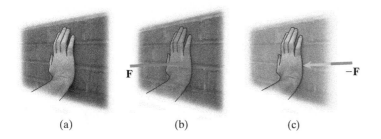

Figure 3.4
(a) Exerting a contact force on a wall by pushing on it.
(b) The vector **F** represents the force you exert on the wall.
(c) The wall exerts a force −**F** on your hand.

The magnitude of an object's weight is related to its mass m by

$$|\mathbf{W}| = mg, \tag{3.1}$$

where g is the acceleration due to gravity at sea level. We will use the values $g = 9.81 \text{ m/s}^2$ in SI units and $g = 32.2 \text{ ft/s}^2$ in U.S. Customary units.

Gravitational forces, and also electromagnetic forces, act at a distance. The objects they act on are not necessarily in contact with the objects exerting the forces. In the next section we discuss forces resulting from contacts between objects.

Contact Forces

Contact forces are the forces that result from contacts between objects. For example, you exert a contact force when you push on a wall (Fig. 3.4a). The surface of your hand exerts a force on the surface of the wall that can be represented by a vector **F** (Fig. 3.4b). The wall exerts an equal and opposite force −**F** on your hand (Fig. 3.4c). (Recall Newton's third law: The forces exerted on each other by any two particles are equal in magnitude and opposite in direction. If you have any doubt that the wall exerts a force on your hand, try pushing on the wall while standing on roller skates.)

We will be concerned with contact forces exerted on objects by contact with the surfaces of other objects and by ropes, cables, and springs.

Surfaces   Consider two plane surfaces in contact (Fig. 3.5a). We represent the force exerted on the right surface by the left surface by the vector **F** in Fig. 3.5b. We can resolve **F** into a component **N** that is normal to the surface and a component **f** that is parallel to the surface (Fig. 3.5c). The component **N** is called the *normal force*, and the component **f** is called the *friction force*. We sometimes assume that the friction force between two surfaces is negligible in comparison to the normal force, a condition we describe by saying that the surfaces are *smooth*. In this case we show only the normal force (Fig. 3.5d). When the friction force cannot be neglected, we say the surfaces are *rough*.

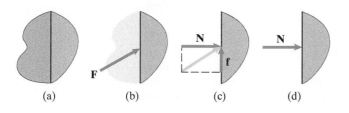

Figure 3.5
(a) Two plane surfaces in contact.
(b) The force **F** exerted on the right surface.
(c) The force **F** resolved into components normal and parallel to the surface.
(d) Only the normal force is shown when friction is neglected.

Figure 3.6
(a) Curved contacting surfaces. The dashed line indicates the plane tangent to the surfaces at their point of contact.
(b) The normal force and friction force on the right surface.

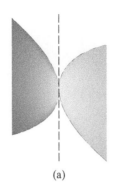
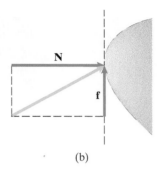

(a)

(b)

If the contacting surfaces are curved (Fig. 3.6a), the normal force and the friction force are perpendicular and parallel to the plane tangent to the surfaces at their point of contact (Fig. 3.6b).

Ropes and Cables A contact force can be exerted on an object by attaching a rope or cable to the object and pulling on it. In Fig. 3.7a, the crane's cable is attached to a container of building materials. We can represent the force the cable exerts on the container by a vector **T** (Fig. 3.7b). The magnitude of **T** is called the *tension* in the cable, and the line of action of **T** is collinear with the cable. The cable exerts an equal and opposite force −**T** on the crane (Fig. 3.7c).

Notice that we have assumed that the cable is straight and that the tension where the cable is connected to the container equals the tension near the crane. This is approximately true if the weight of the cable is small compared to the tension. Otherwise, the cable will sag significantly and the tension will vary along its length. In Chapter 9 we will discuss ropes and cables whose weights are not small in comparison to their tensions. For now, we assume that ropes and cables are straight and that their tensions are constant along their lengths.

A *pulley* is a wheel with a grooved rim that can be used to change the direction of a rope or cable (Fig. 3.8a). For now, we assume that the tension is

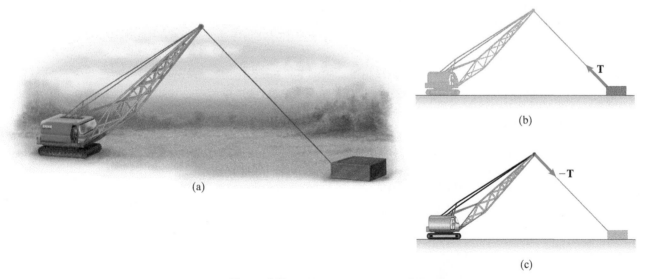

(a)

(b)

(c)

Figure 3.7
(a) A crane with its cable attached to a container.
(b) The force **T** exerted on the container by the cable.
(c) The force −**T** exerted on the crane by the cable.

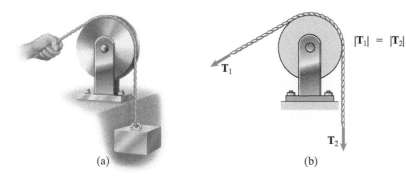

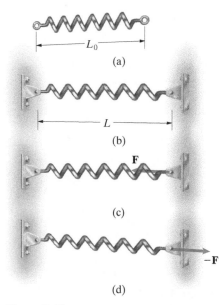

Figure 3.8

(a) A pulley changes the direction of a rope or cable.
(b) For now, you should assume that the tensions on each side of the pulley are equal.

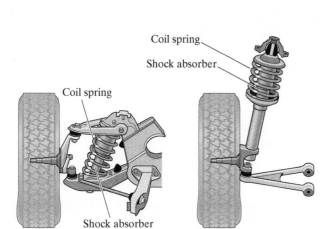

Figure 3.9
Coil springs in car suspensions. The arrangement on the right is called a MacPherson strut.

the same on both sides of a pulley (Fig. 3.8b). This is true, or at least approximately true, when the pulley can turn freely and the rope or cable either is stationary or turns the pulley at a constant rate.

Springs   Springs are used to exert contact forces in mechanical devices, for example, in the suspensions of cars (Fig. 3.9). Let's consider a coil spring whose unstretched length, the length of the spring when its ends are free, is L_0 (Fig. 3.10a). When the spring is stretched to a length L greater than L_0 (Fig. 3.10b), it pulls on the object to which it is attached with a force **F** (Fig. 3.10c). The object exerts an equal and opposite force $-\mathbf{F}$ on the spring (Fig. 3.10d). When the spring is compressed to a length L less than L_0 (Figs. 3.11a, b), the spring pushes on the object with a force **F** and the object exerts an equal and opposite force $-\mathbf{F}$ on the spring (Figs. 3.11c, d). If a spring is compressed too much, it may buckle (Fig. 3.11e). A spring designed to exert a force by being compressed is often provided with lateral support to prevent buckling, for example, by enclosing it in a cylindrical sleeve. In the car suspensions shown in Fig. 3.9, the shock absorbers within the coils prevent the springs from buckling.

The magnitude of the force exerted by a spring depends on the material it is made of, its design, and how much it is stretched or compressed relative to its unstretched length. When the change in length is not too large compared to the unstretched length, the coil springs commonly used in mechanical devices exert a force approximately proportional to the change in length:

$$|\mathbf{F}| = k|L - L_0|. \tag{3.2}$$

Figure 3.10
(a) A spring of unstretched length L_0.
(b) The spring stretched to a length $L > L_0$.
(c, d) The force **F** exerted by the spring and the force $-\mathbf{F}$ on the spring.

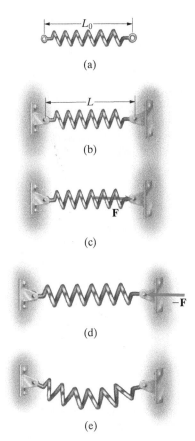

Figure 3.11
(a) A spring of length L_0.
(b) The spring compressed to a length $L < L_0$.
(c, d) The spring pushes on an object with a force **F**, and the object exerts a force $-$**F** on the spring.
(e) A coil spring will buckle if it is compressed too much.

Because the force is a linear function of the change in length (Fig. 3.12), a spring that satisfies this relation is called a *linear spring*. The value of the *spring constant k* depends on the material and design of the spring. Its dimensions are (force)/(length). Notice from Eq. (3.2) that k equals the magnitude of the force required to stretch or compress the spring a unit of length.

Suppose that the unstretched length of a spring is $L_0 = 1$ m and $k = 3000$ N/m. If the spring is stretched to a length $L = 1.2$ m, the magnitude of the pull it exerts is

$$k|L - L_0| = 3000(1.2 - 1) = 600 \text{ N}.$$

Although coil springs are commonly used in mechanical devices, we are also interested in them for a different reason. Springs can be used to *model* situations in which forces depend on displacements. For example, the force necessary to bend the steel beam in Fig. 3.13a is a linear function of the displacement δ, or

$$|\mathbf{F}| = k\delta,$$

if δ is not too large. Therefore we can model the force-deflection behavior of the beam with a linear spring (Fig. 3.13b).

Equilibrium

In everyday conversation, equilibrium means an unchanging state—a state of balance. Before we state precisely what this term means in mechanics, let us consider some familiar examples. If you are in a building as you read this, objects you observe around you that are *at rest (stationary) relative to the building*, such as pieces of furniture, are in equilibrium. A person sitting or standing at rest relative to the building is also in equilibrium. If a train travels at constant speed on a straight track, objects within the train that are at rest relative to the train, such as the passenger seats or a passenger standing in the aisle (Fig. 3.14a), are in equilibrium. *The person at rest relative to the building and also the passenger at rest relative to the train are not accelerating.*

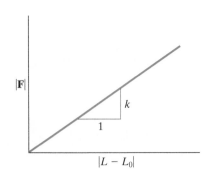

Figure 3.12
The graph of the force exerted by a linear spring as a function of its stretch or compression is a straight line with slope k.

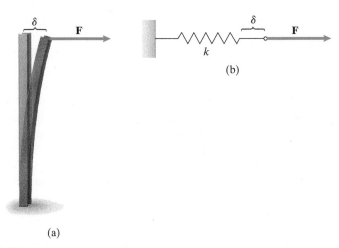

Figure 3.13
(a) A steel beam deflected by a force.
(b) Modeling the beam's behavior with a linear spring.

However, if the train should begin increasing or decreasing its speed, the person standing in the aisle of the train would no longer be in equilibrium and might lose his balance (Fig. 3.14b).

We define an object to be in *equilibrium* only if each point of the object has the same constant velocity, which is referred to as *steady translation*. The velocity must be measured relative to a frame of reference in which Newton's laws are valid. Such a frame is called a *Newtonian* or *inertial reference frame*. In many engineering applications, a frame of reference that is fixed with respect to the earth can be regarded as inertial. Therefore, objects in steady translation relative to the earth can be assumed to be in equilibrium. We make this assumption throughout this book. In the examples cited in the previous paragraph, the furniture and person at rest in a building and also the passenger seats and passenger at rest within the train moving at constant speed are in steady translation relative to the earth and so are in equilibrium.

The vector sum of the external forces acting on an object in equilibrium is zero. We will use the symbol $\Sigma\mathbf{F}$ to denote the sum of the external forces. Thus, when an object is in equilibrium,

$$\Sigma\mathbf{F} = \mathbf{0}. \tag{3.3}$$

In some situations we can use this *equilibrium equation* to determine unknown forces acting on an object in equilibrium. The first step will be to draw a *free-body diagram* of the object to identify the external forces acting on it.

Free-Body Diagrams

A free-body diagram serves to focus attention on the object of interest and helps identify the external forces acting on it. Although in statics we are concerned only with objects in equilibrium, free-body diagrams are also used in dynamics to study the motions of objects.

Although it is one of the most important tools in mechanics, a free-body diagram is a simple concept. It is a drawing of an object and the external forces acting on it. Otherwise, nothing other than the object of interest is included. The drawing shows the object *isolated*, or *freed*, from its surroundings.

Drawing a free-body diagram involves three steps:

1. *Identify the object you want to isolate*—As the following examples show, your choice is often dictated by particular forces you want to determine.

2. *Draw a sketch of the object isolated from its surroundings, and show relevant dimensions and angles*—Your drawing should be reasonably accurate, but it can omit irrelevant details.

3. *Draw vectors representing all of the external forces acting on the isolated object, and label them*—Don't forget to include the gravitational force if you are not intentionally neglecting it.

A coordinate system is necessary to express the forces on the isolated object in terms of components. Often it is convenient to choose the coordinate system before drawing the free-body diagram, but in some situations the best choice of a coordinate system will not be apparent until after it has been drawn.

A simple example demonstrates how you can choose free-body diagrams to determine particular forces and also that you must distinguish carefully between external and internal forces. Two stationary blocks of equal weight W are suspended by cables in Fig. 3.15. The system is in equilibrium. Suppose that we want to determine the tensions in the two cables.

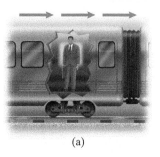

(a)

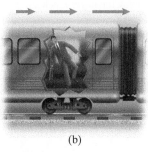

(b)

Figure 3.14

(a) While the train moves at a constant speed, a person standing in the aisle is in equilibrium.

(b) If the train starts to speed up, the person is no longer in equilibrium.

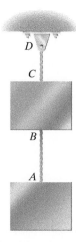

Figure 3.15
Stationary blocks suspended by cables.

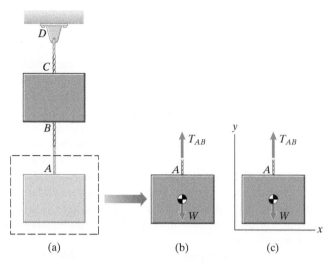

Figure 3.16
(a) Isolating the lower block and part of cable AB.
(b) Indicating the external forces completes the free-body diagram.
(c) Introducing a coordinate system.

To determine the tension in cable AB, we first isolate an "object" consisting of the lower block and part of cable AB (Fig. 3.16a). We then ask ourselves what forces can be exerted on our isolated object by objects not included in the diagram. The earth exerts a gravitational force of magnitude W on the block. Also, where we "cut" cable AB, the cable is subjected to a contact force equal to the tension in the cable (Fig. 3.16b). The arrows in this figure indicate the directions of the forces. The scalar W is the weight of the block and T_{AB} is the tension in cable AB. We assume that the weight of the part of cable AB included in the free-body diagram can be neglected in comparison to the weight of the block.

Since the free-body diagram is in equilibrium, the sum of the external forces equals zero. In terms of a coordinate system with the y axis upward (Fig. 3.16c), we obtain the equilibrium equation

$$\Sigma\mathbf{F} = T_{AB}\mathbf{j} - W\mathbf{j} = (T_{AB} - W)\mathbf{j} = \mathbf{0}.$$

Thus, the tension in cable AB is $T_{AB} = W$.

We can determine the tension in cable CD by isolating the upper block (Fig. 3.17a). The external forces are the weight of the upper block and the tensions in the two cables (Fig. 3.17b). In this case we obtain the equilibrium equation

$$\Sigma\mathbf{F} = T_{CD}\mathbf{j} - T_{AB}\mathbf{j} - W\mathbf{j} = (T_{CD} - T_{AB} - W)\mathbf{j} = \mathbf{0}.$$

Since $T_{AB} = W$, we find that $T_{CD} = 2W$.

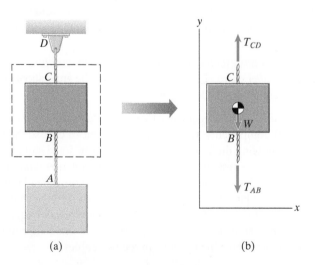

Figure 3.17
(a) Isolating the upper block to determine the tension in cable CD.
(b) Free-body diagram of the upper block.

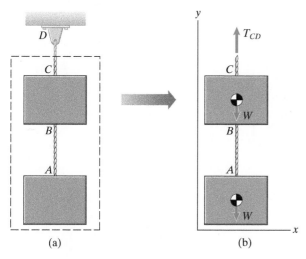

(a)   (b)

Figure 3.18
(a) An alternative choice for determining the tension in cable *CD*.
(b) Free-body diagram including both blocks and cable *AB*.

We could also have determined the tension in cable *CD* by treating the two blocks and the cable *AB* as a single object (Figs. 3.18a, b). The equilibrium equation is

$$\Sigma \mathbf{F} = T_{CD}\mathbf{j} - W\mathbf{j} - W\mathbf{j} = (T_{CD} - 2W)\mathbf{j} = \mathbf{0},$$

and we again obtain $T_{CD} = 2W$.

Why doesn't the tension in cable *AB* appear on the free-body diagram in Fig. 3.18b? Remember that only external forces are shown on free-body diagrams. Since cable *AB* is part of the free-body diagram in this case, the forces it exerts on the upper and lower blocks are internal forces.

RESULTS

Line of Action
The straight line collinear with a vector representing a force is the *line of action* of the force.

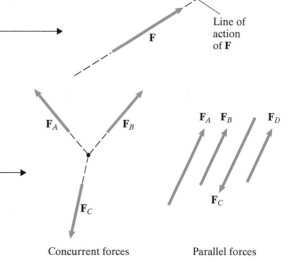

Systems of Forces
A system of forces is *two dimensional* if the lines of action of the forces lie in a plane. Otherwise it is *three dimensional*. A system of forces is *concurrent* if the lines of action intersect at a point and is *parallel* if the lines of action are parallel.

External and Internal Forces
An object is subjected to an *external force* if the force is exerted by a different object. A force exerted on part of an object by a different part of the same object is an *internal force*.

Gravitational Forces
The weight of an object can be represented by a vector. Its magnitude at sea level is related to the mass m of the object by

$$|\mathbf{W}| = mg, \qquad (3.1)$$

where g is the acceleration due to gravity at sea level.

Contact Forces
Contacting objects exert equal and opposite forces on each other.

Objects A and B with plane surfaces in contact.

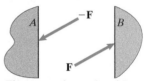

The contact forces A and B exert on each other.

Resolving the force on B into the normal and friction forces.

When friction is neglected there is only a normal force.

Ropes and Cables
If the weight of a rope or cable connecting two objects is negligible in comparison to its tension, it exerts equal and opposite forces on the objects that are parallel to the rope or cable.

Objects A and B connected by a cable.

The forces exerted on A and B.

Linear Springs
The magnitude of the equal and opposite forces exerted on two objects connected by a *linear springs* is

$$|\mathbf{F}| = k|L - L_0|, \tag{3.2}$$

where k is the *spring constant*, L is the length of the spring, and L_0 is its unstretched length.

Objects A and B connected by a spring.

The forces exerted on A and B.

Equilibrium
An object is in equilibrium if it is in *steady translation* (each point of the object has the same constant velocity) relative to an inertial reference frame. The sum of the external forces acting on an object in equilibrium is zero:

$$\Sigma\mathbf{F} = \mathbf{0}. \tag{3.3}$$

Free-Body Diagrams
A *free-body diagram* is a drawing of an object, isolated from its surroundings, that shows the external forces acting on it. Drawing a free-body diagram involves three steps.

1. Identify the object you want to isolate.
2. Draw a sketch of the object isolated from its surroundings.
3. Draw vectors representing the external forces acting on the object.

3.2 Two-Dimensional Force Systems

Suppose that the system of external forces acting on an object in equilibrium is two dimensional (coplanar). By orienting a coordinate system so that the forces lie in the x–y plane, we can express the sum of the external forces as

$$\Sigma\mathbf{F} = (\Sigma F_x)\mathbf{i} + (\Sigma F_y)\mathbf{j} = \mathbf{0},$$

where ΣF_x and ΣF_y are the sums of the x and y components of the forces. Since a vector is zero only if each of its components is zero, we obtain two scalar equilibrium equations:

$$\Sigma F_x = 0, \qquad \Sigma F_y = 0. \tag{3.4}$$

The sums of the x and y components of the external forces acting on an object in equilibrium must each equal zero.

Active Example 3.1 | **Using Equilibrium to Determine Forces** (▶ *Related Problem 3.1*)

The 1440-kg car is held in place on the inclined ramp by the horizontal cable from A to B. The car's brakes are not engaged, so the tires exert only normal forces on the ramp. Determine the magnitude of the force exerted on the car by the cable.

Strategy

Because the car is in equilibrium, we can draw its free-body diagram and use Eqs. (3.4) to determine the force exerted by the cable.

Solution

Draw the Free-Body Diagram of the Car

Draw a sketch of the isolated car. ────────▶

Complete the free-body diagram by showing the forces exerted on the car by its weight, the cable, and the ramp. ────────▶ T

mg

N

Apply the Equilibrium Equations

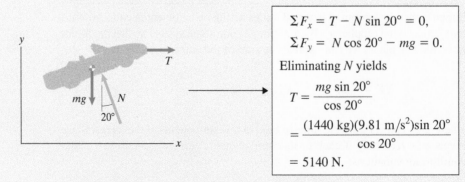

$$\Sigma F_x = T - N \sin 20° = 0,$$
$$\Sigma F_y = N \cos 20° - mg = 0.$$

Eliminating N yields

$$T = \frac{mg \sin 20°}{\cos 20°}$$

$$= \frac{(1440 \text{ kg})(9.81 \text{ m/s}^2)\sin 20°}{\cos 20°}$$

$$= 5140 \text{ N}.$$

Practice Problem Suppose that the cable attachment point B is moved upward so that the cable is parallel to the ramp. Determine the magnitude of the force exerted on the car by the cable.

Answer: 4830 N.

Example 3.2	**Choosing a Free-Body Diagram** (▶ *Related Problem 3.3*)

The automobile engine block is suspended by a system of cables. The mass of the block is 200 kg. The system is stationary. What are the tensions in cables *AB* and *AC*?

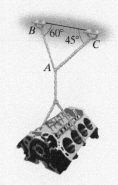

Strategy
We need a free-body diagram that is subjected to the forces we want to determine. By isolating part of the cable system near point *A* where the cables are joined, we can obtain a free-body diagram that is subjected to the weight of the block and the unknown tensions in cables *AB* and *AC*.

Solution
Draw the Free-Body Diagram Isolating part of the cable system near point *A* (Fig. a), we obtain a free-body diagram subjected to the weight of the block $W = mg = (200 \text{ kg}) (9.81 \text{ m/s}^2) = 1962 \text{ N}$ and the tensions in cables *AB* and *AC* (Fig. b).

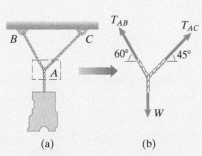
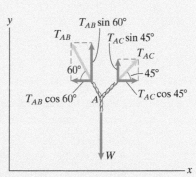

(a)   (b)

(a) Isolating part of the cable system.
(b) The completed free-body diagram.

(c) Selecting a coordinate system and resolving the forces into components.

Apply the Equilibrium Equations We select the coordinate system shown in Fig. c and resolve the cable tensions into *x* and *y* components. The resulting equilibrium equations are

$$\Sigma F_x = T_{AC} \cos 45° - T_{AB} \cos 60° = 0,$$

$$\Sigma F_y = T_{AC} \sin 45° + T_{AB} \sin 60° - 1962 \text{ N} = 0.$$

Solving these equations, we find that the tensions in the cables are $T_{AB} = 1436$ N and $T_{AC} = 1016$ N.

Critical Thinking
How can you choose a free-body diagram that permits you to determine particular unknown forces? There are no definite rules for choosing free-body diagrams. You will learn what to do in many cases from the examples we present, but you will also encounter new situations. It may be necessary to try several free-body diagrams before finding one that provides the information you need. Remember that forces you want to determine should appear as external forces on your free-body diagram, and your objective is to obtain a number of equilibrium equations equal to the number of unknown forces.

Example 3.3 | Applying Equilibrium to a System of Pulleys (▶ *Related Problem 3.54*)

The mass of each pulley of the system is m, and the mass of the suspended object A is m_A. Determine the force T necessary for the system to be in equilibrium.

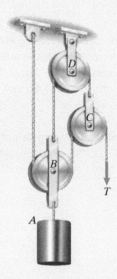

Strategy

By drawing free-body diagrams of the individual pulleys and applying equilibrium, we can relate the force T to the weights of the pulleys and the object A.

Solution

We first draw a free-body diagram of the pulley C to which the force T is applied (Fig. a). Notice that we assume the tension in the cable supported by the pulley to equal T on both sides (see Fig. 3.8). From the equilibrium equation

$$T_D - T - T - mg = 0,$$

we determine that the tension in the cable supported by pulley D is

$$T_D = 2T + mg.$$

We now know the tensions in the cables extending from pulleys C and D to pulley B in terms of T. Drawing the free-body diagram of pulley B (Fig. b), we obtain the equilibrium equation

$$T + T + 2T + mg - mg - m_A g = 0.$$

Solving, we obtain $T = m_A g/4$.

Critical Thinking

Notice that the objects we isolate in Figs. a and b include parts of the cables. The weights of those parts of cable are external forces acting on the free-body diagrams. Why didn't we include them? We tacitly assumed that the weights of those parts of cable could be neglected in comparison to the weights of the pulleys and the suspended object A. You will notice throughout the book that weights of objects are often neglected in analyzing the forces acting on them. This is a valid approximation for a given object if its weight is small compared to the other forces acting on it. But in any real engineering application, this assumption must be carefully evaluated. We discuss the weights of objects in more detail in Chapter 7.

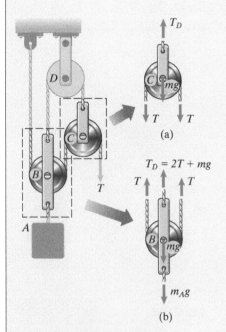

(a) Free-body diagram of pulley C.
(b) Free-body diagram of pulley B.

| Example 3.4 | Forces on an Airplane in Equilibrium (▶ *Related Problems 3.60–3.62*) |

The figure shows an airplane flying in the vertical plane and its free-body diagram. The forces acting on the airplane are its weight W, the thrust T exerted by its engines, and aerodynamic forces resulting from the pressure distribution on the airplane's surface. The dashed line indicates the path along which the airplane is moving. The aerodynamic forces are resolved into a component perpendicular to the path, the lift L, and a component parallel to the path, the drag D. The angle γ between the horizontal and the path is called the flight path angle, and α is the angle of attack. If the airplane remains in equilibrium for an interval of time, it is said to be in steady flight. If $\gamma = 6°$, $D = 125$ kN, $L = 680$ kN, and the mass of the airplane is 72,000 kg, what values of T and α are necessary to maintain steady flight?

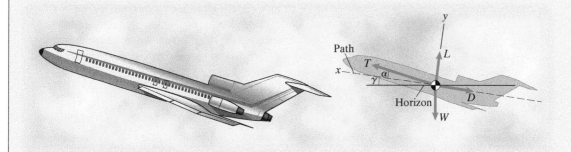

Strategy

The airplane is assumed to be in equilibrium. By applying Eqs. (3.4) to the given free-body diagram, we will obtain two equations with which to determine T and α.

Solution

In terms of the coordinate system in the figure, the equilibrium equations are

$$\Sigma F_x = T \cos \alpha - D - W \sin \gamma = 0, \qquad (1)$$
$$\Sigma F_y = T \sin \alpha + L - W \cos \gamma = 0, \qquad (2)$$

where the airplane's weight is $W = (72{,}000 \text{ kg})(9.81 \text{ m/s}^2) = 706{,}000$ N. We solve Eq. (2) for $\sin \alpha$, solve Eq. (1) for $\cos \alpha$, and divide to obtain an equation for $\tan \alpha$:

$$\tan \alpha = \frac{W \cos \gamma - L}{W \sin \gamma + D}$$

$$= \frac{(706{,}000 \text{ N}) \cos 6° - 680{,}000 \text{ N}}{(706{,}000 \text{ N}) \sin 6° + 125{,}000 \text{ N}} = 0.113.$$

The angle of attack $\alpha = \arctan(0.113) = 6.44°$. Now we use Eq. (1) to determine the thrust:

$$T = \frac{W \sin \gamma + D}{\cos \alpha}$$

$$= \frac{(706{,}000 \text{ N}) \sin 6° + 125{,}000 \text{ N}}{\cos 6.44°} = 200{,}000 \text{ N}.$$

Notice that the thrust necessary for steady flight is 28% of the airplane's weight.

Problems

▶ **3.1** In Active Example 3.1, suppose that the angle between the ramp supporting the car is increased from 20° to 30°. Draw the free-body diagram of the car showing the new geometry. Suppose that the cable from A to B must exert a 1900-lb horizontal force on the car to hold it in place. Determine the car's weight in pounds.

3.2 The ring weighs 5 lb and is in equilibrium. The force $F_1 = 4.5$ lb. Determine the force F_2 and the angle α.

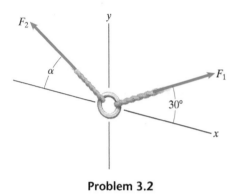

Problem 3.2

▶ **3.3** In Example 3.2, suppose that the attachment point C is moved to the right and cable AC is extended so that the angle between cable AC and the ceiling decreases from 45° to 35°. The angle between cable AB and the ceiling remains 60°. What are the tensions in cables AB and AC?

3.4 The 200-kg engine block is suspended by the cables AB and AC. The angle $\alpha = 40°$. The free-body diagram obtained by isolating the part of the system within the dashed line is shown. Determine the forces T_{AB} and T_{AC}.

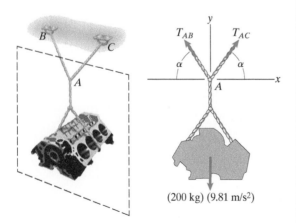

Problem 3.4

3.5 A heavy rope used as a mooring line for a cruise ship sags as shown. If the mass of the rope is 90 kg, what are the tensions in the rope at A and B?

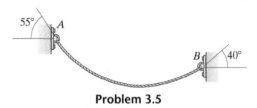

Problem 3.5

3.6 A physiologist estimates that the masseter muscle of a predator, *Martes*, is capable of exerting a force M as large as 900 N. Assume that the jaw is in equilibrium and determine the necessary force T that the temporalis muscle exerts and the force P exerted on the object being bitten.

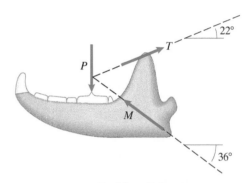

Problem 3.6

3.7 The two springs are identical, with unstretched lengths 250 mm and spring constants $k = 1200$ N/m.

(a) Draw the free-body diagram of block A.

(b) Draw the free-body diagram of block B.

(c) What are the masses of the two blocks?

3.8 The two springs are identical, with unstretched lengths of 250 mm. Suppose that their spring constant k is unknown and the sum of the masses of blocks A and B is 10 kg. Determine the value of k and the masses of the two blocks.

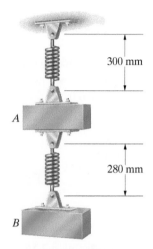

300 mm

A

280 mm

B

Problems 3.7/3.8

3.9 The inclined surface is smooth. (Remember that "smooth" means that friction is negligible.) The two springs are identical, with unstretched lengths of 250 mm and spring constants $k = 1200$ N/m. What are the masses of blocks A and B?

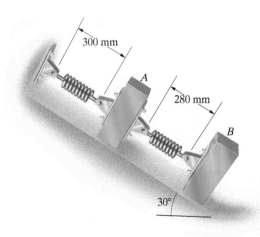

300 mm

A

280 mm

B

30°

Problem 3.9

3.10 The mass of the crane is 20,000 kg. The crane's cable is attached to a caisson whose mass is 400 kg. The tension in the cable is 1 kN.

(a) Determine the magnitudes of the normal and friction forces exerted on the crane by the level ground.

(b) Determine the magnitudes of the normal and friction forces exerted on the caisson by the level ground.

Strategy: To do part (a), draw the free-body diagram of the crane and the part of its cable within the dashed line.

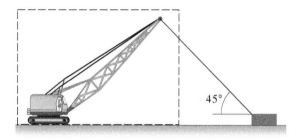

45°

Problem 3.10

3.11 The inclined surface is smooth. The 100-kg crate is held stationary by a force T applied to the cable.

(a) Draw the free-body diagram of the crate.

(b) Determine the force T.

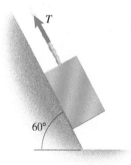

T

60°

Problem 3.11

3.12 The 1200-kg car is stationary on the sloping road.

(a) If $\alpha = 20°$, what are the magnitudes of the total normal and friction forces exerted on the car's tires by the road?

(b) The car can remain stationary only if the total friction force necessary for equilibrium is not greater than 0.6 times the total normal force. What is the largest angle α for which the car can remain stationary?

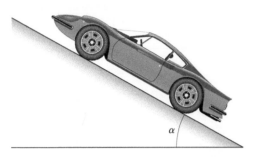

Problem 3.12

3.13 The 100-lb crate is in equilibrium on the smooth surface. The spring constant is $k = 400$ lb/ft. Let S be the stretch of the spring. Obtain an equation for S (in feet) as a function of the angle α.

Problem 3.13

3.14 The 600-lb box is held in place on the smooth bed of the dump truck by the rope AB.

(a) If $\alpha = 25°$, what is the tension in the rope?

(b) If the rope will safely support a tension of 400 lb, what is the maximum allowable value of α?

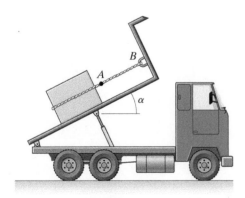

Problem 3.14

3.15 The 80-lb box is held in place on the smooth inclined surface by the rope AB. Determine the tension in the rope and the normal force exerted on the box by the inclined surface.

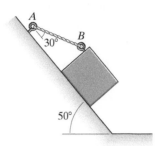

Problem 3.15

3.16 The 1360-kg car and the 2100-kg tow truck are stationary. The muddy surface on which the car's tires rest exerts negligible friction forces on them. What is the tension in the tow cable?

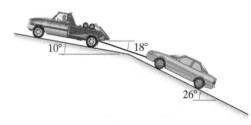

Problem 3.16

3.17 Each box weighs 40 lb. The angles are measured relative to the horizontal. The surfaces are smooth. Determine the tension in the rope A and the normal force exerted on box B by the inclined surface.

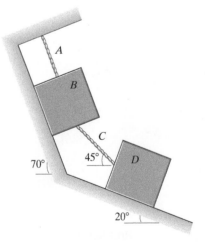

Problem 3.17

3.18 A 10-kg painting is hung with a wire supported by a nail. The length of the wire is 1.3 m.

(a) What is the tension in the wire?

(b) What is the magnitude of the force exerted on the nail by the wire?

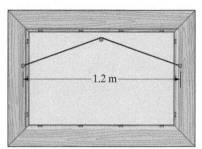

Problem 3.18

3.19 A 10-kg painting is hung with a wire supported by two nails. The length of the wire is 1.3 m.

(a) What is the tension in the wire?

(b) What is the magnitude of the force exerted on each nail by the wire? (Assume that the tension is the same in each part of the wire.)

Compare your answers to the answers to Problem 3.18.

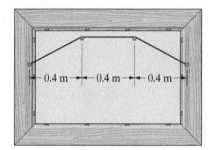

Problem 3.19

3.20 Assume that the 150-lb climber is in equilibrium. What are the tensions in the rope on the left and right sides?

3.21 If the mass of the climber shown in Problem 3.20 is 80 kg, what are the tensions in the rope on the left and right sides?

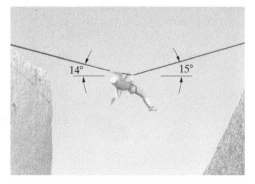

Problems 3.20/3.21

3.22 The construction worker exerts a 20-lb force on the rope to hold the crate in equilibrium in the position shown. What is the weight of the crate?

Problem 3.22

3.23 A construction worker on the moon, where the acceleration due to gravity is 1.62 m/s^2, holds the same crate described in Problem 3.22 in the position shown. What force must she exert on the cable to hold the crate in equilibrium (a) in newtons; (b) in pounds?

Problem 3.23

3.24 The person wants to cause the 200-lb crate to start sliding toward the right. To achieve this, the *horizontal component* of the force exerted on the crate by the rope must equal 0.35 times the normal force exerted on the crate by the floor. In Fig. a, the person pulls on the rope in the direction shown. In Fig. b, the person attaches the rope to a support as shown and pulls upward on the rope. What is the magnitude of the force he must exert on the rope in each case?

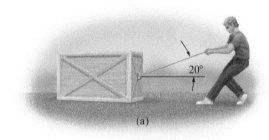

(a)

(b)

Problem 3.24

3.25 A traffic engineer wants to suspend a 200-lb traffic light above the center of the two right lanes of a four-lane thoroughfare as shown. Points *A* and *C* are at the same height. Determine the tensions in the cables *AB* and *BC*.

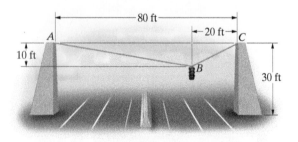

Problem 3.25

3.26 Cable *AB* is 3 m long and cable *BC* is 4 m long. Points *A* and *C* are at the same height. The mass of the suspended object is 350 kg. Determine the tensions in cables *AB* and *BC*.

3.27 The length of cable *AB* is adjustable. Cable *BC* is 4 m long. If you don't want the tension in either cable *AB* or cable *BC* to exceed 3 kN, what is the minimum acceptable length of cable *AB*?

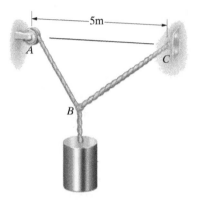

Problems 3.26/3.27

3.28 What are the tensions in the upper and lower cables? (Your answers will be in terms of *W*. Neglect the weight of the pulley.)

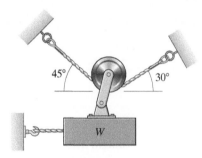

Problem 3.28

3.29 Two tow trucks lift a 660-lb motorcycle out of a ravine following an accident. If the motorcycle is in equilibrium in the position shown, what are the tensions in cables *AB* and *AC*?

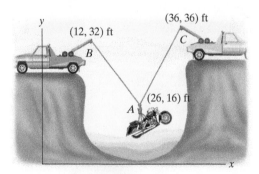

Problem 3.29

3.30 An astronaut candidate conducts experiments on an airbearing platform. While he carries out calibrations, the platform is held in place by the horizontal tethers *AB*, *AC*, and *AD*. The forces exerted by the tethers are the only horizontal forces acting on the platform. If the tension in tether *AC* is 2 N, what are the tensions in the other two tethers?

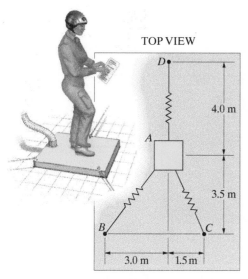

Problem 3.30

3.31 The bucket contains concrete and weighs 5800 lb. What are the tensions in the cables *AB* and *AC*?

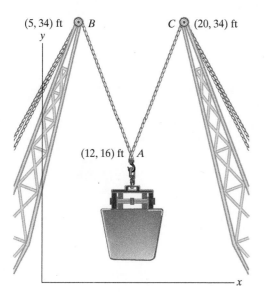

Problem 3.31

3.32 The slider *A* is in equilibrium and the bar is smooth. What is the mass of the slider?

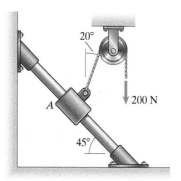

Problem 3.32

3.33 The 20-kg mass is suspended from three cables. Cable *AC* is equipped with a turnbuckle so that its tension can be adjusted and a strain gauge that allows its tension to be measured. If the tension in cable *AC* is 40 N, what are the tensions in cables *AB* and *AD*?

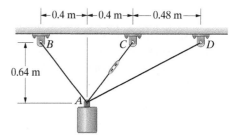

Problem 3.33

3.34 The structural joint is in equilibrium. If $F_A = 1000$ lb and $F_D = 5000$ lb, what are F_B and F_C?

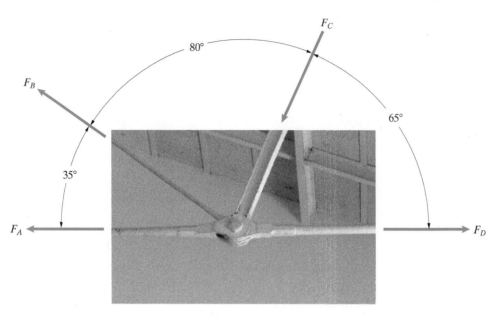

Problem 3.34

3.35 The collar A slides on the smooth vertical bar. The masses $m_A = 20$ kg and $m_B = 10$ kg. When $h = 0.1$ m, the spring is unstretched. When the system is in equilibrium, $h = 0.3$ m. Determine the spring constant k.

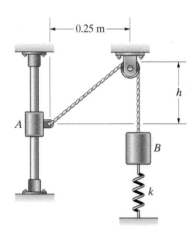

Problem 3.35

3.36* Suppose that you want to design a cable system to suspend an object of weight W from the ceiling. The two wires must be identical, and the dimension b is fixed. The ratio of the tension T in each wire to its cross-sectional area A must equal a specified value $T/A = \sigma$. The "cost" of your design is the total volume of material in the two wires, $V = 2A\sqrt{b^2 + h^2}$. Determine the value of h that minimizes the cost.

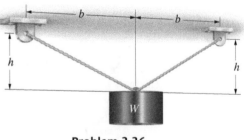

Problem 3.36

3.37 The system of cables suspends a 1000-lb bank of lights above a movie set. Determine the tensions in cables *AB*, *CD*, and *CE*.

3.38 A technician changes the position of the 1000-lb bank of lights by removing the cable *CE*. What is the tension in cable *AB* after the change?

3.39 While working on another exhibit, a curator at the Smithsonian Institution pulls the suspended *Voyager* aircraft to one side by attaching three horizontal cables as shown. The mass of the aircraft is 1250 kg. Determine the tensions in the cable segments *AB*, *BC*, and *CD*.

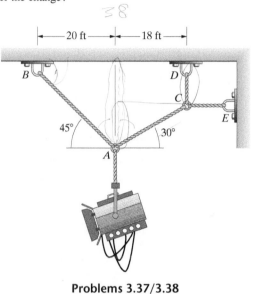

Problems 3.37/3.38

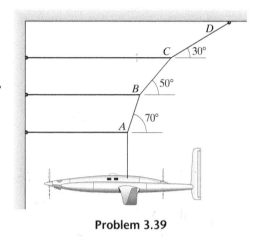

Problem 3.39

3.40 A truck dealer wants to suspend a 4000-kg truck as shown for advertising. The distance $b = 15$ m, and the sum of the lengths of the cables *AB* and *BC* is 42 m. Points *A* and *C* are at the same height. What are the tensions in the cables?

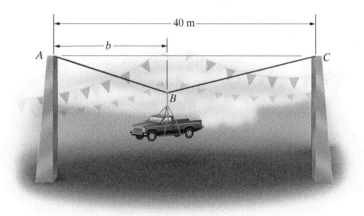

Problem 3.40

3.41 The distance $h = 12$ in, and the tension in cable AD is 200 lb. What are the tensions in cables AB and AC?

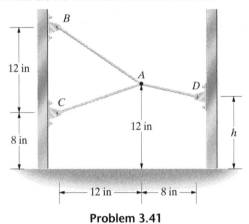

Problem 3.41

3.42 You are designing a cable system to support a suspended object of weight W. Because your design requires points A and B to be placed as shown, you have no control over the angle α, but you can choose the angle β by placing point C wherever you wish. Show that to minimize the tensions in cables AB and BC, you must choose $\beta = \alpha$ if the angle $\alpha \geq 45°$.

Strategy: Draw a diagram of the sum of the forces exerted by the three cables at A.

Problem 3.42

3.43* The length of the cable ABC is 1.4 m. The 2-kN force is applied to a small pulley. The system is stationary. What is the tension in the cable?

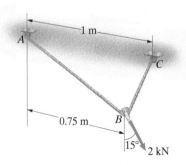

Problem 3.43

3.44 The masses $m_1 = 12$ kg and $m_2 = 6$ kg are suspended by the cable system shown. The cable BC is horizontal. Determine the angle α and the tensions in the cables AB, BC, and CD.

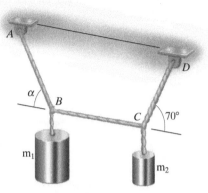

Problem 3.44

3.45 The weights $W_1 = 50$ lb and W_2 are suspended by the cable system shown. Determine the weight W_2 and the tensions in the cables AB, BC, and CD.

3.46 Assume that $W_2 = W_1/2$. If you don't want the tension anywhere in the supporting cable to exceed 200 lb, what is the largest acceptable value of W_1?

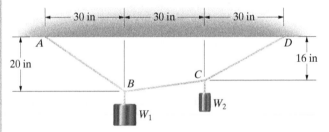

Problems 3.45/3.46

3.47 The hydraulic cylinder is subjected to three forces. An 8-kN force is exerted on the cylinder at B that is parallel to the cylinder and points from B toward C. The link AC exerts a force at C that is parallel to the line from A to C. The link CD exerts a force at C that is parallel to the line from C to D.

(a) Draw the free-body diagram of the cylinder. (The cylinder's weight is negligible.)

(b) Determine the magnitudes of the forces exerted by the links AC and CD.

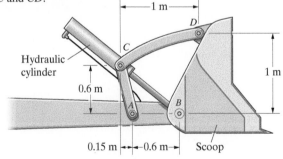

Problem 3.47

3.48 The 50-lb cylinder rests on two smooth surfaces.

(a) Draw the free-body diagram of the cylinder.

(b) If $\alpha = 30°$, what are the magnitudes of the forces exerted on the cylinder by the left and right surfaces?

3.49 Obtain an equation for the force exerted on the 50-lb cylinder by the left surface in terms of the angle α in two ways: (a) using a coordinate system with the y axis vertical, (b) using a coordinate system with the y axis parallel to the right surface.

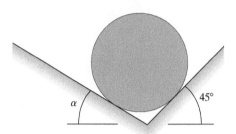

Problems 3.48/3.49

3.50 The two springs are identical, with unstretched length 0.4 m. When the 50-kg mass is suspended at B, the length of each spring increases to 0.6 m. What is the spring constant k?

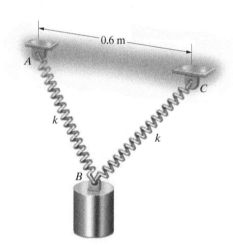

Problem 3.50

3.51 The cable AB is 0.5 m in length. The *unstretched* length of the spring is 0.4 m. When the 50-kg mass is suspended at B, the length of the spring increases to 0.45 m. What is the spring constant k?

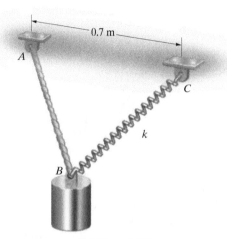

Problem 3.51

3.52* The small sphere of mass m is attached to a string of length L and rests on the smooth surface of a fixed sphere of radius R. The center of the sphere is directly below the point where the string is attached. Obtain an equation for the tension in the string in terms of m, L, h, and R.

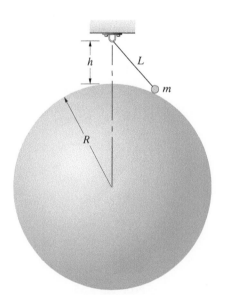

Problem 3.52

3.53 The inclined surface is smooth. Determine the force T that must be exerted on the cable to hold the 100-kg crate in equilibrium and compare your answer to the answer of Problem 3.11.

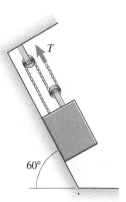

Problem 3.53

▶ **3.54** In Example 3.3, suppose that the mass of the suspended object is m_A and the masses of the pulleys are $m_B = 0.3m_A$, $m_C = 0.2m_A$, and $m_D = 0.2m_A$. Show that the force T necessary for the system to be in equilibrium is $0.275m_Ag$.

3.55 The mass of each pulley of the system is m and the mass of the suspended object A is m_A. Determine the force T necessary for the system to be in equilibrium.

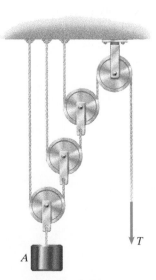

Problem 3.55

3.56 The suspended mass $m_1 = 50$ kg. Neglecting the masses of the pulleys, determine the value of the mass m_2 necessary for the system to be in equilibrium.

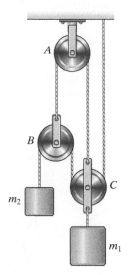

Problem 3.56

3.57 The boy is lifting himself using the block and tackle shown. If the weight of the block and tackle is negligible, and the combined weight of the boy and the beam he is sitting on is 120 lb, what force does he have to exert on the rope to raise himself at a constant rate? (Neglect the deviation of the ropes from the vertical.)

Problem 3.57

3.58 Pulley systems containing one, two, and three pulleys are shown. Neglecting the weights of the pulleys, determine the force T required to support the weight W in each case.

3.59 The number of pulleys in the type of system shown could obviously be extended to an arbitrary number N.

(a) Neglecting the weights of the pulleys, determine the force T required to support the weight W as a function of the number of pulleys N in the system.

(b) Using the result of part (a), determine the force T required to support the weight W for a system with 10 pulleys.

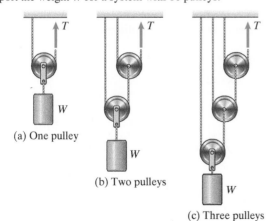

(a) One pulley

(b) Two pulleys

(c) Three pulleys

Problems 3.58/3.59

▶ **3.60** A 14,000-kg airplane is in steady flight in the vertical plane. The flight path angle is $\gamma = 10°$, the angle of attack is $\alpha = 4°$, and the thrust force exerted by the engine is $T = 60$ kN. What are the magnitudes of the lift and drag forces acting on the airplane? (See Example 3.4.)

▶ **3.61** An airplane is in steady flight, the angle of attack $\alpha = 0$, the thrust-to-drag ratio $T/D = 2$, and the lift-to-drag ratio $L/D = 4$. What is the flight path angle γ? (See Example 3.4.)

▶ **3.62** An airplane glides in steady flight ($T = 0$), and its lift-to-drag ratio is $L/D = 4$.

(a) What is the flight path angle γ?

(b) If the airplane glides from an altitude of 1000 m to zero altitude, what horizontal distance does it travel? (See Example 3.4.)

3.3 Three-Dimensional Force Systems

The equilibrium situations we have considered so far have involved only coplanar forces. When the system of external forces acting on an object in equilibrium is three dimensional, we can express the sum of the external forces as

$$\Sigma \mathbf{F} = (\Sigma F_x)\mathbf{i} + (\Sigma F_y)\mathbf{j} + (\Sigma F_z)\mathbf{k} = \mathbf{0}.$$

Each component of this equation must equal zero, resulting in three scalar equilibrium equations:

$$\Sigma F_x = 0, \quad \Sigma F_y = 0, \quad \Sigma F_z = 0. \tag{3.5}$$

The sums of the x, y, and z components of the external forces acting on an object in equilibrium must each equal zero.

Active Example 3.5   (▶ *Related Problem 3.63*)

The 100-kg cylinder is suspended from the ceiling by cables attached at points B, C, and D. What are the tensions in cables AB, AC, and AD?

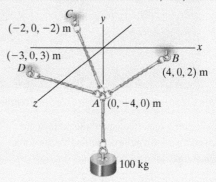

Strategy

By isolating part of the cable system near point A, we will obtain a free-body diagram subjected to forces due to the tensions in the cables. Because the sums of the external forces in the x, y, and z directions must each equal zero, we can obtain three equilibrium equations for the three unknown tensions. To do so, we must express the forces exerted by the tensions in terms of their components.

Solution

Draw the Free-Body Diagram and Apply Equilibrium

Isolate part of the cable system near point A and show the forces exerted due to the tensions in the cables. The sum of the forces must equal zero:

$$\Sigma \mathbf{F} = \mathbf{T}_{AB} + \mathbf{T}_{AC} + \mathbf{T}_{AD} - (981 \text{ N})\mathbf{j} = \mathbf{0}.$$

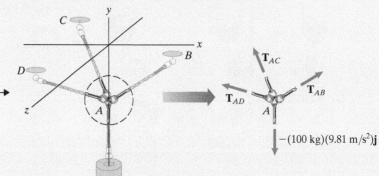

Write the Forces in Terms of Their Components

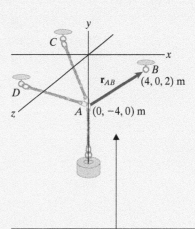

$$\left.\begin{aligned}\mathbf{r}_{AB} &= (x_B - x_A)\mathbf{i} + (y_B - y_A)\mathbf{j} + (z_B - z_A)\mathbf{k}.\\ &= 4\mathbf{i} + 4\mathbf{j} + 2\mathbf{k}\ (\text{m}).\\ \mathbf{e}_{AB} &= \frac{\mathbf{r}_{AB}}{|\mathbf{r}_{AB}|} = 0.667\mathbf{i} + 0.667\mathbf{j} + 0.333\mathbf{k}.\end{aligned}\right\}$$

Obtain a unit vector that has the same direction as the force $\mathbf{T}_{AB}$ by dividing the position vector $\mathbf{r}_{AB}$ from point A to point B by its magnitude.

$$\left.\begin{aligned}\mathbf{T}_{AB} &= T_{AB}\mathbf{e}_{AB}\\ &= T_{AB}(0.667\mathbf{i} + 0.667\mathbf{j} + 0.333\mathbf{k}),\\ \mathbf{T}_{AC} &= T_{AC}(-0.408\mathbf{i} + 0.816\mathbf{j} - 0.408\mathbf{k}),\\ \mathbf{T}_{AD} &= T_{AD}(-0.514\mathbf{i} + 0.686\mathbf{j} + 0.514\mathbf{k}).\end{aligned}\right\}$$

Express the force $\mathbf{T}_{AB}$ in terms of its components by writing it as the product of the tension T_{AB} in cable AB and the unit vector $\mathbf{e}_{AB}$. Express the forces $\mathbf{T}_{AC}$ and $\mathbf{T}_{AD}$ in terms of their components using the same procedure.

Substitute these expressions into the equilibrium equation

$$\mathbf{T}_{AB} + \mathbf{T}_{AC} + \mathbf{T}_{AD} - (981\ \text{N})\mathbf{j} = \mathbf{0}.$$

Because the $\mathbf{i}$, $\mathbf{j}$, and $\mathbf{k}$ components must each equal zero, this results in three equations:

$$0.667T_{AB} - 0.408T_{AC} - 0.514T_{AD} = 0,$$
$$0.667T_{AB} + 0.816T_{AC} + 0.686T_{AD} - 981\ \text{N} = 0,$$
$$0.333T_{AB} - 0.408T_{AC} + 0.514T_{AD} = 0.$$

Solving these three equations yields $T_{AB} = 519\ \text{N}$, $T_{AC} = 636\ \text{N}$, and $T_{AD} = 168\ \text{N}$.

Practice Problem Suppose that cables AB, AC, and AD are lengthened so that the attachment point A is located at the point $(0, -6, 0)$ m. What are the tensions in the cables?

Answer: $T_{AB} = 432\ \text{N}$, $T_{AC} = 574\ \text{N}$, $T_{AD} = 141\ \text{N}$.

| Example 3.6 | Application of the Dot Product (▶ *Related Problem 3.79*) |

The 100-lb "slider" C is held in place on the smooth bar by the cable AC. Determine the tension in the cable and the force exerted on the slider by the bar.

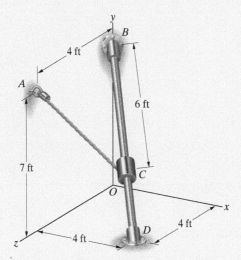

Strategy

Because we want to determine forces that act on the slider, we need to draw its free-body diagram. The external forces acting on the slider are its weight and the forces exerted on it by the cable and the bar. If we approached this example as we did the previous one, our next step would be to express the forces in terms of their components. However, we don't know the direction of the force exerted on the slider by the bar. Since the smooth bar exerts negligible friction force, we do know that the force is normal to the bar's axis. Therefore we can eliminate this force from the equation $\Sigma\mathbf{F} = \mathbf{0}$ by taking the dot product of the equation with a unit vector that is parallel to the bar.

Solution

Draw the Free-Body Diagram   We isolate the slider (Fig. a) and complete the free-body diagram by showing the weight of the slider, the force $\mathbf{T}$ exerted by the tension in the cable, and the normal force $\mathbf{N}$ exerted by the bar (Fig. b).

Apply the Equilibrium Equations   The sum of the external forces acting on the free-body diagram is

$$\Sigma\mathbf{F} = \mathbf{T} + \mathbf{N} - (100\,\text{lb})\mathbf{j} = \mathbf{0}. \tag{1}$$

Let $\mathbf{e}_{BD}$ be the unit vector pointing from point B toward point D. Since $\mathbf{N}$ is perpendicular to the bar, $\mathbf{e}_{BD}\cdot\mathbf{N} = 0$. Therefore,

$$\mathbf{e}_{BD}\cdot(\Sigma\mathbf{F}) = \mathbf{e}_{BD}\cdot[\mathbf{T} - (100\,\text{lb})\mathbf{j}] = 0. \tag{2}$$

Determining $\mathbf{e}_{BD}$: We determine the vector from point B to point D,

$$\mathbf{r}_{BD} = (4-0)\mathbf{i} + (0-7)\mathbf{j} + (4-0)\mathbf{k} = 4\mathbf{i} - 7\mathbf{j} + 4\mathbf{k}\,(\text{ft}),$$

and divide it by its magnitude to obtain the unit vector $\mathbf{e}_{BD}$:

$$\mathbf{e}_{BD} = \frac{\mathbf{r}_{BD}}{|\mathbf{r}_{BD}|} = \frac{4}{9}\mathbf{i} - \frac{7}{9}\mathbf{j} + \frac{4}{9}\mathbf{k}.$$

Expressing **T** *in terms of components:* We need to determine the coordinates of the slider C. We can write the vector from B to C in terms of the unit vector $\mathbf{e}_{BD}$,

$$\mathbf{r}_{BC} = 6\mathbf{e}_{BD} = 2.67\mathbf{i} - 4.67\mathbf{j} + 2.67\mathbf{k} \text{ (ft)},$$

and then add it to the vector from the origin O to B to obtain the vector from O to C:

$$\mathbf{r}_{OC} = \mathbf{r}_{OB} + \mathbf{r}_{BC} = 7\mathbf{j} + (2.67\mathbf{i} - 4.67\mathbf{j} + 2.67\mathbf{k})$$

$$= 2.67\mathbf{i} + 2.33\mathbf{j} + 2.67\mathbf{k} \text{ (ft)}.$$

The components of this vector are the coordinates of point C. Now we can determine a unit vector with the same direction as **T**. The vector from C to A is

$$\mathbf{r}_{CA} = (0 - 2.67)\mathbf{i} + (7 - 2.33)\mathbf{j} + (4 - 2.67)\mathbf{k}$$

$$= -2.67\mathbf{i} + 4.67\mathbf{j} + 1.33\mathbf{k} \text{ (ft)},$$

and the unit vector that points from point C toward point A is

$$\mathbf{e}_{CA} = \frac{\mathbf{r}_{CA}}{|\mathbf{r}_{CA}|} = -0.482\mathbf{i} + 0.843\mathbf{j} + 0.241\mathbf{k}.$$

Let T be the tension in the cable AC. Then we can write the vector **T** as

$$\mathbf{T} = T\mathbf{e}_{CA} = T(-0.482\mathbf{i} + 0.843\mathbf{j} + 0.241\mathbf{k}).$$

Determining **T** *and* **N**: Substituting our expressions for $\mathbf{e}_{BD}$ and **T** in terms of their components into Eq. (2) yields

$$0 = \mathbf{e}_{BD} \cdot [\mathbf{T} - (100 \text{ lb})\mathbf{j}]$$

$$= \left(\frac{4}{9}\mathbf{i} - \frac{7}{9}\mathbf{j} + \frac{4}{9}\mathbf{k}\right) \cdot [-0.482T\mathbf{i} + (0.843T - 100 \text{ lb})\mathbf{j} + 0.241T\mathbf{k}]$$

$$= -0.762T + 77.8 \text{ lb},$$

and we obtain the tension $T = 102$ lb.

Now we can determine the force exerted on the slider by the bar by using Eq. (1):

$$\mathbf{N} = -\mathbf{T} + (100 \text{ lb})\mathbf{j}$$

$$= -(102 \text{ lb})(-0.482\mathbf{i} + 0.843\mathbf{j} + 0.241\mathbf{k}) + (100 \text{ lb})\mathbf{j}$$

$$= 49.1\mathbf{i} + 14.0\mathbf{j} - 24.6\mathbf{k} \text{ (lb)}.$$

Critical Thinking

By taking the dot product of the equilibrium equation for the slider with a unit vector $\mathbf{e}_{BD}$ that is parallel to the smooth bar BD, we obtained Eq. (2), which does not contain the normal force **N**. Why does this happen? The formal answer is that $\mathbf{e}_{BD}$ is perpendicular to **N**, and so $\mathbf{e}_{BD} \cdot \mathbf{N} = 0$. But the physical interpretation of Eq. (2) provides a more compelling explanation: It states that *the component of the slider's weight parallel to the bar is balanced by the component of* **T** *parallel to the bar*. The normal force exerted on the slider by the smooth bar has no component parallel to the bar. We were therefore able to solve for the tension in the cable without knowing the normal force **N**.

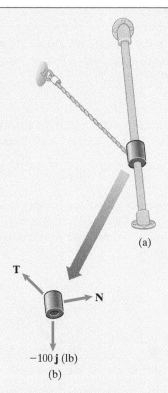

(a)

T

N

$-100\,\mathbf{j}$ (lb)

(b)

(a) Isolating the slider.
(b) Free-body diagram of the slider showing the forces exerted by its weight, the cable, and the bar.

Problems

▶ **3.63** In Active Example 3.5, suppose that the attachment point *B* is moved to the point $(5, 0, 0)$ m. What are the tensions in cables *AB*, *AC*, and *AD*?

3.64 The force $\mathbf{F} = 800\mathbf{i} + 200\mathbf{j}$ (lb) acts at point *A* where the cables *AB*, *AC*, and *AD* are joined. What are the tensions in the three cables?

3.65* Suppose that you want to apply a 1000-lb force **F** at point *A* in a direction such that the resulting tensions in cables *AB*, *AC*, and *AD* are equal. Determine the components of **F**.

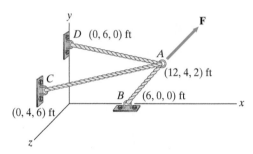

Problems 3.64/3.65

3.66 The 10-lb metal disk *A* is supported by the smooth inclined surface and the strings *AB* and *AC*. The disk is located at coordinates $(5, 1, 4)$ ft. What are the tensions in the strings?

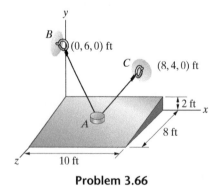

Problem 3.66

3.67 The bulldozer exerts a force $\mathbf{F} = 2\mathbf{i}$ (kip) at *A*. What are the tensions in cables *AB*, *AC*, and *AD*?

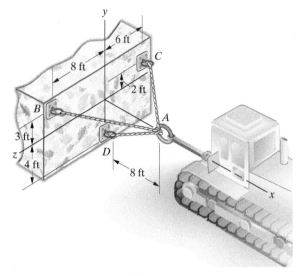

Problem 3.67

3.68 Prior to its launch, a balloon carrying a set of experiments to high altitude is held in place by groups of student volunteers holding the tethers at *B*, *C*, and *D*. The mass of the balloon, experiments package, and the gas it contains is 90 kg, and the buoyancy force on the balloon is 1000 N. The supervising professor conservatively estimates that each student can exert at least a 40-N tension on the tether for the necessary length of time. Based on this estimate, what minimum numbers of students are needed at *B*, *C*, and *D*?

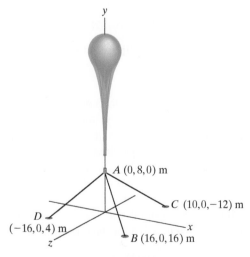

Problem 3.68

3.69 The 20-kg mass is suspended by cables attached to three vertical 2-m posts. Point A is at (0, 1.2, 0) m. Determine the tensions in cables AB, AC, and AD.

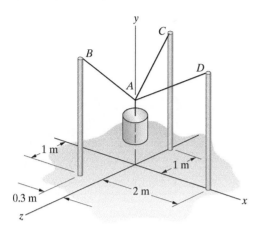

Problem 3.69

3.70 The weight of the horizontal wall section is W = 20,000 lb. Determine the tensions in the cables AB, AC, and AD.

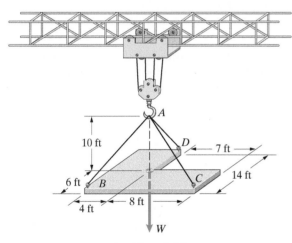

Problem 3.70

3.71 The car in Fig. a and the pallet supporting it weigh 3000 lb. They are supported by four cables AB, AC, AD, and AE. The locations of the attachment points on the pallet are shown in Fig. b. The tensions in cables AB and AE are equal. Determine the tensions in the cables.

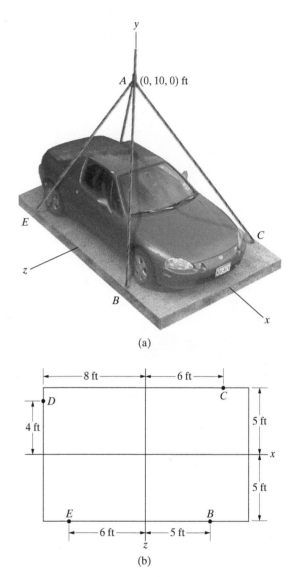

(a)

(b)

Problem 3.71

3.72 The 680-kg load suspended from the helicopter is in equilibrium. The aerodynamic drag force on the load is horizontal. The y axis is vertical, and cable OA lies in the x–y plane. Determine the magnitude of the drag force and the tension in cable OA.

3.73 The coordinates of the three cable attachment points B, C, and D are $(-3.3, -4.5, 0)$ m, $(1.1, -5.3, 1)$ m, and $(1.6, -5.4, -1)$ m, respectively. What are the tensions in cables OB, OC, and OD?

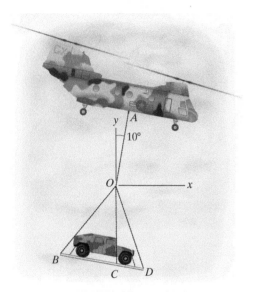

Problems 3.72/3.73

3.74 If the mass of the bar AB is negligible compared to the mass of the suspended object E, the bar exerts a force on the "ball" at B that points from A toward B. The mass of the object E is 200 kg. The y axis points upward. Determine the tensions in the cables BC and BD.

  Strategy: Draw a free-body diagram of the ball at B. (The weight of the ball is negligible.)

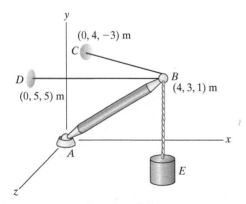

Problem 3.74

3.75* The 3400-lb car is at rest on the plane surface. The unit vector $\mathbf{e_n} = 0.456\mathbf{i} + 0.570\mathbf{j} + 0.684\mathbf{k}$ is perpendicular to the surface. Determine the magnitudes of the total normal force $\mathbf{N}$ and the total friction force $\mathbf{f}$ exerted on the surface by the car's wheels.

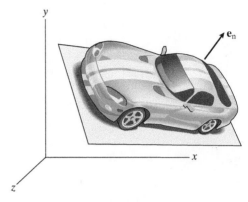

Problem 3.75

3.76 The system shown anchors a stanchion of a cable-suspended roof. If the tension in cable AB is 900 kN, what are the tensions in cables EF and EG?

3.77* The cables of the system will each safely support a tension of 1500 kN. Based on this criterion, what is the largest safe value of the tension in cable AB?

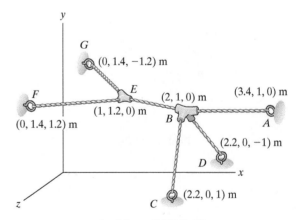

Problems 3.76/3.77

3.78 The 200-kg slider at A is held in place on the smooth vertical bar by the cable AB.

(a) Determine the tension in the cable.

(b) Determine the force exerted on the slider by the bar.

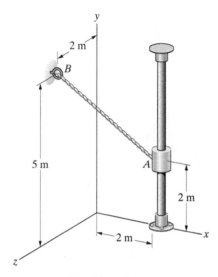

Problem 3.78

▶ **3.79** In Example 3.6, suppose that the cable AC is replaced by a longer one so that the distance from point B to the slider C increases from 6 ft to 8 ft. Determine the tension in the cable.

3.80 The cable AB keeps the 8-kg collar A in place on the smooth bar CD. The y axis points upward. What is the tension in the cable?

3.81* Determine the magnitude of the normal force exerted on the collar A by the smooth bar.

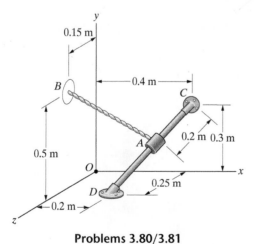

Problems 3.80/3.81

3.82* The 10-kg collar A and 20-kg collar B are held in place on the smooth bars by the 3-m cable from A to B and the force F acting on A. The force F is parallel to the bar. Determine F.

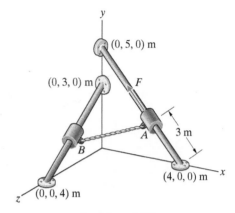

Problem 3.82

Review Problems

3.83 The 100-lb crate is held in place on the smooth surface by the rope AB. Determine the tension in the rope and the magnitude of the normal force exerted on the crate by the surface.

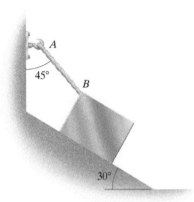

Problem 3.83

3.84 The system shown is called Russell's traction. If the sum of the downward forces exerted at A and B by the patient's leg is 32.2 lb, what is the weight W?

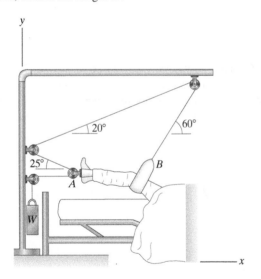

Problem 3.84

3.85 The 400-lb engine block is suspended by the cables AB and AC. If you don't want either T_{AB} or T_{AC} to exceed 400 lb, what is the smallest acceptable value of the angle α?

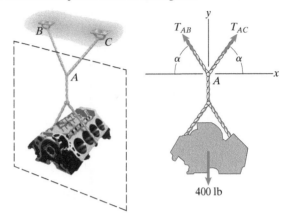

Problem 3.85

3.86 The cable AB is horizontal, and the box on the right weighs 100 lb. The surfaces are smooth.

(a) What is the tension in the cable?

(b) What is the weight of the box on the left?

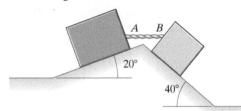

Problem 3.86

3.87 Assume that the forces exerted on the 170-lb climber by the slanted walls of the "chimney" are perpendicular to the walls. If he is in equilibrium and is exerting a 160-lb force on the rope, what are the magnitudes of the forces exerted on him by the left and right walls?

Problem 3.87

3.88 The mass of the suspended object A is m_A and the masses of the pulleys are negligible. Determine the force T necessary for the system to be in equilibrium.

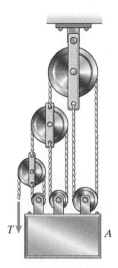

Problem 3.88

3.89 The assembly A, including the pulley, weighs 60 lb. What force F is necessary for the system to be in equilibrium?

Problem 3.89

3.90 The mass of block A is 42 kg, and the mass of block B is 50 kg. The surfaces are smooth. If the blocks are in equilibrium, what is the force F?

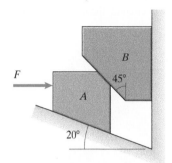

Problem 3.90

3.91 The climber A is being helped up an icy slope by two friends. His mass is 80 kg, and the direction cosines of the force exerted on him by the slope are $\cos \theta_x = -0.286$, $\cos \theta_y = 0.429$, and $\cos \theta_z = 0.857$. The y axis is vertical. If the climber is in equilibrium in the position shown, what are the tensions in the ropes AB and AC and the magnitude of the force exerted on him by the slope?

3.92 Consider the climber A being helped by his friends in Problem 3.91. To try to make the tensions in the ropes more equal, the friend at B moves to the position (4, 2, 0) m. What are the new tensions in the ropes AB and AC and the magnitude of the force exerted on the climber by the slope?

Problems 3.91/3.92

3.93 A climber helps his friend up an icy slope. His friend is hauling a box of supplies. If the mass of the friend is 90 kg and the mass of the supplies is 22 kg, what are the tensions in the ropes *AB* and *CD*? Assume that the slope is smooth. That is, only normal forces are exerted on the man and the box by the slope.

Problem 3.93

3.94 The 2800-lb car is moving at constant speed on a road with the slope shown. The aerodynamics forces on the car are the drag $D = 270$ lb, which is parallel to the road, and the lift $L = 120$ lb, which is perpendicular to the road. Determine the magnitudes of the total normal and friction forces exerted on the car by the road.

Problem 3.94

3.95 An engineer doing preliminary design studies for a new radio telescope envisions a triangular receiving platform suspended by cables from three equally spaced 40-m towers. The receiving platform has a mass of 20 Mg (megagrams) and is 10 m below the tops of the towers. What tension would the cables be subjected to?

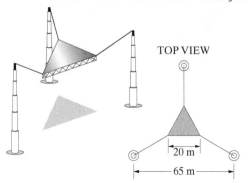

Problem 3.95

3.96 To support the tent, the tension in the rope *AB* must be 35 lb. What are the tensions in the ropes *AC*, *AD*, and *AE*?

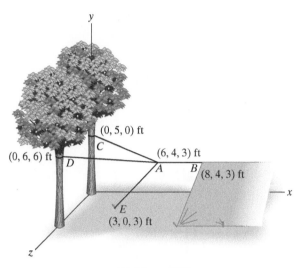

Problem 3.96

3.97 Cable *AB* is attached to the top of the vertical 3-m post, and its tension is 50 kN. What are the tensions in cables *AO*, *AC*, and *AD*?

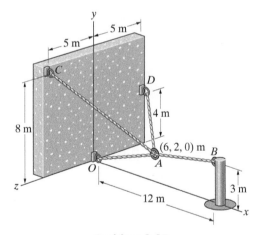

Problem 3.97

3.98* The 1350-kg car is at rest on a plane surface with its brakes locked. The unit vector $e_n = 0.231i + 0.923j + 0.308k$ is perpendicular to the surface. The y axis points upward. The direction cosines of the cable from A to B are $\cos \theta_x = -0.816$, $\cos \theta_y = 0.408$, $\cos \theta_z = -0.408$, and the tension in the cable is 1.2 kN. Determine the magnitudes of the normal and friction forces the car's wheels exert on the surface.

3.99* The brakes of the car are released, and the car is held in place on the plane surface by the cable AB. The car's front wheels are aligned so that the tires exert no friction forces parallel to the car's longitudinal axis. The unit vector $e_p = -0.941i + 0.131j + 0.314k$ is parallel to the plane surface and aligned with the car's longitudinal axis. What is the tension in the cable?

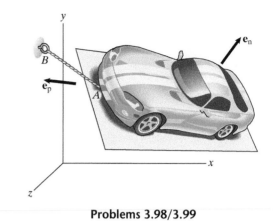

Problems 3.98/3.99

Design Project 1 A possible design for a simple scale to weigh objects is shown. The length of the string AB is 0.5 m. When an object is placed in the pan, the spring stretches and the string AB rotates. The object's weight can be determined by observing the change in the angle α.

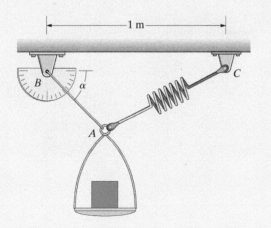

(a) Assume that objects with masses in the range 0.2–2 kg are to be weighed. Choose the unstretched length and spring constant of the spring in order to obtain accurate readings for weights in the desired range. (Neglect the weights of the pan and spring. Notice that a significant change in the angle α is needed to determine the weight accurately.)

(b) Suppose that you can use the same components—the pan, protractor, a spring, string—and also one or more pulleys. Suggest another possible configuration for the scale. Use statics to analyze your proposed configuration and compare its accuracy with that of the configuration shown for objects with masses in the range 0.2–2 kg.

Design Project 2 Suppose that the positions of points A, C, and D of the system of cables suspending the 100-kg mass are fixed, but you are free to choose the x and z coordinates of point B. Investigate the effects of different choices of the location of point B on the tensions in the cables. If the cost of cable AB is proportional to the product of the tension in the cable and its length, investigate the effect of different choices of the location of point B on the cost of the cable. Write a brief report describing the results of your investigations and recommending a location for point B.

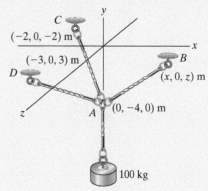

CHAPTER

4

Systems of Forces and Moments

The effects of forces can depend not only on their magnitudes and directions but also on the moments, or torques, they exert. The rotations of objects such as the wheels of a vehicle, the crankshaft of an engine, and the rotor of an electric generator result from the moments of the forces exerted on them. If an object is in equilibrium, the moment about any point due to the forces acting on the object is zero. Before continuing our discussion of free-body diagrams and equilibrium, we must explain how to calculate moments and introduce the concept of equivalent systems of forces and moments.

◀ The counterweight of the building crane exerts a large moment that the crane's structure must support during assembly. In this chapter we calculate moments of forces and analyze systems of forces and moments.

4.1 Two-Dimensional Description of the Moment

Consider a force of magnitude F and a point P, and let's view them in the direction perpendicular to the plane containing the force vector and the point (Fig. 4.1a). The *magnitude of the moment* of the force about P is the product DF, where D is the perpendicular distance from P to the line of action of the force (Fig. 4.1b). In this example, the force would tend to cause counterclockwise rotation about point P. That is, if we imagine that the force acts on

Figure 4.1
(a) The force and point P.
(b) The perpendicular distance D from point P to the line of action of F.
(c) The direction of the moment is counterclockwise.

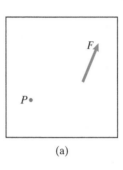
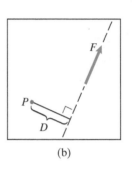

(a)　　　　(b)　　　　(c)

an object that can rotate about point P, the force would cause counterclockwise rotation (Fig. 4.1c). We say that the *direction of the moment* is counterclockwise. *We define counterclockwise moments to be positive and clockwise moments to be negative.* (This is the usual convention, although we occasionally encounter situations in which it is more convenient to define clockwise moments to be positive.) Thus, the moment of the force about P is

$$M_P = DF. \tag{4.1}$$

Notice that if the line of action of F passes through P, the perpendicular distance $D = 0$ and the moment of F about P is zero.

The dimensions of the moment are (distance) $\times$ (force). For example, moments can be expressed in newton-meters in SI units and in foot-pounds in U.S. Customary units.

Suppose that you want to place a television set on a shelf, and you aren't certain the attachment of the shelf to the wall is strong enough to support it. Intuitively, you place it near the wall (Fig. 4.2a), knowing that the attachment is more likely to fail if you place it away from the wall (Fig. 4.2b). What is the difference in the two cases? The magnitude and direction of the force exerted on the shelf by the weight of the television are the same in each case, but the moments exerted on the attachment are different. The moment exerted about P by its weight when it is near the wall, $M_P = -D_1 W$, is smaller in magnitude than the moment about P when it is placed away from the wall, $M_P = -D_2 W$.

The method we describe in this section can be used to determine the sum of the moments of a system of forces about a point if the forces are two-dimensional (coplanar) and the point lies in the same plane. For example, consider the construction crane shown in Fig. 4.3. The sum of the moments exerted about point P by the load W_1 and the counterweight W_2 is

$$\Sigma M_P = D_1 W_1 - D_2 W_2.$$

This moment tends to cause the top of the vertical tower to rotate and could cause it to collapse. If the distance D_2 is adjusted so that $D_1 W_1 = D_2 W_2$, the moment about point P due to the load and the counterweight is zero.

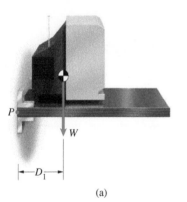

(a)

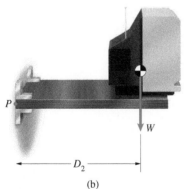

(b)

Figure 4.2
(a) Placing the television near the wall minimizes the moment exerted on the support of the shelf at P.
(b) Placing the television far from the wall exerts a large moment on the support at P and could cause it to fail.

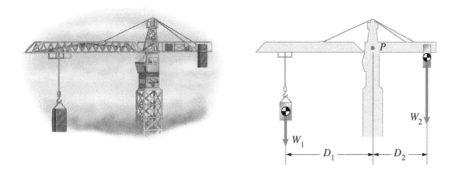

Figure 4.3
A tower crane used in the construction of high-rise buildings.

If a force is expressed in terms of components, the moment of the force about a point P is equal to the sum of the moments of its components about P. We prove this very useful result in the next section.

RESULTS

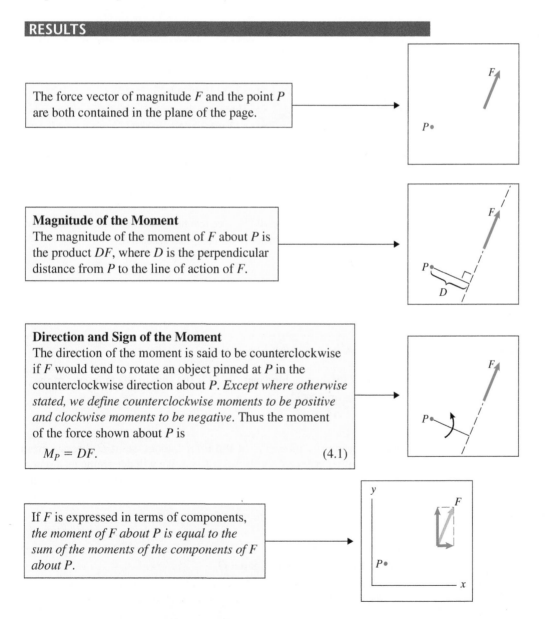

The force vector of magnitude F and the point P are both contained in the plane of the page.

Magnitude of the Moment
The magnitude of the moment of F about P is the product DF, where D is the perpendicular distance from P to the line of action of F.

Direction and Sign of the Moment
The direction of the moment is said to be counterclockwise if F would tend to rotate an object pinned at P in the counterclockwise direction about P. *Except where otherwise stated, we define counterclockwise moments to be positive and clockwise moments to be negative.* Thus the moment of the force shown about P is

$$M_P = DF. \qquad (4.1)$$

If F is expressed in terms of components, *the moment of F about P is equal to the sum of the moments of the components of F about P.*

Active Example 4.1 | Determining a Moment (▶ *Related Problem 4.1*)

What is the moment of the 40-kN force about point *A*?

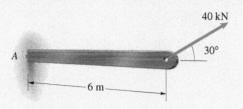

Strategy

We can calculate the magnitude of the moment by determining the perpendicular distance from point *A* to the line of action of the force.

Solution

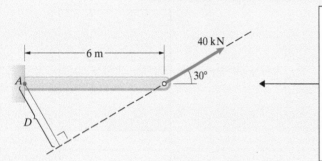

> The perpendicular distance from *A* to the line of action of the force is
> $$D = (6 \text{ m}) \sin 30° = 3 \text{ m}.$$
> Therefore the magnitude of the moment is
> $$(3 \text{ m})(40 \text{ kN}) = 120 \text{ kN-m}.$$
> The direction of the moment is counterclockwise, so
> $$M_A = 120 \text{ kN-m}.$$

Practice Problem Resolve the 40-kN force into horizontal and vertical components and calculate the sum of the moments of the components about *A*.

Answer: 120 kN-m.

Example 4.2 | Moment of a System of Forces (▶ *Related Problem 4.12*)

Four forces act on the machine part. What is the sum of the moments of the forces about the origin *O*?

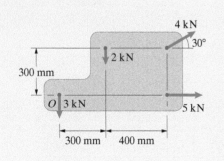

Strategy

We can determine the moments of the forces about point *O* directly from the given information except for the 4-kN force. We will determine its moment by expressing it in terms of components and summing the moments of the components.

Solution

Moment of the 3-kN Force   The line of action of the 3-kN force passes through *O*. It exerts no moment about *O*.

Moment of the 5-kN Force   The line of action of the 5-kN force also passes through O. It too exerts no moment about O.

Moment of the 2-kN Force   The perpendicular distance from O to the line of action of the 2-kN force is 0.3 m, and the direction of the moment about O is clockwise. The moment of the 2-kN force about O is

$$-(0.3 \text{ m})(2 \text{ kN}) = -0.600 \text{ kN-m.}$$

(Notice that we converted the perpendicular distance from millimeters into meters, obtaining the result in terms of kilonewton-meters.)

Moment of the 4-kN Force   In Fig. a, we introduce a coordinate system and express the 4-kN force in terms of x and y components. The perpendicular distance from O to the line of action of the x component is 0.3 m, and the direction of the moment about O is clockwise. The moment of the x component about O is

$$-(0.3 \text{ m})(4 \cos 30° \text{ kN}) = -1.039 \text{ kN-m.}$$

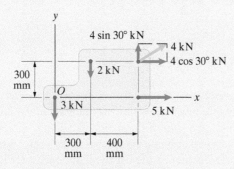

(a) Resolving the 4-kN force into components.

The perpendicular distance from point O to the line of action of the y component is 0.7 m, and the direction of the moment about O is counterclockwise. The moment of the y component about O is

$$(0.7 \text{ m})(4 \sin 30° \text{ kN}) = 1.400 \text{ kN-m.}$$

The sum of the moments of the four forces about point O is

$$\Sigma M_0 = -0.600 - 1.039 + 1.400 = -0.239 \text{ kN-m.}$$

The four forces exert a 0.239 kN-m clockwise moment about point O.

Critical Thinking

If an object is subjected to a system of known forces, why is it useful to determine the sum of the moments of the forces about a given point? As we discuss in Chapter 5, the object is in equilibrium only if the sum of the moments about *any* point is zero, so calculating the sum of the moments provides a test for equilibrium. (Notice that the object in this example is not in equilibrium.) Furthermore, in dynamics the sum of the moments of the forces acting on objects must be determined in order to analyze their angular motions.

| Example 4.3 | Summing Moments to Determine an Unknown Force (▶ *Related Problem 4.23*) |

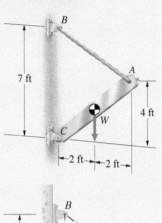

7 ft

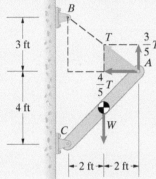

4 ft

←2 ft→←2 ft→

3 ft

4 ft

←2 ft→←2 ft→

(a) Resolving the force exerted by the cable into horizontal and vertical components.

The weight $W = 300$ lb. The sum of the moments about C due to the weight W and the force exerted on the bar CA by the cable AB is zero. What is the tension in the cable?

Strategy
Let T be the tension in cable AB. Using the given dimensions, we can express the horizontal and vertical components of the force exerted on the bar by the cable in terms of T. Then by setting the sum of the moments about C due to the weight of the bar and the force exerted by the cable equal to zero, we can obtain an equation for T.

Solution
Using similar triangles, we express the force exerted on the bar by the cable in terms of horizontal and vertical components (Fig. a). The sum of the moments about C due to the weight of the bar and the force exerted by the cable AB is

$$\Sigma M_C = 4\left(\frac{4}{5}T\right) + 4\left(\frac{3}{5}T\right) - 2W = 0.$$

Solving for T, we obtain

$$T = 0.357W = 107.1 \text{ lb}.$$

Critical Thinking
This example is a preview of the applications we consider in Chapter 5 and demonstrates why you must know how to calculate moments of forces. If the bar is in equilibrium, the sum of the moments about C is zero. Applying this condition allowed us to determine the tension in the cable. Why didn't we need to consider the force exerted on the bar by its support at C? Because we know that the moment of that force about C is zero.

Problems

▶ **4.1** In Active Example 4.1, the 40-kN force points 30° above the horizontal. Suppose that the force points 30° below the horizontal instead. Draw a sketch of the beam with the new orientation of the force. What is the moment of the force about point A?

4.2 The mass $m_1 = 20$ kg. The magnitude of the total moment about B due to the forces exerted on bar AB by the weights of the two suspended masses is 170 N-m. What is the magnitude of the total moment due to the forces about point A?

4.3 The wheels of the overhead crane exert downward forces on the horizontal I-beam at B and C. If the force at B is 40 kip and the force at C is 44 kip, determine the sum of the moments of the forces on the beam about (a) point A, (b) point D.

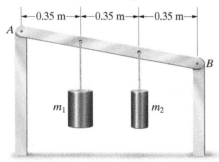

Problem 4.2

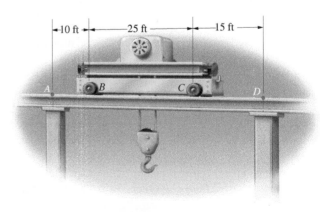

Problem 4.3

4.4 What force F applied to the pliers is required to exert a 4 N-m moment about the center of the bolt at P?

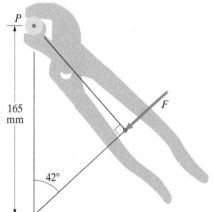

Problem 4.4

4.5 Two forces of equal magnitude F are applied to the wrench as shown. If a 50 N-m moment is required to loosen the nut, what is the necessary value of F?

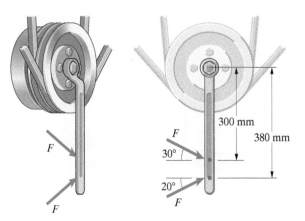

Problem 4.5

4.6 The force $F = 8$ kN. What is the moment of the force about point P?

4.7 If the magnitude of the moment due to the force F about Q is 30 kN-m, what is F?

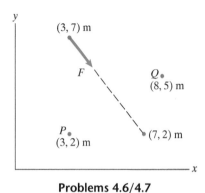

Problems 4.6/4.7

4.8 The support at the left end of the beam will fail if the moment about A of the 15-kN force F exceeds 18 kN-m. Based on this criterion, what is the largest allowable length of the beam?

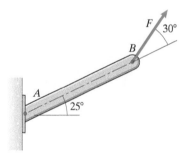

Problem 4.8

4.9 The length of the bar AP is 650 mm. The radius of the pulley is 120 mm. Equal forces $T = 50$ N are applied to the ends of the cable. What is the sum of the moments of the forces (a) about A; (b) about P?

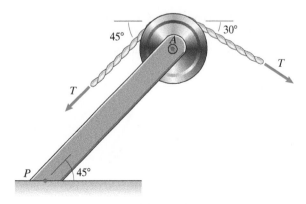

Problem 4.9

4.10 The force $F = 12$ kN. A structural engineer determines that the magnitude of the moment due to F about P should not exceed 5 kN-m. What is the acceptable range of the angle α? Assume that $0 \leq \alpha \leq 90°$.

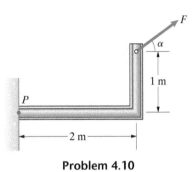

Problem 4.10

4.11 The length of bar AB is 350 mm. The moments exerted about points B and C by the vertical force F are $M_B = -1.75$ kN-m and $M_C = -4.20$ kN-m. Determine the force F and the length of bar AC.

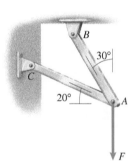

Problem 4.11

▶ **4.12** In Example 4.2, suppose that the 2-kN force points upward instead of downward. Draw a sketch of the machine part showing the orientations of the forces. What is the sum of the moments of the forces about the origin O?

4.13 Two equal and opposite forces act on the beam. Determine the sum of the moments of the two forces (a) about point P; (b) about point Q; (c) about the point with coordinates $x = 7$ m, $y = 5$ m.

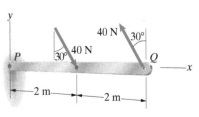

Problem 4.13

4.14 The moment exerted about point E by the weight is 299 in-lb. What moment does the weight exert about point S?

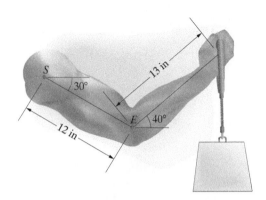

Problem 4.14

4.15 The magnitudes of the forces exerted on the pillar at D by the cables A, B, and C are equal: $F_A = F_B = F_C$. The magnitude of the total moment about E due to the forces exerted by the three cables at D is 1350 kN-m. What is F_A?

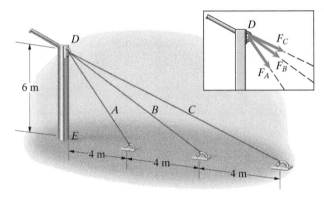

Problem 4.15

4.16 Three forces act on the piping. Determine the sum of the moments of the three forces about point P.

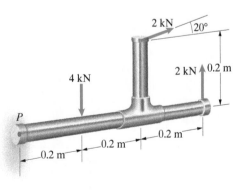

Problem 4.16

4.17 The forces $F_1 = 30$ N, $F_2 = 80$ N, and $F_3 = 40$ N. What is the sum of the moments of the forces about point A?

4.18 The force $F_1 = 30$ N. The vector sum of the three forces is zero. What is the sum of the moments of the forces about point A?

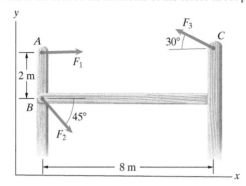

Problems 4.17/4.18

4.19 The forces $F_A = 30$ lb, $F_B = 40$ lb, $F_C = 20$ lb, and $F_D = 30$ lb. What is the sum of the moments of the forces about the origin of the coordinate system?

4.20 The force $F_A = 30$ lb. The vector sum of the forces on the beam is zero, and the sum of the moments of the forces about the origin of the coordinate system is zero. (a) Determine the forces F_B, F_C, and F_D. (b) Determine the sum of the moments of the forces about the right end of the beam.

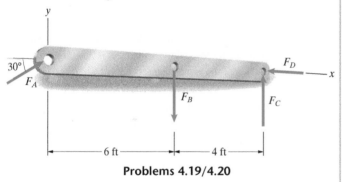

Problems 4.19/4.20

4.21 Three forces act on the car. The sum of the forces is zero and the sum of the moments of the forces about point P is zero.

(a) Determine the forces A and B.

(b) Determine the sum of the moments of the forces about point Q.

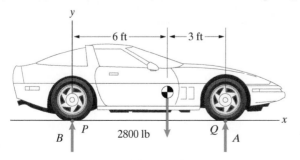

Problem 4.21

4.22 Five forces act on the piping. The vector sum of the forces is zero and the sum of the moments of the forces about point P is zero.

(a) Determine the forces A, B, and C.

(b) Determine the sum of the moments of the forces about point Q.

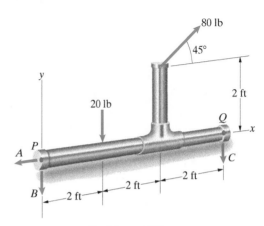

Problem 4.22

▶ **4.23** In Example 4.3, suppose that the attachment point B is moved upward and the cable is lengthened so that the vertical distance from C to B is 9 ft. (The positions of points C and A are unchanged.) Draw a sketch of the system with the cable in its new position. What is the tension in the cable?

4.24 The tension in the cable is the same on both sides of the pulley. The sum of the moments about point A due to the 800-lb force and the forces exerted on the bar by the cable at B and C is zero. What is the tension in the cable?

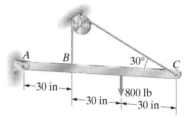

Problem 4.24

4.25 The 160-N weights of the arms AB and BC of the robotic manipulator act at their midpoints. Determine the sum of the moments of the three weights about A.

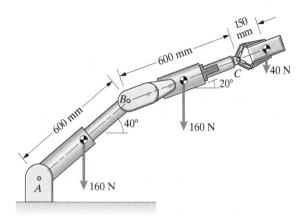

Problem 4.25

4.26 The space shuttle's attitude thrusters exert two forces of magnitude $F = 7.70$ kN. What moment do the thrusters exert about the center of mass G?

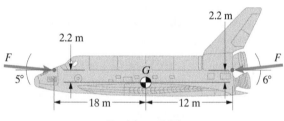

Problem 4.26

4.27 The force F exerts a 200 ft-lb counterclockwise moment about A and a 100 ft-lb clockwise moment about B. What are F and θ?

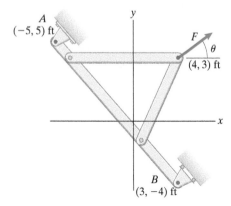

Problem 4.27

4.28 Five forces act on a link in the gear-shifting mechanism of a lawn mower. The vector sum of the five forces on the bar is zero. The sum of their moments about the point where the forces A_x and A_y act is zero.

(a) Determine the forces A_x, A_y, and B.

(b) Determine the sum of the moments of the forces about the point where the force B acts.

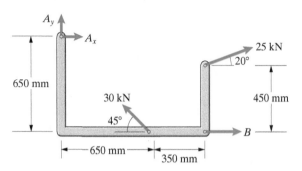

Problem 4.28

4.29 Five forces act on a model truss built by a civil engineering student as part of a design project. The dimensions are $b = 300$ mm and $h = 400$ mm and $F = 100$ N. The sum of the moments of the forces about the point where A_x and A_y act is zero. If the weight of the truss is negligible, what is the force B?

4.30 The dimensions are $b = 3$ ft and $h = 4$ ft and $F = 300$ lb. The vector sum of the forces acting on the truss is zero, and the sum of the moments of the forces about the point where A_x and A_y act is zero.

(a) Determine the forces A_x, A_y, and B.

(b) Determine the sum of the moments of the forces about the point where the force B acts.

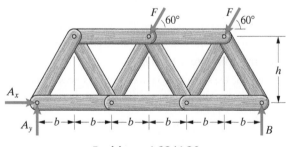

Problems 4.29/4.30

4.31 The mass $m = 70$ kg. What is the moment about A due to the force exerted on the beam at B by the cable?

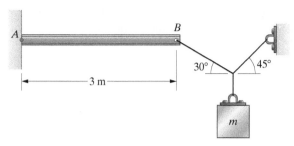

Problem 4.31

4.32 The weights W_1 and W_2 are suspended by the cable system shown. The weight $W_1 = 12$ lb. The cable BC is horizontal. Determine the moment about point P due to the force exerted on the vertical post at D by the cable CD.

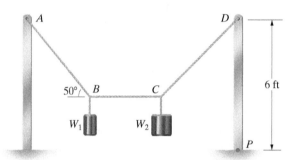

Problem 4.32

4.33 The bar AB exerts a force at B that helps support the vertical retaining wall. The force is parallel to the bar. The civil engineer wants the bar to exert a 38 kN-m moment about O. What is the magnitude of the force the bar must exert?

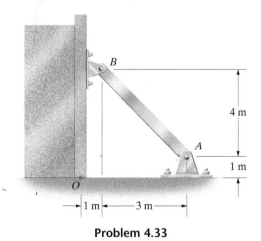

Problem 4.33

4.34 A contestant in a fly-casting contest snags his line in some grass. If the tension in the line is 5 lb, what moment does the force exerted on the rod by the line exert about point H, where he holds the rod?

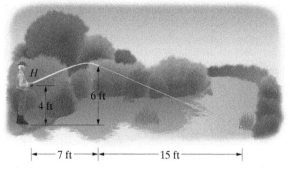

Problem 4.34

4.35 The cables AB and AC help support the tower. The tension in cable AB is 5 kN. The points A, B, C, and O are contained in the same vertical plane. (a) What is the moment about O due to the force exerted on the tower by cable AB? (b) If the sum of the moments about O due to the forces exerted on the tower by the two cables is zero, what is the tension in cable AC?

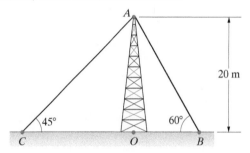

Problem 4.35

4.36 The cable from B to A (the sailboat's forestay) exerts a 230-N force at B. The cable from B to C (the backstay) exerts a 660-N force at B. The bottom of the sailboat's mast is located at $x = 4$ m, $y = 0$. What is the sum of the moments about the bottom of the mast due to the forces exerted at B by the forestay and backstay?

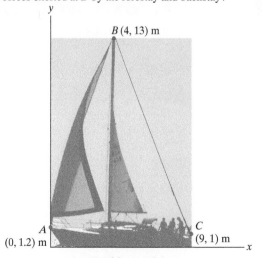

Problem 4.36

4.37 The cable AB exerts a 290-kN force on the crane's boom at B. The cable AC exerts a 148-kN force on the boom at C. Determine the sum of the moments about P due to the forces the cables AB and AC exert on the boom.

4.38 The mass of the crane's boom is 9000 kg. Its weight acts at G. The sum of the moments about P due to the boom's weight, the force exerted at B by the cable AB, and the force exerted at C by the cable AC is zero. Assume that the tensions in cables AB and AC are equal. Determine the tension in the cables.

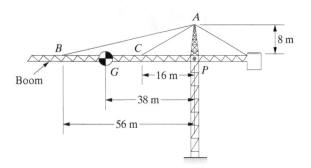

Problems 4.37/4.38

4.39 The mass of the luggage carrier and the suitcase combined is 12 kg. Their weight acts at A. The sum of the moments about the origin of the coordinate system due to the weight acting at A and the vertical force F applied to the handle of the luggage carrier is zero. Determine the force F (a) if $\alpha = 30°$; (b) if $\alpha = 50°$.

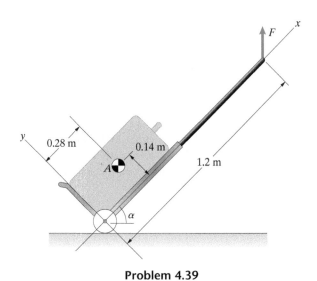

Problem 4.39

4.40 The hydraulic cylinder BC exerts a 300-kN force on the boom of the crane at C. The force is parallel to the cylinder. What is the moment of the force about A?

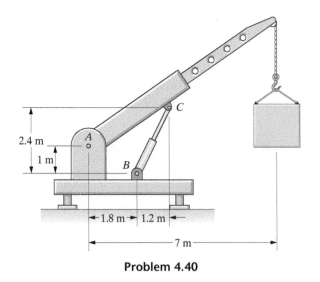

Problem 4.40

4.41 The hydraulic piston AB exerts a 400-lb force on the ladder at B in the direction parallel to the piston. The sum of the moments about C due to the force exerted on the ladder by the piston and the weight W of the ladder is zero. What is the weight of the ladder?

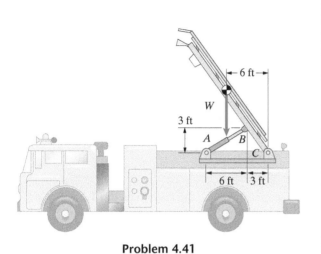

Problem 4.41

4.42 The hydraulic cylinder exerts an 8-kN force at B that is parallel to the cylinder and points from C toward B. Determine the moments of the force about points A and D.

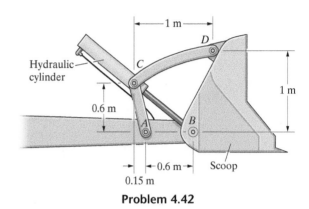

Problem 4.42

4.43 The structure shown in the diagram is one of two identical structures that support the scoop of the excavator. The bar BC exerts a 700-N force at C that points from C toward B. What is the moment of this force about K?

4.44 The bar BC exerts a force at C that points from C toward B. The hydraulic cylinder DH exerts a 1550-N force at D that points from D toward H. The sum of the moments of these two forces about K is zero. What is the magnitude of the force that bar BC exerts at C?

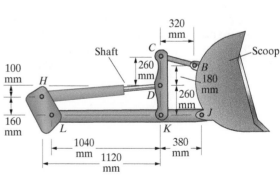

Problems 4.43/4.44

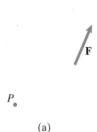

(a)

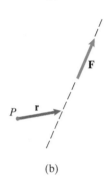

(b)

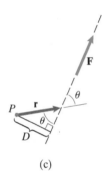

(c)

Figure 4.4
(a) The force **F** and point *P*.
(b) A vector **r** from *P* to a point on the line
of action of **F**.
(c) The angle θ and the perpendicular
distance *D*.

4.2 The Moment Vector

BACKGROUND

The moment of a force about a point is a vector. In this section we define this vector and explain how it is evaluated. We then show that when we use the two-dimensional description of the moment described in Section 4.1, we are specifying the magnitude and direction of the moment vector.

Consider a force vector **F** and point *P* (Fig. 4.4a). The *moment* of **F** about *P* is the vector

$$\mathbf{M}_P = \mathbf{r} \times \mathbf{F}, \tag{4.2}$$

where **r** is a position vector from *P* to *any* point on the line of action of **F** (Fig. 4.4b).

Magnitude of the Moment

From the definition of the cross product, the magnitude of $\mathbf{M}_P$ is

$$|\mathbf{M}_P| = |\mathbf{r}||\mathbf{F}| \sin \theta,$$

where θ is the angle between the vectors **r** and **F** when they are placed tail to tail. The perpendicular distance from *P* to the line of action of **F** is $D = |\mathbf{r}| \sin \theta$ (Fig. 4.4c). Therefore the magnitude of the moment $\mathbf{M}_P$ equals the product of the perpendicular distance from *P* to the line of action of **F** and the magnitude of **F**:

$$|\mathbf{M}_P| = D|\mathbf{F}|. \tag{4.3}$$

Notice that if we know the vectors $\mathbf{M}_P$ and **F**, this equation can be solved for the perpendicular distance *D*.

Direction of the Moment

We know from the definition of the cross product that $\mathbf{M}_P$ is perpendicular to both **r** and **F**. That means that $\mathbf{M}_P$ is perpendicular to the plane containing *P* and **F** (Fig. 4.5a). Notice in this figure that we denote a moment by a circular arrow around the vector.

Figure 4.5
(a) $\mathbf{M}_P$ is perpendicular to the plane
containing *p* and **F**.
(b) The direction of $\mathbf{M}_P$ indicates the
direction of the moment.

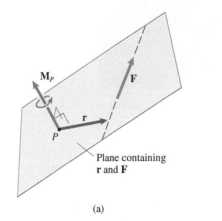

Plane containing
r and **F**

(a)

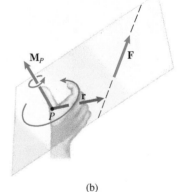

(b)

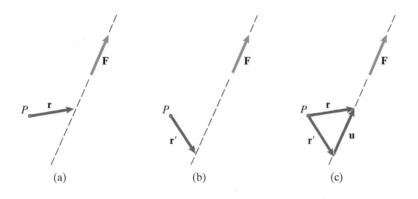

Figure 4.6
(a) A vector **r** from P to the line of action of **F**.
(b) A different vector **r**′.
(c) **r** = **r**′ + **u**.

The direction of $\mathbf{M}_P$ also indicates the direction of the moment: Pointing the thumb of the right hand in the direction of $\mathbf{M}_P$, the "arc" of the fingers indicates the direction of the rotation that **F** tends to cause about P (Fig. 4.5b).

The result obtained from Eq. (4.2) doesn't depend on where the vector **r** intersects the line of action of **F**. Instead of using the vector **r** in Fig. 4.6a, we could use the vector **r**′ in Fig. 4.6b. The vector **r** = **r**′ + **u**, where **u** is parallel to **F** (Fig. 4.6c). Therefore,

$$\mathbf{r} \times \mathbf{F} = (\mathbf{r}' + \mathbf{u}) \times \mathbf{F} = \mathbf{r}' \times \mathbf{F}$$

because the cross product of the parallel vectors **u** and **F** is zero.

In summary, the moment of a force **F** about a point P has three properties:

1. The magnitude of $\mathbf{M}_P$ is equal to the product of the magnitude of **F** and the perpendicular distance from P to the line of action of **F**. If the line of action of **F** passes through P, $\mathbf{M}_P = \mathbf{0}$.
2. $\mathbf{M}_P$ is perpendicular to the plane containing P and **F**.
3. The direction of $\mathbf{M}_P$ indicates the direction of the moment through a right-hand rule (Fig. 4.5b). Since the cross product is not commutative, it is essential to maintain the correct sequence of the vectors in the equation $\mathbf{M}_P = \mathbf{r} \times \mathbf{F}$.

Let us determine the moment of the force **F** in Fig. 4.7a about the point P. Since the vector **r** in Eq. (4.2) can be a position vector to any point on the line of action of **F**, we can use the vector from P to the point of application of **F** (Fig. 4.7b):

$$\mathbf{r} = (12 - 3)\mathbf{i} + (6 - 4)\mathbf{j} + (-5 - 1)\mathbf{k} = 9\mathbf{i} + 2\mathbf{j} - 6\mathbf{k} \text{ (ft)}.$$

The moment is

$$\mathbf{M}_P = \mathbf{r} \times \mathbf{F} = \begin{vmatrix} \mathbf{i} & \mathbf{j} & \mathbf{k} \\ 9 & 2 & -6 \\ 4 & 4 & 7 \end{vmatrix} = 38\mathbf{i} - 87\mathbf{j} + 28\mathbf{k} \text{ (ft-lb)}.$$

The magnitude of $\mathbf{M}_P$,

$$|\mathbf{M}_P| = \sqrt{(38)^2 + (-87)^2 + (28)^2} = 99.0 \text{ ft-lb},$$

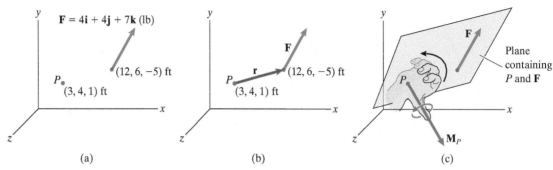

Figure 4.7
(a) A force **F** and point *P*.
(b) The vector **r** from *P* to the point of application of **F**.
(c) **M**$_P$ is perpendicular to the plane containing *P* and **F**.
    The right-hand rule indicates the direction of the moment.

equals the product of the magnitude of **F** and the perpendicular distance *D* from point *P* to the line of action of **F**. Therefore,

$$D = \frac{|\mathbf{M}_P|}{|\mathbf{F}|} = \frac{99.0 \text{ ft-lb}}{9 \text{ lb}} = 11.0 \text{ ft.}$$

The direction of **M**$_P$ tells us both the orientation of the plane containing *P* and **F** and the direction of the moment (Fig. 4.7c).

Relation to the Two-Dimensional Description

If our view is perpendicular to the plane containing the point *P* and the force **F**, the two-dimensional description of the moment we used in Section 4.1 specifies both the magnitude and direction of the vector **M**$_P$. In this situation, **M**$_P$ is perpendicular to the page, and the right-hand rule indicates whether it points out of or into the page.

For example, in Fig. 4.8a, the view is perpendicular to the *x*–*y* plane and the 10-N force is contained in the *x*–*y* plane. Suppose that we want to determine the

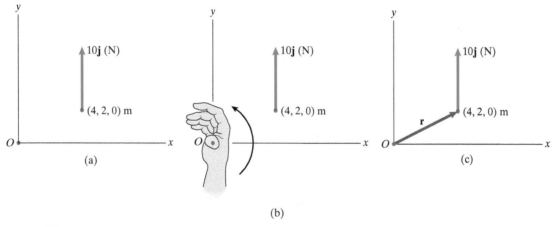

Figure 4.8
(a) The force is contained in the *x*–*y* plane.
(b) The counterclockwise direction of the moment indicates that **M**$_O$ points out of the page.
(c) The vector **r** from *O* to the point of application of **F**.

moment of the force about the origin O. The perpendicular distance from O to the line of action of the force is 4 m. The two-dimensional description of the moment of the force about O is that its magnitude is $(4\text{ m})(10\text{ N}) = 40\text{ N-m}$ and its direction is counterclockwise, or

$$M_O = 40\text{ N-m}.$$

That tells us that the magnitude of the vector $\mathbf{M}_O$ is 40 N-m, and the right-hand rule (Fig. 4.8b) indicates that it points out of the page. Therefore,

$$\mathbf{M}_O = 40\mathbf{k}\ (\text{N-m}).$$

We can confirm this result by using Eq. (4.2). If we let $\mathbf{r}$ be the vector from O to the point of application of the force (Fig. 4.8c),

$$\mathbf{M}_O = \mathbf{r} \times \mathbf{F} = (4\mathbf{i} + 2\mathbf{j}) \times 10\mathbf{j} = 40\mathbf{k}\ (\text{N-m}).$$

As this example illustrates, the two-dimensional description of the moment determines the moment vector. The converse is also true. The magnitude of $\mathbf{M}_O$ equals the product of the magnitude of the force and the perpendicular distance from O to the line of action of the force, 40 N-m, and the direction of the vector $\mathbf{M}_O$ indicates that the moment is counterclockwise (Fig. 4.8b).

Varignon's Theorem

Let $\mathbf{F}_1, \mathbf{F}_2, \ldots, \mathbf{F}_N$ be a concurrent system of forces whose lines of action intersect at a point Q. The moment of the system about a point P is

$$(\mathbf{r}_{PQ} \times \mathbf{F}_1) + (\mathbf{r}_{PQ} \times \mathbf{F}_2) + \cdots + (\mathbf{r}_{PQ} \times \mathbf{F}_N)$$

$$= \mathbf{r}_{PQ} \times (\mathbf{F}_1 + \mathbf{F}_2 + \cdots + \mathbf{F}_N),$$

where $\mathbf{r}_{PQ}$ is the vector from P to Q (Fig. 4.9). This result, known as *Varignon's theorem*, follows from the distributive property of the cross product, Eq. (2.31). It confirms that the moment of a force about a point P is equal to the sum of the moments of its components about P.

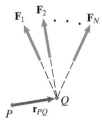

Figure 4.9
A system of concurrent forces and a point P.

RESULTS

Moment
The moment of a force $\mathbf{F}$ about a point P is defined by

$$\mathbf{M}_P = \mathbf{r} \times \mathbf{F}, \tag{4.2}$$

where $\mathbf{r}$ is a position vector from P to *any* point on the line of action of $\mathbf{F}$.

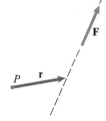

Magnitude of the Moment
The magnitude of the vector $\mathbf{M}_P$ is

$$|\mathbf{M}_P| = D|\mathbf{F}|, \tag{4.3}$$

where D is the perpendicular distance from P to the line of action of $\mathbf{F}$.

Direction of the Moment
The vector $\mathbf{M}_P$ is perpendicular to the plane containing the point P and the vector $\mathbf{F}$. Pointing the thumb of the right hand in the direction of $\mathbf{M}_P$, the fingers point in the direction of the rotation that $\mathbf{F}$ tends to cause about P.

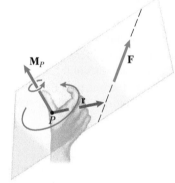

Active Example 4.4　**Determining a Moment** (▶ *Related Problem 4.45*)

Determine the moment of the 90-lb force $\mathbf{F}$ about point A.

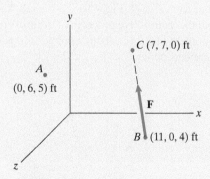

Strategy
To apply Eq. (4.2), we must express the force $\mathbf{F}$ in terms of its components. The vector $\mathbf{r}$ is a vector from point A to any point on the line of action of $\mathbf{F}$, so we can use the vector from point A to point B.

Solution

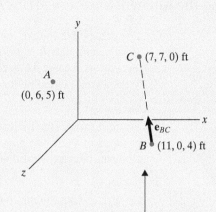

$$\mathbf{r}_{BC} = (x_C - x_B)\mathbf{i} + (y_C - y_B)\mathbf{j} + (z_C - z_B)\mathbf{k}$$
$$= -4\mathbf{i} + 7\mathbf{j} - 4\mathbf{k} \text{ (ft)}.$$

$$\mathbf{e}_{BC} = \frac{\mathbf{r}_{BC}}{|\mathbf{r}_{BC}|} = -\frac{4}{9}\mathbf{i} + \frac{7}{9}\mathbf{j} - \frac{4}{9}\mathbf{k}.$$

> Obtain a unit vector that has the same direction as the force **F** by dividing the position vector from point B to point C by its magnitude.

$$\mathbf{F} = (90 \text{ lb})\mathbf{e}_{BC}$$
$$= (90 \text{ lb})\left(-\frac{4}{9}\mathbf{i} + \frac{7}{9}\mathbf{j} - \frac{4}{9}\mathbf{k}\right)$$
$$= -40\mathbf{i} + 70\mathbf{j} - 40\mathbf{k} \text{ (lb)}.$$

> Express the force **F** in terms of its components by writing it as the product of its magnitude and the unit vector $\mathbf{e}_{BC}$.

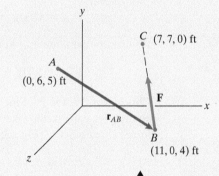

$$\mathbf{r}_{AB} = (x_B - x_A)\mathbf{i} + (y_B - y_A)\mathbf{j} + (z_B - z_A)\mathbf{k}$$
$$= 11\mathbf{i} - 6\mathbf{j} - \mathbf{k} \text{ (ft)}.$$

$$\mathbf{M}_A = \mathbf{r}_{AB} \times \mathbf{F}$$
$$= \begin{vmatrix} \mathbf{i} & \mathbf{j} & \mathbf{k} \\ 11 & -6 & -1 \\ -40 & 70 & -40 \end{vmatrix}$$
$$= 310\mathbf{i} + 480\mathbf{j} + 530\mathbf{k} \text{ (ft-lb)}.$$

> Apply Eq. (4.2) to determine the moment of **F** about point A.

Practice Problem (a) Use Eq. (4.2) to determine the moment of **F** about point A, letting the vector **r** be the position vector from point A to point C. (b) Determine the perpendicular distance from point A to the line of action of **F**.

Answer: (a) $\mathbf{M}_A = 310\mathbf{i} + 480\mathbf{j} + 530\mathbf{k}$ (ft-lb). (b) 8.66 ft.

| Example 4.5 | Applying the Moment Vector (► *Related Problem 4.57*) |

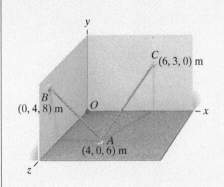

The cables *AB* and *AC* extend from an attachment point *A* on the floor to attachment points *B* and *C* in the walls. The tension in cable *AB* is 10 kN, and the tension in cable *AC* is 20 kN. What is the sum of the moments about *O* due to the forces exerted on the attachment point *A* by the two cables?

Strategy

We must express the forces exerted on the attachment point *A* by the two cables in terms of their components. Then we can use Eq. (4.2) to determine the moments the forces exert about *O*.

Solution

Let $\mathbf{F}_{AB}$ and $\mathbf{F}_{AC}$ be the forces exerted on the attachment point *A* by the two cables (Fig. a). To express $\mathbf{F}_{AB}$ in terms of its components, we determine the position vector from *A* to *B*,

$$(0 - 4)\mathbf{i} + (4 - 0)\mathbf{j} + (8 - 6)\mathbf{k} = -4\mathbf{i} + 4\mathbf{j} + 2\mathbf{k} \ (\text{m}),$$

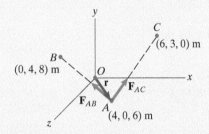

(a) The forces $\mathbf{F}_{AB}$ and $\mathbf{F}_{AC}$ exerted at *A* by the cables.

and divide it by its magnitude to obtain a unit vector $\mathbf{e}_{AB}$ with the same direction as $\mathbf{F}_{AB}$ (Fig. b):

$$\mathbf{e}_{AB} = \frac{-4\mathbf{i} + 4\mathbf{j} + 2\mathbf{k} \ (\text{m})}{\sqrt{(-4 \ \text{m})^2 + (4 \ \text{m})^2 + (2 \ \text{m})^2}} = -\frac{2}{3}\mathbf{i} + \frac{2}{3}\mathbf{j} + \frac{1}{3}\mathbf{k}.$$

Now we write $\mathbf{F}_{AB}$ as

$$\mathbf{F}_{AB} = 10\mathbf{e}_{AB} = -6.67\mathbf{i} + 6.67\mathbf{j} + 3.33\mathbf{k} \ (\text{kN}).$$

We express the force $\mathbf{F}_{AC}$ in terms of its components in the same way:

$$\mathbf{F}_{AC} = 5.71\mathbf{i} + 8.57\mathbf{j} - 17.14\mathbf{k} \ (\text{kN}).$$

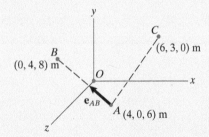

(b) The unit vector $\mathbf{e}_{AB}$ has the same direction as $\mathbf{F}_{AB}$.

Choose the Vector r Since the lines of action of both forces pass through point *A*, we can use the vector from *O* to *A* to determine the moments of both forces about point *O* (Fig. a):

$$\mathbf{r} = 4\mathbf{i} + 6\mathbf{k} \ (\text{m}).$$

Evaluate r × F The sum of the moments is

$$\Sigma \mathbf{M}_O = (\mathbf{r} \times \mathbf{F}_{AB}) + (\mathbf{r} \times \mathbf{F}_{AC})$$

$$= \begin{vmatrix} \mathbf{i} & \mathbf{j} & \mathbf{k} \\ 4 & 0 & 6 \\ -6.67 & 6.67 & 3.33 \end{vmatrix} + \begin{vmatrix} \mathbf{i} & \mathbf{j} & \mathbf{k} \\ 4 & 0 & 6 \\ 5.71 & 8.57 & -17.14 \end{vmatrix}$$

$$= -91.4\mathbf{i} + 49.5\mathbf{j} + 61.0\mathbf{k} \ (\text{kN-m}).$$

Critical Thinking

The lines of action of the forces $\mathbf{F}_{AB}$ and $\mathbf{F}_{AC}$ intersect at *A*. Notice that, according to Varignon's theorem, we could have summed the forces first, obtaining

$$\mathbf{F}_{AB} + \mathbf{F}_{AC} = -0.952\mathbf{i} + 15.24\mathbf{j} - 13.81\mathbf{k} \ (\text{kN}),$$

and then determined the sum of the moments of the two forces about O by calculating the moment of the sum of the two forces about O:

$$\Sigma \mathbf{M}_O = \mathbf{r} \times (\mathbf{F}_{AB} + \mathbf{F}_{AC})$$

$$= \begin{vmatrix} \mathbf{i} & \mathbf{j} & \mathbf{k} \\ 4 & 0 & 6 \\ -0.952 & 15.24 & -13.81 \end{vmatrix}$$

$$= -91.4\mathbf{i} + 49.5\mathbf{j} + 61.0\mathbf{k} \ (\text{kN-m}).$$

Problems

▶ **4.45** In Active Example 4.4, what is the moment of **F** about the origin of the coordinate system?

4.46 Use Eq. (4.2) to determine the moment of the 80-N force about the origin O letting **r** be the vector (a) from O to A; (b) from O to B.

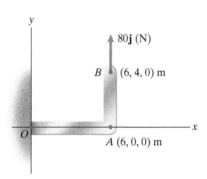

Problem 4.46

4.47 A bioengineer studying an injury sustained in throwing the javelin estimates that the magnitude of the maximum force exerted was $|\mathbf{F}| = 360$ N and the perpendicular distance from O to the line of action of **F** was 550 mm. The vector **F** and point O are contained in the x–y plane. Express the moment of **F** about the shoulder joint at O as a vector.

Problem 4.47

4.48 Use Eq. (4.2) to determine the moment of the 100-kN force (a) about A; (b) about B.

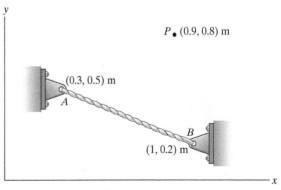

Problem 4.48

4.49 The cable AB exerts a 200-N force on the support at A that points from A toward B. Use Eq. (4.2) to determine the moment of this force about point P, (a) letting **r** be the vector from P to A; (b) letting **r** be the vector from P to B.

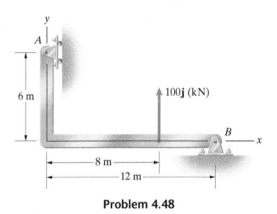

Problem 4.49

4.50 The line of action of **F** is contained in the *x–y* plane. The moment of **F** about *O* is 140**k** (N-m), and the moment of **F** about *A* is 280**k** (N-m). What are the components of **F**?

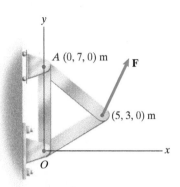

Problem 4.50

4.51 Use Eq. (4.2) to determine the sum of the moments of the three forces (a) about *A*; (b) about *B*.

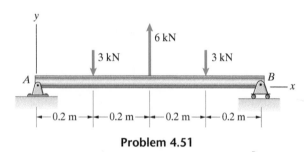

Problem 4.51

4.52 Three forces are applied to the plate. Use Eq. (4.2) to determine the sum of the moments of the three forces about the origin *O*.

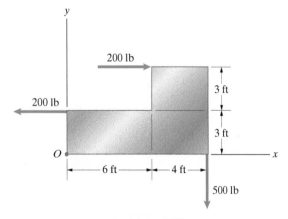

Problem 4.52

4.53 Three forces act on the plate. Use Eq. (4.2) to determine the sum of the moments of the three forces about point *P*.

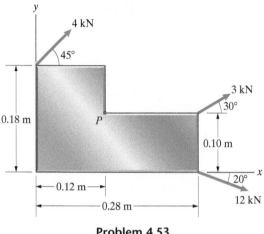

Problem 4.53

4.54 (a) Determine the magnitude of the moment of the 150-N force about *A* by calculating the perpendicular distance from *A* to the line of action of the force.

(b) Use Eq. (4.2) to determine the magnitude of the moment of the 150-N force about *A*.

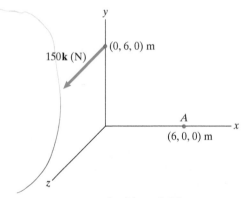

Problem 4.54

4.55 (a) Determine the magnitude of the moment of the 600-N force about A by calculating the perpendicular distance from A to the line of action of the force.

(b) Use Eq. (4.2) to determine the magnitude of the moment of the 600-N force about A.

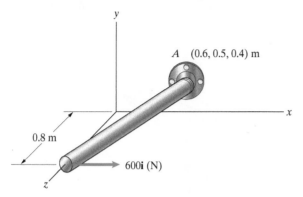

Problem 4.55

4.56 What is the magnitude of the moment of **F** about point B?

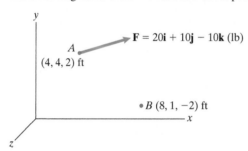

Problem 4.56

▶ **4.57** In Example 4.5, suppose that the attachment point C is moved to the location (8, 2, 0) m and the tension in cable AC changes to 25 kN. What is the sum of the moments about O due to the forces exerted on the attachment point A by the two cables?

4.58 The rope exerts a force of magnitude $|\mathbf{F}| = 200$ lb on the top of the pole at B. Determine the magnitude of the moment of **F** about A.

Problem 4.58

4.59 The force $\mathbf{F} = 30\mathbf{i} + 20\mathbf{j} - 10\mathbf{k}$ (N).

(a) Determine the magnitude of the moment of **F** about A.

(b) Suppose that you can change the direction of **F** while keeping its magnitude constant, and you want to choose a direction that maximizes the moment of **F** about A. What is the magnitude of the resulting maximum moment?

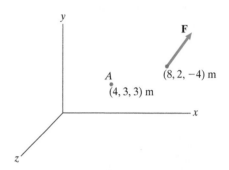

Problem 4.59

4.60 The direction cosines of the force **F** are $\cos \theta_x = 0.818$, $\cos \theta_y = 0.182$, and $\cos \theta_z = -0.545$. The support of the beam at O will fail if the magnitude of the moment of **F** about O exceeds 100 kN-m. Determine the magnitude of the largest force **F** that can safely be applied to the beam.

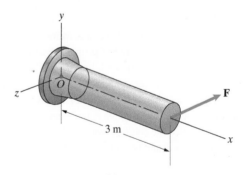

Problem 4.60

4.61 The force $\mathbf{F}$ exerted on the grip of the exercise machine points in the direction of the unit vector $\mathbf{e} = \frac{2}{3}\mathbf{i} - \frac{2}{3}\mathbf{j} + \frac{1}{3}\mathbf{k}$ and its magnitude is 120 N. Determine the magnitude of the moment of $\mathbf{F}$ about the origin O.

4.62 The force $\mathbf{F}$ points in the direction of the unit vector $\mathbf{e} = \frac{2}{3}\mathbf{i} - \frac{2}{3}\mathbf{j} + \frac{1}{3}\mathbf{k}$. The support at O will safely support a moment of 560 N-m magnitude. (a) Based on this criterion, what is the largest safe magnitude of $\mathbf{F}$? (b) If the force $\mathbf{F}$ may be exerted in any direction, what is its largest safe magnitude?

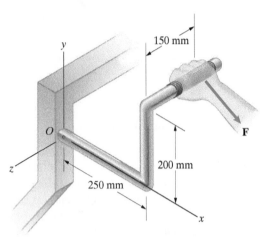

Problems 4.61/4.62

4.63 A civil engineer in Boulder, Colorado, estimates that under the severest expected Chinook winds, the total force on the highway sign will be $\mathbf{F} = 2.8\mathbf{i} - 1.8\mathbf{j}$ (kN). Let $\mathbf{M}_O$ be the moment due to $\mathbf{F}$ about the base O of the cylindrical column supporting the sign. The y component of $\mathbf{M}_O$ is called the *torsion* exerted on the cylindrical column at the base, and the component of $\mathbf{M}_O$ parallel to the x–z plane is called the *bending moment*. Determine the magnitudes of the torsion and bending moment.

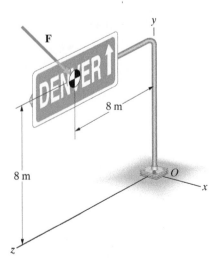

Problem 4.63

4.64 The weights of the arms OA and AB of the robotic manipulator act at their midpoints. The direction cosines of the centerline of arm OA are $\cos\theta_x = 0.500$, $\cos\theta_y = 0.866$, and $\cos\theta_z = 0$, and the direction cosines of the centerline of arm AB are $\cos\theta_x = 0.707$, $\cos\theta_y = 0.619$, and $\cos\theta_z = -0.342$. What is the sum of the moments about O due to the two forces?

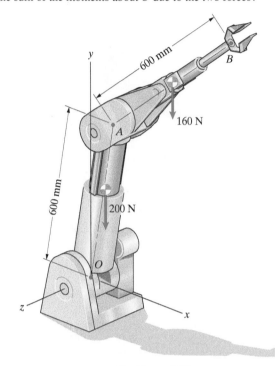

Problem 4.64

4.65 The tension in cable AB is 100 lb. If you want the magnitude of the moment due to the forces exerted on the tree by the two ropes about the base O of the tree to be 1500 ft-lb, what is the necessary tension in rope AC?

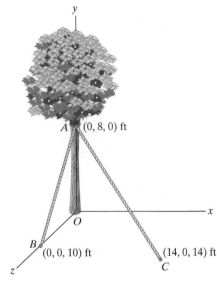

Problem 4.65

4.66* A force **F** acts at the top end A of the pole. Its magnitude is $|\mathbf{F}| = 6$ kN and its x component is $F_x = 4$ kN. The coordinates of point A are shown. Determine the components of **F** so that the magnitude of the moment due to **F** about the base P of the pole is as large as possible.

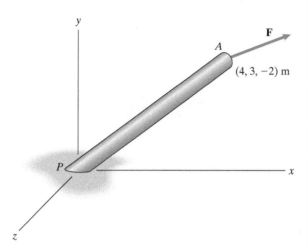

Problem 4.66

4.67 The force $\mathbf{F} = 5\mathbf{i}$ (kN) acts on the ring A where the cables $AB, AC,$ and AD are joined. What is the sum of the moments about point D due to the force **F** and the three forces exerted on the ring by the cables?

 Strategy: The ring is in equilibrium. Use what you know about the four forces acting on it.

4.68 In Problem 4.67, determine the moment about point D due to the force exerted on the ring A by the cable AB.

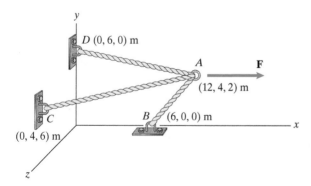

Problems 4.67/4.68

4.69 The tower is 70 m tall. The tensions in cables $AB, AC,$ and AD are 4 kN, 2 kN, and 2 kN, respectively. Determine the sum of the moments about the origin O due to the forces exerted by the cables at point A.

4.70 Suppose that the tension in cable AB is 4 kN, and you want to adjust the tensions in cables AC and AD so that the sum of the moments about the origin O due to the forces exerted by the cables at point A is zero. Determine the tensions.

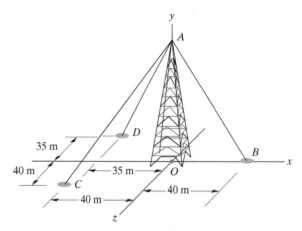

Problems 4.69/4.70

4.71 The tension in cable AB is 150 N. The tension in cable AC is 100 N. Determine the sum of the moments about D due to the forces exerted on the wall by the cables.

4.72 The total force exerted by the two cables in the direction perpendicular to the wall is 2 kN. The magnitude of the sum of the moments about D due to the forces exerted on the wall by the cables is 18 kN-m. What are the tensions in the cables?

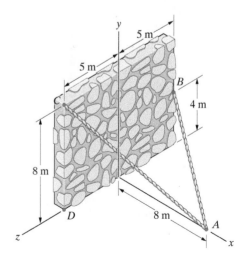

Problems 4.71/4.72

4.73 The tension in the cable BD is 1 kN. As a result, cable BD exerts a 1-kN force on the "ball" at B that points from B toward D. Determine the moment of this force about point A.

4.74* Suppose that the mass of the suspended object E is 100 kg and the mass of the bar AB is 20 kg. Assume that the weight of the bar acts at its midpoint. If the sum of the moments about point A due to the weight of the bar and the forces exerted on the "ball" at B by the three cables BC, BD, and BE is zero, determine the tensions in the cables BC and BD.

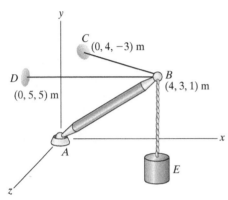

Problems 4.73/4.74

4.75 The 200-kg slider at A is held in place on the smooth vertical bar by the cable AB. Determine the moment about the bottom of the bar (point C with coordinates x = 2 m, y = z = 0) due to the force exerted on the slider by the cable.

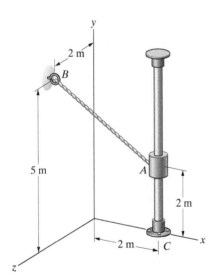

Problem 4.75

4.76 To evaluate the adequacy of the design of the vertical steel post, you must determine the moment about the bottom of the post due to the force exerted on the post at B by the cable AB. A calibrated strain gauge mounted on cable AC indicates that the tension in cable AC is 22 kN. What is the moment?

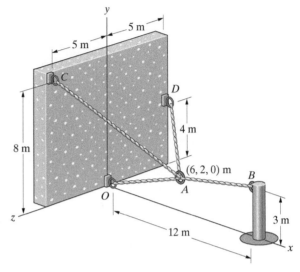

Problem 4.76

4.3 Moment of a Force About a Line

BACKGROUND

The device in Fig. 4.10, called a *capstan*, was used in the days of square-rigged sailing ships. Crewmen turned it by pushing on the handles as shown in Fig. 4.10a, providing power for such tasks as raising anchors and hoisting yards. A vertical force **F** applied to one of the handles as shown in Fig. 4.10b does not cause the capstan to turn, even though the magnitude of the moment about point P is $d|\mathbf{F}|$ in both cases.

The measure of the tendency of a force to cause rotation about a line, or axis, is called the moment of the force about the line. Suppose that a force **F** acts on an object such as a turbine that rotates about an axis L, and we resolve **F** into components in terms of the coordinate system shown in Fig. 4.11. The components F_x and F_z do not tend to rotate the turbine, just as the force parallel to the axis of the capstan did not cause it to turn. It is the component F_y that tends to cause rotation, by exerting a moment of magnitude aF_y about the turbine's axis. In this example we can determine the moment of **F** about L easily because the coordinate system is conveniently placed. We now introduce an expression that determines the moment of a force about any line.

(a)   (b)

Figure 4.10
(a) Turning a capstan.
(b) A vertical force does not turn the capstan.

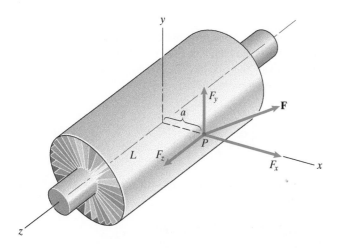

Figure 4.11
Applying a force to a turbine with axis of rotation L.

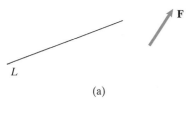

(a)

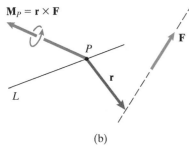

(b)

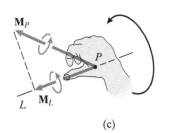

(c)

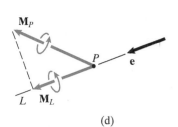

(d)

Figure 4.12
(a) The line L and force $\mathbf{F}$.
(b) $\mathbf{M}_P$ is the moment of $\mathbf{F}$ about any point P on L.
(c) The component $\mathbf{M}_L$ is the moment of $\mathbf{F}$ about L.
(d) A unit vector $\mathbf{e}$ along L.

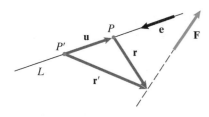

Figure 4.13
Using different points P and P' to determine the moment of $\mathbf{F}$ about L.

Definition

Consider a line L and force $\mathbf{F}$ (Fig. 4.12a). Let $\mathbf{M}_P$ be the moment of $\mathbf{F}$ about an arbitrary point P on L (Fig. 4.12b). The moment of $\mathbf{F}$ about L is the component of $\mathbf{M}_P$ parallel to L, which we denote by $\mathbf{M}_L$ (Fig. 4.12c). The magnitude of the moment of $\mathbf{F}$ about L is $|\mathbf{M}_L|$, and when the thumb of the right hand is pointed in the direction of $\mathbf{M}_L$, the arc of the fingers indicates the direction of the moment about L. In terms of a unit vector $\mathbf{e}$ along L (Fig. 4.12d), $\mathbf{M}_L$ is given by

$$\mathbf{M}_L = (\mathbf{e} \cdot \mathbf{M}_P)\mathbf{e}. \tag{4.4}$$

(The unit vector $\mathbf{e}$ can point in either direction. See our discussion of vector components parallel and normal to a line in Section 2.5.) The moment $\mathbf{M}_P = \mathbf{r} \times \mathbf{F}$, so we can also express $\mathbf{M}_L$ as

$$\mathbf{M}_L = [\mathbf{e} \cdot (\mathbf{r} \times \mathbf{F})]\mathbf{e}. \tag{4.5}$$

The mixed triple product in this expression is given in terms of the components of the three vectors by

$$\mathbf{e} \cdot (\mathbf{r} \times \mathbf{F}) = \begin{vmatrix} e_x & e_y & e_z \\ r_x & r_y & r_z \\ F_x & F_y & F_z \end{vmatrix}. \tag{4.6}$$

Notice that the value of the scalar $\mathbf{e} \cdot \mathbf{M}_P = \mathbf{e} \cdot (\mathbf{r} \times \mathbf{F})$ determines both the magnitude and direction of $\mathbf{M}_L$. The absolute value of $\mathbf{e} \cdot \mathbf{M}_P$ is the magnitude of $\mathbf{M}_L$. If $\mathbf{e} \cdot \mathbf{M}_P$ is positive, $\mathbf{M}_L$ points in the direction of $\mathbf{e}$, and if $\mathbf{e} \cdot \mathbf{M}_P$ is negative, $\mathbf{M}_L$ points in the direction opposite to $\mathbf{e}$.

The result obtained with Eq. (4.4) or (4.5) doesn't depend on which point on L is chosen to determine $\mathbf{M}_P = \mathbf{r} \times \mathbf{F}$. If we use point P in Fig. 4.13 to determine the moment of $\mathbf{F}$ about L, we get the result given by Eq. (4.5). If we use P' instead, we obtain the same result,

$$[\mathbf{e} \cdot (\mathbf{r}' \times \mathbf{F})]\mathbf{e} = \{\mathbf{e} \cdot [(\mathbf{r} + \mathbf{u}) \times \mathbf{F}]\}\mathbf{e}$$
$$= [\mathbf{e} \cdot (\mathbf{r} \times \mathbf{F}) + \mathbf{e} \cdot (\mathbf{u} \times \mathbf{F})]\mathbf{e}$$
$$= [\mathbf{e} \cdot (\mathbf{r} \times \mathbf{F})]\mathbf{e},$$

because $\mathbf{u} \times \mathbf{F}$ is perpendicular to $\mathbf{e}$.

Applications

To demonstrate that $\mathbf{M}_L$ is the measure of the tendency of $\mathbf{F}$ to cause rotation about L, we return to the turbine in Fig. 4.11. Let Q be a point on L at an arbitrary distance b from the origin (Fig. 4.14a). The vector $\mathbf{r}$ from Q to P is $\mathbf{r} = a\mathbf{i} - b\mathbf{k}$, so the moment of $\mathbf{F}$ about Q is

$$\mathbf{M}_Q = \mathbf{r} \times \mathbf{F} = \begin{vmatrix} \mathbf{i} & \mathbf{j} & \mathbf{k} \\ a & 0 & -b \\ F_x & F_y & F_z \end{vmatrix} = bF_y\mathbf{i} - (aF_z + bF_x)\mathbf{j} + aF_y\mathbf{k}.$$

Since the z axis is coincident with L, the unit vector $\mathbf{k}$ is along L. Therefore the moment of $\mathbf{F}$ about L is

$$\mathbf{M}_L = (\mathbf{k} \cdot \mathbf{M}_Q)\mathbf{k} = aF_y\mathbf{k}.$$

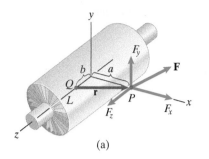
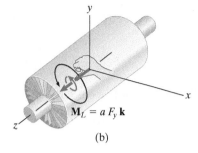

(a)   (b)

Figure 4.14
(a) An arbitrary point Q on L and the vector $\mathbf{r}$ from Q to P.
(b) $\mathbf{M}_L$ and the direction of the moment about L.

The components F_x and F_z exert no moment about L. If we assume that F_y is positive, it exerts a moment of magnitude aF_y about the turbine's axis in the direction shown in Fig. 4.14b.

Now let us determine the moment of a force about an arbitrary line L (Fig. 4.15a). The first step is to choose a point on the line. If we choose point A (Fig. 4.15b), the vector $\mathbf{r}$ from A to the point of application of $\mathbf{F}$ is

$$\mathbf{r} = (8 - 2)\mathbf{i} + (6 - 0)\mathbf{j} + (4 - 4)\mathbf{k} = 6\mathbf{i} + 6\mathbf{j} \ (\text{m}).$$

The moment of $\mathbf{F}$ about A is

$$\mathbf{M}_A = \mathbf{r} \times \mathbf{F} = \begin{vmatrix} \mathbf{i} & \mathbf{j} & \mathbf{k} \\ 6 & 6 & 0 \\ 10 & 60 & -20 \end{vmatrix}$$

$$= -120\mathbf{i} + 120\mathbf{j} + 300\mathbf{k} \ (\text{N-m}).$$

The next step is to determine a unit vector along L. The vector from A to B is

$$(-7 - 2)\mathbf{i} + (6 - 0)\mathbf{j} + (2 - 4)\mathbf{k} = -9\mathbf{i} + 6\mathbf{j} - 2\mathbf{k} \ (\text{m}).$$

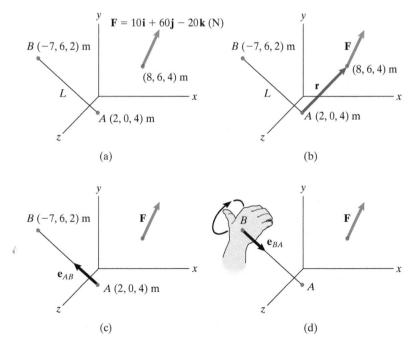

(a)   (b)

(c)   (d)

Figure 4.15
(a) A force $\mathbf{F}$ and line L.
(b) The vector $\mathbf{r}$ from A to the point of application of $\mathbf{F}$.
(c) $\mathbf{e}_{AB}$ points from A toward B.
(d) The right-hand rule indicates the direction of the moment.

Dividing this vector by its magnitude, we obtain a unit vector $\mathbf{e}_{AB}$ that points from A toward B (Fig. 4.15c):

$$\mathbf{e}_{AB} = -\frac{9}{11}\mathbf{i} + \frac{6}{11}\mathbf{j} - \frac{2}{11}\mathbf{k}.$$

The moment of $\mathbf{F}$ about L is

$$\mathbf{M}_L = (\mathbf{e}_{AB} \cdot \mathbf{M}_A)\mathbf{e}_{AB}$$

$$= \left[\left(-\frac{9}{11}\right)(-120 \text{ N-m}) + \left(\frac{6}{11}\right)(120 \text{ N-m}) + \left(-\frac{2}{11}\right)(300 \text{ N-m})\right]\mathbf{e}_{AB}$$

$$= 109\mathbf{e}_{AB} \text{ (N-m)}.$$

The magnitude of $\mathbf{M}_L$ is 109 N-m; pointing the thumb of the right hand in the direction of $\mathbf{e}_{AB}$ indicates the direction.

If we calculate $\mathbf{M}_L$ using the unit vector $\mathbf{e}_{BA}$ that points from B toward A instead, we obtain

$$\mathbf{M}_L = -109\mathbf{e}_{BA} \text{ (N-m)}.$$

We obtain the same magnitude, and the minus sign indicates that $\mathbf{M}_L$ points in the direction opposite to $\mathbf{e}_{BA}$, so the direction of $\mathbf{M}_L$ is the same. Therefore the right-hand rule indicates the same direction (Fig. 4.15d).

The preceding examples demonstrate three useful results that we can state in more general terms:

- When the line of action of $\mathbf{F}$ is perpendicular to a plane containing L (Fig. 4.16a), the magnitude of the moment of $\mathbf{F}$ about L is equal to the product of the magnitude of $\mathbf{F}$ and the perpendicular distance D from L to the point where the line of action intersects the plane: $|\mathbf{M}_L| = |\mathbf{F}|D$.

- When the line of action of $\mathbf{F}$ is parallel to L (Fig. 4.16b), the moment of $\mathbf{F}$ about L is zero: $\mathbf{M}_L = 0$. Since $\mathbf{M}_P = \mathbf{r} \times \mathbf{F}$ is perpendicular to $\mathbf{F}$, $\mathbf{M}_P$ is perpendicular to L and the vector component of $\mathbf{M}_P$ parallel to L is zero.

- When the line of action of $\mathbf{F}$ intersects L (Fig. 4.16c), the moment of $\mathbf{F}$ about L is zero. Since we can choose any point on L to evaluate $\mathbf{M}_P$, we can use the point where the line of action of $\mathbf{F}$ intersects L. The moment $\mathbf{M}_P$ about that point is zero, so its vector component parallel to L is zero.

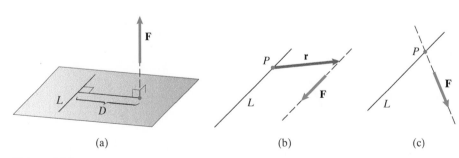

(a)   (b)   (c)

Figure 4.16
(a) $\mathbf{F}$ is perpendicular to a plane containing L.
(b) $\mathbf{F}$ is parallel to L.
(c) The line of action of $\mathbf{F}$ intersects L at P.

RESULTS

Determining the Moment of a Force F About a Line *L*

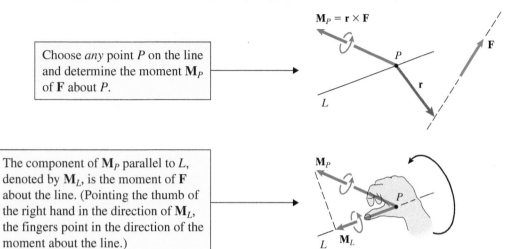

Choose *any* point *P* on the line and determine the moment $\mathbf{M}_P$ of **F** about *P*.

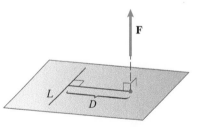

The component of $\mathbf{M}_P$ parallel to *L*, denoted by $\mathbf{M}_L$, is the moment of **F** about the line. (Pointing the thumb of the right hand in the direction of $\mathbf{M}_L$, the fingers point in the direction of the moment about the line.)

If **e** is a unit vector parallel to *L*, $$\mathbf{M}_L = (\mathbf{e} \cdot \mathbf{M}_P)\, \mathbf{e}. \qquad (4.4)$$

Special Cases

When the line of action of **F** is perpendicular to a plane containing *L*, $|\mathbf{M}_L| = |\mathbf{F}|D$, where *D* is the perpendicular distance from *L* to the point where the line of action intersects the plane.

When the line of action of **F** is parallel to *L*, $\mathbf{M}_L = \mathbf{0}$.

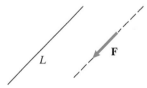

When the line of action of **F** intersects *L*, $\mathbf{M}_L = \mathbf{0}$.

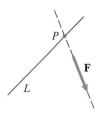

Active Example 4.6 Moment of a Force About a Line (▶ *Related Problem 4.87*)

What is the moment of the force **F** about the axis of the bar *BC*?

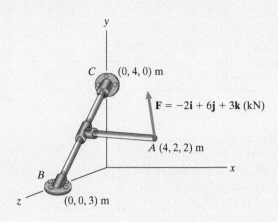

Strategy

Because we know the coordinates of points *A*, *B*, and *C*, we can determine the moment due to **F** about a point on the axis of the bar. We will determine the moment about point *B*. The component of that moment parallel to the axis *BC* is the moment of **F** about the axis. By obtaining a unit vector parallel to the axis, we can use Eq. (4.4) to determine the parallel component.

Solution

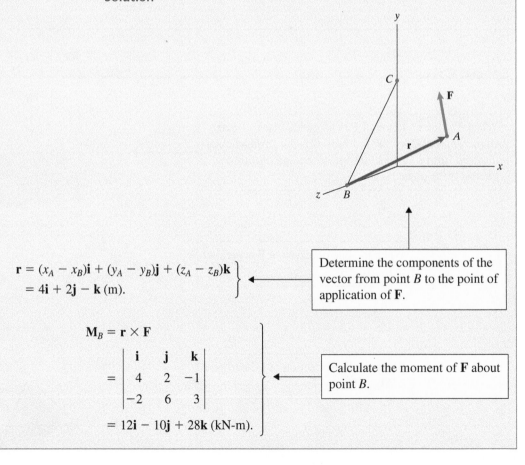

$$\mathbf{r} = (x_A - x_B)\mathbf{i} + (y_A - y_B)\mathbf{j} + (z_A - z_B)\mathbf{k}$$
$$= 4\mathbf{i} + 2\mathbf{j} - \mathbf{k} \ (\text{m}).$$

Determine the components of the vector from point *B* to the point of application of **F**.

$$\mathbf{M}_B = \mathbf{r} \times \mathbf{F}$$

$$= \begin{vmatrix} \mathbf{i} & \mathbf{j} & \mathbf{k} \\ 4 & 2 & -1 \\ -2 & 6 & 3 \end{vmatrix}$$

$$= 12\mathbf{i} - 10\mathbf{j} + 28\mathbf{k} \ (\text{kN-m}).$$

Calculate the moment of **F** about point *B*.

$$\mathbf{r}_{BC} = (x_C - x_B)\mathbf{i} + (y_C - y_B)\mathbf{j} + (z_C - z_B)\mathbf{k}$$
$$= 4\mathbf{j} - 3\mathbf{k} \text{ (m)}.$$

$$\mathbf{e}_{BC} = \frac{\mathbf{r}_{BC}}{|\mathbf{r}_{BC}|} = 0.8\mathbf{j} - 0.6\mathbf{k}.$$

> Obtain a unit vector parallel to the axis BC by dividing the position vector from point B to point C by its magnitude.

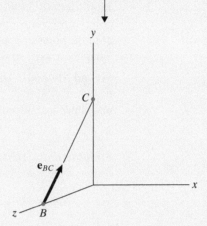

$$\mathbf{M}_{BC} = (\mathbf{e}_{BC} \cdot \mathbf{M}_B)\,\mathbf{e}_{BC}$$
$$= [(0)(12) + (0.8)(-10) + (-0.6)(28)]\mathbf{e}_{BC}$$
$$= -24.8\mathbf{e}_{BC} \text{ (kN-m)}.$$

> Apply Eq. (4.4) to determine the moment of $\mathbf{F}$ about the axis BC. Notice the negative result. Pointing the thumb of the right hand *opposite* to the direction of the unit vector $\mathbf{e}_{BC}$, the fingers point in the direction of the moment of $\mathbf{F}$ about the axis BC.

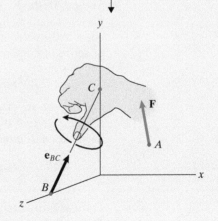

Practice Problem Determine the moment $\mathbf{M}_C$ of the force $\mathbf{F}$ about point C. Use it to calculate the moment of $\mathbf{F}$ about the axis BC by determining the component of $\mathbf{M}_C$ parallel to the axis.

Answer: $\mathbf{M}_{BC} = -24.8\mathbf{e}_{BC}$ (kN-m).

| Example 4.7 | Moment of a Force About the *x* Axis (► *Related Problem 4.77*) |

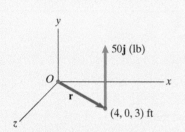

What is the moment of the 50-lb force about the *x* axis?

Strategy

We can determine the moment in two ways.

First Method   We can use Eqs. (4.5) and (4.6). Since **r** can extend from any point on the *x* axis to the line of action of the force, we can use the vector from *O* to the point of application of the force. The vector **e** must be a unit vector along the *x* axis, so we can use either **i** or −**i**.

Second Method   This example is the first of the special cases we discussed, because the 50-lb force is perpendicular to the *x*–*z* plane. We can determine the magnitude and direction of the moment directly from the given information.

Solution

First Method   *Determine a vector* **r**. The vector from *O* to the point of application of the force is (Fig. a)

$$\mathbf{r} = 4\mathbf{i} + 3\mathbf{k} \ (\text{ft}).$$

Determine a vector **e**. We can use the unit vector **i**.

Evaluate $\mathbf{M}_L$. From Eq. (4.6), the mixed triple product is

$$\mathbf{i} \cdot (\mathbf{r} \times \mathbf{F}) = \begin{vmatrix} 1 & 0 & 0 \\ 4 & 0 & 3 \\ 0 & 50 & 0 \end{vmatrix} = -150 \text{ ft-lb.}$$

Then from Eq. (4.5), the moment of the force about the *x* axis is

$$\mathbf{M}_{x \text{ axis}} = [\mathbf{i} \cdot (\mathbf{r} \times \mathbf{F})]\mathbf{i} = -150\mathbf{i} \ (\text{ft-lb}).$$

The magnitude of the moment is 150 ft-lb, and its direction is as shown in Fig. b.

Second Method   Since the 50-lb force is perpendicular to a plane (the *x*–*z* plane) containing the *x* axis, the magnitude of the moment about the *x* axis is equal to the perpendicular distance from the *x* axis to the point where the line of action of the force intersects the *x*–*z* plane (Fig. c):

$$\left| \mathbf{M}_{x \text{ axis}} \right| = (3 \text{ ft})(50 \text{ lb}) = 150 \text{ ft-lb.}$$

Pointing the arc of the fingers in the direction of the moment about the *x* axis (Fig. c), we find that the right-hand rule indicates that $\mathbf{M}_{x \text{ axis}}$ points in the negative *x* axis direction. Therefore,

$$\mathbf{M}_{x \text{ axis}} = -150\mathbf{i} \ (\text{ft-lb}).$$

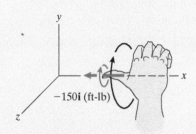

(a) The vector **r** from *O* to the point of application of the force.

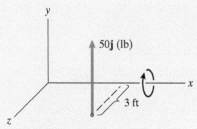

(b) The direction of the moment.

(c) The distance from the *x* axis to the point where the line of action of the force intersects the *x*–*z* plane is 3 ft. The arrow indicates the direction of the moment about the *x* axis.

Critical Thinking

The hinged door in this example is designed to rotate about the *x* axis. If no other forces act on the door, you can see that the 50-lb upward force would tend to cause the door to rotate upward. It is the moment of the force about the *x* axis, and *not* the moment of the force about some point, that measures the tendency of the force to cause the door to rotate on its hinges. Furthermore, the direction of the moment of the force about the *x* axis indicates the direction in which the force tends to cause the door to rotate. (See Fig. b.)

Example 4.8   Rotating Machines (▶ *Related Problem 4.100*)

The crewman exerts the forces shown on the handles of the coffee grinder winch, where $\mathbf{F} = 4\mathbf{j} + 32\mathbf{k}$ N. Determine the total moment he exerts (a) about point O; (b) about the axis of the winch, which coincides with the x axis.

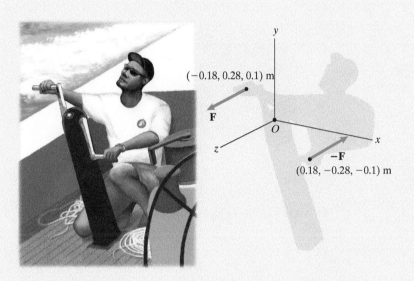

Strategy

(a) To obtain the total moment about point O, we must sum the moments of the two forces about O. Let the sum be denoted by $\Sigma\mathbf{M}_O$.

(b) Because point O is on the x axis, the total moment about the x axis is the component of $\Sigma\mathbf{M}_O$ parallel to the x axis, which is the x component of $\Sigma\mathbf{M}_O$.

Solution

(a) The total moment about point O is

$$\Sigma\mathbf{M}_O = \begin{vmatrix} \mathbf{i} & \mathbf{j} & \mathbf{k} \\ -0.18 & 0.28 & 0.1 \\ 0 & 4 & 32 \end{vmatrix} + \begin{vmatrix} \mathbf{i} & \mathbf{j} & \mathbf{k} \\ 0.18 & -0.28 & -0.1 \\ 0 & -4 & -32 \end{vmatrix}$$

$$= 17.1\mathbf{i} + 11.5\mathbf{j} - 1.4\mathbf{k} \text{ (N-m)}.$$

(b) The total moment about the x axis is the x component of $\Sigma\mathbf{M}_O$ (Fig. a):

$$\Sigma\mathbf{M}_{x\text{ axis}} = 17.1 \text{ (N-m)}.$$

Notice that this is the result given by Eq. (4.4): Since $\mathbf{i}$ is a unit vector parallel to the x axis,

$$\Sigma\mathbf{M}_{x\text{ axis}} = (\mathbf{i} \cdot \Sigma\mathbf{M}_O)\mathbf{i} = 17.1 \text{ (N-m)}.$$

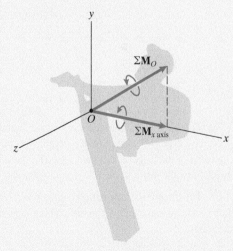

(a) The total moment about the x axis.

Problems

▶ **4.77** The force $\mathbf{F} = 20\mathbf{i} + 40\mathbf{j} - 10\mathbf{k}$ (N). Use both of the procedures described in Example 4.7 to determine the moment due to $\mathbf{F}$ about the z axis.

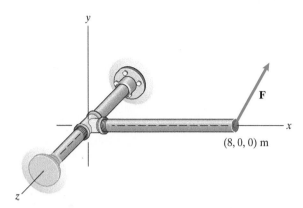

Problem 4.77

4.78 Use Eqs. (4.5) and (4.6) to determine the moment of the 20-N force about (a) the x axis, (b) the y axis, (c) the z axis. (First see if you can write down the results without using the equations.)

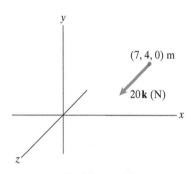

Problem 4.78

4.79 Three forces parallel to the y axis act on the rectangular plate. Use Eqs. (4.5) and (4.6) to determine the sum of the moments of the forces about the x axis. (First see if you can write down the result without using the equations.)

4.80 The three forces are parallel to the y axis. Determine the sum of the moments of the forces (a) about the y axis; (b) about the z axis.

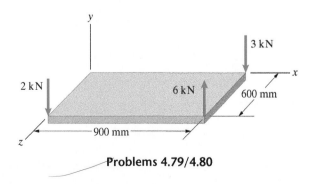

Problems 4.79/4.80

4.81 The person exerts a force $\mathbf{F} = 0.2\mathbf{i} - 0.4\mathbf{j} + 1.2\mathbf{k}$ (lb) on the gate at C. Point C lies in the x–y plane. What moment does the person exert about the gate's hinge axis, which is coincident with the y axis?

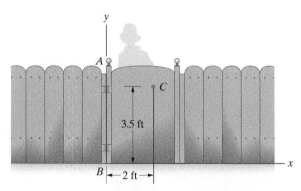

Problem 4.81

4.82 Four forces act on the plate. Their components are

$$\mathbf{F}_A = -2\mathbf{i} + 4\mathbf{j} + 2\mathbf{k} \ (\text{kN}),$$

$$\mathbf{F}_B = 3\mathbf{j} - 3\mathbf{k} \ (\text{kN}),$$

$$\mathbf{F}_C = 2\mathbf{j} + 3\mathbf{k} \ (\text{kN}),$$

$$\mathbf{F}_D = 2\mathbf{i} + 6\mathbf{j} + 4\mathbf{k} \ (\text{kN}).$$

Determine the sum of the moments of the forces (a) about the x axis; (b) about the z axis.

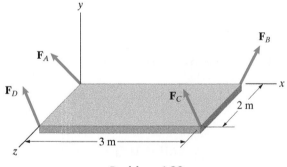

Problem 4.82

4.83 The force $\mathbf{F} = 30\mathbf{i} + 20\mathbf{j} - 10\mathbf{k}$ (lb).

(a) What is the moment of $\mathbf{F}$ about the y axis?

(b) Suppose that you keep the magnitude of $\mathbf{F}$ fixed, but you change its direction so as to make the moment of $\mathbf{F}$ about the y axis as large as possible. What is the magnitude of the resulting moment?

4.84 The moment of the force $\mathbf{F}$ about the x axis is $-80\mathbf{i}$ (ft-lb), the moment about the y axis is zero, and the moment about the z axis is $160\mathbf{k}$ (ft-lb). If $F_y = 80$ lb, what are F_x and F_z?

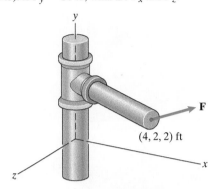

Problems 4.83/4.84

4.85 The robotic manipulator is stationary. The weights of the arms AB and BC act at their midpoints. The direction cosines of the centerline of arm AB are $\cos \theta_x = 0.500$, $\cos \theta_y = 0.866$, $\cos \theta_z = 0$, and the direction cosines of the centerline of arm BC are $\cos \theta_x = 0.707$, $\cos \theta_y = 0.619$, $\cos \theta_z = -0.342$. What total moment is exerted about the z axis by the weights of the arms?

4.86 In Problem 4.85, what total moment is exerted about the x axis by the weights of the arms?

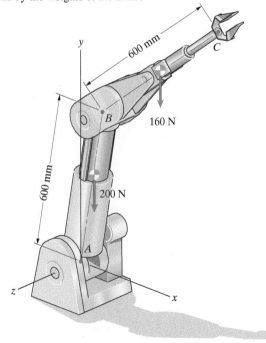

Problems 4.85/4.86

4.87 In Active Example 4.6, suppose that the force changes to $\mathbf{F} = -2\mathbf{i} + 3\mathbf{j} + 6\mathbf{k}$ (kN). Determine the magnitude of the moment of the force about the axis of the bar BC.

4.88 Determine the moment of the 20-N force about the line AB. Use Eqs. (4.5) and (4.6), letting the unit vector $\mathbf{e}$ point (a) from A toward B; (b) from B toward A.

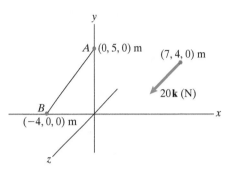

Problem 4.88

4.89 The force $\mathbf{F} = -10\mathbf{i} + 5\mathbf{j} - 5\mathbf{k}$ (kip). Determine the moment of $\mathbf{F}$ about the line AB. Draw a sketch to indicate the direction of the moment.

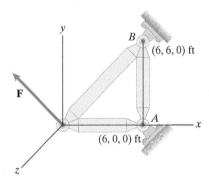

Problem 4.89

4.90 The force $\mathbf{F} = 10\mathbf{i} + 12\mathbf{j} - 6\mathbf{k}$ (N). What is the moment of $\mathbf{F}$ about the line AO? Draw a sketch to indicate the direction of the moment.

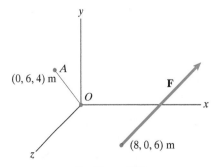

Problem 4.90

4.91 The tension in the cable AB is 1 kN. Determine the moment about the x axis due to the force exerted on the hatch by the cable at point B. Draw a sketch to indicate the direction of the moment.

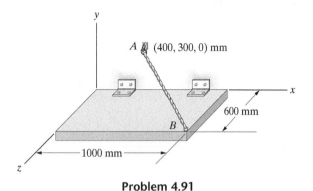

Problem 4.91

4.92 Determine the moment of the force applied at D about the straight line through the hinges A and B. (The line through A and B lies in the y–z plane.)

4.93 The tension in the cable CE is 160 lb. Determine the moment of the force exerted by the cable on the hatch at C about the straight line through the hinges A and B.

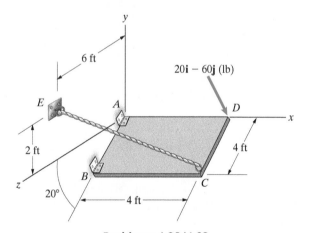

Problems 4.92/4.93

4.94 The coordinates of A are $(-2.4, 0, -0.6)$ m, and the coordinates of B are $(-2.2, 0.7, -1.2)$ m. The force exerted at B by the sailboat's main sheet AB is 130 N. Determine the moment of the force about the centerline of the mast (the y axis). Draw a sketch to indicate the direction of the moment.

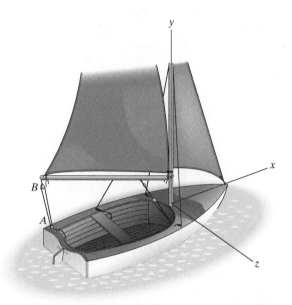

Problem 4.94

4.95 The tension in cable AB is 200 lb. Determine the moments about each of the coordinate axes due to the force exerted on point B by the cable. Draw sketches to indicate the direction of the moments.

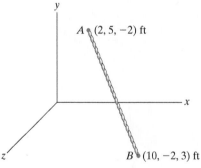

Problem 4.95

4.96 The total force exerted on the blades of the turbine by the steam nozzle is **F** = 20**i** − 120**j** + 100**k** (N), and it effectively acts at the point (100, 80, 300) mm. What moment is exerted about the axis of the turbine (the *x* axis)?

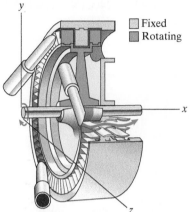

Problem 4.96

4.97 The pneumatic support *AB* holds a trunk lid in place. It exerts a 35-N force on the fixture at *B* that points in the direction from *A* toward *B*. Determine the magnitude of the moment of the force about the hinge axis of the lid, which is the *z* axis.

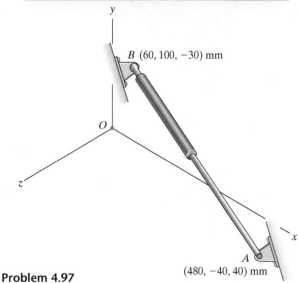

B (60, 100, −30) mm

O

A
(480, −40, 40) mm

Problem 4.97

4.98 The tension in cable *AB* is 80 lb. What is the moment about the line *CD* due to the force exerted by the cable on the wall at *B*?

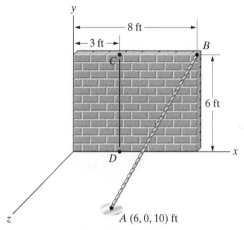

A (6, 0, 10) ft

Problem 4.98

4.99 The magnitude of the force **F** is 0.2 N and its direction cosines are cos θ_x = 0.727, cos θ_y = −0.364, and cos θ_z = 0.582. Determine the magnitude of the moment of **F** about the axis *AB* of the spool.

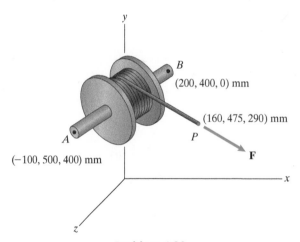

B
(200, 400, 0) mm

(160, 475, 290) mm

P

F

A

(−100, 500, 400) mm

Problem 4.99

▶ **4.100** A motorist applies the two forces shown to loosen a lug nut. The direction cosines of **F** are $\cos \theta_x = \frac{4}{13}$, $\cos \theta_y = \frac{12}{13}$, and $\cos \theta_z = \frac{3}{13}$. If the magnitude of the moment about the x axis must be 32 ft-lb to loosen the nut, what is the magnitude of the forces the motorist must apply? (See Example 4.8.)

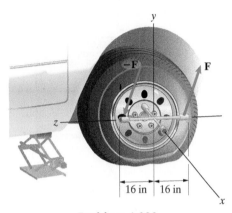

Problem 4.100

4.101 The tension in cable AB is 2 kN. What is the magnitude of the moment about the shaft CD due to the force exerted by the cable at A? Draw a sketch to indicate the direction of the moment about the shaft.

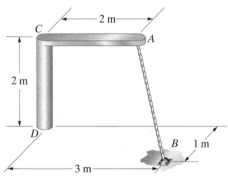

Problem 4.101

4.102 The axis of the car's wheel passes through the origin of the coordinate system and its direction cosines are $\cos \theta_x = 0.940$, $\cos \theta_y = 0$, $\cos \theta_z = 0.342$. The force exerted on the tire by the road effectively acts at the point $x = 0$, $y = -0.36$ m, $z = 0$ and has components $\mathbf{F} = -720\mathbf{i} + 3660\mathbf{j} + 1240\mathbf{k}$ (N). What is the moment of **F** about the wheel's axis?

Problem 4.102

4.103 The direction cosines of the centerline OA are $\cos \theta_x = 0.500$, $\cos \theta_y = 0.866$, and $\cos \theta_z = 0$, and the direction cosines of the line AG are $\cos \theta_x = 0.707$, $\cos \theta_y = 0.619$, and $\cos \theta_z = -0.342$. What is the moment about OA due to the 250-N weight? Draw a sketch to indicate the direction of the moment about the shaft.

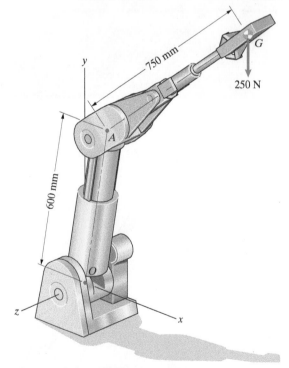

Problem 4.103

4.104 The radius of the steering wheel is 200 mm. The distance from O to C is 1 m. The center C of the steering wheel lies in the x–y plane. The driver exerts a force $\mathbf{F} = 10\mathbf{i} + 10\mathbf{j} - 5\mathbf{k}$ (N) on the wheel at A. If the angle $\alpha = 0$, what is the magnitude of the moment about the shaft OC? Draw a sketch to indicate the direction of the moment about the shaft.

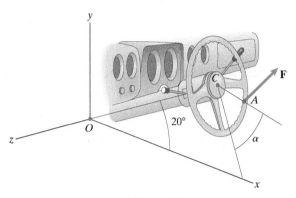

Problem 4.104

4.105* The magnitude of the force $\mathbf{F}$ is 10 N. Suppose that you want to choose the direction of the force $\mathbf{F}$ so that the magnitude of its moment about the line L is a maximum. Determine the components of $\mathbf{F}$ and the magnitude of its moment about L. (There are two solutions for $\mathbf{F}$.)

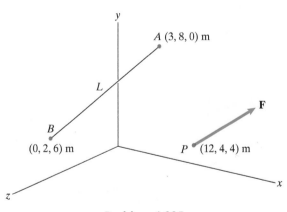

Problem 4.105

4.106 The weight W causes a tension of 100 lb in cable CD. If $d = 2$ ft, what is the moment about the z axis due to the force exerted by the cable CD at point C?

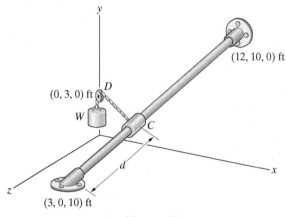

Problem 4.106

4.107* The y axis points upward. The weight of the 4-kg rectangular plate acts at the midpoint G of the plate. The sum of the moments about the straight line through the supports A and B due to the weight of the plate and the force exerted on the plate by the cable CD is zero. What is the tension in the cable?

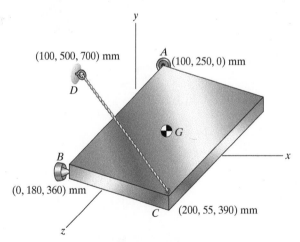

Problem 4.107

4.4 Couples

BACKGROUND

Now that we have described how to calculate the moment due to a force, consider this question: Is it possible to exert a moment on an object without subjecting it to a net force? The answer is yes, and it occurs when a compact disk begins rotating or a screw is turned by a screwdriver. Forces are exerted on these objects, but in such a way that the net force is zero while the net moment is not zero.

Two forces that have equal magnitudes, opposite directions, and different lines of action are called a *couple* (Fig. 4.17a). A couple tends to cause rotation of an object even though the vector sum of the forces is zero, and it has the remarkable property that *the moment it exerts is the same about any point*.

The moment of a couple is simply the sum of the moments of the forces about a point P (Fig. 4.17b):

$$\mathbf{M} = [\mathbf{r}_1 \times \mathbf{F}] + [\mathbf{r}_2 \times (-\mathbf{F})] = (\mathbf{r}_1 - \mathbf{r}_2) \times \mathbf{F}.$$

The vector $\mathbf{r}_1 - \mathbf{r}_2$ is equal to the vector $\mathbf{r}$ shown in Fig. 4.17c, so we can express the moment as

$$\mathbf{M} = \mathbf{r} \times \mathbf{F}.$$

Since $\mathbf{r}$ doesn't depend on the position of P, the moment $\mathbf{M}$ is the same for *any* point P.

Because a couple exerts a moment but the sum of the forces is zero, it is often represented in diagrams simply by showing the moment (Fig. 4.17d). Like the Cheshire cat in *Alice's Adventures in Wonderland,* which vanished except for its grin, the forces don't appear; only the moment they exert is visible. But we recognize the origin of the moment by referring to it as a *moment of a couple,* or simply a *couple*.

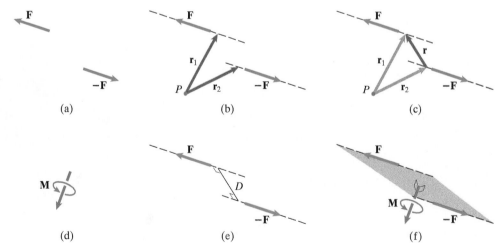

(a)   (b)   (c)

(d)   (e)   (f)

Figure 4.17
(a) A couple.
(b) Determining the moment about P.
(c) The vector $\mathbf{r} = \mathbf{r}_1 - \mathbf{r}_2$.
(d) Representing the moment of the couple.
(e) The distance D between the lines of action.
(f) $\mathbf{M}$ is perpendicular to the plane containing $\mathbf{F}$ and $-\mathbf{F}$.

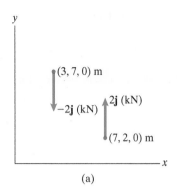

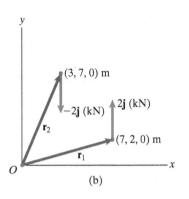

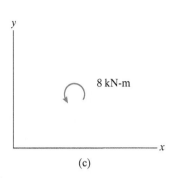

(a) (b) (c)

Figure 4.18
(a) A couple consisting of 2-kN forces.
(b) Determining the sum of the moments of the forces about O.
(c) Representing a couple in two dimensions.

Notice in Fig. 4.17c that $\mathbf{M} = \mathbf{r} \times \mathbf{F}$ is the moment of $\mathbf{F}$ about a point on the line of action of the force $-\mathbf{F}$. The magnitude of the moment of a force about a point equals the product of the magnitude of the force and the perpendicular distance from the point to the line of action of the force, so $|\mathbf{M}| = D|\mathbf{F}|$, where D is the perpendicular distance between the lines of action of the two forces (Fig. 4.17e). The cross product $\mathbf{r} \times \mathbf{F}$ is perpendicular to $\mathbf{r}$ and $\mathbf{F}$, which means that $\mathbf{M}$ is perpendicular to the plane containing $\mathbf{F}$ and $-\mathbf{F}$ (Fig. 4.17f). Pointing the thumb of the right hand in the direction of $\mathbf{M}$, the arc of the fingers indicates the direction of the moment.

In Fig. 4.18a, our view is perpendicular to the plane containing the two forces. The distance between the lines of action of the forces is 4 m, so the magnitude of the moment of the couple is $|\mathbf{M}| = (4 \text{ m})(2 \text{ kN}) = 8$ kN-m. The moment $\mathbf{M}$ is perpendicular to the plane containing the two forces. Pointing the arc of the fingers of the right hand counterclockwise, we find that the right-hand rule indicates that $\mathbf{M}$ points out of the page. Therefore, the moment of the couple is

$$\mathbf{M} = 8\mathbf{k} \text{ (kN-m)}.$$

We can also determine the moment of the couple by calculating the sum of the moments of the two forces about *any* point. The sum of the moments of the forces about the origin O is (Fig. 4.18b)

$$\mathbf{M} = [\mathbf{r}_1 \times (2\mathbf{j})] + [\mathbf{r}_2 \times (-2\mathbf{j})]$$
$$= [(7\mathbf{i} + 2\mathbf{j}) \times (2\mathbf{j})] + [(3\mathbf{i} + 7\mathbf{j}) \times (-2\mathbf{j})]$$
$$= 8\mathbf{k} \text{ (kN-m)}.$$

In a two-dimensional situation like this example, it isn't convenient to represent a couple by showing the moment vector, because the vector is perpendicular to the page. Instead, we represent the couple by showing its magnitude and a circular arrow that indicates its direction (Fig. 4.18c).

By grasping a bar and twisting it (Fig. 4.19a), a moment can be exerted about its axis (Fig. 4.19b). Although the system of forces exerted is distributed over the surface of the bar in a complicated way, the effect is the same as if two equal and opposite forces are exerted (Fig. 4.19c). When we represent a couple as in Fig. 4.19b, or by showing the moment vector $\mathbf{M}$, we imply that some system of forces exerts that moment. The system of forces (such as the forces exerted in twisting the bar, or the forces on the crankshaft that exert a moment on

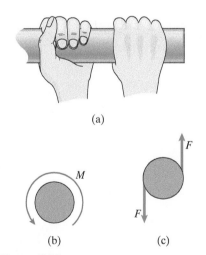

(a)

(b) (c)

Figure 4.19
(a) Twisting a bar.
(b) The moment about the axis of the bar.
(c) The same effect is obtained by applying two equal and opposite forces.

the drive shaft of a car) is nearly always more complicated than two equal and opposite forces, but the effect is the same. For this reason, we can *model* the actual system as a simple system of two forces.

RESULTS

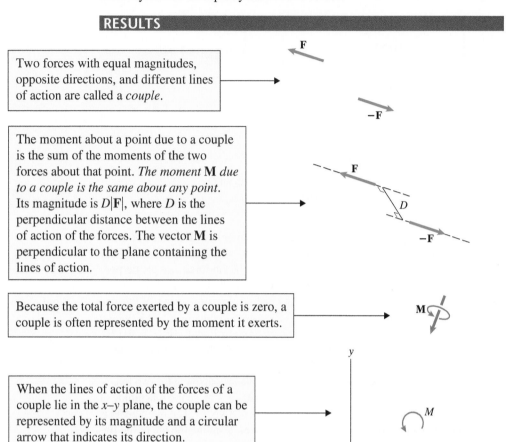

Two forces with equal magnitudes, opposite directions, and different lines of action are called a *couple*.

The moment about a point due to a couple is the sum of the moments of the two forces about that point. *The moment* **M** *due to a couple is the same about any point.* Its magnitude is $D|\mathbf{F}|$, where D is the perpendicular distance between the lines of action of the forces. The vector **M** is perpendicular to the plane containing the lines of action.

Because the total force exerted by a couple is zero, a couple is often represented by the moment it exerts.

When the lines of action of the forces of a couple lie in the *x–y* plane, the couple can be represented by its magnitude and a circular arrow that indicates its direction.

| Active Example 4.9 | Moment of a Couple (▶ *Related Problem 4.108*) |

The force $\mathbf{F} = 10\mathbf{i} - 4\mathbf{j}$ (N). Determine the moment due to the couple. Represent the moment by its magnitude and a circular arrow indicating its direction.

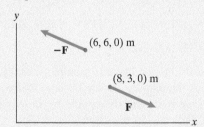

Strategy
We will determine the moment in two ways. In the first method, we will choose a point and calculate the sum of the moments of the two forces about that point. Because the moment due to a couple is the same about any point, we can choose any convenient point. In the second method, we will sum the moments of the two couples formed by the *x* and *y* components of the forces.

Solution

First Method

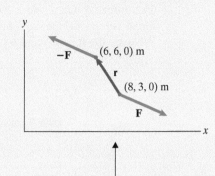

$$M = r \times (-F)$$
$$= (-2i + 3j) \times (-10i + 4j)$$
$$= 22k \text{ (N-m)}.$$

Calculate the sum of the moments of the two forces about the point of application of the force **F**.

The magnitude of the moment is 22 N-m. Pointing the thumb of the right hand in the direction of the unit vector **k**, the direction of the moment in the x–y plane is counterclockwise.

Second Method

The components of the two forces form two couples.

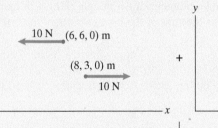

The magnitude of the moment due to the 10-N couple is (3 m)(10 N) = 30 N-m, and the moment is counterclockwise. The magnitude of the moment due to the 4-N couple is (2 m)(4 N) = 8 N-m, and the moment is clockwise. Therefore the total counterclockwise moment is 30 − 8 = 22 N-m.

Practice Problem Use the cross product to calculate the sum of the moments of the forces **F** and −**F** about the point P with coordinates (10, 7, 3) m. Represent the moment by its magnitude and a circular arrow indicating its direction.

Answer: 22k (N-m), or 22 N-m counterclockwise.

Example 4.10 Determining Unknown Forces (▶ *Related Problem 4.113*)

Two forces *A* and *B* and a 200 ft-lb couple act on the beam. The sum of the forces is zero, and the sum of the moments about the left end of the beam is zero. What are the forces *A* and *B*?

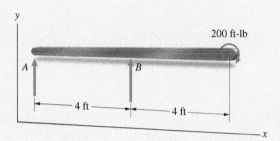

Strategy

By summing the two forces (the couple exerts no net force on the beam) and summing the moments due to the forces and the couple about the left end of the beam, we will obtain two equations in terms of the two unknown forces.

Solution

The sum of the forces is

$$\Sigma F_y = A + B = 0.$$

The moment of the couple (200 ft-lb clockwise) is the same about any point, so the sum of the moments about the left end of the beam is

$$\Sigma M_{\text{left end}} = (4 \text{ ft}) B - 200 \text{ ft-lb} = 0.$$

The forces are $B = 50$ lb and $A = -50$ lb.

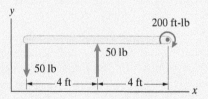

The forces on the beam form a couple.

Critical Thinking

Notice that the total moment about the left end of the beam is the sum of the moment due to the force *B* and the moment due to the 200 ft-lb couple. As we observe in Chapter 5, if an object subjected to forces and couples is in equilibrium, the sum of the forces is zero and the sum of the moments about any point, *including moments due to couples*, is zero. In this example we needed both these conditions to determine the unknown forces *A* and *B*.

Example 4.11 | **Sum of the Moments Due to Two Couples** (▶ *Related Problem 4.119*)

Determine the sum of the moments exerted on the pipe by the two couples.

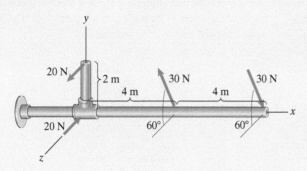

Strategy
We will express the moment exerted by each couple as a vector. To express the 30-N couple in terms of a vector, we will express the forces in terms of their components. We can then sum the moment vectors to determine the sum of the moments exerted by the couples.

Solution
Consider the 20-N couple. The magnitude of the moment of the couple is $(2\text{ m})(20\text{ N}) = 40$ N-m. The direction of the moment vector is perpendicular to the y–z plane, and the right-hand rule indicates that it points in the positive x axis direction. The moment of the 20-N couple is $40\mathbf{i}$ (N-m).

By resolving the 30-N forces into y and z components, we obtain the two couples in Fig. a. The moment of the couple formed by the y components is $-(30\sin 60°)(4)\mathbf{k}$ (N-m), and the moment of the couple formed by the z components is $(30\cos 60°)(4)\mathbf{j}$ (N-m).

The sum of the moments is therefore

$$\Sigma\mathbf{M} = 40\mathbf{i} + (30\cos 60°)(4)\mathbf{j} - (30\sin 60°)(4)\mathbf{k} \text{ (N-m)}$$

$$= 40\mathbf{i} + 60\mathbf{j} - 104\mathbf{k} \text{ (N-m)}.$$

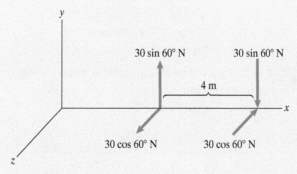

(a) Resolving the 30-N forces into y and z components.

Critical Thinking
Although the method we used in this example helps you recognize the contributions of the individual couples to the sum of the moments, it is convenient only when the orientations of the forces and their points of application relative to the coordinate system are fairly simple. When that is not the case, you can determine the sum of the moments by choosing any point and calculating the sum of the moments of the forces about that point.

Problems

▶ **4.108** In Active Example 4.9, suppose that the point of application of the force **F** is moved from (8, 3, 0) m to (8, 8, 0) m. Draw a sketch showing the new position of the force. From your sketch, will the moment due to the couple be clockwise or counterclockwise? Calculate the moment due to the couple. Represent the moment by its magnitude and a circular arrow indicating its direction.

4.109 The forces are contained in the *x*–*y* plane.

(a) Determine the moment of the couple and represent it as shown in Fig. 4.18c.

(b) What is the sum of the moments of the two forces about the point (10, −40, 20) ft?

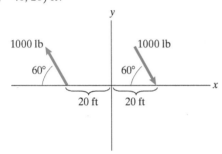

Problem 4.109

4.110 The moment of the couple is 600**k** (N-m). What is the angle *α*?

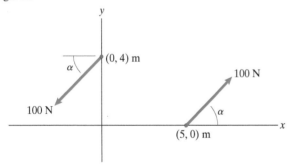

Problem 4.110

4.111 Point *P* is contained in the *x*–*y* plane, $|\mathbf{F}| = 100$ N, and the moment of the couple is −500**k** (N-m). What are the coordinates of *P*?

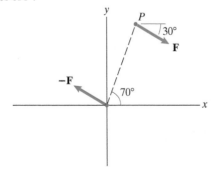

Problem 4.111

4.112 Three forces of equal magnitude are applied parallel to the sides of an equilateral triangle. (a) Show that the sum of the moments of the forces is the same about any point. (b) Determine the magnitude of the sum of the moments.

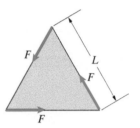

Problem 4.112

▶ **4.113** In Example 4.10, suppose that the 200 ft-lb couple is counterclockwise instead of clockwise. Draw a sketch of the beam showing the forces and couple acting on it. What are the forces *A* and *B*?

4.114 The moments of two couples are shown. What is the sum of the moments about point *P*?

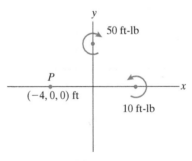

Problem 4.114

4.115 Determine the sum of the moments exerted on the plate by the two couples.

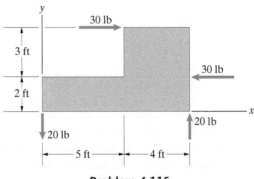

Problem 4.115

4.116 Determine the sum of the moments exerted about A by the couple and the two forces.

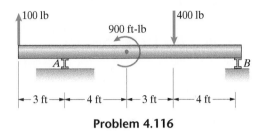

Problem 4.116

4.117 Determine the sum of the moments exerted about A by the couple and the two forces.

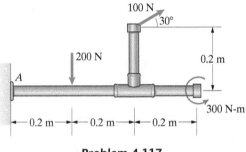

Problem 4.117

4.118 The sum of the moments about point A due to the forces and couples acting on the bar is zero.

(a) What is the magnitude of the couple C?

(b) Determine the sum of the moments about point B due to the forces and couples acting on the bar.

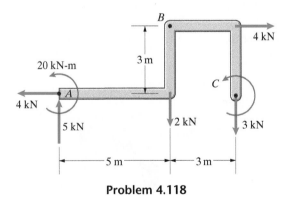

Problem 4.118

▶ **4.119** In Example 4.11, suppose that instead of acting in the positive z axis direction, the upper 20-N force acts in the positive x axis direction. Instead of acting in the negative z axis direction, let the lower 20-N force act in the negative x axis direction. Draw a sketch of the pipe showing the forces acting on it. Determine the sum of the moments exerted on the pipe by the two couples.

4.120 (a) What is the moment of the couple?

(b) Determine the perpendicular distance between the lines of action of the two forces.

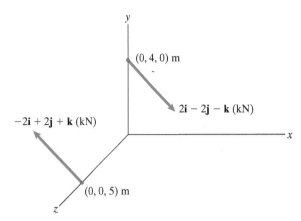

Problem 4.120

4.121 Determine the sum of the moments exerted on the plate by the three couples. (The 80-lb forces are contained in the x–z plane.)

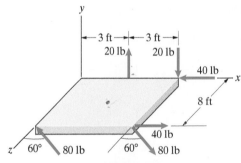

Problem 4.121

4.122 What is the magnitude of the sum of the moments exerted on the T-shaped structure by the two couples?

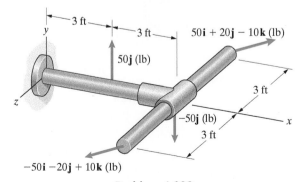

Problem 4.122

4.123 The tension in cables AB and CD is 500 N.

(a) Show that the two forces exerted by the cables on the rectangular hatch at B and C form a couple.

(b) What is the moment exerted on the plate by the cables?

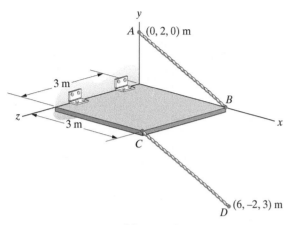

Problem 4.123

4.124 The cables AB and CD exert a couple on the vertical pipe. The tension in each cable is 8 kN. Determine the magnitude of the moment the cables exert on the pipe.

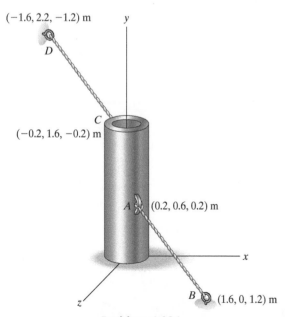

Problem 4.124

4.125 The bar is loaded by the forces

$$\mathbf{F}_B = 2\mathbf{i} + 6\mathbf{j} + 3\mathbf{k} \text{ (kN)},$$
$$\mathbf{F}_C = \mathbf{i} - 2\mathbf{j} + 2\mathbf{k} \text{ (kN)},$$

and the couple

$$\mathbf{M}_C = 2\mathbf{i} + \mathbf{j} - 2\mathbf{k} \text{ (kN-m)}.$$

Determine the sum of the moments of the two forces and the couple about A.

4.126 The forces

$$\mathbf{F}_B = 2\mathbf{i} + 6\mathbf{j} + 3\mathbf{k} \text{ (kN)},$$
$$\mathbf{F}_C = \mathbf{i} - 2\mathbf{j} + 2\mathbf{k} \text{ (kN)},$$

and the couple

$$\mathbf{M}_C = M_{Cy}\mathbf{j} + M_{Cz}\mathbf{k} \text{ (kN-m)}.$$

Determine the values of $\mathbf{M}_{Cy}$ and $\mathbf{M}_{Cz}$ so that the sum of the moments of the two forces and the couple about A is zero.

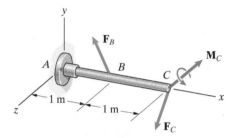

Problems 4.125/4.126

4.127 Two wrenches are used to tighten an elbow fitting. The force $\mathbf{F} = 10\mathbf{k}$ (lb) on the right wrench is applied at $(6, -5, -3)$ in, and the force $-\mathbf{F}$ on the left wrench is applied at $(4, -5, 3)$ in.

(a) Determine the moment about the x axis due to the force exerted on the right wrench.

(b) Determine the moment of the couple formed by the forces exerted on the two wrenches.

(c) Based on the results of (a) and (b), explain why two wrenches are used.

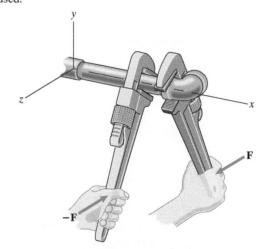

Problem 4.127

4.5 Equivalent Systems

A *system of forces and moments* is simply a particular set of forces and moments of couples. The systems of forces and moments dealt with in engineering can be complicated. This is especially true in the case of distributed forces, such as the pressure forces exerted by water on a dam. Fortunately, if we are concerned only with the total force and moment exerted, we can represent complicated systems of forces and moments by much simpler systems.

Conditions for Equivalence

We define two systems of forces and moments, designated as system 1 and system 2, to be *equivalent* if the sums of the forces are equal, or

$$(\Sigma \mathbf{F})_1 = (\Sigma \mathbf{F})_2, \tag{4.7}$$

and the sums of the moments about a point P are equal, or

$$(\Sigma \mathbf{M}_P)_1 = (\Sigma \mathbf{M}_P)_2. \tag{4.8}$$

To see what the conditions for equivalence mean, consider the systems of forces and moments in Fig. 4.20a. In system 1, an object is subjected to two forces $\mathbf{F}_A$ and $\mathbf{F}_B$ and a couple $\mathbf{M}_C$. In system 2, the object is subjected to a force $\mathbf{F}_D$ and two couples $\mathbf{M}_E$ and $\mathbf{M}_F$. The first condition for equivalence is

$$(\Sigma \mathbf{F})_1 = (\Sigma \mathbf{F})_2:$$
$$\mathbf{F}_A + \mathbf{F}_B = \mathbf{F}_D. \tag{4.9}$$

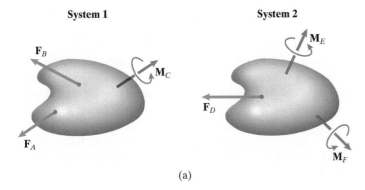

(a)

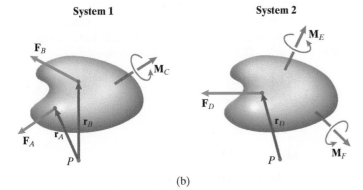

(b)

Figure 4.20
(a) Different systems of forces and moments applied to an object.
(b) Determining the sum of the moments about a point P for each system.

If we determine the sums of the moments about the point P in Fig. 4.20b, the second condition for equivalence is

$$(\Sigma \mathbf{M}_P)_1 = (\Sigma \mathbf{M}_P)_2:$$

$$(\mathbf{r}_A \times \mathbf{F}_A) + (\mathbf{r}_B \times \mathbf{F}_B) + \mathbf{M}_C = (\mathbf{r}_D \times \mathbf{F}_D) + \mathbf{M}_E + \mathbf{M}_F. \quad (4.10)$$

If these conditions are satisfied, systems 1 and 2 are equivalent.

We will use this example to demonstrate that *if the sums of the forces are equal for two systems of forces and moments and the sums of the moments about one point P are equal, then the sums of the moments about any point are equal.* Suppose that Eq. (4.9) is satisfied, and Eq. (4.10) is satisfied for the point P in Fig. 4.20b. For a different point P' (Fig. 4.21), we will show that

$$(\Sigma \mathbf{M}_{P'})_1 = (\Sigma \mathbf{M}_{P'})_2:$$

$$(\mathbf{r}'_A \times \mathbf{F}_A) + (\mathbf{r}'_B \times \mathbf{F}_B) + \mathbf{M}_C = (\mathbf{r}'_D \times \mathbf{F}_D) + \mathbf{M}_E + \mathbf{M}_F. \quad (4.11)$$

In terms of the vector $\mathbf{r}$ from P' to P, the relations between the vectors $\mathbf{r}'_A$, $\mathbf{r}'_B$, and $\mathbf{r}'_D$ in Fig. 4.21 and the vectors $\mathbf{r}_A$, $\mathbf{r}_B$, and $\mathbf{r}_D$ in Fig. 4.20b are

$$\mathbf{r}'_A = \mathbf{r} + \mathbf{r}_A, \qquad \mathbf{r}'_B = \mathbf{r} + \mathbf{r}_B, \qquad \mathbf{r}'_D = \mathbf{r} + \mathbf{r}_D.$$

Substituting these expressions into Eq. (4.11), we obtain

$$[(\mathbf{r} + \mathbf{r}_A) \times \mathbf{F}_A] + [(\mathbf{r} + \mathbf{r}_B) \times \mathbf{F}_B] + \mathbf{M}_C$$
$$= [(\mathbf{r} + \mathbf{r}_D) \times \mathbf{F}_D] + \mathbf{M}_E + \mathbf{M}_F.$$

Rearranging terms, we can write this equation as

$$[\mathbf{r} \times (\Sigma \mathbf{F})_1] + (\Sigma \mathbf{M}_P)_1 = [\mathbf{r} \times (\Sigma \mathbf{F})_2] + (\Sigma \mathbf{M}_P)_2,$$

which holds in view of Eqs. (4.9) and (4.10). The sums of the moments of the two systems about any point are equal.

Representing Systems by Equivalent Systems

If we are concerned only with the total force and total moment exerted on an object by a given system of forces and moments, we can *represent* the system by an equivalent one. By this we mean that instead of showing the actual forces and couples acting on an object, we would show a different system that exerts the same total force and moment. In this way, we can replace a given system by a less complicated one to simplify the analysis of the forces and moments acting on an object and to gain a better intuitive understanding of their effects on the object.

Representing a System by a Force and a Couple Let us consider an arbitrary system of forces and moments and a point P (system 1 in Fig. 4.22). We can represent this system by one consisting of a single force acting at P and a single couple (system 2). The conditions for equivalence are

$$(\Sigma \mathbf{F})_2 = (\Sigma \mathbf{F})_1:$$

$$\mathbf{F} = (\Sigma \mathbf{F})_1$$

and

$$(\Sigma \mathbf{M}_P)_2 = (\Sigma \mathbf{M}_P)_1:$$

$$\mathbf{M} = (\Sigma \mathbf{M}_P)_1.$$

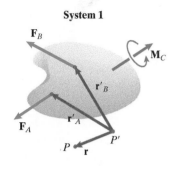

System 1

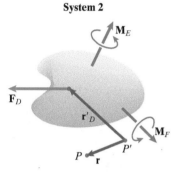

System 2

Figure 4.21
Determining the sums of the moments about a different point P'.

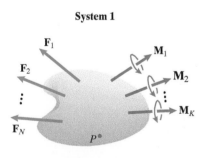

System 1

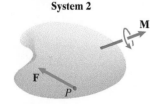

System 2

Figure 4.22
(a) An arbitrary system of forces and moments.
(b) A force acting at P and a couple.

These conditions are satisfied if **F** equals the sum of the forces in system 1 and **M** equals the sum of the moments about P in system 1.

Thus *no matter how complicated a system of forces and moments may be, it can be represented by a single force acting at a given point and a single couple.*

Representing a Force by a Force and a Couple   A force $\mathbf{F}_P$ acting at a point P (system 1 in Fig. 4.23a) can be represented by a force **F** acting at a different point Q and a couple **M** (system 2). The moment of system 1 about point Q is $\mathbf{r} \times \mathbf{F}_P$, where **r** is the vector from Q to P (Fig. 4.23b). The conditions for equivalence are

$$(\Sigma\mathbf{F})_2 = (\Sigma\mathbf{F})_1:$$

$$\mathbf{F} = \mathbf{F}_P$$

and

$$(\Sigma\mathbf{M}_Q)_2 = (\Sigma\mathbf{M}_Q)_1:$$

$$\mathbf{M} = \mathbf{r} \times \mathbf{F}_P.$$

The systems are equivalent if the force **F** equals the force $\mathbf{F}_P$ and the couple **M** equals the moment of $\mathbf{F}_P$ about Q.

Concurrent Forces Represented by a Force   A system of concurrent forces whose lines of action intersect at a point P (system 1 in Fig. 4.24) can be represented by a single force whose line of action intersects P (system 2). The sums of the forces in the two systems are equal if

$$\mathbf{F} = \mathbf{F}_1 + \mathbf{F}_2 + \cdots + \mathbf{F}_N.$$

The sum of the moments about P equals zero for each system, so the systems are equivalent if the force **F** equals the sum of the forces in system 1.

Parallel Forces Represented by a Force   A system of parallel forces whose sum is not zero can be represented by a single force **F** (Fig. 4.25). We demonstrate this result in Example 4.14.

Representing a System by a Wrench

We have shown that *any* system of forces and moments can be represented by a single force acting at a given point and a single couple. This raises an interesting question: What is the simplest system that can be equivalent to any system of forces and moments?

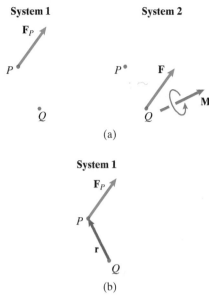

(a)

(b)

Figure 4.23
(a) System 1 is a force $\mathbf{F}_P$ acting at point P. System 2 consists of a force **F** acting at point Q and a couple **M**.
(b) Determining the moment of system 1 about point Q.

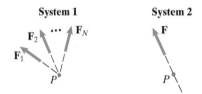

Figure 4.24
A system of concurrent forces and a system consisting of a single force **F**.

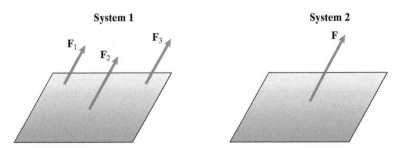

Figure 4.25
A system of parallel forces and a system consisting of a single force **F**.

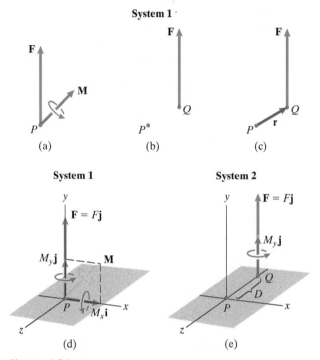

Figure 4.26
(a) System 1 is a single force and a single couple.
(b) Can system 1 be represented by a single force and no couple?
(c) The moment of **F** about P is $\mathbf{r} \times \mathbf{F}$.
(d) **F** is along the y axis, and **M** is contained in the x–y plane.
(e) System 2 is the force **F** and the component of **M** parallel to **F**.

To consider this question, let us begin with an arbitrary force **F** acting at a point P and an arbitrary couple **M** (system 1 in Fig. 4.26a) and see whether we can represent this system by a simpler one. For example, can we represent it by the force **F** acting at a different point Q and no couple (Fig. 4.26b)? The sum of the forces is the same as in system 1. If we can choose the point Q so that $\mathbf{r} \times \mathbf{F} = \mathbf{M}$, where **r** is the vector from P to Q (Fig. 4.26c), the sum of the moments about P is the same as in system 1 and the systems are equivalent. But the vector $\mathbf{r} \times \mathbf{F}$ is perpendicular to **F**, so it can equal **M** only if **M** is perpendicular to **F**. That means that, in general, we can't represent system 1 by the force **F** alone.

However, we can represent system 1 by the force **F** acting at a point Q and the component of **M** that is parallel to **F**. Figure 4.26d shows system 1 with a coordinate system placed so that **F** is along the y axis and **M** is contained in the x–y plane. In terms of this coordinate system, we can express the force and couple as $\mathbf{F} = F\mathbf{j}$ and $\mathbf{M} = M_x\mathbf{i} + M_y\mathbf{j}$. System 2 in Fig. 4.26e consists of the force **F** acting at a point on the z axis and the component of **M** parallel to **F**. If we choose the distance D so that $D = M_x/F$, system 2 is equivalent to system 1. The sum of the forces in each system is **F**. The sum of the moments about P in system 1 is **M**, and the sum of the moments about P in system 2 is

$$(\Sigma \mathbf{M}_P)_2 = [(-D\mathbf{k}) \times (F\mathbf{j})] + M_y\mathbf{j} = M_x\mathbf{i} + M_y\mathbf{j} = \mathbf{M}.$$

A force **F** and a couple $\mathbf{M}_p$ that is parallel to **F** is called a *wrench. It is the simplest system that can be equivalent to an arbitrary system of forces and moments.*

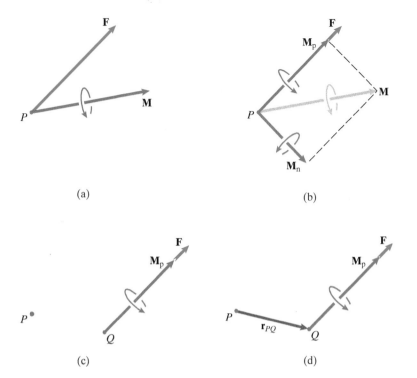

Figure 4.27
(a) If necessary, first represent the system by a single force and a single couple.
(b) The components of **M** parallel and normal to **F**.
(c) The wrench.
(d) Choose Q so that the moment of **F** about P equals the normal component of **M**.

How can we represent a given system of forces and moments by a wrench? If the system is a single force or a single couple or if it consists of a force **F** and a couple that is parallel to **F**, it is a wrench, and we can't simplify it further. If the system is more complicated than a single force and a single couple, we can begin by choosing a convenient point P and representing the system by a force **F** acting at P and a couple **M** (Fig. 4.27a). Then representing this system by a wrench requires two steps:

1. Determine the components of **M** parallel and normal to **F** (Fig. 4.27b).

2. The wrench consists of the force **F** acting at a point Q and the parallel component $\mathbf{M}_P$ (Fig. 4.27c). To achieve equivalence, the point Q must be chosen so that the moment of **F** about P equals the normal component $\mathbf{M}_n$ (Fig. 4.27d)—that is, so that $\mathbf{r}_{PQ} \times \mathbf{F} = \mathbf{M}_n$.

RESULTS

Equivalent Systems of Forces and Moments

A *system of forces and moments* is simply a particular set of forces and moments due to couples. We define two systems of forces and moments, designated as system 1 and system 2, to be *equivalent* if two conditions are satisfied:

1. The sum of the forces in system 1 is equal to the sum of the forces in system 2.

2. The sum of the moments about any point P due to the forces and moments in system 1 is equal to the sum of the moments about *the same point P* due to the forces and moments in system 2.

Representing Systems of Forces and Moments by Equivalent Systems

System 1

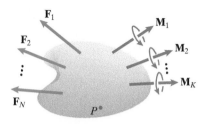

Representing an Arbitrary System by a Force and Couple

Any system of forces and moments (system 1) can be represented by an equivalent system consisting of a force $\mathbf{F}$ acting at any point P and a couple $\mathbf{M}$ (system 2). The systems are equivalent if $\mathbf{F}$ equals the sum of the forces in system 1 and $\mathbf{M}$ equals the sum of the moments about P due to the forces and moments in system 1.

System 2

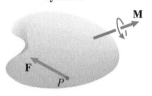

Representing a Force by a Force and Couple

A force $\mathbf{F}$ acting at a point P (system 1) can be represented by an equivalent system consisting of the force $\mathbf{F}$ acting at a different point Q and a couple $\mathbf{M}$ (system 2). The systems are equivalent if $\mathbf{M}$ equals the moment about point Q due to system 1.

System 1   **System 2**

Representing Concurrent Forces by a Force

A system of concurrent forces whose lines of action intersect at a point P (system 1) can be represented by an equivalent system consisting of a force $\mathbf{F}$ whose line of action passes through P (system 2). The systems are equivalent if $\mathbf{F}$ equals the sum of the forces in system 1.

System 1   **System 2**

Representing Parallel Forces by a Force

A system of parallel forces whose sum is not zero (system 1) can be represented by an equivalent system consisting of a force $\mathbf{F}$ acting at a point P (system 2). The systems are equivalent if $\mathbf{F}$ equals the sum of the forces in system 1 and the sum of the moments about any point due to the forces in system 1 is equal to the sum of the moments about the same point due to the forces in system 2.

System 1   **System 2**

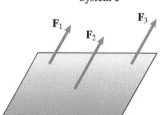   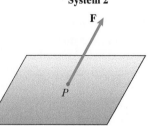

Active Example 4.12 (▶ *Related Problem 4.151*)

System 1 consists of the following forces and couples:

$$\mathbf{F}_A = -10\mathbf{i} + 10\mathbf{j} - 15\mathbf{k} \ (\text{kN}),$$

$$\mathbf{F}_B = 30\mathbf{i} + 5\mathbf{j} + 10\mathbf{k} \ (\text{kN}),$$

$$\mathbf{M}_C = -90\mathbf{i} + 150\mathbf{j} + 60\mathbf{k} \ (\text{kN-m}).$$

Suppose that you want to represent system 1 by an equivalent system consisting of a force **F** acting at the point *P* with coordinates (4, 3, −2) m and a couple **M** (system 2). Determine **F** and **M**.

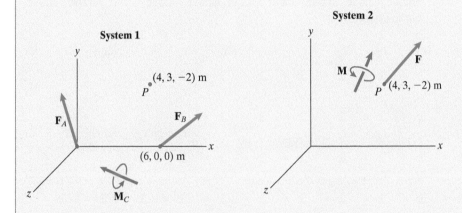

Strategy

The conditions for equivalence are satisfied if **F** equals the sum of the forces in system 1 and **M** equals the sum of the moments about point *P* due to the forces and moments in system 1. We can use these conditions to determine **F** and **M**.

Solution

$$\mathbf{F} = \mathbf{F}_A + \mathbf{F}_B$$
$$= 20\mathbf{i} + 15\mathbf{j} - 5\mathbf{k} \ (\text{kN}).$$

> The force **F** must equal the sum of the forces in system 1.

$$\mathbf{M} = \begin{vmatrix} \mathbf{i} & \mathbf{j} & \mathbf{k} \\ -4 & -3 & 2 \\ -10 & 10 & -15 \end{vmatrix} + \begin{vmatrix} \mathbf{i} & \mathbf{j} & \mathbf{k} \\ 2 & -3 & 2 \\ 30 & 5 & 10 \end{vmatrix}$$
$$+ \ (-90\mathbf{i} + 150\mathbf{j} + 60\mathbf{k})$$
$$= -105\mathbf{i} + 110\mathbf{j} + 90\mathbf{k} \ (\text{kN-m}).$$

> The couple **M** must equal the sum of the moments about point *P* due to the forces and moments in system 1.

Practice Problem Suppose that you want to represent system 2 by an equivalent system consisting of a force **F′** acting at the origin of the coordinate system and a couple **M′** (system 3). Determine **F′** and **M′**.

Answer: $\mathbf{F}' = 20\mathbf{i} + 15\mathbf{j} - 5\mathbf{k} \ (\text{kN})$, $\mathbf{M}' = -90\mathbf{i} + 90\mathbf{j} + 90\mathbf{k} \ (\text{kN-m})$.

Example 4.13 | **Representing a System by a Simpler Equivalent System** (▶ *Related Problem 4.137*)

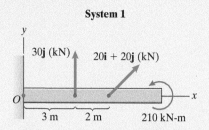

System 1

System 1 consists of two forces and a couple acting on a pipe. Represent system 1 by (a) a single force acting at the origin O of the coordinate system and a single couple and (b) a single force.

Strategy

(a) We can represent system 1 by a force $\mathbf{F}$ acting at the origin and a couple M (system 2 in Fig. a) and use the conditions for equivalence to determine $\mathbf{F}$ and $\mathbf{M}$.
(b) Suppose that we place the force $\mathbf{F}$ with its point of application a distance D along the x axis (system 3 in Fig. b). The sums of the forces in systems 2 and 3 are equal. If we can choose the distance D so that the moment about O in system 3 equals $\mathbf{M}$, system 3 will be equivalent to system 2 and therefore equivalent to system 1.

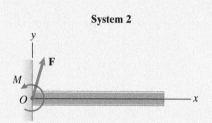

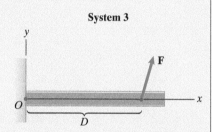

(a) A force $\mathbf{F}$ acting at O and a couple M. **(b)** A system consisting of the force $\mathbf{F}$ acting at a point on the x axis.

Solution

(a) The conditions for equivalence are

$$(\Sigma\mathbf{F})_2 = (\Sigma\mathbf{F})_1:$$

$$\mathbf{F} = 30\mathbf{j} + (20\mathbf{i} + 20\mathbf{j})\ (\text{kN}) = 20\mathbf{i} + 50\mathbf{j}\ (\text{kN}),$$

and

$$(\Sigma M_O)_2 = (\Sigma M_O)_1:$$

$$M = (30\ \text{kN})(3\ \text{m}) + (20\ \text{kN})(5\ \text{m}) + 210\ \text{kN-m}$$

$$= 400\ \text{kN-m}.$$

(b) The sums of the forces in systems 2 and 3 are equal. Equating the sums of the moments about O yields

$$(\Sigma M_O)_3 = (\Sigma M_O)_2:$$

$$(50\ \text{kN})D = 400\ \text{kN-m},$$

and we find that system 3 is equivalent to system 2 if $D = 8$ m.

Critical Thinking

In part (b), why did we assume that the point of application of the force is on the x axis? In order to represent the system in Fig. a by a single force, we needed to place the line of action of the force so that the force would exert a 400 kN-m counterclockwise moment about O. Placing the point of application of the force a distance D along the x axis was simply a convenient way to accomplish that.

| Example 4.14 | **Representing Parallel Forces by a Single Force** (▶ *Related Problem 4.154*) |

System 1 consists of parallel forces. Suppose you want to represent it by a force
F (system 2). What is **F**, and where does its line of action intersect the *x*–*z* plane?

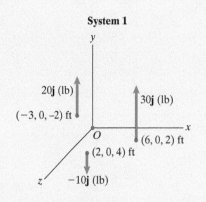

System 1

Strategy
We can determine **F** from the condition that the sums of the forces in the two systems must be equal. For the two systems to be equivalent, we must choose the
point of application P so that the sums of the moments about a point are equal.
This condition will tell us where the line of action intersects the *x*–*z* plane.

Solution
The sums of the forces must be equal.

$$(\Sigma\mathbf{F})_2 = (\Sigma\mathbf{F})_1:$$
$$\mathbf{F} = 30\mathbf{j} + 20\mathbf{j} - 10\mathbf{j} \text{ (lb)} = 40\mathbf{j} \text{ (lb)}.$$

The sums of the moments about an arbitrary point must be equal: Let the coordinates of point P be (x, y, z). The sums of the moments about the origin O
must be equal.

$$(\Sigma\mathbf{M}_O)_2 = (\Sigma\mathbf{M}_O)_1:$$

$$\begin{vmatrix} \mathbf{i} & \mathbf{j} & \mathbf{k} \\ x & y & z \\ 0 & 40 & 0 \end{vmatrix} = \begin{vmatrix} \mathbf{i} & \mathbf{j} & \mathbf{k} \\ 6 & 0 & 2 \\ 0 & 30 & 0 \end{vmatrix} + \begin{vmatrix} \mathbf{i} & \mathbf{j} & \mathbf{k} \\ 2 & 0 & 4 \\ 0 & -10 & 0 \end{vmatrix} + \begin{vmatrix} \mathbf{i} & \mathbf{j} & \mathbf{k} \\ -3 & 0 & -2 \\ 0 & 20 & 0 \end{vmatrix}$$

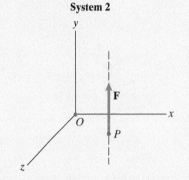

System 2

Expanding the determinants, we obtain

$$[20 \text{ ft-lb} + (40 \text{ lb})z]\mathbf{i} + [100 \text{ ft-lb} - (40 \text{ lb})x]\mathbf{k} = \mathbf{0}.$$

The sums of the moments about the origin are equal if

$$x = 2.5 \text{ ft},$$
$$z = -0.5 \text{ ft}.$$

The systems are equivalent if $\mathbf{F} = 40\mathbf{j}$ (lb) and its line of action intersects
the *x*–*z* plane at $x = 2.5$ ft and $z = -0.5$ ft. Notice that we did not obtain an
equation for the *y* coordinate of P. The systems are equivalent if **F** is applied at
any point along the line of action.

Critical Thinking
In this example we could have determined the *x* and *z* coordinates of point P
in a simpler way. Since the sums of the moments about any point must be
equal for the systems to be equivalent, the sums of the moments about any *line*
must also be equal. Equating the sums of the moments about the *x* axis yields

$$(\Sigma M_{x\text{ axis}})_2 = (\Sigma M_{x\text{ axis}})_1:$$
$$-(40 \text{ lb})z = -(30 \text{ lb})(2 \text{ ft}) + (10 \text{ lb})(4 \text{ ft}) + (20 \text{ lb})(2 \text{ ft}),$$

and we obtain $z = -0.5$ ft. Also, equating the sums of the moments about the
z axis gives

$$(\Sigma M_{z\text{ axis}})_2 = (\Sigma M_{z\text{ axis}})_1:$$
$$(40 \text{ lb})x = (30 \text{ lb})(6 \text{ ft}) - (10 \text{ lb})(2 \text{ ft}) - (20 \text{ lb})(3 \text{ ft}),$$

and we obtain $x = 2.5$ ft.

| **Example 4.15** | **Representing a Force and Couple by a Wrench** (▶ *Related Problems 4.170, 4.171*) |

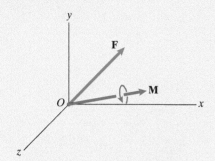

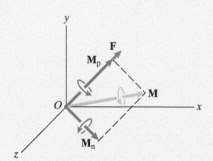

(a) Resolving **M** into components parallel and normal to **F**.

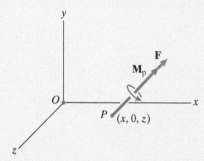

(b) The wrench acting at a point in the x–z plane.

The system consists of the force and couple

$$\mathbf{F} = 3\mathbf{i} + 6\mathbf{j} + 2\mathbf{k} \ (\text{N}),$$

$$\mathbf{M} = 12\mathbf{i} + 4\mathbf{j} + 6\mathbf{k} \ (\text{N-m}).$$

Represent it by a wrench, and determine where the line of action of the wrench's force intersects the x–z plane.

Strategy

The wrench is the force **F** and the component of **M** parallel to **F** (Figs. a, b). We must choose the point of application P so that the moment of **F** about O equals the normal component $\mathbf{M_n}$. By letting P be an arbitrary point of the x–z plane, we can determine where the line of action of **F** intersects that plane.

Solution

Dividing **F** by its magnitude, we obtain a unit vector **e** with the same direction as **F**:

$$\mathbf{e} = \frac{\mathbf{F}}{|\mathbf{F}|} = \frac{3\mathbf{i} + 6\mathbf{j} + 2\mathbf{k} \ (\text{N})}{\sqrt{(3\,\text{N})^2 + (6\,\text{N})^2 + (2\,\text{N})^2}} = 0.429\mathbf{i} + 0.857\mathbf{j} + 0.286\mathbf{k}.$$

We can use **e** to calculate the component of **M** parallel to **F**:

$$\mathbf{M_p} = (\mathbf{e} \cdot \mathbf{M})\mathbf{e} = [(0.429)(12\,\text{N-m}) + (0.857)(4\,\text{N-m}) + (0.286)(6\,\text{N-m})]\mathbf{e}$$

$$= 4.408\mathbf{i} + 8.816\mathbf{j} + 2.939\mathbf{k} \ (\text{N-m}).$$

The component of **M** normal to **F** is

$$\mathbf{M_n} = \mathbf{M} - \mathbf{M_p} = 7.592\mathbf{i} - 4.816\mathbf{j} + 3.061\mathbf{k} \ (\text{N-m}).$$

The wrench is shown in Fig. b. Let the coordinates of P be $(x, 0, z)$. The moment of **F** about O is

$$\mathbf{r}_{OP} \times \mathbf{F} = \begin{vmatrix} \mathbf{i} & \mathbf{j} & \mathbf{k} \\ x & 0 & z \\ 3 & 6 & 2 \end{vmatrix} = -6z\mathbf{i} - (2x - 3z)\mathbf{j} + 6x\mathbf{k} \ (\text{N-m}).$$

By equating this moment to $\mathbf{M_n}$, or

$$-6z\mathbf{i} - (2x - 3z)\mathbf{j} + 6x\mathbf{k} \ (\text{N-m}) = 7.592\mathbf{i} - 4.816\mathbf{j} + 3.061\mathbf{k} \ (\text{N-m}),$$

we obtain the equations

$$-6z = 7.592,$$

$$-2x + 3z = -4.816,$$

$$6x = 3.061.$$

Solving these equations, we find the coordinates of point P are $x = 0.510$ m, $z = -1.265$ m.

Critical Thinking

Why did we place point P at an arbitrary point $(x, 0, z)$ in the x–z plane? Our objective was to place the line of action of the force **F** of the wrench so as to satisfy the condition that the moment of **F** about O would equal $\mathbf{M_n}$. Placing the point of application of **F** at a point $(x, 0, z)$ and then using this condition to determine x and z was a convenient way to determine the necessary location of the line of action. The point $(x, 0, z) = (0.510, 0, -1.265)$ m is the intersection of the line of action with the x–z plane.

Problems

4.128 Two systems of forces act on the beam. Are they equivalent?

 Strategy: Check the two conditions for equivalence. The sums of the forces must be equal, and the sums of the moments about an arbitrary point must be equal.

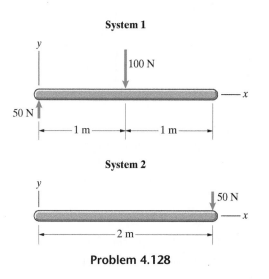

Problem 4.128

4.129 Two systems of forces and moments act on the beam. Are they equivalent?

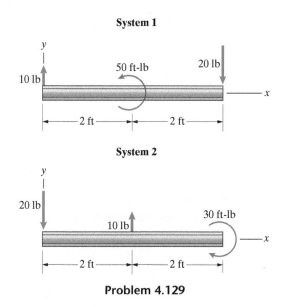

Problem 4.129

4.130 Four systems of forces and moments act on an 8-m beam. Which systems are equivalent?

4.131 The four systems can be made equivalent by adding a couple to one of the systems. Which system is it, and what couple must be added?

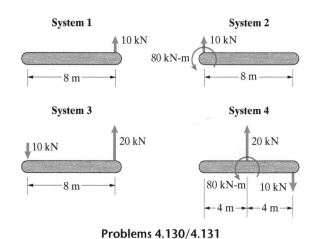

Problems 4.130/4.131

4.132 System 1 is a force **F** acting at a point O. System 2 is the force **F** acting at a different point O' along the same line of action. Explain why these systems are equivalent. (This simple result is called the *principle of transmissibility*.)

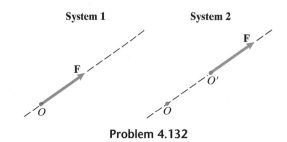

Problem 4.132

4.133 The vector sum of the forces exerted on the log by the cables is the same in the two cases. Show that the systems of forces exerted on the log are equivalent.

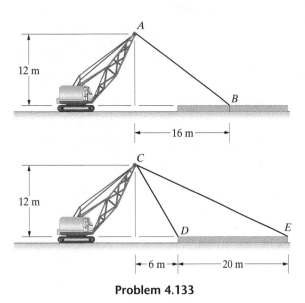

Problem 4.133

4.134 Systems 1 and 2 each consist of a couple. If they are equivalent, what is F?

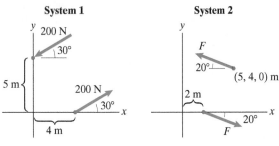

Problem 4.134

4.135 Two equivalent systems of forces and moments act on the L-shaped bar. Determine the forces F_A and F_B and the couple M.

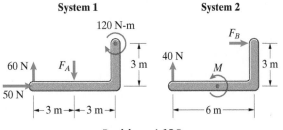

Problem 4.135

4.136 Two equivalent systems of forces and moments act on the plate. Determine the force F and the couple M.

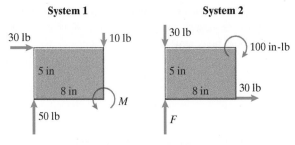

Problem 4.136

▶ **4.137** In Example 4.13, suppose that the 30-kN vertical force in system 1 is replaced by a 230-kN vertical force. Draw a sketch of the new system 1. If you represent system 1 by a single force **F** as in system 3, at what position D on the x axis must the force be placed?

4.138 Three forces and a couple are applied to a beam (system 1).

(a) If you represent system 1 by a force applied at A and a couple (system 2), what are **F** and M?

(b) If you represent system 1 by the force **F** (system 3), what is the distance D?

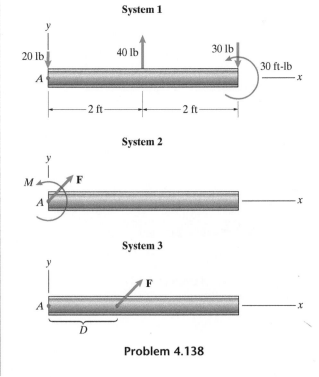

Problem 4.138

4.139 Represent the two forces and couple acting on the beam by a force **F**. Determine **F** and determine where its line of action intersects the x axis.

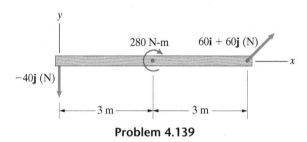

Problem 4.139

4.140 The bracket is subjected to three forces and a couple. If you represent this system by a force **F**, what is **F** and where does its line of action intersect the x axis?

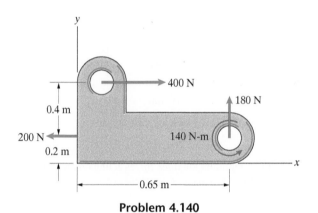

Problem 4.140

4.141 The vector sum of the forces acting on the beam is zero, and the sum of the moments about the left end of the beam is zero.

(a) Determine the forces A_x and A_y, and the couple M_A.

(b) Determine the sum of the moments about the right end of the beam.

(c) If you represent the 600-N force, the 200-N force, and the 30 N-m couple by a force **F** acting at the left end of the beam and a couple M, what are **F** and M?

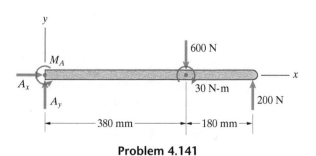

Problem 4.141

4.142 The vector sum of the forces acting on the truss is zero, and the sum of the moments about the origin O is zero.

(a) Determine the forces A_x, A_y, and B.

(b) If you represent the 2-kip, 4-kip, and 6-kip forces by a force **F**, what is **F**, and where does its line of action intersect the y axis?

(c) If you replace the 2-kip, 4-kip, and 6-kip forces by the force you determined in (b), what are the vector sum of the forces acting on the truss and the sum of the moments about O?

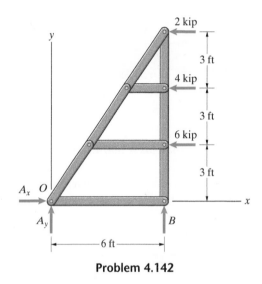

Problem 4.142

4.143 The distributed force exerted on part of a building foundation by the soil is represented by five forces. If you represent them by a force **F**, what is **F**, and where does its line of action intersect the x axis?

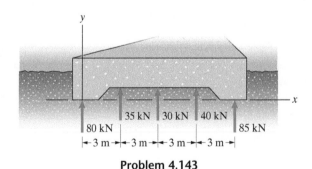

Problem 4.143

4.144 At a particular instant, aerodynamic forces distributed over the airplane's surface exert the 88-kN and 16-kN vertical forces and the 22 kN-m counterclockwise couple shown. If you represent these forces and couple by a system consisting of a force **F** acting at the center of mass G and a couple M, what are **F** and M?

4.145 If you represent the two forces and couple acting on the airplane by a force **F**, what is **F**, and where does its line of action intersect the x axis?

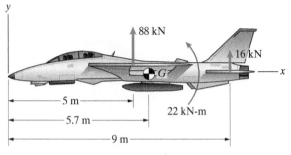

Problems 4.144/4.145

4.146 The system is in equilibrium. If you represent the forces F_{AB} and F_{AC} by a force **F** acting at A and a couple M, what are **F** and M?

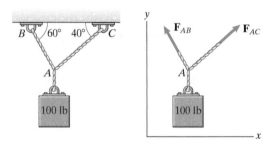

Problem 4.146

4.147 Three forces act on the beam.

(a) Represent the system by a force **F** acting at the origin O and a couple M.

(b) Represent the system by a single force. Where does the line of action of the force intersect the x axis?

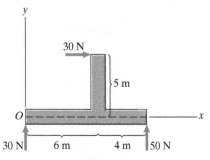

Problem 4.147

4.148 The tension in cable AB is 400 N, and the tension in cable CD is 600 N.

(a) If you represent the forces exerted on the left post by the cables by a force **F** acting at the origin O and a couple M, what are **F** and M?

(b) If you represent the forces exerted on the left post by the cables by the force **F** alone, where does its line of action intersect the y axis?

4.149 The tension in each of the cables AB and CD is 400 N. If you represent the forces exerted on the right post by the cables by a force **F**, what is **F**, and where does its line of action intersect the y axis?

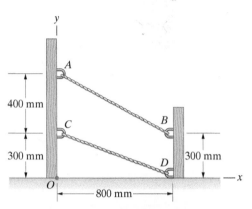

Problems 4.148/4.149

4.150 If you represent the three forces acting on the beam cross section by a force **F**, what is **F**, and where does its line of action intersect the x axis?

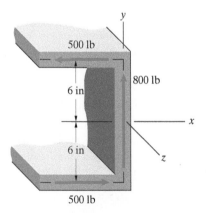

Problem 4.150

▶ **4.151** In Active Example 4.12, suppose that the force F_B is changed to $F_B = 20\mathbf{i} - 15\mathbf{j} + 30\mathbf{k}$ (kN), and you want to represent system 1 by an equivalent system consisting of a force **F** acting at the point P with coordinates $(4, 3, -2)$ m and a couple M (system 2). Determine **F** and M.

4.152 The wall bracket is subjected to the force shown.

(a) Determine the moment exerted by the force about the *z* axis.

(b) Determine the moment exerted by the force about the *y* axis.

(c) If you represent the force by a force **F** acting at *O* and a couple **M**, what are **F** and **M**?

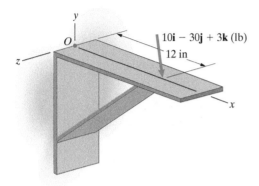

Problem 4.152

4.153 A basketball player executes a "slam dunk" shot, then hangs momentarily on the rim, exerting the two 100-lb forces shown. The dimensions are $h = 14\frac{1}{2}$ in and $r = 9\frac{1}{2}$ in, and the angle $\alpha = 120°$.

(a) If you represent the forces he exerts by a force **F** acting at *O* and a couple **M**, what are **F** and **M**?

(b) The glass backboard will shatter if $|\mathbf{M}| > 4000$ in-lb. Does it break?

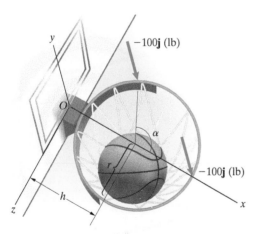

Problem 4.153

▶ **4.154** In Example 4.14, suppose that the 30-lb upward force in system 1 is changed to a 25-lb upward force. If you want to represent system 1 by a single force **F** (system 2), where does the line of action of **F** intersect the *x*–*z* plane?

4.155 The normal forces exerted on the car's tires by the road are

$$\mathbf{N}_A = 5104\mathbf{j} \ (\text{N}),$$
$$\mathbf{N}_B = 5027\mathbf{j} \ (\text{N}),$$
$$\mathbf{N}_C = 3613\mathbf{j} \ (\text{N}),$$
$$\mathbf{N}_D = 3559\mathbf{j} \ (\text{N}).$$

If you represent these forces by a single equivalent force **N**, what is **N** and where does its line of action intersect the *x*–*z* plane?

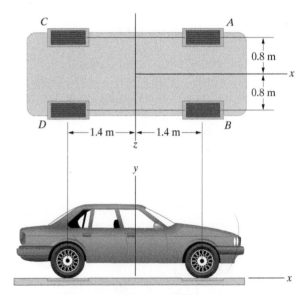

Problem 4.155

4.156 Two forces act on the beam. If you represent them by a force **F** acting at *C* and a couple **M**, what are **F** and **M**?

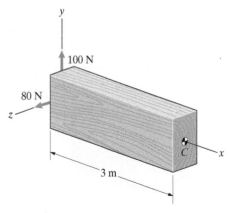

Problem 4.156

4.157 An axial force of magnitude P acts on the beam. If you represent it by a force $\mathbf{F}$ acting at the origin O and a couple $\mathbf{M}$, what are $\mathbf{F}$ and $\mathbf{M}$?

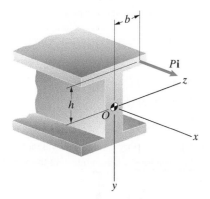

Problem 4.157

4.158 The brace is being used to remove a screw.

(a) If you represent the forces acting on the brace by a force $\mathbf{F}$ acting at the origin O and a couple $\mathbf{M}$, what are $\mathbf{F}$ and $\mathbf{M}$?

(b) If you represent the forces acting on the brace by a force $\mathbf{F}'$ acting at a point P with coordinates (x_P, y_P, z_P) and a couple $\mathbf{M}'$, what are $\mathbf{F}'$ and $\mathbf{M}'$?

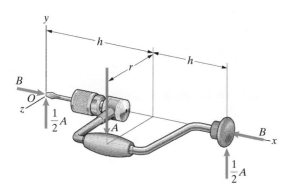

Problem 4.158

4.159 Two forces and a couple act on the cube. If you represent them by a force $\mathbf{F}$ acting at point P and a couple $\mathbf{M}$, what are $\mathbf{F}$ and $\mathbf{M}$?

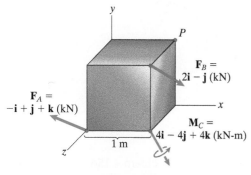

Problem 4.159

4.160 The two shafts are subjected to the torques (couples) shown.

(a) If you represent the two couples by a force $\mathbf{F}$ acting at the origin O and a couple $\mathbf{M}$, what are $\mathbf{F}$ and $\mathbf{M}$?

(b) What is the magnitude of the total moment exerted by the two couples?

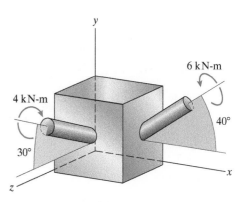

Problem 4.160

4.161 The two systems of forces and moments acting on the bar are equivalent. If

$$\mathbf{F}_A = 30\mathbf{i} + 30\mathbf{j} - 20\mathbf{k} \text{ (kN)},$$
$$\mathbf{F}_B = 40\mathbf{i} - 20\mathbf{j} + 25\mathbf{k} \text{ (kN)},$$
$$\mathbf{M}_B = 10\mathbf{i} + 40\mathbf{j} - 10\mathbf{k} \text{ (kN-m)},$$

what are $\mathbf{F}$ and $\mathbf{M}$?

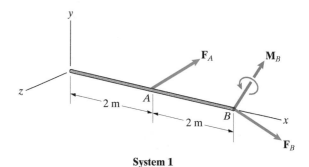

System 1

System 2

Problem 4.161

4.162 Point G is at the center of the block. The forces are

$$\mathbf{F}_A = -20\mathbf{i} + 10\mathbf{j} + 20\mathbf{k} \text{ (lb)},$$

$$\mathbf{F}_B = 10\mathbf{j} - 10\mathbf{k} \text{ (lb)}.$$

If you represent the two forces by a force $\mathbf{F}$ acting at G and a couple $\mathbf{M}$, what are $\mathbf{F}$ and $\mathbf{M}$?

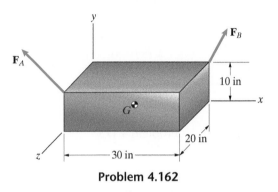

Problem 4.162

4.163 The engine above the airplane's fuselage exerts a thrust $T_0 = 16$ kip, and each of the engines under the wings exerts a thrust $T_U = 12$ kip. The dimensions are $h = 8$ ft, $c = 12$ ft, and $b = 16$ ft. If you represent the three thrust forces by a force $\mathbf{F}$ acting at the origin O and a couple $\mathbf{M}$, what are $\mathbf{F}$ and $\mathbf{M}$?

4.164 Consider the airplane described in Problem 4.163 and suppose that the engine under the wing to the pilot's right loses thrust.

(a) If you represent the two remaining thrust forces by a force $\mathbf{F}$ acting at the origin O and a couple $\mathbf{M}$, what are $\mathbf{F}$ and $\mathbf{M}$?

(b) If you represent the two remaining thrust forces by the force $\mathbf{F}$ alone, where does its line of action intersect the x–y plane?

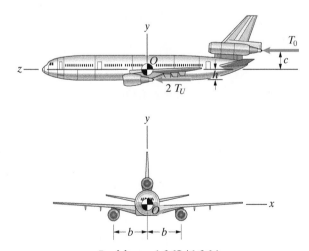

Problems 4.163/4.164

4.165 The tension in cable AB is 100 lb, and the tension in cable CD is 60 lb. Suppose that you want to replace these two cables by a single cable EF so that the force exerted on the wall at E is equivalent to the two forces exerted by cables AB and CD on the walls at A and C. What is the tension in cable EF, and what are the coordinates of points E and F?

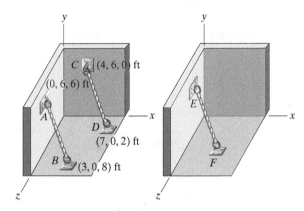

Problem 4.165

4.166 The distance $s = 4$ m. If you represent the force and the 200-N-m couple by a force $\mathbf{F}$ acting at the origin O and a couple $\mathbf{M}$, what are $\mathbf{F}$ and $\mathbf{M}$?

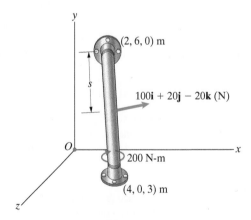

Problem 4.166

4.167 The force **F** and couple **M** in system 1 are

$$\mathbf{F} = 12\mathbf{i} + 4\mathbf{j} - 3\mathbf{k} \text{ (lb)},$$

$$\mathbf{M} = 4\mathbf{i} + 7\mathbf{j} + 4\mathbf{k} \text{ (ft-lb)}.$$

Suppose you want to represent system 1 by a wrench (system 2). Determine the couple $\mathbf{M}_p$ and the coordinates x and z where the line of action of the force intersects the x–z plane.

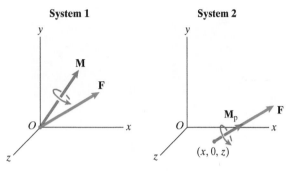

Problem 4.167

4.168 A system consists of a force **F** acting at the origin O and a couple **M**, where

$$\mathbf{F} = 10\mathbf{i} \text{ (lb)}, \qquad \mathbf{M} = 20\mathbf{j} \text{ (ft-lb)}.$$

If you represent the system by a wrench consisting of the force **F** and a parallel couple $\mathbf{M}_p$, what is $\mathbf{M}_p$, and where does the line of action of **F** intersect the y–z plane?

4.169 A system consists of a force **F** acting at the origin O and a couple **M**, where

$$\mathbf{F} = \mathbf{i} + 2\mathbf{j} + 5\mathbf{k} \text{ (N)}, \qquad \mathbf{M} = 10\mathbf{i} + 8\mathbf{j} - 4\mathbf{k} \text{ (N-m)}.$$

If you represent it by a wrench consisting of the force **F** and a parallel couple $\mathbf{M}_p$, (a) determine $\mathbf{M}_p$, and determine where the line of action of **F** intersects (b) the x–z plane, (c) the y–z plane.

▶ **4.170** Consider the force **F** acting at the origin O and the couple **M** given in Example 4.15. If you represent this system by a wrench, where does the line of action of the force intersect the x–y plane?

▶ **4.171** Consider the force **F** acting at the origin O and the couple **M** given in Example 4.15. If you represent this system by a wrench, where does the line of action of the force intersect the plane $y = 3$ m?

4.172 A wrench consists of a force of magnitude 100 N acting at the origin O and a couple of magnitude 60 N-m. The force and couple point in the direction from O to the point $(1, 1, 2)$ m. If you represent the wrench by a force **F** acting at the point $(5, 3, 1)$ m and a couple **M**, what are **F** and **M**?

4.173 System 1 consists of two forces and a couple. Suppose that you want to represent it by a wrench (system 2). Determine the force **F**, the couple $\mathbf{M}_p$, and the coordinates x and z where the line of action of **F** intersects the x–z plane.

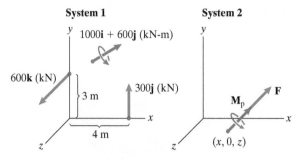

Problem 4.173

4.174 A plumber exerts the two forces shown to loosen a pipe.

(a) What total moment does he exert about the axis of the pipe?

(b) If you represent the two forces by a force **F** acting at O and a couple **M**, what are **F** and **M**?

(c) If you represent the two forces by a wrench consisting of the force **F** and a parallel couple $\mathbf{M}_p$, what is $\mathbf{M}_p$, and where does the line of action of **F** intersect the x–y plane?

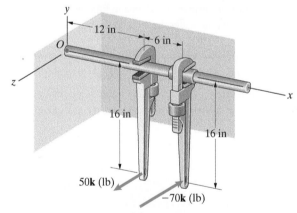

Problem 4.174

Review Problems

4.175 The Leaning Tower of Pisa is approximately 55 m tall and 7 m in diameter. The horizontal displacement of the top of the tower from the vertical is approximately 5 m. Its mass is approximately 3.2×10^6 kg. If you model the tower as a cylinder and assume that its weight acts at the center, what is the magnitude of the moment exerted by the weight about the point at the center of the tower's base?

Problem 4.175

4.176 The cable AB exerts a 300-N force on the support A that points from A toward B. Determine the magnitude of the moment the force exerts about point P.

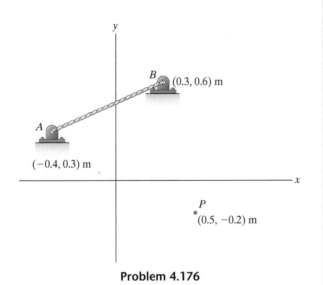

Problem 4.176

4.177 Three forces act on the structure. The sum of the moments due to the forces about A is zero. Determine the magnitude of the force F.

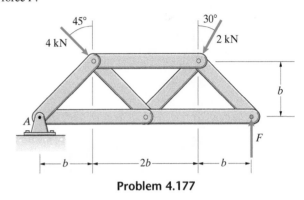

Problem 4.177

4.178 Determine the moment of the 400-N force (a) about A, (b) about B.

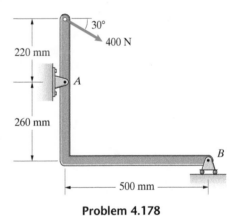

Problem 4.178

4.179 Determine the sum of the moments exerted about A by the three forces and the couple.

4.180 If you represent the three forces and the couple by an equivalent system consisting of a force $\mathbf{F}$ acting at A and a couple $\mathbf{M}$, what are the magnitudes of $\mathbf{F}$ and $\mathbf{M}$?

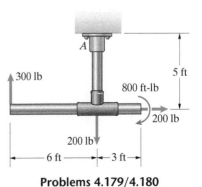

Problems 4.179/4.180

4.181 The vector sum of the forces acting on the beam is zero, and the sum of the moments about A is zero.

(a) What are the forces A_x, A_y, and B?

(b) What is the sum of the moments about B?

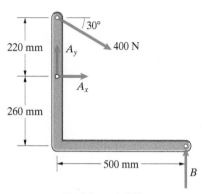

Problem 4.181

4.182 The hydraulic piston BC exerts a 970-lb force on the boom at C in the direction parallel to the piston. The angle $\alpha = 40°$. The sum of the moments about A due to the force exerted on the boom by the piston and the weight of the suspended load is zero. What is the weight of the suspended load?

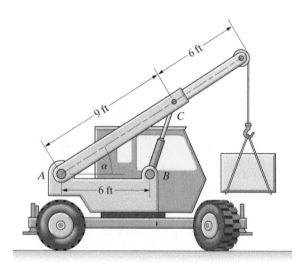

Problem 4.182

4.183 The force $\mathbf{F} = -60\mathbf{i} + 60\mathbf{j}$ (lb).

(a) Determine the moment of **F** about point A.

(b) What is the perpendicular distance from point A to the line of action of **F**?

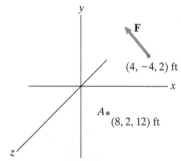

Problem 4.183

4.184 The 20-kg mass is suspended by cables attached to three vertical 2-m posts. Point A is at (0, 1.2, 0) m. Determine the moment about the base E due to the force exerted on the post BE by the cable AB.

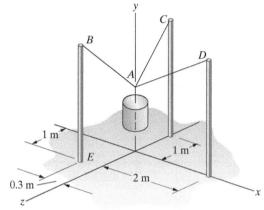

Problem 4.184

4.185 What is the total moment due to the two couples?

(a) Express the answer by giving the magnitude and stating whether the moment is clockwise or counterclockwise.

(b) Express the answer as a vector.

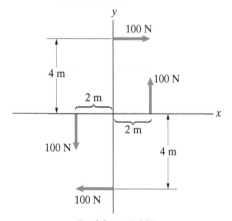

Problem 4.185

4.186 The bar AB supporting the lid of the grand piano exerts a force $\mathbf{F} = -6\mathbf{i} + 35\mathbf{j} - 12\mathbf{k}$ (lb) at B. The coordinates of B are $(3, 4, 3)$ ft. What is the moment of the force about the hinge line of the lid (the x axis)?

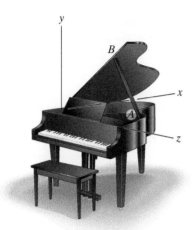

Problem 4.186

4.187 Determine the moment of the vertical 800-lb force about point C.

4.188 Determine the moment of the vertical 800-lb force about the straight line through points C and D.

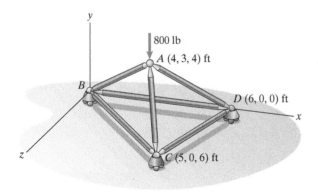

Problems 4.187/4.188

4.189 The system of cables and pulleys supports the 300-lb weight of the work platform. If you represent the upward force exerted at E by cable EF and the upward force exerted at G by cable GH by a single equivalent force $\mathbf{F}$, what is $\mathbf{F}$, and where does its line of action intersect the x axis?

4.190 The system of cables and pulleys supports the 300-lb weight of the work platform.

(a) What are the tensions in cables AB and CD?

(b) If you represent the forces exerted on the work platform by the cables at A and C by a single equivalent force $\mathbf{F}$, what is $\mathbf{F}$ and where does its line of action intersect the x axis?

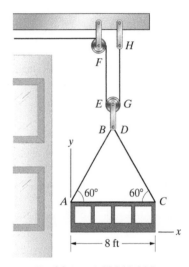

Problems 4.189/4.190

4.191 The two systems are equivalent. Determine the forces A_x and A_y, and the couple M_A.

4.192 If you represent the equivalent systems in Problem 4.191 by a force **F** acting at the origin and a couple M, what are **F** and M?

4.193 If you represent the equivalent systems in Problem 4.191 by a force **F**, what is **F**, and where does its line of action intersect the x axis?

System 1

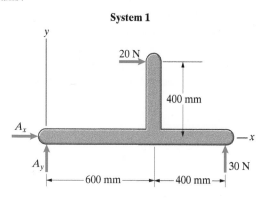

System 2

Problems 4.191–4.193

4.194 The two systems are equivalent. If

$$\mathbf{F} = -100\mathbf{i} + 40\mathbf{j} + 30\mathbf{k} \text{ (lb)},$$
$$\mathbf{M}' = -80\mathbf{i} + 120\mathbf{j} + 40\mathbf{k} \text{ (in-lb)},$$

determine **F**′ and **M**.

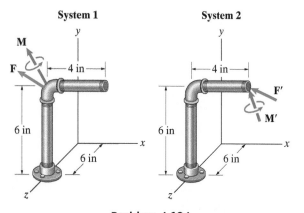

Problem 4.194

4.195 The tugboats A and B exert forces $F_A = 1$ kN and $F_B = 1.2$ kN on the ship. The angle $\theta = 30°$. If you represent the two forces by a force **F** acting at the origin O and a couple M, what are **F** and M?

4.196 The tugboats A and B exert forces $F_A = 600$ N and $F_B = 800$ N on the ship. The angle $\theta = 45°$. If you represent the two forces by a force **F**, what is **F**, and where does its line of action intersect the y axis?

4.197 The tugboats A and B want to exert two forces on the ship that are equivalent to a force **F** acting at the origin O of 2-kN magnitude. If $F_A = 800$ N, determine the necessary values of F_B and θ.

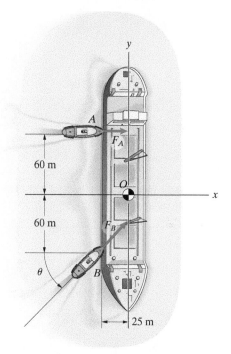

Problems 4.195–4.197

4.198 If you represent the forces exerted by the floor on the table legs by a force **F** acting at the origin O and a couple **M**, what are **F** and **M**?

4.199 If you represent the forces exerted by the floor on the table legs by a force **F**, what is **F**, and where does its line of action intersect the x–z plane?

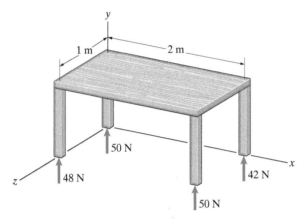

Problems 4.198/4.199

4.200 Two forces are exerted on the crankshaft by the connecting rods. The direction cosines of $\mathbf{F}_A$ are $\cos\theta_x = -0.182$, $\cos\theta_y = 0.818$, and $\cos\theta_z = 0.545$, and its magnitude is 4 kN. The direction cosines of $\mathbf{F}_B$ are $\cos\theta_x = 0.182$, $\cos\theta_y = 0.818$, and $\cos\theta_z = -0.545$, and its magnitude is 2 kN. If you represent the two forces by a force **F** acting at the origin O and a couple **M**, what are **F** and **M**?

4.201 If you represent the two forces exerted on the crankshaft in Problem 4.200 by a wrench consisting of a force **F** and a parallel couple $\mathbf{M_p}$, what are **F** and $\mathbf{M_p}$, and where does the line of action of **F** intersect the x–z plane?

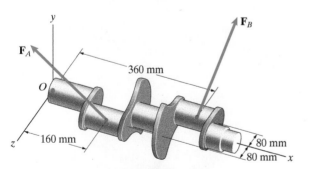

Problems 4.200/4.201

Design Project   A relatively primitive device for exercising the biceps muscle is shown. Suggest an improved configuration for the device. You can use elastic cords (which behave like linear springs), weights, and pulleys. Seek a design such that the variation of the moment about the elbow joint as the device is used is small in comparison to the design shown. Give consideration to the safety of your device, its reliability, and the requirement to accommodate users having a range of dimensions and strengths. Choosing specific dimensions, determine the range of the magnitude of the moment exerted about the elbow joint as your device is used.

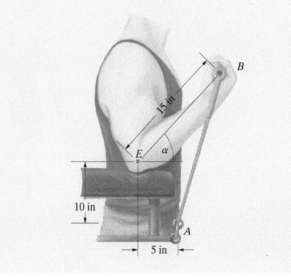

CHAPTER

5

Objects in Equilibrium

Building on concepts developed in Chapters 3 and 4, we first state the general equilibrium equations. We describe various ways that structural members can be supported, or held in place. Using free-body diagrams and equilibrium equations, we then show how to determine unknown forces and couples exerted on structural members by their supports. The principal motivation for this procedure is that it is the initial step in answering an essential question in structural analysis: How do engineers design structural elements so that they will support the loads to which they are subjected?

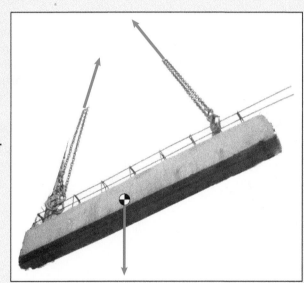

◀ The beam is in equilibrium under the actions of its weight and the forces exerted by the chains. In this chapter we apply the equilibrium equations to determine unknown forces and couples acting on objects.

5.1 Two-Dimensional Applications

When an object acted upon by a system of forces and moments is in equilibrium, the following conditions are satisfied:

1. The sum of the forces is zero:

$$\Sigma \mathbf{F} = \mathbf{0}. \tag{5.1}$$

2. The sum of the moments about any point is zero:

$$\Sigma \mathbf{M}_{\text{any point}} = \mathbf{0}. \tag{5.2}$$

From our discussion of equivalent systems of forces and moments in Chapter 4, Eqs. (5.1) and (5.2) imply that the system of forces and moments acting on an object in equilibrium is equivalent to a system consisting of no forces and no couples. This provides insight into the nature of equilibrium. From the standpoint of the total force and total moment exerted on an object in equilibrium, the effects are the same as if no forces or couples acted on the object. This observation also makes it clear that if the sum of the forces on an object is zero and the sum of the moments about one point is zero, then the sum of the moments about every point is zero.

The Scalar Equilibrium Equations

When the loads and reactions on an object in equilibrium form a two-dimensional system of forces and moments, they are related by three scalar equilibrium equations:

$$\Sigma F_x = 0, \tag{5.3}$$

$$\Sigma F_y = 0, \tag{5.4}$$

$$\Sigma M_{\text{any point}} = 0. \tag{5.5}$$

A natural question is whether more than one equation can be obtained from Eq. (5.5) by evaluating the sum of the moments about more than one point. The answer is yes, and in some cases it is convenient to do so. But there is a catch—the additional equations will not be independent of Eqs. (5.3)–(5.5). In other words, *more than three independent equilibrium equations cannot be obtained from a two-dimensional free-body diagram, which means we can solve for at most three unknown forces or couples*. We discuss this point further in Section 5.2.

Supports

When you are standing, the floor supports you. When you sit in a chair with your feet on the floor, the chair and floor support you. In this section we are concerned with the ways objects can be supported, or held in place. Forces and couples exerted on an object by its supports are called *reactions,* expressing the fact that the supports "react" to the other forces and couples, or *loads,* acting on the object. For example, a bridge is held up by the reactions exerted by its supports, and the loads are the forces exerted by the weight of the bridge itself, the traffic crossing it, and the wind.

Some very common kinds of supports are represented by stylized models called *support conventions*. Actual supports often closely resemble the support

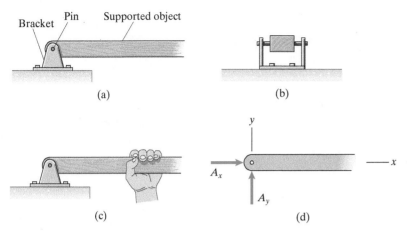

Figure 5.1
(a) A pin support.
(b) Side view showing the pin passing through the beam.
(c) Holding a supported bar.
(d) The pin support is capable of exerting two components of force.

conventions, but even when they don't, we represent them by these conventions if the actual supports exert the same (or approximately the same) reactions as the models.

The Pin Support   Figure 5.1a shows a *pin support*. The diagram represents a bracket to which an object (such as a beam) is attached by a smooth pin that passes through the bracket and the object. The side view is shown in Fig. 5.1b.

To understand the reactions that a pin support can exert, it's helpful to imagine holding a bar attached to a pin support (Fig. 5.1c). If you try to move the bar without rotating it (that is, translate the bar), the support exerts a reactive force that prevents this movement. However, you can rotate the bar about the axis of the pin. The support cannot exert a couple about the pin axis to prevent rotation. Thus a pin support can't exert a couple about the pin axis, but it can exert a force on an object in any direction, which is usually expressed by representing the force in terms of components (Fig. 5.1d). The arrows indicate the directions of the reactions if A_x and A_y are positive. If you determine A_x or A_y to be negative, the reaction is in the direction opposite to that of the arrow.

The pin support is used to represent any real support capable of exerting a force in any direction but not exerting a couple. Pin supports are used in many common devices, particularly those designed to allow connected parts to rotate relative to each other (Fig. 5.2).

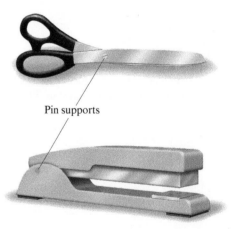

Pin supports

Figure 5.2
Pin supports in a pair of scissors and a stapler.

The Roller Support   The convention called a *roller support* (Fig. 5.3a) represents a pin support mounted on wheels. Like the pin support, it cannot exert a couple about the axis of the pin. Since it can move freely in the direction parallel to the surface on which it rolls, it can't exert a force parallel to the surface but can only exert a force normal (perpendicular) to this surface (Fig. 5.3b). Figures 5.3c–e are other commonly used conventions equivalent to the roller support. The wheels of vehicles and wheels supporting parts of machines are roller supports if the friction forces exerted on them are negligible in comparison to the normal forces. A plane smooth surface can also be modeled by a roller

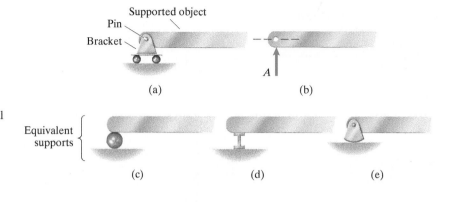

Figure 5.3
(a) A roller support.
(b) The reaction consists of a force normal to the surface.
(c)–(e) Supports equivalent to the roller support.

Figure 5.4
Supporting an object with a plane smooth surface.

support (Fig. 5.4). Beams and bridges are sometimes supported in this way so that they will be free to undergo thermal expansion and contraction.

The supports shown in Fig. 5.5 are similar to the roller support in that they cannot exert a couple and can only exert a force normal to a particular direction. (Friction is neglected.) In these supports, the supported object is attached to a pin or slider that can move freely in one direction but is constrained in the perpendicular direction. Unlike the roller support, these supports can exert a normal force in either direction.

The Fixed Support   The *fixed support* shows the supported object literally built into a wall (Fig. 5.6a). This convention is also called a *built-in* support. To understand the reactions, imagine holding a bar attached to a fixed support (Fig. 5.6b). If you try to translate the bar, the support exerts a reactive force that

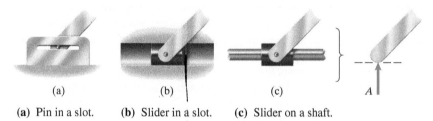

Figure 5.5
Supports similar to the roller support except that the normal force can be exerted in either direction.

(a) Pin in a slot.   **(b)** Slider in a slot.   **(c)** Slider on a shaft.

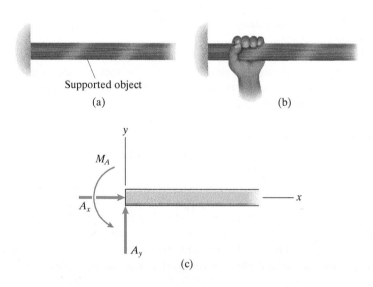

Figure 5.6
(a) Fixed support.
(b) Holding a supported bar.
(c) The reactions a fixed support is capable of exerting.

prevents translation, and if you try to rotate the bar, the support exerts a reactive couple that prevents rotation. A fixed support can exert two components of force and a couple (Fig. 5.6c). The term M_A is the couple exerted by the support, and the curved arrow indicates its direction. Fence posts and lampposts have fixed supports. The attachments of parts connected so that they cannot move or rotate relative to each other, such as the head of a hammer and its handle, can be modeled as fixed supports.

Table 5.1 summarizes the support conventions commonly used in two-dimensional applications, including those we discussed in Chapter 3. Although

Table 5.1 Supports used in two-dimensional applications.

Supports	Reactions
Rope or Cable Spring	A Collinear Force
Contact with a Smooth Surface	A Force Normal to the Supporting Surface
Contact with a Rough Surface	Two Force Components
Pin Support	Two Force Components
Roller Support — Equivalents	A Force Normal to the Supporting Surface
Constrained Pin or Slider	A Normal Force
Fixed (Built-in) Support	Two Force Components and a Couple

the number of conventions may appear daunting, the examples and problems will help you become familiar with them. You should also observe how various objects you see in your everyday experience are supported and think about whether each support could be represented by one of the conventions.

Free-Body Diagrams

We introduced free-body diagrams in Chapter 3 and used them to determine forces acting on simple objects in equilibrium. By using the support conventions, we can model more elaborate objects and construct their free-body diagrams in a systematic way.

For example, the beam in Fig. 5.7a has a pin support at the left end and a roller support at the right end and is loaded by a force F. The roller support rests on a surface inclined at $30°$ to the horizontal. To obtain the free-body diagram of the beam, we first isolate it from its supports (Fig. 5.7b), since the free-body diagram must contain no object other than the beam. We complete the free-body diagram by showing the reactions that may be exerted on the beam by the supports (Fig. 5.7c). Notice that the reaction B exerted by the roller support is normal to the surface on which the support rests.

The object in Fig. 5.8a has a fixed support at the left end. A cable passing over a pulley is attached to the object at two points. We isolate it from its supports (Fig. 5.8b) and complete the free-body diagram by showing the reactions at the fixed support and the forces exerted by the cable (Fig. 5.8c). *Don't forget the couple at a fixed support.* Since we assume the tension in the cable is the same on both sides of the pulley, the two forces exerted by the cable have the same magnitude T.

Once you have obtained the free-body diagram of an object in equilibrium to identify the loads and reactions acting on it, you can apply the equilibrium equations.

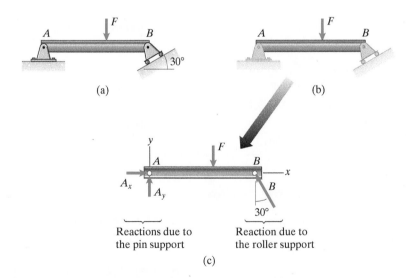

Figure 5.7
(a) A beam with pin and roller supports.
(b) Isolating the beam from its supports.
(c) The completed free-body diagram.

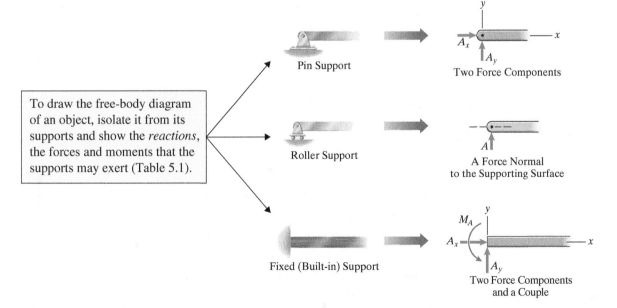

(a)   (b)   (c)

Figure 5.8
(a) An object with a fixed support.
(b) Isolating the object.
(c) The completed free-body diagram.

RESULTS

Equilibrium Equations

When an object is in equilibrium, the system of forces and moments acting on it satisfies two conditions.

> The sum of the forces is zero:
> $$\Sigma\mathbf{F} = \mathbf{0}. \qquad (5.1)$$

> The sum of the moments about any point is zero:
> $$\Sigma\mathbf{M}_{\text{any point}} = \mathbf{0}. \qquad (5.2)$$

When the system of forces and moments acting on an object in equilibrium is two dimensional, it satisfies three scalar equilibrium equations.

> $$\Sigma F_x = 0, \qquad (5.3)$$
> $$\Sigma F_y = 0, \qquad (5.4)$$
> $$\Sigma M_{\text{any point}} = 0. \qquad (5.5)$$

Supports

To draw the free-body diagram of an object, isolate it from its supports and show the *reactions*, the forces and moments that the supports may exert (Table 5.1).

Pin Support

Two Force Components

Roller Support

A Force Normal
to the Supporting Surface

Fixed (Built-in) Support

Two Force Components
and a Couple

Active Example 5.1 **Reactions at a Fixed Support** (▶ *Related Problem 5.1*)

The beam has a fixed support at *A* and is subjected to a 4-kN force. (a) Draw the free-body diagram of the beam. (b) Determine the reactions at the fixed support.

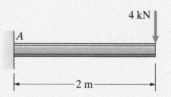

Strategy

To draw the free-body diagram of the beam we must isolate it from the built-in support and show the reactions that the support may exert. Then we can apply the equilibrium equations to determine the unknown reactions.

Solution

(a) Draw a diagram of the beam isolated from its fixed support and show the reactions due to the support.

(b) Write the equilibrium equations,

$$\Sigma F_x = A_x = 0,$$
$$\Sigma F_y = A_y - 4 \text{ kN} = 0,$$
$$\Sigma M_{\text{left end}} = M_A - (2 \text{ m}) (4 \text{ kN}) = 0,$$

and solve them, obtaining

$$A_x = 0, \ A_y = 4 \text{ kN}, \ M_A = 8 \text{ kN-m}.$$

Practice Problem The beam has pin and roller supports and is subjected to a 4-kN force. (a) Draw the free-body diagram of the beam. (b) Determine the reactions at the supports.

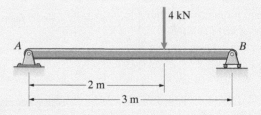

Answer: $A_x = 0, A_y = 1.33 \text{ kN}, B = 2.67 \text{ kN}.$

| Example 5.2 | **Reactions at a Fixed Support** (▶ *Related Problem 5.9*) |

The object has a fixed support at A and is subjected to two forces and a couple. What are the reactions at the support?

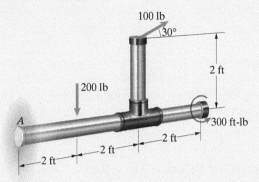

Strategy
We will obtain a free-body diagram by isolating the object from the fixed support at A and showing the reactions exerted at A, *including the couple that may be exerted by a fixed support*. Then we can determine the unknown reactions by applying the equilibrium equations.

Solution

Draw the Free-Body Diagram   We isolate the object from its support and show the reactions at the fixed support (Fig. a). There are three unknown reactions: two force components A_x and A_y and a couple M_A. (Remember that we can choose the directions of these arrows arbitrarily.) We also resolve the 100-lb force into its components.

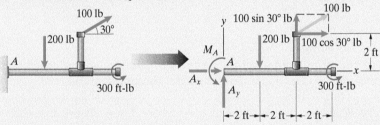

(a) Drawing the free-body diagram.

Apply the Equilibrium Equations   Summing the moments about point A, the equilibrium equations are

$$\Sigma F_x = A_x + 100 \cos 30° \text{ lb} = 0,$$
$$\Sigma F_y = A_y - 200 \text{ lb} + 100 \sin 30° \text{ lb} = 0,$$
$$\Sigma M_{\text{point }A} = M_A + 300 \text{ ft-lb} - (2\text{ft})(200 \text{ lb}) - (2 \text{ ft})(100 \cos 30° \text{ lb})$$
$$+ (4 \text{ ft})(100 \sin 30° \text{ lb}) = 0.$$

Solving these equations, we obtain the reactions $A_x = -86.6$ lb, $A_y = 150$ lb, and $M_A = 73.2$ ft-lb.

Critical Thinking
Why don't the 300 ft-lb couple and the couple M_A exerted by the fixed support appear in the first two equilibrium equations? Remember that a couple exerts no net force. Also, because the moment due to a couple is the same about any point, the moment about A due to the 300 ft-lb counterclockwise couple is 300 ft-lb counterclockwise.

| Example 5.3 | Choosing the Point About Which to Evaluate Moments (▶ *Related Problem 5.15*) |

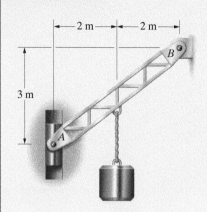

The structure AB supports a suspended 2-Mg (megagram) mass. The structure is attached to a slider in a vertical slot at A and has a pin support at B. What are the reactions at A and B?

Strategy

We will draw the free-body diagram of the structure and the suspended mass by removing the supports at A and B. Notice that the support at A can exert only a horizontal reaction. Then we can use the equilibrium equations to determine the reactions at A and B.

Solution

Draw the Free-Body Diagram   We isolate the structure and mass from the supports and show the reactions at the supports and the force exerted by the weight of the 2000-kg mass (Fig. a). The slot at A can exert only a horizontal force on the slider.

Apply the Equilibrium Equations   Summing moments about point B, we find that the equilibrium equations are

$$\Sigma F_x = A + B_x = 0,$$
$$\Sigma F_y = B_y - (2000)(9.81) \text{ N} = 0,$$
$$\Sigma M_{\text{point } B} = (3 \text{ m})A + (2 \text{ m})[(2000)(9.81) \text{ N}] = 0.$$

The reactions are $A = -13.1$ kN, $B_x = 13.1$ kN, and $B_y = 19.6$ kN.

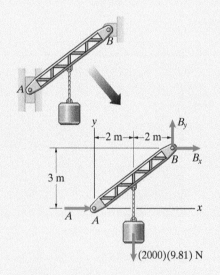

(a) Drawing the free-body diagram.

Critical Thinking

Although the point about which moments are evaluated in writing equilibrium equations can be chosen arbitrarily, a careful choice can often simplify your solution. In this example, point B lies on the lines of action of the two unknown reactions B_x and B_y. By evaluating moments about B, we obtained an equation containing only one unknown, the reaction at A.

| Example 5.4 | Analysis of a Luggage Carrier (▶ *Related Problems 5.65–5.68*) |

The figure shows an airport luggage carrier and its free-body diagram when it is held in equilibrium in the tilted position. If the luggage carrier supports a weight $W = 50$ lb, the angle $\alpha = 30°$, $a = 8$ in, $b = 16$ in, and $d = 48$ in, what force F must the user exert?

Strategy

The unknown reactions on the free-body diagram are the force F and the normal force N exerted by the floor. If we sum moments about the center of the wheel C, we obtain an equation in which F is the only unknown reaction.

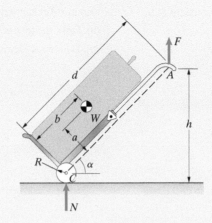

Solution
Summing moments about C,

$$\Sigma M_{(\text{point } C)} = d(F \cos \alpha) + a(W \sin \alpha) - b(W \cos \alpha) = 0,$$

and solving for F, we obtain

$$F = \frac{(b - a \tan \alpha)W}{d}.$$

Substituting the values of W, α, a, b, and d yields the solution $F = 11.9$ lb.

Problems

Assume that objects are in equilibrium. In the statements of the answers, x components are positive to the right and y components are positive upward.

▶ **5.1** In Active Example 5.1, suppose that the beam is subjected to a 6 kN-m counterclockwise couple at the right end in addition to the 4-kN downward force. Draw a sketch of the beam showing its new loading. Draw the free-body diagram of the beam and apply the equilibrium equations to determine the reactions at A.

5.2 The beam has a fixed support at A and is loaded by two forces and a couple. Draw the free-body diagram of the beam and apply equilibrium to determine the reactions at A.

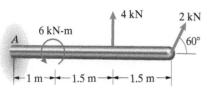

Problem 5.2

5.3 The beam is subjected to a load $F = 400$ N and is supported by the rope and the smooth surfaces at A and B.

(a) Draw the free-body diagram of the beam.

(b) What are the magnitudes of the reactions at A and B?

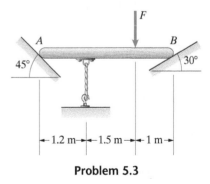

Problem 5.3

5.4 (a) Draw the free-body diagram of the beam.
(b) Determine the tension in the rope and the reactions at *B*.

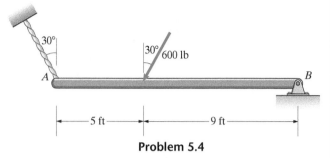

Problem 5.4

5.5 (a) Draw the free-body diagram of the 60-lb drill press, assuming that the surfaces at *A* and *B* are smooth.
(b) Determine the reactions at *A* and *B*.

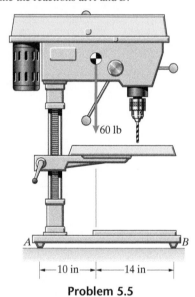

Problem 5.5

5.6 The masses of the person and the diving board are 54 kg and 36 kg, respectively. Assume that they are in equilibrium.
(a) Draw the free-body diagram of the diving board.
(b) Determine the reactions at the supports *A* and *B*.

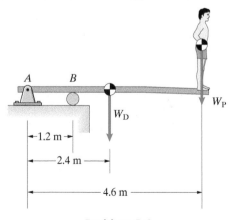

Problem 5.6

5.7 The ironing board has supports at *A* and *B* that can be modeled as roller supports.
(a) Draw the free-body diagram of the ironing board.
(b) Determine the reactions at *A* and *B*.

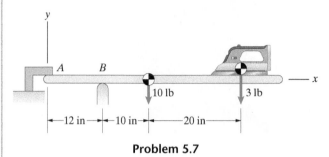

Problem 5.7

5.8 The distance $x = 9$ m.
(a) Draw the free-body diagram of the beam.
(b) Determine the reactions at the supports.

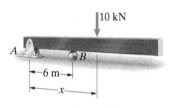

Problem 5.8

▶ **5.9** In Example 5.2, suppose that the 200-lb downward force and the 300 ft-lb counterclockwise couple change places; the 200-lb downward force acts at the right end of the horizontal bar, and the 300 ft-lb counterclockwise couple acts on the horizontal bar 2 ft to the right of the support *A*. Draw a sketch of the object showing the new loading. Draw the free-body diagram of the object and apply the equilibrium equations to determine the reactions at *A*.

5.10 (a) Draw the free-body diagram of the beam.
(b) Determine the reactions at the supports.

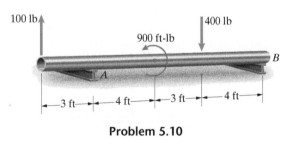

Problem 5.10

5.11 The person exerts 20-N forces on the pliers. The free-body diagram of one part of the pliers is shown. Notice that the pin at *C* connecting the two parts of the pliers behaves like a pin support. Determine the reactions at *C* and the force *B* exerted on the pliers by the bolt.

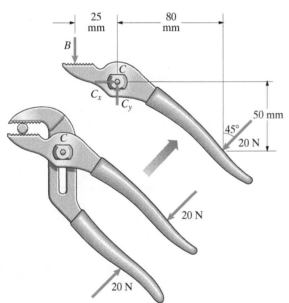

Problem 5.11

5.12 (a) Draw the free-body diagram of the beam.
(b) Determine the reactions at the pin support *A*.

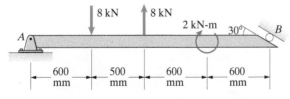

Problem 5.12

5.13 (a) Draw the free-body diagram of the beam.
(b) Determine the reactions at the supports.

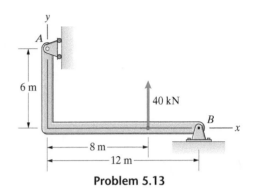

Problem 5.13

5.14 (a) Draw the free-body diagram of the beam.
(b) If *F* = 4 kN, what are the reactions at *A* and *B*?

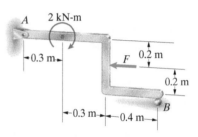

Problem 5.14

▶ **5.15** In Example 5.3, suppose that the attachment point for the suspended mass is moved toward point *B* such that the horizontal distance from *A* to the attachment point increases from 2 m to 3 m. Draw a sketch of the beam *AB* showing the new geometry. Draw the free-body diagram of the beam and apply the equilibrium equations to determine the reactions at *A* and *B*.

5.16 A person doing push-ups pauses in the position shown. His 180-lb weight *W* acts at the point shown. The dimensions *a* = 15 in, *b* = 42 in, and *c* = 16 in. Determine the normal force exerted by the floor on each of his hands and on each of his feet.

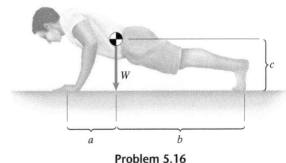

Problem 5.16

5.17 The hydraulic piston AB exerts a 400-lb force on the ladder at B in the direction parallel to the piston. Determine the weight of the ladder and the reactions at C.

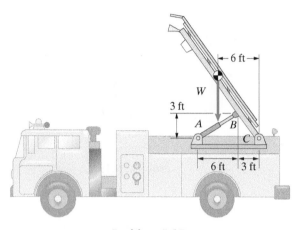

Problem 5.17

5.18 Draw the free-body diagram of the structure by isolating it from its supports at A and E. Determine the reactions at A and E.

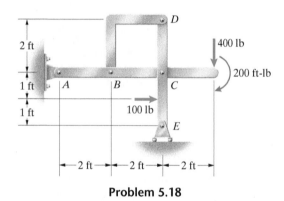

Problem 5.18

5.19 (a) Draw the free-body diagram of the beam.
(b) Determine the tension in the cable and the reactions at A.

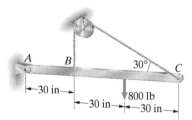

Problem 5.19

5.20 The unstretched length of the spring CD is 350 mm. Suppose that you want the lever ABC to exert a 120-N normal force on the smooth surface at A. Determine the necessary value of the spring constant k and the resulting reactions at B.

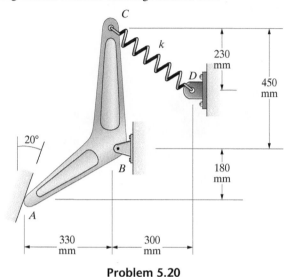

Problem 5.20

5.21 The mobile is in equilibrium. The fish B weighs 27 oz. Determine the weights of the fish A, C, and D. (The weights of the crossbars are negligible.)

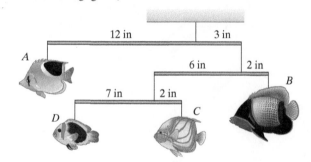

Problem 5.21

5.22 The car's wheelbase (the distance between the wheels) is 2.82 m. The mass of the car is 1760 kg and its weight acts at the point $x = 2.00$ m, $y = 0.68$ m. If the angle $\alpha = 15°$, what is the total normal force exerted on the two rear tires by the sloped ramp?

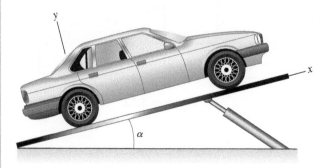

Problem 5.22

5.23 The link AB exerts a force on the bucket of the excavator at A that is parallel to the link. The weight $W = 1500$ lb. Draw the free-body diagram of the bucket and determine the reactions at C. (The connection at C is equivalent to a pin support of the bucket.)

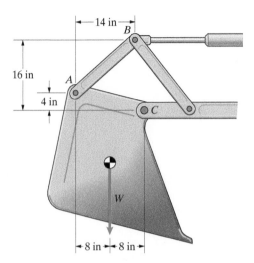

Problem 5.23

5.24 The 14.5-lb chain saw is subjected to the loads at A by the log it cuts. Determine the reactions R, B_x, and B_y that must be applied by the person using the saw to hold it in equilibrium.

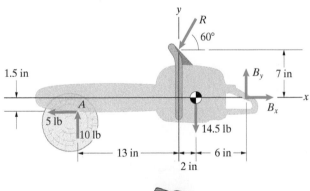

Problem 5.24

5.25 The mass of the trailer is 2.2 Mg (megagrams). The distances $a = 2.5$ m and $b = 5.5$ m. The truck is stationary, and the wheels of the trailer can turn freely, which means the road exerts no horizontal force on them. The hitch at B can be modeled as a pin support.

(a) Draw the free-body diagram of the trailer.

(b) Determine the total normal force exerted on the rear tires at A and the reactions exerted on the trailer at the pin support B.

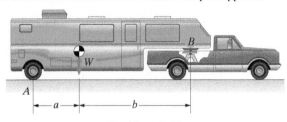

Problem 5.25

5.26 The total weight of the wheelbarrow and its load is $W = 100$ lb. (a) What is the magnitude of the upward force F necessary to lift the support at A off the ground? (b) What is the magnitude of the downward force necessary to raise the wheel off the ground?

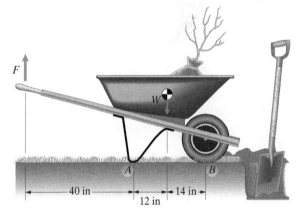

Problem 5.26

5.27 The airplane's weight is $W = 2400$ lb. Its brakes keep the rear wheels locked. The front (nose) wheel can turn freely, and so the ground exerts no horizontal force on it. The force T exerted by the airplane's propeller is horizontal.

(a) Draw the free-body diagram of the airplane. Determine the reaction exerted on the nose wheel and the total normal reaction exerted on the rear wheels

(b) when $T = 0$;

(c) when $T = 250$ lb.

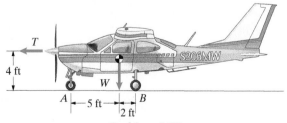

Problem 5.27

5.28 A safety engineer establishing limits on the loads that can be carried by a forklift analyzes the situation shown. The dimensions are $a = 32$ in, $b = 30$ in, and $c = 26$ in. The combined weight of the forklift and operator is $W_F = 1200$ lb. As the weight W_L supported by the forklift increases, the normal force exerted on the floor by the rear wheels at B decreases. The forklift is on the verge of tipping forward when the normal force at B is zero. Determine the value of W_L that will cause this condition.

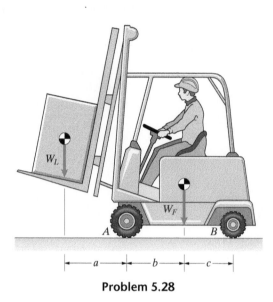

Problem 5.28

5.29 Paleontologists speculate that the stegosaur could stand on its hind limbs for short periods to feed. Based on the free-body diagram shown and assuming that $m = 2000$ kg, determine the magnitudes of the forces B and C exerted by the ligament–muscle brace and vertebral column, and determine the angle α.

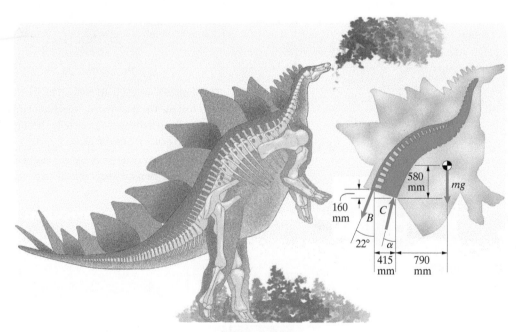

Problem 5.29

5.30 The weight of the fan is $W = 20$ lb. Its base has four equally spaced legs of length $b = 12$ in. Each leg has a pad near the end that contacts the floor and supports the fan. The height $h = 32$ in. If the fan's blade exerts a thrust $T = 2$ lb, what total normal force is exerted on the two legs at A?

5.31 The weight of the fan is $W = 20$ lb. Its base has four equally spaced legs of length $b = 12$ in. Each leg has a pad near the end that contacts the floor and supports the fan. The height $h = 32$ in. As the thrust T of the fan increases, the normal force supported by the two legs at A decreases. When the normal force at A is zero, the fan is on the verge of tipping over. Determine the value of T that will cause this condition.

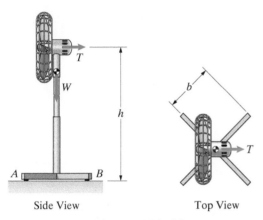

Side View   Top View

Problems 5.30/5.31

5.32 In a measure to decrease costs, the manufacturer of the fan described in Problem 5.31 proposes to support the fan with three equally spaced legs instead of four. An engineer is assigned to analyze the safety implications of the change. The weight of the fan decreases to $W = 19.6$ lb. The dimensions b and h are unchanged. What thrust T will cause the fan to be on the verge of tipping over in this case? Compare your answer to the answer to Problem 5.31.

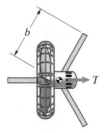

Problem 5.32

5.33 A force $F = 400$ N acts on the bracket. What are the reactions at A and B?

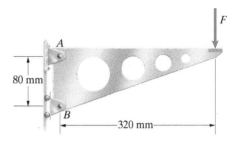

Problem 5.33

5.34 The sign's weight $W_s = 32$ lb acts at the point shown. The 10-lb weight of bar AD acts at the midpoint of the bar. Determine the tension in the cable AE and the reactions at D.

Problem 5.34

5.35 The device shown, called a *swape* or *shadoof*, helps a person lift a heavy load. (Devices of this kind were used in Egypt at least as early as 1550 B.C. and are still in use in various parts of the world.) The dimensions $a = 3.6$ m and $b = 1.2$ m. The mass of the bar and counterweight is 90 kg, and their weight W acts at the point shown. The mass of the load being lifted is 45 kg. Determine the vertical force the person must exert to support the stationary load (a) when the load is just above the ground (the position shown); (b) when the load is 1 m above the ground. Assume that the rope remains vertical.

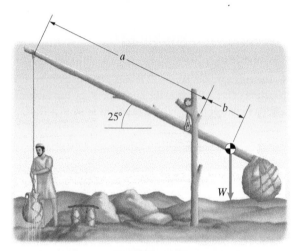

Problem 5.35

5.36 This structure, called a *truss*, has a pin support at A and a roller support at B and is loaded by two forces. Determine the reactions at the supports.

Strategy: Draw a free-body diagram treating the entire truss as a single object.

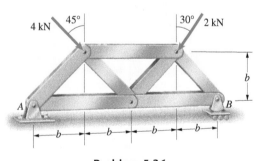

Problem 5.36

5.37 An Olympic gymnast is stationary in the "iron cross" position. The weight of his left arm and the weight of his body *not including his arms* are shown. The distances are $a = b = 9$ in and $c = 13$ in. Treat his shoulder S as a fixed support, and determine the magnitudes of the reactions at his shoulder. That is, determine the force and couple his shoulder must support.

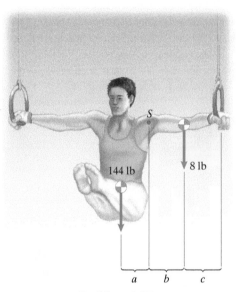

Problem 5.37

5.38 Determine the reactions at A.

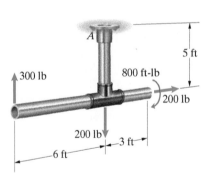

Problem 5.38

5.39 The car's brakes keep the rear wheels locked, and the front wheels are free to turn. Determine the forces exerted on the front and rear wheels by the road when the car is parked (a) on an upslope with $\alpha = 15°$; (b) on a downslope with $\alpha = -15°$.

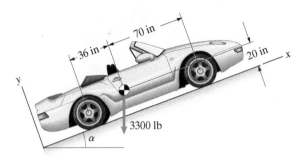

Problem 5.39

5.40 The length of the bar is $L = 4$ ft. Its weight $W = 6$ lb acts at the midpoint of the bar. The floor and wall are smooth. The spring is unstretched when the angle $\alpha = 0$. If the bar is in equilibrium when $\alpha = 40°$, what is the spring constant k?

5.41 The weight W of the bar acts at its midpoint. The floor and wall are smooth. The spring is unstretched when the angle $\alpha = 0$. Determine the angle α at which the bar is in equilibrium in terms of W, k, and L.

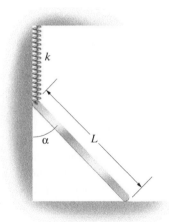

Problems 5.40/5.41

5.42 The plate is supported by a pin in a smooth slot at B. What are the reactions at the supports?

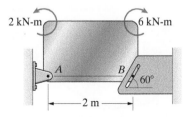

Problem 5.42

5.43 Determine the reactions at the fixed support A.

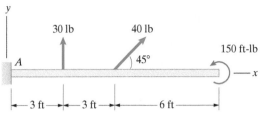

Problem 5.43

5.44 Suppose that you want to represent the two forces and couple acting on the beam in Problem 5.43 by an equivalent force F as shown. (a) Determine F and the distance D at which its line of action crosses the x axis. (b) Assume that F is the only load acting on the beam and determine the reactions at the fixed support A. Compare your answers to the answers to Problem 5.43.

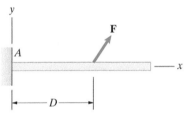

Problem 5.44

5.45 The bicycle brake on the right is pinned to the bicycle's frame at A. Determine the force exerted by the brake pad on the wheel rim at B in terms of the cable tension T.

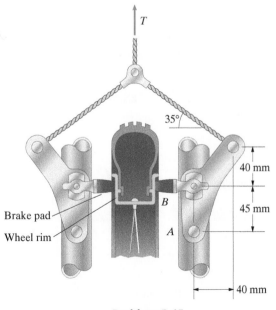

Problem 5.45

5.46 The mass of each of the suspended weights is 80 kg. Determine the reactions at the supports at A and E.

5.47 The suspended weights are each of mass m. The supports at A and E will each safely support a force of 6 kN magnitude. Based on this criterion, what is the largest safe value of m?

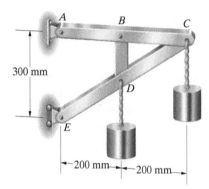

Problems 5.46/5.47

5.48 The tension in cable BC is 100 lb. Determine the reactions at the fixed support.

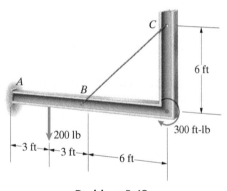

Problem 5.48

5.49 The tension in cable AB is 2 kN. What are the reactions at C in the two cases?

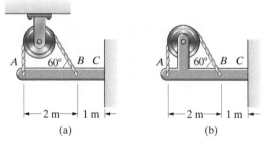

(a)   (b)

Problem 5.49

5.50 Determine the reactions at the supports.

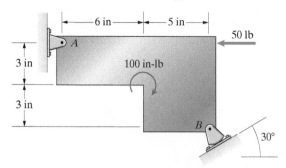

Problem 5.50

5.51 The weight $W = 2$ kN. Determine the tension in the cable and the reactions at A.

5.52 The cable will safely support a tension of 6 kN. Based on this criterion, what is the largest safe value of the weight W?

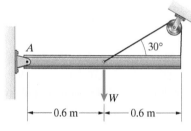

Problems 5.51/5.52

5.53 The blocks being compressed by the clamp exert a 200-N force on the pin at D that points from A toward D. The threaded shaft BE exerts a force on the pin at E that points from B toward E.
(a) Draw a free-body diagram of the arm DCE of the clamp, assuming that the pin at C behaves like a pin support.
(b) Determine the reactions at C.

5.54 The blocks being compressed by the clamp exert a 200-N force on the pin at A that points from D toward A. The threaded shaft BE exerts a force on the pin at B that points from E toward B.
(a) Draw a free-body diagram of the arm ABC of the clamp, assuming that the pin at C behaves like a pin support.
(b) Determine the reactions at C.

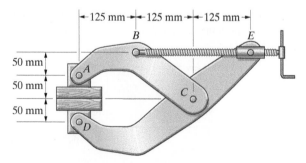

Problems 5.53/5.54

5.55 Suppose that you want to design the safety valve to open when the difference between the pressure p in the circular pipe (diameter = 150 mm) and atmospheric pressure is 10 MPa (megapascals; a pascal is 1 N/m²). The spring is compressed 20 mm when the valve is closed. What should the value of the spring constant be?

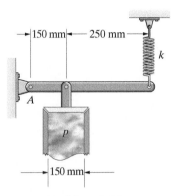

Problem 5.55

5.56 The 10-lb weight of the bar AB acts at the midpoint of the bar. The length of the bar is 3 ft. Determine the tension in the string BC and the reactions at A.

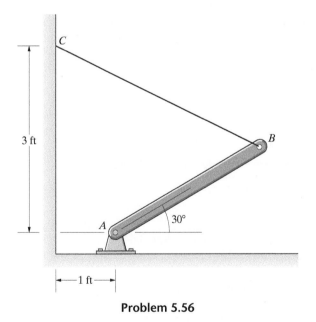

Problem 5.56

5.57 The crane's arm has a pin support at A. The hydraulic cylinder BC exerts a force on the arm at C in the direction parallel to BC. The crane's arm has a mass of 200 kg, and its weight can be assumed to act at a point 2 m to the right of A. If the mass of the suspended box is 800 kg and the system is in equilibrium, what is the magnitude of the force exerted by the hydraulic cylinder?

5.58 In Problem 5.57, what is the magnitude of the force exerted on the crane's arm by the pin support at A?

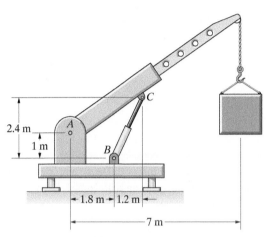

Problems 5.57/5.58

5.59 A speaker system is suspended by the cables attached at D and E. The mass of the speaker system is 130 kg, and its weight acts at G. Determine the tensions in the cables and the reactions at A and C.

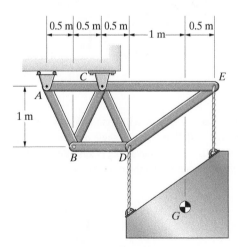

Problem 5.59

5.60 The weight $W_1 = 1000$ lb. Neglect the weight of the bar AB. The cable goes over a pulley at C. Determine the weight W_2 and the reactions at the pin support A.

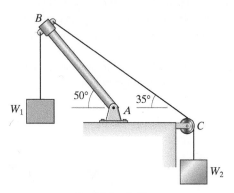

Problem 5.60

5.61 The dimensions $a = 2$ m and $b = 1$ m. The couple $M = 2400$ N-m. The spring constant is $k = 6000$ N/m, and the spring would be unstretched if $h = 0$. The system is in equilibrium when $h = 2$ m and the beam is horizontal. Determine the force F and the reactions at A.

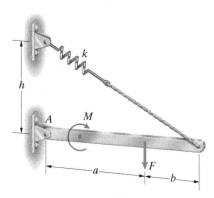

Problem 5.61

5.62 The bar is 1 m long, and its weight W acts at its midpoint. The distance $b = 0.75$ m, and the angle $\alpha = 30°$. The spring constant is $k = 100$ N/m, and the spring is unstretched when the bar is vertical. Determine W and the reactions at A.

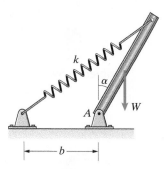

Problem 5.62

5.63 The boom derrick supports a suspended 15-kip load. The booms BC and DE are each 20 ft long. The distances are $a = 15$ ft and $b = 2$ ft, and the angle $\theta = 30°$. Determine the tension in cable AB and the reactions at the pin supports C and D.

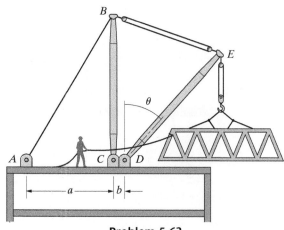

Problem 5.63

5.64 The arrangement shown controls the elevators of an airplane. (The elevators are the horizontal control surfaces in the airplane's tail.) The elevators are attached to member EDG. Aerodynamic pressures on the elevators exert a clockwise couple of 120 in-lb. Cable BG is slack, and its tension can be neglected. Determine the force F and the reactions at the pin support A.

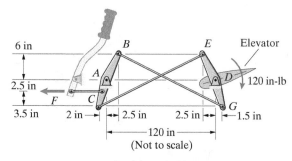

Problem 5.64

▶ **5.65** In Example 5.4, suppose that $\alpha = 40°$, $d = 1$ m, $a = 200$ mm, $b = 500$ mm, $R = 75$ mm, and the mass of the luggage is 40 kg. Determine F and N.

▶ **5.66** In Example 5.4, suppose that $\alpha = 35°$, $d = 46$ in, $a = 10$ in, $b = 14$ in, $R = 3$ in, and you don't want the user to have to exert a force F larger than 20 lb. What is the largest luggage weight that can be placed on the carrier?

▶ **5.67** One of the difficulties in making design decisions is that you don't know how the user will place the luggage on the carrier in Example 5.4. Suppose you assume that the point where the weight acts may be anywhere within the "envelope" $R \leq a \leq 0.75c$ and $0 \leq b \leq 0.75d$. If $\alpha = 30°$, $c = 14$ in, $d = 48$ in, $R = 3$ in, and $W = 80$ lb, what is the largest force F the user will have to exert for any luggage placement?

▶ **5.68** In Example 5.4, assume a user that would hold the carrier's handle at $h = 36$ in above the floor. Assume that $R = 3$ in, $a = 6$ in, $b = 12$ in, and $d = 4$ ft. The resulting ratio of the force the user must exert to the weight of the luggage is $F/W = 0.132$. Suppose that people with a range of heights use this carrier. Obtain a graph of F/W as a function of h for $24 \leq h \leq 36$ in.

5.2 Statically Indeterminate Objects

BACKGROUND

In Section 5.1 we discussed examples in which we were able to use the equilibrium equations to determine unknown forces and couples acting on objects in equilibrium. It is important to be aware of two common situations in which this procedure doesn't lead to a solution. First, the free-body diagram of an object can have more unknown forces or couples than the number of independent equilibrium equations that can be obtained. For example, because no more than three independent equilibrium equations can be obtained from a given free-body diagram in a two-dimensional problem, if there are more than three unknowns they can't all be determined from the equilibrium equations alone. This occurs, for example, when an object has more supports than the minimum number necessary to maintain it in equilibrium. Such an object is said to have *redundant supports*. The second situation is when the supports of an object are improperly designed such that they cannot maintain equilibrium under the loads acting on it. The object is said to have *improper supports*. In either situation, the object is said to be *statically indeterminate*.

Engineers use redundant supports whenever possible for strength and safety. Some designs, however, require that the object be incompletely supported so that it is free to undergo certain motions. These two situations—more supports than necessary for equilibrium or not enough—are so common that we consider them in detail.

Redundant Supports

Consider a beam with a fixed support (Fig. 5.9a). From its free-body diagram (Fig. 5.9b), we obtain the equilibrium equations

$$\Sigma F_x = A_x = 0,$$
$$\Sigma F_y = A_y - F = 0,$$
$$\Sigma M_{\text{point } A} = M_A - \left(\frac{L}{2}\right)F = 0.$$

Assuming we know the load F, we have three equations and three unknown reactions, for which we obtain the solutions $A_x = 0$, $A_y = F$, and $M_A = FL/2$.

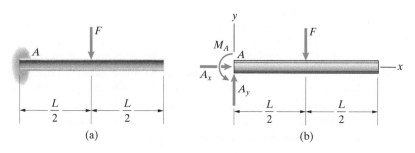

(a)

(b)

Figure 5.9
(a) A beam with a fixed support.
(b) The free-body diagram has three unknown reactions.

Figure 5.10
(a) A beam with fixed and roller supports.
(b) The free-body diagram has four
unknown reactions.

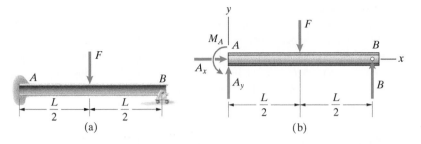

(a)   (b)

Now suppose we add a roller support at the right end of the beam (Fig. 5.10a). From the new free-body diagram (Fig. 5.10b), we obtain the equilibrium equations

$$\Sigma F_x = A_x = 0, \tag{5.6}$$

$$\Sigma F_y = A_y - F + B = 0, \tag{5.7}$$

$$\Sigma M_{\text{point } A} = M_A - \left(\frac{L}{2}\right)F + LB = 0. \tag{5.8}$$

Now we have three equations and four unknown reactions. Although the first equation tells us that $A_x = 0$, we can't solve the two equations (5.7) and (5.8) for the three reactions A_y, B, and M_A.

When faced with this situation, students often attempt to sum the moments about another point, such as point B, to obtain an additional equation:

$$\Sigma M_{\text{point } B} = M_A + \left(\frac{L}{2}\right)F - LA_y = 0.$$

Unfortunately, this doesn't help. This is not an independent equation, but is a linear combination of Eqs. (5.7) and (5.8):

$$\Sigma M_{\text{point } B} = M_A + \left(\frac{L}{2}\right)F - LA_y$$

$$= \underbrace{M_A - \left(\frac{L}{2}\right)F + LB}_{\text{Eq. (5.8)}} - \underbrace{L(A_y - F + B)}_{\text{Eq. (5.7)}}.$$

As this example demonstrates, each support added to an object results in additional reactions. The difference between the number of reactions and the number of independent equilibrium equations is called the *degree of redundancy*. Even if an object is statically indeterminate due to redundant supports, it may be possible to determine some of the reactions from the equilibrium equations. Notice that in our previous example we were able to determine the reaction A_x even though we could not determine the other reactions.

Since redundant supports are so ubiquitous, you may wonder why we devote so much effort to teaching you how to analyze objects whose reactions can be determined with the equilibrium equations. We want to develop your understanding of equilibrium and give you practice writing equilibrium equations. The reactions on an object with redundant supports *can* be determined by supplementing the equilibrium equations with additional equations that relate the forces and couples acting on the object to its deformation, or change in shape. Thus obtaining the equilibrium equations is the first step of the solution.

Improper Supports

We say that an object has improper supports if it will not remain in equilibrium under the action of the loads exerted on it. Thus an object with improper supports will move when the loads are applied. In two-dimensional problems, this can occur in two ways:

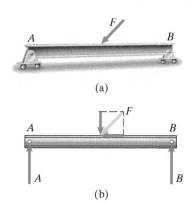

(a)

(b)

Figure 5.11
(a) A beam with two roller supports is not in equilibrium when subjected to the load shown.
(b) The sum of the forces in the horizontal direction is not zero.

1. *The supports can exert only parallel forces.* This leaves the object free to move in the direction perpendicular to the support forces. If the loads exert a component of force in that direction, the object is not in equilibrium. Figure 5.11a shows an example of this situation. The two roller supports can exert only vertical forces, while the force *F* has a horizontal component. The beam will move horizontally when *F* is applied. This is particularly apparent from the free-body diagram (Fig. 5.11b). The sum of the forces in the horizontal direction cannot be zero because the roller supports can exert only vertical reactions.

2. *The supports can exert only concurrent forces.* If the loads exert a moment about the point where the lines of action of the support forces intersect, the object is not in equilibrium. For example, consider the beam in Fig. 5.12a. From its free-body diagram (Fig. 5.12b) we see that the reactions *A* and *B* exert no moment about the point *P*, where their lines of action intersect, but the load *F* does. The sum of the moments about point *P* is not zero, and the beam will rotate when the load is applied.

Except for problems that deal explicitly with improper supports, objects in our examples and problems have proper supports. You should develop the habit of examining objects in equilibrium and thinking about why they are properly supported for the loads acting on them.

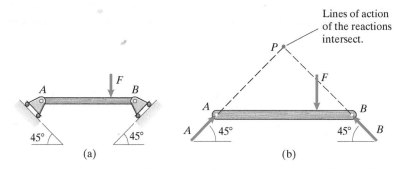

(a)

(b)

Figure 5.12
(a) A beam with roller supports on sloped surfaces.
(b) The sum of the moments about point *P* is not zero.

RESULTS

A supported object is said to be *statically indeterminate* in two circumstances:

Redundant Supports
The object has more supports than the minimum number necessary to maintain equilibrium. The difference between the number of reactions due to the supports and the number of independent equilibrium equations is called the *degree of redundancy*.

Improper Supports
The supports cannot maintain the object in equilibrium under the loads acting on it.

Active Example 5.5	Recognizing a Statically Indeterminate Object (▶ *Related Problem 5.69*)

The beam has two pin supports and is loaded by a 2-kN force.

(a) Show that the beam is statically indeterminate and determine the degree of redundancy.
(b) Determine as many reactions as possible.

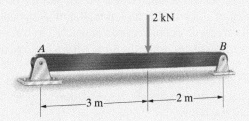

Strategy
The beam is statically indeterminate if its free-body diagram has more unknown reactions than the number of independent equilibrium equations we can obtain. The difference between the number of reactions and the number of equilibrium equations is the degree of redundancy. Even if the beam is statically indeterminate, it may be possible to solve the equilibrium equation for some of the reactions.

Solution

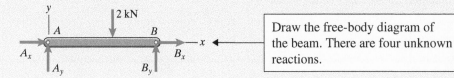

Draw the free-body diagram of the beam. There are four unknown reactions.

$$\Sigma F_x = A_x + B_x = 0,$$
$$\Sigma F_y = A_y + B_y - 2 \text{ kN} = 0,$$
$$\Sigma M_{\text{point } A} = (5 \text{ m})B_y - (3 \text{ m})(2 \text{ kN}) = 0.$$

Write the equilibrium equations.

There are three independent equilibrium equations, so the beam is statically indeterminate and the degree of redundancy is $4 - 3 = 1$. We cannot determine A_x or B_x from the equilibrium equations, but we can determine A_y and B_y.

$$B_y = \frac{(3 \text{ m})(2 \text{ kN})}{(5 \text{ m})} = 1.2 \text{ kN},$$
$$A_y = 2 \text{ kN} - B_y = 0.8 \text{ kN}.$$

Determine the reactions A_y and B_y.

Practice Problem Suppose that the pin support at point A of the beam is replaced by a fixed support. (a) Show that the beam is statically indeterminate and determine the degree of redundancy. (b) Determine as many reactions as possible.

Answer: (a) Degree of redundancy is 2. (b) No reactions can be determined.

Example 5.6   **Proper and Improper Supports** (▶ *Related Problems 5.75, 5.76*)

State whether each L-shaped bar is properly or improperly supported. If a bar is properly supported, determine the reactions at its supports.

Strategy

By drawing the free-body diagram of each bar, we can determine whether the reactions of the supports can exert only parallel or concurrent forces on it. If so, we can then recognize whether the applied load results in the bar not being in equilibrium.

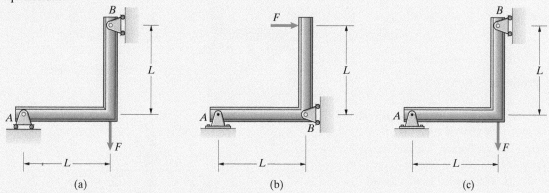

(a)   (b)   (c)

Solution

Consider the free-body diagrams of the bars (shown below):

Bar (a)   The lines of action of the reactions due to the two roller supports intersect at P, and the load F exerts a moment about P. This bar is improperly supported.

Bar (b)   The lines of action of the reactions intersect at A, and the load F exerts a moment about A. This bar is also improperly supported.

Bar (c)   The three support forces are neither parallel nor concurrent. This bar is properly supported. The equilibrium equations are

$$\Sigma F_x = A_x - B = 0,$$
$$\Sigma F_y = A_y - F = 0,$$
$$\Sigma M_{\text{point } A} = BL - FL = 0.$$

Solving these equations, the reactions are $A_x = F, A_y = F,$ and $B = F$.

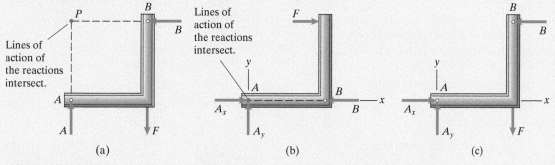

(a)   (b)   (c)

Critical Thinking

An essential part of learning mechanics is developing your intuition about the behaviors of the physical systems we study. In this example, think about the effects of the loads on the three systems, and see if you can predict whether they are properly supported. Will the loads cause the bars to move or not? Then see if your judgment is confirmed by the analyses given in the example.

Problems

▶ **5.69** (a) Draw the free-body diagram of the beam and show that it is statically indeterminate. (See Active Example 5.5.)

(b) Determine as many of the reactions as possible.

5.70 Choose supports at *A* and *B* so that the beam is not statically indeterminate. Determine the reactions at the supports.

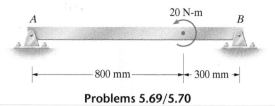

Problems 5.69/5.70

5.71 (a) Draw the free-body diagram of the beam and show that it is statically indeterminate. (The external couple M_0 is known.)

(b) By an analysis of the beam's deflection, it is determined that the vertical reaction *B* exerted by the roller support is related to the couple M_0 by $B = 2M_0/L$. What are the reactions at *A*?

5.72 Choose supports at *A* and *B* so that the beam is not statically indeterminate. Determine the reactions at the supports.

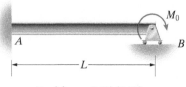

Problems 5.71/5.72

5.73 Draw the free-body diagram of the L-shaped pipe assembly and show that it is statically indeterminate. Determine as many of the reactions as possible.

Strategy: Place the coordinate system so that the *x* axis passes through points *A* and *B*.

5.74 Choose supports at *A* and *B* so that the pipe assembly is not statically indeterminate. Determine the reactions at the supports.

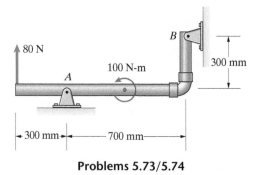

Problems 5.73/5.74

▶ **5.75** State whether each of the L-shaped bars shown is properly or improperly supported. If a bar is properly supported, determine the reactions at its supports. (See Active Example 5.6.)

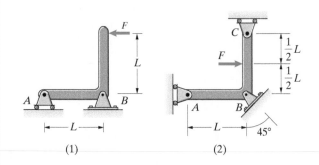

(1)   (2)

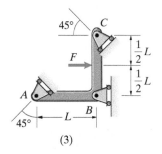

(3)

Problem 5.75

▶ **5.76** State whether each of the L-shaped bars shown is properly or improperly supported. If a bar is properly supported, determine the reactions at its supports. (See Active Example 5.6.)

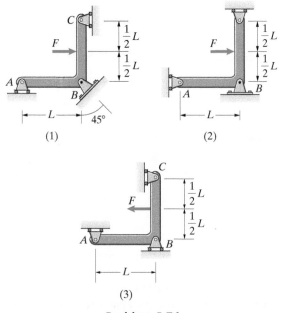

(1)   (2)

(3)

Problem 5.76

5.3 Three-Dimensional Applications

BACKGROUND

We have seen that when an object in equilibrium is subjected to a two-dimensional system of forces and moments, no more than three independent equilibrium equations can be obtained. In the case of a three-dimensional system of forces and moments, up to six independent equilibrium equations can be obtained. The three components of the sum of the forces must equal zero and the three components of the sum of the moments about a point must equal zero. The procedure for determining the reactions on an object subjected to a three-dimensional system of forces and moments—drawing a free-body diagram and applying the equilibrium equations—is the same as in two dimensions.

The Scalar Equilibrium Equations

When an object is in equilibrium, the system of forces and couples acting on it satisfy Eqs. (5.1) and (5.2). The sum of the forces is zero and the sum of the moments about any point is zero. Expressing these equations in terms of cartesian components in three dimensions yields the six scalar equilibrium equations.

$$\Sigma F_x = 0, \tag{5.9}$$

$$\Sigma F_y = 0, \tag{5.10}$$

$$\Sigma F_z = 0, \tag{5.11}$$

$$\Sigma M_x = 0, \tag{5.12}$$

$$\Sigma M_y = 0, \tag{5.13}$$

$$\Sigma M_z = 0. \tag{5.14}$$

The sums of the moments can be evaluated about any point. Although more equations can be obtained by summing moments about other points, they will not be independent of these equations. *More than six independent equilibrium equations cannot be obtained from a given free-body diagram, so at most six unknown forces or couples can be determined.*

The steps required to determine reactions in three dimensions are familiar from the two-dimensional applications we have discussed. First obtain a free-body diagram by isolating an object and showing the loads and reactions acting on it, then use Eqs. (5.9)–(5.14) to determine the reactions.

Supports

We present five conventions frequently used in three-dimensional problems. Even when actual supports do not physically resemble these models, we represent them by the models if they exert the same (or approximately the same) reactions.

The Ball and Socket Support   In the *ball and socket support*, the supported object is attached to a ball enclosed within a spherical socket (Fig. 5.13a). The socket permits the ball to rotate freely (friction is neglected) but prevents it from translating in any direction.

Imagine holding a bar attached to a ball and socket support (Fig. 5.13b). If you try to translate the bar (move it without rotating it) in any direction, the support exerts a reactive force to prevent the motion. However, you can rotate

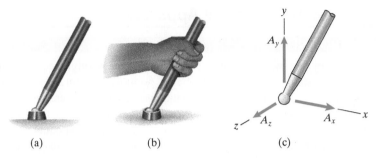

Figure 5.13
(a) A ball and socket support.
(b) Holding a supported bar.
(c) The ball and socket support can exert three components of force.

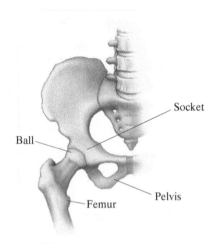

Figure 5.14
The human femur is attached to the pelvis by a ball and socket support.

the bar about the support. The support cannot exert a couple to prevent rotation. Thus a ball and socket support can't exert a couple but can exert three components of force (Fig. 5.13c). It is the three-dimensional analog of the two-dimensional pin support.

The human hip joint is an example of a ball and socket support (Fig. 5.14). The support of the gear shift lever of a car can be modeled as a ball and socket support within the lever's range of motion.

The Roller Support The *roller support* (Fig. 5.15a) is a ball and socket support that can roll freely on a supporting surface. A roller support can exert only a force normal to the supporting surface (Fig. 5.15b). The rolling "casters" sometimes used to support furniture legs are supports of this type.

The Hinge The hinge support is the familiar device used to support doors. It permits the supported object to rotate freely about a line, the *hinge axis*. An object is attached to a hinge in Fig. 5.16a. The z axis of the coordinate system is aligned with the hinge axis.

If you imagine holding a bar attached to a hinge (Fig. 5.16b), notice that you can rotate the bar about the hinge axis. The hinge cannot exert a couple about the hinge axis (the z axis) to prevent rotation. However, you can't rotate the bar about the x or y axis because the hinge can exert couples about those

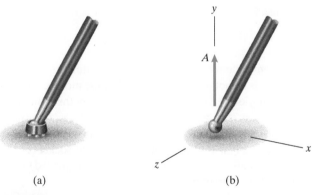

Figure 5.15
(a) A roller support.
(b) The reaction is normal to the supporting surface.

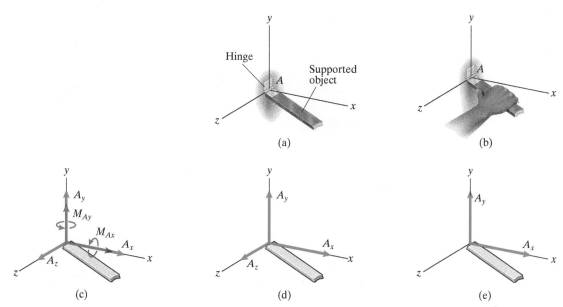

Figure 5.16
(a) A hinge. The z axis is aligned with the hinge axis.
(b) Holding a supported bar.
(c) In general, a hinge can exert five reactions: three force
    components and two couple components.
(d) The reactions when the hinge exerts no couples.
(e) The reactions when the hinge exerts neither couples nor
    a force parallel to the hinge axis.

axes to resist the motion. In addition, you can't translate the bar in any direction. The reactions a hinge can exert on an object are shown in Fig. 5.16c. There are three components of force, A_x, A_y, and A_z, and couples about the x and y axes, M_{Ax} and M_{Ay}.

In some situations, either a hinge exerts no couples on the object it supports, or they are sufficiently small to neglect. An example of the latter case is when the axes of the hinges supporting a door are properly aligned (the axes of the individual hinges coincide). In these situations the hinge exerts only forces on an object (Fig. 5.16d). Situations also arise in which a hinge exerts no couples on an object and exerts no force in the direction of the hinge axis. (The hinge may actually be designed so that it cannot support a force parallel to the hinge axis.) Then the hinge exerts forces only in the directions perpendicular to the hinge axis (Fig. 5.16e). In examples and problems, we indicate when a hinge does not exert all five of the reactions in Fig. 5.16c.

The Bearing   The type of bearing shown in Fig. 5.17a supports a circular shaft while permitting it to rotate about its axis. The reactions are identical to those exerted by a hinge. In the most general case (Fig. 5.17b), the bearing can exert a force on the supported shaft in each coordinate direction and can exert couples about axes perpendicular to the shaft but cannot exert a couple about the axis of the shaft.

As in the case of the hinge, situations can occur in which the bearing exerts no couples (Fig. 5.17c) or exerts no couples and no force parallel to the shaft axis (Fig. 5.17d). Some bearings are designed in this way for specific

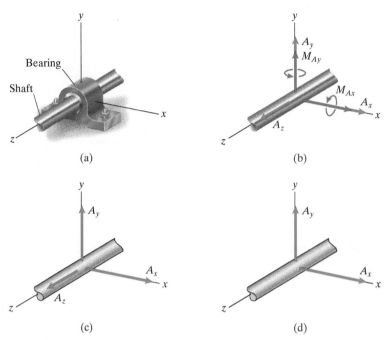

Figure 5.17
(a) A bearing. The z axis is aligned with the axis of the shaft.
(b) In general, a bearing can exert five reactions: three force components and two couple components.
(c) The reactions when the bearing exerts no couples.
(d) The reactions when the bearing exerts neither couples nor a force parallel to the axis of the shaft.

applications. In examples and problems, we indicate when a bearing does not exert all of the reactions in Fig. 5.17b.

The Fixed Support You are already familiar with the fixed, or built-in, support (Fig. 5.18a). Imagine holding a bar with a fixed support (Fig. 5.18b). You cannot translate it in any direction, and you cannot rotate it about any axis.

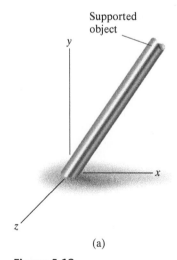
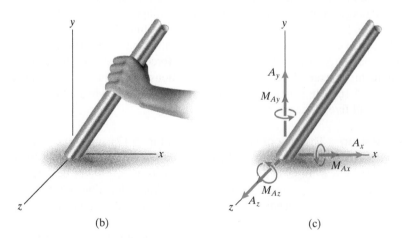

Figure 5.18
(a) A fixed support.
(b) Holding a supported bar.
(c) A fixed support can exert six reactions: three force components and three couple components.

The support is capable of exerting forces A_x, A_y, and A_z in each coordinate direction and couples M_{Ax}, M_{Ay}, and M_{Az} about each coordinate axis (Fig. 5.18c).

Table 5.2 summarizes the support conventions commonly used in three-dimensional applications.

Table 5.2   Supports used in three-dimensional applications.

Supports	**Reactions**
Rope or Cable	A Collinear Force
Contact with a Smooth Surface	A Normal Force
Contact with a Rough Surface	Three Force Components
Ball and Socket Support	Three Force Components
Roller Support	A Normal Force

Table 5.2 *continued*

Supports	Reactions
 Hinge (The *z* axis is parallel to the hinge axis.)	 Three Force Components, Two Couple Components (When no couples are exerted)
 Bearing (The *z* axis is parallel to the axis of the supported shaft.)	 (When no couples and no axial force are exerted)
 Fixed (Built-in) Support	 Three Force Components, Three Couple Components

RESULTS

Equilibrium Equations

If an object is in equilibrium, the sum of the external forces acting on it equals zero,

$$\Sigma F_x = 0, \quad (5.9)$$

$$\Sigma \mathbf{F} = \mathbf{0} \longrightarrow \quad \Sigma F_y = 0, \quad (5.10)$$

$$\Sigma F_z = 0, \quad (5.11)$$

and the sum of the moments about any point due to the forces and couples acting on it is zero,

$$\Sigma M_x = 0, \quad (5.12)$$

$$\Sigma \mathbf{M}_{\text{any point}} = \mathbf{0} \longrightarrow \quad \Sigma M_y = 0, \quad (5.13)$$

$$\Sigma M_z = 0. \quad (5.14)$$

Supports

Examples of supports used in three-dimensional applications. (See Table 5.2.)

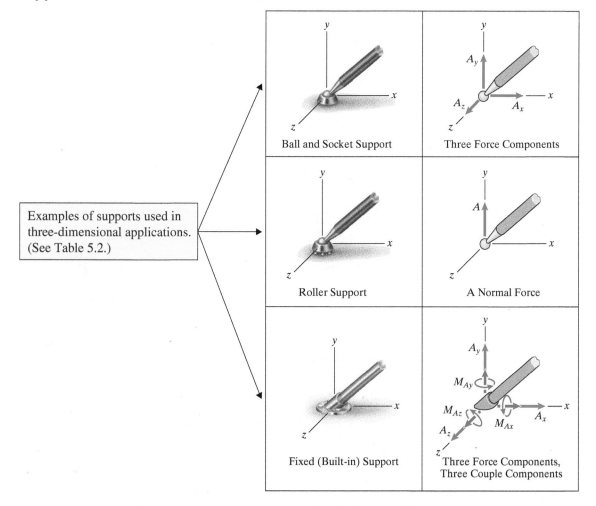

Ball and Socket Support

Three Force Components

Roller Support

A Normal Force

Fixed (Built-in) Support

Three Force Components, Three Couple Components

Determining Reactions in Three Dimensions (▶ *Related Problem 5.86*)

The bar *AB* is supported by the cables *BC* and *BD* and a ball and socket support at *A*. Cable *BC* is parallel to the *z* axis and cable *BD* is parallel to the *x* axis. The 200-N force acts at the midpoint of the bar. Determine the tensions in the cables and the reactions at *A*.

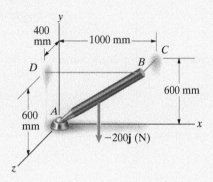

Strategy

We must obtain the free-body diagram of the bar by isolating it and showing the reactions exerted by the cables and the ball and socket support. Then we can apply the equilibrium equations to determine the reactions.

Solution

Draw the Free-Body Diagram of the Bar

Isolate the bar and show the reactions exerted by the cables and the ball and socket support.

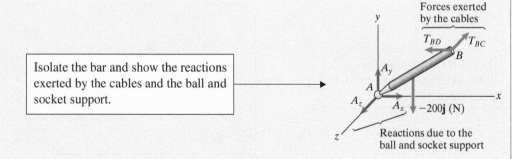

Forces exerted by the cables

Reactions due to the ball and socket support

Apply the Equilibrium Equations

$$\Sigma F_x = A_x - T_{BD} = 0,$$
$$\Sigma F_y = A_y - 200 \text{ N} = 0,$$
$$\Sigma F_z = A_z - T_{BC} = 0.$$

The sums of the forces in each coordinate direction equal zero.

$$\Sigma \mathbf{M}_{\text{point } A} = [\mathbf{r}_{AB} \times (-T_{BC}\mathbf{k})] + [\mathbf{r}_{AB} \times (-T_{BD}\mathbf{i})] + \left[\frac{1}{2}\,\mathbf{r}_{AB} \times (-200\mathbf{j})\right]$$

$$= \begin{vmatrix} \mathbf{i} & \mathbf{j} & \mathbf{k} \\ 1 & 0.6 & 0.4 \\ 0 & 0 & -T_{BC} \end{vmatrix} + \begin{vmatrix} \mathbf{i} & \mathbf{j} & \mathbf{k} \\ 1 & 0.6 & 0.4 \\ -T_{BD} & 0 & 0 \end{vmatrix} + \begin{vmatrix} \mathbf{i} & \mathbf{j} & \mathbf{k} \\ 0.5 & 0.3 & 0.2 \\ 0 & -200 & 0 \end{vmatrix}$$

$$= (-0.6T_{BC} + 40)\mathbf{i} + (T_{BC} - 0.4T_{BD})\mathbf{j} + (0.6T_{BD} - 100)\mathbf{k}.$$

> The sum of the moments about any point equals zero.

> The components of this vector (the sums of the moments about the three coordinate axes) must each equal zero.

$$\Sigma M_x = -(0.6 \text{ m})T_{BC} + 40 \text{ N-m} = 0,$$
$$\Sigma M_y = (1 \text{ m})T_{BC} - (0.4 \text{ m})T_{BD} = 0,$$
$$\Sigma M_z = (0.6 \text{ m})T_{BD} - 100 \text{ N-m} = 0.$$

> Solving the six scalar equilibrium equations yields
> $A_x = 166.7$ N, $A_y = 200$ N, $A_z = 66.7$ N, $T_{BC} = 66.7$ N, and $T_{BD} = 166.7$ N.

Practice Problem Suppose that the cables *BC* and *BD* are removed and the ball and socket joint at *A* is replaced by a fixed support. Determine the reactions at *A*.

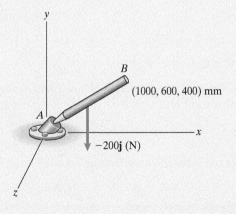

Answer: $A_x = 0$, $A_y = 200$ N, $A_z = 0$, $M_{Ax} = -40$ N-m, $M_{Ay} = 0$, $M_{Az} = 100$ N-m.

| Example 5.8 | Reactions at a Hinge Support (▶ *Related Problem 5.104*) |

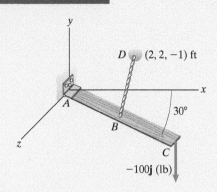

The bar AC is 4 ft long and is supported by a hinge at A and the cable BD. The hinge axis is along the z axis. The centerline of the bar lies in the x–y plane, and the cable attachment point B is the midpoint of the bar. Determine the tension in the cable and the reactions exerted on the bar by the hinge.

Strategy

We will obtain a free-body diagram of bar AC by isolating it from the cable and hinge. (The reactions the hinge can exert on the bar are shown in Table 5.2.) Then we can determine the reactions by applying the equilibrium equations.

Solution

Draw the Free-Body Diagram   We isolate the bar from the hinge support and the cable and show the reactions they exert (Fig. a). The terms A_x, A_y, and A_z are the components of force exerted by the hinge, and the terms M_{Ax} and M_{Ay} are the couples exerted by the hinge about the x and y axes. (Remember that the hinge cannot exert a couple on the bar about the hinge axis.) The term T is the tension in the cable.

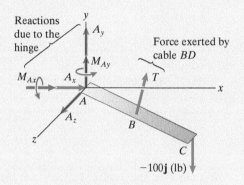

(a) The free-body diagram of the bar.

Apply the Equilibrium Equations   To write the equilibrium equations, we must first express the cable force in terms of its components. The coordinates of point B are $(2 \cos 30°, -2 \sin 30°, 0)$ ft, so the position vector from B to D is

$$\mathbf{r}_{BD} = (2 - 2 \cos 30°)\mathbf{i} + [2 - (-2 \sin 30°)]\mathbf{j} + (-1 - 0)\mathbf{k}$$

$$= 0.268\mathbf{i} + 3\mathbf{j} - \mathbf{k} \text{ (ft)}.$$

We divide this vector by its magnitude to obtain a unit vector $\mathbf{e}_{BD}$ that points from point B toward point D:

$$\mathbf{e}_{BD} = \frac{\mathbf{r}_{BD}}{|\mathbf{r}_{BD}|} = 0.084\mathbf{i} + 0.945\mathbf{j} - 0.315\mathbf{k}.$$

Now we can write the cable force as the product of its magnitude and $\mathbf{e}_{BD}$:

$$T\mathbf{e}_{BD} = T(0.084\mathbf{i} + 0.945\mathbf{j} - 0.315\mathbf{k}).$$

The sums of the forces in each coordinate direction must equal zero:

$$\Sigma F_x = A_x + 0.084T = 0,$$

$$\Sigma F_y = A_y + 0.945T - 100 \text{ lb} = 0, \qquad (1)$$

$$\Sigma F_z = A_z - 0.315T = 0.$$

If we sum moments about A, the resulting equations do not contain the unknown reactions A_x, A_y, and A_z. The position vectors from A to B and from A to C are

$$\mathbf{r}_{AB} = 2 \cos 30°\mathbf{i} - 2 \sin 30°\mathbf{j} \text{ (ft)},$$

$$\mathbf{r}_{AC} = 4 \cos 30°\mathbf{i} - 4 \sin 30°\mathbf{j} \text{ (ft)}.$$

The sum of the moments about A, with forces in lb and distances in ft, is

$$\Sigma\mathbf{M}_{\text{point } A} = M_{Ax}\mathbf{i} + M_{Ay}\mathbf{j} + [\mathbf{r}_{AB} \times (T\mathbf{e}_{BD})] + [\mathbf{r}_{AC} \times (-100\mathbf{j})]$$

$$= M_{Ax}\mathbf{i} + M_{Ay}\mathbf{j} + \begin{vmatrix} \mathbf{i} & \mathbf{j} & \mathbf{k} \\ 1.732 & -1 & 0 \\ 0.084T & 0.945T & -0.315T \end{vmatrix}$$

$$+ \begin{vmatrix} \mathbf{i} & \mathbf{j} & \mathbf{k} \\ 3.464 & -2 & 0 \\ 0 & -100 & 0 \end{vmatrix}$$

$$= (M_{Ax} + 0.315T)\mathbf{i} + (M_{Ay} + 0.546T)\mathbf{j}$$

$$+ (1.72T - 346)\mathbf{k} = 0.$$

From this vector equation, we obtain the scalar equations

$$\Sigma M_x = M_{Ax} + (0.315 \text{ ft})T = 0,$$

$$\Sigma M_y = M_{Ay} + (0.546 \text{ ft})T = 0,$$

$$\Sigma M_z = (1.72 \text{ ft})T_{BD} - 346 \text{ ft-lb} = 0.$$

Solving these equations yields the reactions

$$T = 201 \text{ lb}, \qquad M_{Ax} = -63.4 \text{ ft-lb}, \qquad M_{Ay} = -109.8 \text{ ft-lb}.$$

Then from Eqs. (1) we obtain the forces exerted on the bar by the hinge:

$$A_x = -17.0 \text{ lb}, \qquad A_y = -90.2 \text{ lb}, \qquad A_z = 63.4 \text{ lb}.$$

Critical Thinking

Notice in Table 5.2 that there are three possibilities for the reactions exerted by a hinge or bearing. How do you know which one to choose? Under certain circumstances, a hinge may not exert significant couples on the object to which it is connected, and it also may not exert a significant force in the direction of the hinge axis. For example, when an object has two hinge supports and their axes are aligned (see Example 5.9), you can often assume that each individual hinge does not exert couples on the object. But in general, it requires experience to make such judgments. In upcoming examples and problems, we will indicate the reactions that you can assume are exerted by a hinge. Whenever you are in doubt, you should assume that a hinge may exert the most general set of reactions shown in Table 5.2 (three force components and two couple components).

| Example 5.9 | Reactions at Properly Aligned Hinges (▶ *Related Problem 5.112*) |

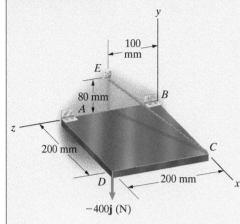

The plate is supported by hinges at *A* and *B* and the cable *CE*. The properly aligned hinges do not exert couples on the plate, and the hinge at *A* does not exert a force on the plate in the direction of the hinge axis. Determine the reactions at the hinges and the tension in the cable.

Strategy

We will draw the free-body diagram of the plate, using the given information about the reactions exerted by the hinges at *A* and *B*. Before the equilibrium equations can be applied, we must express the force exerted on the plate by the cable in terms of its components.

Solution

Draw the Free-Body Diagram   We isolate the plate and show the reactions at the hinges and the force exerted by the cable (Fig. a). The term *T* is the force exerted on the plate by cable *CE*.

Apply the Equilibrium Equations   Since we know the coordinates of points *C* and *E*, we can express the cable force as the product of its magnitude *T* and a unit vector directed from *C* toward *E*. The result is

$$T(-0.842\mathbf{i} + 0.337\mathbf{j} + 0.421\mathbf{k}).$$

The sums of the forces in each coordinate direction equal zero:

$$\Sigma F_x = A_x + B_x - 0.842T = 0,$$
$$\Sigma F_y = A_y + B_y + 0.337T - 400 = 0, \tag{1}$$
$$\Sigma F_z = B_z + 0.421T = 0.$$

If we sum the moments about *B*, the resulting equations will not contain the three unknown reactions at *B*. The sum of the moments about *B*, with forces in N and distances in m, is

$$\Sigma \mathbf{M}_{\text{point } B} = \begin{vmatrix} \mathbf{i} & \mathbf{j} & \mathbf{k} \\ 0.2 & 0 & 0 \\ -0.842T & 0.337T & 0.421T \end{vmatrix} + \begin{vmatrix} \mathbf{i} & \mathbf{j} & \mathbf{k} \\ 0 & 0 & 0.2 \\ A_x & A_y & 0 \end{vmatrix}$$

$$+ \begin{vmatrix} \mathbf{i} & \mathbf{j} & \mathbf{k} \\ 0.2 & 0 & 0.2 \\ 0 & -400 & 0 \end{vmatrix}$$

$$= (-0.2A_y + 80)\mathbf{i} + (-0.0842T + 0.2A_x)\mathbf{j}$$
$$+ (0.0674T - 80)\mathbf{k} = 0.$$

The scalar equations are

$$\Sigma M_x = -(0.2 \text{ m})A_y + 80 \text{ N-m} = 0,$$
$$\Sigma M_y = -(0.0842 \text{ m})T + (0.2 \text{ m})A_x = 0,$$
$$\Sigma M_z = (0.0674 \text{ m})T - 80 \text{ N-m} = 0.$$

Solving these equations, we obtain the reactions

$$T = 1187 \text{ N}, \qquad A_x = 500 \text{ N}, \qquad A_y = 400 \text{ N}.$$

Then from Eqs. (1), the reactions at *B* are

$$B_x = 500 \text{ N}, \qquad B_y = -400 \text{ N}, \qquad B_z = -500 \text{ N}.$$

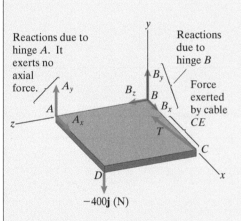

(a) The free-body diagram of the plate.

Critical Thinking

"Properly aligned hinges" means hinges that are mounted on an object so that their axes are aligned. When this is the case, as in this example, it can usually be assumed that each individual hinge does not exert couples on the object. Notice that it is also assumed in this example that the hinge at A exerts no reaction parallel to the hinge axis but the hinge at B does. The hinges can be intentionally designed so that this is the case, or it can result from the way they are installed.

If our only objective in this example had been to determine the tension T, we could have done so easily by evaluating the sum of the moments about the line AB (the z axis). Because the reactions at the hinges exert no moment about the z axis, we obtain the equation

$$(0.2 \text{ m})(0.337T) - (0.2 \text{ m})(400 \text{ N}) = 0,$$

which yields $T = 1187$ N.

Problems

5.77 The bar AB has a fixed support at A and is loaded by the forces

$$\mathbf{F}_B = 2\mathbf{i} + 6\mathbf{j} + 3\mathbf{k} \text{ (kN)},$$
$$\mathbf{F}_C = \mathbf{i} - 2\mathbf{j} + 2\mathbf{k} \text{ (kN)}.$$

(a) Draw the free-body diagram of the bar.

(b) Determine the reactions at A.

    Strategy: (a) Draw a diagram of the bar isolated from its supports. Complete the free-body diagram of the bar by adding the two external forces and the reactions due to the fixed support (see Table 5.2). (b) Use the scalar equilibrium equations (5.9)–(5.14) to determine the reactions.

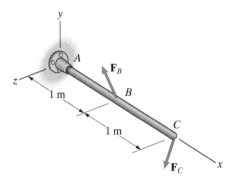

Problem 5.77

5.78 The bar AB has a fixed support at A. The tension in cable BC is 8 kN. Determine the reactions at A.

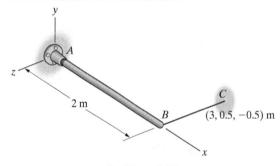

Problem 5.78

5.79 The bar AB has a fixed support at A. The collar at B is fixed to the bar. The tension in the rope BC is 300 lb. (a) Draw the free-body diagram of the bar. (b) Determine the reactions at A.

5.80 The bar AB has a fixed support at A. The collar at B is fixed to the bar. Suppose that you don't want the support at A to be subjected to a couple of magnitude greater than 3000 ft-lb. What is the largest allowable tension in the rope BC?

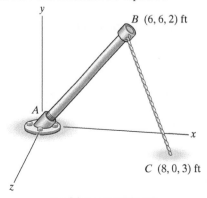

Problems 5.79/5.80

5.81 The total force exerted on the highway sign by its weight and the most severe anticipated winds is $\mathbf{F} = 2.8\mathbf{i} - 1.8\mathbf{j}$ (kN). Determine the reactions at the fixed support.

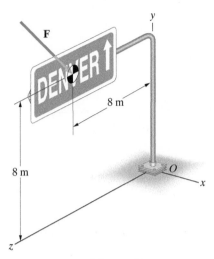

Problem 5.81

5.82 The tension in cable AB is 800 lb. Determine the reactions at the fixed support C.

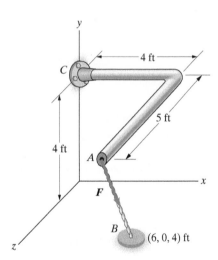

Problem 5.82

5.83 The tension in cable AB is 24 kN. Determine the reactions at the fixed support D.

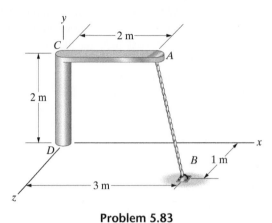

Problem 5.83

5.84 The robotic manipulator is stationary and the y axis is vertical. The weights of the arms AB and BC act at their midpoints. The direction cosines of the centerline of arm AB are $\cos \theta_x = 0.174$, $\cos \theta_y = 0.985$, $\cos \theta_z = 0$, and the direction cosines of the centerline of arm BC are $\cos \theta_x = 0.743$, $\cos \theta_y = 0.557$, $\cos \theta_z = -0.371$. The support at A behaves like a fixed support.

(a) What is the sum of the moments about A due to the weights of the two arms?

(b) What are the reactions at A?

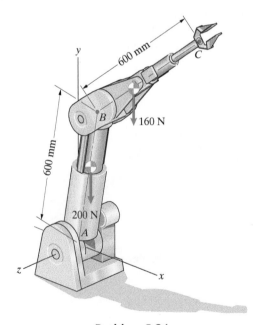

Problem 5.84

5.85 The force exerted on the grip of the exercise machine is **F** = 260**i** − 130**j** (N). What are the reactions at the fixed support at *O*?

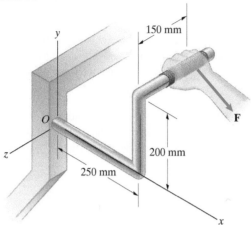

Problem 5.85

▶ **5.86** In Active Example 5.7, suppose that cable *BD* is lengthened and the attachment point *D* moved from (0, 600, 400) mm to (0, 600, 600) mm. (The end *B* of bar *AB* remains where it is.) Draw a sketch of the bar and its supports showing cable *BD* in its new position. Draw the free-body diagram of the bar and apply equilibrium to determine the tensions in the cables and the reactions at *A*.

5.87 The force **F** acting on the boom *ABC* at *C* points in the direction of the unit vector 0.512**i** − 0.384**j** + 0.768**k** and its magnitude is 8 kN. The boom is supported by a ball and socket at *A* and the cables *BD* and *BE*. The collar at *B* is fixed to the boom.

(a) Draw the free-body diagram of the boom.

(b) Determine the tensions in the cables and the reactions at *A*.

5.88 The cables *BD* and *BE* in Problem 5.87 will each safely support a tension of 25 kN. Based on this criterion, what is the largest acceptable magnitude of the force **F**?

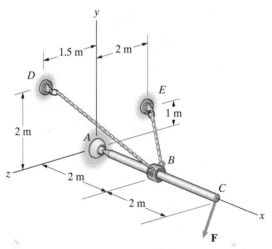

Problems 5.87/5.88

5.89 The suspended load exerts a force *F* = 600 lb at *A*, and the weight of the bar *OA* is negligible. Determine the tensions in the cables and the reactions at the ball and socket support *O*.

5.90 The suspended load exerts a force *F* = 600 lb at *A* and bar *OA* weighs 200 lb. Assume that the bar's weight acts at its midpoint. Determine the tensions in the cables and the reactions at the ball and socket support *O*.

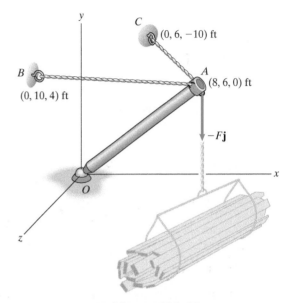

Problems 5.89/5.90

5.91 The 158,000-kg airplane is at rest on the ground (*z* = 0 is ground level). The landing gear carriages are at *A*, *B*, and *C*. The coordinates of the point *G* at which the weight of the plane acts are (3, 0.5, 5) m. What are the magnitudes of the normal reactions exerted on the landing gear by the ground?

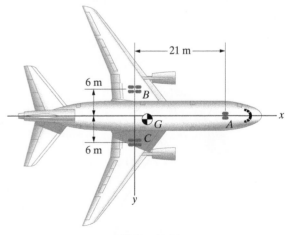

Problem 5.91

5.92 The horizontal triangular plate is suspended by the three vertical cables A, B, and C. The tension in each cable is 80 N. Determine the x and z coordinates of the point where the plate's weight effectively acts.

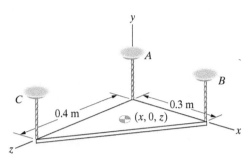

Problem 5.92

5.93 The 800-kg horizontal wall section is supported by the three vertical cables A, B, and C. What are the tensions in the cables?

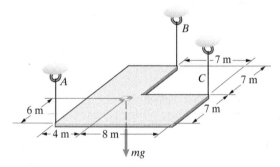

Problem 5.93

5.94 The bar AC is supported by the cable BD and a bearing at A that can rotate about the z axis. The person exerts a force $\mathbf{F} = 10\mathbf{j}$ (lb) at C. Determine the tension in the cable and the reactions at A.

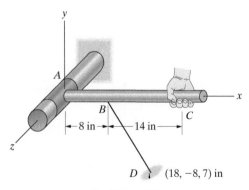

Problem 5.94

5.95 The L-shaped bar is supported by a bearing at A and rests on a smooth horizontal surface at B. The vertical force $F = 4$ kN and the distance $b = 0.15$ m. Determine the reactions at A and B.

5.96 The vertical force $F = 4$ kN and the distance $b = 0.15$ m. If you represent the reactions at A and B by an equivalent system consisting of a single force, what is the force and where does its line of action intersect the x–z plane?

5.97 The vertical force $F = 4$ kN. The bearing at A will safely support a force of 2.5-kN magnitude and a couple of 0.5 kN-m magnitude. Based on these criteria, what is the allowable range of the distance b?

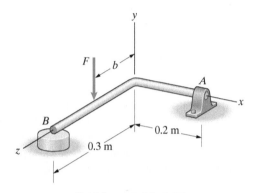

Problems 5.95–5.97

5.98 The 1.1-m bar is supported by a ball and socket support at A and the two smooth walls. The tension in the vertical cable CD is 1 kN.

(a) Draw the free-body diagram of the bar.

(b) Determine the reactions at A and B.

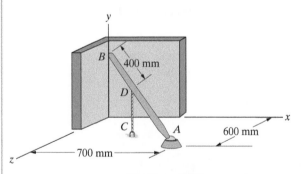

Problem 5.98

5.99 The 8-ft bar is supported by a ball and socket support at A, the cable BD, and a roller support at C. The collar at B is fixed to the bar at its midpoint. The force $\mathbf{F} = -50\mathbf{k}$ (lb). Determine the tension in cable BD and the reactions at A and C.

5.100 The bar is 8 ft in length. The force $\mathbf{F} = F_y\mathbf{j} - 50\mathbf{k}$ (lb). What is the largest value of F_y for which the roller support at C will remain on the floor?

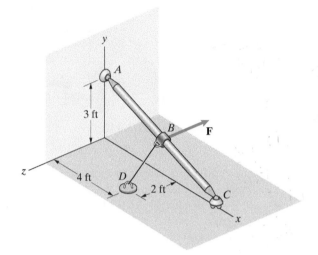

Problems 5.99/5.100

5.101 The tower is 70 m tall. The tension in each cable is 2 kN. Treat the base of the tower A as a fixed support. What are the reactions at A?

5.102 The tower is 70 m tall. If the tension in cable BC is 2 kN, what must the tensions in cables BD and BE be if you want the couple exerted on the tower by the fixed support at A to be zero? What are the resulting reactions at A?

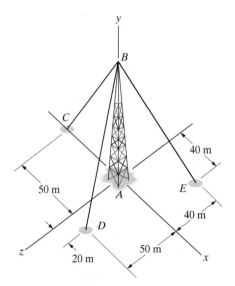

Problems 5.101/5.102

5.103 The space truss has roller supports at B, C, and D and is subjected to a vertical force $F = 20$ kN at A. What are the reactions at the roller supports?

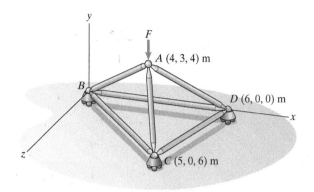

Problem 5.103

▶ **5.104** In Example 5.8, suppose that the cable BD is lengthened and the attachment point B is moved to the end of the bar at C. The positions of the attachment point D and the bar are unchanged. Draw a sketch of the bar showing cable BD in its new position. Draw the free-body diagram of the bar and apply equilibrium to determine the tension in the cable and the reactions at A.

5.105 The 40-lb door is supported by hinges at A and B. The y axis is vertical. The hinges do not exert couples on the door, and the hinge at B does not exert a force parallel to the hinge axis. The weight of the door acts at its midpoint. What are the reactions at A and B?

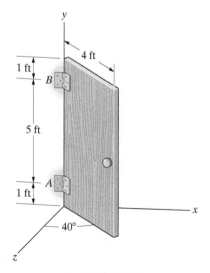

Problem 5.105

5.106 The vertical cable is attached at *A*. Determine the tension in the cable and the reactions at the bearing *B* due to the force $\mathbf{F} = 10\mathbf{i} - 30\mathbf{j} - 10\mathbf{k}$ (N).

5.107 Suppose that the *z* component of the force **F** is zero, but otherwise **F** is unknown. If the couple exerted on the shaft by the bearing at *B* is $\mathbf{M}_B = 6\mathbf{j} - 6\mathbf{k}$ N-m, what are the force **F** and the tension in the cable?

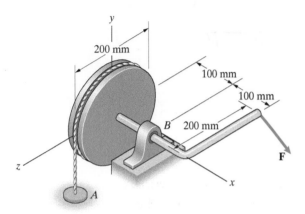

Problems 5.106/5.107

5.108 The device in Problem 5.106 is badly designed because of the couples that must be supported by the bearing at *B*, which would cause the bearing to "bind." (Imagine trying to open a door supported by only one hinge.) In this improved design, the bearings at *B* and *C* support no couples, and the bearing at *C* does not exert a force in the *x* direction. If the force $\mathbf{F} = 10\mathbf{i} - 30\mathbf{j} - 10\mathbf{k}$ (N), what are the tension in the vertical cable and the reactions at the bearings *B* and *C*?

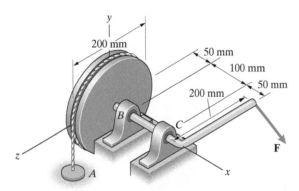

Problem 5.108

5.109 The rocket launcher is supported by the hydraulic jack *DE* and the bearings *A* and *B*. The bearings lie on the *x* axis and support shafts parallel to the *x* axis. The hydraulic cylinder *DE* exerts a force on the launcher that points along the line from *D* to *E*. The coordinates of *D* are (7, 0, 7) ft, and the coordinates of *E* are (9, 6, 4) ft. The weight *W* = 30 kip acts at (4.5, 5, 2) ft. What is the magnitude of the reaction on the launcher at *E*?

5.110 Consider the rocket launcher described in Problem 5.109. The bearings at *A* and *B* do not exert couples, and the bearing *B* does not exert a force in the *x* direction. Determine the reactions at *A* and *B*.

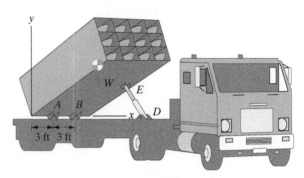

Problems 5.109/5.110

5.111 The crane's cable *CD* is attached to a stationary object at *D*. The crane is supported by the bearings *E* and *F* and the horizontal cable *AB*. The tension in cable *AB* is 8 kN. Determine the tension in the cable *CD*.

Strategy: Since the reactions exerted on the crane by the bearings do not exert moments about the *z* axis, the sum of the moments about the *z* axis due to the forces exerted on the crane by the cables *AB* and *CD* equals zero.

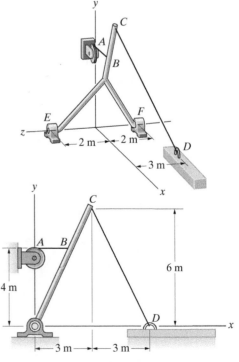

Problem 5.111

▶ **5.112** In Example 5.9, suppose that the cable *CE* is shortened and its attachment point *E* is moved to the point (0, 80, 0) mm. The plate remains in the same position. Draw a sketch of the plate and its supports showing the new position of cable *CE*. Draw the free-body diagram of the plate and apply equilibrium to determine the reactions at the hinges and the tension in the cable.

5.113 The plate is supported by hinges at *A* and *B* and the cable *CE*, and it is loaded by the force at *D*. The edge of the plate to which the hinges are attached lies in the *y–z* plane, and the axes of the hinges are parallel to the line through points *A* and *B*. The hinges do not exert couples on the plate. What is the tension in cable *CE*?

5.114 In Problem 5.113, the hinge at *B* does not exert a force on the plate in the direction of the hinge axis. What are the magnitudes of the forces exerted on the plate by the hinges at *A* and *B*?

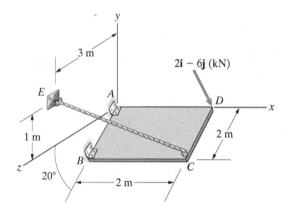

Problems 5.113/5.114

5.115 The bar *ABC* is supported by ball and socket supports at *A* and *C* and the cable *BD*. The suspended mass is 1800 kg. Determine the tension in the cable.

5.116* In Problem 5.115, assume that the ball and socket support at *A* is designed so that it exerts no force parallel to the straight line from *A* to *C*. Determine the reactions at *A* and *C*.

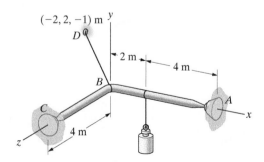

Problems 5.115/5.116

5.117 The bearings at *A*, *B*, and *C* do not exert couples on the bar and do not exert forces in the direction of the axis of the bar. Determine the reactions at the bearings due to the two forces on the bar.

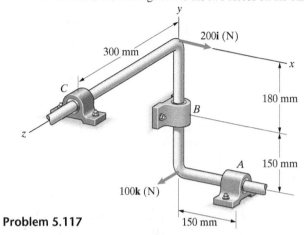

Problem 5.117

5.118 The support that attaches the sailboat's mast to the deck behaves like a ball and socket support. The line that attaches the spinnaker (the sail) to the top of the mast exerts a 200-lb force on the mast. The force is in the horizontal plane at 15° from the centerline of the boat. (See the top view.) The spinnaker pole exerts a 50-lb force on the mast at *P*. The force is in the horizontal plane at 45° from the centerline. (See the top view.) The mast is supported by two cables, the backstay *AB* and the port shroud *ACD*. (The forestay *AE* and the starboard shroud *AFG* are slack, and their tensions can be neglected.) Determine the tensions in the cables *AB* and *CD* and the reactions at the bottom of the mast.

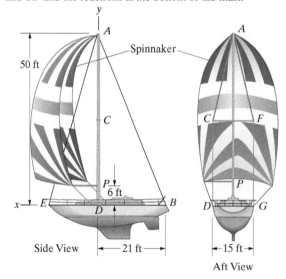

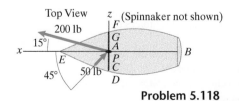

Problem 5.118

5.119* The bar AC is supported by the cable BD and a bearing at A that can rotate about the axis AE. The person exerts a force $\mathbf{F} = 50\mathbf{j}$ (N) at C. Determine the tension in the cable.

Strategy: Use the fact that the sum of the moments about the axis AE due to the forces acting on the free-body diagram of the bar must equal zero.

5.120* In Problem 5.119, determine the reactions at the bearing A.

Strategy: Write the couple exerted on the free-body diagram of the bar by the bearing as $\mathbf{M}_A = M_{Ax}\mathbf{i} + M_{Ay}\mathbf{j} + M_{Az}\mathbf{k}$. Then, in addition to the equilibrium equations, obtain an equation by requiring the component of $\mathbf{M}_A$ parallel to the axis AE to equal zero.

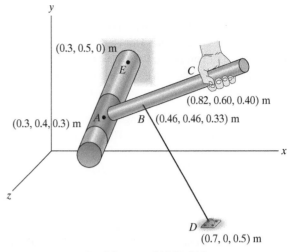

Problems 5.119/5.120

5.4 Two-Force and Three-Force Members

BACKGROUND

We have shown how the equilibrium equations are used to analyze objects that are supported and loaded in different ways. Here we discuss two particular types of loading that occur so frequently they deserve particular attention. The first type, the two-force member, is especially important and plays an important role in our analysis of structures in Chapter 6.

Two-Force Members

If the system of forces and moments acting on an object is equivalent to two forces acting at different points, we refer to the object as a *two-force member*. For example, the object in Fig. 5.19a is subjected to two sets of concurrent forces whose lines of action intersect at A and B. Since we can represent them by single forces acting at A and B (Fig. 5.19b), where $\mathbf{F} = \mathbf{F}_1 + \mathbf{F}_2 + \cdots + \mathbf{F}_N$ and $\mathbf{F}' = \mathbf{F}'_1 + \mathbf{F}'_2 + \cdots + \mathbf{F}'_M$, this object is a two-force member.

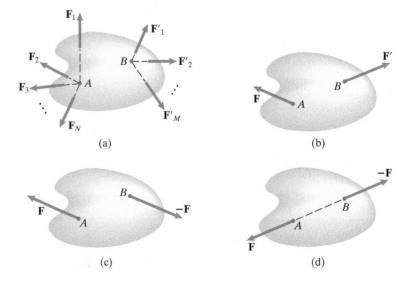

Figure 5.19
(a) An object subjected to two sets of concurrent forces.
(b) Representing the concurrent forces by two forces $\mathbf{F}$ and $\mathbf{F}'$.
(c) If the object is in equilibrium, the forces must be equal and opposite.
(d) The forces form a couple unless they have the same line of action.

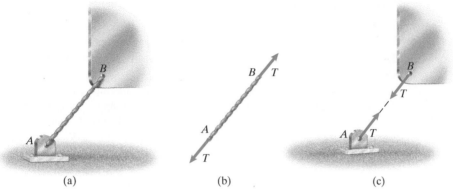

Figure 5.20
(a) A cable attached at A and B.
(b) The cable is a two-force member.
(c) The forces exerted by the cable.

If the object is in equilibrium, what can we infer about the forces $\mathbf{F}$ and $\mathbf{F'}$? The sum of the forces equals zero only if $\mathbf{F'} = -\mathbf{F}$ (Fig. 5.19c). Furthermore, the forces $\mathbf{F}$ and $-\mathbf{F}$ form a couple, so the sum of the moments is not zero unless the lines of action of the forces lie along the line through the points A and B (Fig. 5.19d). Thus equilibrium tells us that *the two forces are equal in magnitude, are opposite in direction, and have the same line of action.* However, without additional information, we cannot determine their magnitude.

A cable attached at two points (Fig. 5.20a) is a familiar example of a two-force member (Fig. 5.20b). The cable exerts forces on the attachment points that are directed along the line between them (Fig. 5.20c).

A bar that has two supports that exert only forces on it (no couples) and is not subjected to any loads is a two-force member (Fig. 5.21a). Such bars are often used as supports for other objects. Because the bar is a two-force member, the lines of action of the forces exerted on the bar must lie along the line between the supports (Fig. 5.21b). Notice that, unlike the cable, the bar can exert forces at A and B either in the directions shown in Fig. 5.21c or in the opposite directions. (In other words, the cable can only pull on its supports, while the bar can either pull or push.)

In these examples we assumed that the weights of the cable and the bar could be neglected in comparison with the forces exerted on them by their supports. When that is not the case, they are clearly not two-force members.

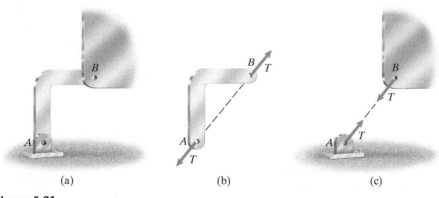

Figure 5.21
(a) The bar AB attaches the object to the pin support.
(b) The bar AB is a two-force member.
(c) The force exerted on the supported object by the bar AB.

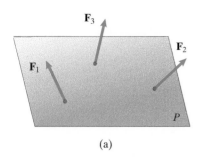

(a)

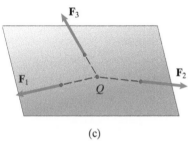

(b)

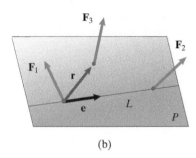

(c)

Figure 5.22
(a) The three forces and the plane P.
(b) Determining the moment due to force $\mathbf{F}_3$ about L.
(c) If the forces are not parallel, they must be concurrent.

Three-Force Members

If the system of forces and moments acting on an object is equivalent to three forces acting at different points, we call it a *three-force member*. We can show that if a three-force member is in equilibrium, the three forces are coplanar and are either parallel or concurrent.

We first prove that the forces are coplanar. Let them be called $\mathbf{F}_1$, $\mathbf{F}_2$, and $\mathbf{F}_3$, and let P be the plane containing the three points of application (Fig. 5.22a). Let L be the line through the points of application of $\mathbf{F}_1$ and $\mathbf{F}_2$. Since the moments due to $\mathbf{F}_1$ and $\mathbf{F}_2$ about L are zero, the moment due to $\mathbf{F}_3$ about L must equal zero (Fig. 5.22b):

$$[\mathbf{e} \cdot (\mathbf{r} \times \mathbf{F}_3)]\mathbf{e} = [\mathbf{F}_3 \cdot (\mathbf{e} \times \mathbf{r})]\mathbf{e} = \mathbf{0}.$$

This equation requires that $\mathbf{F}_3$ be perpendicular to $\mathbf{e} \times \mathbf{r}$, which means that $\mathbf{F}_3$ is contained in P. The same procedure can be used to show that $\mathbf{F}_1$ and $\mathbf{F}_2$ are contained in P, so the forces are coplanar. (A different proof is required if the points of application lie on a straight line, but the result is the same.)

If the three coplanar forces are not parallel, there will be points where their lines of action intersect. Suppose that the lines of action of two of the forces intersect at a point Q. Then the moments of those two forces about Q are zero, and the sum of the moments about Q is zero only if the line of action of the third force also passes through Q. Therefore, either the forces are parallel or they are concurrent (Fig. 5.22c).

The analysis of an object in equilibrium can often be simplified by recognizing that it is a two-force or three-force member. However, in doing so we are not getting something for nothing. Once the free-body diagram of a two-force member is drawn, as shown in Figs. 5.20b and 5.21b, no further information can be obtained from the equilibrium equations. And when we require that the lines of action of nonparallel forces acting on a three-force member be coincident, we have used the fact that the sum of the moments about a point must be zero and cannot obtain further information from that condition.

RESULTS

Two-Force Member
If an object in equilibrium is subjected to two forces acting at different points and *no other forces or couples*, it is called a two-force member. Equilibrium requires that the two forces be equal and opposite and parallel to the line between the two points.

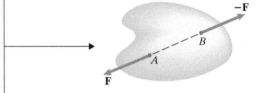

Three-Force Member
If an object in equilibrium is subjected to three forces acting at different points and *no other forces or couples*, it is called a three-force member. Equilibrium requires that the three forces be coplanar and either parallel or concurrent.

Active Example 5.10   Two- and Three-Force Members (▶ *Related Problem 5.121*)

The 100-lb weight of the rectangular plate acts at its midpoint. Neglect the weight of the link *AB*. Determine the reactions exerted on the plate at *B* and *C*.

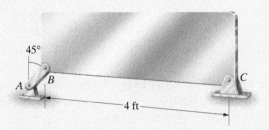

Strategy

The plate is subjected to its weight and the reactions exerted by the pin supports at *B* and *C*, so it is a three-force member. The link *BC* is a two-force member, so the line of action of the reaction it exerts on the plate at *B* must be directed along the line between *A* and *B*. We can use this information to simplify the free-body diagram of the plate.

The reaction exerted on the plate by the two-force member *AB* must be directed along the line between *A* and *B*.

Solution

> The force exerted on the plate by the bar *AB* must be directed along the line between *A* and *B*, and the line of action of the weight of the plate is vertical, so the three forces on the plate are not parallel. Therefore they must be concurrent.

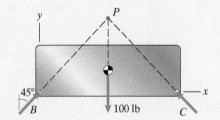

$\Sigma F_x = B \sin 45° - C \sin 45° = 0,$

$\Sigma F_y = B \cos 45° + C \cos 45° - 100 \text{ lb} = 0.$

Solving yields the reactions $B = C = 70.7$ lb.

> Apply the equilibrium equations.

Practice Problem Suppose that the plate is replaced with a 100-lb plate whose thickness (the dimension perpendicular to the page) is not uniform. The line of action of the weight of the nonuniform plate is 3 ft to the right of point *B*. Determine the reactions exerted on the plate at *B* and *C*.

Answer: $B = 35.4$ lb, $C = 79.1$ lb.

Example 5.11 **A Two-Force Member** (▶ *Related Problem 5.122*)

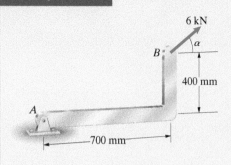

The L-shaped bar has a pin support at A and is loaded by a 6-kN force at B. Neglect the weight of the bar. Determine the angle α and the reactions at A.

Strategy

The bar is a two-force member because it is subjected only to the 6-kN force at B and the force exerted by the pin support. (If we could not neglect the weight of the bar, it would not be a two-force member.) We will determine the angle α and the reactions at A in two ways, first by applying the equilibrium equations in the usual way and then by using the fact that the bar is a two-force member.

Solution

Applying the Equilibrium Equations We draw the free-body diagram of the bar in Fig. a, showing the reactions at the pin support. Summing moments about point A, the equilibrium equations are

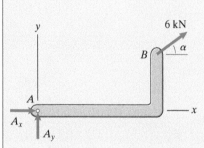

(a) The free-body diagram of the bar.

$$\Sigma F_x = A_x + 6 \cos \alpha \text{ kN} = 0,$$
$$\Sigma F_y = A_y + 6 \sin \alpha \text{ kN} = 0,$$
$$\Sigma M_{\text{point } A} = (0.7 \text{ m})(6 \sin \alpha \text{ kN}) - (0.4 \text{ m})(6 \cos \alpha \text{ kN}) = 0.$$

From the third equation we see that $\alpha = \arctan(0.4/0.7)$. In the range $0 \le \alpha \le 360°$, this equation has the two solutions $\alpha = 29.7°$ and $\alpha = 209.7°$. Knowing α, we can determine A_x and A_y from the first two equilibrium equations. The solutions for the two values of α are

$$\alpha = 29.7°, \quad A_x = -5.21 \text{ kN}, \quad A_y = -2.98 \text{ kN},$$

and

$$\alpha = 209.7°, \quad A_x = 5.21 \text{ kN}, \quad A_y = 2.98 \text{ kN}.$$

Treating the Bar as a Two-Force Member We know that the 6-kN force at B and the force exerted by the pin support must be equal in magnitude, opposite in direction, and directed along the line between points A and B. The two possibilities are shown in Figs. b and c. Thus by recognizing that the bar is a two-force member, we immediately know the possible directions of the forces and the magnitude of the reaction at A.

In Fig. b we can see that $\tan \alpha = 0.4/0.7$, so $\alpha = 29.7°$ and the components of the reaction at A are

$$A_x = -6 \cos 29.7° \text{ kN} = -5.21 \text{ kN},$$
$$A_y = -6 \sin 29.7° \text{ kN} = -2.98 \text{ kN}.$$

In Fig. c, $\alpha = 180° + 29.7° = 209.7°$, and the components of the reaction at A are

$$A_x = 6 \cos 29.7° \text{ kN} = 5.21 \text{ kN}$$
$$A_y = 6 \sin 29.7° \text{ kN} = 2.98 \text{ kN}.$$

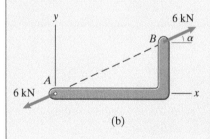

(b)

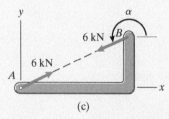

(c)

(b), (c) The possible directions of the forces.

Critical Thinking

Why is it worthwhile to recognize that an object is a two-force member? Doing so tells you the directions of the forces acting on the object and also that the forces are equal and opposite. As this example demonstrates, such information frequently simplifies the solution of a problem.

Problems

▶ **5.121** In Active Example 5.10, suppose that the support at *A* is moved so that the angle between the bar *AB* and the vertical decreases from 45° to 30°. The position of the rectangular plate does not change. Draw the free-body diagram of the plate showing the point *P* where the lines of action of the three forces acting on the plate intersect. Determine the magnitudes of the reactions on the plate at *B* and *C*.

▶ **5.122** The magnitude of the reaction exerted on the L-shaped bar at *B* is 60 lb. (See Example 5.11.)

(a) What is the magnitude of the reaction exerted on the bar by the support at *A*?

(b) What are the *x* and *y* components of the reaction exerted on the bar by the support at *A*?

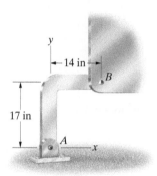

Problem 5.122

5.123 The suspended load weighs 1000 lb. The structure is a three-force member if its weight is neglected. Use this fact to determine the magnitudes of the reactions at *A* and *B*.

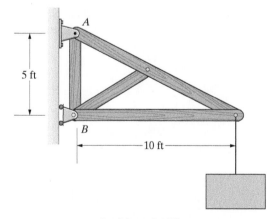

Problem 5.123

5.124 The weight *W* = 50 lb acts at the center of the disk. Use the fact that the disk is a three-force member to determine the tension in the cable and the magnitude of the reaction at the pin support.

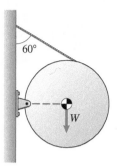

Problem 5.124

5.125 The weight *W* = 40 N acts at the center of the disk. The surfaces are rough. What force *F* is necessary to lift the disk off the floor?

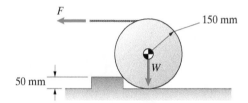

Problem 5.125

5.126 Use the fact that the horizontal bar is a three-force member to determine the angle *α* and the magnitudes of the reactions at *A* and *B*. Assume that $0 \le \alpha \le 90°$.

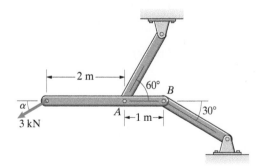

Problem 5.126

5.127 The suspended load weighs 600 lb. Use the fact that *ABC* is a three-force member to determine the magnitudes of the reactions at *A* and *B*.

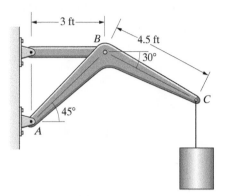

Problem 5.127

5.128 (a) Is the L-shaped bar a three-force member?

(b) Determine the magnitudes of the reactions at *A* and *B*.

(c) Are the three forces acting on the L-shaped bar concurrent?

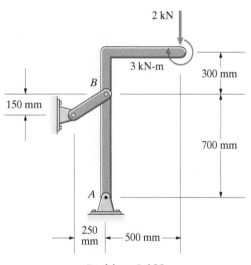

Problem 5.128

5.129 The hydraulic piston exerts a horizontal force at *B* to support the weight *W* = 1500 lb of the bucket of the excavator. Determine the magnitude of the force the hydraulic piston must exert. (The vector sum of the forces exerted at *B* by the hydraulic piston, the two-force member *AB*, and the two-force member *BD* must equal zero.)

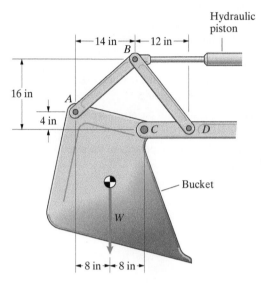

Problem 5.129

5.130 The member *ACG* of the front-end loader is subjected to a load *W* = 2 kN and is supported by a pin support at *A* and the hydraulic cylinder *BC*. Treat the hydraulic cylinder as a two-force member.

(a) Draw the free-body diagrams of the hydraulic cylinder and the member *ACG*.

(b) Determine the reactions on the member *ACG*.

5.131 In Problem 5.130, determine the reactions on the member *ACG* by using the fact that it is a three-force member.

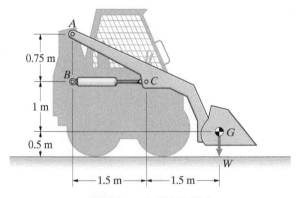

Problems 5.130/5.131

5.132 A rectangular plate is subjected to two forces A and B (Fig. a). In Fig. b, the two forces are resolved into components. By writing equilibrium equations in terms of the components A_x, A_y, B_x, and B_y, show that the two forces A and B are equal in magnitude, opposite in direction, and directed along the line between their points of application.

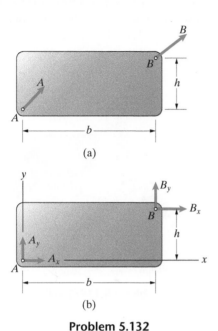

(a)

(b)

Problem 5.132

5.133 An object in equilibrium is subjected to three forces whose points of application lie on a straight line. Prove that the forces are coplanar.

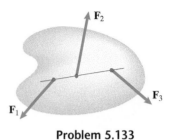

Problem 5.133

Review Problems

5.134 The suspended cable weighs 12 lb.

(a) Draw the free-body diagram of the cable. (The tensions in the cable at A and B are *not* equal.)

(b) Determine the tensions in the cable at A and B.

(c) What is the tension in the cable at its lowest point?

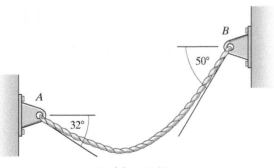

Problem 5.134

5.135 Determine the reactions at the fixed support.

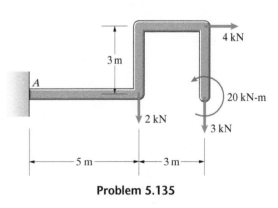

Problem 5.135

5.136 (a) Draw the free-body diagram of the 50-lb plate, and explain why it is statically indeterminate.

(b) Determine as many of the reactions at A and B as possible.

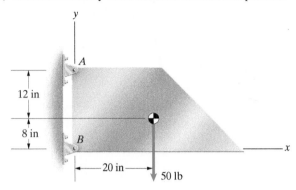

Problem 5.136

5.137 The mass of the truck is 4000 kg. Its wheels are locked, and the tension in its cable is $T = 10$ kN.

(a) Draw the free-body diagram of the truck.

(b) Determine the normal forces exerted on the truck's wheels at A and B by the road.

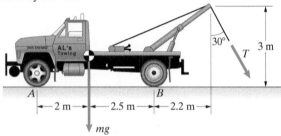

Problem 5.137

5.138 Assume that the force exerted on the head of the nail by the hammer is vertical, and neglect the hammer's weight.

(a) Draw the free-body diagram of the hammer.

(b) If $F = 10$ lb, what are the magnitudes of the force exerted on the nail by the hammer and the normal and friction forces exerted on the floor by the hammer?

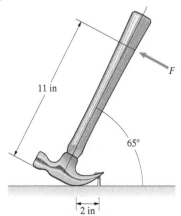

Problem 5.138

5.139 The spring constant is $k = 9600$ N/m and the unstretched length of the spring is 30 mm. Treat the bolt at A as a pin support and assume that the surface at C is smooth. Determine the reactions at A and the normal force at C.

5.140 The engineer designing the release mechanism wants the normal force exerted at C to be 120 N. If the unstretched length of the spring is 30 mm, what is the necessary value of the spring constant k?

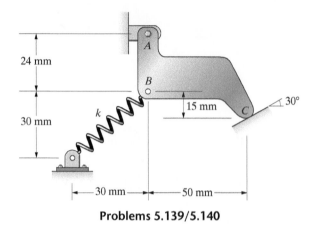

Problems 5.139/5.140

5.141 The truss supports a 90-kg suspended object. What are the reactions at the supports A and B?

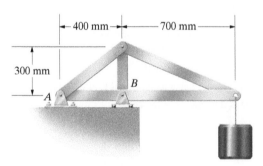

Problem 5.141

5.142 The trailer is parked on a 15° slope. Its wheels are free to turn. The hitch *H* behaves like a pin support. Determine the reactions at *A* and *H*.

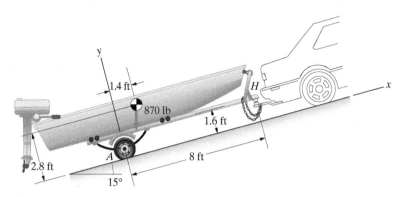

Problem 5.142

5.143 To determine the location of the point where the weight of a car acts (the *center of mass*), an engineer places the car on scales and measures the normal reactions at the wheels for two values of α, obtaining the following results.

α	A_y (kN)	B (kN)
10°	10.134	4.357
20°	10.150	3.677

What are the distances *b* and *h*?

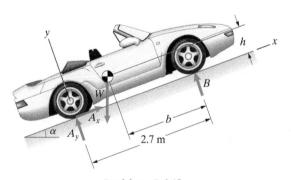

Problem 5.143

5.144 The bar is attached by pin supports to collars that slide on the two fixed bars. Its mass is 10 kg, it is 1 m in length, and its weight acts at its midpoint. Neglect friction and the masses of the collars. The spring is unstretched when the bar is vertical ($\alpha = 0$), and the spring constant is $k = 100$ N/m. Determine the values of α in the range $0 \le \alpha \le 60°$ at which the bar is in equilibrium.

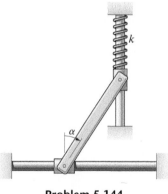

Problem 5.144

5.145 With each of the devices shown you can support a load R by applying a force F. They are called levers of the first, second, and third class.

(a) The ratio R/F is called the *mechanical advantage*. Determine the mechanical advantage of each lever.

(b) Determine the magnitude of the reaction at A for each lever. (Express your answers in terms of F.)

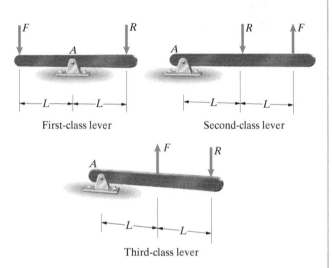

First-class lever   Second-class lever

Third-class lever

Problem 5.145

5.146 The force exerted by the weight of the horizontal rectangular plate is 800 N. The weight of the rectangular plate acts at its midpoint. If you represent the reactions exerted on the plate by the three cables by a single equivalent force, what is the force, and where does its line of action intersect the plate?

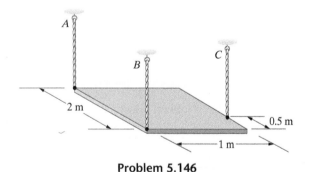

Problem 5.146

5.147 The 20-kg mass is suspended by cables attached to three vertical 2-m posts. Point A is at $(0, 1.2, 0)$ m. Determine the reactions at the fixed support at E.

5.148 In Problem 5.147, the fixed support of each vertical post will safely support a couple of 800 N-m magnitude. Based on this criterion, what is the maximum safe value of the suspended mass?

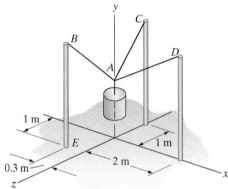

Problems 5.147/148

5.149 The 80-lb bar is supported by a ball and socket support at A, the smooth wall it leans against, and the cable BC. The weight of the bar acts at its midpoint.

(a) Draw the free-body diagram of the bar.

(b) Determine the tension in cable BC and the reactions at A.

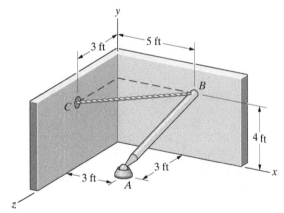

Problem 5.149

5.150 The horizontal bar of weight W is supported by a roller support at A and the cable BC. Use the fact that the bar is a three-force member to determine the angle α, the tension in the cable, and the magnitude of the reaction at A.

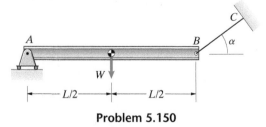

Problem 5.150

Design Project 1 The traditional wheelbarrow shown is designed to transport a load W while being supported by an upward force F applied to the handles by the user. (a) Use statics to analyze the effects of a range of choices of the dimensions a and b on the size of load that could be carried. Also consider the implications of these dimensions on the wheelbarrow's ease and practicality of use. (b) Suggest a different design for this classic device that achieves the same function. Use statics to compare your design to the wheelbarrow with respect to load-carrying ability and ease of use.

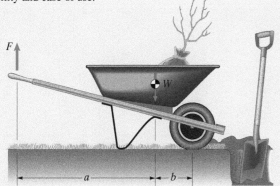

Design Project 2 The figure shows an example of the popular devices called "mobiles," which were introduced as an art form by American artist Alexander Calder (1898–1976). Suppose that you want to design a mobile representing the solar system, and have chosen colored spheres to represent the planets. The masses of the spheres that represent Mercury, Venus, Earth, Mars, Jupiter, Saturn, Uranus, Neptune, and Pluto are 10 g, 25 g, 25 g, 10 g, 50 g, 40 g, 40 g, 40 g, and 10 g. Assume that the cross bars and string you use are of negligible mass. Design your mobile so that the planets are in their correct order relative to the sun. Write a brief report including a drawing of your design and the analysis proving that your mobile is balanced.

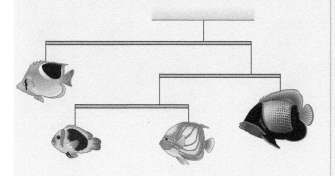

Design Project 3 The bed of the dump truck (Fig. a) is raised by two tandem hydraulic cylinders AB (Fig. b). The mass of the truck's bed and load is 16,000 kg and its weight acts at point G. (Assume that the position of point G *relative to the bed* does not change when the bed is raised.)

(a) Draw a graph of the magnitude of the total force the hydraulic cylinders must exert to support the stationary bed for values of the angle α from zero to 30°.

(b) Consider other choices for the locations of the attachment points A and B that appear to be feasible and investigate how your choices affect the magnitude of the total force the hydraulic cylinders must exert as α varies from zero to 30°. Also compare the costs of your choices of the attachment points to the choices shown in Fig. a, assuming that the cost of the hydraulic cylinders is proportional to the product of the maximum force they must exert as α varies from zero to 30° and their length when $\alpha = 30°$.

(c) Write a brief report presenting your investigations and making a recommendation for the locations of points A and B.

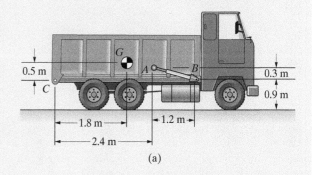

(a)

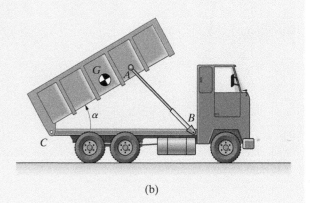

(b)

CHAPTER
6

Structures in Equilibrium

In engineering, the term *structure* can refer to any object that has the capacity to support and exert loads. In this chapter we consider structures composed of interconnected parts, or *members*. To design such a structure, or to determine whether an existing one is adequate, it is necessary to determine the forces and couples acting on the structure as a whole as well as on its individual members. We first demonstrate how this is done for the structures called trusses, which are composed entirely of two-force members. The familiar frameworks of steel members that support some highway bridges are trusses. We then consider other structures, called *frames* if they are designed to remain stationary and support loads and *machines* if they are designed to move and exert loads.

◀ The Neolithic engineers who built Stonehenge set an example for the design of enduring structures. In this chapter we describe techniques for determining the forces and couples acting on individual members of structures.

6.1 Trusses

We can explain the nature of truss structures such as the beams supporting a house (Fig. 6.1) by starting with very simple examples. Suppose we pin three bars together at their ends to form a triangle. If we add supports as shown in Fig. 6.2a, we obtain a structure that will support a load F. We can construct more elaborate structures by adding more triangles (Figs. 6.2b and c). The bars are the members of these structures, and the places where the bars are pinned together are called the *joints*. Even though these examples are quite simple, you can see that Fig. 6.2c, which is called a Warren truss, begins to resemble the structures used to support bridges and the roofs of houses (Fig. 6.3). If these structures are supported and loaded at their joints and we neglect the weights of the bars, each bar is a two-force member. We call such a structure a *truss*.

We draw the free-body diagram of a member of a truss in Fig. 6.4a. Because it is a two-force member, the forces at the ends, which are the sums of the forces exerted on the member at its joints, must be equal in magnitude, opposite in direction, and directed along the line between the joints. We call the force T the *axial force* in the member. When T is positive in the direction shown (that is, when the forces are directed away from each other), the member is in *tension*. When the forces are directed toward each other, the member is in *compression*.

In Fig. 6.4b, we "cut" the member by a plane and draw the free-body diagram of the part of the member on one side of the plane. We represent the system of internal forces and moments exerted by the part not included in the free-body diagram by a force **F** acting at the point P where the plane intersects

Figure 6.1
A typical house is supported by trusses made of wood beams.

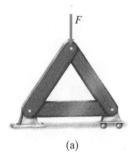

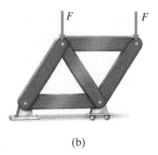

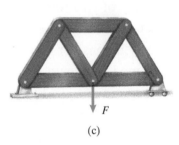

(a)   (b)   (c)

Figure 6.2
Making structures by pinning bars together to form triangles.

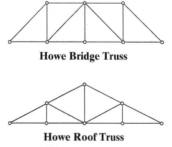

Howe Bridge Truss   Pratt Bridge Truss

Howe Roof Truss

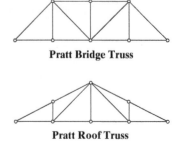

Pratt Roof Truss

Figure 6.3
Simple examples of bridge and roof structures. (The lines represent members, the circles represent joints.)

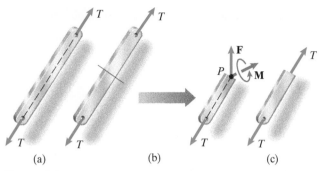

Figure 6.4
(**a**) Each member of a truss is a two-force member.
(**b**) Obtaining the free-body diagram of part of the member.
(**c**) The internal force is equal and opposite to the force acting at
the joint, and the internal couple is zero.

the axis of the member and a couple $\mathbf{M}$. The sum of the moments about P must
equal zero, so $\mathbf{M} = \mathbf{0}$. Therefore we have a two-force member, which means
that $\mathbf{F}$ must be equal in magnitude and opposite in direction to the force T acting at the joint (Fig. 6.4c). The internal force is a tension or compression equal
to the tension or compression exerted at the joint. Notice the similarity to a
rope or cable, in which the internal force is a tension equal to the tension applied at the ends.

Although many actual structures, including "roof trusses" and "bridge
trusses," consist of bars connected at the ends, very few have pinned joints.
For example, a joint of a bridge truss is shown in Fig. 6.5. The ends of the
members are welded at the joint and are not free to rotate. It is obvious that
such a joint can exert couples on the members. Why are these structures called
trusses?

The reason is that they are designed to function as trusses, meaning that they
support loads primarily by subjecting their members to axial forces. They can
usually be *modeled* as trusses, treating the joints as pinned connections under
the assumption that couples they exert on the members are small in comparison
to axial forces. When we refer to structures with riveted joints as trusses in problems, we mean that you can model them as trusses.

Figure 6.5
A joint of a bridge truss.

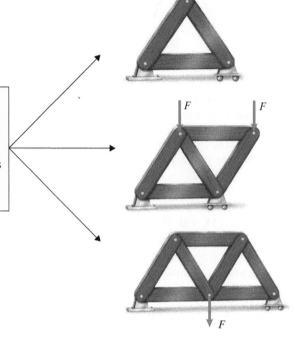

Trusses

Structures that consist of straight bars pinned at the ends and are supported and loaded only at the *joints* where the members are connected are called *trusses*. It is assumed that the weights of the members are negligible in comparison to the applied loads.

Free-Body Diagram of an Individual Member

Because *each member of a truss is a two-force member*, it is subjected only to equal and opposite axial loads. We call the force T the *axial force* in a member. When T is positive in the direction shown (that is, when the forces are directed away from each other), the member is in *tension* (T). When the forces are directed toward each other, the member is in *compression* (C).

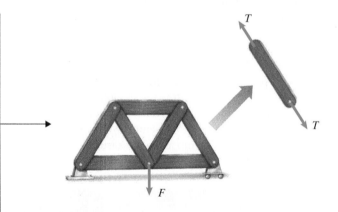

6.2 The Method of Joints

The method of joints involves drawing free-body diagrams of the joints of a truss one by one and using the equilibrium equations to determine the axial forces in the members. Before beginning, it is usually necessary to draw a free-body diagram of the entire truss (that is, treat the truss as a single object) and determine the reactions at its supports. For example, let's consider the Warren truss in Fig. 6.6a, which has members 2 m in length and supports

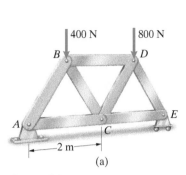

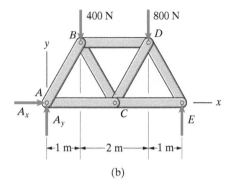

Figure 6.6
(a) A Warren truss supporting two loads.
(b) Free-body diagram of the truss.

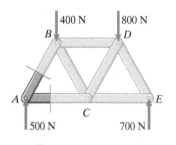

loads at B and D. We draw its free-body diagram in Fig. 6.6b. From the equilibrium equations,

$$\Sigma F_x = A_x = 0,$$
$$\Sigma F_y = A_y + E - 400 \text{ N} - 800 \text{ N} = 0,$$
$$\Sigma M_{\text{point } A} = -(1 \text{ m})(400 \text{ N}) - (3 \text{ m})(800 \text{ N}) + (4 \text{ m})E = 0,$$

we obtain the reactions $A_x = 0$, $A_y = 500$ N, and $E = 700$ N.

Our next step is to choose a joint and draw its free-body diagram. In Fig. 6.7a, we isolate joint A by cutting members AB and AC. The terms T_{AB} and T_{AC} are the axial forces in members AB and AC, respectively. Although the directions of the arrows representing the unknown axial forces can be chosen arbitrarily, notice that we have chosen them so that a member is in tension if we obtain a positive value for the axial force. Consistently choosing the directions in this way helps avoid errors.

The equilibrium equations for joint A are

$$\Sigma F_x = T_{AC} + T_{AB} \cos 60° = 0,$$
$$\Sigma F_y = T_{AB} \sin 60° + 500 \text{ N} = 0.$$

Solving these equations, we obtain the axial forces $T_{AB} = -577$ N and $T_{AC} = 289$ N. Member AB is in compression, and member AC is in tension (Fig. 6.7b).

Although we use a realistic figure for the joint in Fig. 6.7a to help you understand the free-body diagram, in your own work you can use a simple figure showing only the forces acting on the joint (Fig. 6.7c).

We next obtain a free-body diagram of joint B by cutting members AB, BC, and BD (Fig. 6.8a). From the equilibrium equations for joint B,

$$\Sigma F_x = T_{BD} + T_{BC} \cos 60° + 577 \cos 60° \text{ N} = 0,$$
$$\Sigma F_y = -400 \text{ N} + 577 \sin 60° \text{ N} - T_{BC} \sin 60° = 0,$$

we obtain $T_{BC} = 115$ N and $T_{BD} = -346$ N. Member BC is in tension, and member BD is in compression (Fig. 6.8b). By continuing to draw free-body diagrams of the joints, we can determine the axial forces in all of the members.

In two dimensions, you can obtain only two independent equilibrium equations from the free-body diagram of a joint. Summing the moments about a point does not result in an additional independent equation because the forces are concurrent. Therefore when applying the method of joints, you should choose joints to analyze that are subjected to no more than two unknown forces. In our

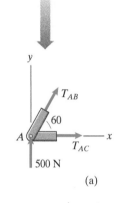

(a)

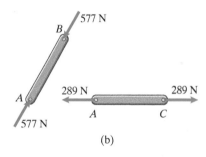

(b)

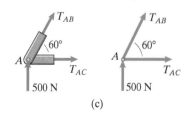

(c)

Figure 6.7
(a) Obtaining the free-body diagram of joint A.
(b) The axial forces on members AB and AC.
(c) Realistic and simple free-body diagrams of joint A.

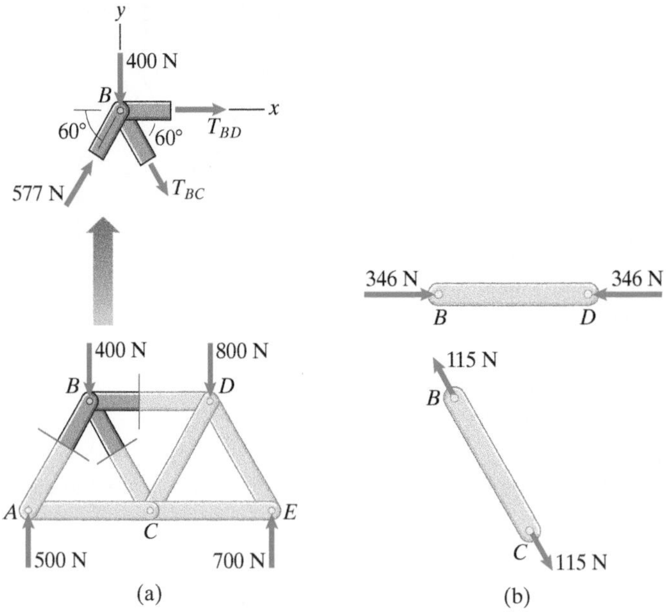

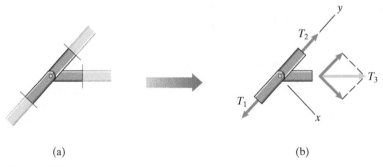

Figure 6.8
(a) Obtaining the free-body diagram of joint B.
(b) Axial forces in members BD and BC.

(a)

(b)

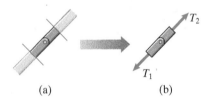

(a)   (b)

Figure 6.9
(a) A joint with two collinear members and no load.
(b) Free-body diagram of the joint.

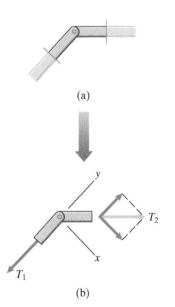

(a)

(b)

Figure 6.10
(a) A joint with two noncollinear members and no load.
(b) Free-body diagram of the joint.

example, we analyzed joint A first because it was subjected to the known reaction exerted by the pin support and two unknown forces, the axial forces T_{AB} and T_{AC} (Fig. 6.7a). We could then analyze joint B because it was subjected to two known forces and two unknown forces, T_{BC} and T_{BD} (Fig. 6.8a). If we had attempted to analyze joint B first, there would have been three unknown forces.

When you determine the axial forces in the members of a truss, your task will often be simpler if you are familiar with three particular types of joints.

- **Truss joints with two collinear members and no load** (Fig. 6.9). The sum of the forces must equal zero, $T_1 = T_2$. The axial forces are equal.
- **Truss joints with two noncollinear members and no load** (Fig. 6.10). Because the sum of the forces in the x direction must equal zero, $T_2 = 0$. Therefore T_1 must also equal zero. The axial forces are zero.
- **Truss joints with three members, two of which are collinear, and no load** (Fig. 6.11). Because the sum of the forces in the x direction must equal zero, $T_3 = 0$. The sum of the forces in the y direction must equal zero, so $T_1 = T_2$. The axial forces in the collinear members are equal, and the axial force in the third member is zero.

(a)   (b)

Figure 6.11
(a) A joint with three members, two of which are collinear, and no load.
(b) Free-body diagram of the joint.

RESULTS

Method of Joints

Before beginning, it is usually necessary to draw the free-body diagram of the entire truss considered as a single object and apply the equilibrium equations to determine the reactions at the supports.

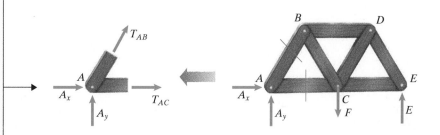

Isolate an individual joint by passing planes through the connected members. Complete the free-body diagram by showing the axial forces in the members. Apply the equilibrium equations $\Sigma F_x = 0$ and $\Sigma F_y = 0$ to the free-body diagram of the joint. Repeat this process for other joints until the desired axial loads have been determined.

Special Joints

If a joint consists of two collinear members and no external load is applied to the joint, the axial forces in the members are equal.

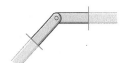

If a joint consists of two noncollinear members and no external load is applied to the joint, there is no axial force in either member.

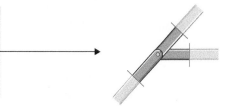

If a joint consists of three members, two of which are collinear, and no external load is applied to the joint, the axial forces in the collinear members are equal and the axial force in the third member is zero.

Active Example 6.1   The Method of Joints (▶ *Related Problem 6.1*)

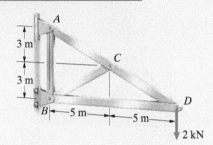

Determine the axial forces in members *AB* and *AC* of the truss.

Strategy
We will first draw a free-body diagram of the entire truss, treating it as a single object, and determine the reactions at the supports. Then we can determine the axial forces in members *AB* and *AC* by drawing the free-body diagram of joint *A*.

Solution

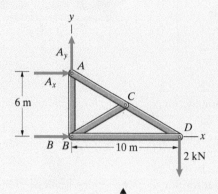

$\Sigma F_x = A_x + B = 0,$

$\Sigma F_y = A_y - 2\ \text{kN} = 0,$

$\Sigma M_{\text{point } B} = -(6\ \text{m})A_x - (10\ \text{m})(2\ \text{kN}) = 0.$

Solving yields $A_x = -3.33\ \text{kN}$, $A_y = 2\ \text{kN}$,
and $B = 3.33\ \text{kN}$.

Draw the free-body diagram of the entire truss and apply the equilibrium equations.

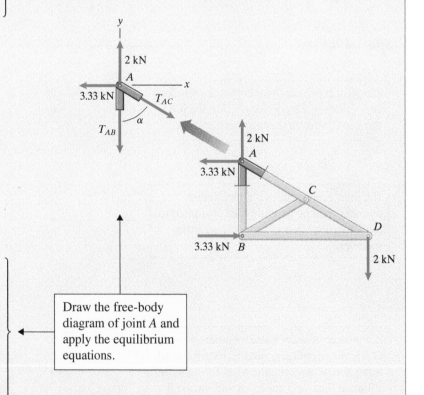

Draw the free-body diagram of joint *A* and apply the equilibrium equations.

The angle $\alpha = \arctan(5/3) = 59.0°$.

$\Sigma F_x = T_{AC} \sin\alpha - 3.33\ \text{kN} = 0,$

$\Sigma F_y = 2\ \text{kN} - T_{AB} - T_{AC}\cos\alpha = 0.$

Solving yields $T_{AB} = 0$ and $T_{AC} = 3.89\ \text{kN}$.
The axial force in member *AB* is zero and
the axial force in member *AC* is 3.89 kN
in tension, which we write as

  AB: zero, *AC*: 3.89 kN (T).

Practice Problem Determine the axial forces in members BC and BD of the truss. In doing so, use the fact that it is already known from the analysis of joint A that the axial force in member AB is zero.

Answer: BC: zero, BD: 3.33 kN (C).

Example 6.2   A Bridge Truss (▶ *Related Problem 6.31*)

The loads a bridge structure must support and pin supports where the structure is to be attached are shown in Fig. 1. Assigned to design the structure, a civil engineering student proposes the structure shown in Fig. 2. What are the axial forces in the members?

Strategy
The vertical members AG, BH, CI, DJ, and EK are subjected to compressive forces of magnitude F. Because of the symmetry of the structure, we can determine the axial loads in the remaining members by analyzing joints C and B.

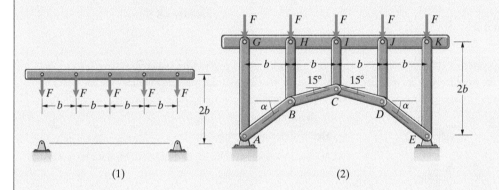

(1)   (2)

Solution
We will leave it as an exercise to show by drawing the free-body diagram of joint C that members BC and CD are subjected to equal compressive loads of magnitude $1.93F$. We draw the free-body diagram of joint B in Fig. a, where $T_{BC} = -1.93F$.

From the equilibrium equations

$$\Sigma F_x = -T_{AB} \cos \alpha + T_{BC} \cos 15° = 0,$$

$$\Sigma F_y = -T_{AB} \sin \alpha + T_{BC} \sin 15° - F = 0,$$

we obtain $T_{AB} = -2.39F$ and $\alpha = 38.8°$. By symmetry, $T_{DE} = T_{AB}$. The axial forces in the members are shown in the table.

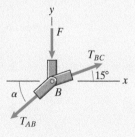

(a) Free-body diagram of joint B.

Axial forces in the members of the bridge structure

Members	Axial Force
AG, BH, CI, DJ, EK	F (C)
AB, DE	$2.39F$ (C)
BC, CD	$1.93F$ (C)

Problems

▶ **6.1** In Active Example 6.1, suppose that in addition to the 2-kN downward force acting at point *D*, a 2-kN downward force acts at point *C*. Draw a sketch of the truss showing the new loading. Determine the axial forces in members *AB* and *AC* of the truss.

6.2 Determine the axial forces in the members of the truss and indicate whether they are in tension (T) or compression (C).

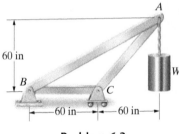

Problem 6.2

6.3 Member *AB* of the truss is subjected to a 1000-lb tensile force. Determine the weight *W* and the axial force in member *AC*.

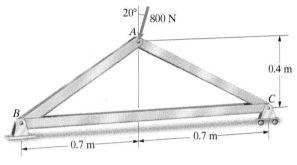

Problem 6.3

6.4 Determine the axial forces in members *BC* and *CD* of the truss.

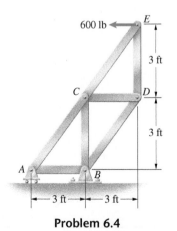

Problem 6.4

6.5 Each suspended weight has mass *m* = 20 kg. Determine the axial forces in the members of the truss and indicate whether they are in tension (T) or compression (C).

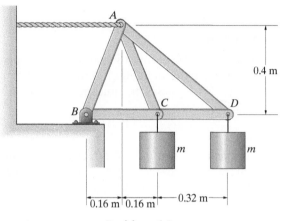

Problem 6.5

6.6 Determine the largest tensile and compressive forces that occur in the members of the truss, and indicate the members in which they occur if

(a) the dimension *h* = 0.1 m;

(b) the dimension *h* = 0.5 m.

Observe how a simple change in design affects the maximum axial loads.

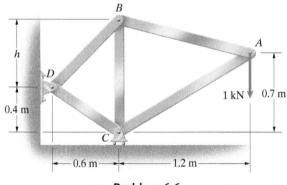

Problem 6.6

6.7 This steel truss bridge is in the Gallatin National Forest south of Bozeman, Montana. Suppose that one of the tandem trusses supporting the bridge is loaded as shown. Determine the axial forces in members *AB*, *BC*, *BD*, and *BE*.

6.8 Determine the largest tensile and compressive forces that occur in the members of the bridge truss, and indicate the members in which they occur.

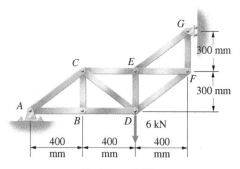

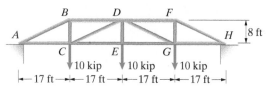

Problems 6.7/6.8

6.9 The trusses supporting the bridge in Problems 6.7 and 6.8 are called Pratt trusses. Suppose that the bridge designers had decided to use the truss shown instead, which is called a Howe truss. Determine the largest tensile and compressive forces that occur in the members, and indicate the members in which they occur. Compare your answers to the answers to Problem 6.8.

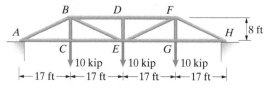

Problem 6.9

6.10 Determine the axial forces in members *BD*, *CD*, and *CE* of the truss.

Problem 6.10

6.11 The loads $F_1 = F_2 = 8$ kN. Determine the axial forces in members *BD*, *BE*, and *BG*.

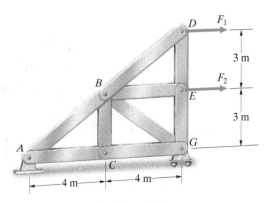

Problem 6.11

6.12 Determine the largest tensile and compressive forces that occur in the members of the truss, and indicate the members in which they occur if

(a) the dimension $h = 5$ in;

(b) the dimension $h = 10$ in.

Observe how a simple change in design affects the maximum axial loads.

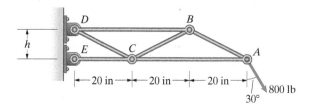

Problem 6.12

6.13 The truss supports loads at *C* and *E*. If $F = 3$ kN, what are the axial forces in members *BC* and *BE*?

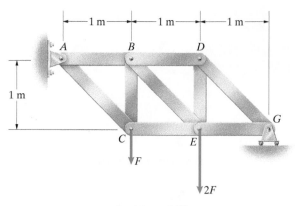

Problem 6.13

6.14 If you don't want the members of the truss to be subjected to an axial load (tension or compression) greater than 20 kN, what is the largest acceptable magnitude of the downward force F?

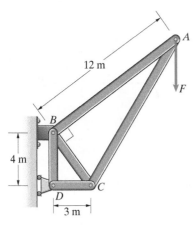

Problem 6.14

6.15 The truss is a preliminary design for a structure to attach one end of a stretcher to a rescue helicopter. Based on dynamic simulations, the design engineer estimates that the downward forces the stretcher will exert will be no greater than 1.6 kN at A and at B. What are the resulting axial forces in members CF, DF, and FG?

6.16 Upon learning of an upgrade in the helicopter's engine, the engineer designing the truss does new simulations and concludes that the downward forces the stretcher will exert at A and at B may be as large as 1.8 kN. What are the resulting axial forces in members DE, DF, and DG?

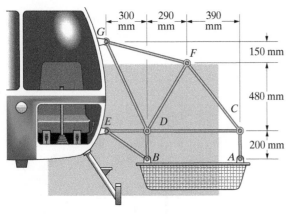

Problems 6.15/6.16

6.17 Determine the axial forces in the members in terms of the weight W.

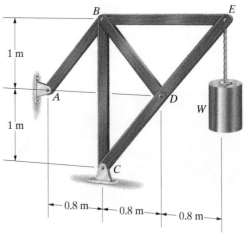

Problem 6.17

6.18 The lengths of the members of the truss are shown. The mass of the suspended crate is 900 kg. Determine the axial forces in the members.

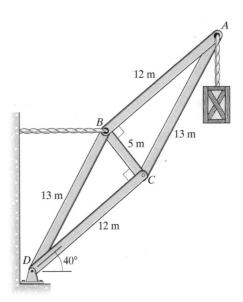

Problem 6.18

6.19 The loads $F_1 = 600$ lb and $F_2 = 300$ lb. Determine the axial forces in members AE, BD, and CD.

6.20 The loads $F_1 = 450$ lb and $F_2 = 150$ lb. Determine the axial forces in members AB, AC, and BC.

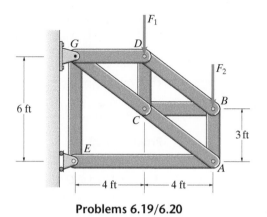

Problems 6.19/6.20

6.21 Determine the axial forces in members BC, CD, and CE of the truss.

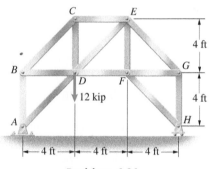

Problem 6.21

6.22 The Warren truss supporting the walkway is designed to support vertical 50-kN loads at B, D, F, and H. If the truss is subjected to these loads, what are the resulting axial forces in members BC, CD, and CE?

6.23 For the Warren truss in Problem 6.22, determine the axial forces in members DF, EF, and FG.

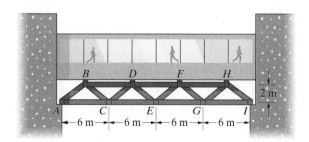

Problems 6.22/6.23

6.24 The Pratt bridge truss supports five forces ($F = 300$ kN). The dimension $L = 8$ m. Determine the axial forces in members BC, BI, and BJ.

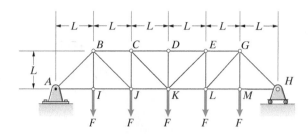

Problem 6.24

6.25 For the roof truss shown, determine the axial forces in members AD, BD, DE, and DG. Model the supports at A and I as roller supports.

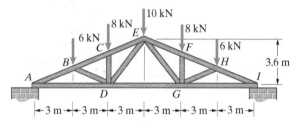

Problem 6.25

6.26 The Howe truss helps support a roof. Model the supports at A and G as roller supports. Determine the axial forces in members AB, BC, and CD.

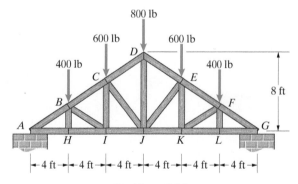

Problem 6.26

6.27 The plane truss forms part of the supports of a crane on an offshore oil platform. The crane exerts vertical 75-kN forces on the truss at B, C, and D. You can model the support at A as a pin support and model the support at E as a roller support that can exert a force normal to the dashed line but cannot exert a force parallel to it. The angle $\alpha = 45°$. Determine the axial forces in the members of the truss.

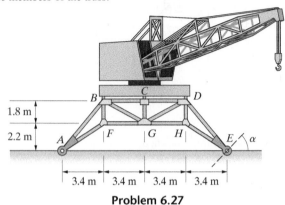

Problem 6.27

6.28 (a) Design a truss attached to the supports A and B that supports the loads applied at points C and D. (b) Determine the axial forces in the members of the truss you designed in (a).

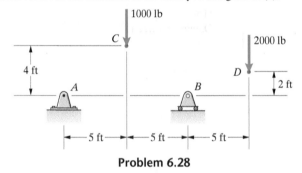

Problem 6.28

6.29 (a) Design a truss attached to the supports A and B that goes over the obstacle and supports the load applied at C.

(b) Determine the axial forces in the members of the truss you designed in (a).

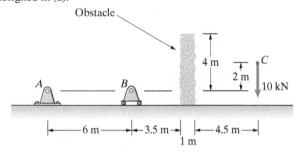

Problem 6.29

6.30 Suppose that you want to design a truss supported at A and B (Fig. a) to support a 3-kN downward load at C. The simplest design (Fig. b) subjects member AC to a 5-kN tensile force. Redesign the truss so that the largest tensile force is less than 3 kN.

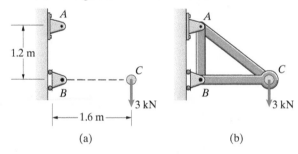

Problem 6.30

▶ **6.31** The bridge structure shown in Example 6.2 can be given a higher arch by increasing the 15° angles to 20°. If this is done, what are the axial forces in members AB, BC, CD, and DE?

6.3 The Method of Sections

BACKGROUND

When we need to know the axial forces only in certain members of a truss, we often can determine them more quickly using the method of sections than using the method of joints. For example, let's reconsider the Warren truss we used to introduce the method of joints (Fig. 6.12a). It supports loads at B and D, and each member is 2 m in length. Suppose that we need to determine only the axial force in member BC.

Figure 6.12
(a) A Warren truss supporting two loads.
(b) Free-body diagram of the truss, showing the reactions at the supports.

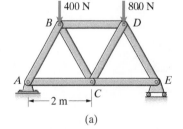

(a)

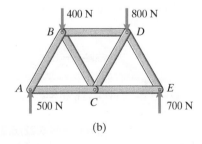

(b)

Just as in the method of joints, we begin by drawing a free-body diagram of the entire truss and determining the reactions at the supports. The results of this step are shown in Fig. 6.12b. Our next step is to cut the members AC, BC, and BD to obtain a free-body diagram of a part, or *section*, of the truss (Fig. 6.13). Summing moments about point B, the equilibrium equations for the section are

$$\Sigma F_x = T_{AC} + T_{BD} + T_{BC} \cos 60° = 0,$$
$$\Sigma F_y = 500 \text{ N} - 400 \text{ N} - T_{BC} \sin 60° = 0,$$
$$\Sigma M_{\text{point } B} = (2 \sin 60° \text{ m})T_{AC} - (2 \cos 60° \text{ m})(500 \text{ N}) = 0.$$

Solving them, we obtain $T_{AC} = 289$ N, $T_{BC} = 115$ N, and $T_{BD} = -346$ N.

Notice how similar this method is to the method of joints. Both methods involve cutting members to obtain free-body diagrams of parts of a truss. In the method of joints, we move from joint to joint, drawing free-body diagrams of the joints and determining the axial forces in the members as we go. In the method of sections, we try to obtain a single free-body diagram that allows us to determine the axial forces in specific members. In our example, we obtained a free-body diagram by cutting three members, including the one (member BC) whose axial force we wanted to determine.

In contrast to the free-body diagrams of joints, the forces on the free-body diagrams used in the method of sections are not usually concurrent, and as in our example, we can obtain three independent equilibrium equations. Although there are exceptions, it is usually necessary to choose a section that requires cutting no more than three members, or there will be more unknown axial forces than equilibrium equations.

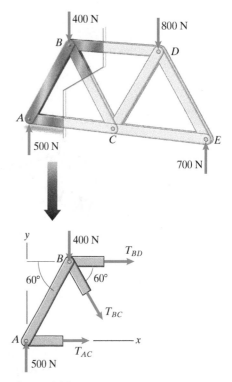

Figure 6.13
Obtaining a free-body diagram of a section of the truss.

The Method of Sections

When the axial forces in particular members of a truss must be determined, the method of sections can often provide the needed results more efficiently than the method of joints.

Before beginning, it is usually advantageous to draw the free-body diagram of the entire truss considered as a single object and apply the equilibrium equations to determine the reactions at the supports.	

Pass planes through enough members to isolate a part, or *section*, of the truss. In doing so, attempt to pass planes through members whose axial forces are to be determined. Complete the free-body diagram of the section by showing the axial forces in the members. Apply the equilibrium equations to the free-body diagram of the section.	

Active Example 6.3 | **The Method of Sections** (▶ *Related Problem 6.32*)

The horizontal members of the truss are each 1 m in length. Determine the axial forces in members *CD*, *CJ*, and *IJ*.

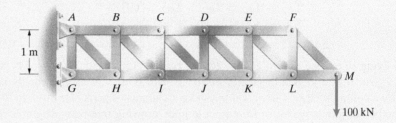

Strategy

By passing planes through members *CD*, *CJ*, and *IJ*, we will obtain a section from which we can obtain the desired axial forces.

Solution

Pass planes through members *CD*, *CJ*, and *IJ* and draw the free-body diagram of the section.

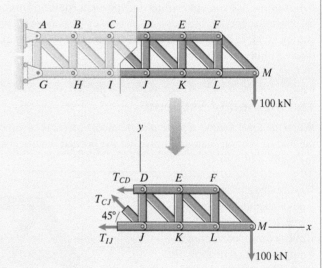

$$\Sigma F_x = -T_{CD} - T_{CJ}\cos 45° - T_{IJ} = 0,$$

$$\Sigma F_y = T_{CJ}\sin 45° - 100 \text{ kN} = 0,$$

$$\Sigma M_{\text{point } J} = (1 \text{ m})T_{CD} - (3 \text{ m})(100 \text{ kN}) = 0.$$

Solving yields $T_{CD} = 300$ kN, $T_{CJ} = 141$ kN, and $T_{IJ} = -400$ kN. The axial loads are *CD*: 300 kN (T), *CJ*: 141 kN (T), *IJ*: 400 kN (C).

Apply the equilibrium equations.

Practice Problem Use the method of sections to determine the axial forces in members *DE*, *DK*, and *JK* of the truss.

Answer: *DE*: 200 kN (T), *DK*: 141 kN (T), *JK*: 300 kN (C).

Example 6.4   Choosing an Appropriate Section (▶ *Related Problem 6.33*)

Determine the axial forces in members *DG* and *BE* of the truss.

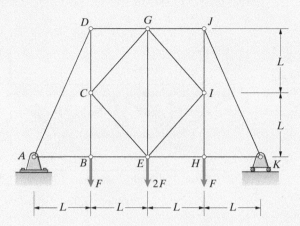

Strategy
We can't obtain a section that involves cutting members *DG* and *BE* without cutting more than three members. However, cutting members *DG*, *BE*, *CD*, and *BC* results in a section with which we can determine the axial forces in members *DG* and *BE*.

Solution
Determine the Reactions at the Supports   We draw the free-body diagram of the entire truss in Fig. a. From the equilibrium equations,

$$\Sigma F_x = A_x = 0,$$

$$\Sigma F_y = A_y + K - F - 2F - F = 0,$$

$$\Sigma M_{\text{point } A} = -LF - (2L)(2F) - (3L)F + (4L)K = 0,$$

we obtain the reactions $A_x = 0$, $A_y = 2F$, and $K = 2F$.

Choose a Section
In Fig. b, we obtain a section by cutting members *DG*, *CD*, *BC*, and *BE*. Because the lines of action of T_{BE}, T_{BC}, and T_{CD} pass through point *B*, we can determine T_{DG} by summing moments about *B*:

$$\Sigma M_{\text{point } B} = -L(2F) - (2L)T_{DG} = 0.$$

The axial force $T_{DG} = -F$. Then, from the equilibrium equation

$$\Sigma F_x = T_{DG} + T_{BE} = 0,$$

we see that $T_{BE} = -T_{DG} = F$. Member *DG* is in compression, and member *BE* is in tension.

Critical Thinking
This is a clever example, but not one that is typical of problems faced in practice. The section used to solve it might not be obvious even to a person with experience analyzing structures. Notice that the free-body diagram in Fig. b is statically indeterminate, although it can be used to determine the axial forces in members *DG* and *BE*.

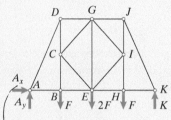

(a) Free-body diagram of the entire truss.

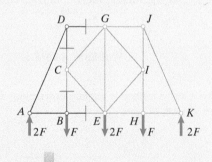

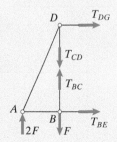

(b) A section of the truss obtained by passing planes through members *DG*, *CD*, *BC*, and *BE*.

Problems

▶ **6.32** In Active Example 6.3, use the method of sections to determine the axial forces in members *BC*, *BI*, and *HI*.

▶ **6.33** In Example 6.4, obtain a section of the truss by passing planes through members *BE*, *CE*, *CG*, and *DG*. Using the fact that the axial forces in members *DG* and *BE* have already been determined, use your section to determine the axial forces in members *CE* and *CG*.

6.34 The truss supports a 100-kN load at *J*. The horizontal members are each 1 m in length.

(a) Use the method of joints to determine the axial force in member *DG*.

(b) Use the method of sections to determine the axial force in member *DG*.

6.35 The horizontal members are each 1 m in length. Use the method of sections to determine the axial forces in members *BC*, *CF*, and *FG*.

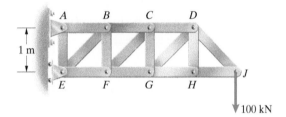

Problems 6.34/6.35

6.36 Use the method of sections to determine the axial forces in members *AB*, *BC*, and *CE*.

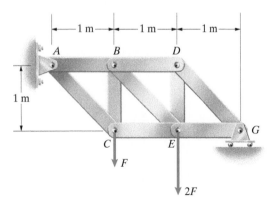

Problem 6.36

6.37 Use the method of sections to determine the axial forces in members *DF*, *EF*, and *EG*.

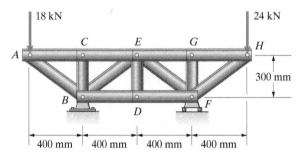

Problem 6.37

6.38 The Pratt bridge truss is loaded as shown. Use the method of sections to determine the axial forces in members *BD*, *BE*, and *CE*.

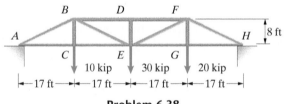

Problem 6.38

6.39 The Howe bridge truss is loaded as shown. Use the method of sections to determine the axial forces in members *BD*, *CD*, and *CE*.

6.40 For the Howe bridge truss, use the method of sections to determine the axial forces in members *DF*, *DG*, and *EG*.

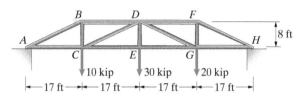

Problems 6.39/6.40

6.41 The Pratt bridge truss supports five forces $F = 340$ kN. The dimension $L = 8$ m. Use the method of sections to determine the axial force in member *JK*.

6.42 For the Pratt bridge truss in Problem 6.41, use the method of sections to determine the axial force in member *EK*.

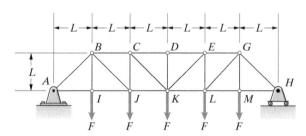

Problems 6.41/6.42

6.43 The walkway exerts vertical 50-kN loads on the Warren truss at *B*, *D*, *F*, and *H*. Use the method of sections to determine the axial force in member *CE*.

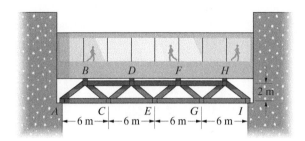

Problem 6.43

6.44 Use the method of sections to determine the axial forces in members *AC*, *BC*, and *BD*.

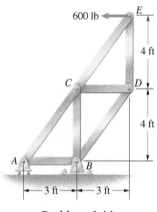

Problem 6.44

6.45 Use the method of sections to determine the axial forces in members *FH*, *GH*, and *GI*.

6.46 Use the method of sections to determine the axial forces in members *DF*, *DG*, and *EG*.

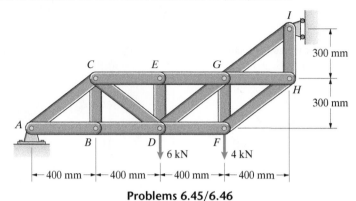

Problems 6.45/6.46

6.47 The Howe truss helps support a roof. Model the supports at *A* and *G* as roller supports.

(a) Use the method of joints to determine the axial force in member *BI*.

(b) Use the method of sections to determine the axial force in member *BI*.

6.48 Use the method of sections to determine the axial force in member *EJ*.

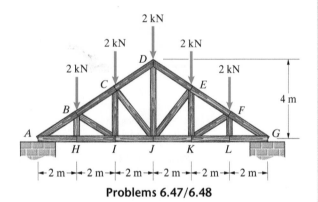

Problems 6.47/6.48

6.49 Use the method of sections to determine the axial forces in members *CE*, *DE*, and *DF*.

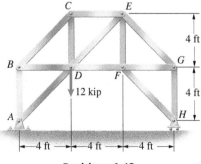

Problem 6.49

6.50 For the bridge truss shown, use the method of sections to determine the axial forces in members *CE*, *CF*, and *DF*.

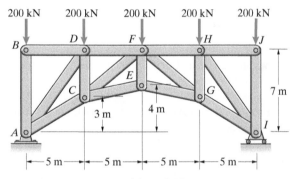

Problem 6.50

6.51 The load $F = 20$ kN and the dimension $L = 2$ m. Use the method of sections to determine the axial force in member *HK*.

Strategy: Obtain a section by cutting members *HK*, *HI*, *IJ*, and *JM*. You can determine the axial forces in members *HK* and *JM* even though the resulting free-body diagram is statically indeterminate.

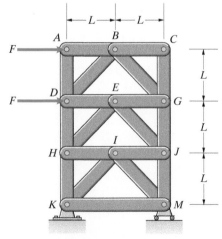

Problem 6.51

6.52 The weight of the bucket is $W = 1000$ lb. The cable passes over pulleys at A and D.

(a) Determine the axial forces in members FG and HI.

(b) By drawing free-body diagrams of sections, explain why the axial forces in members FG and HI are equal.

6.53 The weight of the bucket is $W = 1000$ lb. The cable passes over pulleys at A and D. Determine the axial forces in members IK and JL.

6.54 The truss supports loads at N, P, and R. Determine the axial forces in members IL and KM.

6.55 Determine the axial forces in members HJ and GI.

6.56 By drawing free-body diagrams of sections, explain why the axial forces in members DE, FG, and HI are zero.

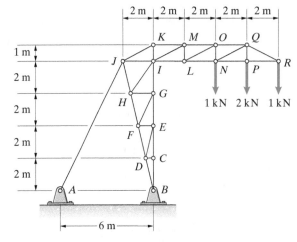

Problems 6.54–6.56

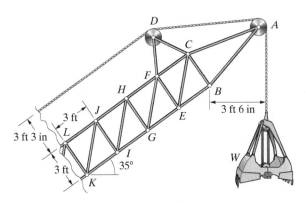

Problems 6.52/6.53

6.4 Space Trusses

BACKGROUND

We can form a simple three-dimensional structure by connecting six bars at their ends to obtain a tetrahedron, as shown in Fig. 6.14a. By adding members, we can obtain more elaborate structures (Figs. 6.14b and c). Three-dimensional structures such as these are called *space trusses* if they have joints that do not exert couples on the members (that is, the joints behave like ball and socket supports) and they are loaded and supported at their joints. Space trusses are analyzed by the same methods we described for two-dimensional trusses. The only difference is the need to cope with the more complicated geometry.

Consider the space truss in Fig. 6.15a. Suppose that the load $\mathbf{F} = -2\mathbf{i} - 6\mathbf{j} - \mathbf{k}$ (kN). The joints A, B, and C rest on the smooth floor. Joint

(a)

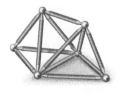
(b)

(c)

Figure 6.14
Space trusses with 6, 9, and 12 members.

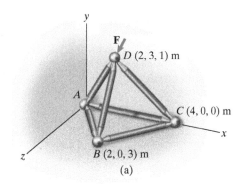

y

F

$D\,(2,3,1)$ m

A

$C\,(4,0,0)$ m

x

z

$B\,(2,0,3)$ m

(a)

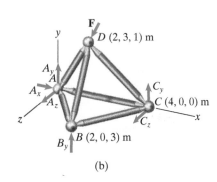

F

y

$D\,(2,3,1)$ m

A_y

A

A_x

A_z

C_y

$C\,(4,0,0)$ m

z

C_z

x

B_y $B\,(2,0,3)$ m

(b)

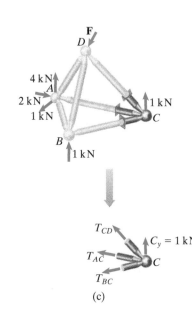

F

D

4 kN

A

2 kN

1 kN

1 kN

C

B

1 kN

T_{CD}

$C_y = 1$ kN

T_{AC}

C

T_{BC}

(c)

Figure 6.15
(a) A space truss supporting a load **F**.
(b) Free-body diagram of the entire truss.
(c) Obtaining the free-body diagram of joint C.

A is supported by the corner where the smooth walls meet, and joint C rests against the back wall. We can apply the method of joints to this truss.

First we must determine the reactions exerted by the supports (the floor and walls). We draw the free-body diagram of the entire truss in Fig. 6.15b. The corner can exert three components of force at A, the floor and wall can exert two components of force at C, and the floor can exert a normal force at B. Summing moments about A, we find that the equilibrium equations, with forces in kN and distances in m, are

$$\Sigma F_x = A_x - 2 = 0,$$

$$\Sigma F_y = A_y + B_y + C_y - 6 = 0,$$

$$\Sigma F_z = A_z + C_z - 1 = 0,$$

$$\Sigma M_{\text{point } A} = (\mathbf{r}_{AB} \times B_y\mathbf{j}) + [\mathbf{r}_{AC} \times (C_y\mathbf{j} + C_z\mathbf{k})] + (\mathbf{r}_{AD} \times \mathbf{F})$$

$$= \begin{vmatrix} \mathbf{i} & \mathbf{j} & \mathbf{k} \\ 2 & 0 & 3 \\ 0 & B_y & 0 \end{vmatrix} + \begin{vmatrix} \mathbf{i} & \mathbf{j} & \mathbf{k} \\ 4 & 0 & 0 \\ 0 & C_y & C_z \end{vmatrix} + \begin{vmatrix} \mathbf{i} & \mathbf{j} & \mathbf{k} \\ 2 & 3 & 1 \\ -2 & -6 & -1 \end{vmatrix}$$

$$= (-3B_y + 3)\mathbf{i} + (-4C_z)\mathbf{j}$$

$$+ (2B_y + 4C_y - 6)\mathbf{k} = 0.$$

Solving these equations, we obtain the reactions $A_x = 2$ kN, $A_y = 4$ kN, $A_z = 1$ kN, $B_y = 1$ kN, $C_y = 1$ kN, and $C_z = 0$.

In this example, we can determine the axial forces in members AC, BC, and CD from the free-body diagram of joint C (Fig. 6.15c). To write the equilibrium equations for the joint, we must express the three axial forces in terms of their components. Because member AC lies along the x axis, we express the force exerted on joint C by the axial force T_{AC} as the vector $-T_{AC}\mathbf{i}$. Let $\mathbf{r}_{CB}$ be the position vector from C to B:

$$\mathbf{r}_{CB} = (2 - 4)\mathbf{i} + (0 - 0)\mathbf{j} + (3 - 0)\mathbf{k} = -2\mathbf{i} + 3\mathbf{k} \text{ (m)}.$$

Dividing this vector by its magnitude to obtain a unit vector that points from C toward B yields

$$\mathbf{e}_{CB} = \frac{\mathbf{r}_{CB}}{|\mathbf{r}_{CB}|} = -0.555\mathbf{i} + 0.832\mathbf{k},$$

and we express the force exerted on joint C by the axial force T_{BC} as the vector

$$T_{BC}\,\mathbf{e}_{CB} = T_{BC}(-0.555\mathbf{i} + 0.832\mathbf{k}).$$

In the same way, we express the force exerted on joint C by the axial force T_{CD} as the vector

$$T_{CD}(-0.535\mathbf{i} + 0.802\mathbf{j} + 0.267\mathbf{k}).$$

Setting the sum of the forces on the joint equal to zero, we obtain

$$-T_{AC}\mathbf{i} + T_{BC}(-0.555\mathbf{i} + 0.832\mathbf{k})$$
$$+T_{CD}(-0.535\mathbf{i} + 0.802\mathbf{j} + 0.267\mathbf{k}) + (1\ \text{kN})\mathbf{j} = 0,$$

and then get the three equilibrium equations

$$\Sigma F_x = -T_{AC} - 0.555T_{BC} - 0.535T_{CD} = 0,$$
$$\Sigma F_y = 0.802T_{CD} + 1\ \text{kN} = 0,$$
$$\Sigma F_z = 0.832T_{BC} + 0.267T_{CD} = 0.$$

Solving these equations, the axial forces are $T_{AC} = 0.444$ kN, $T_{BC} = 0.401$ kN, and $T_{CD} = -1.247$ kN. Members AC and BC are in tension, and member CD is in compression. By continuing to draw free-body diagrams of the joints, we can determine the axial forces in all the members.

As our example demonstrates, three equilibrium equations can be obtained from the free-body diagram of a joint in three dimensions, so it is usually necessary to choose joints to analyze that are subjected to known forces and no more than three unknown forces.

RESULTS

A *space truss* is a truss whose members are not coplanar. Axial forces in the members of a statically determinate space truss can be determined by applying the method of joints.

Before beginning, it is usually necessary to draw the free-body diagram of the entire truss considered as a single object and apply the equilibrium equations to determine the reactions at the supports.

Isolate an individual joint by passing planes through the connected members. Complete the free-body diagram by showing the axial forces in the members. Apply the equilibrium equation $\Sigma \mathbf{F} = \mathbf{0}$ to the free-body diagram of the joint. Repeat this process for other joints until the desired axial loads have been determined.

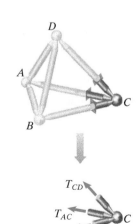

Active Example 6.5   Space Truss (► *Related Problem 6.57*)

The space truss has roller supports at B, C, and D and supports a vertical 1200-lb load at A. Determine the axial forces in members AD, BD, and CD.

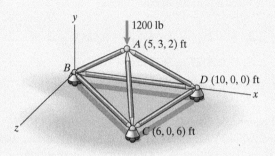

Strategy

We will first draw a free-body diagram of the entire truss, treating it as a single object, and determine the reactions at the supports. Then we can determine the axial forces in members AD, BD, and CD by drawing the free-body diagram of joint D.

Solution

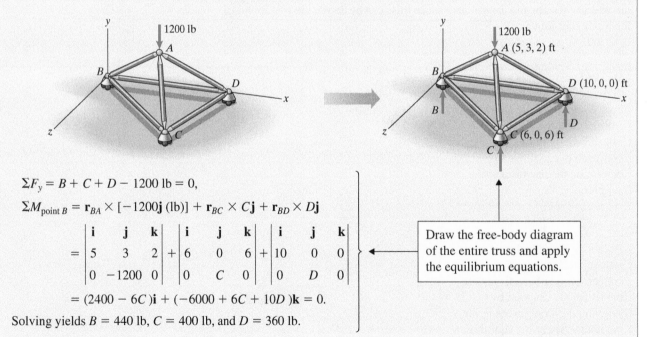

$\Sigma F_y = B + C + D - 1200 \text{ lb} = 0,$

$\Sigma M_{\text{point }B} = \mathbf{r}_{BA} \times [-1200\mathbf{j} \text{ (lb)}] + \mathbf{r}_{BC} \times C\mathbf{j} + \mathbf{r}_{BD} \times D\mathbf{j}$

$$= \begin{vmatrix} \mathbf{i} & \mathbf{j} & \mathbf{k} \\ 5 & 3 & 2 \\ 0 & -1200 & 0 \end{vmatrix} + \begin{vmatrix} \mathbf{i} & \mathbf{j} & \mathbf{k} \\ 6 & 0 & 6 \\ 0 & C & 0 \end{vmatrix} + \begin{vmatrix} \mathbf{i} & \mathbf{j} & \mathbf{k} \\ 10 & 0 & 0 \\ 0 & D & 0 \end{vmatrix}$$

Draw the free-body diagram of the entire truss and apply the equilibrium equations.

$= (2400 - 6C)\mathbf{i} + (-6000 + 6C + 10D)\mathbf{k} = 0.$

Solving yields $B = 440$ lb, $C = 400$ lb, and $D = 360$ lb.

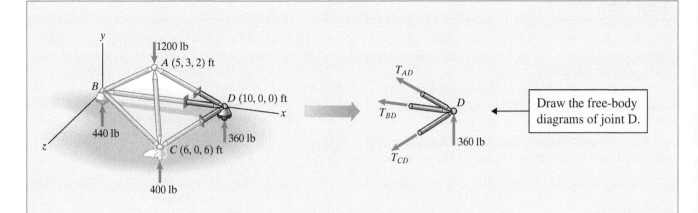

Draw the free-body diagrams of joint D.

$$\mathbf{r}_{DA} = -5\mathbf{i} + 3\mathbf{j} + 2\mathbf{k} \text{ (ft).}$$

$$\mathbf{e}_{DA} = \frac{\mathbf{r}_{DA}}{|\mathbf{r}_{DA}|} = -0.811\mathbf{i} + 0.487\mathbf{j} + 0.324\mathbf{k}.$$

$$T_{AD}\mathbf{e}_{DA} = T_{AD}(-0.811\mathbf{i} + 0.487\mathbf{j} + 0.324\mathbf{k}),$$

$$T_{BD}\mathbf{e}_{DB} = -T_{BD}\mathbf{i},$$

$$T_{CD}\mathbf{e}_{DC} = T_{CD}(-0.555\mathbf{i} + 0.832\mathbf{k}).$$

Divide the position vector from D to A by its magnitude to obtain a unit vector $\mathbf{e}_{DA}$ that points from D toward A. Express the axial force in member AD in terms of its components by writing it as $T_{AD}\mathbf{e}_{DA}$. Express the axial forces in members BD and CD in terms of their components in the same way.

$$T_{AD}\mathbf{e}_{DA} + T_{BD}\mathbf{e}_{DB} + T_{CD}\mathbf{e}_{DC} + (360 \text{ lb})\mathbf{j} = 0.$$

The $\mathbf{i}$, $\mathbf{j}$, and $\mathbf{k}$ components of this equation must each equal zero, resulting in the three equations

$$-0.811T_{AD} - T_{BD} - 0.555T_{CD} = 0,$$
$$0.487T_{AD} + 360 \text{ lb} = 0,$$
$$0.324T_{AD} + 0.832T_{CD} = 0.$$

Solving yields $T_{AD} = -740$ lb, $T_{BD} = 440$ lb, and $T_{CD} = 288$ lb. The axial forces are AD: 740 lb (C), BD: 440 lb (T), CD: 288 lb (T).

Apply equilibrium.

Practice Problem Determine the axial forces in members AB and AC of the truss.

Answer: AB: 904 lb (C), AC: 680 lb (C).

Problems

▶ **6.57** In Active Example 6.5, draw the free-body diagram of joint B of the space truss and use it to determine the axial forces in members AB, BC, and BD.

6.58 The space truss supports a vertical 10-kN load at D. The reactions at the supports at joints A, B, and C are shown. What are the axial forces in members AD, BD, and CD?

6.59 The reactions at the supports at joints A, B, and C are shown. What are the axial forces in members AB, AC, and AD?

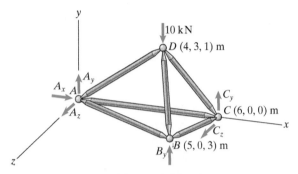

Problems 6.58/6.59

6.60 The space truss supports a vertical load F at A. Each member is of length L, and the truss rests on the horizontal surface on roller supports at B, C, and D. Determine the axial forces in members AB, AC, and AD.

6.61 For the truss in Problem 6.60, determine the axial forces in members AB, BC, and BD.

Problems 6.60/6.61

6.62 The space truss has roller supports at B, C, and D and supports a vertical 800-lb load at A. What are the axial forces in members AB, AC, and AD?

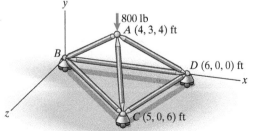

Problem 6.62

6.63 The space truss shown models an airplane's landing gear. It has ball and socket supports at C, D, and E. If the force exerted at A by the wheel is $\mathbf{F} = 40\mathbf{j}$ (kN), what are the axial forces in members AB, AC, and AD?

6.64 If the force exerted at point A of the truss in Problem 6.63 is $\mathbf{F} = 10\mathbf{i} + 60\mathbf{j} + 20\mathbf{k}$ (kN), what are the axial forces in members BC, BD, and BE?

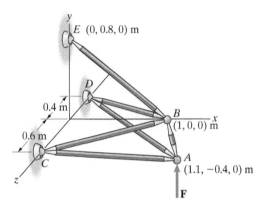

Problems 6.63/6.64

6.65 The space truss is supported by roller supports on the horizontal surface at C and D and a ball and socket support at E. The y axis points upward. The mass of the suspended object is 120 kg. The coordinates of the joints of the truss are A: (1.6, 0.4, 0) m, B: (1.0, 1.0, −0.2) m, C: (0.9, 0, 0.9) m, D: (0.9, 0, −0.6) m, and E: (0, 0.8, 0) m. Determine the axial forces in members AB, AC, and AD.

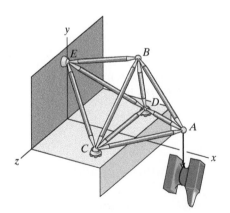

Problem 6.65

6.66 The free-body diagram of the part of the construction crane to the left of the plane is shown. The coordinates (in meters) of the joints A, B, and C are $(1.5, 1.5, 0)$, $(0, 0, 1)$, and $(0, 0, -1)$, respectively. The axial forces P_1, P_2, and P_3 are parallel to the x axis. The axial forces P_4, P_5, and P_6 point in the directions of the unit vectors

$$\mathbf{e}_4 = 0.640\mathbf{i} - 0.640\mathbf{j} - 0.426\mathbf{k},$$

$$\mathbf{e}_5 = 0.640\mathbf{i} - 0.640\mathbf{j} + 0.426\mathbf{k},$$

$$\mathbf{e}_6 = 0.832\mathbf{i} - 0.555\mathbf{k}.$$

The total force exerted on the free-body diagram by the weight of the crane and the load it supports is $-F\mathbf{j} = -44\mathbf{j}$ (kN) acting at the point $(-20, 0, 0)$ m. What is the axial force P_3?

Strategy: Use the fact that the moment about the line that passes through joints A and B equals zero.

6.67 In Problem 6.66, what are the axial forces P_1, P_4, and P_5?

Strategy: Write the equilibrium equations for the entire free-body diagram.

6.68 The mirror housing of the telescope is supported by a 6-bar space truss. The mass of the housing is 3 Mg (megagrams), and its weight acts at G. The distance from the axis of the telescope to points A, B, and C is 1 m, and the distance from the axis to points D, E, and F is 2.5 m. If the telescope axis is vertical ($\alpha = 90°$), what are the axial forces in the members of the truss?

6.69 Consider the telescope described in Problem 6.68. Determine the axial forces in the members of the truss if the angle α between the horizontal and the telescope axis is 20°.

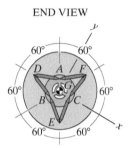

END VIEW

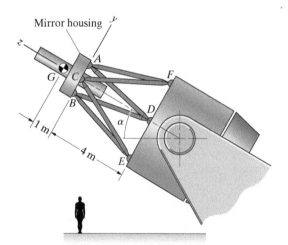

Problems 6.68/6.69

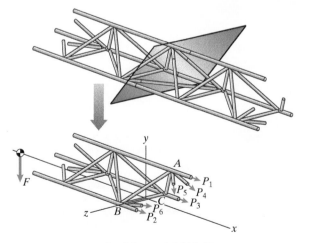

Problems 6.66/6.67

6.5 Frames and Machines

Many structures, such as the frame of a car and the human structure of bones, tendons, and muscles (Fig. 6.16), are not composed entirely of two-force members and thus cannot be modeled as trusses. In this section we consider structures of interconnected members that do not satisfy the definition of a truss. Such structures are called *frames* if they are designed to remain stationary and support loads and *machines* if they are designed to move and apply loads.

When trusses are analyzed by cutting members to obtain free-body diagrams of joints or sections, the internal forces acting at the "cuts" are simple axial forces (see Fig. 6.4). This is not generally true for frames or machines, and a different method of analysis is necessary. Instead of cutting members, we isolate entire members, or in some cases combinations of members, from the structure.

To begin analyzing a frame or machine, we draw a free-body diagram of the entire structure (that is, treat the structure as a single object) and determine the reactions at its supports. In some cases the entire structure will be statically indeterminate, but it is helpful to determine as many of the reactions as possible. We then draw free-body diagrams of individual members, or selected combinations of members, and apply the equilibrium equations to determine the forces and couples acting on them. For example, consider the stationary structure in

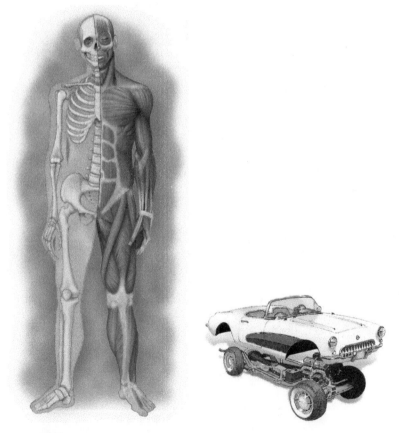

Figure 6.16
The internal structure of a person and a car's frame are not trusses.

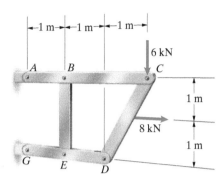

Figure 6.17
A frame supporting two loads.

Fig. 6.17. Member *BE* is a two-force member, but the other three members—*ABC*, *CD*, and *DEG*—are not. This structure is a frame. Our objective is to determine the forces on its members.

Analyzing the Entire Structure

We draw the free-body diagram of the entire frame in Fig. 6.18. It is statically indeterminate: There are four unknown reactions, A_x, A_y, G_x, and G_y, whereas we can write only three independent equilibrium equations. However, notice that the lines of action of three of the unknown reactions intersect at A. Summing moments about A yields

$$\Sigma M_{\text{point } A} = (2 \text{ m})G_x + (1 \text{ m})(8 \text{ kN}) - (3 \text{ m})(6 \text{ kN}) = 0,$$

and we obtain the reaction $G_x = 5$ kN. Then, from the equilibrium equation

$$\Sigma F_x = A_x + G_x + 8 \text{ kN} = 0,$$

we obtain the reaction $A_x = -13$ kN. Although we cannot determine A_y or G_y from the free-body diagram of the entire structure, we can do so by analyzing the individual members.

Analyzing the Members

Our next step is to draw free-body diagrams of the members. To do so, we treat the attachment of a member to another member just as if it were a support. Looked at in this way, we can think of each member as a supported object of the kind analyzed in Chapter 5. Furthermore, the forces and couples the members exert on one another are *equal in magnitude and opposite in direction*. A simple

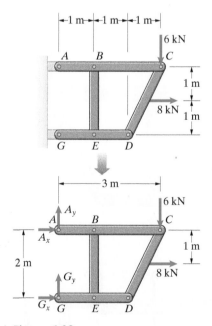

Figure 6.18
Obtaining the free-body diagram of the
entire frame.

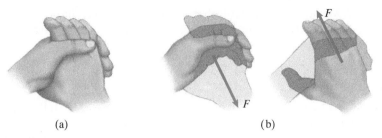

Figure 6.19
Demonstrating Newton's third law:
(a) Clasp your hands and pull on your left hand.
(b) Your hands exert equal and opposite forces.

demonstration is instructive. If you clasp your hands as shown in Fig. 6.19a and exert a force on your left hand with your right hand, your left hand exerts an equal and opposite force on your right hand (Fig. 6.19b). Similarly, if you exert a couple on your left hand, your left hand exerts an equal and opposite couple on your right hand.

In Fig. 6.20 we "disassemble" the frame and draw free-body diagrams of its members. Observe that the forces exerted on one another by the members are equal and opposite. For example, at point C on the free-body diagram of member ABC, the force exerted by member CD is denoted by the components

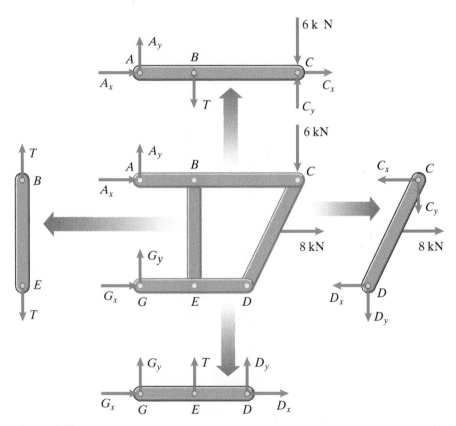

Figure 6.20
Obtaining the free-body diagrams of the members.

C_x and C_y. The forces exerted by member *ABC* on member *CD* at point *C* must be equal and opposite, as shown.

We need to discuss two important aspects of these free-body diagrams before completing the analysis.

Two-Force Members Member *BE* is a two-force member, and we have taken this into account in drawing its free-body diagram in Fig. 6.20. The force *T* is the axial force in member *BE*, and an equal and opposite force is subjected on member *ABC* at *B* and on member *GED* at *E*.

Recognizing two-force members in frames and machines and drawing their free-body diagrams as we have done will reduce the number of unknowns and will greatly simplify the analysis. In our example, if we did not treat member *BE* as a two-force member, its free-body diagram would have four unknown forces (Fig. 6.21a). By treating it as a two-force member (Fig. 6.21b), we reduce the number of unknown forces by three.

Loads Applied at Joints A question arises when a load is applied at a joint: Where does the load appear on the free-body diagrams of the individual members? The answer is that you can place the load on *any one* of the members attached at the joint. For example, in Fig. 6.17, the 6-kN load acts at the joint where members *ABC* and *CD* are connected. In drawing the free-body diagrams of the individual members (Fig. 6.20), we assumed that the 6-kN load acted on member *ABC*. The force components C_x and C_y on the free-body diagram of member *ABC* are the forces exerted by the member *CD*.

To explain why we can draw the free-body diagrams in this way, let us assume that the 6-kN force acts on the pin connecting members *ABC* and *CD*, and draw separate free-body diagrams of the pin and the two members (Fig. 6.22a). The force components C_x' and C_y' are the forces exerted by the pin on member *ABC*, and C_x and C_y are the forces exerted by the pin on member *CD*. If we superimpose the free-body diagrams of the pin and member *ABC*, we obtain the two free-body diagrams in Fig. 6.22b, which is the way we drew them in Fig. 6.20. Alternatively, by superimposing the free-body diagrams of the pin and member *CD*, we obtain the two free-body diagrams in Fig. 6.22c.

Thus if a load acts at a joint, it can be placed on any one of the members attached at the joint when drawing the free-body diagrams of the individual members. Just make sure not to place it on more than one member.

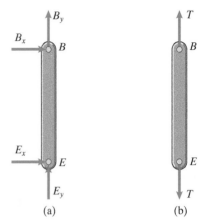

Figure 6.21
Free-body diagram of member *BE*:
(a) Not treating it as a two-force member.
(b) Treating it as a two-force member.

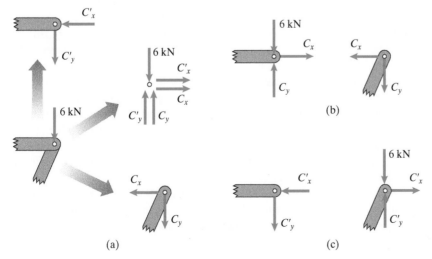

Figure 6.22
(a) Drawing free-body diagrams of the pin and the two members.
(b) Superimposing the pin on member *ABC*.
(c) Superimposing the pin on member *CD*.

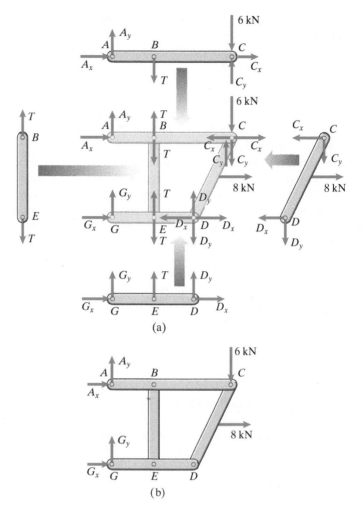

(a)

(b)

Figure 6.23
(a) "Reassembling" the free-body diagrams of the individual members.
(b) The free-body diagram of the entire frame is recovered.

To detect errors in the free-body diagrams of the members, it is helpful to "reassemble" them (Fig. 6.23a). The forces at the connections between the members cancel (they are internal forces once the members are reassembled), and the free-body diagram of the entire structure is recovered (Fig. 6.23b).

Our final step is to apply the equilibrium equations to the free-body diagrams of the members (Fig. 6.24). In two dimensions, we can obtain three independent equilibrium equations from the free-body diagram of each member of a structure that we do not treat as a two-force member. (By assuming that the forces on a two-force member are equal and opposite axial forces, we have already used the three equilibrium equations for that member.) In this example, there are three members in addition to the two-force member, so we can write $3 \times 3 = 9$ independent equilibrium equations, and there are nine unknown forces: $A_x, A_y, C_x, C_y, D_x, D_y, G_x, G_y$, and T.

Recall that we determined that $A_x = -13$ kN and $G_x = 5$ kN from our analysis of the entire structure. The equilibrium equations we obtained from the free-body diagram of the entire structure are not independent of the equilibrium

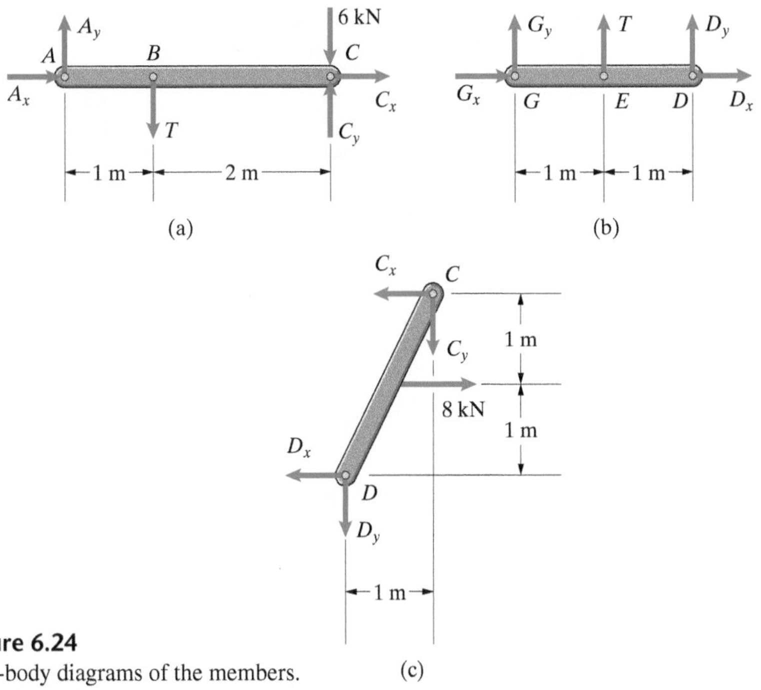

(a)

(b)

Figure 6.24
Free-body diagrams of the members.   (c)

equations obtained from the free-body diagrams of the members, but by using them to determine A_x and G_x, we get a head start on solving the equations for the members. Consider the free-body diagram of member ABC (Fig. 6.24a). Because we know A_x, we can determine C_x from the equation

$$\Sigma F_x = A_x + C_x = 0,$$

obtaining $C_x = -A_x = 13$ kN. Now consider the free-body diagram of GED (Fig. 6.24b). We can determine D_x from the equation

$$\Sigma F_x = G_x + D_x = 0,$$

obtaining $D_x = -G_x = -5$ kN. Now consider the free-body diagram of member CD (Fig. 6.24c). Because we know C_x, we can determine C_y by summing moments about D:

$$\Sigma M_{\text{point } D} = (2 \text{ m})C_x - (1 \text{ m})C_y - (1 \text{ m})(8 \text{ kN}) = 0.$$

We obtain $C_y = 18$ kN. Then, from the equation

$$\Sigma F_y = -C_y - D_y = 0,$$

we find that $D_y = -C_y = -18$ kN. Now we can return to the free-body diagrams of members ABC and GED to determine A_y and G_y. Summing moments about point B of member ABC yields

$$\Sigma M_{\text{point } B} = -(1 \text{ m})A_y + (2 \text{ m})C_y - (2 \text{ m})(6 \text{ kN}) = 0,$$

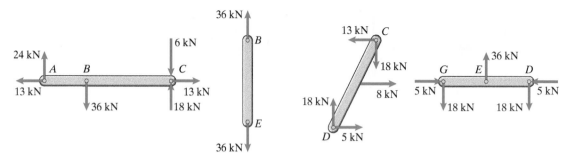

Figure 6.25
Forces on the members of the frame.

and we obtain $A_y = 2C_y - 12$ kN $= 24$ kN. Then, summing moments about point E of member GED, we have

$$\Sigma M_{\text{point } E} = (1 \text{ m})D_y - (1 \text{ m})G_y = 0,$$

from which we obtain $G_y = D_y = -18$ kN. Finally, from the free-body diagram of member GED, we use the equilibrium equation

$$\Sigma F_y = D_y + G_y + T = 0,$$

which gives us the result $T = -D_y - G_y = 36$ kN. The forces on the members are shown in Fig. 6.25. As this example demonstrates, determination of the forces on the members can often be simplified by carefully choosing the order in which the equations are solved.

We see that determining the forces and couples on the members of frames and machines involves two steps:

1. **Determine the reactions at the supports**—Draw the free-body diagram of the entire structure, and determine the reactions at its supports. Although this step is not essential, it can greatly simplify your analysis of the members. If the free-body diagram is statically indeterminant, determine as many of the reactions as possible.

2. **Analyze the members**—Draw free-body diagrams of the members, and apply the equilibrium equations to determine the forces acting on them. You can simplify this step by identifying two-force members. If a load acts at a joint of the structure, you can place the load on the free-body diagram of any one of the members attached at that joint.

RESULTS

A structure of interconnected members that cannot be modeled as a truss is called a *frame* if it is designed to remain stationary and support loads and a *machine* if it is designed to move and apply loads. The forces and couples acting on the individual members of a frame or machine in equilibrium can often be determined by applying the equilibrium equations to the individual members.

It is often advantageous to begin by drawing the free-body diagram of the entire structure considered as a single object and applying the equilibrium equations. *Even if the free-body diagram of the entire structure is statically indeterminate, it may be possible to determine the reactions from the subsequent analysis of the individual members.*

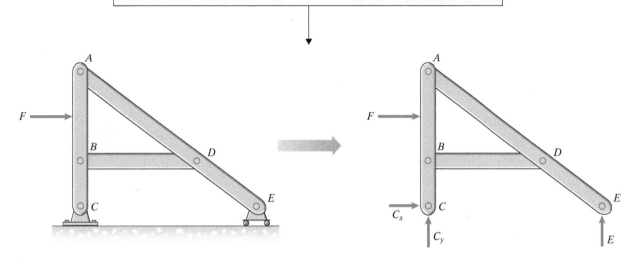

Draw the free-body diagrams of the individual members and apply the equilibrium equations to them. Notice that where two members are connected, *the reactions they exert on each other are equal and opposite*. Notice that member *BD* is a two-force member. Recognizing two-force members will simplify the analysis of a structure.

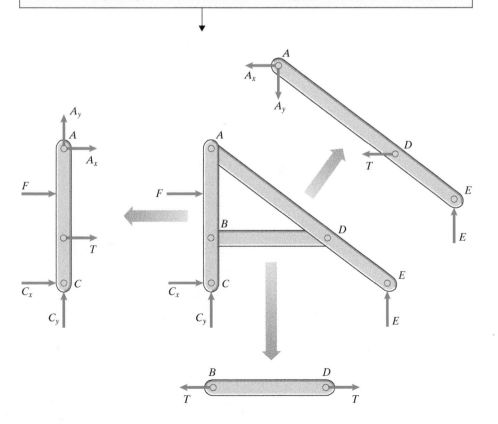

| Active Example 6.6 | Analyzing a Frame (▶ *Related Problem 6.70*) |

Determine the forces and couples acting on the members of the frame.

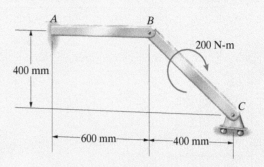

Strategy

We will first draw a free-body diagram of the entire frame, treating it as a single object, and attempt to determine the reactions at the supports. We will then draw free-body diagrams of the individual members and apply the equilibrium equations to determine the forces and couples acting on them.

Solution

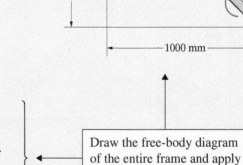

$$\Sigma F_x = A_x = 0,$$

$$\Sigma F_y = A_y + C = 0,$$

$$\Sigma M_{\text{point } A} = M_A - 200 \text{ N-m} + (1.0 \text{ m})C = 0.$$

The reaction $A_x = 0$, but A_y, C, and M_A cannot be determined from these equations. The free-body diagram of the entire frame is statically indeterminate.

> Draw the free-body diagram of the entire frame and apply the equilibrium equations.

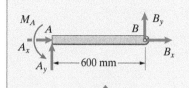

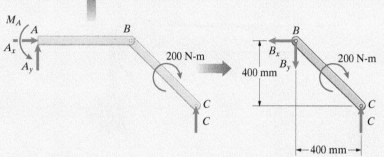

Draw the free-body diagrams of the individual members.

$\Sigma F_x = -B_x = 0,$

$\Sigma F_y = -B_y + C = 0,$

$\Sigma M_{\text{point } B} = -200 \text{ N-m} + (0.4 \text{ m})C = 0.$

Solving yields $B_x = 0$, $B_y = 500$ N, and $C = 500$ N.

Apply equilibrium to member BC.

$\Sigma F_x = A_x + B_x = 0,$

$\Sigma F_y = A_y + B_y = 0,$

$\Sigma M_{\text{point } A} = M_A + (0.6 \text{ m})B_y = 0.$

Because A_x, B_x, and B_y have already been determined, these equations can be solved for A_y and M_A. The results are $A_y = -500$ N and $M_A = -300$ N-m, which completes the solution.

Apply equilibrium to member AB.

Practice Problem The frame has pin supports at A and C. Determine the forces and couples acting on member BC at B and C.

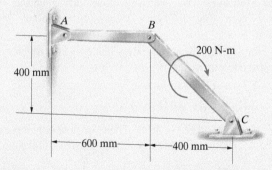

Answer: $B_x = -500$ N, $B_y = 0$, $C_x = 500$ N, $C_y = 0$. (In the statements of the answers, x components are positive to the right and y components are positive upward.)

Example 6.7   **Determining Forces on Members of a Frame** (▶ *Related Problem 6.74*)

The frame supports a suspended weight $W = 40$ lb. Determine the forces on members *ABCD* and *CEG*.

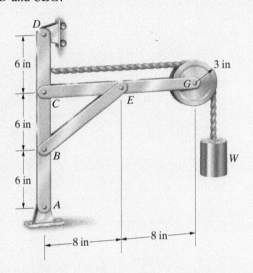

Strategy

We will draw a free-body diagram of the entire frame and attempt to determine the reactions at the supports. We will then draw free-body diagrams of the individual members and use the equilibrium equations to determine the forces and couples acting on them. In doing so, we can take advantage of the fact that the bar *BE* is a two-force member.

Solution

Determine the Reactions at the Supports   We draw the free-body diagram of the entire frame in Fig. a. From the equilibrium equations

$$\Sigma F_x = A_x - D = 0,$$
$$\Sigma F_y = A_y - 40 \text{ lb} = 0,$$
$$\Sigma M_{\text{point } A} = (18 \text{ in})D - (19 \text{ in})(40 \text{ lb}) = 0,$$

we obtain the reactions $A_x = 42.2$ lb, $A_y = 40$ lb, and $D = 42.2$ lb.

Analyze the Members   We obtain the free-body diagrams of the members in Fig. b. Notice that *BE* is a two-force member. The angle $\alpha = \arctan(6/8) = 36.9°$.

     The free-body diagram of the pulley has only two unknown forces. From the equilibrium equations

$$\Sigma F_x = G_x - 40 \text{ lb} = 0,$$
$$\Sigma F_y = G_y - 40 \text{ lb} = 0,$$

we obtain $G_x = 40$ lb and $G_y = 40$ lb. There are now only three unknown forces on the free-body diagram of member *CEG*. From the equilibrium equations

$$\Sigma F_x = -C_x - R\cos\alpha - 40 \text{ lb} = 0,$$
$$\Sigma F_y = -C_y - R\sin\alpha - 40 \text{ lb} = 0,$$
$$\Sigma M_{\text{point } C} = -(8 \text{ in})R\sin\alpha - (16 \text{ in})(40 \text{ lb}) = 0,$$

we obtain $C_x = 66.7$ lb, $C_y = 40$ lb, and $R = -133.3$ lb, completing the solution (Fig. c).

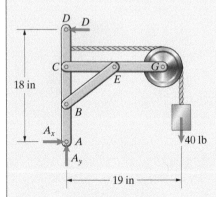

(a) Free-body diagram of the entire frame.

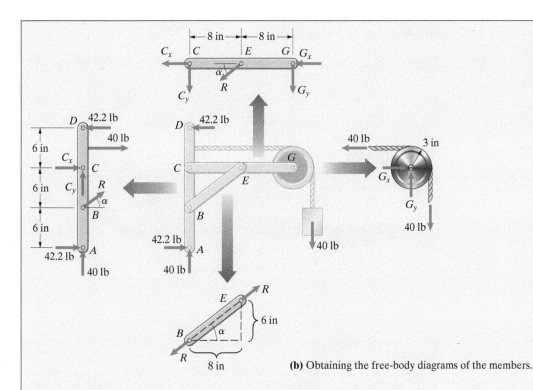

(b) Obtaining the free-body diagrams of the members.

Critical Thinking

In problems of this kind, the reactions on the individual members of the frame can be determined from the free-body diagrams of the members. Why did we draw the free-body diagram of the entire frame and solve the associated equilibrium equations? The reason is that it gave us a head start on solving the equilibrium equations for the members. In this example, when we drew the free-body diagrams of the members we already knew the reactions at A and D, which simplified the remaining analysis. Analyzing the entire frame can also provide a check on your work. Notice that we did not use the equilibrium equations for member $ABCD$. We can check our analysis by confirming that this member is in equilibrium (Fig. c):

$$\Sigma F_x = 42.2 \text{ lb} - 133.3 \cos 36.9° \text{ lb} + 66.7 \text{ lb} + 40 \text{ lb} - 42.2 \text{ lb} = 0,$$

$$\Sigma F_y = 40 \text{ lb} - 133.3 \sin 36.9° \text{ lb} + 40 \text{ lb} = 0,$$

$$\Sigma M_{\text{point } A} = (6 \text{ in})(133.3 \cos 36.9° \text{ lb}) - (12 \text{ in})(66.7 \text{ lb})$$

$$- (15 \text{ in})(40 \text{ lb}) + (18 \text{ in})(42.2 \text{ lb}) = 0.$$

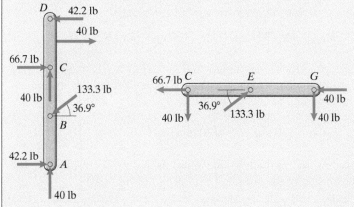

(c) Forces on members $ABCD$ and CEG.

| Example 6.8 | Analyzing a Machine (▶ *Related Problem 6.103*) |

What forces are exerted on the ball at E as a result of the 150-N forces on the pliers?

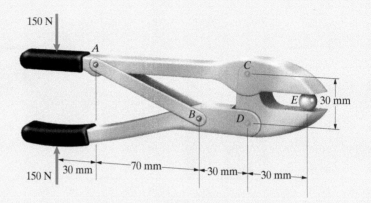

Strategy

A pair of pliers is a simple example of a machine, a structure designed to move and exert forces. The interconnections of the members are designed to create a mechanical advantage, subjecting an object to forces greater than the forces exerted by the user.

In this case there is no information to be gained from the free-body diagram of the entire structure. We must determine the forces exerted on the ball by drawing free-body diagrams of the members.

Solution

We "disassemble" the pliers in Fig. a to obtain the free-body diagrams of the members, labeled (1), (2), and (3). The force R on free-body diagrams (1) and (3) is exerted by the two-force member AB. The angle $\alpha = \arctan(30/70) = 23.2°$. Our objective is to determine the force E exerted by the ball.

The free-body diagram of member (3) has only three unknown forces and the 150-N load, so we can determine R, D_x, and D_y from this free-body diagram alone. The equilibrium equations are

$$\Sigma F_x = D_x + R \cos \alpha = 0,$$

$$\Sigma F_y = D_y - R \sin \alpha + 150 \text{ N} = 0,$$

$$\Sigma M_{\text{point } B} = (30 \text{ mm})D_y - (100 \text{ mm})(150 \text{ N}) = 0.$$

Solving these equations, we obtain $D_x = -1517$ N, $D_y = 500$ N, and $R = 1650$ N. Knowing D_x, we can determine E from the free-body diagram of member (2) by summing moments about C:

$$\Sigma M_{\text{point } C} = -(30 \text{ mm})E - (30 \text{ mm})D_x = 0.$$

The force exerted on the ball by the pliers is $E = -D_x = 1517$ N. The mechanical advantage of the pliers is $(1517 \text{ N})/(150 \text{ N}) = 10.1$.

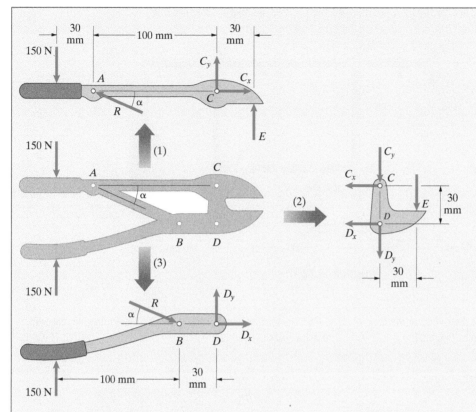

(a) Obtaining the free-body diagrams of the members.

Critical Thinking

What is the motivation for determining the reactions on the members of the pliers? This process is essential for machine and tool design. To design the configuration of the pliers and choose the materials and dimensions of its members, it is necessary to determine all the forces acting on the members, as we have done in this example. Once the forces are known, the methods of mechanics of materials can be used to assess the adequacy of the members to support them.

Problems

Assume that objects are in equilibrium. In the statements of the answers, x components are positive to the right and y components are positive upward.

▶ **6.70** In Active Example 6.6, suppose that in addition to being loaded by the 200 N-m couple, the frame is subjected to a 400-N force at C that is horizontal and points toward the left. Draw a sketch of the frame showing the new loading. Determine the forces and couples acting on member AB of the frame.

6.71 The object suspended at E weighs 200 lb. Determine the reactions on member ACD at A and C.

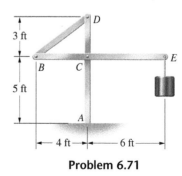

Problem 6.71

6.72 The mass of the object suspended at *G* is 100 kg. Determine the reactions on member *CDE* at *C* and *E*.

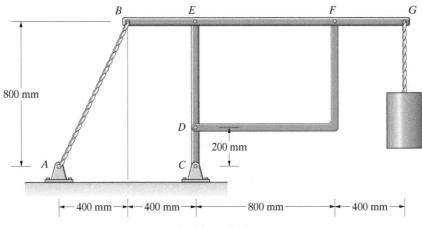

Problem 6.72

6.73 The force *F* = 10 kN. Determine the forces on member *ABC*, presenting your answers as shown in Fig. 6.25.

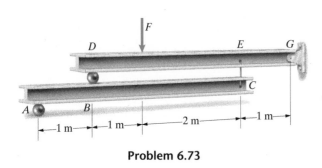

Problem 6.73

▶ **6.74** In Example 6.7, suppose that the frame is redesigned so that the distance from point *C* to the attachment point *E* of the two-force member *BE* is increased from 8 in to 10 in. Determine the forces acting at *C* on member *ABCD*.

6.75 The tension in cable *BD* is 500 lb. Determine the reactions at *A* for cases (1) and (2).

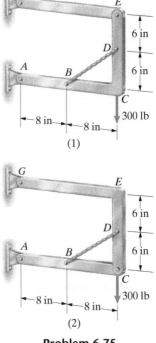

(1)

(2)

Problem 6.75

6.76 Determine the reactions on member *ABCD* at *A*, *C*, and *D*.

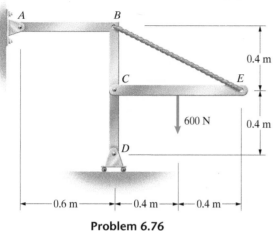

Problem 6.76

6.77 Determine the forces exerted on member *ABC* at *A* and *C*.

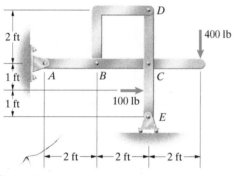

Problem 6.77

6.78 An athlete works out with a squat thrust machine. To rotate the bar *ABD*, she must exert a vertical force at *A* that causes the magnitude of the axial force in the two-force member *BC* to be 1800 N. When the bar *ABD* is on the verge of rotating, what are the reactions on the vertical bar *CDE* at *D* and *E*?

Problem 6.78

6.79 The frame supports a 6-kN vertical load at *C*. The bars *ABC* and *DEF* are horizontal. Determine the reactions on the frame at *A* and *D*.

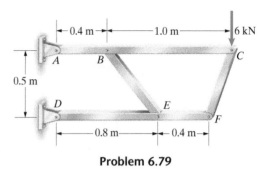

Problem 6.79

6.80 The mass *m* = 120 kg. Determine the forces on member *ABC*, presenting your answers as shown in Fig. 6.25.

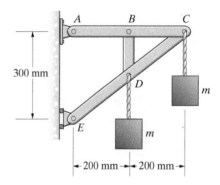

Problem 6.80

6.81 Determine the reactions on member *BCD*.

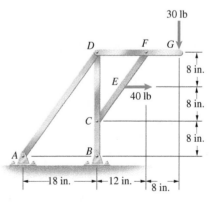

Problem 6.81

6.82 The weight of the suspended object is $W = 50$ lb. Determine the tension in the spring and the reactions at F. (The slotted member DE is vertical.)

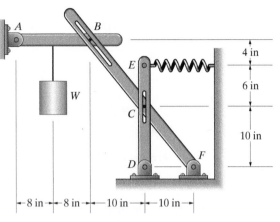

Problem 6.82

6.83 The mass $m = 50$ kg. Bar DE is horizontal. Determine the forces on member $ABCD$, presenting your answers as shown in Fig. 6.25.

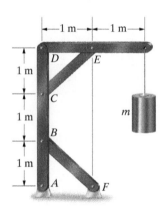

Problem 6.83

6.84 Determine the forces on member BCD.

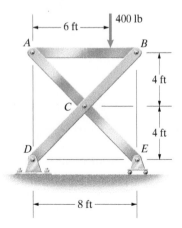

Problem 6.84

6.85 Determine the forces on member ABC.

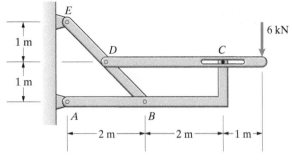

Problem 6.85

6.86 Determine the forces on member ABD.

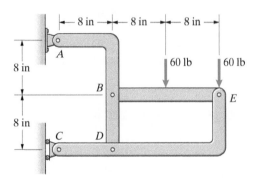

Problem 6.86

6.87 The mass $m = 12$ kg. Determine the forces on member CDE.

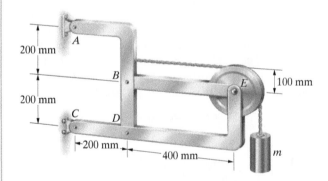

Problem 6.87

6.88 The weight $W = 80$ lb. Determine the forces on member $ABCD$.

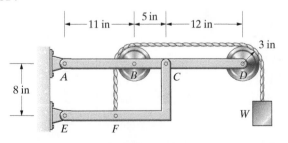

Problem 6.88

6.89 The woman using the exercise machine is holding the 80-lb weight stationary in the position shown. What are the reactions at the fixed support E and the pin support F? (A and C are pinned connections.)

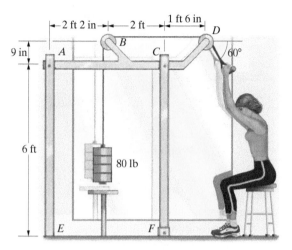

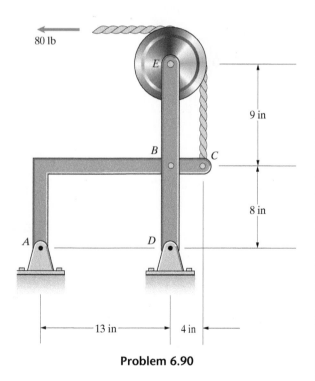

Problem 6.89

6.90 Determine the reactions on member ABC at A and B.

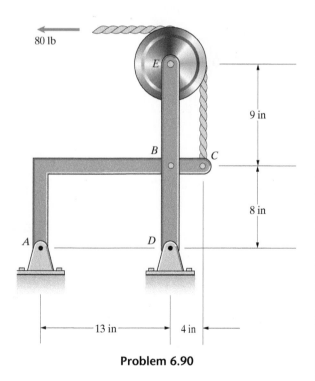

Problem 6.90

6.91 The mass of the suspended object is $m = 50$ kg. Determine the reactions on member ABC.

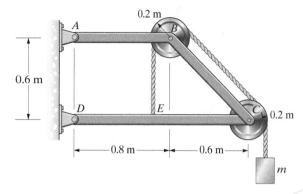

Problem 6.91

6.92 The unstretched length of the spring is L_0. Show that when the system is in equilibrium the angle α satisfies the relation $\sin \alpha = 2(L_0 - 2F/k)/L$.

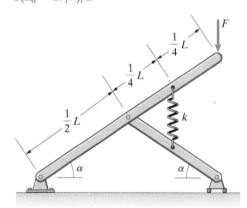

Problem 6.92

6.93 The pin support B will safely support a force of 24-kN magnitude. Based on this criterion, what is the largest mass m that the frame will safely support?

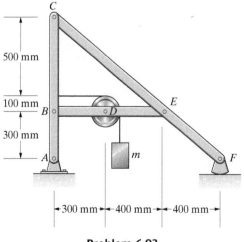

Problem 6.93

6.94 Determine the reactions at *A* and *C*.

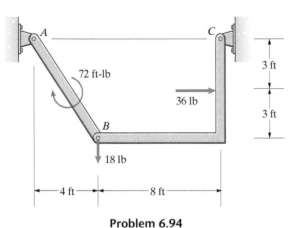

Problem 6.94

6.95 Determine the forces on member *AD*.

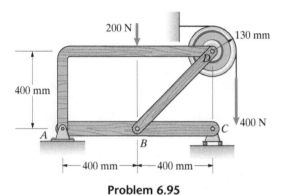

Problem 6.95

6.96 The frame shown is used to support high-tension wires. If $b = 3$ ft, $\alpha = 30°$, and $W = 200$ lb, what is the axial force in member *HJ*?

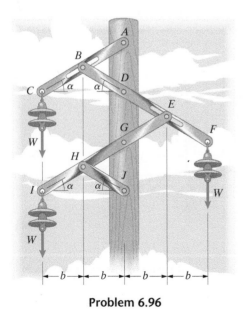

Problem 6.96

6.97 Determine the force exerted on the ball by the bolt cutters and the magnitude of the axial force in the two-force member *AB*.

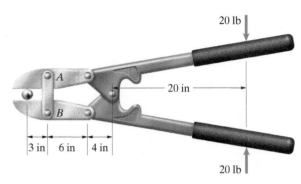

Problem 6.97

6.98 The woman exerts 20-N forces to the pliers as shown.

(a) What is the magnitude of the forces the pliers exert on the bolt at *B*?

(b) Determine the magnitude of the force the members of the pliers exert on each other at the pinned connection *C*.

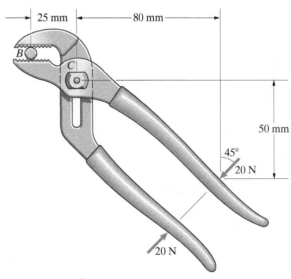

Problem 6.98

6.99 Figure a is a diagram of the bones and biceps muscle of a person's arm supporting a mass. Tension in the biceps muscle holds the forearm in the horizontal position, as illustrated in the simple mechanical model in Fig. b. The weight of the forearm is 9 N, and the mass $m = 2$ kg.

(a) Determine the tension in the biceps muscle AB.

(b) Determine the magnitude of the force exerted on the upper arm by the forearm at the elbow joint C.

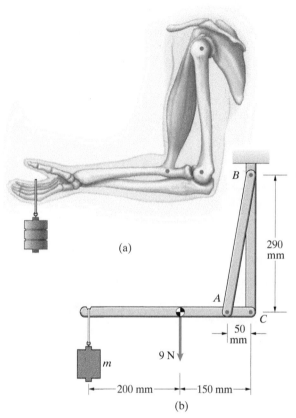

Problem 6.99

6.100 The bones and tendons in a horse's rear leg are shown in Fig. a. A biomechanical model of the leg is shown in Fig. b. If the horse is stationary and the normal force exerted on its leg by the ground is $N = 1200$ N, determine the tensions in the superficial digital flexor BC and the patellar ligament DF.

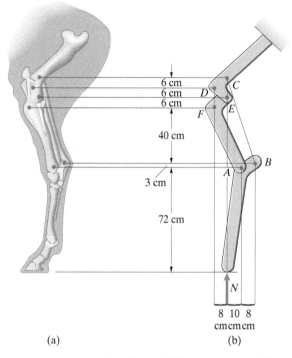

Problem 6.100

6.101 The pressure force exerted on the piston is 2 kN toward the left. Determine the couple M necessary to keep the system in equilibrium.

6.102 In Problem 6.101, determine the forces on member AB at A and B.

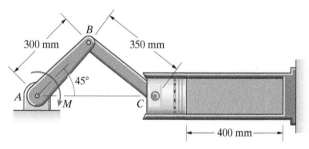

Problems 6.101/6.102

▶ **6.103** In Example 6.8, suppose that the object being held by the pliers is moved to the left so that the horizontal distance from D to the object at E decreases from 30 mm to 20 mm. Draw a sketch of the pliers showing the new position of the object. What forces are exerted on the object at E as a result of the 150-N forces on the pliers?

6.104 The shovel of the excavator is supported by a pin support at *E* and the two-force member *BC*. The 300-lb weight *W* of the shovel acts at the point shown. Determine the reactions on the shovel at *E* and the magnitude of the axial force in the two-force member *BC*.

6.105 The shovel of the excavator has a pin support at *E*. The position of the shovel is controlled by the horizontal hydraulic piston *AB*, which is attached to the shovel through a linkage of the two-force members *BC* and *BD*. The 300-lb weight *W* of the shovel acts at the point shown. What is the magnitude of the force the hydraulic piston must exert to hold the shovel in equilibrium?

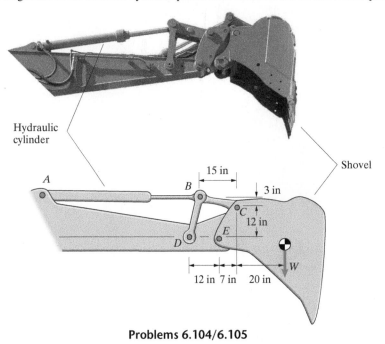

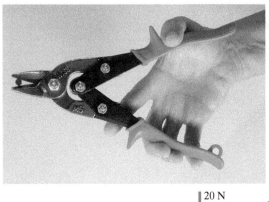

Problems 6.104/6.105

6.106 The woman exerts 20-N forces on the handles of the shears. Determine the magnitude of the forces exerted on the branch at *A*.

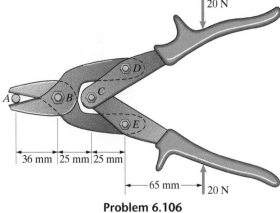

Problem 6.106

6.107 The person exerts 40-N forces on the handles of the locking wrench. Determine the magnitude of the forces the wrench exerts on the bolt at *A*.

6.108 Determine the magnitude of the force the members of the wrench exert on each other at *B* and the axial force in the two-force member *DE*.

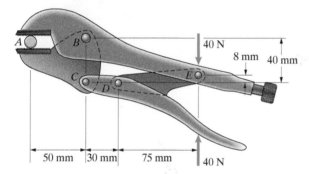

Problems 6.107/6.108

6.109 This device is designed to exert a large force on the horizontal bar at *A* for a stamping operation. If the hydraulic cylinder *DE* exerts an axial force of 800 N and $\alpha = 80°$, what horizontal force is exerted on the horizontal bar at *A*?

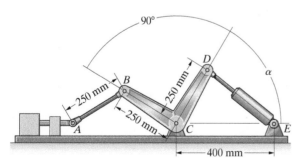

Problem 6.109

6.110 This device raises a load *W* by extending the hydraulic actuator *DE*. The bars *AD* and *BC* are 4 ft long, and the distances $b = 2.5$ ft and $h = 1.5$ ft. If $W = 300$ lb, what force must the actuator exert to hold the load in equilibrium?

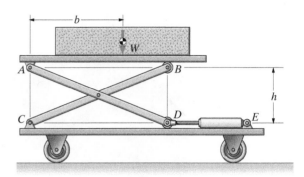

Problem 6.110

6.111 The four-bar linkage operates the forks of a fork lift truck. The force supported by the forks is $W = 8$ kN. Determine the reactions on member *CDE*.

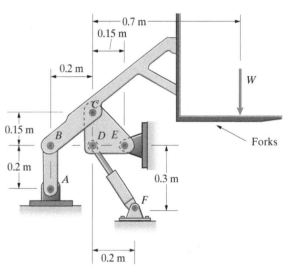

Problem 6.111

6.112 If the horizontal force on the scoop is $F = 2000$ lb, what is the magnitude of the axial force in the hydraulic actuator AC?

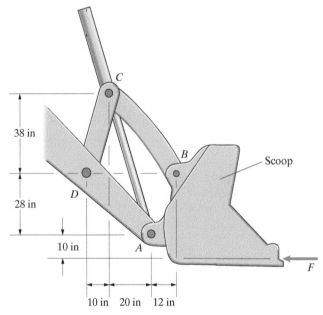

38 in

28 in

10 in

C

B

Scoop

D

A

F

10 in   20 in   12 in

Problem 6.112

6.113 A 10-kip horizontal force acts on the bucket of the excavator. Determine the reactions on member *ACF* at *A* and *F*.

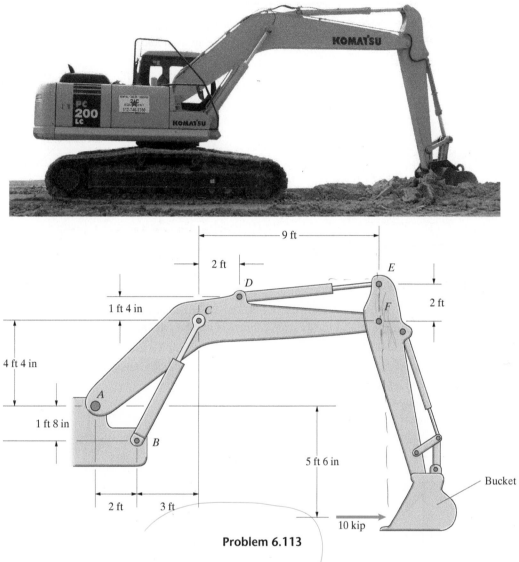

Problem 6.113

6.114 The structure shown in the diagram (one of the two identical structures that support the scoop of the excavator) supports a downward force *F* = 1800 N at *G*. Members *BC* and *DH* can be treated as two-force members. Determine the reactions on member *CDK* at *K*.

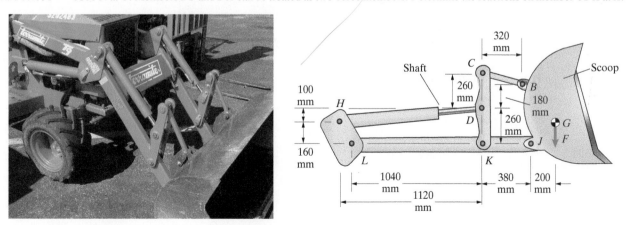

Problem 6.114

Review Problems

6.115 The loads $F_1 = 440$ N and $F_2 = 160$ N. Determine the axial forces in the members. Indicate whether they are in tension (T) or compression (C).

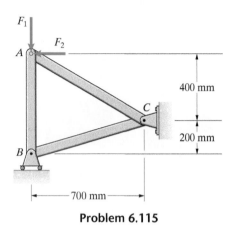

Problem 6.115

6.116 The truss supports a load $F = 10$ kN. Determine the axial forces in members AB, AC, and BC.

6.117 Each member of the truss will safely support a tensile force of 40 kN and a compressive force of 32 kN. Based on this criterion, what is the largest downward load F that can safely be applied at C?

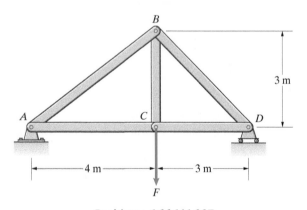

Problems 6.116/6.117

6.118 The Pratt bridge truss supports loads at F, G, and H. Determine the axial forces in members BC, BG, and FG.

6.119 Determine the axial forces in members CD, GD, and GH.

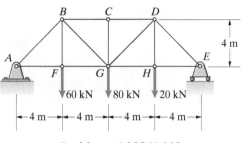

Problems 6.118/6.119

6.120 The truss supports loads at F and H. Determine the axial forces in members AB, AC, BC, BD, CD, and CE.

6.121 Determine the axial forces in members EH and FH.

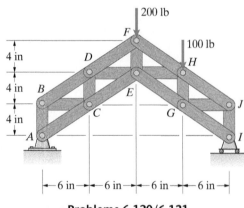

Problems 6.120/6.121

6.122 Determine the axial forces in members *BD*, *CD*, and *CE*.

6.123 Determine the axial forces in members *DF*, *EF*, and *EG*.

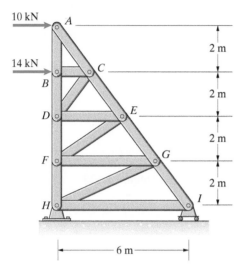

Problems 6.122/6.123

6.124 The truss supports a 400-N load at *G*. Determine the axial forces in members *AC*, *CD*, and *CF*.

6.125 Determine the axial forces in members *CE*, *EF*, and *EH*.

6.126 Which members have the largest tensile and compressive forces, and what are their values?

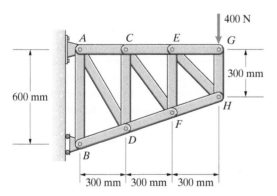

Problems 6.124–6.126

6.127 The Howe truss helps support a roof. Model the supports at *A* and *G* as roller supports. Use the method of joints to determine the axial forces in members *BC*, *CD*, *CI*, and *CJ*.

6.128 Use the method of sections to determine the axial forces in members *CD*, *CJ*, and *IJ*.

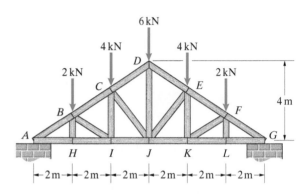

Problems 6.127/6.128

6.129 A speaker system is suspended from the truss by cables attached at *D* and *E*. The mass of the speaker system is 130 kg, and its weight acts at *G*. Determine the axial forces in members *BC* and *CD*.

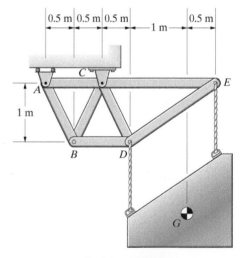

Problem 6.129

6.130 The mass of the suspended object is 900 kg. Determine the axial forces in the bars AB and AC.

Strategy: Draw the free-body diagram of joint A.

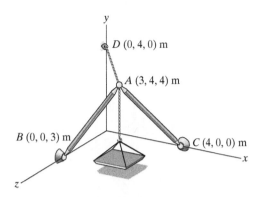

Problem 6.130

6.131 Determine the forces on member ABC, presenting your answers as shown in Fig. 6.25. Obtain the answers in two ways:

(a) When you draw the free-body diagrams of the individual members, place the 400-lb load on the free-body diagram of member ABC.

(b) When you draw the free-body diagrams of the individual members, place the 400-lb load on the free-body diagram of member CD.

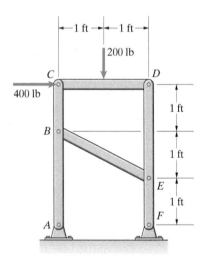

Problem 6.131

6.132 The mass $m = 120$ kg. Determine the forces on member ABC.

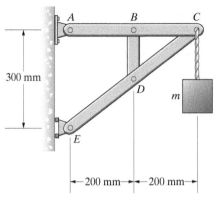

Problem 6.132

6.133 Determine the reactions on member ABC at B and C.

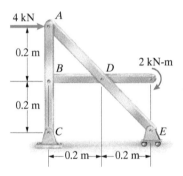

Problem 6.133

6.134 The truck and trailer are parked on a 10° slope. The 14,000-lb weight of the truck and the 8000-lb weight of the trailer act at the points shown. The truck's brakes prevent its rear wheels at B from turning. The truck's front wheels at C and the trailer's wheels at A can turn freely, which means they do not exert friction forces on the road. The trailer hitch at D behaves like a pin support. Determine the forces exerted on the truck at B, C, and D.

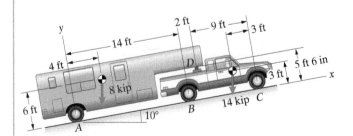

Problem 6.134

6.135 The 600-lb weight of the scoop acts at a point 1 ft 6 in to the right of the vertical line *CE*. The line *ADE* is horizontal. The hydraulic actuator *AB* can be treated as a two-force member. Determine the axial force in the hydraulic actuator *AB* and the forces exerted on the scoop at *C* and *E*.

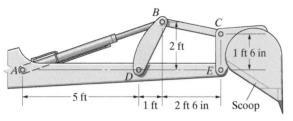

Problem 6.135

6.136 Determine the force exerted on the bolt by the bolt cutters.

6.137 Determine the magnitude of the force the members of the bolt cutters exert on each other at the pin connection *B* and the axial force in the two-force member *CD*.

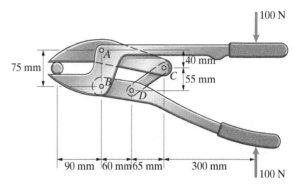

Problems 6.136/6.137

Design Project 1 Design a truss structure to support a foot bridge with an unsupported span (width) of 8 m. Make conservative estimates of the loads the structure will need to support if the pathway supported by the truss is made of wood. Consider two options: (1) Your client wants the bridge to be supported by a truss below the bridge so that the upper surface will be unencumbered by structure. (2) The client wants the truss to be above the bridge and designed so that it can serve as handrails. For each option, use statics to estimate the maximum axial forces to which the members of the structure will be subjected. Investigate alternative designs and compare the resulting axial loads.

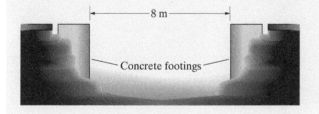

Design Project 2 The truss shown connects one end of a stretcher to a rescue helicopter. Consider alternative truss designs that support the stretcher at *A* and *B* and are supported at *E* and *G*. Compare the maximum tensile and compressive loads in the members of your designs to those in the truss shown. Assuming that the cost of a truss is proportional to the sum of the lengths of its members, compare the costs of your designs to that of the truss shown. Write a brief report describing your analysis and recommending the design you would choose.

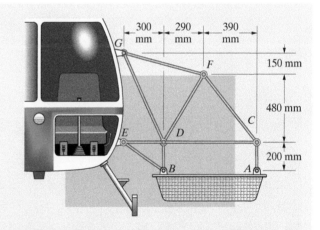

Design Project 3 Go to a fitness center and choose an exercise device that seems mechanically interesting. (For example, it may employ weights, pulleys, and levers.) By measuring dimensions (while the device is not in use), drawing sketches, and perhaps taking photographs, gather the information necessary to analyze the device. Use statics to determine the range of forces a person must exert in using the device.

Suggest changes to the design of the device (other than simply increasing weights) that will increase the maximum force the user must exert.

Prepare a brief report that (1) describes the original device; (2) presents your model and analysis of the device; (3) describes your proposed changes and any analyses supporting them; and (4) recommends the design change you would choose to increase the maximum force the user must employ.

CHAPTER
7

Centroids and Centers of Mass

An object's weight does not act at a single point—it is distributed over the entire volume of the object. But the weight can be represented by a single equivalent force acting at a point called the center of mass. When the equilibrium equations are used to determine the reactions exerted on an object by its supports, the location of the center of mass must be known if the weight of the object is to be included in the analysis. The dynamic behaviors of objects also depend on the locations of their centers of mass. In this chapter we define the center of mass and show how it is determined for various kinds of objects. We also introduce definitions that can be interpreted as the average positions of areas, volumes, and lines. These average positions are called centroids. Centroids coincide with the centers of mass of particular classes of objects, and they also arise in many other engineering applications.

◀ To be balanced, the woman's center of mass—the point at which her weight effectively acts—must be directly above her hands. In this chapter we introduce the concept of an average position, or centroid, and show how to locate the centers of mass of objects.

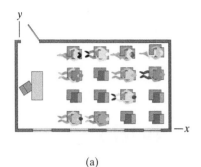

(a)

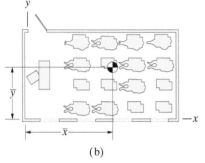

(b)

Figure 7.1
(a) A group of students in a classroom.
(b) Their average position.

7.1 Centroids of Areas

BACKGROUND

Suppose that we want to determine the average position of a group of students sitting in a room. First, we introduce a coordinate system so that we can specify the position of each student. For example, we can align the axes with the walls of the room (Fig. 7.1a). We number the students from 1 to N and denote the position of student 1 by (x_1, y_1), the position of student 2 by (x_2, y_2), and so on. The average x coordinate, which we denote by $\bar{x}$, is the sum of their x coordinates divided by N; that is,

$$\bar{x} = \frac{x_1 + x_2 + \cdots + x_N}{N} = \frac{\sum_i x_i}{N}, \tag{7.1}$$

where the symbol $\sum_i$ means "sum over the range of i." The average y coordinate is

$$\bar{y} = \frac{\sum_i y_i}{N}. \tag{7.2}$$

We indicate the average position by the symbol shown in Fig. 7.1b.

Now suppose that we pass out some pennies to the students. Let the number of coins given to student 1 be c_1, the number given to student 2 be c_2, and so on. What is the average position of the coins in the room? Clearly, the average position of the coins may not be the same as the average position of the students. For example, if the students in the front of the room have more coins, the average position of the coins will be closer to the front of the room than the average position of the students.

To determine the x coordinate of the average position of the coins, we need to sum the x coordinates of the coins and divide by the number of coins. We can obtain the sum of the x coordinates of the coins by multiplying the number of coins each student has by his or her x coordinate and summing. We can obtain the number of coins by summing the numbers $c_1, c_2, \ldots$. Thus, the average x coordinate of the coins is

$$\bar{x} = \frac{\sum_i x_i c_i}{\sum_i c_i}. \tag{7.3}$$

We can determine the average y coordinate of the coins in the same way:

$$\bar{y} = \frac{\sum_i y_i c_i}{\sum_i c_i}. \tag{7.4}$$

By assigning other meanings to $c_1, c_2, \ldots$, we can determine the average positions of other measures associated with the students. For example, we could determine the average position of their age or the average position of their height.

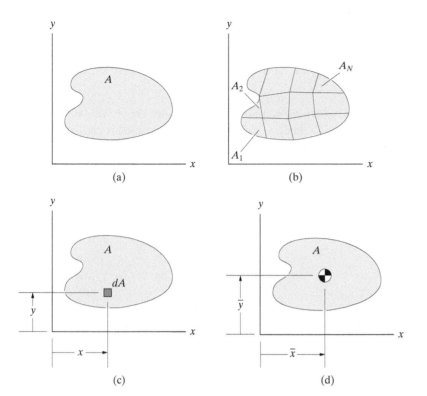

Figure 7.2
(a) The area A.
(b) Dividing A into N parts.
(c) A differential element of area dA with coordinates (x, y).
(d) The centroid of the area.

More generally, we can use Eqs. (7.3) and (7.4) to determine the average position of any set of quantities with which we can associate positions. An average position obtained from these equations is called a *weighted average position*, or *centroid*. The "weight" associated with position (x_1, y_1) is c_1, the weight associated with position (x_2, y_2) is c_2, and so on. In Eqs. (7.1) and (7.2), the weight associated with the position of each student is 1. When the census is taken, the centroid of the population of the United States—the average position of the population—is determined in this way.

Let us consider an arbitrary area A in the x–y plane (Fig. 7.2a). Divide the area into parts $A_1, A_2, \ldots, A_N$ (Fig. 7.2b) and denote the positions of the parts by $(x_1, y_1), (x_2, y_2), \ldots, (x_N, y_N)$. We can obtain the centroid, or average position of the area, by using Eqs. (7.3) and (7.4) with the areas of the parts as the weights:

$$\bar{x} = \frac{\sum_i x_i A_i}{\sum_i A_i}, \qquad \bar{y} = \frac{\sum_i y_i A_i}{\sum_i A_i}. \tag{7.5}$$

A question arises if we try to carry out this procedure: What are the exact positions of the areas $A_1, A_2, \ldots, A_N$? We could reduce the uncertainty in their positions by dividing A into smaller parts, but we would still obtain only approximate values for $\bar{x}$ and $\bar{y}$. To determine the exact location of the centroid, we must take the limit as the sizes of the parts approach zero. We obtain this limit by replacing Eqs. (7.5) by the integrals

$$\bar{x} = \frac{\int_A x \, dA}{\int_A dA}, \tag{7.6}$$

$$\bar{y} = \frac{\displaystyle\int_A y\, dA}{\displaystyle\int_A dA}, \tag{7.7}$$

where x and y are the coordinates of the differential element of area dA (Fig. 7.2c). The subscript A on the integral signs means the integration is carried out over the entire area. The centroid of the area is shown in Fig. 7.2d.

<hr />

RESULTS

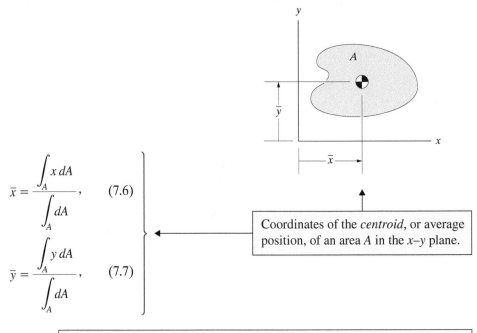

$$\bar{x} = \frac{\displaystyle\int_A x\, dA}{\displaystyle\int_A dA}, \qquad (7.6)$$

$$\bar{y} = \frac{\displaystyle\int_A y\, dA}{\displaystyle\int_A dA}, \qquad (7.7)$$

Coordinates of the *centroid*, or average position, of an area A in the x–y plane.

Keeping in mind that the centroid of an area is its average position will often help in locating it. If an area has "mirror image" symmetry about an axis, its centroid lies on the axis. If an area is symmetric about two axes, the centroid lies at the intersection of the axes.

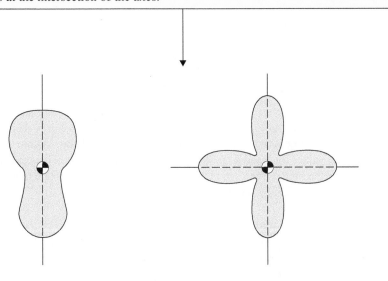

Active Example 7.1   Centroid of an Area by Integration (▶ *Related Problem 7.1*)

Determine the x coordinate of the centroid of the triangular area.

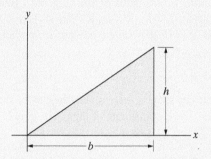

Strategy

We will evaluate Eq. (7.6) using an element of area dA in the form of a vertical "strip" of width dx.

Solution

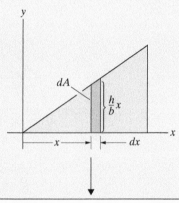

$$\bar{x} = \frac{\displaystyle\int_A x\, dA}{\displaystyle\int_A dA} = \frac{\displaystyle\int_0^b x\left(\frac{h}{b}x\, dx\right)}{\displaystyle\int_0^b \frac{h}{b}x\, dx} = \frac{\dfrac{h}{b}\left[\dfrac{x^3}{3}\right]_0^b}{\dfrac{h}{b}\left[\dfrac{x^2}{2}\right]_0^b} = \frac{2}{3}b.$$

The height of a strip of width dx at position x is $(h/b)x$, so its area is $dA = (h/b)x\, dx$. Use this expression to evaluate Eq. (7.6).

Practice Problem Determine the y coordinate of the centroid of the triangular area. Evaluate Eq. (7.7) by using an element of area dA in the form of a vertical "strip" of width dx, and let y be the height of the midpoint of the strip.

Answer: $\bar{y} = \dfrac{1}{3}h.$

| Example 7.2 | **Area Defined by Two Equations** (▶ *Related Problems 7.2, 7.3*) |

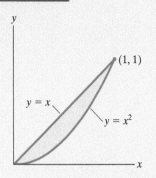

Determine the centroid of the area.

Strategy
We can determine the coordinates of the centroid using an element of area in the form of a vertical strip, just as we did in Active Example 7.1. In this case the strip must be defined so that it extends from the lower curve ($y = x^2$) to the upper curve ($y = x$).

Solution
Let dA be the vertical strip in Fig. a. The height of the strip is $x - x^2$, so $dA = (x - x^2)\,dx$. The x coordinate of the centroid is

$$\bar{x} = \frac{\int_A x\,dA}{\int_A dA} = \frac{\int_0^1 x(x - x^2)\,dx}{\int_0^1 (x - x^2)\,dx} = \frac{\left[\dfrac{x^3}{3} - \dfrac{x^4}{4}\right]_0^1}{\left[\dfrac{x^2}{2} - \dfrac{x^3}{3}\right]_0^1} = \frac{1}{2}.$$

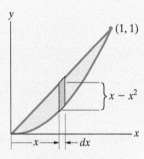

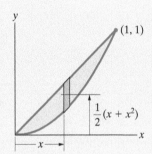

(a) A vertical strip of width dx. The height of the strip is equal to the difference in the two functions.

(b) The y coordinate of the midpoint of the strip.

The y coordinate of the midpoint of the strip is $x^2 + \frac{1}{2}(x - x^2) = \frac{1}{2}(x + x^2)$ (Fig. b). Substituting this expression for y in Eq. (7.7), we obtain the y coordinate of the centroid:

$$\bar{y} = \frac{\int_A y\,dA}{\int_A dA} = \frac{\int_0^1 \left[\dfrac{1}{2}(x + x^2)\right](x - x^2)\,dx}{\int_0^1 (x - x^2)\,dx} = \frac{\dfrac{1}{2}\left[\dfrac{x^3}{3} - \dfrac{x^5}{5}\right]_0^1}{\left[\dfrac{x^2}{2} - \dfrac{x^3}{3}\right]_0^1} = \frac{2}{5}.$$

Critical Thinking
Notice the generality of the approach we use in this example. It can be used to determine the x and y coordinates of the centroid of any area whose upper and lower boundaries are defined by two functions.

Problems

▶ **7.1** In Active Example 7.1, suppose that the triangular area is oriented as shown. Use integration to determine the x and y coordinates of its centroid. (Notice that you already know the answers based on the results of Active Example 7.1.)

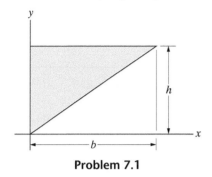

Problem 7.1

▶ **7.2** In Example 7.2, suppose that the area is redefined as shown. Determine the x coordinate of the centroid.

▶ **7.3** In Example 7.2, suppose that the area is redefined as shown. Determine the y coordinate of the centroid.

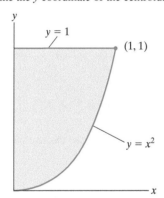

Problems 7.2/7.3

7.4 Determine the centroid of the area.

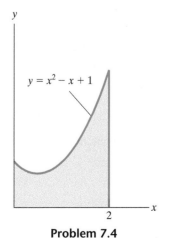

Problem 7.4

7.5 Determine the coordinates of the centroid of the area.

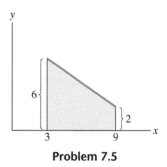

Problem 7.5

7.6 Determine x coordinate of the centroid of the area and compare your answer to the value given in Appendix B.

7.7 Determine the y coordinate of the centroid of the area and compare your answer to the value given in Appendix B.

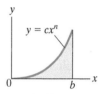

Problems 7.6/7.7

7.8 Suppose that an art student wants to paint a panel of wood as shown, with the horizontal and vertical lines passing through the centroid of the painted area, and asks you to determine the coordinates of the centroid. What are they?

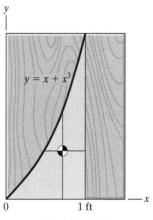

Problem 7.8

7.9 Determine the value of the constant c so that the y coordinate of the centroid of the area is $\bar{y} = 2$. What is the x coordinate of the centroid?

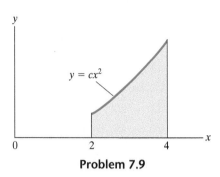

$y = cx^2$

0   2   4

Problem 7.9

7.10 Determine the coordinates of the centroid of the metal plate's cross-sectional area.

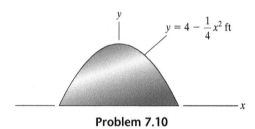

$y = 4 - \dfrac{1}{4}x^2$ ft

Problem 7.10

7.11 An architect wants to build a wall with the profile shown. To estimate the effects of wind loads, he must determine the wall's area and the coordinates of its centroid. What are they?

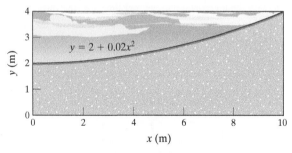

$y = 2 + 0.02x^2$

x (m)

Problem 7.11

7.12 Determine the coordinates of the centroid of the area.

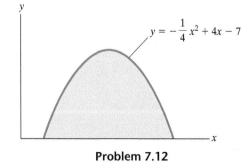

$y = -\dfrac{1}{4}x^2 + 4x - 7$

Problem 7.12

7.13 Determine the coordinates of the centroid of the area.

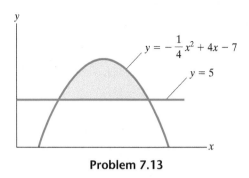

$y = -\dfrac{1}{4}x^2 + 4x - 7$

$y = 5$

Problem 7.13

7.14 Determine the x coordinate of the centroid of the area.

7.15 Determine the y coordinate of the centroid of the area.

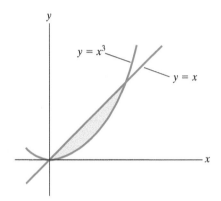

$y = x^3$

$y = x$

Problems 7.14/7.15

7.16 Determine the x component of the centroid of the area.

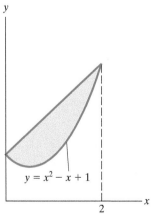

$y = x^2 - x + 1$

2

Problem 7.16

7.17 Determine the x coordinate of the centroid of the area.

7.18 Determine the y coordinate of the centroid of the area.

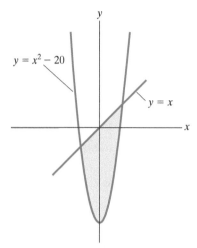

$y = x^2 - 20$

$y = x$

Problems 7.17/7.18

7.19 What is the x coordinate of the centroid of the area?

7.20 What is the y coordinate of the centroid of the area?

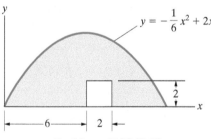

$y = -\dfrac{1}{6}x^2 + 2x$

Problems 7.19/7.20

7.21 An agronomist wants to measure the rainfall at the centroid of a plowed field between two roads. What are the coordinates of the point where the rain gauge should be placed?

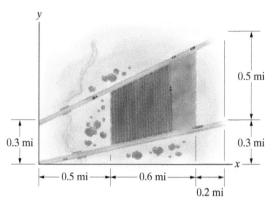

0.5 mi

0.3 mi

0.3 mi

0.5 mi

0.6 mi

0.2 mi

Problem 7.21

7.22 The cross section of an earth-fill dam is shown. Determine the coefficients a and b so that the y coordinate of the centroid of the cross section is 10 m.

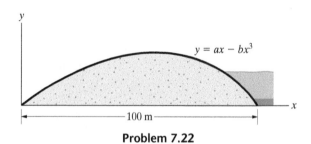

$y = ax - bx^3$

100 m

Problem 7.22

7.23 The Supermarine Spitfire used by Great Britain in World War II had a wing with an elliptical profile. Determine the coordinates of its centroid.

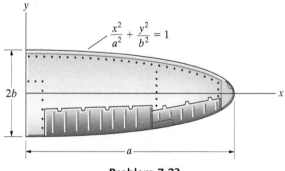

$\dfrac{x^2}{a^2} + \dfrac{y^2}{b^2} = 1$

$2b$

a

Problem 7.23

7.24 Determine the coordinates of the centroid of the area.

Strategy: Write the equation for the circular boundary in the form $y = (R^2 - x^2)^{1/2}$ and use a vertical "strip" of width dx as the element of area dA.

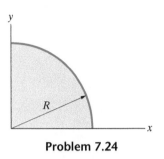

Problem 7.24

7.25* If $R = 6$ and $b = 3$, what is the y coordinate of the centroid of the area?

7.26* What is the x coordinate of the centroid of the area in Problem 7.25?

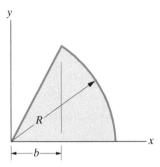

Problems 7.25/7.26

7.2 Composite Areas

BACKGROUND

Although centroids of areas can be determined by integration, the process becomes difficult and tedious for complicated areas. In this section we describe a much easier approach that can be used if an area consists of a combination of simple areas, which we call a *composite area*. We can determine the centroid of a composite area without integration if the centroids of its parts are known.

The area in Fig. 7.3a consists of a triangle, a rectangle, and a semicircle, which we call parts 1, 2, and 3. The x coordinate of the centroid of the composite area is

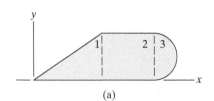

(a)

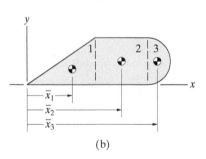

(b)

Figure 7.3
(a) A composite area composed of three simple areas.
(b) The centroids of the parts.

$$\bar{x} = \frac{\displaystyle\int_A x\, dA}{\displaystyle\int_A dA} = \frac{\displaystyle\int_{A_1} x\, dA + \int_{A_2} x\, dA + \int_{A_3} x\, dA}{\displaystyle\int_{A_1} dA + \int_{A_2} dA + \int_{A_3} dA}. \qquad (7.8)$$

The x coordinates of the centroids of the parts are shown in Fig. 7.3b. From the equation for the x coordinate of the centroid of part 1,

$$\bar{x}_1 = \frac{\displaystyle\int_{A_1} x\, dA}{\displaystyle\int_{A_1} dA},$$

we obtain

$$\int_{A_1} x\, dA = \bar{x}_1 A_1.$$

Using this equation and equivalent equations for parts 2 and 3, we can write Eq. (7.8) as

$$\bar{x} = \frac{\bar{x}_1 A_1 + \bar{x}_2 A_2 + \bar{x}_3 A_3}{A_1 + A_2 + A_3}.$$

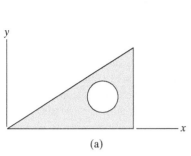 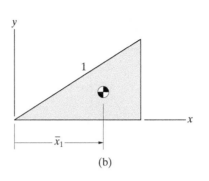 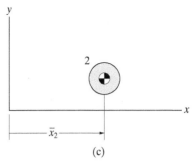

(a) (b) (c)

Figure 7.4
(a) An area with a cutout.
(b) The triangular area.
(c) The area of the cutout.

We have obtained an equation for the x coordinate of the composite area in terms of those of its parts. The coordinates of the centroid of a composite area with an arbitrary number of parts are

$$\bar{x} = \frac{\sum_i \bar{x}_i A_i}{\sum_i A_i}, \qquad \bar{y} = \frac{\sum_i \bar{y}_i A_i}{\sum_i A_i}. \tag{7.9}$$

When we can divide an area into parts whose centroids are known, we can use these expressions to determine its centroid. The centroids of some simple areas are tabulated in Appendix B.

We began our discussion of the centroid of an area by dividing an area into finite parts and writing equations for its weighted average position. The results, Eqs. (7.5), are approximate because of the uncertainty in the positions of the parts of the area. The exact Eqs. (7.9) are identical except that the positions of the parts are their centroids.

The area in Fig. 7.4a consists of a triangular area with a circular hole, or cutout. Designating the triangular area (without the cutout) as part 1 of the composite area (Fig. 7.4b) and the area of the cutout as part 2 (Fig. 7.4c), we obtain the x coordinate of the centroid of the composite area:

$$\bar{x} = \frac{\int_{A_1} x\, dA - \int_{A_2} x\, dA}{\int_{A_1} dA - \int_{A_2} dA} = \frac{\bar{x}_1 A_1 - \bar{x}_2 A_2}{A_1 - A_2}.$$

This equation is identical in form to the first of Eqs. (7.9) except that the terms corresponding to the cutout are negative. As this example demonstrates, we can use Eqs. (7.9) to determine the centroids of composite areas containing cutouts by treating the cutouts as negative areas.

We see that determining the centroid of a composite area requires three steps:

1. Choose the parts—Try to divide the composite area into parts whose centroids you know or can easily determine.

2. Determine the values for the parts—Determine the centroid and the area of each part. Watch for instances of symmetry that can simplify your task.

3. Calculate the centroid—Use Eqs. (7.9) to determine the centroid of the composite area.

RESULTS

$$\bar{x} = \frac{\bar{x}_1 A_1 + \bar{x}_2 A_2 + \cdots}{A_1 + A_2 + \cdots} = \frac{\sum_i \bar{x}_i A_i}{\sum_i A_i}$$

$$\bar{y} = \frac{\bar{y}_1 A_1 + \bar{y}_2 A_2 + \cdots}{A_1 + A_2 + \cdots} = \frac{\sum_i \bar{y}_i A_i}{\sum_i A_i}$$

(7.9)

Coordinates of the centroid of a composite area consisting of parts 1, 2, ... The term A_i is the area of the ith part, and x_i, y_i are the coordinates of the centroid of A_i.

If an area contains a hole or *cutout*, the centroid of the area can be determined from Eqs. (7.9) by treating the cutout as a negative area.

A triangular area with a circular cutout.

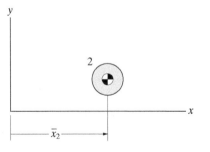

The triangular area without the cutout. Let its area be A_1 and let $\bar{x}_1$ be the x coordinate of its centroid.

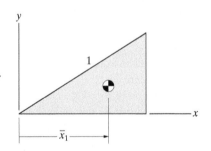

The area of the circular cutout. Let its area be A_2 and let $\bar{x}_2$ be the x coordinate of its centroid.

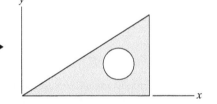

The x coordinate of the centroid of the triangular area with the cutout is

$$\bar{x} = \frac{\bar{x}_1 A_1 - \bar{x}_2 A_2}{A_1 - A_2}.$$

Active Example 7.3   Centroid of a Composite Area (▶ *Related Problem 7.27*)

Determine the x coordinate of the centroid of the composite area.

Strategy
We must divide the area into simple parts (in this example the parts are obvious), determine the areas and centroid locations for the parts, and apply Eq. (7.9)$_1$.

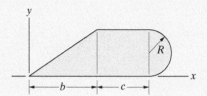

Solution

Choose the Parts
Divide the area into simple parts. The x coordinates of the centroids of the parts are shown.

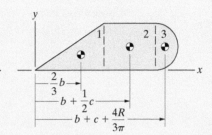

Determine the Values for the Parts
Tabulate the terms needed to apply Eq. (7.9)$_1$. See Appendix B.

	$\bar{x}_i$	A_i	$\bar{x}_i A_i$
Part 1 (triangle)	$\dfrac{2}{3}b$	$\dfrac{1}{2}b(2R)$	$\left(\dfrac{2}{3}b\right)\left[\dfrac{1}{2}b(2R)\right]$
Part 2 (rectangle)	$b + \dfrac{1}{2}c$	$c(2R)$	$\left(b + \dfrac{1}{2}c\right)[c(2R)]$
Part 3 (semicircle)	$b + c + \dfrac{4R}{3\pi}$	$\dfrac{1}{2}\pi R^2$	$\left(b + c + \dfrac{4R}{3\pi}\right)\left(\dfrac{1}{2}\pi R^2\right)$

$$\bar{x} = \frac{\bar{x}_1 A_1 + \bar{x}_2 A_2 + \bar{x}_3 A_3}{A_1 + A_2 + A_3}$$

$$= \frac{\left(\dfrac{2}{3}b\right)\left[\dfrac{1}{2}b(2R)\right] + \left(b + \dfrac{1}{2}c\right)[c(2R)] + \left(b + c + \dfrac{4R}{3\pi}\right)\left(\dfrac{1}{2}\pi R^2\right)}{\dfrac{1}{2}b(2R) + c(2R) + \dfrac{1}{2}\pi R^2}$$

Calculate the Centroid
Use Eq. (7.9)$_1$ to determine the x component of the centroid.

Practice Problem Determine the y coordinate of the centroid of the composite area.

Answer: $\bar{y} = \dfrac{\left[\frac{1}{3}(2R)\right]\left[\frac{1}{2}b(2R)\right] + R\left[c(2R)\right] + R\left(\frac{1}{2}\pi R^2\right)}{\frac{1}{2}b(2R) + c(2R) + \frac{1}{2}\pi R^2}.$

Example 7.4	Centroid of an Area with a Cutout (▶ *Related Problem 7.28*)

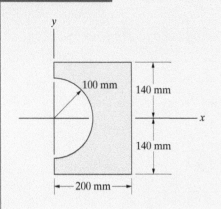

Determine the centroid of the area.

Strategy
Instead of attempting to divide the area into parts, a simpler approach is to treat it as a composite of a rectangular area with a semicircular cutout. Then we can apply Eq. (7.9) by treating the cutout as a negative area.

Solution

Choose the Parts We call the rectangle without the semicircular cutout and the area of the cutout parts 1 and 2, respectively (Fig. a).

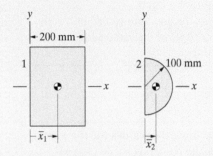

(a) The rectangle and the semicircular cutout.

Determine the Values for the Parts From Appendix B, the x coordinate of the centroid of the cutout is

$$\overline{x}_2 = \frac{4R}{3\pi} = \frac{4(100)}{3\pi} \text{ mm}.$$

The information for determining the x coordinate of the centroid is summarized in the table. Notice that we treat the cutout as a negative area.

Information for determining $\overline{x}$

	$\overline{x}_i$ (mm)	A_i (mm²)	$\overline{x}_i A_i$ (mm³)
Part 1 (rectangle)	100	(200)(280)	(100)[(200)(280)]
Part 2 (cutout)	$\dfrac{4(100)}{3\pi}$	$-\frac{1}{2}\pi(100)^2$	$-\dfrac{4(100)}{3\pi}\left[\frac{1}{2}\pi(100)^2\right]$

Calculate the Centroid The x coordinate of the centroid is

$$\overline{x} = \frac{\overline{x}_1 A_1 + \overline{x}_2 A_2}{A_1 + A_2} = \frac{(100)[(200)(280)] - \dfrac{4(100)}{3\pi}\left[\frac{1}{2}\pi(100)^2\right]}{(200)(280) - \frac{1}{2}\pi(100)^2} = 122 \text{ mm}$$

Because of the symmetry of the area, $\overline{y} = 0$.

Critical Thinking
If you try to divide the area into simple parts, you will gain appreciation for the approach we used. We were able to determine the centroid by dealing with two simple areas, the rectangular area without the cutout and the semicircular cutout. Determining centroids of areas can often be simplified in this way.

Problems

▶ **7.27** In Active Example 7.3, suppose that the area is placed as shown. Let the dimensions $R = 6$ in, $c = 14$ in, and $b = 18$ in. Use Eq. $(7.9)_1$ to determine the x coordinate of the centroid.

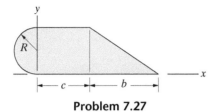

Problem 7.27

▶ **7.28** In Example 7.4, suppose that the area is given a second semicircular cutout as shown. Determine the x coordinate of the centroid.

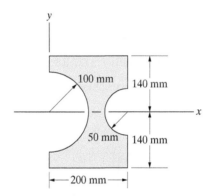

Problem 7.28

For Problems 7.29–7.36, determine the coordinates of the centroids.

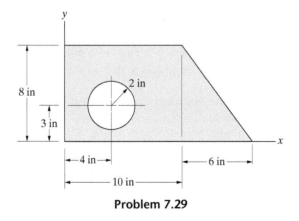

Problem 7.29

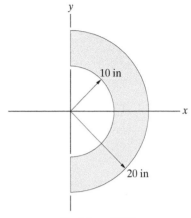

Problem 7.30

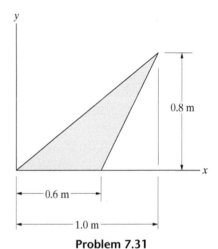

Problem 7.31

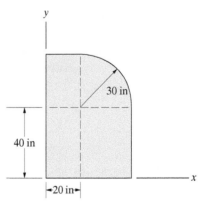

Problem 7.32

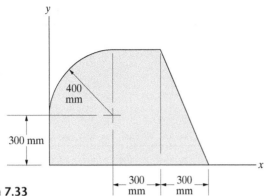

Problem 7.33

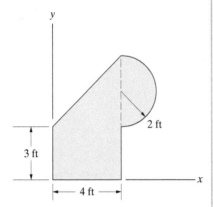

Problem 7.34

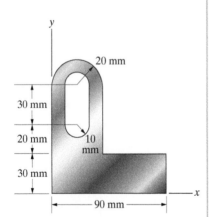

Problem 7.35

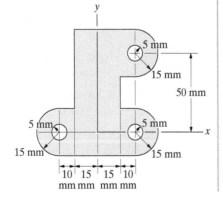

Problem 7.36

7.37 The dimensions $b = 42$ mm and $h = 22$ mm. Determine the y coordinate of the centroid of the beam's cross section.

7.38 If the cross-sectional area of the beam is 8400 mm^2 and the y coordinate of the centroid of the area is $\bar{y} = 90$ mm, what are the dimensions b and h?

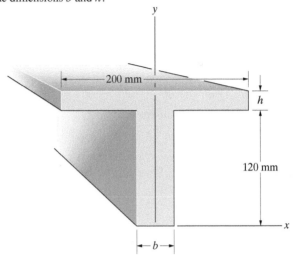

Problems 7.37/7.38

7.39 Determine the y coordinate of the centroid of the beam's cross section.

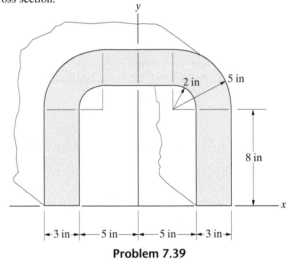

Problem 7.39

7.40 Determine the coordinates of the centroid of the airplane's vertical stabilizer.

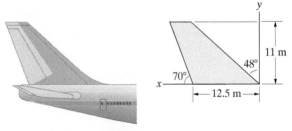

Problem 7.40

7.41 The area has elliptical boundaries. If $a = 30$ mm, $b = 15$ mm, and $\varepsilon = 6$ mm, what is the x coordinate of the centroid of the area?

7.42 By determining the x coordinate of the centroid of the area shown in Problem 7.41 in terms of a, b, and ε, and evaluating its limit as $\varepsilon \to 0$, show that the x coordinate of the centroid of a quarter-elliptical line is

$$\bar{x} = \frac{4a(a + 2b)}{3\pi(a + b)}.$$

7.43 Three sails of a New York pilot schooner are shown. The coordinates of the points are in feet. Determine the centroid of sail 1.

7.44 Determine the centroid of sail 2.

7.45 Determine the centroid of sail 3.

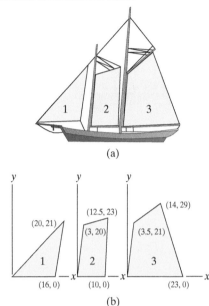

(a)

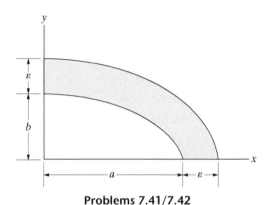

Problems 7.41/7.42

(b)

Problems 7.43–7.45

7.3 Distributed Loads

BACKGROUND

The load exerted on a beam (stringer) supporting a floor of a building is distributed over the beam's length (Fig. 7.5a). The load exerted by wind on a television transmission tower is distributed along the tower's height (Fig. 7.5b). In many engineering applications, loads are continuously distributed along lines. We will show that the concept of the centroid of an area can be useful in the analysis of objects subjected to such loads.

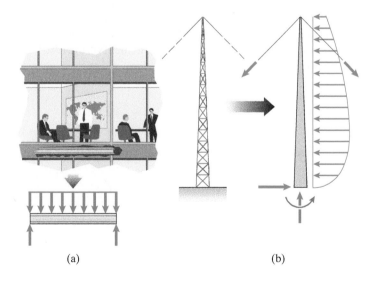

(a)   (b)

Figure 7.5
Examples of distributed forces:
(a) Uniformly distributed load exerted on a beam of a building's frame by the floor.
(b) Wind load distributed along the height of a tower.

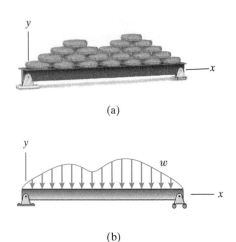

Figure 7.6
(a) Loading a beam with bags of sand.
(b) The distributed load w models the load exerted by the bags.

Describing a Distributed Load

We can use a simple example to demonstrate how such loads are expressed analytically. Suppose that we pile bags of sand on a beam, as shown in Fig. 7.6a. It is clear that the load exerted by the bags is distributed over the length of the beam and that its magnitude at a given position x depends on how high the bags are piled at that position. To describe the load, we define a function w such that the *downward* force exerted on an infinitesimal element dx of the beam is $w\,dx$. With this function we can model the varying magnitude of the load exerted by the sand bags (Fig. 7.6b). The arrows in the figure indicate that the load acts in the downward direction. Loads distributed along lines, from simple examples such as a beam's own weight to complicated ones such as the lift distributed along the length of an airplane's wing, are modeled by the function w. Since the product of w and dx is a force, the dimensions of w are (force)/(length). For example, w can be expressed in newtons per meter in SI units or in pounds per foot in U.S. Customary units.

Determining Force and Moment

Let's assume that the function w describing a particular distributed load is known (Fig. 7.7a). The graph of w is called the *loading curve*. Since the force acting on an element dx of the line is $w\,dx$, we can determine the total force F exerted by the distributed load by integrating the loading curve with respect to x:

$$F = \int_L w\,dx. \tag{7.10}$$

We can also integrate to determine the moment about a point exerted by the distributed load. For example, the moment about the origin due to the force exerted on the element dx is $xw\,dx$, so the total moment about the origin due to the distributed load is

$$M = \int_L xw\,dx. \tag{7.11}$$

When you are concerned only with the total force and moment exerted by a distributed load, you can represent it by a single equivalent force F (Fig. 7.7b). For equivalence, the force must act at a position $\bar{x}$ on the x axis such that the moment of F about the origin is equal to the moment of the distributed load about the origin:

$$\bar{x}F = \int_L xw\,dx.$$

Therefore the force F is equivalent to the distributed load if we place it at the position

$$\bar{x} = \frac{\displaystyle\int_L xw\,dx}{\displaystyle\int_L w\,dx}. \tag{7.12}$$

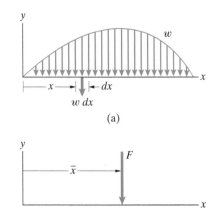

Figure 7.7
(a) A distributed load and the force exerted on a differential element dx.
(b) The equivalent force.

The Area Analogy

Notice that the term $w \, dx$ is equal to an element of "area" dA between the loading curve and the x axis (Fig. 7.8a). (We use quotation marks because $w \, dx$ is actually a force and not an area.) Interpreted in this way, Eq. (7.10) states that the total force exerted by the distributed load is equal to the "area" A between the loading curve and the x axis:

$$F = \int_L w \, dx = \int_A dA = A. \tag{7.13}$$

Substituting $w \, dx = dA$ into Eq. (7.12), we obtain

$$\bar{x} = \frac{\displaystyle\int_L xw \, dx}{\displaystyle\int_L w \, dx} = \frac{\displaystyle\int_A x \, dA}{\displaystyle\int_A dA}. \tag{7.14}$$

The force F is equivalent to the distributed load if it acts at the centroid of the "area" between the loading curve and the x axis (Fig. 7.8b). Using this analogy to represent a distributed load by an equivalent force can be very useful when the loading curve is relatively simple.

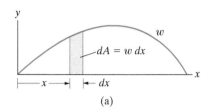

(a)

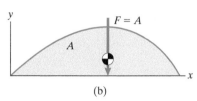

(b)

Figure 7.8
(a) Determining the "area" between the function w and the x axis.
(b) The equivalent force is equal to the "area," and the line of action passes through its centroid.

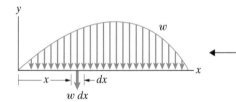

To represent a load that is distributed along the x axis, we define a function w such that the downward force on an element dx of the x axis is $w \, dx$. The graph of w is called the *loading curve*.

$$F = \int_L w \, dx, \quad (7.10)$$

$$M = \int_L xw \, dx, \quad (7.11)$$

The total downward force and the total clockwise moment about the origin due to a distributed load w acting on an interval L of the x axis can be determined by integration.

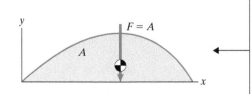

The total downward force F due to a distributed load is equal to the "area" A between the loading curve and the x axis. When this force is represented by a vector, the force vector is *equivalent* to the distributed load if it is placed at the centroid of the "area." (That is, the clockwise moment about the origin due to the force vector is equal to M.) This is called the *area analogy*.

Active Example 7.5 **Beam with a Distributed Load** (▶ *Related Problem 7.46*)

The beam is subjected to a "triangular" distributed load whose value at B is 100 N/m. (That is, the function w increases linearly from $w = 0$ at A to $w = 100$ N/m at B.) Determine the reactions on the beam at A and B.

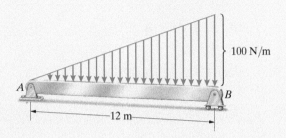

Strategy

We can use the area analogy to represent the distributed load by an equivalent force. Then we can apply the equilibrium equations to determine the reactions at A and B.

Solution

The "area" of the triangular distributed load is one-half its base times its height, or $\frac{1}{2}(12 \text{ m}) \times (100 \text{ N/m}) = 600$ N. The centroid of the triangular "area" is located at $\overline{x} = \frac{2}{3}(12 \text{ m}) = 8$ m.

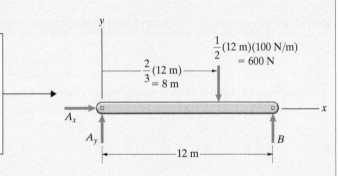

$$\Sigma F_x = A_x = 0,$$
$$\Sigma F_y = A_y + B - 600 \text{ N} = 0,$$
$$\Sigma M_{\text{point } A} = (12 \text{ m})B - (8 \text{ m})(600 \text{ N}) = 0.$$

Apply equilibrium.

Solving yields $A_x = 0$, $A_y = 200$ N, and $B = 400$ N.

Practice Problem (a) Determine w as a function of x for the triangular distributed load in this example. (b) Use Eqs. (7.10) and (7.11) to determine the total downward force and the total clockwise moment about the left end of the beam due to the triangular distributed load.

Answer: (a) $w = \frac{100}{12}x$ N/m. (b) $F = 600$ N, $M = 4800$ N-m.

Example 7.6	Beam Subjected to Distributed Loads (▶ *Related Problem 7.48*)

The beam is subjected to two distributed loads. Determine the reactions at A and B.

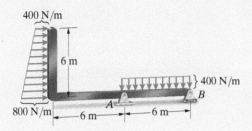

Strategy

We can easily apply the area analogy to the uniformly distributed load between A and B. We will treat the distributed load on the vertical section of the beam as the sum of uniform and triangular distributed loads and use the area analogy to represent each distributed load by an equivalent force.

Solution

We draw the free-body diagram of the beam in Fig. a, expressing the left distributed load as the sum of uniform and triangular loads. In Fig. b, we represent the three distributed loads by equivalent forces. The "area" of the uniform distributed load on the right is $(6\text{ m}) \times (400\text{ N/m}) = 2400\text{ N}$, and its centroid is 3 m from B. The area of the uniform distributed load on the vertical part of the beam is $(6\text{ m}) \times (400\text{ N/m}) = 2400\text{ N}$, and its centroid is located at $y = 3$ m. The area of the triangular distributed load is $\frac{1}{2}(6\text{ m}) \times (400\text{ N/m}) = 1200\text{ N}$, and its centroid is located at $y = \frac{1}{3}(6\text{ m}) = 2$ m.

From the equilibrium equations

$$\Sigma F_x = A_x + 1200\text{ N} + 2400\text{ N} = 0,$$

$$\Sigma F_y = A_y + B - 2400\text{ N} = 0,$$

$$\Sigma M_{\text{point }A} = (6\text{ m})B - (3\text{ m})(2400\text{ N}) - (2\text{ m})(1200\text{ N}) - (3\text{ m})(2400\text{ N}) = 0,$$

we obtain $A_x = -3600$ N, $A_y = -400$ N, and $B = 2800$ N.

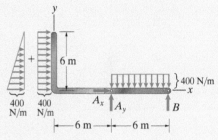

(a) Free-body diagram of the beam.

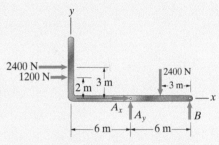

(b) Representing the distributed loads by equivalent forces.

Critical Thinking

When you analyze a problem involving distributed loads, should you always use the area analogy to represent them as we did in this example? The area analogy is useful when a loading curve is sufficiently simple that its area and the location of its centroid are easy to determine. When that is not the case, you can use Eqs. (7.10) and (7.11) to determine the force and moment exerted by a distributed load. We illustrate this approach in Example 7.7.

Example 7.7	**Beam with a Distributed Load** (▶ *Related Problem 7.49*)

The beam is subjected to a distributed load, a force, and a couple. The distributed load is $w = 300x - 50x^2 + 0.3x^4$ lb/ft. Determine the reactions at the fixed support A.

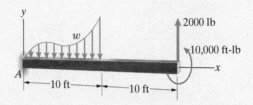

Strategy
Since we know the function w, we can use Eqs. (7.10) and (7.11) to determine the force and moment exerted on the beam by the distributed load. We can then use the equilibrium equations to determine the reactions at A.

Solution
We isolate the beam and show the reactions at the fixed support in Fig. a. The *downward* force exerted by the distributed load is

$$\int_L w \, dx = \int_0^{10} (300x - 50x^2 + 0.3x^4) \, dx = 4330 \text{ lb.}$$

The *clockwise* moment about A exerted by the distributed load is

$$\int_L xw \, dx = \int_0^{10} x(300x - 50x^2 + 0.3x^4) \, dx = 25{,}000 \text{ ft-lb.}$$

From the equilibrium equations

$$\Sigma F_x = A_x = 0,$$

$$\Sigma F_y = A_y - 4330 \text{ lb} + 2000 \text{ lb} = 0,$$

$$\Sigma M_{\text{point } A} = M_A - 25{,}000 \text{ ft-lb} + (20 \text{ ft})(2000 \text{ lb}) + 10{,}000 \text{ ft-lb} = 0,$$

we obtain $A_x = 0$, $A_y = 2330$ lb, and $M_A = -25{,}000$ ft-lb.

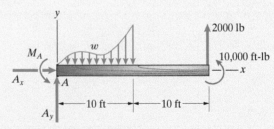

(a) Free-body diagram of the beam.

Critical Thinking
When you use Eq. (7.11), it is important to be aware that you are calculating the *clockwise* moment due to the distributed load w *about the origin* $x = 0$.

Problems

▶ **7.46** In Active Example 7.5, suppose that the distributed load is modified as shown. Determine the reactions on the beam at A and B.

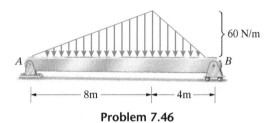

Problem 7.46

7.47 Determine the reactions at A and B.

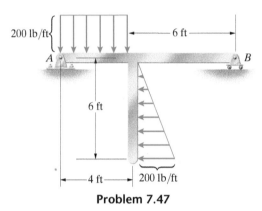

Problem 7.47

▶ **7.48** In Example 7.6, suppose that the distributed loads are modified as shown. Determine the reactions on the beam at A and B.

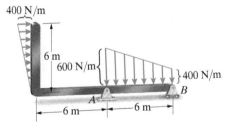

Problem 7.48

▶ **7.49** In Example 7.7, suppose that the distributed load acting on the beam from $x = 0$ to $x = 10$ ft is given by $w = 350 + 0.3x^3$ lb/ft. (a) Determine the downward force and the clockwise moment about A exerted by the distributed load. (b) Determine the reactions at the fixed support.

7.50 Determine the reactions at the fixed support A.

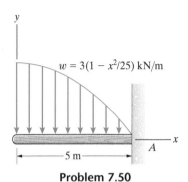

Problem 7.50

7.51 An engineer measures the forces exerted by the soil on a 10-m section of a building foundation and finds that they are described by the distributed load $w = -10x - x^2 + 0.2x^3$ kN/m.

(a) Determine the magnitude of the total force exerted on the foundation by the distributed load.

(b) Determine the magnitude of the moment about A due to the distributed load.

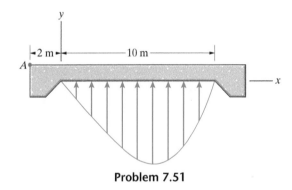

Problem 7.51

7.52 Determine the reactions on the beam at A and B.

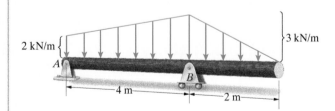

Problem 7.52

7.53 The aerodynamic lift of the wing is described by the distributed load $w = -300 \sqrt{1 - 0.04x^2}$ N/m. The mass of the wing is 27 kg, and its center of mass is located 2 m from the wing root R.

(a) Determine the magnitudes of the force and the moment about R exerted by the lift of the wing.

(b) Determine the reactions on the wing at R.

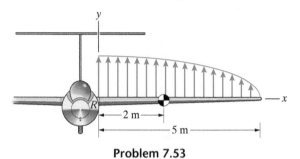

Problem 7.53

7.54 Determine the reactions on the bar at A and B.

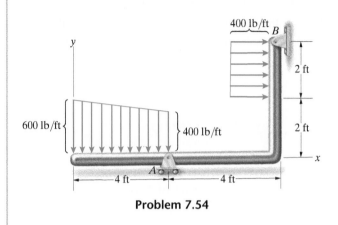

Problem 7.54

7.55 Determine the reactions on member AB at A and B.

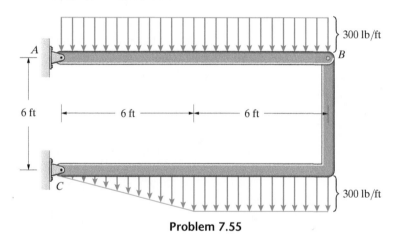

Problem 7.55

7.56 Determine the axial forces in members BD, CD, and CE of the truss and indicate whether they are in tension (T) or compression (C).

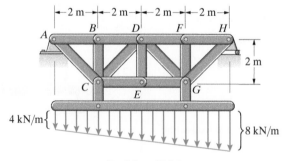

Problem 7.56

7.57 Determine the reactions on member *ABC* at *A* and *B*.

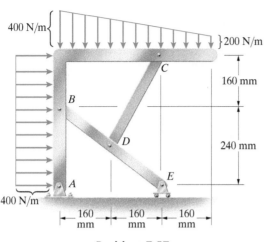

Problem 7.57

7.58 Determine the forces on member *ABC* of the frame.

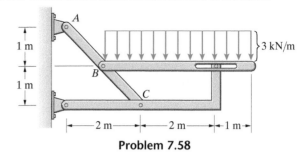

Problem 7.58

7.4 Centroids of Volumes and Lines

BACKGROUND

Here we define the centroids, or average positions, of volumes and lines, and show how to determine the centroids of composite volumes and lines. We will show in Section 7.7 that knowing the centroids of volumes and lines allows you to determine the centers of mass of certain types of objects, which tells you where their weights effectively act.

Volumes   Consider a volume *V*, and let *dV* be a differential element of *V* with coordinates *x*, *y*, and *z* (Fig. 7.9). By analogy with Eqs. (7.6) and (7.7), the coordinates of the centroid of *V* are

$$\bar{x} = \frac{\int_V x \, dV}{\int_V dV}, \qquad \bar{y} = \frac{\int_V y \, dV}{\int_V dV}, \qquad \bar{z} = \frac{\int_V z \, dV}{\int_V dV}. \qquad (7.15)$$

The subscript *V* on the integral signs means that the integration is carried out over the entire volume.

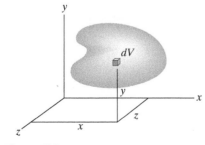

Figure 7.9
A volume *V* and differential element *dV*.

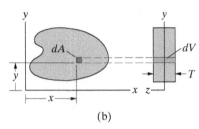

Front View   Side View

(a)

(b)

Figure 7.10
(a) A volume of uniform thickness.
(b) Obtaining dV by projecting dA through the volume.

If a volume has the form of a plate with uniform thickness and cross-sectional area A (Fig. 7.10a), its centroid coincides with the centroid of A and lies at the midpoint between the two faces. To show that this is true, we obtain a volume element dV by projecting an element dA of the cross-sectional area through the thickness T of the volume, so that $dV = T\,dA$ (Fig. 7.10b). Then the x and y coordinates of the centroid of the volume are

$$\bar{x} = \frac{\int_V x\,dV}{\int_V dV} = \frac{\int_A xT\,dA}{\int_A T\,dA} = \frac{\int_A x\,dA}{\int_A dA},$$

$$\bar{y} = \frac{\int_V y\,dV}{\int_V dV} = \frac{\int_A yT\,dA}{\int_A T\,dA} = \frac{\int_A y\,dA}{\int_A dA}.$$

The coordinate $\bar{z} = 0$ by symmetry. Thus you know the centroid of this type of volume if you know (or can determine) the centroid of its cross-sectional area.

Lines   The coordinates of the centroid of a line L are

$$\bar{x} = \frac{\int_L x\,dL}{\int_L dL}, \qquad \bar{y} = \frac{\int_L y\,dL}{\int_L dL}, \qquad \bar{z} = \frac{\int_L z\,dL}{\int_L dL}, \qquad (7.16)$$

where dL is a differential length of the line with coordinates x, y, and z. (Fig. 7.11).

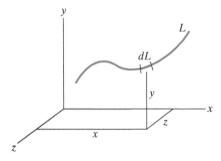

Figure 7.11
A line L and differential element dL.

RESULTS

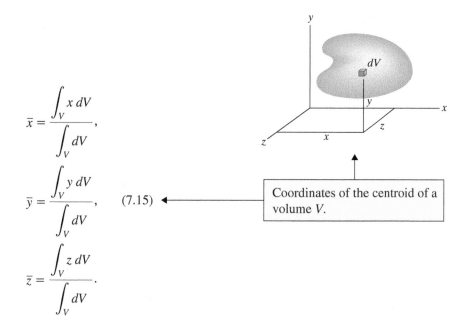

$$\bar{x} = \frac{\displaystyle\int_V x\,dV}{\displaystyle\int_V dV},$$

$$\bar{y} = \frac{\displaystyle\int_V y\,dV}{\displaystyle\int_V dV}, \qquad (7.15)$$

$$\bar{z} = \frac{\displaystyle\int_V z\,dV}{\displaystyle\int_V dV}.$$

Coordinates of the centroid of a volume V.

If a volume has the form of a plate with uniform thickness and cross-sectional area A, its centroid coincides with the centroid of A and lies at the midpoint between the two faces.

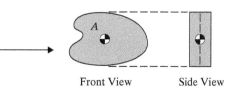

Front View   Side View

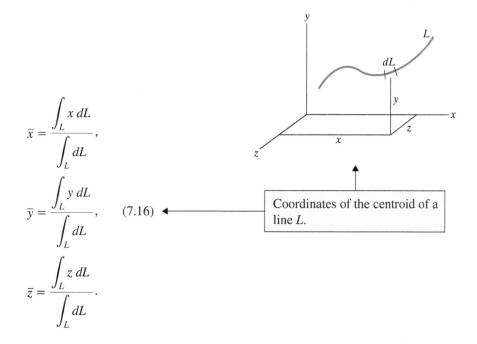

$$\bar{x} = \frac{\displaystyle\int_L x\,dL}{\displaystyle\int_L dL},$$

$$\bar{y} = \frac{\displaystyle\int_L y\,dL}{\displaystyle\int_L dL}, \qquad (7.16)$$

$$\bar{z} = \frac{\displaystyle\int_L z\,dL}{\displaystyle\int_L dL}.$$

Coordinates of the centroid of a line L.

Active Example 7.8   Centroid of a Cone by Integration (▶ *Related Problem 7.59*)

Determine the centroid of the cone.

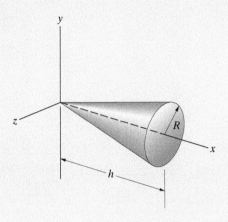

Strategy

Because of the axial symmetry of the cone, the centroid must lie on the x axis. We will determine the x coordinate of the centroid by applying Eq. $(7.15)_1$ using an element of volume dV in the form of a disk of thickness dx.

Solution

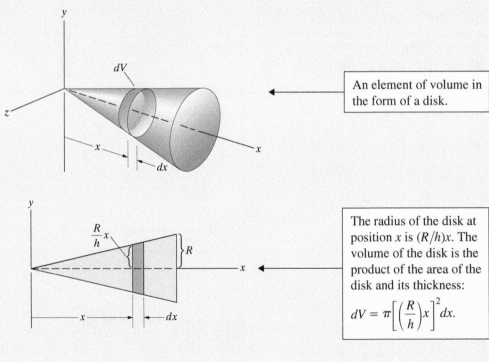

An element of volume in the form of a disk.

The radius of the disk at position x is $(R/h)x$. The volume of the disk is the product of the area of the disk and its thickness:

$$dV = \pi\left[\left(\frac{R}{h}\right)x\right]^2 dx.$$

$$\bar{x} = \frac{\displaystyle\int_V x\, dV}{\displaystyle\int_V dV} = \frac{\displaystyle\int_0^h x\pi\left[\left(\frac{R}{h}\right)x\right]^2}{\displaystyle\int_0^h \pi\left[\left(\frac{R}{h}\right)x\right]^2 dx} = \frac{3}{4}h.$$

Apply Eq. $(7.15)_1$.

Practice Problem The radius in feet of the circular cross section of the truncated cone is given as a function of x by $r = 1 + \frac{1}{4}x$. Determine the x coordinate of its centroid.

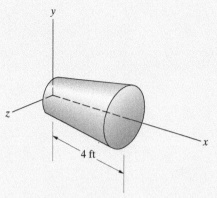

Answer: 2.43 ft.

Example 7.9   Centroid of a Line by Integration (▶ *Related Problem 7.66*)

The line L is defined by the function $y = x^2$. Determine the x coordinate of its centroid.

Strategy
We can express a differential element dL of a line (Fig. a) in terms of dx and dy:

$$dL = \sqrt{dx^2 + dy^2} = \sqrt{1 + \left(\frac{dy}{dx}\right)^2}\, dx.$$

From the equation describing the line, the derivative $dy/dx = 2x$, so we obtain an expression for dL in terms of x:

$$dL = \sqrt{1 + 4x^2}\, dx.$$

Solution
To integrate over the entire line, we must integrate from $x = 0$ to $x = 1$. The x coordinate of the centroid is

$$\bar{x} = \frac{\displaystyle\int_L x\,dL}{\displaystyle\int_L dL} = \frac{\displaystyle\int_0^1 x\sqrt{1 + 4x^2}\, dx}{\displaystyle\int_0^1 \sqrt{1 + 4x^2}\, dx} = 0.574.$$

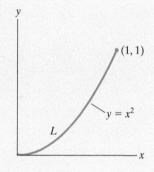

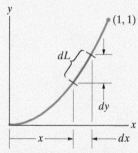

(a) A differential line element dL.

Critical Thinking
Our approach in this example is appropriate to determine the centroid of a line that is described by a function of the form $y = f(x)$. In Example 7.10 we show how to determine the centroid of a line that is described in terms of polar coordinates.

Example 7.10	Centroid of a Semicircular Line by Integration (▶ *Related Problem 7.70*)

Determine the centroid of the semicircular line.

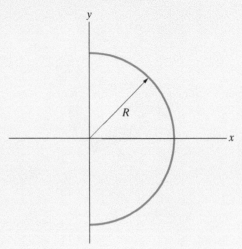

Strategy

Because of the symmetry of the line, the centroid lies on the x axis. To determine $\bar{x}$, we will integrate in terms of polar coordinates. By letting θ change by an amount $d\theta$, we obtain a differential line element of length $dL = R\,d\theta$ (Fig. a). The x coordinate of dL is $x = R\cos\theta$.

Solution

To integrate over the entire line, we must integrate with respect to θ from $\theta = -\pi/2$ to $\theta = +\pi/2$:

$$\bar{x} = \frac{\displaystyle\int_L x\,dL}{\displaystyle\int_L dL} = \frac{\displaystyle\int_{-\pi/2}^{\pi/2} (R\cos\theta)R\,d\theta}{\displaystyle\int_{-\pi/2}^{\pi/2} R\,d\theta} = \frac{R^2[\sin\theta]_{-\pi/2}^{\pi/2}}{R[\theta]_{-\pi/2}^{\pi/2}} = \frac{2R}{\pi}.$$

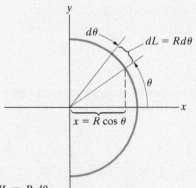

(a) A differential line element $dL = R\,d\theta$.

Critical Thinking

Notice that our integration procedure gives the correct length of the line:

$$\int_L dL = \int_{-\pi/2}^{\pi/2} R\,d\theta = R[\theta]_{-\pi/2}^{\pi/2} = \pi R.$$

Problems

▶ **7.59** Use the method described in Active Example 7.8 to determine the centroid of the truncated cone.

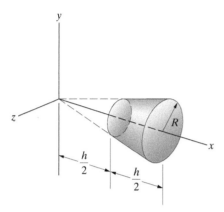

Problem 7.59

7.60 A grain storage tank has the form of a surface of revolution with the profile shown. The height of the tank is 7 m and its diameter at ground level is 10 m. Determine the volume of the tank and the height *above ground level* of the centroid of its volume.

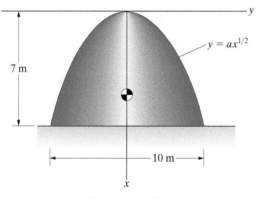

Problem 7.60

7.61 The object shown, designed to serve as a pedestal for a speaker, has a profile obtained by revolving the curve $y = 0.167x^2$ about the x axis. What is the x coordinate of the centroid of the object?

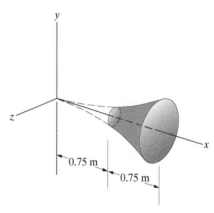

Problem 7.61

7.62 The volume of a nose cone is generated by rotating the function $y = x - 0.2x^2$ about the x axis.

(a) What is the volume of the nose cone?

(b) What is the x coordinate of the centroid of the volume?

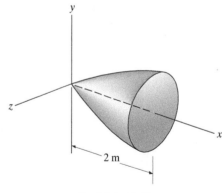

Problem 7.62

7.63 Determine the centroid of the hemispherical volume.

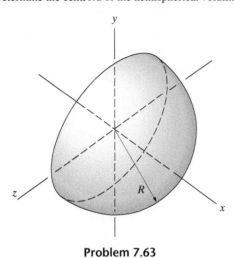

Problem 7.63

7.64 The volume consists of a segment of a sphere of radius R. Determine its centroid.

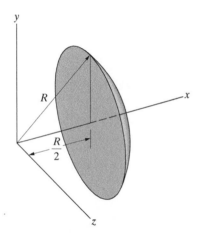

Problem 7.64

7.65 A volume of revolution is obtained by revolving the curve $x^2/a^2 + y^2/b^2 = 1$ about the x axis. Determine its centroid.

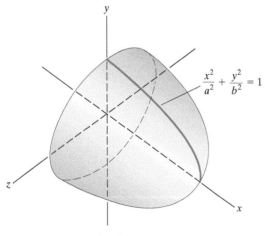

Problem 7.65

▶ **7.66** In Example 7.9, determine the y coordinate of the centroid of the line.

7.67 Determine the coordinates of the centroid of the line.

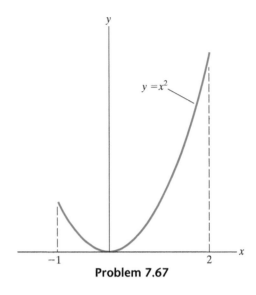

Problem 7.67

7.68 Determine the x coordinate of the centroid of the line.

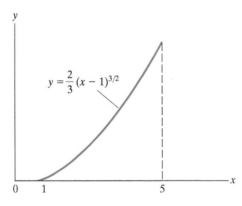

Problem 7.68

7.69 Determine the x coordinate of the centroid of the line.

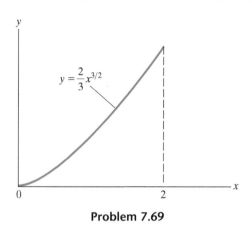

$y = \dfrac{2}{3} x^{3/2}$

Problem 7.69

▶ **7.70** Use the method described in Example 7.10 to determine the centroid of the circular arc.

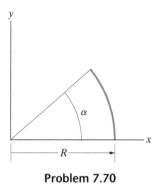

Problem 7.70

7.5 Composite Volumes and Lines

BACKGROUND

The centroids of composite volumes and lines can be derived using the same approach we applied to areas. The coordinates of the centroid of a composite volume are

$$\bar{x} = \frac{\sum_i \bar{x}_i V_i}{\sum_i V_i}, \qquad \bar{y} = \frac{\sum_i \bar{y}_i V_i}{\sum_i V_i}, \qquad \bar{z} = \frac{\sum_i \bar{z}_i V_i}{\sum_i V_i}, \qquad (7.17)$$

and the coordinates of the centroid of a composite line are

$$\bar{x} = \frac{\sum_i \bar{x}_i L_i}{\sum_i L_i}, \qquad \bar{y} = \frac{\sum_i \bar{y}_i L_i}{\sum_i L_i}, \qquad \bar{z} = \frac{\sum_i \bar{z}_i L_i}{\sum_i L_i}. \qquad (7.18)$$

The centroids of some simple volumes and lines are tabulated in Appendices B and C.

Determining the centroid of a composite volume or line requires three steps:

1. Choose the parts—Try to divide the composite into parts whose centroids you know or can easily determine.
2. Determine the values for the parts—Determine the centroid and the volume or length of each part. Watch for instances of symmetry that can simplify your task.
3. Calculate the centroid—Use Eqs. (7.17) or (7.18) to determine the centroid of the composite volume or line.

| Active Example 7.11 | Centroid of a Composite Volume (▶ *Related Problem 7.71*) |

Determine the x coordinate of the centroid of the composite volume.

Strategy

We must divide the volume into simple parts (in this example the parts are obvious), determine the volumes and centroid locations for the parts, and apply Eq. (7.17)₁.

Solution

Choose the Parts
Divide the volume into simple parts. The x coordinates of the centroids of the parts are shown. See Appendix C.

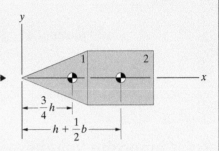

Determine the Values for the Parts
Tabulate the terms needed to apply Eq. (7.17)₁.

	$\bar{x}_i$	V_i	$\bar{x}_i V_i$
Part 1 (cone)	$\dfrac{3}{4}h$	$\dfrac{1}{3}\pi R^2 h$	$\left(\dfrac{3}{4}h\right)\left(\dfrac{1}{3}\pi R^2 h\right)$
Part 2 (cylinder)	$h + \dfrac{1}{2}b$	$\pi R^2 b$	$\left(h + \dfrac{1}{2}b\right)(\pi R^2 b)$

$$\bar{x} = \frac{\bar{x}_1 V_1 + \bar{x}_2 V_2}{V_1 + V_2}.$$

$$= \frac{\left(\dfrac{3}{4}h\right)\left(\dfrac{1}{3}\pi R^2 h\right) + \left(h + \dfrac{1}{2}b\right)\left(\pi R^2 b\right)}{\dfrac{1}{3}\pi R^2 h + \pi R^2 b}.$$

Calculate the Centroid
Use Eq. (7.17)₁ to determine the x component of the centroid.

Practice Problem The composite volume consists of a circular cylinder and a hemisphere. Determine the x coordinate of its centroid.

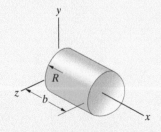

Answer: $\bar{x} = \dfrac{\left(\frac{1}{2}b\right)\left(\pi R^2 b\right) + \left(b + \frac{3}{8}R\right)\left(\frac{2}{3}\pi R^3\right)}{\pi R^2 b + \frac{2}{3}\pi R^3}.$

| Example 7.12 | Centroid of a Volume Containing a Cutout (▶ *Related Problem 7.72*) |

Determine the centroid of the volume.

Strategy

We can divide this volume into the five simple parts shown in Fig. a. Notice that parts 2 and 3 *do not* have the cutout. It is assumed to be "filled in," which simplifies the geometries of those parts. Part 5, which is the volume of the 20-mm-diameter hole, will be treated as a negative volume in Eqs. (7.17).

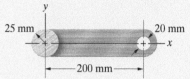

Side View

Solution

Choose the Parts We can divide the volume into the five simple parts shown in Fig. a. Part 5 is the volume of the 20-mm-diameter hole.

Determine the Values for the Parts The centroids of parts 1 and 3 are located at the centroids of their semicircular cross sections (Fig. b). The information for determining the x-coordinate of the centroid is summarized in the table. Part 5 is a negative volume.

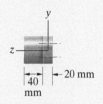

End View

Information for determining $\bar{x}$

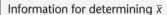

	$\bar{x}_i$ (mm)	V_i (mm^3)	$\bar{x}_i V_i$ (mm^4)
Part 1	$-\dfrac{4(25)}{3\pi}$	$\dfrac{\pi(25)^2}{2}(20)$	$\left[-\dfrac{4(25)}{3\pi}\right]\left[\dfrac{\pi(25)^2}{2}(20)\right]$
Part 2	100	$(200)(50)(20)$	$(100)[(200)(50)(20)]$
Part 3	$200 + \dfrac{4(25)}{3\pi}$	$\dfrac{\pi(25)^2}{2}(20)$	$\left[200 + \dfrac{4(25)}{3\pi}\right]\left[\dfrac{\pi(25)^2}{2}(20)\right]$
Part 4	0	$\pi(25)^2(40)$	0
Part 5	200	$-\pi(10)^2(20)$	$-(200[\pi(10)^2(20)]$

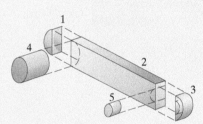

(a) Dividing the line into three parts.

Calculate the Centroid The x coordinate of the centroid of the composite volume is

$$\bar{x} = \frac{\bar{x}_1 V_1 + \bar{x}_2 V_2 + \bar{x}_3 V_3 + \bar{x}_4 V_4 + \bar{x}_5 V_5}{V_1 + V_2 + V_3 + V_4 + V_5}$$

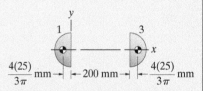

(b) Positions of the centroids of parts 1 and 3.

$$= \frac{\left[-\dfrac{4(25)}{3\pi}\right]\left[\dfrac{\pi(25)^2}{2}(20)\right] + (100)[(200)(50)(20)] + \left[200 + \dfrac{4(25)}{3\pi}\right]\left[\dfrac{\pi(25)^2}{2}(20)\right] + 0 - (200)[\pi(10)^2(20)]}{\dfrac{\pi(25)^2}{2}(20) + (200)(50)(20) + \dfrac{\pi(25)^2}{2}(20) + \pi(25)^2(40) - \pi(10)^2(20)}$$

$$= 72.77 \text{ mm.}$$

The z coordinates of the centroids of the parts are zero except $\bar{z}_4 = 30$ mm. Therefore the z coordinate of the centroid of the composite volume is

$$\bar{z} = \frac{\bar{z}_4 V_4}{V_1 + V_2 + V_3 + V_4 + V_5}$$

$$= \frac{30[\pi(25)^2(40)]}{\dfrac{\pi(25)^2}{2}(20) + (200)(50)(20) + \dfrac{\pi(25)^2}{2}(20) + \pi(25)^2(40) - \pi(10)^2(20)}$$

$$= 7.56 \text{ mm}.$$

Because of symmetry, $\bar{y} = 0$.

Critical Thinking
You can recognize that the volume in this example could be part of a mechanical device. Many manufactured parts have volumes that are composites of simple volumes, and the method used in this example can be used to determine their centroids and, if they are homogeneous, their centers of mass.

Example 7.13 Centroid of a Composite Line (▶ *Related Problem 7.81*)

Determine the centroid of the line. The quarter-circular arc lies in the y–z plane.

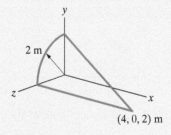

Strategy
We must divide the line into parts (in this case the quarter-circular arc and the two straight segments), determine the centroids of the parts, and apply Eqs. (7.18).

Solution
Choose the Parts   The line consists of a quarter-circular arc and two straight segments, which we call parts 1, 2, and 3 (Fig. a).

Determine the Values for the Parts   From Appendix B, the coordinates of the centroid of the quarter-circular arc are $\bar{x}_1 = 0, \bar{y}_1 = \bar{z}_1 = 2(2)/\pi$ m. The centroids of the straight segments lie at their midpoints. For segment 2, $\bar{x}_2 = 2$ m, $\bar{y}_2 = 0$, and $\bar{z}_2 = 2$ m, and for segment 3, $\bar{x}_3 = 2$ m, $\bar{y}_3 = 1$ m, and $\bar{z}_3 = 1$ m. The length of segment 3 is $L_3 = \sqrt{(4)^2 + (2)^2 + (2)^2} = 4.90$ m. This information is summarized in the table.

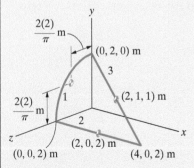

(a) Dividing the line into three parts.

Information for determining the centroid.

	$\bar{x}_i$ (m)	$\bar{y}_i$ (m)	$\bar{z}_i$ (m)	L_i (m)
Part 1	0	$2(2)/\pi$	$2(2)/\pi$	$\pi(2)/2$
Part 2	2	0	2	4
Part 3	2	1	1	4.90

Calculate the Centroid   The coordinates of the centroid of the composite line are

$$\bar{x} = \frac{\bar{x}_1 L_1 + \bar{x}_2 L_2 + \bar{x}_3 L_3}{L_1 + L_2 + L_3} = \frac{0 + (2)(4) + (2)(4.90)}{\pi + 4 + 4.90} = 1.478 \text{ m,}$$

$$\bar{y} = \frac{\bar{y}_1 L_1 + \bar{y}_2 L_2 + \bar{y}_3 L_3}{L_1 + L_2 + L_3} = \frac{[2(2)/\pi][\pi(2)/2] + 0 + (1)(4.90)}{\pi + 4 + 4.90} = 0.739 \text{ m,}$$

$$\bar{z} = \frac{\bar{z}_1 L_1 + \bar{z}_2 L_2 + \bar{z}_3 L_3}{L_1 + L_2 + L_3} = \frac{[2(2)/\pi][\pi(2)/2] + (2)(4) + (1)(4.90)}{\pi + 4 + 4.90} = 1.404 \text{ m.}$$

Critical Thinking
What possible reason could you have for wanting to know the centroid (average position) of a line? In Section 7.7 we show that the center of mass of a slender homogeneous bar, which is the point at which the weight of the bar can be represented by an equivalent force, lies approximately at the centroid of the bar's axis.

Problems

▶ **7.71** In Active Example 7.11, suppose that the cylinder is hollow with inner radius $R/2$ as shown. If the dimensions $R = 6$ in, $h = 12$ in, and $b = 10$ in, what is the x coordinate of the centroid of the volume?

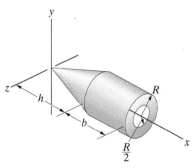

Problem 7.71

▶ **7.72** Use the procedure described in Example 7.12 to determine the x component of the centroid of the volume.

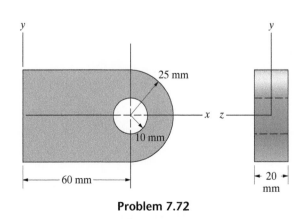

Problem 7.72

For Problems 7.73–7.78, determine the centroids of the volumes.

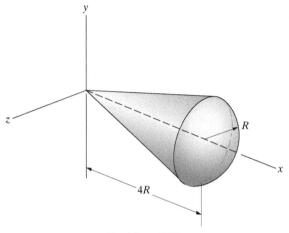

Problem 7.73

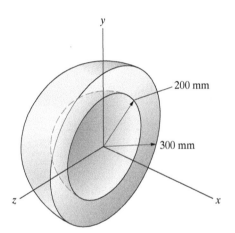

Problem 7.74

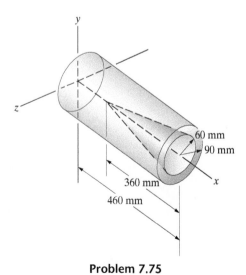

Problem 7.75

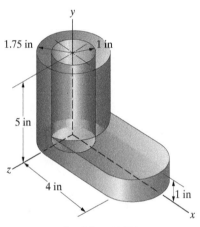

Problem 7.76

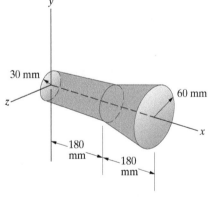

Problem 7.77

Problem 7.78

7.79 The dimensions of the *Gemini* spacecraft (in meters) were $a = 0.70$, $b = 0.88$, $c = 0.74$, $d = 0.98$, $e = 1.82$, $f = 2.20$, $g = 2.24$, and $h = 2.98$. Determine the centroid of its volume.

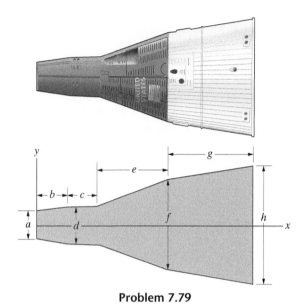

Problem 7.79

7.80 Two views of a machine element are shown. Determine the centroid of its volume.

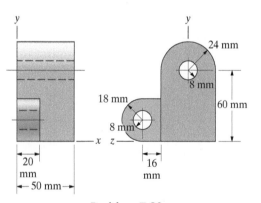

Problem 7.80

▶ **7.81** In Example 7.13, suppose that the circular arc is replaced by a straight line as shown. Determine the centroid of the three-segment line.

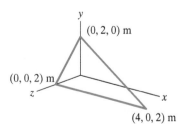

Problem 7.81

For Problems 7.82 and 7.83, determine the centroids of the lines.

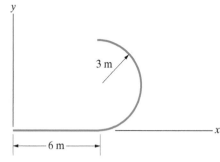

Problem 7.82

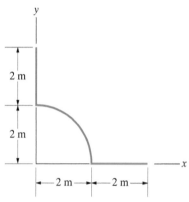

Problem 7.83

7.84 The semicircular part of the line lies in the *x–z* plane. Determine the centroid of the line.

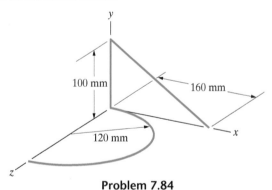

Problem 7.84

7.85 Determine the centroid of the line.

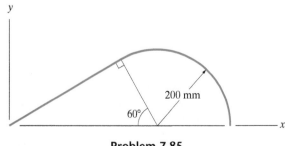

Problem 7.85

7.6 The Pappus–Guldinus Theorems

In this section we discuss two simple and useful theorems relating surfaces and volumes of revolution to the centroids of the lines and areas that generate them.

First Theorem

Consider a line L in the x–y plane that does not intersect the x axis (Fig. 7.12a). Let the coordinates of the centroid of the line be $(\bar{x}, \bar{y})$. We can generate a surface by revolving the line about the x axis (Fig. 7.12b). As the line revolves about the x axis, the centroid of the line moves in a circular path of radius $\bar{y}$.

The first Pappus–Guldinus theorem states that the area of the surface of revolution is equal to the product of the distance through which the centroid of the line moves and the length of the line:

$$A = 2\pi\bar{y}\,L. \tag{7.19}$$

To prove this result, we observe that as the line revolves about the x axis, the area dA generated by an element dL of the line is $dA = 2\pi y\,dL$, where y is the y coordinate of the element dL (Fig. 7.12c). Therefore, the total area of the surface of revolution is

$$A = 2\pi \int_L y\,dL. \tag{7.20}$$

From the definition of the y coordinate of the centroid of the line,

$$\bar{y} = \frac{\displaystyle\int_L y\,dL}{\displaystyle\int_L dL},$$

we obtain

$$\int_L y\,dL = \bar{y}L.$$

Substituting this result into Eq. (7.20), we obtain Eq. (7.19).

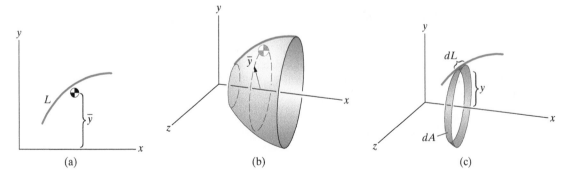

Figure 7.12
(a) A line L and the y coordinate of its centroid.
(b) The surface generated by revolving the line L about the x axis and the path followed by the centroid of the line.
(c) An element dL of the line and the element of area dA it generates.

Second Theorem

Consider an area A in the x–y plane that does not intersect the x axis (Fig. 7.13a). Let the coordinates of the centroid of the area be $(\bar{x}, \bar{y})$. We can generate a volume by revolving the area about the x axis (Fig. 7.13b). As the area revolves about the x axis, the centroid of the area moves in a circular path of length $2\pi\bar{y}$.

The second Pappus–Guldinus theorem states that the volume V of the volume of revolution is equal to the product of the distance through which the centroid of the area moves and the area:

$$V = 2\pi\bar{y}A. \tag{7.21}$$

As the area revolves about the x axis, the volume dV generated by an element dA of the area is $dV = 2\pi y\, dA$, where y is the y coordinate of the element dA (Fig. 7.13c). Therefore, the total volume is

$$V = 2\pi \int_A y\, dA. \tag{7.22}$$

From the definition of the y coordinate of the centroid of the area,

$$\bar{y} = \frac{\displaystyle\int_A y\, dA}{\displaystyle\int_A dA},$$

we obtain

$$\int_A y\, dA = \bar{y}A.$$

Substituting this result into Eq. (7.22), we obtain Eq. (7.21).

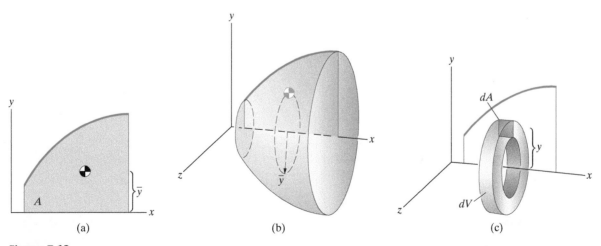

(a)   (b)   (c)

Figure 7.13
(a) An area A and the y coordinate of its centroid.
(b) The volume generated by revolving the area A about the x axis and the path followed by the centroid of the area.
(c) An element dA of the area and the element of volume dV it generates.

The First Pappus–Guldinus Theorem

The line L is in the x–y plane. The y coordinate of the centroid of L is $\bar{y}$.

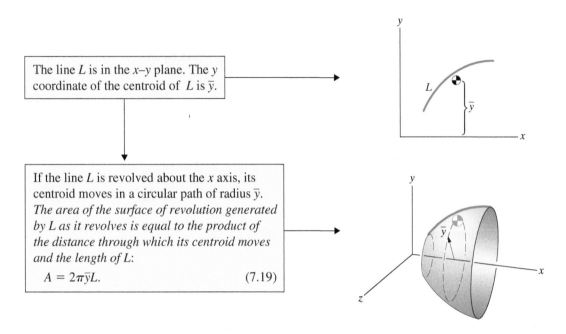

If the line L is revolved about the x axis, its centroid moves in a circular path of radius $\bar{y}$. *The area of the surface of revolution generated by L as it revolves is equal to the product of the distance through which its centroid moves and the length of L:*

$A = 2\pi\bar{y}L.$ (7.19)

The Second Pappus–Guldinus Theorem

The area A is in the x–y plane. The y coordinate of the centroid of A is $\bar{y}$.

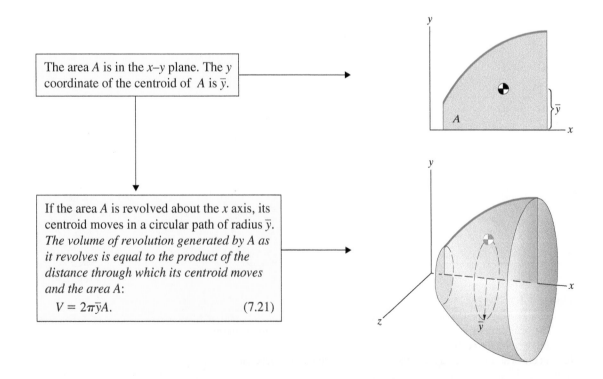

If the area A is revolved about the x axis, its centroid moves in a circular path of radius $\bar{y}$. *The volume of revolution generated by A as it revolves is equal to the product of the distance through which its centroid moves and the area A:*

$V = 2\pi\bar{y}A.$ (7.21)

| **Active Example 7.14** | **The Pappus–Guldinus Theorems** (▶ *Related Problem 7.86*) |

Use the first Pappus–Guldinus theorem to determine the surface area of the cone.

Strategy
We can generate the curved surface of the cone by revolving a straight line about an axis. Because the location of the centroid of the straight line is known, we can use the first Pappus–Guldinus theorem to determine the area of the curved surface.

Solution

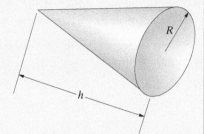

> Revolving this straight line about the x axis generates the curved surface of the cone. The y coordinate of the centroid of the line is shown.
>
> The length of the line is $L = \sqrt{h^2 + R^2}$.
> The area of the curved surface is
>
> $$A = 2\pi \bar{y}_L L = \pi R \sqrt{h^2 + R^2}.$$
>
> Adding the area of the base, the total surface area of the cone is $\pi R \sqrt{h^2 + R^2} + \pi R^2$.

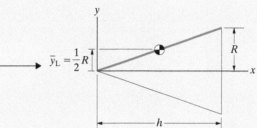

$\bar{y}_L = \frac{1}{2}R$

Practice Problem Use the second Pappus–Guldinus theorem to determine the volume of the cone.

Answer: $V = \frac{1}{3}\pi h R^2.$

| **Example 7.15** | **Determining a Centroid with a Pappus–Guldinus Theorem** (▶ *Related Problem 7.88*) |

The circumference of a sphere of radius R is $2\pi R$ and its surface area is $4\pi R^2$. Use this information to determine the centroid of a semicircular line.

Strategy
Revolving a semicircular line about an axis generates a spherical area. Knowing the area, we can use the first Pappus–Guldinus theorem to determine the centroid of the generating line.

Solution
The length of the semicircular line is $L = \pi R$, and $\bar{y}_L$ is the y coordinate of its centroid. Rotating the line about the x axis generates the surface of a sphere. The first Pappus–Guldinus theorem states that the surface area of the sphere is

$$(2\pi \bar{y}_L)L = 2\pi^2 R \bar{y}_L.$$

By equating this expression to the given surface area $4\pi R^2$, we obtain $\bar{y}_L$:

$$\bar{y}_L = \frac{2R}{\pi}.$$

Critical Thinking
If you can obtain a result by using the Pappus–Guldinus theorems, you will often save time and effort in comparison with other approaches. Compare this example with Example 7.10, in which we used integration to determine the centroid of a semicircular line.

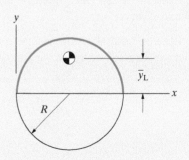

Revolving a semicircular line about the x axis.

Problems

▶ **7.86** Use the method described in Active Example 7.14 to determine the area of the curved part of the surface of the truncated cone.

7.87 Use the second Pappus–Guldinus theorem to determine the volume of the truncated cone.

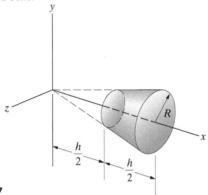

Problems 7.86/7.87

▶ **7.88** The area of the shaded semicircle is $\frac{1}{2}\pi R^2$. The volume of a sphere is $\frac{4}{3}\pi R^3$. Extend the approach described in Example 7.15 to the second Pappus–Guldinus theorem and determine the centroid $\bar{y}_S$ of the semicircular area.

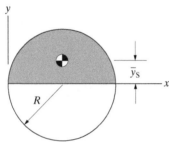

Problem 7.88

7.89 Use the second Pappus–Guldinus theorem to determine the volume generated by revolving the curve about the y axis.

7.90 The length of the curve is $L = 1.479$, and the area generated by rotating it about the x axis is $A = 3.810$. Use the first Pappus–Guldinus theorem to determine the y coordinate of the centroid of the curve.

7.91 Use the first Pappus–Guldinus theorem to determine the area of the surface generated by revolving the curve about the y axis.

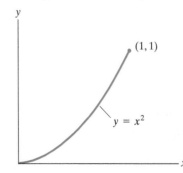

Problems 7.89–7.91

7.92 A nozzle for a large rocket engine is designed by revolving the function $y = \frac{2}{3}(x - 1)^{3/2}$ about the y axis. Use the first Pappus–Guldinus theorem to determine the surface area of the nozzle.

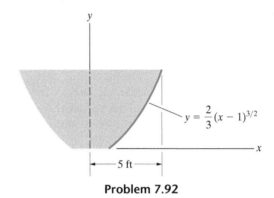

Problem 7.92

7.93 The coordinates of the centroid of the line are $\bar{x} = 332$ mm and $\bar{y} = 118$ mm. Use the first Pappus–Guldinus theorem to determine the area of the surface of revolution obtained by revolving the line about the x axis.

7.94 The coordinates of the centroid of the area between the x axis and the line are $\bar{x} = 355$ mm and $\bar{y} = 78.4$ mm. Use the second Pappus–Guldinus theorem to determine the volume obtained by revolving the area about the x axis.

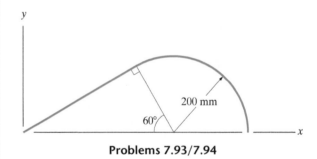

Problems 7.93/7.94

7.95 The volume of revolution contains a hole of radius R.

(a) Use integration to determine its volume.

(b) Use the second Pappus–Guldinus theorem to determine its volume.

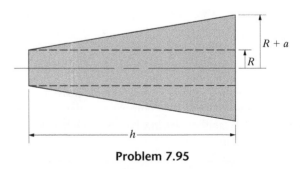

Problem 7.95

7.96 Determine the volume of the volume of revolution.

7.97 Determine the surface area of the volume of revolution.

7.98 The volume of revolution has an elliptical cross section. Determine its volume.

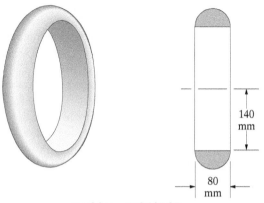

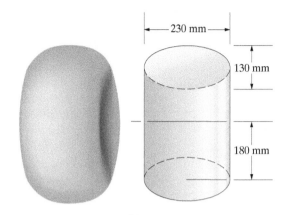

Problems 7.96/7.97

Problem 7.98

7.7 Centers of Mass of Objects

BACKGROUND

The *center of mass* of an object is the centroid, or average position, of its mass. Here we give the analytical definition of the center of mass and demonstrate one of its most important properties: *An object's weight can be represented by a single equivalent force acting at its center of mass*. We then discuss how to locate centers of mass and show that for particular classes of objects, the center of mass coincides with the centroid of a volume, area, or line.

The center of mass of an object is defined by

$$\bar{x} = \frac{\int_m x \, dm}{\int_m dm}, \qquad \bar{y} = \frac{\int_m y \, dm}{\int_m dm}, \qquad \bar{z} = \frac{\int_m z \, dm}{\int_m dm}, \qquad (7.23)$$

where x, y, and z are the coordinates of the differential element of mass dm (Fig. 7.14). The subscripts m indicate that the integration must be carried out over the entire mass of the object.

Before considering how to determine the center of mass of an object, we will demonstrate that the weight of an object can be represented by a single equivalent force acting at its center of mass. Consider an element of mass dm of an object (Fig. 7.15a). If the y axis of the coordinate system points upward, the weight of dm is $-dm g \, \mathbf{j}$. Integrating this expression over the mass m, we obtain the total weight of the object,

$$\int_m - g\mathbf{j} \, dm = -mg\mathbf{j} = -W\mathbf{j}.$$

The moment of the weight of the element dm about the origin is

$$(x\mathbf{i} + y\mathbf{j} + z\mathbf{k}) \times (-dm g \, \mathbf{j}) = gz\mathbf{i} \, dm - gx\mathbf{k} \, dm.$$

Integrating this expression over m, we obtain the total moment about the origin due to the weight of the object:

$$\int_m (gz\mathbf{i} \, dm - gx\mathbf{k} \, dm) = mg\bar{z}\mathbf{i} - mg\bar{x}\mathbf{k} = W\bar{z}\mathbf{i} - W\bar{x}\mathbf{k}.$$

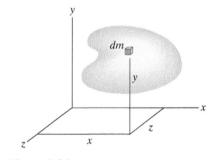

Figure 7.14
An object and differential element of mass dm.

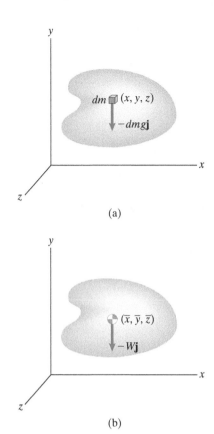

(a)

(b)

Figure 7.15
(a) Weight of the element dm.
(b) Representing the weight by a single force at the center of mass.

If we represent the weight of the object by the force $-W\mathbf{j}$ acting at the center of mass (Fig. 7.15b), the moment of this force about the origin is equal to the total moment due to the weight:

$$(\bar{x}\mathbf{i} + \bar{y}\mathbf{j} + \bar{z}\mathbf{k}) \times (-W\mathbf{j}) = W\bar{z}\mathbf{i} - W\bar{x}\mathbf{k}.$$

This result shows that when we are concerned only with the total force and total moment exerted by the weight of an object, we can assume that its weight acts at the center of mass.

To apply Eqs. (7.23) to specific objects, we will change the variable of integration from mass to volume by introducing the *density*. The density ρ of an object is defined such that the mass of a differential element dV of the volume of the object is $dm = \rho\, dV$. The dimensions of ρ are therefore (mass/volume). For example, it can be expressed in kg/m^3 in SI units or in slug/ft^3 in U.S. Customary units. The total mass of an object is

$$m = \int_m dm = \int_V \rho\, dV. \tag{7.24}$$

An object whose density is uniform throughout its volume is said to be *homogeneous*. In this case, the total mass equals the product of the density and the volume:

$$m = \rho \int_V dV = \rho V. \quad \text{Homogeneous object} \tag{7.25}$$

The *weight density* is defined by $\gamma = g\rho$. It can be expressed in N/m^3 in SI units or in lb/ft^3 in U.S. Customary units. The weight of an element of volume dV of an object is $dW = \gamma\, dV$, and the total weight of a homogeneous object equals γV.

By substituting $dm = \rho\, dV$ into Eq. (7.23), we can express the coordinates of the center of mass in terms of volume integrals:

$$\bar{x} = \frac{\int_V \rho x\, dV}{\int_V \rho\, dV}, \qquad \bar{y} = \frac{\int_V \rho y\, dV}{\int_V \rho\, dV}, \qquad \bar{z} = \frac{\int_V \rho z\, dV}{\int_V \rho\, dV}. \tag{7.26}$$

If ρ is known as a function of position in an object, these expressions determine its center of mass. Furthermore, we can use these expressions to show that the centers of mass of particular classes of objects coincide with centroids of volumes, areas, and lines:

- **The center of mass of a homogeneous object coincides with the centroid of its volume.** If an object is homogeneous, $\rho = $ constant and Eqs. (7.26) become the equations for the centroid of the volume,

$$\bar{x} = \frac{\int_V x\, dV}{\int_V dV}, \qquad \bar{y} = \frac{\int_V y\, dV}{\int_V dV}, \qquad \bar{z} = \frac{\int_V z\, dV}{\int_V dV}.$$

- **The center of mass of a homogeneous plate of uniform thickness coincides with the centroid of its cross-sectional area** (Fig. 7.16). The center of mass of the plate coincides with the centroid of its volume, and we showed in Section 7.4 that the centroid of the volume of a plate of uniform thickness coincides with the centroid of its cross-sectional area.

- **The center of mass of a homogeneous slender bar of uniform cross-sectional area coincides approximately with the centroid of the axis of**

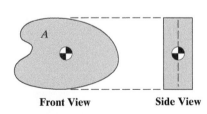

Front View   Side View

Figure 7.16
A plate of uniform thickness.

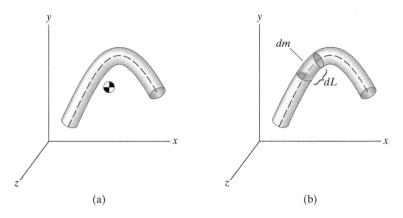

Figure 7.17
(**a**) A slender bar and the centroid of its axis.
(**b**) The element dm.

the bar (Fig. 7.17a). The axis of the bar is defined to be the line through the centroid of its cross section. Let $dm = \rho A\, dL$, where A is the cross-sectional area of the bar and dL is a differential element of length of its axis (Fig. 7.17b). If we substitute this expression into Eqs. (7.26), they become the equations for the centroid of the axis:

$$\bar{x} = \frac{\displaystyle\int_L x\, dL}{\displaystyle\int_L dL}, \qquad \bar{y} = \frac{\displaystyle\int_L y\, dL}{\displaystyle\int_L dL}, \qquad \bar{z} = \frac{\displaystyle\int_L z\, dL}{\displaystyle\int_L dL}.$$

This result is approximate because the center of mass of the element dm does not coincide with the centroid of the cross section in regions where the bar is curved.

RESULTS

$$\bar{x} = \frac{\displaystyle\int_m x\, dm}{\displaystyle\int_m dm} = \frac{\displaystyle\int_V \rho x\, dV}{\displaystyle\int_i \rho\, dV},$$

$$\bar{y} = \frac{\displaystyle\int_m y\, dm}{\displaystyle\int_m dm} = \frac{\displaystyle\int_V \rho y\, dV}{\displaystyle\int_V \rho\, dV}, \qquad (7.23),\ (7.26).$$

$$\bar{z} = \frac{\displaystyle\int_m z\, dm}{\displaystyle\int_m dm} = \frac{\displaystyle\int_V \rho z\, dV}{\displaystyle\int_V \rho\, dV}.$$

Coordinates of the center of mass of an object, where dm is an infinitesimal element of its mass and ρ is its *density*.

An object is *homogeneous* if its density ρ is constant, or uniform. *The center of mass of a homogeneous object coincides with the centroid of its volume.*

The center of mass of a homogeneous plate of uniform thickness coincides with the centroid of its cross-sectional area.

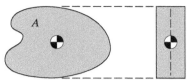

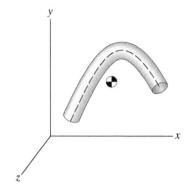

Front View   **Side View**

The center of mass of a homogeneous slender bar of uniform cross-sectional area coincides approximately with the centroid of the axis of the bar.

Active Example 7.16   **Representing the Weight of an L-Shaped Bar** (▶ *Related Problem 7.99*)

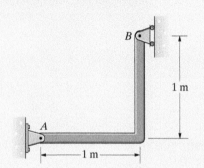

The mass of the homogeneous slender bar is 80 kg. What are the reactions at A and B?

Strategy
We can determine the reactions in two ways.

First Method   By representing the weight of each straight segment of the bar by a force acting at the center of mass of the segment.

Second Method   By determining the center of mass of the entire bar, which is located at the centroid of its axis, and representing the weight of the entire bar by a force acting at its center of mass.

Solution
First Method

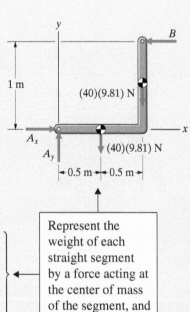

Represent the weight of each straight segment by a force acting at the center of mass of the segment, and apply equilibrium.

$$\Sigma F_x = A_x - B = 0,$$

$$\Sigma F_y = A_y - (40)(9.81)\,\text{N} - (40)(9.81)\,\text{N} = 0,$$

$$\Sigma M_{\text{point } A} = (1\,\text{m})B - (1\,\text{m})[(40)(9.81)\,\text{N}] - (0.5\,\text{m})[(40)(9.81)\,\text{N}] = 0.$$

Solving yields $A_x = 589$ N, $A_y = 785$ N, and $B = 589$ N.

Second Method

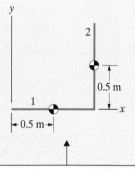

$$\bar{x} = \frac{\bar{x}_1 L_1 + \bar{x}_2 L_2}{L_1 + L_2} = \frac{(0.5)(1) + (1)(1)}{1 + 1} = 0.75 \text{ m},$$

$$\bar{y} = \frac{\bar{y}_1 L_1 + \bar{y}_2 L_2}{L_1 + L_2} = \frac{(0)(1) + (0.5)(1)}{1 + 1} = 0.25 \text{ m},$$

> Treat the axis of the bar as a composite line with parts 1 and 2 and calculate the coordinates of its centroid.

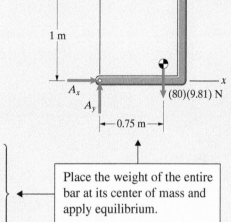

$$\Sigma F_x = A_x - B = 0,$$

$$\Sigma F_y = A_y - (80)(9.81) \text{ N} = 0,$$

$$\Sigma M_{\text{point } A} = (1 \text{ m}) B - (0.75 \text{ m}) [(80)(9.81) \text{ N}] = 0.$$

Solving again yields $A_x = 589$ N, $A_y = 785$ N, and $B = 589$ N.

> Place the weight of the entire bar at its center of mass and apply equilibrium.

Practice Problem The mass of the homogeneous circular bar is 80 kg. What are the reactions at A and B?

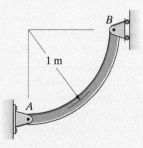

Answer: $A_x = 500$ N, $A_y = 785$ N, $B = 500$ N.

Example 7.17 Cylinder with Nonuniform Density (▶ *Related Problem 7.105*)

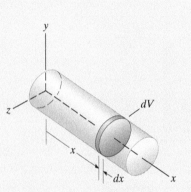

(a) An element of volume dV in the form of a disk.

Determine the mass of the cylinder and the position of its center of mass if (a) it is homogeneous with density ρ_0; (b) its density is given by the equation $\rho = \rho_0(1 + x/L)$.

Strategy

In (a), the mass of the cylinder is simply the product of its density and its volume and the center of mass is located at the centroid of its volume. In (b), the cylinder is inhomogeneous and we must use Eqs. (7.24) and (7.26) to determine its mass and center of mass.

Solution

(a) The volume of the cylinder is LA, so its mass is $\rho_0 LA$. Since the center of mass is coincident with the centroid of the volume of the cylinder, the coordinates of the center of mass are $\bar{x} = \frac{1}{2}L, \bar{y} = 0, \bar{z} = 0$.

(b) We can determine the mass of the cylinder by using an element of volume dV in the form of a disk of thickness dx (Fig. a). The volume $dV = A\,dx$. The mass of the cylinder is

$$m = \int_v \rho\,dV = \int_0^L \rho_0\left(1 + \frac{x}{L}\right)A\,dx = \frac{3}{2}\rho_0 AL.$$

The x coordinate of the center of mass is

$$\bar{x} = \frac{\displaystyle\int_v x\rho\,dV}{\displaystyle\int_v \rho\,dV} = \frac{\displaystyle\int_0^L \rho_0\left(x + \frac{x^2}{L}\right)A\,dx}{\dfrac{3}{2}\rho_0 AL} = \frac{5}{9}L.$$

Because the density does not depend on y or z, we know from symmetry that $\bar{y} = 0$ and $\bar{z} = 0$.

Critical Thinking

Notice that the center of mass of the inhomogeneous cylinder is *not* located at the centroid of its volume. Its density increases from left to right, so the center of mass is located to the right of the midpoint of the cylinder. Many of the objects we deal with in engineering are not homogeneous, but it is not common for an object's density to vary continuously through its volume as in this example. More often, objects consist of assemblies of parts (composites) that have different densities because they consist of different materials. Frequently the individual parts are approximately homogeneous. We discuss the determination of the centers of mass of such composite objects in the next section.

Problems

▶ **7.99** Suppose that the bar in Active Example 7.16 is replaced with this 100-kg homogeneous bar. (a) What is the x coordinate of the bar's center of mass? (b) Determine the reactions at A and B.

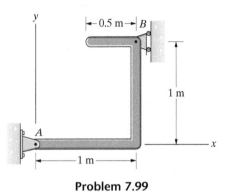

Problem 7.99

7.100 The mass of the homogeneous flat plate is 50 kg. Determine the reactions at the supports A and B.

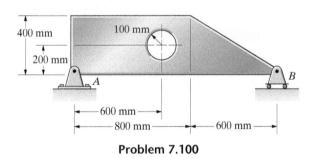

Problem 7.100

7.101 The suspended sign is a homogeneous flat plate that has a mass of 130 kg. Determine the axial forces in members AD and CE. (Notice that the y axis is positive downward.)

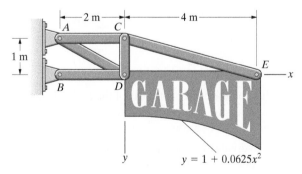

Problem 7.101

7.102 The bar has a mass of 80 kg. What are the reactions at A and B?

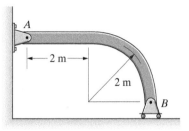

Problem 7.102

7.103 The mass of the bar per unit length is 2 kg/m. Choose the dimension b so that part BC of the suspended bar is horizontal. What is the dimension b, and what are the resulting reactions on the bar at A?

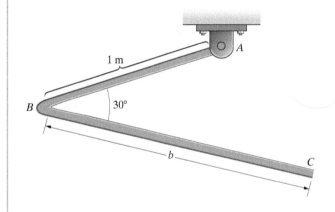

Problem 7.103

7.104 The semicircular part of the homogeneous slender bar lies in the x–z plane. Determine the center of mass of the bar.

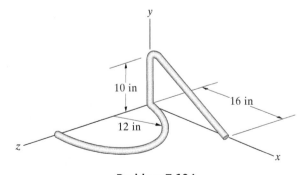

Problem 7.104

▶ **7.105** The density of the cone is given by the equation $\rho = \rho_0(1 + x/h)$, where ρ_0 is a constant. Use the procedure described in Example 7.17 to show that the mass of the cone is given by $m = (7/4)\rho_0 V$, where V is the volume of the cone, and that the x coordinate of the center of mass of the cone is $\bar{x} = (27/35)h$.

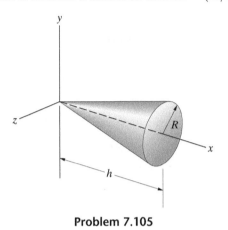

Problem 7.105

7.106 A horizontal cone with 800-mm length and 200-mm radius has a fixed support at A. Its density is $\rho = 6000(1 + 0.4x^2)$ kg/m³, where x is in meters. What are the reactions at A?

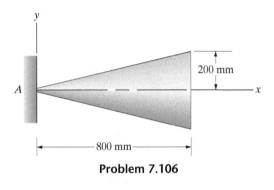

Problem 7.106

7.8 Centers of Mass of Composite Objects

BACKGROUND

The center of mass of an object consisting of a combination of parts can be determined if the centers of mass of its parts are known. The coordinates of the center of mass of a composite object composed of parts with masses $m_1, m_2, \ldots$, are

$$\bar{x} = \frac{\sum_i \bar{x}_i m_i}{\sum_i m_i}, \qquad \bar{y} = \frac{\sum_i \bar{y}_i m_i}{\sum_i m_i}, \qquad \bar{z} = \frac{\sum_i \bar{z}_i m_i}{\sum_i m_i}, \qquad (7.27)$$

where $\bar{x}_i, \bar{y}_i, \bar{z}_i$ are the coordinates of the centers of mass of the parts. Because the weights of the parts are related to their masses by $W_i = gm_i$, Eqs. (7.27) can also be expressed as

$$\bar{x} = \frac{\sum_i \bar{x}_i W_i}{\sum_i W_i}, \qquad \bar{y} = \frac{\sum_i \bar{y}_i W_i}{\sum_i W_i}, \qquad \bar{z} = \frac{\sum_i \bar{z}_i W_i}{\sum_i W_i}. \qquad (7.28)$$

When the masses or weights and the centers of mass of the parts of a composite object are known, these equations determine its center of mass.

Determining the center of mass of a composite object requires three steps:

1. **Choose the parts**—Try to divide the object into parts whose centers of mass you know or can easily determine.

2. **Determine the values for the parts**—Determine the center of mass and the mass or weight of each part. Watch for instances of symmetry that can simplify your task.

3. **Calculate the center of mass**—Use Eqs. (7.27) or (7.28) to determine the center of mass of the composite object.

Active Example 7.18   Center of Mass of a Composite Object (▶ *Related Problem 7.107*)

The L-shaped machine part is composed to two homogeneous bars. Bar 1 is tungsten alloy with a density of 14,000 kg/m^3. Bar 2 is steel with a density of 7800 kg/m^3. Determine the *x* coordinate of the center of mass of the machine part.

Strategy
We can determine the mass and the *x* coordinate of the center of mass of each homogeneous bar and apply Eq. (7.27)$_1$.

Solution

The volume of bar 1 is
$$V_1 = (80 \text{ mm})(240 \text{ mm})(40 \text{ mm})$$
$$= 7.68 \times 10^5 \text{ mm}^3$$
$$= 7.68 \times 10^{-4} \text{ m}^3,$$
so its mass is
$$m_1 = \rho_1 V_1$$
$$= (14{,}000 \text{ kg/m}^3)(7.68 \times 10^{-4} \text{ m}^3)$$
$$= 10.8 \text{ kg}.$$

◀ ⎯ Mass of bar 1.

The center of mass coincides with the centroid of the volume of the bar, so
$$\bar{x}_1 = \frac{1}{2}(80 \text{ mm}) = 40 \text{ mm}.$$

◀ ⎯ Center of mass of bar 1.

Bar 2 has the same volume as bar 1, so the mass of bar 2 is
$$m_2 = \rho_2 V_2$$
$$= (7800 \text{ kg/m}^3)(7.68 \times 10^{-4} \text{ m}^3)$$
$$= 5.99 \text{ kg}.$$

◀ ⎯ Mass of bar 2.

The *x* coordinate of the centroid of the volume of the bar is
$$\bar{x}_2 = 80 \text{ mm} + \frac{1}{2}(240 \text{ mm}) = 200 \text{ mm}.$$

◀ ⎯ Center of mass of bar 2.

$$\bar{x} = \frac{\bar{x}_1 m_1 + \bar{x}_2 m_2}{m_1 + m_2}$$
$$= \frac{(40 \text{ mm})(10.8 \text{ kg}) + (200 \text{ mm})(5.99 \text{ kg})}{10.8 \text{ kg} + 5.99 \text{ kg}}$$
$$= 97.2 \text{ mm}.$$

◀ ⎯ Apply Eq. (7.27)$_1$.

Practice Problem Determine the *y* coordinate of the center of mass of the L-shaped machine part.

Answer: $\bar{y} = 91.4$ mm.

| Example 7.19 | Center of Mass of a Composite Object (▶ *Related Problem 7.109*) |

The composite object consists of a bar welded to a cylinder. The homogeneous bar is aluminum (weight density 168 lb/ft³), and the homogeneous cylinder is bronze (weight density 530 lb/ft³). Determine the center of mass of the object.

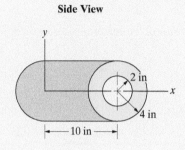

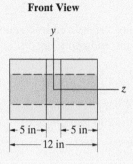

Strategy

We can determine the weight of each homogeneous part by multiplying its volume by its weight density. We also know that the center of mass of each part coincides with the centroid of its volume. The centroid of the cylinder is located at its center, but we must determine the location of the centroid of the bar by treating it as a composite volume.

Solution

The volume of the cylinder is

$$V_{\text{cylinder}} = (12 \text{ in})[\pi(4 \text{ in})^2 - \pi(2 \text{ in})^2]$$

$$= 452 \text{ in}^3 = 0.262 \text{ ft}^3,$$

so its weight is

$$W_{\text{cylinder}} = (0.262 \text{ ft}^3)(530 \text{ lb/ft}^3) = 138.8 \text{ lb}.$$

The x coordinate of its center of mass is $\bar{x}_{\text{cylinder}} = 10$ in. The volume of the bar is

$$V_{\text{bar}} = (10 \text{ in})(8 \text{ in})(2 \text{ in}) + \tfrac{1}{2}\pi(4 \text{ in})^2(2 \text{ in}) - \tfrac{1}{2}\pi(4 \text{ in})^2(2 \text{ in})$$

$$= 160 \text{ in}^3 = 0.0926 \text{ ft}^3,$$

and its weight is

$$W_{\text{bar}} = (0.0926 \text{ ft}^3)(168 \text{ lb/ft}^3) = 15.6 \text{ lb}.$$

We can determine the centroid of the volume of the bar by treating it as a composite volume consisting of three parts (Fig. a). Part 3 is a semicircular "cutout." The centroids of part 1 and the semicircular cutout 3 are located at the

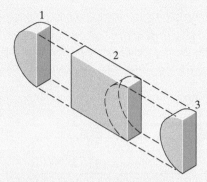
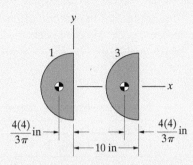

(a) Dividing the bar into three parts.
(b) The centroids of the two semicircular parts.

centroids of their semicircular cross sections (Fig b). Using the information summarized in the table, we have

$$\bar{x}_{bar} = \frac{\bar{x}_1 V_1 + \bar{x}_2 V_2 + \bar{x}_3 V_3}{V_1 + V_2 + V_3}$$

$$= \frac{-\dfrac{4(4)}{3\pi}\left[\frac{1}{2}\pi(4)^2(2)\right] + 5[(10)(8)(2)] - \left[10 - \dfrac{4(4)}{3\pi}\right]\left[\frac{1}{2}\pi(4)^2(2)\right]}{\frac{1}{2}\pi(4)^2(2) + (10)(8)(2) - \frac{1}{2}\pi(4)^2(2)}$$

$$= 1.86 \text{ in.}$$

Information for determining the x coordinate of the centroid of the bar

	$\bar{x}_i$ (in)	V_i (in^3)	$\bar{x}_i V_i$ (in^4)
Part 1	$-\dfrac{4(4)}{3\pi}$	$\frac{1}{2}\pi(4)^2(2)$	$-\dfrac{4(4)}{3\pi}\left[\frac{1}{2}\pi(4)^2(2)\right]$
Part 2	5	$(10)(8)(2)$	$5[(10)(8)(2)]$
Part 3	$10 - \dfrac{4(4)}{3\pi}$	$-\frac{1}{2}\pi(4)^2(2)$	$-\left[10 - \dfrac{4(4)}{3\pi}\right]\left[\frac{1}{2}\pi(4)^2(2)\right]$

Therefore, the x coordinate of the center of mass of the composite object is

$$\bar{x} = \frac{\bar{x}_{bar} W_{bar} + \bar{x}_{cylinder} W_{cylinder}}{W_{bar} + W_{cylinder}}$$

$$= \frac{(1.86 \text{ in})(15.6 \text{ lb}) + (10 \text{ in})(138.8 \text{ lb})}{15.6 \text{ lb} + 138.8 \text{ lb}}$$

$$= 9.18 \text{ in.}$$

Because of the symmetry of the bar, the y and z coordinates of its center of mass are $\bar{y} = 0$ and $\bar{z} = 0$.

Critical Thinking

The composite object in this example is not homogeneous, which means we could not assume that its center of mass coincides with the centroid of its volume. But the bar and the cylinder are each homogeneous, so we *could* determine their individual centers of mass by finding the centroids of their volumes. The primary challenge in this example was determining the centroid of the volume of the bar with its semicircular end and semicircular cutout.

Example 7.20 | **Centers of Mass of Vehicles** (▶ *Related Problems 7.115, 7.116*)

A car is placed on a platform that measures the normal force exerted by each tire independently. Measurements made with the platform horizontal and with the platform tilted at $\alpha = 15°$ are shown in the table. Determine the position of the car's center of mass.

Measurements of the normal forces exerted by the tires

Wheelbase = 2.82 m		
Track = 1.55 m		**Measured Loads (N)**
	$\alpha = 0$	$\alpha = 15°$
Left front wheel, N_{LF}	5104	4463
Right front wheel, N_{RF}	5027	4396
Left rear wheel, N_{LR}	3613	3956
Right rear wheel, N_{RR}	3559	3898

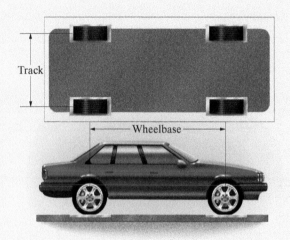

Strategy

The given measurements tell us the normal reactions exerted on the car's tires by the platform. By drawing free-body diagrams of the car in the two positions and applying equilibrium equations, we will obtain equations that can be solved for the unknown coordinates of the car's center of mass.

Solution

We draw the free-body diagram of the car when the platform is in the horizontal position in Figs. a and b. The car's weight is

$$W = N_{LF} + N_{RF} + N_{LR} + N_{RR}$$

$$= 5104 + 5027 + 3613 + 3559$$

$$= 17,303 \text{ N.}$$

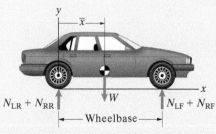

(a) Side view of the free-body diagram with the platform horizontal.

From Fig. a, we obtain the equilibrium equation

$$\Sigma M_{z \text{ axis}} = (\text{wheelbase})(N_{LF} + N_{RF}) - \bar{x}W = 0,$$

which we can solve for $\bar{x}$:

$$\bar{x} = \frac{(\text{wheelbase})(N_{\text{LF}} + N_{\text{RF}})}{W}$$

$$= \frac{(2.82 \text{ m})(5104 \text{ N} + 5027 \text{ N})}{17{,}303 \text{ N}}$$

$$= 1.651 \text{ m}.$$

From Fig. b,

$$\Sigma M_{x \text{ axis}} = \bar{z}W - (\text{track})(N_{\text{RF}} + N_{\text{RR}}) = 0,$$

which we can solve for $\bar{z}$:

$$\bar{z} = \frac{(\text{track})(N_{\text{RF}} + N_{\text{RR}})}{W}$$

$$= \frac{(1.55 \text{ m})(5027 \text{ N} + 3559 \text{ N})}{17{,}303 \text{ N}}$$

$$= 0.769 \text{ m}.$$

Now that we know $\bar{x}$, we can determine $\bar{y}$ from the free-body diagram of the car when the platform is in the tilted position (Fig. c). From the equilibrium equation

$$\Sigma M_{z \text{ axis}} = (\text{wheelbase})(N_{\text{LF}} + N_{\text{RF}}) + \bar{y}W \sin 15° - \bar{x}W \cos 15°$$

$$= 0,$$

we obtain

$$\bar{y} = \frac{\bar{x}W \cos 15° - (\text{wheelbase})(N_{\text{LF}} + N_{\text{RF}})}{W \sin 15°}$$

$$= \frac{(1.651 \text{ m})(17{,}303 \text{ N}) \cos 15° - (2.82 \text{ m})(4463 \text{ N} + 4396 \text{ N})}{(17{,}303 \text{ N}) \sin 15°}$$

$$= 0.584 \text{ m}.$$

Notice that we could not have determined $\bar{y}$ without the measurements made with the car in the tilted position.

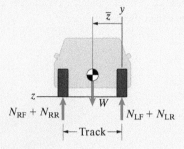

(b) Front view of the free-body diagram with the platform horizontal.

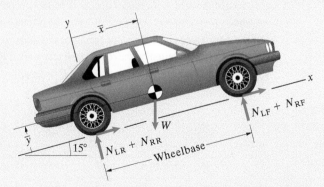

(c) Side view of the free-body diagram with the platform tilted.

Problems

▶ **7.107** In Active Example 7.18, suppose that bar 1 is replaced by a bar with the same dimensions that consists of aluminum alloy with a density of 2600 kg/m³. Determine the x coordinate of the center of mass of the machine part.

7.108 The cylindrical tube is made of aluminum with density 2700 kg/m³. The cylindrical plug is made of steel with density 7800 kg/m³. Determine the coordinates of the center of mass of the composite object.

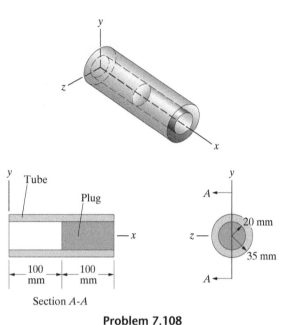

Section A-A

Problem 7.108

▶ **7.109** In Example 7.19, suppose that the object is redesigned so that the radius of the hole in the hollow cylinder is increased from 2 in to 3 in. What is the x coordinate of the center of mass of the object?

7.110 A machine consists of three parts. The masses and the locations of the centers of mass of two of the parts are

Part	Mass (kg)	$\bar{x}$ (mm)	$\bar{y}$ (mm)	$\bar{z}$ (mm)
1	2.0	100	50	−20
2	4.5	150	70	0

The mass of part 3 is 2.5 kg. The design engineer wants to position part 3 so that the center of mass location of the machine is $\bar{x} = 120$ mm, $\bar{y} = 80$ mm, $\bar{z} = 0$. Determine the necessary position of the center of mass of part 3.

7.111 Two views of a machine element are shown. Part 1 is aluminum alloy with density 2800 kg/m³, and part 2 is steel with density 7800 kg/m³. Determine the coordinates of its center of mass.

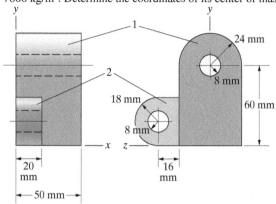

Problem 7.111

7.112 The loads $F_1 = F_2 = 25$ kN. The mass of the truss is 900 kg. The members of the truss are homogeneous bars with the same uniform cross section. (a) What is the x coordinate of the center of mass of the truss? (b) Determine the reactions at A and G.

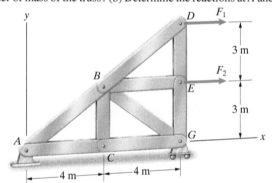

Problem 7.112

7.113 With its engine removed, the mass of the car is 1100 kg and its center of mass is at C. The mass of the engine is 220 kg.

(a) Suppose that you want to place the center of mass E of the engine so that the center of mass of the car is midway between the front wheels A and the rear wheels B. What is the distance b?

(b) If the car is parked on a 15° slope facing up the slope, what total normal force is exerted by the road on the rear wheels B?

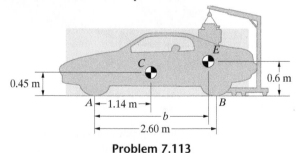

Problem 7.113

7.114 The airplane is parked with its landing gear resting on scales. The weights measured at A, B, and C are 30 kN, 140 kN, and 146 kN, respectively. After a crate is loaded onto the plane, the weights measured at A, B, and C are 31 kN, 142 kN, and 147 kN, respectively. Determine the mass and the x and y coordinates of the center of mass of the crate.

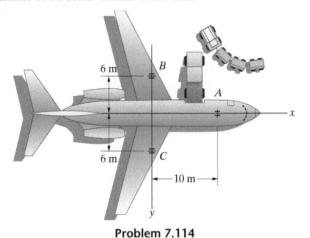

Problem 7.114

▶ **7.115** A suitcase with a mass of 90 kg is placed in the trunk of the car described in Example 7.20. The position of the center of mass of the suitcase is $\bar{x}_s = -0.533$ m, $\bar{y}_s = 0.762$ m, $\bar{z}_s = -0.305$ m. If the suitcase is regarded as part of the car, what is the new position of the car's center of mass?

▶ **7.116** A group of engineering students constructs a miniature device of the kind described in Example 7.20 and uses it to determine the center of mass of a miniature vehicle. The data they obtain are shown in the following table:

Wheelbase = 36 in		
Track = 30 in	**Measured Loads (lb)**	
	$\alpha = 0$	$\alpha = 10°$
Left front wheel, N_{LF}	35	32
Right front wheel, N_{RF}	36	33
Left rear wheel, N_{LR}	27	34
Right rear wheel, N_{RR}	29	30

Determine the center of mass of the vehicle. Use the same coordinate system as in Example 7.20.

Review Problems

7.117 Determine the centroid of the area by letting dA be a vertical strip of width dx.

7.118 Determine the centroid of the area by letting dA be a horizontal strip of height dy.

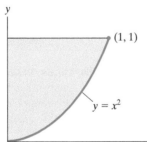

Problems 7.117/7.118

7.119 Determine the centroid of the area.

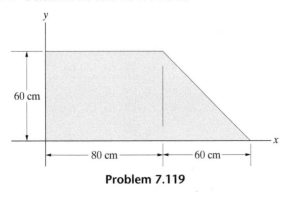

Problem 7.119

7.120 Determine the centroid of the area.

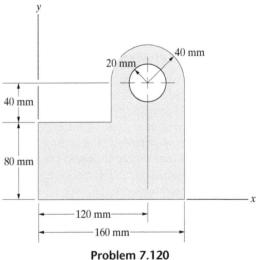

Problem 7.120

7.121 The cantilever beam is subjected to a triangular distributed load. What are the reactions at A?

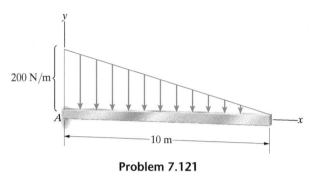

Problem 7.121

7.122 What is the axial load in member BD of the frame?

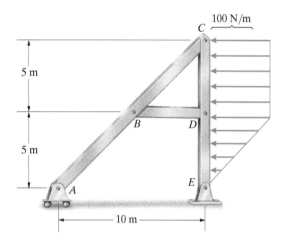

Problem 7.122

7.123 An engineer estimates that the maximum wind load on the 40-m tower in Fig. a is described by the distributed load in Fig. b. The tower is supported by three cables, A, B, and C, from the top of the tower to equally spaced points 15 m from the bottom of the tower (Fig. c). If the wind blows from the west and cables B and C are slack, what is the tension in cable A? (Model the base of the tower as a ball and socket support.)

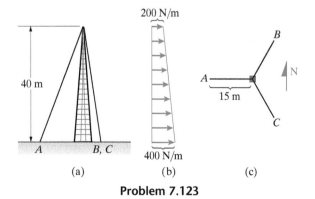

Problem 7.123

7.124 Determine the reactions on member $ABCD$ at A and D.

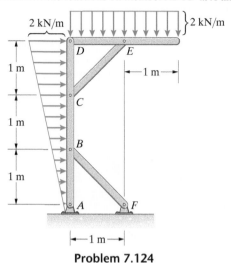

Problem 7.124

7.125 Estimate the centroid of the volume of the *Apollo* lunar return configuration (not including its rocket nozzle) by treating it as a cone and a cylinder.

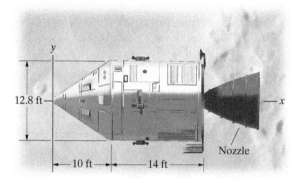

Problem 7.125

7.126 The shape of the rocket nozzle of the *Apollo* lunar return configuration is approximated by revolving the curve shown around the x axis. In terms of the coordinate system shown, determine the centroid of the volume of the nozzle.

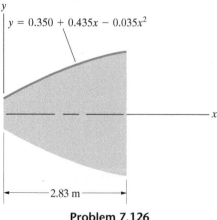

Problem 7.126

7.127 Determine the coordinates of the centroid of the volume.

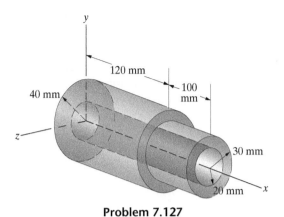

Problem 7.127

7.128 Determine the surface area of the volume of revolution.

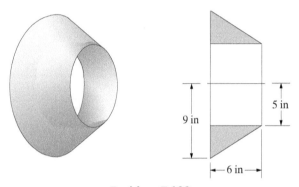

Problem 7.128

7.129 Determine the y coordinate of the center of mass of the homogeneous steel plate.

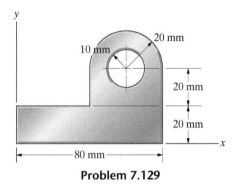

Problem 7.129

7.130 Determine the x coordinate of the center of mass of the homogeneous steel plate.

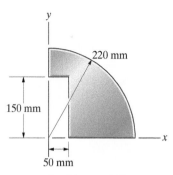

Problem 7.130

7.131 The area of the homogeneous plate is 10 ft². The vertical reactions on the plate at A and B are 80 lb and 84 lb, respectively. Suppose that you want to equalize the reactions at A and B by drilling a 1-ft-diameter hole in the plate. What horizontal distance from A should the center of the hole be? What are the resulting reactions at A and B?

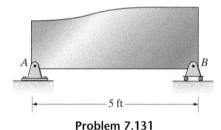

Problem 7.131

7.132 The plate is of uniform thickness and is made of homogeneous material whose mass per unit area of the plate is 2 kg/m². The vertical reactions at A and B are 6 N and 10 N, respectively. What is the x coordinate of the centroid of the hole?

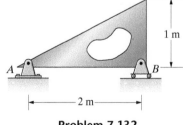

Problem 7.132

7.133 Determine the center of mass of the homogeneous sheet of metal.

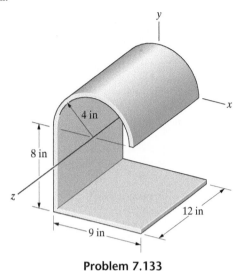

Problem 7.133

7.134 Determine the center of mass of the homogeneous object.

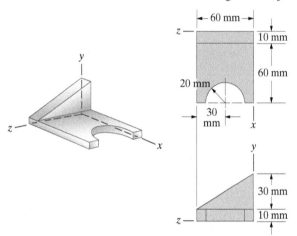

Problem 7.134

7.135 Determine the center of mass of the homogeneous object.

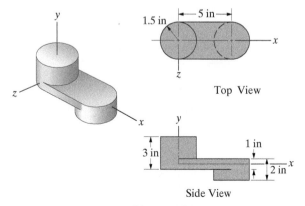

Problem 7.135

7.136 The arrangement shown can be used to determine the location of the center of mass of a person. A horizontal board has a pin support at A and rests on a scale that measures weight at B. The distance from A to B is 2.3 m. When the person is not on the board, the scale at B measures 90 N.

(a) When a 63-kg person is in position (1), the scale at B measures 496 N. What is the x coordinate of the person's center of mass?

(b) When the same person is in position (2), the scale measures 523 N. What is the x coordinate of his center of mass?

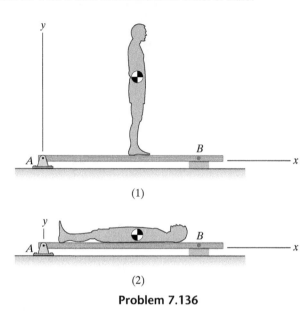

(1)

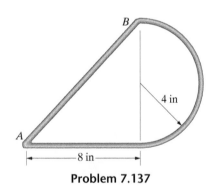

(2)

Problem 7.136

7.137 If a string is tied to the slender bar at A and the bar is allowed to hang freely, what will be the angle between AB and the vertical?

Problem 7.137

7.138 When the truck is unloaded, the total reactions at the front and rear wheels are $A = 54$ kN and $B = 36$ kN. The density of the load of gravel is $\rho = 1600$ kg/m^3. The dimension of the load in the z direction is 3 m, and its surface profile, given by the function shown, does not depend on z. What are the total reactions at the front and rear wheels of the loaded truck?

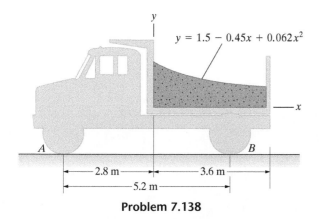

$$y = 1.5 - 0.45x + 0.062x^2$$

Problem 7.138

7.139 The mass of the moon is 0.0123 times the mass of the earth. If the moon's center of mass is 383,000 km from the center of mass of the earth, what is the distance from the center of mass of the earth to the center of mass of the earth–moon system?

Design Project

7.140 Construct a homogeneous thin flat plate with the shape shown in Fig. a. (Use the cardboard back of a pad of paper to construct the plate. Choose your dimensions so that the plate is as large as possible.) Calculate the location of the center of mass of the plate. Measuring as carefully as possible, mark the center of mass clearly on both sides of the plate. Then carry out the following experiments.

(a) Balance the plate on your finger (Fig. b) and observe that it balances at its center of mass. Explain the result of this experiment by drawing a free-body diagram of the plate.

(b) This experiment requires a needle or slender nail, a length of string, and a small weight. Tie the weight to one end of the string and make a small loop at the other end. Stick the needle through the plate at any point other than its center of mass. Hold the needle horizontal so that the plate hangs freely from it (Fig. c). Use the loop to hang the weight from the needle, and let the weight hang freely so that the string lies along the face of the plate. Observe that the string passes through the center of mass of the plate. Repeat this experiment several times, sticking the needle through various points on the plate. Explain the results of this experiment by drawing a free-body diagram of the plate.

(c) Hold the plate so that the plane of the plate is vertical, and throw the plate upward, spinning it like a Frisbee. Observe that the plate spins about its center of mass.

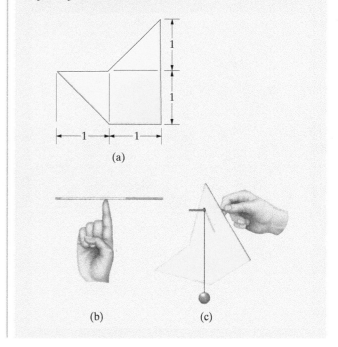

CHAPTER
9

Friction

Friction forces have many important effects, both desirable and undesirable, in engineering applications. The Coulomb theory of friction allows us to estimate the maximum friction forces that can be exerted by contacting surfaces and the friction forces exerted by sliding surfaces. This opens the path to the analysis of important new classes of supports and machines, including wedges (shims), threaded connections, bearings, and belts.

◄ The workpiece exerts normal and friction forces on the grinding wheel. In this chapter we analyze friction forces between contacting surfaces.

9.1 Theory of Dry Friction

Suppose that a person climbs a ladder that leans against a smooth wall. Figure 9.1a shows the free-body diagram of the person and ladder. If the person is stationary on the ladder, we can use the equilibrium equations to determine the friction force. But there is another question that we cannot answer using the equilibrium equations alone: Will the ladder remain in place, or will it slip on the floor? If a truck is parked on an incline, the total friction force exerted on its tires by the road prevents it from sliding down the incline (Fig. 9.1b). We can use the equilibrium equations to determine the total friction force. But here too there is another question that we cannot answer: What is the steepest incline on which the truck could be parked without slipping?

To answer these questions, we must examine the nature of friction forces in more detail. Place a book on a table and push it with a small horizontal force, as shown in Fig. 9.2a. If the force you exert is sufficiently small, the book does not move. The free-body diagram of the book is shown in Fig. 9.2b. The force W is the book's weight, and N is the total normal force exerted by the table on the surface of the book that is in contact with the table. The force F is the horizontal force you apply, and f is the total friction force exerted by the table. Because the book is in equilibrium, $f = F$.

Now slowly increase the force you apply to the book. As long as the book remains in equilibrium, the friction force must increase correspondingly, since it equals the force you apply. When the force you apply becomes too large, the book moves. It slips on the table. After reaching some maximum value, the friction force can no longer maintain the book in equilibrium. Also, notice that the force you must apply to keep the book moving on the table is smaller than the force required to cause it to slip. (You are familiar with this phenomenon if you've ever pushed a piece of furniture across a floor.)

(a)   (b)

Figure 9.1
Objects supported by friction forces.

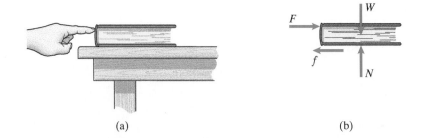

(a)   (b)

Figure 9.2
(a) Exerting a horizontal force on a book.
(b) The free-body diagram of the book.

How does the table exert a friction force on the book? Why does the book slip? Why is less force required to slide the book across the table than is required to start it moving? If the surfaces of the table and the book are magnified sufficiently, they will appear rough (Fig. 9.3). Friction forces arise in part from the interactions of the roughnesses, or *asperities,* of the contacting surfaces. We can gain insight into this mechanism of friction by considering a simple two-dimensional model of the rough surfaces of the book and table.

Suppose that we idealize the asperities of the book and table as the mating two-dimensional "saw-tooth" profiles in Fig. 9.4a. As the horizontal force F increases, the book will remain stationary until the force is sufficiently large to cause the book to slide upward as shown in Fig. 9.4b. What horizontal force is necessary for this to occur? To find out, we must determine the value of F necessary for the book to be in equilibrium in the "slipped" position in Fig. 9.4b. The normal force C_i exerted on the ith saw-tooth asperity of the book is shown in Fig. 9.4c. (Notice that in this simple model we assume the contacting surfaces of the asperities to be smooth.) Denoting the sum of the normal forces exerted on the asperities of the book by the table by $C = \sum_i C_i$, we obtain the equilibrium equations

$$\Sigma F_x = F - C \sin \alpha = 0,$$

$$\Sigma F_y = C \cos \alpha - W = 0.$$

Eliminating C from these equations, we obtain the force necessary to cause the book to slip on the table:

$$F = (\tan \alpha)W.$$

We see that *the force necessary to cause the book to slip is proportional to the force pressing the saw-tooth surfaces together* (the book's weight). Think about stacking increasing numbers of books and applying a horizontal force to them. A progressively larger force is required to cause them to slip as the number of books increases. Also, in our two-dimensional thought experiment, *the angle α is a measure of the roughness of the saw-tooth surfaces.* As $\alpha \rightarrow 0$, the surfaces become smooth and the force necessary to cause the book to slip approaches zero. As α increases, the roughness increases and the force necessary to cause the book to slip increases.

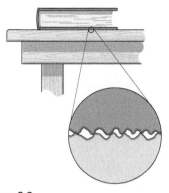

Figure 9.3
The roughnesses of the surfaces can be seen in a magnified view.

Figure 9.4
(a) Two-dimensional model of rough surfaces in contact.
(b) Slip of the book relative to the table.
(c) Normal force on one of the book's asperities.

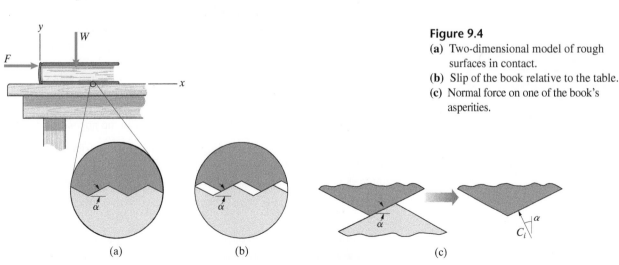

(a)   (b)   (c)

In the sections that follow, we present a theory that incorporates the basic phenomena we have just described and that has been found useful for determining friction forces between dry surfaces. (Friction between lubricated surfaces is a hydrodynamic phenomenon and must be analyzed in the context of fluid mechanics.)

Coefficients of Friction

The theory of dry friction, or *Coulomb friction,* predicts the maximum friction forces that can be exerted by dry, contacting surfaces that are stationary relative to each other. It also predicts the friction forces exerted by the surfaces when they are in relative motion, or sliding. We first consider surfaces that are not in relative motion.

TABLE 9.1 Typical values of the coefficient of static friction.

Materials	Coefficient of Static Friction μ_s
Metal on metal	0.15–0.20
Masonry on masonry	0.60–0.70
Wood on wood	0.25–0.50
Metal on masonry	0.30–0.70
Metal on wood	0.20–0.60
Rubber on concrete	0.50–0.90

The Static Coefficient   The magnitude of the *maximum* friction force that can be exerted between two plane, dry surfaces in contact that are not in motion relative to one another is

$$f = \mu_s N, \tag{9.1}$$

where N is the normal component of the contact force between the surfaces and μ_s is a constant called the *coefficient of static friction*. The value of μ_s is assumed to depend only on the materials of the contacting surfaces and the conditions (smoothness and degree of contamination by other materials) of the surfaces. Typical values of μ_s for various materials are shown in Table 9.1. The relatively large range of values for each pair of materials reflects the sensitivity of μ_s to the conditions of the surfaces. In engineering applications it is usually necessary to measure the value of μ_s for the actual surfaces used.

Let us return to the example of the book on the table (Fig. 9.2). If a *specified* horizontal force F is applied to the book, and the book remains in equilibrium, what friction force is exerted on the book by the table? We can see from the free-body diagram in Fig. 9.2b that $f = F$. Notice that we do not use Eq. (9.1) to answer this question. But suppose that we want to know the *largest* force F that can be applied to the book without causing it to slip. If we know the coefficient of static friction μ_s between the book and the table, Eq. (9.1) tells us the largest friction force that the table can exert on the book. Therefore, the largest force F that can be applied without causing the book to slip is $F = f = \mu_s N$. We also know from the free-body diagram in Fig. 9.2b that $N = W$, so the largest force that will not cause the book to slip is $F = \mu_s W$.

Equation (9.1) determines the magnitude of the maximum friction force but not its direction. The friction force is a maximum, and Eq. (9.1) is applicable, when two surfaces are on the verge of slipping relative to each other. We say that slip is *impending*, and the friction forces resist the impending motion. In Fig. 9.5a, suppose that the lower surface is fixed and slip of the upper surface toward the right is impending. The friction force on the upper surface resists its impending motion (Fig. 9.5b). The friction force on the lower surface is in the opposite direction.

The Kinetic Coefficient   According to the theory of dry friction, the magnitude of the friction force between two plane dry contacting surfaces that are in motion (sliding) relative to each other is

$$f = \mu_k N, \tag{9.2}$$

where N is the normal force between the surfaces and μ_k is the *coefficient of kinetic friction*. The value of μ_k is assumed to depend only on the compositions

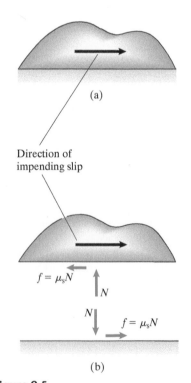

Direction of impending slip

Figure 9.5
(a) The upper surface is on the verge of slipping to the right.
(b) Directions of the friction forces.

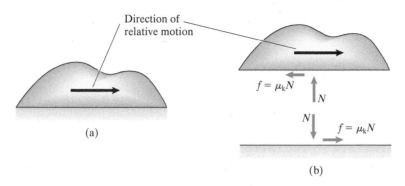

Direction of relative motion

$f = \mu_k N$

N

N

$f = \mu_k N$

(a)

(b)

Figure 9.6
(a) The upper surface is moving to the right relative to the lower surface.
(b) Directions of the friction forces.

of the surfaces and their conditions. For a given pair of surfaces, its value is generally smaller than that of μ_s.

Once you have caused the book in Fig. 9.2 to begin sliding on the table, the friction force $f = \mu_k N = \mu_k W$. Therefore, the force you must exert to keep the book in uniform motion is $F = f = \mu_k W$.

When two surfaces are sliding relative to each other, the friction forces resist the relative motion. In Fig. 9.6a, suppose that the lower surface is fixed and the upper surface is moving to the right. The friction force on the upper surface acts in the direction opposite to its motion (Fig. 9.6b). The friction force on the lower surface is in the opposite direction.

Angles of Friction

We have expressed the reaction exerted on a surface due to its contact with another surface in terms of its components parallel and perpendicular to the surface, the friction force f and normal force N (Fig. 9.7a). In some situations it is more convenient to express the reaction in terms of its magnitude R and the *angle of friction* θ between the reaction and the normal to the surface (Fig. 9.7b). The forces f and N are related to R and θ by

$$f = R \sin\theta, \tag{9.3}$$
$$N = R \cos\theta. \tag{9.4}$$

The value of θ when slip is impending is called the *angle of static friction* θ_s, and its value when the surfaces are sliding relative to each other is called the *angle of kinetic friction* θ_k. By using Eqs. (9.1)–(9.4), we can express the angles of static and kinetic friction in terms of the coefficients of friction:

$$\tan\theta_s = \mu_s, \tag{9.5}$$
$$\tan\theta_k = \mu_k. \tag{9.6}$$

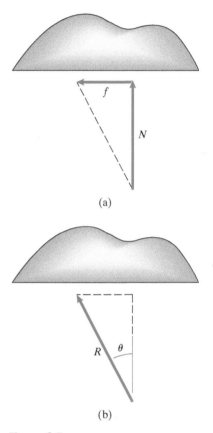

(a)

f

N

(b)

R θ

Figure 9.7
(a) The friction force f and the normal force N.
(b) The magnitude R and the angle of friction θ.

RESULTS

The forces resulting from the contact of plane surfaces can be expressed in two alternative ways:

In terms of the normal force N and friction force f.

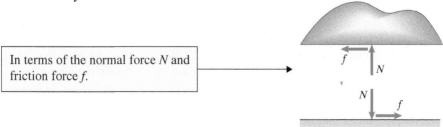

f

N

N

f

In terms of the magnitude R and angle of friction θ.

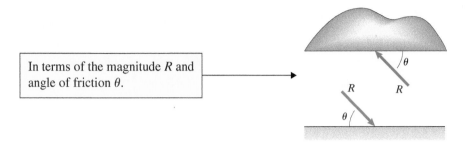

Friction Coefficients

The magnitude of the maximum friction force that can be exerted by dry surfaces that are stationary relative to each other (that is, when slip is impending) is

$$f = \mu_s N, \tag{9.1}$$

where μ_s is the *coefficient of static friction*. The angle of friction when slip is impending is related to the coefficient of static friction by

$$\tan \theta_s = \mu_s. \tag{9.5}$$

The magnitude of the friction force exerted by dry surfaces that are in motion (sliding) relative to each other is

$$f = \mu_k N, \tag{9.2}$$

where μ_k is the *coefficient of kinetic friction*. The angle of friction when the surfaces are sliding is related to the coefficient of kinetic friction by

$$\tan \theta_k = \mu_k \tag{9.6}$$

Evaluating the friction force and angle of friction requires a sequence of decisions:

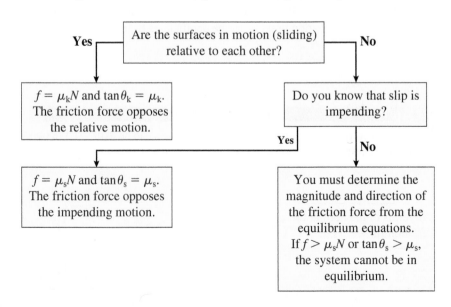

Active Example 9.1   Determining a Friction Force (▶ *Related Problem 9.1*)

The rope exerts a horizontal force on the stationary 180-lb crate. The coefficient of static friction between the crate and the ramp is $\mu_s = 0.4$. If the rope exerts a 90-lb force on the crate, what friction force is exerted on the crate by the ramp?

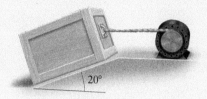

20°

Strategy

The crate is not sliding on the ramp, and we don't know whether slip is impending, so we must determine the friction force by applying the equilibrium equations.

Solution

Draw the free-body diagram of the crate. The direction of the friction force f is not known, so choose it arbitrarily. The sign of the answer for f will indicate its direction.	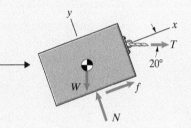

Apply equilibrium. The negative value of the friction force indicates that its direction is down the ramp.	$\begin{cases} \Sigma F_x = f + T\cos 20° - W\sin 20° = 0, \\ \Sigma F_y = N - T\sin 20° - W\cos 20° = 0. \end{cases}$ Setting $W = 180$ lb and $T = 90$ lb and solving yields $N = 200$ lb and $f = -23.0$ lb.

Calculate the maximum friction force the surfaces will support to confirm that it is not exceeded by the magnitude of the friction force necessary for equilibrium.	$\mu_s N = (0.4)(200 \text{ lb}) = 80 \text{ lb}.$

Practice Problem What is the largest horizontal force the rope can exert on the crate without causing it to start sliding up the ramp?

Answer: 161 lb.

Example 9.2 | Analyzing a Friction Brake (▶ *Related Problem 9.22*)

The motion of the disk is controlled by the friction force exerted at C by the brake ABC. The hydraulic actuator BE exerts a horizontal force of magnitude F on the brake at B. The coefficients of friction between the disk and the brake are μ_s and μ_k. What couple M is necessary to rotate the disk at a constant rate in the counterclockwise direction?

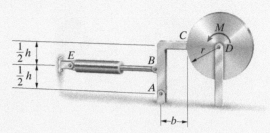

Strategy

We can use the free-body diagram of the disk to obtain a relation between M and the reaction exerted on the disk by the brake, then use the free-body diagram of the brake to determine the reaction in terms of F.

Solution

We draw the free-body diagram of the disk in Fig. a, representing the force exerted by the brake by a single force R. The force R opposes the counterclockwise rotation of the disk, and the friction angle is the angle of kinetic friction $\theta_k = \arctan \mu_k$. Summing moments about D, we obtain

$$\Sigma M_{\text{point } D} = M - (R \sin \theta_k) r = 0.$$

Then, from the free-body diagram of the brake (Fig. b), we get

$$\Sigma M_{\text{point } A} = -F\left(\frac{1}{2}h\right) + (R \cos \theta_k)h - (R \sin \theta_k)b = 0.$$

We can solve these two equations for M and R. The solution for the couple M is

$$M = \frac{(1/2)hr\, F \sin \theta_k}{h \cos \theta_k - b \sin \theta_k} = \frac{(1/2)hr\, F\mu_k}{h - b\mu_k}.$$

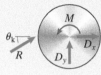

(a) The free-body diagram of the disk.

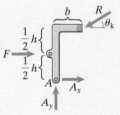

(b) The free-body diagram of the brake.

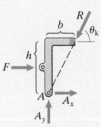

(c) The line of action of R passing through point A.

Critical Thinking

If the friction coefficient μ_k is sufficiently small, the denominator in our solution for the couple M, the term $h \cos \theta_k - b \sin \theta_k$, is positive. As μ_k increases, the denominator becomes smaller, because $\cos \theta_k$ decreases and $\sin \theta_k$ increases. As the denominator approaches zero, the couple required to rotate the disk approaches infinity. To understand this result, notice that the denominator equals zero when $\tan \theta_k = h/b$, which means that the line of action of the force R passes through point A (Fig. c). As μ_k increases and the line of action of R approaches point A, the magnitude of R necessary to balance the moment due to F about A approaches infinity. As a result, the *analytical prediction* for M approaches infinity. Of course, at some value of M, the forces F and R would exceed the values the brake could support.

Example 9.3   Determining Whether an Object Will Tip Over (▶ *Related Problem 9.45*)

Suppose that we want to push the tool chest across the floor by applying the horizontal force F. If we apply the force at too great a height h, the chest will tip over before it slips. If the coefficient of static friction between the floor and the chest is μ_s, what is the largest value of h for which the chest will slip before it tips over?

Strategy
When the chest is on the verge of tipping over, it is in equilibrium with no reaction at B. We can use this condition to determine F in terms of h. Then, by determining the value of F that will cause the chest to slip, we will obtain the value of h that causes the chest to be on the verge of tipping over *and* on the verge of slipping.

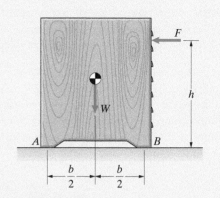

Solution
We draw the free-body diagram of the chest when it is on the verge of tipping over in Fig. a. Summing moments about A, we obtain

$$\Sigma M_{\text{point } A} = Fh - W\left(\frac{1}{2}b\right) = 0.$$

Equilibrium also requires that $f = F$ and $N = W$.
   When the chest is on the verge of slipping,

$$f = \mu_s N,$$

so

$$F = f = \mu_s N = \mu_s W.$$

Substituting this expression into the moment equation, we obtain

$$\mu_s W h - W\left(\frac{1}{2}b\right) = 0.$$

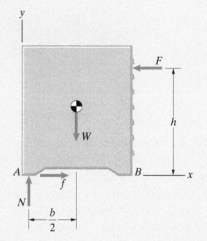

(a) The free-body diagram when the chest is on the verge of tipping over.

Solving this equation for h, we find that when the chest is on the verge of slipping, it is also on the verge of tipping over if it is pushed at the height

$$h = \frac{b}{2\mu_s}.$$

If h is smaller than this value, the chest will begin sliding before it tips over.

Critical Thinking
Notice that the largest value of h for which the chest will slip before it tips over is independent of F. Whether the chest will tip over depends only on where the force is applied, not how large it is. What is the motivation for the solution in this example? The possibility of heavy objects falling over is an obvious safety hazard, and analyses of this kind can influence their design. Once they are in use, safety engineers can establish guidelines (for example, by marking a horizontal line on a vertical cabinet or machine above which it should not be pushed) to prevent tipping.

Problems

▶ **9.1** In Active Example 9.1, suppose that the coefficient of static friction between the 180-lb crate and the ramp is $\mu_s = 0.3$. What is the magnitude of the smallest horizontal force the rope must exert on the crate to prevent it from sliding down the ramp?

9.2 A person places a 2-lb book on a table that is tilted at 15° relative to the horizontal. She finds that if she exerts a very small force on the book as shown, the book remains in equilibrium, but if she removes the force, the book slides down the table. What force would she need to exert on the book (in the direction parallel to the table) to cause it to slide up the table?

15°

Problem 9.2

9.3 A student pushes a 200-lb box of books across the floor. The coefficient of kinetic friction between the carpet and the box is $\mu_k = 0.15$.

(a) If he exerts the force F at angle $\alpha = 25°$, what is the magnitude of the force he must exert to slide the box across the floor?

(b) If he bends his knees more and exerts the force F at angle $\alpha = 10°$, what is the magnitude of the force he must exert to slide the box?

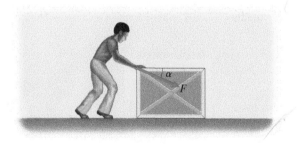

α

F

Problem 9.3

9.4 The 2975-lb car is parked on a sloped street. The brakes are applied to both its front and rear wheels.

(a) If the coefficient of static friction between the car's tires and the road is $\mu_s = 0.8$, what is the steepest slope (in degrees relative to the horizontal) on which the car could remain in equilibrium?

(b) If the street were icy and the coefficient of static friction between the car's tires and the road was $\mu_s = 0.2$, what is the steepest slope on which the car could remain in equilibrium?

Problem 9.4

9.5 The truck's winch exerts a horizontal force on the 200-kg crate in an effort to pull it down the ramp. The coefficient of static friction between the crate and the ramp is $\mu_s = 0.6$.

(a) If the winch exerts a 200-N horizontal force on the crate, what is the magnitude of the friction force exerted on the crate by the ramp?

(b) What is the magnitude of the horizontal force the winch must exert on the crate to cause it to start moving down the ramp?

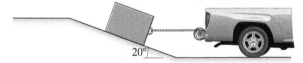

20°

Problem 9.5

9.6 The device shown is designed to position pieces of luggage on a ramp. It exerts a force parallel to the ramp. The suitcase weighs 40 lb. The coefficients of friction between the suitcase and the ramp are $\mu_s = 0.20$ and $\mu_k = 0.18$.

(a) Will the suitcase remain stationary on the ramp when the device exerts no force on it?

(b) What force must the device exert to push the suitcase up the ramp at a constant speed?

20°

Problem 9.6

9.7 The coefficient of static friction between the 50-kg crate and the ramp is $\mu_s = 0.35$. The unstretched length of the spring is 800 mm, and the spring constant is $k = 660$ N/m. What is the minimum value of x at which the crate can remain stationary on the ramp?

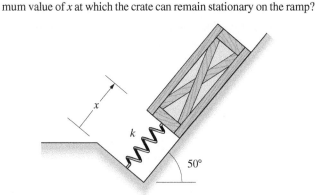

Problem 9.7

9.8 The coefficient of kinetic friction between the 40-kg crate and the slanting floor is $\mu_k = 0.3$. If the angle $\alpha = 20°$, what tension must the person exert on the rope to move the crate at constant speed?

9.9 In Problem 9.8, for what angle α is the tension necessary to move the crate at constant speed a minimum? What is the necessary tension?

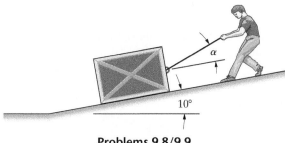

Problems 9.8/9.9

9.10 Box A weighs 100 lb and box B weighs 30 lb. The coefficients of friction between box A and the ramp are $\mu_s = 0.30$ and $\mu_k = 0.28$. What is the magnitude of the friction force exerted on box A by the ramp?

9.11 Box A weighs 100 lb, and the coefficients of friction between box A and the ramp are $\mu_s = 0.30$ and $\mu_k = 0.28$. For what range of weights of the box B will the system remain stationary?

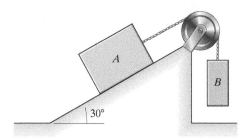

Problems 9.10/9.11

9.12 The mass of the box on the left is 30 kg, and the mass of the box on the right is 40 kg. The coefficient of static friction between each box and the inclined surface is $\mu_s = 0.2$. Determine the minimum angle α for which the boxes will remain stationary.

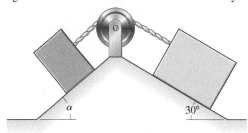

Problem 9.12

9.13 The coefficient of kinetic friction between the 100-kg box and the inclined surface is 0.35. Determine the tension T necessary to pull the box up the surface at a constant rate.

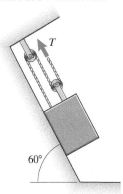

Problem 9.13

9.14 The box is stationary on the inclined surface. The coefficient of static friction between the box and the surface is μ_s.

(a) If the mass of the box is 10 kg, $\alpha = 20°$, $\beta = 30°$, and $\mu_s = 0.24$, what force T is necessary to start the box sliding up the surface?

(b) Show that the force T necessary to start the box sliding up the surface is a minimum when $\tan \beta = \mu_s$.

9.15 In explaining observations of ship launchings at the port of Rochefort in 1779, Coulomb analyzed the system shown to determine the minimum force T necessary to hold the box stationary on the inclined surface. Show that the result is

$$T = \frac{(\sin \alpha - \mu_s \cos \alpha)mg}{\cos \beta - \mu_s \sin \beta}.$$

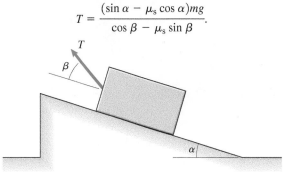

Problems 9.14/9.15

9.16 Two sheets of plywood A and B lie on the bed of the truck. They have the same weight W, and the coefficient of static friction between the two sheets of wood and between sheet B and the truck bed is μ_s.

(a) If you apply a horizontal force to sheet A and apply no force to sheet B, can you slide sheet A off the truck without causing sheet B to move? What force is necessary to cause sheet A to start moving?

(b) If you prevent sheet A from moving by exerting a horizontal force on it, what horizontal force on sheet B is necessary to start it moving?

Problem 9.16

9.17 The weights of the two boxes are $W_1 = 100$ lb and $W_2 = 50$ lb. The coefficients of friction between the left box and the inclined surface are $\mu_s = 0.12$ and $\mu_k = 0.10$. Determine the tension the man must exert on the rope to pull the boxes upward at a constant rate.

9.18 In Problem 9.17, for what range of tensions exerted on the rope by the man will the boxes remain stationary?

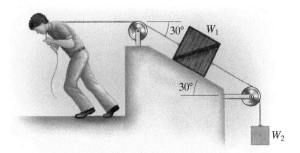

Problems 9.17/9.18

9.19 Each box weighs 10 lb. The coefficient of static friction between box A and box B is 0.24, and the coefficient of static friction between box B and the inclined surface is 0.3. What is the largest angle α for which box B will not slip?

Strategy: Draw individual free-body diagrams of the two boxes and write their equilibrium equations assuming that slip of box B is impending.

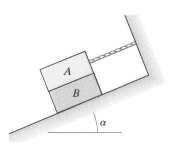

Problem 9.19

9.20 The masses of the boxes are $m_A = 15$ kg and $m_B = 60$ kg. The coefficient of static friction between boxes A and B and between box B and the inclined surface is 0.12. What is the largest force F for which the boxes will not slip?

9.21 In Problem 9.20, what is the smallest force F for which the boxes will not slip?

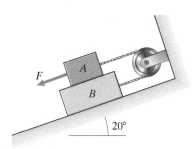

Problems 9.20/9.21

▶ **9.22** In Example 9.2, what clockwise couple M would need to be applied to the disk to cause it to rotate at a constant rate in the clockwise direction?

9.23 The homogeneous horizontal bar AB weighs 20 lb. The homogeneous disk weighs 30 lb. The coefficient of kinetic friction between the disk and the sloping surface is $\mu_k = 0.24$. What is the magnitude of the couple that would need to be applied to the disk to cause it to rotate at a constant rate in the clockwise direction?

9.24 The homogeneous horizontal bar AB weighs 20 lb. The homogeneous disk weighs 30 lb. The coefficient of kinetic friction between the disk and the sloping surface is $\mu_k = 0.24$. What is the magnitude of the couple that would need to be applied to the disk to cause it to rotate at a constant rate in the counterclockwise direction?

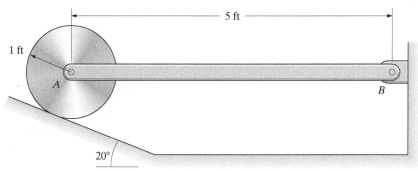

Problems 9.23/9.24

9.25 The mass of the bar is 4 kg. The coefficient of static friction between the bar and the floor is 0.3. Neglect friction between the bar and the wall.

(a) If $\alpha = 20°$, what is the magnitude of the friction force exerted on the bar by the floor?

(b) What is the maximum angle α for which the bar will not slip?

9.26 The coefficient of static friction between the bar and the floor and between the 4-kg bar and the wall is 0.3. What is the maximum angle α for which the bar will not slip?

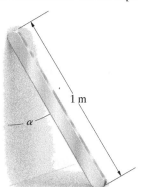

Problems 9.25/9.26

9.27 The ladder and the person weigh 30 lb and 180 lb, respectively. The center of mass of the 12-ft ladder is at its midpoint. The angle $\alpha = 30°$. Assume that the wall exerts a negligible friction force on the ladder.

(a) If $x = 4$ ft, what is the magnitude of the friction force exerted on the ladder by the floor?

(b) What minimum coefficient of static friction between the ladder and the floor is necessary for the person to be able to climb to the top of the ladder without slipping?

9.28 The ladder and the person weigh 30 lb and 180 lb, respectively. The center of mass of the 12-ft ladder is at its midpoint. The coefficient of static friction between the ladder and the floor is $\mu_s = 0.5$. What is the largest value of the angle α for which the person could climb to the top of the ladder without it slipping?

9.29 The ladder and the person weigh 30 lb and 180 lb, respectively. The center of mass of the 12-ft ladder is at its midpoint. The coefficient of static friction between the ladder and the floor is 0.5 and the coefficient of friction between the ladder and the wall is 0.3. What is the largest value of the angle α for which the person could climb to the top of the ladder without it slipping? Compare your answer to the answer to Problem 9.28.

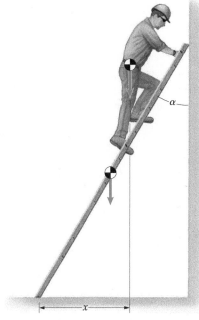

Problems 9.27–9.29

9.30 The disk weighs 50 lb and the bar weighs 25 lb. The coefficients of friction between the disk and the inclined surface are $\mu_s = 0.6$ and $\mu_k = 0.5$.

(a) What is the largest couple M that can be applied to the stationary disk without causing it to start rotating?

(b) What couple M is necessary to rotate the disk at a constant rate?

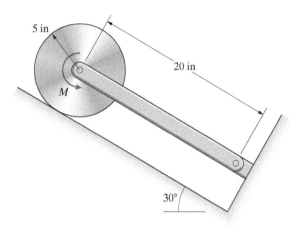

Problem 9.30

9.31 The radius of the 40-kg homogeneous cylinder is $R = 0.15$ m. The slanted wall is smooth and the angle $\alpha = 30°$. The coefficient of static friction between the cylinder and the floor is $\mu_s = 0.2$. What is the largest couple M that can be applied to the cylinder without causing it to slip?

9.32 The homogeneous cylinder has weight W. The coefficient of static friction between the cylinder and both surfaces is μ_s. What is the largest couple M that can be applied to the cylinder without causing it to slip? (Assume that the cylinder slips before rolling up the inclined surface.)

9.33 The homogeneous cylinder has weight W. The coefficient of static friction between the cylinder and both surfaces is μ_s. What is the minimum value of μ_s for which the couple M will cause the cylinder to roll up the inclined surface without slipping?

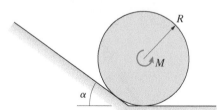

Problems 9.31–9.33

9.34 The coefficient of static friction between the blades of the shears and the object they are gripping is 0.36. What is the largest value of the angle α for which the object will not slip out? Neglect the object's weight.

Strategy: Draw the free-body diagram of the object and assume that slip is impending.

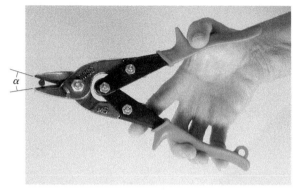

Problem 9.34

9.35 A stationary disk of 300-mm radius is attached to a pin support at D. The disk is held in place by the brake ABC in contact with the disk at C. The hydraulic actuator BE exerts a horizontal 400-N force on the brake at B. The coefficients of friction between the disk and the brake are $\mu_s = 0.6$ and $\mu_k = 0.5$. What couple must be applied to the stationary disk to cause it to slip in the counterclockwise direction?

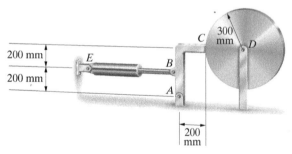

Problem 9.35

9.36 The figure shows a preliminary conceptual idea for a device to exert a braking force on a rope when the rope is pulled downward by the force T. The coefficient of kinetic friction between the rope and the two bars is $\mu_k = 0.28$. Determine the force T necessary to pull the rope downward at a constant rate if $F = 10$ lb and (a) $\alpha = 30°$; (b) $\alpha = 20°$.

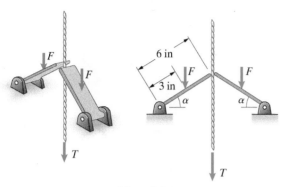

Problem 9.36

9.37 The mass of block B is 8 kg. The coefficient of static friction between the surfaces of the clamp and the block is $\mu_s = 0.2$. When the clamp is aligned as shown, what minimum force must the spring exert to prevent the block from slipping out?

9.38 By altering its dimensions, redesign the clamp in Problem 9.37 so that the minimum force the spring must exert to prevent the block from slipping out is 180 N. Draw a sketch of your new design.

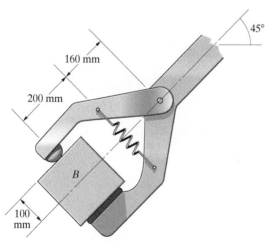

Problems 9.37/9.38

9.39 The horizontal bar is attached to a collar that slides on the smooth vertical bar. The collar at P slides on the smooth horizontal bar. The total mass of the horizontal bar and the two collars is 12 kg. The system is held in place by the pin in the circular slot. The pin contacts only the lower surface of the slot, and the coefficient of static friction between the pin and the slot is 0.8. If the system is in equilibrium and $y = 260$ mm, what is the magnitude of the friction force exerted on the pin by the slot?

9.40 In Problem 9.39, what is the minimum height y at which the system can be in equilibrium?

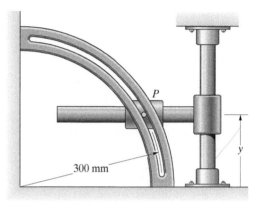

Problems 9.39/9.40

9.41 The rectangular 100-lb plate is supported by the pins A and B. If friction can be neglected at A and the coefficient of static friction between the pin at B and the slot is $\mu_s = 0.4$, what is the largest angle α for which the plate will not slip?

9.42 If you can neglect friction at B and the coefficient of static friction between the pin at A and the slot is $\mu_s = 0.4$, what is the largest angle α for which the 100-lb plate will not slip?

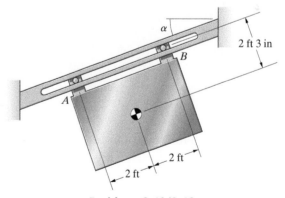

Problems 9.41/9.42

9.43 The airplane's weight is $W = 2400$ lb. Its brakes keep the rear wheels locked, and the coefficient of static friction between the wheels and the runway is $\mu_s = 0.6$. The front (nose) wheel can turn freely and so exerts a negligible friction force on the runway. Determine the largest horizontal thrust force T the plane's propeller can generate without causing the rear wheels to slip.

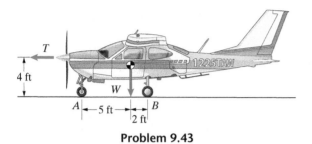

Problem 9.43

9.44 The refrigerator weighs 220 lb. It is supported at A and B. The coefficient of static friction between the supports and the floor is $\mu_s = 0.2$. If you assume that the refrigerator does not tip over before it slips, what force F is necessary for impending slip?

▶ **9.45** The refrigerator weighs 220 lb. It is supported at A and B. The coefficient of static friction between the supports and the floor is $\mu_s = 0.2$. The distance $h = 60$ in and the dimension $b = 30$ in. When the force F is applied to push the refrigerator across the floor, will it tip over before it slips? (See Example 9.3.)

Problems 9.44/9.45

9.46 To obtain a preliminary evaluation of the stability of a turning car, imagine subjecting the stationary car to an increasing lateral force F at the height of its center of mass, and determine whether the car will slip (skid) laterally before it tips over. Show that this will be the case if $b/h > 2\mu_s$. (Notice the importance of the height of the center of mass relative to the width of the car. This reflects on recent discussions of the stability of sport utility vehicles and vans that have relatively high centers of mass.)

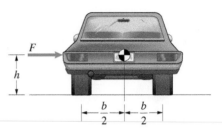

Problem 9.46

9.47 The man exerts a force P on the car at an angle $\alpha = 20°$. The 1760-kg car has front wheel drive. The driver spins the front wheels, and the coefficient of kinetic friction is $\mu_k = 0.02$. Snow behind the rear tires exerts a horizontal resisting force S. Getting the car to move requires overcoming a resisting force $S = 420$ N. What force P must the man exert?

9.48 In Problem 9.47, what value of the angle α minimizes the magnitude of the force P the man must exert to overcome the resisting force $S = 420$ N exerted on the rear tires by the snow? What force must he exert?

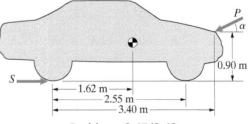

Problems 9.47/9.48

9.49 The coefficient of static friction between the 3000-lb car's tires and the road is $\mu_s = 0.5$. Determine the steepest grade (the largest value of the angle α) the car can drive up at constant speed if the car has (a) rear-wheel drive; (b) front-wheel drive; (c) four-wheel drive.

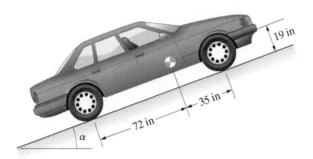

Problem 9.49

9.50 The stationary cabinet has weight W. Determine the force F that must be exerted to cause it to move if (a) the coefficient of static friction at A and at B is μ_s; (b) the coefficient of static friction at A is μ_{sA} and the coefficient of static friction at B is μ_{sB}.

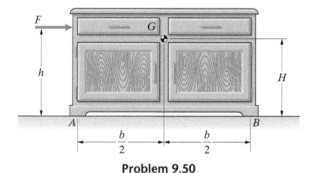

Problem 9.50

9.51 The table weighs 50 lb and the coefficient of static friction between its legs and the inclined surface is 0.7.

(a) If you apply a force at A parallel to the inclined surface to push the table up the inclined surface, will the table tip over before it slips? If not, what force is required to start the table moving up the surface?

(b) If you apply a force at B parallel to the inclined surface to push the table down the inclined surface, will the table tip over before it slips? If not, what force is required to start the table moving down the surface?

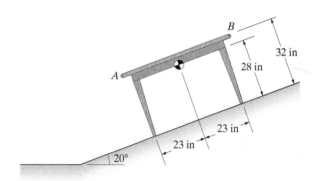

Problem 9.51

9.52 The coefficient of static friction between the right bar and the surface at A is $\mu_s = 0.6$. Neglect the weights of the bars. If $\alpha = 20°$, what is the magnitude of the friction force exerted at A?

9.53 The coefficient of static friction between the right bar and the surface at A is $\mu_s = 0.6$. Neglect the weights of the bars. What is the largest angle α at which the truss will remain stationary without slipping?

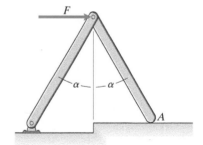

Problems 9.52/9.53

9.54 The bar BC is supported by a rough floor at C. If $F = 2$ kN and bar BC does not slip at C, what is the magnitude of the friction force exerted on the bar at C?

9.55 The bar BC is supported by a rough floor at C. If $F = 2$ kN, what is the minimum coefficient of static friction for which bar BC will not slip at C?

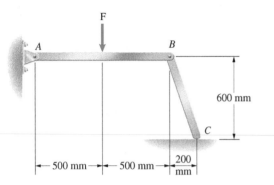

Problems 9.54/9.55

9.56 The weight of the box is 20 lb and the coefficient of static friction between the box and the floor is $\mu_s = 0.65$. Neglect the weights of the bars. What is the largest value of the force F that will not cause the box to slip?

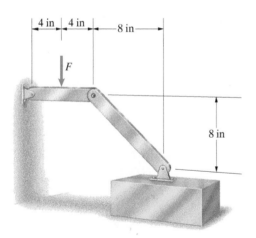

Problem 9.56

9.57 The mass of the suspended object is 6 kg. The structure is supported at B by the normal and friction forces exerted on the plate by the wall. Neglect the weights of the bars.

(a) What is the magnitude of the friction force exerted on the plate at B?

(b) What is the minimum coefficient of static friction at B necessary for the structure to remain in equilibrium?

9.58 Suppose that the lengths of the bars in Problem 9.57 are $L_{AB} = 1.2$ m and $L_{AC} = 1.0$ m and their masses are $m_{AB} = 3.6$ kg and $m_{AC} = 3.0$ kg.

(a) What is the magnitude of the friction force exerted on the plate at B?

(b) What is the minimum coefficient of static friction at B necessary for the structure to remain in equilibrium?

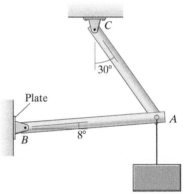

Problems 9.57/9.58

9.59 The frame is supported by the normal and friction forces exerted on the plates at A and G by the fixed surfaces. The coefficient of static friction at A is $\mu_s = 0.6$. Will the frame slip at A when it is subjected to the loads shown?

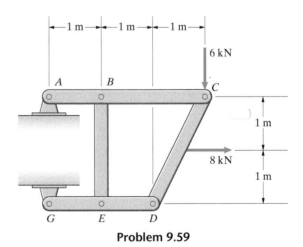

Problem 9.59

9.60 The frame is supported by the normal and friction forces exerted on the plate at A by the wall.

(a) What is the magnitude of the friction force exerted on the plate at A?

(b) What is the minimum coefficient of static friction at A necessary for the structure to remain in equilibrium?

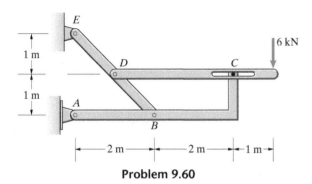

Problem 9.60

9.61 The direction cosines of the crane's cable are $\cos \theta_x = 0.588$, $\cos \theta_y = 0.766$, $\cos \theta_z = 0.260$. The y axis is vertical. The stationary caisson to which the cable is attached weighs 2000 lb and rests on horizontal ground. If the coefficient of static friction between the caisson and the ground is $\mu_s = 0.4$, what tension in the cable is necessary to cause the caisson to slip?

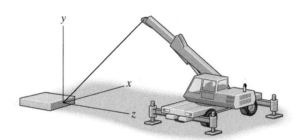

Problem 9.61

9.62* The 10-lb metal disk A is at the center of the inclined surface. The tension in the string AB is 5 lb. What minimum coefficient of static friction between the disk and the surface is necessary to keep the disk from slipping?

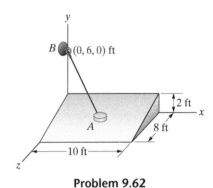

Problem 9.62

9.63* The 5-kg box is at rest on the sloping surface. The y axis points upward. The unit vector $0.557\mathbf{i} + 0.743\mathbf{j} + 0.371\mathbf{k}$ is perpendicular to the sloping surface. What is the magnitude of the friction force exerted on the box by the surface?

9.64* In Problem 9.63, what is the minimum coefficient of static friction necessary for the box to remain at rest on the sloping surface?

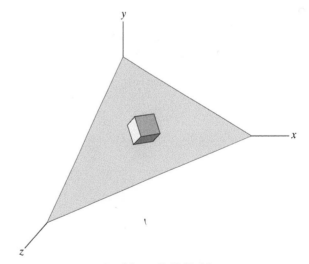

Problems 9.63/9.64

9.2 Wedges

A *wedge* is a bifacial tool with the faces set at a small acute angle (Figs. 9.8a and b). When a wedge is pushed forward, the faces exert large normal forces as a result of the small angle between them (Fig. 9.8c). In various forms, wedges are used in many engineering applications.

The large lateral force generated by a wedge can be used to lift a load (Fig. 9.9a). Let W_L be the weight of the load and W_W the weight of the wedge. To determine the force F necessary to start raising the load, we assume that slip of the load and wedge are impending (Fig. 9.9b). From the free-body diagram of the load, we obtain the equilibrium equations

$$\Sigma F_x = Q - N \sin \alpha - \mu_s N \cos \alpha = 0$$

and

$$\Sigma F_y = N \cos \alpha - \mu_s N \sin \alpha - \mu_s Q - W_L = 0.$$

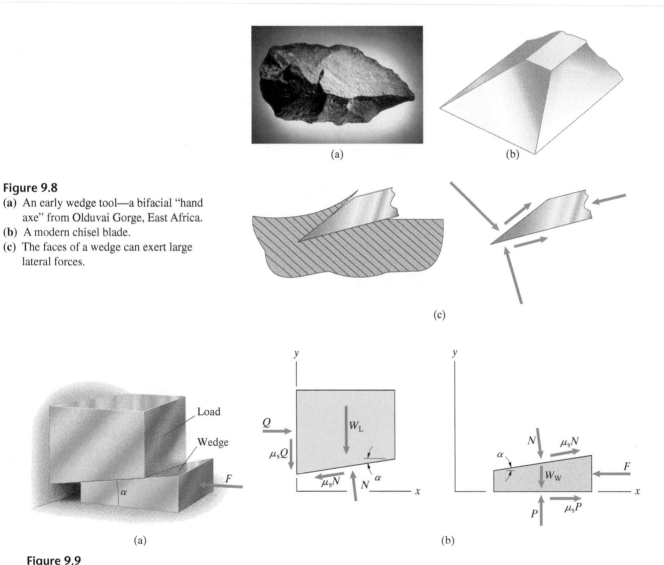

Figure 9.8

(a) An early wedge tool—a bifacial "hand axe" from Olduvai Gorge, East Africa.

(b) A modern chisel blade.

(c) The faces of a wedge can exert large lateral forces.

(a)

(b)

Figure 9.9

(a) Raising a load with a wedge.

(b) Free-body diagrams of the load and the wedge when slip is impending.

From the free-body diagram of the wedge, we obtain the equations

$$\Sigma F_x = N \sin \alpha + \mu_s N \cos \alpha + \mu_s P - F = 0$$

and

$$\Sigma F_y = P - N \cos \alpha + \mu_s N \sin \alpha - W_W = 0.$$

These four equations determine the three normal forces Q, N, and P, and the force F. The solution for F is

$$F = \mu_s W_W + \left[\frac{(1 - \mu_s^2) \tan \alpha + 2\mu_s}{(1 - \mu_s^2) - 2\mu_s \tan \alpha} \right] W_L.$$

Suppose that $W_W = 0.2W_L$ and $\alpha = 10°$. If $\mu_s = 0$, the force necessary to lift the load is only $0.176W_L$. But if $\mu_s = 0.2$, the force becomes $0.680W_L$, and if $\mu_s = 0.4$, it becomes $1.44W_L$. From this standpoint, friction is undesirable. But if there were no friction, the wedge would not remain in place when the force F is removed.

Active Example 9.4   **Forces on a Wedge** (▶ *Related Problems 9.65, 9.66, 9.67*)

A wedge is used to split a log. The angle $\alpha = 10°$. The coefficients of friction between the wedge and the log are $\mu_s = 0.22$ and $\mu_k = 0.20$. If the wedge is driven into the log at a constant speed by a vertical force F, what are the magnitudes of the normal forces exerted on the log by the wedge (that is, what are the magnitudes of the forces causing the log to split)?

Strategy

The friction forces exerted on the wedge by the log resist the motion of the wedge into the log and are of magnitude $\mu_k N$. We can apply equilibrium to the wedge to determine N in terms of F.

Solution

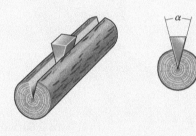

Draw the free-body diagram of the wedge.

The sum of the forces in the vertical direction is

$$2N \sin\left(\frac{\alpha}{2}\right) + 2\mu_k N \cos\left(\frac{\alpha}{2}\right) - F = 0.$$

Solving for N yields

$$N = \frac{F}{2[\sin(\alpha/2) + \mu_k \cos(\alpha/2)]}$$

$$= \frac{F}{2[\sin(10°/2) + (0.20)\cos(10°/2)]}$$

$$= 1.75F.$$

Apply equilibrium.

Practice Problem If the force F is removed, will the wedge remain in place in the log?

Answer: Yes.

Problems

▶ **9.65** In Active Example 9.4, the coefficients of friction between the wedge and the log are $\mu_s = 0.22$ and $\mu_k = 0.20$. What is the largest value of the wedge angle α for which the wedge would remain in place in the log when the force F is removed?

▶ **9.66** The wedge shown is being used to split the log. The wedge weighs 20 lb and the angle α equals 30°. The coefficient of kinetic friction between the faces of the wedge and the log is 0.28. If the normal force exerted by each face of the wedge must equal 150 lb to split the log, what vertical force F is necessary to drive the wedge into the log at a constant rate? (See Active Example 9.4.)

▶ **9.67** The coefficient of static friction between the faces of the wedge and the log in Problem 9.67 is 0.30. Will the wedge remain in place in the log when the vertical force F is removed? (See Active Example 9.4.)

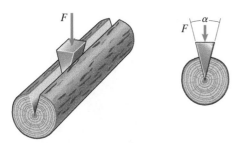

Problems 9.66/9.67

9.68 The weights of the blocks are $W_A = 100$ lb and $W_B = 25$ lb. Between all of the contacting surfaces, $\mu_s = 0.32$ and $\mu_k = 0.30$. What force F is necessary to move B to the left at a constant rate?

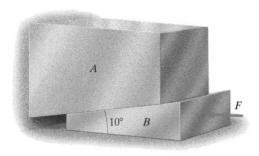

Problem 9.68

9.69 The masses of the blocks are $m_A = 30$ kg and $m_B = 70$ kg. Between all of the contacting surfaces, $\mu_s = 0.1$. What is the largest force F that can be applied without causing the blocks to slip?

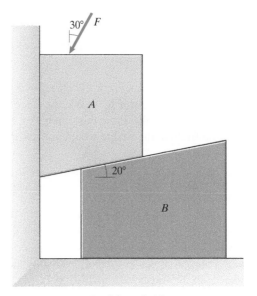

Problem 9.69

9.70 Each block weighs 200 lb. Between all of the contacting surfaces, $\mu_s = 0.1$. What is the largest force F that can be applied without causing block B to slip upward?

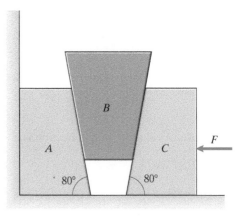

Problem 9.70

9.71 Small wedges called *shims* can be used to hold an object in place. The coefficient of kinetic friction between the contacting surfaces is 0.4. What force F is needed to push the shim downward until the horizontal force exerted on the object A is 200 N?

9.72 The coefficient of static friction between the contacting surfaces is 0.44. If the shims are in place and exert a 200-N horizontal force on the object A, what upward force must be exerted on the left shim to loosen it?

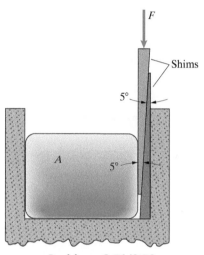

Problems 9.71/9.72

9.73 The crate A weighs 600 lb. Between all contacting surfaces, $\mu_s = 0.32$ and $\mu_k = 0.30$. Neglect the weights of the wedges. What force F is required to move A to the right at a constant rate?

9.74 Suppose that between all contacting surfaces, $\mu_s = 0.32$ and $\mu_k = 0.30$. Neglect the weights of the 5° wedges. If a force $F = 800$ N is required to move A to the right at a constant rate, what is the mass of A?

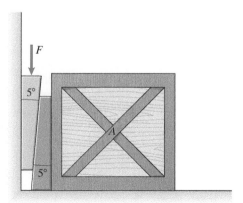

Problems 9.73/9.74

9.75 The box A has a mass of 80 kg, and the wedge B has a mass of 40 kg. Between all contacting surfaces, $\mu_s = 0.15$ and $\mu_k = 0.12$. What force F is required to raise A at a constant rate?

9.76 Suppose that A weighs 800 lb and B weighs 400 lb. The coefficients of friction between all of the contacting surfaces are $\mu_s = 0.15$ and $\mu_k = 0.12$. Will B remain in place if the force F is removed?

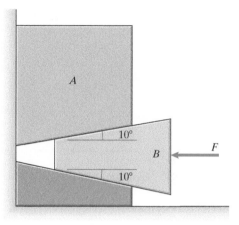

Problems 9.75/9.76

9.77 Between A and B, $\mu_s = 0.20$, and between B and C, $\mu_s = 0.18$. Between C and the wall, $\mu_s = 0.30$. The weights $W_B = 20$ lb and $W_C = 80$ lb. What force F is required to start C moving upward?

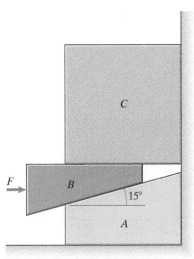

Problem 9.77

9.78 The masses of A, B, and C are 8 kg, 12 kg, and 80 kg, respectively. Between all contacting surfaces, $\mu_s = 0.4$. What force F is required to start C moving upward?

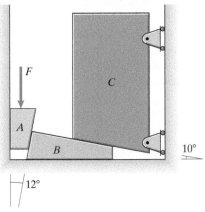

Problem 9.78

9.3 Threads

BACKGROUND

Threads are familiar from their use on wood screws, machine screws, and other machine elements. We show a shaft with square threads in Fig. 9.10a. The axial distance p from one thread to the next is called the *pitch* of the thread, and the angle α is its *slope*. We will consider only the case in which the shaft has a single continuous thread, so the relation between the pitch and slope is

$$\tan \alpha = \frac{p}{2\pi r}, \qquad (9.7)$$

where r is the mean radius of the thread.

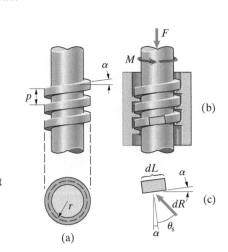

Figure 9.10
(a) A shaft with a square thread.
(b) The shaft within a sleeve with a mating groove and the direction of M that can cause the shaft to start moving in the axial direction opposite to F.
(c) A differential element of the thread when slip is impending.

Suppose that the threaded shaft is enclosed in a fixed sleeve with a mating groove and is subjected to an axial load F (Fig. 9.10b). Applying a couple M in the direction shown will tend to cause the shaft to start rotating and moving in the axial direction opposite to F. Our objective is to determine the couple M necessary to cause the shaft to start rotating.

We draw the free-body diagram of a differential element of the thread of length dL in Fig. 9.10c, representing the reaction exerted by the mating groove by the force dR. If the shaft is on the verge of rotating, dR resists the impending motion and the friction angle is the angle of static friction θ_s. The vertical component of the reaction on the element is $dR \cos(\theta_s + \alpha)$. To determine the total vertical force on the thread, we must integrate this expression over the length L of the thread. For equilibrium, the result must equal the axial force F acting on the shaft:

$$\cos(\theta_s + \alpha) \int_L dR = F. \tag{9.8}$$

The moment about the center of the shaft due to the reaction on the element is $r\,dR \sin(\theta_s + \alpha)$. The total moment must equal the couple M exerted on the shaft:

$$r \sin(\theta_s + \alpha) \int_L dR = M.$$

Dividing this equation by Eq. (9.8), we obtain the couple M necessary for the shaft to be on the verge of rotating and moving in the axial direction opposite to F:

$$M = rF \tan(\theta_s + \alpha). \tag{9.9}$$

Replacing the angle of static friction θ_s in this expression with the angle of kinetic friction θ_k gives the couple required to cause the shaft to rotate at a constant rate.

If the couple M is applied to the shaft in the opposite direction (Fig. 9.11a), the shaft tends to start rotating and moving in the axial direction of the load F. Figure 9.11b shows the reaction on a differential element of the thread of length dL when slip is impending. The direction of the reaction opposes the rotation of the shaft. In this case, the vertical component of the reaction on the element is $dR \cos(\theta_s - \alpha)$. Equilibrium requires that

$$\cos(\theta_s - \alpha) \int_L dR = F. \tag{9.10}$$

The moment about the center of the shaft due to the reaction is $r\,dR \sin(\theta_s - \alpha)$, so

$$r \sin(\theta_s - \alpha) \int_L dR = M.$$

Dividing this equation by Eq. (9.10), we obtain the couple M necessary for the shaft to be on the verge of rotating and moving in the direction of the force F:

$$M = rF \tan(\theta_s - \alpha). \tag{9.11}$$

Replacing θ_s with θ_k in this expression gives the couple necessary to rotate the shaft at a constant rate.

Notice in Eq. (9.11) that the couple required for impending motion is zero when $\theta_s = \alpha$. When the angle of static friction is less than this value, the shaft will rotate and move in the direction of the force F with no couple applied.

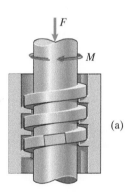

(a)

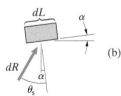

(b)

Figure 9.11
(a) The direction of M that can cause the shaft to move in the axial direction of F.
(b) A differential element of the thread when slip is impending.

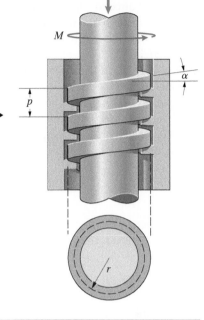

The slope α of the thread is related to its pitch p and the radius r by

$$\tan \alpha = \frac{p}{2\pi r}. \tag{9.7}$$

$$M = rF \tan(\theta_s + \alpha). \tag{9.9}$$

The couple M required for impending rotation and axial motion of the shaft opposite to the direction of F, where

$$\theta_s = \arctan \mu_s.$$

$$M = rF \tan(\theta_s - \alpha). \tag{9.11}$$

The couple M (opposite to the direction shown) required for impending rotation and axial motion of the shaft in the direction of F. If $\theta_s < \alpha$, the shaft will rotate and move in the direction of F with no couple applied.

Active Example 9.5 Rotating a Threaded Collar (▶ *Related Problem 9.79*)

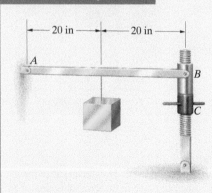

The right end of bar AB is pinned to an unthreaded collar B that rests on a threaded collar C. The mean radius of the threaded vertical shaft is $r = 1.6$ in and its pitch is $p = 0.2$ in. The coefficients of friction between the threads of the collar C and the vertical shaft are $\mu_s = 0.25$ and $\mu_k = 0.22$. The 400-lb suspended object can be raised or lowered by rotating the collar C. When the system is in the position shown, with bar AB horizontal, what is the magnitude of the couple that must be applied to the collar C to cause it to turn at a constant rate and move the suspended object upward?

Strategy
By drawing the free-body diagram of bar AB and the collar B, we can determine the axial force exerted on the collar C. Then we can use Eq. (9.9), with θ_s replaced by θ_k, to determine the required couple.

Solution

Draw the free-body diagram of the bar and collar B.

From the sum of the moments about point A,

$$\Sigma M_{\text{point } A} = (40 \text{ in})F - (20 \text{ in})(400 \text{ lb}) = 0,$$

the force $F = 200$ lb. This is the axial force exerted on collar C.

Apply equilibrium.

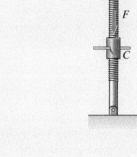

From Eq. (9.7),

$$\tan \alpha = \frac{p}{2\pi r} = \frac{0.2 \text{ in}}{2\pi(1.6 \text{ in})} = 0.0199,$$

the slope of the thread is $\alpha = 1.14°$.
The kinetic angle of friction is

$$\theta_k = \arctan \mu_k = \arctan(0.22) = 12.4°.$$

Substituting these values into Eq. (9.9),

$$M = rF \tan(\theta_k + \alpha)$$
$$= (1.6 \text{ in})(200 \text{ lb}) \tan(12.4° + 1.14°)$$
$$= 77.1 \text{ in-lb}.$$

Apply Eq. (9.9).

Practice Problem When the system is in the position shown, with bar AB horizontal, what is the magnitude of the couple that must be applied to the collar C to cause it to turn at a constant rate and move the suspended object downward?

Answer: 63.8 in-lb.

Problems

▶ **9.79** In Active Example 9.5, suppose that the pitch of the thread is changed from $p = 0.2$ in to $p = 0.24$ in. What is the slope of the thread? What is the magnitude of the couple that must be applied to the collar C to cause it to turn at a constant rate and move the suspended object upward?

9.80 The pitch of the threaded shaft is $p = 2$ mm and the mean radius of the thread is $r = 20$ mm. The coefficients of friction between the thread and the mating groove are $\mu_s = 0.22$ and $\mu_k = 0.20$. The weight $W = 500$ N. Neglect the weight of the threaded shaft. What couple must be applied to the threaded shaft to lower the weight at a constant rate?

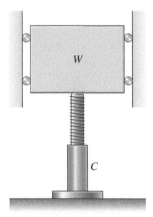

Problem 9.80

9.81 The position of the horizontal beam can be adjusted by turning the machine screw A. Neglect the weight of the beam. The pitch of the screw is $p = 1$ mm, and the mean radius of the thread is $r = 4$ mm. The coefficients of friction between the thread and the mating groove are $\mu_s = 0.20$ and $\mu_k = 0.18$. If the system is initially stationary, determine the couple that must be applied to the screw to cause the beam to start moving (a) upward; (b) downward.

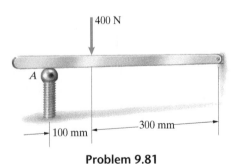

Problem 9.81

9.82 The pitch of the threaded shaft of the C clamp is $p = 0.05$ in, and the mean radius of the thread is $r = 0.15$ in. The coefficients of friction between the threaded shaft and the mating collar are $\mu_s = 0.18$ and $\mu_k = 0.16$.

(a) What maximum couple must be applied to the shaft to exert a 30-lb force on the clamped object?

(b) If a 30-lb force is exerted on the clamped object, what couple must be applied to the shaft to begin loosening the clamp?

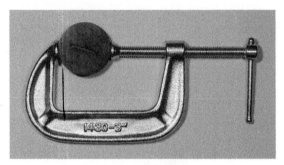

Problem 9.82

9.83 The mass of block A is 60 kg. Neglect the weight of the 5° wedge. The coefficient of kinetic friction between the contacting surfaces of the block A, the wedge, the table, and the wall is $\mu_k = 0.4$. The pitch of the threaded shaft is 5 mm, the mean radius of the thread is 15 mm, and the coefficient of kinetic friction between the thread and the mating groove is 0.2. What couple must be exerted on the threaded shaft to raise the block A at a constant rate?

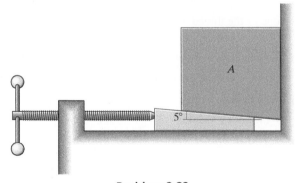

Problem 9.83

9.84 The vise exerts 80-lb forces on A. The threaded shafts are subjected only to axial loads by the jaws of the vise. The pitch of their threads is $p = 1/8$ in, the mean radius of the threads is $r = 1$ in, and the coefficient of static friction between the threads and the mating grooves is 0.2. Suppose that you want to loosen the vise by turning one of the shafts. Determine the couple you must apply (a) to shaft B; (b) to shaft C.

9.85 Suppose that you want to tighten the vise in Problem 9.84 by turning one of the shafts. Determine the couple you must apply

(a) to shaft B;

(b) to shaft C.

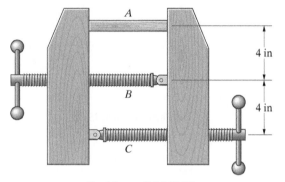

Problems 9.84/9.85

9.86 The threaded shaft has a ball and socket support at B. The 400-lb load A can be raised or lowered by rotating the threaded shaft, causing the threaded collar at C to move relative to the shaft. Neglect the weights of the members. The pitch of the shaft is $p = \frac{1}{4}$ in, the mean radius of the thread is $r = 1$ in, and the coefficient of static friction between the thread and the mating groove is 0.24. If the system is stationary in the position shown, what couple is necessary to start the shaft rotating to raise the load?

9.87 In Problem 9.86, if the system is stationary in the position shown, what couple is necessary to start the shaft rotating to lower the load?

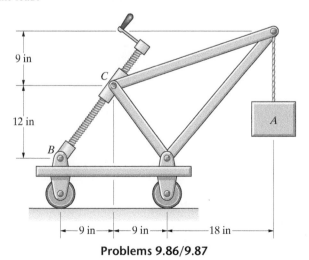

Problems 9.86/9.87

9.88 The car jack is operated by turning the horizontal threaded shaft at A. The threaded shaft fits into a mating threading collar at B. As the shaft turns, points A and B move closer together or farther apart, thereby raising or lowering the jack. The pitch of the threaded shaft is $p = 0.1$ in, the mean radius of the thread is $r = 0.2$ in, and the coefficient of kinetic friction between the threaded shaft and the mating collar at B is 0.15. What couple must be applied at A to rotate the shaft at a constant rate and raise the jack when it is in the position shown if the load $L = 1400$ lb?

9.89 The car jack is operated by turning the horizontal threaded shaft at A. The threaded shaft fits into a mating threading collar at B. As the shaft turns, points A and B move closer together or farther apart, thereby raising or lowering the jack. The pitch of the threaded shaft is $p = 0.1$ in, the mean radius of the thread is $r = 0.2$ in, and the coefficient of kinetic friction between the threaded shaft and the mating collar at B is 0.15. What couple must be applied at A to rotate the shaft at a constant rate and lower the jack when it is in the position shown if the load $L = 1400$ lb?

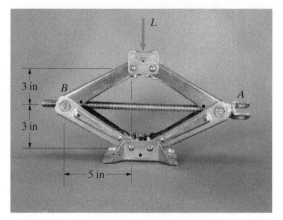

Problems 9.88/9.89

9.90 A *turnbuckle,* used to adjust the length or tension of a bar or cable, is threaded at both ends. Rotating it draws threaded ends of the bar or cable together or moves them apart. Suppose that the pitch of the threads is $p = 0.05$ in, their mean radius is $r = 0.25$ in, and the coefficient of static friction between the threads and the mating grooves is 0.24. If $T = 200$ lb, what couple must be exerted on the turnbuckle to start tightening it?

9.91 Suppose that the pitch of the threads of the turnbuckle is $p = 0.05$ in, their mean radius is $r = 0.25$ in, and the coefficient of static friction between the threads and the mating grooves is 0.24. If $T = 200$ lb, what couple must be exerted on the turnbuckle to start loosening it?

Problems 9.90/9.91

9.92 Member *BE* of the frame has a turnbuckle. (See Problem 9.90.) The threads have pitch $p = 1$ mm, their mean radius is $r = 6$ mm, and the coefficient of static friction between the threads and the mating grooves is 0.2. What couple must be exerted on the turnbuckle to start loosening it?

9.93 In Problem 9.92, what couple must be exerted on the turnbuckle to start tightening it?

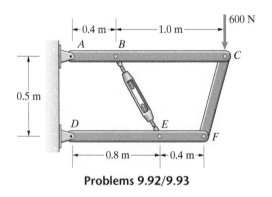

Problems 9.92/9.93

9.94 Members *CD* and *DG* of the truss have turnbuckles. (See Problem 9.90.) The pitch of the threads is $p = 4$ mm, their mean radius is $r = 10$ mm, and the coefficient of static friction between the threads and the mating grooves is 0.18. What couple must be exerted on the turnbuckle of member *CD* to start loosening it?

9.95 In Problem 9.94, what couple must be exerted on the turnbuckle of member *DG* to start loosening it?

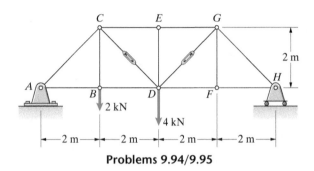

Problems 9.94/9.95

9.96* The load $W = 800$ N can be raised or lowered by rotating the threaded shaft. The distances are $b = 75$ mm and $h = 200$ mm. The pinned bars are each 300 mm in length. The pitch of the threaded shaft is $p = 5$ mm, the mean radius of the thread is $r = 15$ mm, and the coefficient of kinetic friction between the thread and the mating groove is 0.2. When the system is in the position shown, what couple must be exerted to turn the threaded shaft at a constant rate, raising the load?

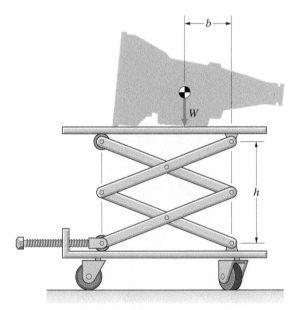

Problem 9.96

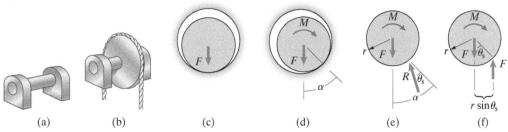

Figure 9.12
(a) A shaft supported by journal bearings.
(b) A pulley supported by the shaft.
(c) The shaft and bearing when no couple is applied to the shaft.
(d) A couple causes the shaft to roll within the bearing.
(e) Free-body diagram of the shaft.
(f) The two forces on the shaft must be equal and opposite.

9.4 Journal Bearings

BACKGROUND

A *bearing* is a support. This term usually refers to supports designed to allow the supported object to move. For example, in Fig. 9.12a, a horizontal shaft is supported by two *journal bearings*, which allow the shaft to rotate. The shaft can then be used to support a load perpendicular to its axis, such as that subjected by a pulley (Fig. 9.12b).

Here we analyze journal bearings consisting of brackets with holes through which the shaft passes. The radius of the shaft is slightly smaller than the radius of the holes in the bearings. Our objective is to determine the couple that must be applied to the shaft to cause it to rotate in the bearings. Let F be the total load supported by the shaft including the weight of the shaft itself. When no couple is exerted on the shaft, the force F presses it against the bearings as shown in Fig. 9.12c. When a couple M is exerted on the shaft, it rolls up the surfaces of the bearings (Fig. 9.12d). The term α is the angle from the original point of contact of the shaft to its point of contact when M is applied.

In Fig. 9.12e, we draw the free-body diagram of the shaft when M is sufficiently large that slip is impending. The force R is the total reaction exerted on the shaft by the two bearings. Since R and F are the only forces acting on the shaft, equilibrium requires that $\alpha = \theta_s$ and $R = F$ (Fig. 9.12f). The reaction exerted on the shaft by the bearings is displaced a distance $r \sin \theta_s$ from the vertical line through the center of the shaft. By summing moments about the center of the shaft, we obtain the couple M that causes the shaft to be on the verge of slipping:

$$M = rF \sin \theta_s. \tag{9.12}$$

This is the largest couple that can be exerted on the shaft without causing it to start rotating. Replacing θ_s in this expression by the angle of kinetic friction θ_k gives the couple necessary to rotate the shaft at a constant rate.

The simple type of journal bearing we have described is too primitive for most applications. The surfaces where the shaft and bearing are in contact would quickly become worn. Designers usually incorporate "ball" or "roller" bearings in journal bearings to minimize friction (Fig. 9.13).

(a)

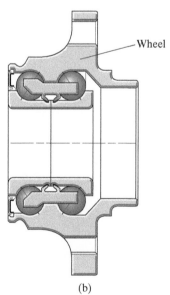

(b)

Figure 9.13
(a) A journal bearing with one row of balls.
(b) Journal bearing assembly of the wheel of a car. There are two rows of balls between the rotating wheel and the fixed inner cylinder.

RESULTS

RESULTS

A journal bearing has a circular hole slightly larger than the circular shaft it supports.

The couple M that must be applied to the circular shaft in order for slip to impend relative to a journal bearing is

$$M = rF \sin \theta_s, \qquad (9.12)$$

where r is the radius of the shaft, F is the lateral load supported by the shaft, and $\theta_s = \arctan \mu_s$.

Active Example 9.6	Pulley Supported by Journal Bearings (▶ *Related Problem 9.97*)

The weight of the suspended load is $W = 1000$ lb. The pulley P has a 6-in radius and is rigidly attached to a horizontal circular shaft that is supported by journal bearings. The radius of the shaft is 0.5 in, and the coefficient of kinetic friction between the shaft and the bearings is $\mu_k = 0.2$. The weights of the pulley and shaft are negligible. What tension must the winch A exert on the rope to raise the load at a constant rate?

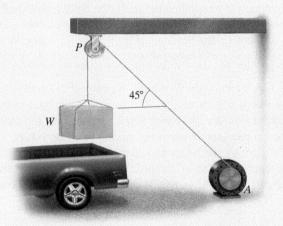

Strategy
Eq. (9.12) with θ_s replaced by θ_k relates the couple M required to turn the pulley at a constant rate to the lateral force F supported by the shaft. By expressing M and F in terms of the forces exerted on the pulley by the rope and applying Eq. (9.12), we can obtain an equation for the tension the winch must exert.

Solution

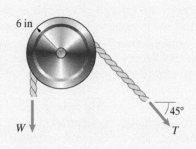

Forces exerted on the pulley by the rope. The force T is the tension exerted by the winch.

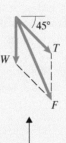

The vector sum of the forces exerted on the pulley by the rope is the lateral force F the shaft of the pulley must support. The magnitude of F can be expressed in terms of W and T.

$$F = \sqrt{(W + T \sin 45°)^2 + (T \cos 45°)^2}.$$

The pulley moves in the clockwise direction. Express the clockwise couple on the pulley in terms of T and W.

$$M = (6 \text{ in})(T - W).$$

The angle of kinetic friction is

$$\theta_k = \arctan \mu_k = \arctan(0.2) = 11.3°.$$

Equation (9.12) is

$$M = rF \sin \theta_k:$$

Apply Eq. (9.12).

$$(6 \text{ in})(T - W) = (0.5 \text{ in}) \sqrt{(W + T \sin 45°)^2 + (T \cos 45°)^2} \sin 11.3°.$$

Setting $W = 1000$ lb and solving yields

$$T = 1030 \text{ lb}.$$

Practice Problem What tension must the winch A exert on the rope to lower the load at a constant rate?

Answer: $T = 970$ lb.

Problems

▶ **9.97** In Active Example 9.6, suppose that the placement of the winch at A is changed so that the angle between the rope from A to P and the horizontal increases from 45° to 60°. If the suspended load weighs 1500 lb, what tension must the winch exert on the rope to raise the load at a constant rate?

9.98 The radius of the pulley is 4 in. The pulley is rigidly attached to the horizontal shaft, which is supported by two journal bearings. The radius of the shaft is 1 in, and the combined weight of the pulley and shaft is 20 lb. The coefficients of friction between the shaft and the bearings are $\mu_s = 0.30$ and $\mu_k = 0.28$. Determine the largest weight W that can be suspended as shown without causing the stationary shaft to slip in the bearings.

9.99 In Problem 9.98, suppose that the weight $W = 4$ lb. What couple would have to be applied to the horizontal shaft to raise the weight at a constant rate?

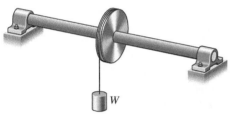

Problems 9.98/9.99

9.100 The pulley is mounted on a horizontal shaft supported by journal bearings. The coefficient of kinetic friction between the shaft and the bearings is $\mu_k = 0.3$. The radius of the shaft is 20 mm, and the radius of the pulley is 150 mm. The mass $m = 10$ kg. Neglect the masses of the pulley and shaft. What force T must be applied to the cable to move the mass upward at a constant rate?

9.101 In Problem 9.100, what force T must be applied to the cable to lower the mass at a constant rate?

Problems 9.100/9.101

9.102 The pulley of 8-in radius is mounted on a shaft of 1-in radius. The shaft is supported by two journal bearings. The coefficient of static friction between the bearings and the shaft is $\mu_s = 0.15$. Neglect the weights of the pulley and shaft. The 50-lb block A rests on the floor. If sand is slowly added to the bucket B, what do the bucket and sand weigh when the shaft slips in the bearings?

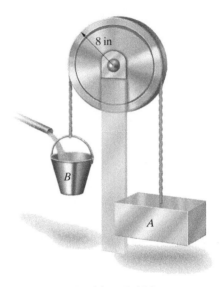

Problem 9.102

9.103 The pulley of 50-mm radius is mounted on a shaft of 10-mm radius. The shaft is supported by two journal bearings. The mass of the block A is 8 kg. Neglect the weights of the pulley and shaft. If a force $T = 84$ N is necessary to raise block A at a constant rate, what is the coefficient of kinetic friction between the shaft and the bearings?

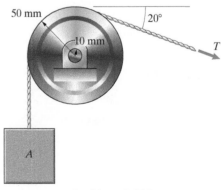

Problem 9.103

9.104 The mass of the suspended object is 4 kg. The pulley has a 100-mm radius and is rigidly attached to a horizontal shaft supported by journal bearings. The radius of the horizontal shaft is 10 mm and the coefficient of kinetic friction between the shaft and the bearings is 0.26. What tension must the person exert on the rope to raise the load at a constant rate?

9.105 In Problem 9.104, what tension must the person exert to lower the load at a constant rate?

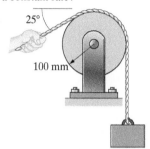

Problems 9.104/9.105

9.106 The radius of the pulley is 200 mm, and it is mounted on a shaft of 20-mm radius. The coefficient of static friction between the pulley and shaft is $\mu_s = 0.18$. If $F_A = 200$ N, what is the largest force F_B that can be applied without causing the pulley to turn? Neglect the weight of the pulley.

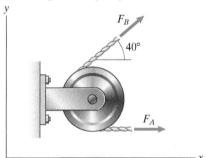

Problem 9.106

9.107 The masses of the boxes are $m_A = 15$ kg and $m_B = 60$ kg. The coefficient of static friction between boxes A and B and between box B and the inclined surface is 0.12. The pulley has a radius of 60 mm and is mounted on a shaft of 10-mm radius. The coefficient of static friction between the pulley and shaft is 0.16. What is the largest force F for which the boxes will not slip?

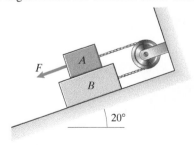

Problem 9.107

9.108 The two pulleys have a radius of 4 in and are mounted on shafts of 1-in radius supported by journal bearings. Neglect the weights of the pulleys and shafts. The tension in the spring is 40 lb. The coefficient of kinetic friction between the shafts and the bearings is $\mu_k = 0.3$. What couple M is required to turn the left pulley at a constant rate?

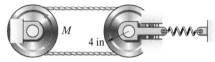

Problem 9.108

9.109 The weights of the boxes are $W_A = 65$ lb and $W_B = 130$ lb. The coefficient of static friction between boxes A and B and between box B and the floor is 0.12. The pulley has a radius of 4 in and is mounted on a shaft of 0.8-in radius. The coefficient of static friction between the pulley and shaft is 0.16. What is the largest force F for which the boxes will not slip?

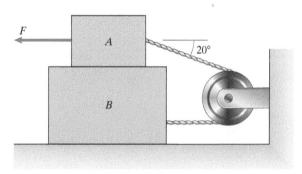

Problem 9.109

9.110 The coefficient of kinetic friction between the 100-kg box and the inclined surface is 0.35. Each pulley has a radius of 100 mm and is mounted on a shaft of 5-mm radius supported by journal bearings. The coefficient of kinetic friction between the shafts and the journal bearings is 0.18. Determine the tension T necessary to pull the box up the surface at a constant rate.

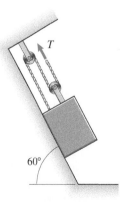

Problem 9.110

9.5 Thrust Bearings and Clutches

BACKGROUND

A *thrust bearing* supports a rotating shaft that is subjected to an axial load. In the type shown in Figs. 9.14a and b, the conical end of the shaft is pressed against the mating conical cavity by an axial load F. Let us determine the couple M necessary to rotate the shaft.

The differential element of area dA in Fig. 9.14c is

$$dA = 2\pi r\, ds = 2\pi r\left(\frac{dr}{\cos \alpha}\right).$$

Integrating this expression from $r = r_i$ to $r = r_o$, we obtain the area of contact:

$$A = \frac{\pi(r_o^2 - r_i^2)}{\cos \alpha}.$$

If we assume that the mating surface exerts a uniform pressure p, the axial component of the total force due to p must equal F: $pA \cos \alpha = F$. Therefore, the pressure is

$$p = \frac{F}{A \cos \alpha} = \frac{F}{\pi(r_o^2 - r_i^2)}.$$

As the shaft rotates about its axis, the moment about the axis due to the friction force on the element dA is $r\mu_k(p\, dA)$. The total moment is

$$M = \int_A \mu_k rp\, dA = \int_{r_i}^{r_o} \mu_k r\left[\frac{F}{\pi(r_o^2 - r_i^2)}\right]\left(\frac{2\pi r\, dr}{\cos \alpha}\right).$$

Integrating, we obtain the couple M necessary to rotate the shaft at a constant rate:

$$M = \frac{2\mu_k F}{3 \cos \alpha}\left(\frac{r_o^3 - r_i^3}{r_o^2 - r_i^2}\right). \tag{9.13}$$

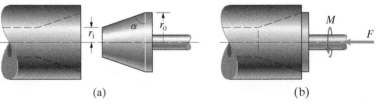

(a)　　　　　　　　(b)

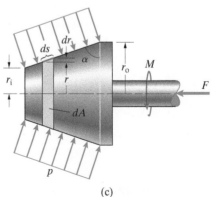

(c)

Figure 9.14

(a), (b) A thrust bearing supports a shaft subjected to an axial load.

(c) The differential element dA and the uniform pressure p exerted by the cavity.

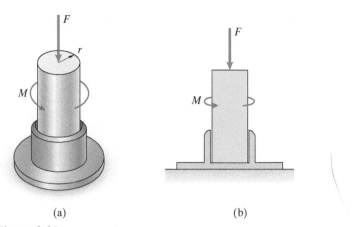

(a)   (b)

Figure 9.15
A thrust bearing that supports a flat-ended shaft.

A simpler thrust bearing is shown in Figs. 9.15a and b. The bracket supports the flat end of a shaft of radius r that is subjected to an axial load F. We can obtain the couple necessary to rotate the shaft at a constant rate from Eq. (9.13) by setting $\alpha = 0$, $r_i = 0$, and $r_o = r$:

$$M = \frac{2}{3}\mu_k Fr. \tag{9.14}$$

Although they are good examples of the analysis of friction forces, the thrust bearings we have described would become worn too quickly to be used in most applications. The designer of the thrust bearing in Fig. 9.16 minimizes friction by incorporating "roller" bearings.

A *clutch* is a device used to connect and disconnect two coaxial rotating shafts. The type shown in Figs. 9.17a and b consists of disks of radius r attached to the ends of the shafts. When the disks are separated (Fig. 9.17a), the clutch is *disengaged,* and the shafts can rotate freely relative to each other. When the clutch is engaged by pressing the disks together with axial forces F (Fig. 9.17b), the shafts can support a couple M due to the friction forces between the disks. If the couple M becomes too large, the clutch slips.

The friction forces exerted on one face of the clutch by the other face are identical to the friction forces exerted on the flat-ended shaft by the bracket in Fig. 9.15. We can therefore determine the largest couple the clutch can support without slipping by replacing μ_k with μ_s in Eq. (9.14):

$$M = \frac{2}{3}\mu_s Fr. \tag{9.15}$$

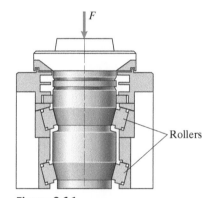

Figure 9.16
A thrust bearing with two rows of cylindrical rollers between the shaft and the fixed support.

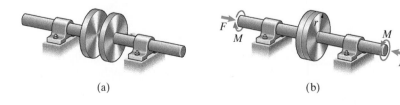

(a)   (b)

Figure 9.17
A clutch.
(**a**) Disengaged position.
(**b**) Engaged position.

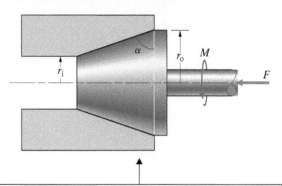

$$M = \frac{2\mu_k F}{3 \cos \alpha} \left(\frac{r_o^3 - r_i^3}{r_o^2 - r_i^2} \right). \quad (9.13)$$

The couple required to rotate a shaft supported by a *thrust bearing* in terms of the axial force supported by the shaft.

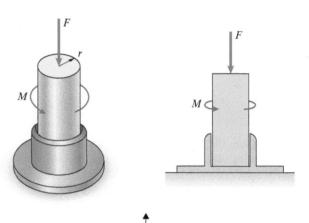

$$M = \frac{2}{3} \mu_k Fr. \quad (9.14)$$

The couple required to rotate a flat-ended shaft supported by a thrust bearing in terms of the axial force supported by the shaft.

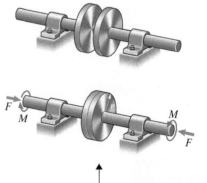

$$M = \frac{2}{3} \mu_s Fr. \quad (9.15)$$

The couple required to cause impending slip of a *clutch* in terms of the axial force applied to the clutch.

Active Example 9.7   Thrust Bearing (▶ *Related Problem 9.111*)

The axial force on the thrust bearing is $F = 200$ lb. The diameters $D_o = 3\frac{1}{2}$ in and $D_i = 1$ in, and the angle $\alpha = 72°$. The coefficient of kinetic friction is $\mu_k = 0.18$. What couple is required to turn the shaft at a constant rate?

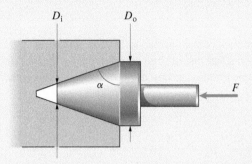

Strategy

The couple is given by Eq. (9.13).

Solution

The radii $r_o = 1.75$ in and $r_i = 0.5$ in.

$$M = \frac{2\mu_k F}{3 \cos \alpha} \left(\frac{r_o^3 - r_i^3}{r_o^2 - r_i^2} \right)$$

$$= \frac{2(0.18)(200 \text{ lb})}{3 \cos 72°} \left[\frac{(1.75 \text{ in})^3 - (0.5 \text{ in})^3}{(1.75 \text{ in})^2 - (0.5 \text{ in})^2} \right]$$

$$= 145 \text{ in-lb}.$$

Apply Eq. (9.13).

Practice Problem The axial force on the thrust bearing is $F = 200$ lb. The diameters $D_o = 3\frac{1}{2}$ in and $D_i = 1$ in, and the dimension $b = 5$ in. The coefficient of kinetic friction is $\mu_k = 0.18$. What couple is required to turn the shaft at a constant rate?

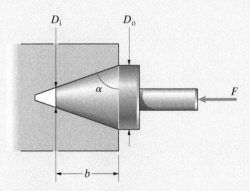

Answer: $M = 184$ in-lb.

| Example 9.8 | Friction on a Disk Sander (▶ *Related Problem 9.118*) |

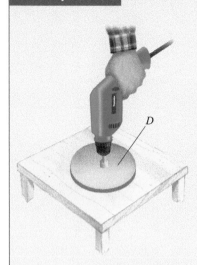

The handheld sander has a rotating disk D of 4-in radius with sandpaper bonded to it. The total downward force exerted by the operator and the weight of the sander is 15 lb. The coefficient of kinetic friction between the sandpaper and the surface is $\mu_k = 0.6$. What couple (torque) M must the motor exert to turn the sander at a constant rate?

Strategy
As the disk D rotates, it is subjected to friction forces analogous to the friction forces exerted on a flat-ended shaft supported by a thrust bearing. We can determine the couple required to turn the disk D at a constant rate from Eq. (9.14).

Solution
The couple required to turn the disk at a constant rate is

$$M = \frac{2}{3}\mu_k rF = \frac{2}{3}(0.6)(4 \text{ in})(15 \text{ lb}) = 24 \text{ in-lb}.$$

Critical Thinking
Equations (9.13)–(9.15) were derived under the assumption that the normal force (and consequently the friction force) is uniformly distributed over the contacting surfaces. Evaluating and improving upon this assumption would require analysis of the deformations of the contacting surfaces in specific applications such as the disk sander in this example.

Problems

▶ **9.111** In Active Example 9.7, suppose that the diameters $D_o = 3\frac{1}{2}$ in and $D_i = 1\frac{1}{2}$ in and the angle $\alpha = 72°$. What couple is required to turn the shaft at a constant rate?

9.112 The circular flat-ended shaft is pressed into the thrust bearing by an axial load of 600 lb. The weight of the shaft is negligible. The coefficients of friction between the end of the shaft and the bearing are $\mu_s = 0.20$ and $\mu_k = 0.15$. What is the largest couple M that can be applied to the stationary shaft without causing it to rotate in the bearing?

9.113 The circular flat-ended shaft is pressed into the thrust bearing by an axial load of 600 lb. The weight of the shaft is negligible. The coefficients of friction between the end of the shaft and the bearing are $\mu_s = 0.20$ and $\mu_k = 0.15$. What couple M is required to rotate the shaft at a constant rate?

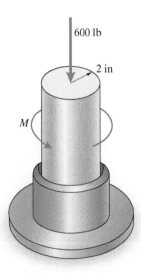

600 lb

2 in

M

Problems 9.112/9.113

9.114 The disk D is rigidly attached to the vertical shaft. The shaft has flat ends supported by thrust bearings. The disk and the shaft together have a mass of 220 kg and the diameter of the shaft is 50 mm. The vertical force exerted on the end of the shaft by the upper thrust bearing is 440 N. The coefficient of kinetic friction between the ends of the shaft and the bearings is 0.25. What couple M is required to rotate the shaft at a constant rate?

9.115 Suppose that the ends of the shaft in Problem 9.114 are supported by thrust bearings of the type shown in Fig. 9.14, where $r_o = 25$ mm, $r_i = 6$ mm, $\alpha = 45°$, and $\mu_k = 0.25$. What couple M is required to rotate the shaft at a constant rate?

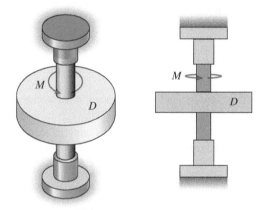

Problems 9.114/9.115

9.116 The shaft is supported by thrust bearings that subject it to an axial load of 800 N. The coefficients of kinetic friction between the shaft and the left and right bearings are 0.20 and 0.26, respectively. What couple is required to rotate the shaft at a constant rate?

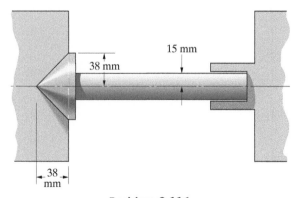

Problem 9.116

9.117 A motor is used to rotate a paddle for mixing chemicals. The shaft of the motor is coupled to the paddle using a friction clutch of the type shown in Fig. 9.17. The radius of the disks of the clutch is 120 mm, and the coefficient of static friction between the disks is 0.6. If the motor transmits a maximum torque of 15 N-m to the paddle, what minimum normal force between the plates of the clutch is necessary to prevent slipping?

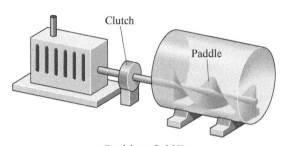

Problem 9.117

▶ **9.118** The thrust bearing is supported by contact of the collar C with a fixed plate. The area of contact is an annulus with an inside diameter $D_1 = 40$ mm and an outside diameter $D_2 = 120$ mm. The coefficient of kinetic friction between the collar and the plate is $\mu_k = 0.3$. The force $F = 400$ N. What couple M is required to rotate the shaft at a constant rate? (See Example 9.8.)

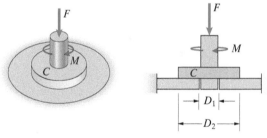

Problem 9.118

9.119 An experimental automobile brake design works by pressing the fixed red annular plate against the rotating wheel. If $\mu_k = 0.6$, what force F pressing the plate against the wheel is necessary to exert a couple of 200 N-m on the wheel?

9.120 An experimental automobile brake design works by pressing the fixed red annular plate against the rotating wheel. Suppose that $\mu_k = 0.65$ and the force pressing the plate against the wheel is $F = 2$ kN.

(a) What couple is exerted on the wheel?

(b) What percentage increase in the couple exerted on the wheel is obtained if the outer radius of the brake is increased from 90 mm to 100 mm?

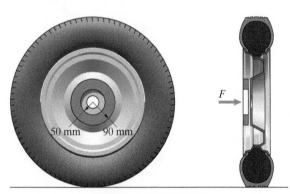

Problems 9.119/9.120

9.121 The coefficient of static friction between the plates of the car's clutch is 0.8. If the plates are pressed together with a force $F = 2.60$ kN, what is the maximum torque the clutch will support without slipping?

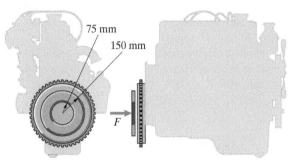

Problem 9.121

9.122* The "Morse taper" is used to support the workpiece on a machinist's lathe. The taper is driven into the spindle and is held in place by friction. If the spindle exerts a uniform pressure $p = 15$ psi on the taper and $\mu_s = 0.2$, what couple must be exerted about the axis of the taper to loosen it?

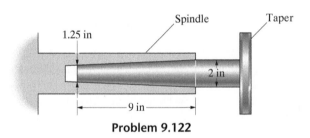

Problem 9.122

9.6 Belt Friction

BACKGROUND

If a rope is wrapped around a fixed post as shown in Fig. 9.18, a large force T_2 exerted on one end can be supported by a relatively small force T_1 applied to the other end. In this section we analyze this familiar phenomenon. It is referred to as *belt friction* because a similar approach can be used to analyze belts used in machines, such as the belts that drive alternators and other devices in a car.

Let us consider a rope wrapped through an angle β around a fixed cylinder (Fig. 9.19a). We will assume that the tension T_1 is known. Our objective is to determine the largest force T_2 that can be applied to the other end of the rope without causing the rope to slip.

We begin by drawing the free-body diagram of an element of the rope whose boundaries are at angles α and $\alpha + \Delta\alpha$ from the point where the rope comes into contact with the cylinder (Figs. 9.19b and c). The force T is the tension in the rope at the position defined by the angle α. We know that the tension in the rope varies with position, because it increases from T_1 at $\alpha = 0$ to T_2 at $\alpha = \beta$. We therefore write the tension in the rope at the position $\alpha + \Delta\alpha$ as $T + \Delta T$. The force ΔN is the normal force exerted on the element by the cylinder. Because we want to determine the largest value of T_2 that will not cause the rope to slip, we assume that the friction force is equal to its maximum possible value $\mu_s \Delta N$, where μ_s is the coefficient of static friction between the rope and the cylinder.

The equilibrium equations in the directions tangential to and normal to the centerline of the rope are

$$\Sigma F_{\text{tangential}} = \mu_s \Delta N + T \cos\left(\frac{\Delta\alpha}{2}\right) - (T + \Delta T) \cos\left(\frac{\Delta\alpha}{2}\right) = 0,$$

(9.16)

$$\Sigma F_{\text{normal}} = \Delta N - (T + \Delta T) \sin\left(\frac{\Delta\alpha}{2}\right) - T \sin\left(\frac{\Delta\alpha}{2}\right) = 0.$$

Eliminating ΔN, we can write the resulting equation as

$$\left[\cos\left(\frac{\Delta\alpha}{2}\right) - \mu_s \sin\left(\frac{\Delta\alpha}{2}\right)\right]\frac{\Delta T}{\Delta\alpha} - \mu_s T \frac{\sin(\Delta\alpha/2)}{\Delta\alpha/2} = 0.$$

Figure 9.18
A rope wrapped around a post.

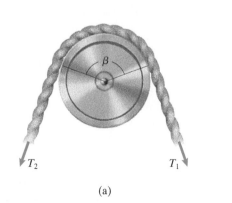

(a)

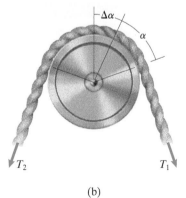

(b)

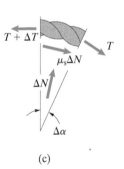

(c)

Figure 9.19
(a) A rope wrapped around a fixed cylinder.
(b) A differential element with boundaries at angles α and $\alpha + \Delta\alpha$.
(c) Free-body diagram of the element.

Evaluating the limit of this equation as $\Delta\alpha \to 0$ and observing that

$$\frac{\sin(\Delta\alpha/2)}{\Delta\alpha/2} \to 1,$$

we obtain

$$\frac{dT}{d\alpha} - \mu_s T = 0.$$

This differential equation governs the variation of the tension in the rope. Separating variables yields

$$\frac{dT}{T} = \mu_s\, d\alpha.$$

We can now integrate to determine the tension T_2 in terms of the tension T_1 and the angle β:

$$\int_{T_1}^{T_2} \frac{dT}{T} = \int_0^\beta \mu_s\, d\alpha.$$

Thus, we obtain the largest force T_2 that can be applied without causing the rope to slip when the force on the other end is T_1:

$$T_2 = T_1 e^{\mu_s \beta}. \tag{9.17}$$

The angle β in this equation must be expressed in radians. Replacing μ_s by the coefficient of kinetic friction μ_k gives the force T_2 required to cause the rope to slide at a constant rate.

Equation (9.17) explains why a large force can be supported by a relatively small force when a rope is wrapped around a fixed support. The force required to cause the rope to slip increases exponentially as a function of the angle through which the rope is wrapped. Suppose that $\mu_s = 0.3$. When the rope is wrapped one complete turn around the post $(\beta = 2\pi)$, the ratio $T_2/T_1 = 6.59$. When the rope is wrapped four complete turns around the post $(\beta = 8\pi)$, the ratio $T_2/T_1 = 1880$.

RESULTS

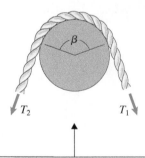

$$T_2 = T_1 e^{\mu_s \beta}. \tag{9.17}$$

The force T_2 necessary for impending slip of the rope relative to the fixed support in the direction of T_2, where the angle β is in radians and μ_s is the coefficient of static friction between the rope and the support.

Active Example 9.9   Rope Wrapped Around Fixed Cylinders (▶ *Related Problem 9.123*)

The 100-lb box is suspended from a rope that passes over two *fixed* cylinders. The coefficient of static friction is 0.2 between the rope and the left cylinder and 0.4 between the rope and the right cylinder. What is the smallest force the woman needs to exert on the rope to support the stationary box?

Strategy

She exerts the smallest necessary force when slip of the rope is impending on both cylinders. If we assume that slip is impending and apply Eq. (9.17) to each cylinder, we can determine the force she must apply.

Solution

Let T be the tension in the rope between the two cylinders. The weight $W = 100$ lb and F is the force the woman exerts. The rope is wrapped around each cylinder through an angle (in radians) $\beta = \pi/2$.

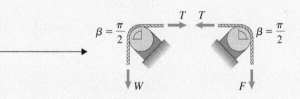

$\beta = \dfrac{\pi}{2}$ $T \quad T$ $\beta = \dfrac{\pi}{2}$

W F

$W = Te^{\mu_s\beta} = Te^{(0.2)(\pi/2)}$.

Solving for T yields

$T = We^{-(0.2)(\pi/2)} = (100\ \text{lb})e^{-(0.2)(\pi/2)} = 73.0\ \text{lb}.$

> Apply Eq. (9.17) to the left cylinder. Assume that slip of the rope in the direction of the force W is impending.

$T = Fe^{\mu_s\beta} = Fe^{(0.4)(\pi/2)}$.

Solving for F yields

$F = Te^{-(0.4)(\pi/2)} = (73.0\ \text{lb})e^{-(0.4)(\pi/2)} = 39.0\ \text{lb}.$

> Apply Eq. (9.17) to the right cylinder. Assume that slip of the rope in the direction of the force T is impending.

Practice Problem What force would the woman need to exert on the rope for slip to be impending in the direction she is pulling? That is, how hard would she have to pull for the box to be on the verge of moving upward? Would she need help?

Answer: 257 lb. Yes.

Example 9.10	Belts and Pulleys (▶ *Related Problem 9.134*)

The pulleys turn at a constant rate. The large pulley is attached to a fixed support. The small pulley is supported by a smooth horizontal slot and is pulled to the right by the force $F = 200$ N. The coefficient of static friction between the pulleys and the belt is $\mu_s = 0.8$, the dimension $b = 500$ mm, and the radii of the pulleys are $R_A = 200$ mm and $R_B = 100$ mm. What are the largest values of the couples M_A and M_B for which the belt will not slip?

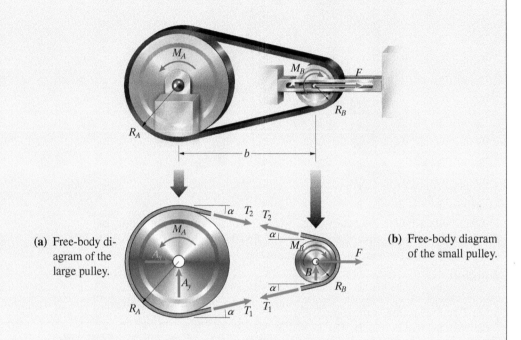

(a) Free-body diagram of the large pulley.

(b) Free-body diagram of the small pulley.

Strategy

By drawing free-body diagrams of the pulleys, we can use the equilibrium equations to relate the tensions in the belt to M_A and M_B and obtain a relation between the tensions in the belt and the force F. When slip is impending, the tensions are also related by Eq. (9.17). From these equations we can determine M_A and M_B.

Solution

From the free-body diagram of the large pulley (Fig. a), we obtain the equilibrium equation

$$M_A = R_A(T_2 - T_1), \tag{1}$$

and from the free-body diagram of the small pulley (Fig. b), we obtain

$$F = (T_1 + T_2) \cos \alpha, \tag{2}$$

$$M_B = R_B(T_2 - T_1). \tag{3}$$

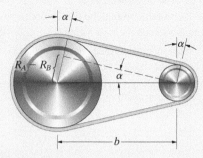

(c) Determining the angle α.

The belt is in contact with the small pulley through the angle $\pi - 2\alpha$ (Fig. c). From the dashed line parallel to the belt, we see that the angle α satisfies the relation

$$\sin \alpha = \frac{R_A - R_B}{b} = \frac{200 \text{ mm} - 100 \text{ mm}}{500 \text{ mm}} = 0.2.$$

Therefore, $\alpha = 11.5° = 0.201$ rad. If we assume that slip impends between the small pulley and the belt, Eq. (9.17) states that

$$T_2 = T_1 e^{\mu_s \beta} = T_1 e^{0.8(\pi - 2\alpha)} = 8.95 T_1.$$

We solve this equation together with Eq. (2) for the two tensions, obtaining $T_1 = 20.5$ N and $T_2 = 183.6$ N. Then from Eqs. (1) and (3), the couples are $M_A = 32.6$ N-m and $M_B = 16.3$ N-m.

If we assume that slip impends between the large pulley and the belt, we obtain $M_A = 36.3$ N-m and $M_B = 18.1$ N-m, so the belt slips on the small pulley at smaller values of the couples.

Problems

▶ **9.123** In Active Example 9.9, suppose that the left fixed cylinder is replaced by a pulley. Assume that the tensions in the rope on each side of the pulley are approximately equal. What is the smallest force the woman needs to exert on the rope to support the stationary box?

9.124 Suppose that you want to lift a 50-lb crate off the ground by using a rope looped over a tree limb as shown. The coefficient of static friction between the rope and the limb is 0.2, and the rope is wound 135° around the limb. What force must you exert to begin lifting the crate?

Problem 9.124

9.125 *Winches* are used on sailboats to help support the forces exerted by the sails on the ropes (*sheets*) holding them in position. The winch shown is a post that will rotate in the clockwise direction (seen from above), but will not rotate in the counterclockwise direction. The sail exerts a tension $T_S = 800$ N on the sheet, which is wrapped two complete turns around the winch. The coefficient of static friction between the sheet and the winch is $\mu_s = 0.2$. What tension T_C must the crew member exert on the sheet to prevent it from slipping on the winch?

9.126 The coefficient of kinetic friction between the sheet and the winch in Problem 9.125 is $\mu_k = 0.16$. If the crew member wants to let the sheet slip at a constant rate, releasing the sail, what initial tension T_C must he exert on the sheet as it begins slipping?

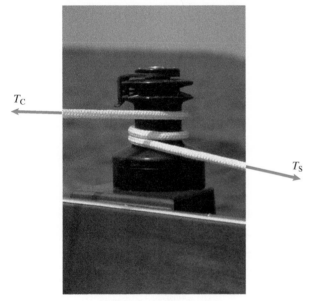

Problems 9.125/9.126

9.127 The box A weighs 20 lb. The rope is wrapped one and one-fourth turns around the fixed wooden post. The coefficients of friction between the rope and post are $\mu_s = 0.15$ and $\mu_k = 0.12$.

(a) What minimum force does the man need to exert to support the stationary box?

(b) What force would the man have to exert to raise the box at a constant rate?

Problem 9.127

9.128 The weight of block A is W. The disk is supported by a smooth bearing. The coefficient of kinetic friction between the disk and the belt is μ_k. What couple M is necessary to turn the disk at a constant rate?

Problem 9.128

9.129 The couple required to turn the wheel of the exercise bicycle is adjusted by changing the weight W. The coefficient of kinetic friction between the wheel and the belt is μ_k. Assume the wheel turns clockwise.

(a) Show that the couple M required to turn the wheel is
$M = WR\,(1 - e^{-3.4\mu_k})$.

(b) If $W = 40$ lb and $\mu_k = 0.2$, what force will the scale S indicate when the bicycle is in use?

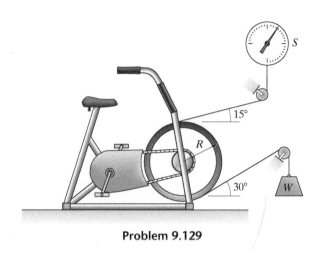

Problem 9.129

9.130 The box B weighs 50 lb. The coefficients of friction between the cable and the fixed round supports are $\mu_s = 0.4$ and $\mu_k = 0.3$.

(a) What is the minimum force F required to support the box?

(b) What force F is required to move the box upward at a constant rate?

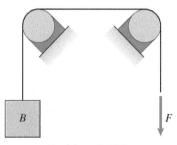

Problem 9.130

9.131 The coefficient of static friction between the 50-lb box and the inclined surface is 0.10. The coefficient of static friction between the rope and the fixed cylinder is 0.05. Determine the force the woman must exert on the rope to cause the box to start moving up the inclined surface.

9.132 In Problem 9.131, what is the minimum force the woman must exert on the rope to hold the box in equilibrium on the inclined surface?

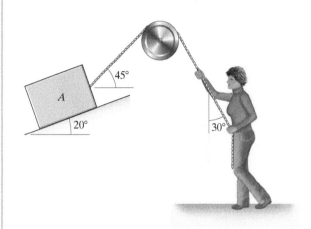

Problems 9.131/9.132

9.133 Blocks B and C each have a mass of 20 kg. The coefficient of static friction at the contacting surfaces is 0.2. Block A is suspended by a rope that passes over a fixed cylinder and is attached to block B. The coefficient of static friction between the rope and the cylinder is 0.3. What is the largest mass block A can have without causing block B to slip to the left?

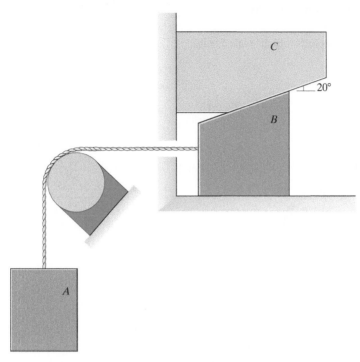

Problem 9.133

▶ **9.134** If the force F in Example 9.10 is increased to 400 N, what are the largest values of the couples M_A and M_B for which the belt will not slip?

9.135 The spring exerts a 320-N force on the left pulley. The coefficient of static friction between the flat belt and the pulleys is $\mu_s = 0.5$. The right pulley cannot rotate. What is the largest couple M that can be exerted on the left pulley without causing the belt to slip?

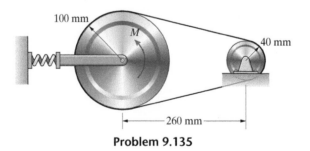

Problem 9.135

Review Problems

9.136 The weight of the box is $W = 30$ lb, and the force F is perpendicular to the inclined surface. The coefficient of static friction between the box and the inclined surface is $\mu_s = 0.2$.

(a) If $F = 30$ lb, what is the magnitude of the friction force exerted on the stationary box?

(b) If $F = 10$ lb, show that the box cannot remain at rest on the inclined surface.

9.137 In Problem 9.136, what is the smallest force F necessary to hold the box stationary on the inclined surface?

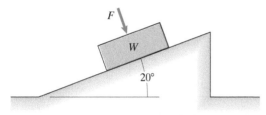

Problems 9.136/9.137

9.138 Blocks A and B are connected by a horizontal bar. The coefficient of static friction between the inclined surface and the 400-lb block A is 0.3. The coefficient of static friction between the surface and the 300-lb block B is 0.5. What is the smallest force F that will prevent the blocks from slipping down the surface?

9.139 What force F is necessary to cause the blocks in Problem 9.138 to start sliding up the plane?

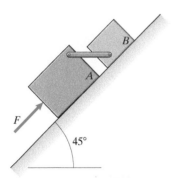

Problems 9.138/9.139

9.140 The masses of crates A and B are 25 kg and 30 kg, respectively. The coefficient of static friction between the contacting surfaces is $\mu_s = 0.34$. What is the largest value of α for which the crates will remain in equilibrium?

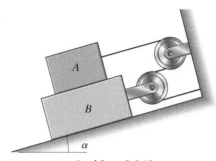

Problem 9.140

9.141 The side of a soil embankment has a 45° slope (Fig. a). If the coefficient of static friction of soil on soil is $\mu_s = 0.6$, will the embankment be stable or will it collapse? If it will collapse, what is the smallest slope that can be stable?

Strategy: Draw a free-body diagram by isolating part of the embankment as shown in Fig. b.

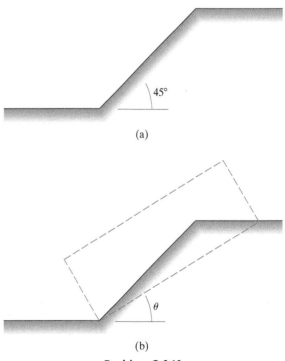

Problem 9.141

9.142 The mass of the van is 2250 kg, and the coefficient of static friction between its tires and the road is 0.6. If its front wheels are locked and its rear wheels can turn freely, what is the largest value of α for which it can remain in equilibrium?

9.143 In Problem 9.142, what is the largest value of α for which the van can remain in equilibrium if it points up the slope?

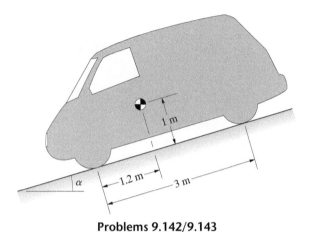

Problems 9.142/9.143

9.144 The shelf is designed so that it can be placed at any height on the vertical beam. The shelf is supported by friction between the two horizontal cylinders and the vertical beam. The combined weight of the shelf and camera is W. If the coefficient of static friction between the vertical beam and the horizontal cylinders is μ_s, what is the minimum distance b necessary for the shelf to stay in place?

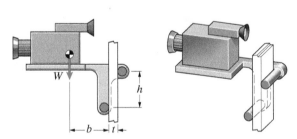

Problem 9.144

9.145 The 20-lb homogeneous object is supported at A and B. The distance $h = 4$ in, friction can be neglected at B, and the coefficient of static friction at A is 0.4. Determine the largest force F that can be exerted without causing the object to slip.

9.146 In Problem 9.145, suppose that the coefficient of static friction at B is 0.36. What is the largest value of h for which the object will slip before it tips over?

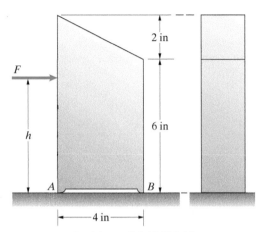

Problems 9.145/9.146

9.147 The 180-lb climber is supported in the "chimney" by the normal and friction forces exerted on his shoes and back. The static coefficients of friction between his shoes and the wall and between his back and the wall are 0.8 and 0.6, respectively. What is the minimum normal force his shoes must exert?

Problem 9.147

9.148 The sides of the 200-lb door fit loosely into grooves in the walls. Cables at A and B raise the door at a constant rate. The coefficient of kinetic friction between the door and the grooves is $\mu_k = 0.3$. What force must the cable at A exert to continue raising the door at a constant rate if the cable at B breaks?

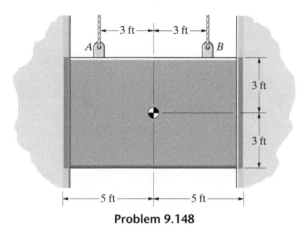

Problem 9.148

9.149 The coefficients of static friction between the tires of the 1000-kg tractor and the ground and between the 450-kg crate and the ground are 0.8 and 0.3, respectively. Starting from rest, what torque must the tractor's engine exert on the rear wheels to cause the crate to move? (The front wheels can turn freely.)

9.150 In Problem 9.149, what is the most massive crate the tractor can cause to move from rest if its engine can exert sufficient torque? What torque is necessary?

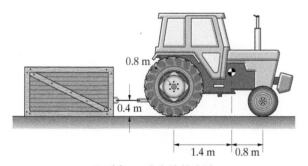

Problems 9.149/9.150

9.151 The mass of the vehicle is 900 kg, it has rear-wheel drive, and the coefficient of static friction between its tires and the surface is 0.65. The coefficient of static friction between the crate and the surface is 0.4. If the vehicle attempts to pull the crate up the incline, what is the largest value of the mass of the crate for which it will slip up the incline before the vehicle's tires slip?

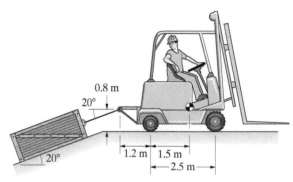

Problem 9.151

9.152 Each 1-m bar has a mass of 4 kg. The coefficient of static friction between the bar and the surface at B is 0.2. If the system is in equilibrium, what is the magnitude of the friction force exerted on the bar at B?

9.153 Each 1-m bar has a mass of 4 kg. What is the minimum coefficient of static friction between the bar and the surface at B necessary for the system to be in equilibrium?

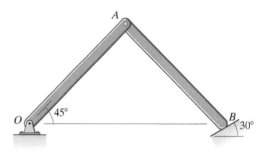

Problems 9.152/9.153

9.154 The collars A and B each have a mass of 2 kg. If friction between collar B and the bar can be neglected, what minimum coefficient of static friction between collar A and the bar is necessary for the collars to remain in equilibrium in the position shown?

9.155 If the coefficient of static friction has the same value μ_s between the 2-kg collars A and B and the bars, what minimum value of μ_s is necessary for the collars to remain in equilibrium in the position shown? (Assume that slip impends at A and B.)

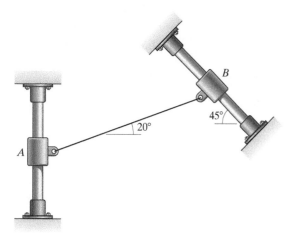

Problems 9.154/9.155

9.156 The clamp presses two pieces of wood together. The pitch of the threads is $p = 2$ mm, the mean radius of the thread is $r = 8$ mm, and the coefficient of kinetic friction between the thread and the mating groove is 0.24. What couple must be exerted on the threaded shaft to press the pieces of wood together with a force of 200 N?

9.157 In Problem 9.156, the coefficient of static friction between the thread and the mating groove is 0.28. After the threaded shaft is rotated sufficiently to press the pieces of wood together with a force of 200 N, what couple must be exerted on the shaft to loosen it?

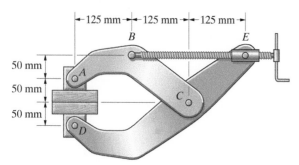

Problems 9.156/9.157

9.158 The axles of the tram are supported by journal bearings. The radius of the wheels is 75 mm, the radius of the axles is 15 mm, and the coefficient of kinetic friction between the axles and the bearings is $\mu_k = 0.14$. The mass of the tram and its load is 160 kg. If the weight of the tram and its load is evenly divided between the axles, what force P is necessary to push the tram at a constant speed?

Problem 9.158

9.159 The two pulleys have a radius of 6 in and are mounted on shafts of 1-in radius supported by journal bearings. Neglect the weights of the pulleys and shafts. The coefficient of kinetic friction between the shafts and the bearings is $\mu_k = 0.2$. If a force $T = 200$ lb is required to raise the man at a constant rate, what is his weight?

9.160 If the man in Problem 9.159 weighs 160 lb, what force T is necessary to lower him at a constant rate?

Problems 9.159/9.160

9.161 If the two cylinders are held fixed, what is the range of W for which the two weights will remain stationary?

9.162 If the system is initially stationary and the left cylinder is slowly rotated, determine the largest weight W that can be

(a) raised;

(b) lowered.

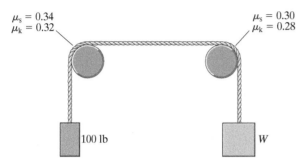

$\mu_s = 0.34$
$\mu_k = 0.32$

$\mu_s = 0.30$
$\mu_k = 0.28$

100 lb

W

Problems 9.161/9.162

Design Project 1

The wedge is used to split firewood by hammering it into a log as shown (see Active Example 9.4). Suppose that you want to design such a wedge to be marketed at hardware stores. Experiments indicate that the coefficient of static friction between the steel wedge and various types of wood varies from 0.2 to 0.4.

(a) Based on the given range of static friction coefficients, determine the maximum wedge angle α for which the wedge would remain in place in a log with no external force acting on it.

(b) Using the wedge angle determined in part (a), and assuming that the coefficient of kinetic friction is 0.9 times the coefficient of static friction, determine the range of vertical forces necessary to drive the wedge into a log at a constant rate.

(c) Write a brief report describing your analysis and recommending a wedge angle for the manufactured product. Consider whether a margin of safety in the chosen wedge angle might be appropriate.

Design Project 2

Design and build a device to measure the coefficient of static friction μ_s between two materials. Use it to measure μ_s for several of the materials listed in Table 9.1 and compare your results with the values in the table. Discuss possible sources of error in your device and determine how closely your values agree when you perform repeated experiments with the same two materials.

APPENDIX

A

Review of Mathematics

A.1 Algebra

Quadratic Equations

The solutions of the quadratic equation

$$ax^2 + bx + c = 0$$

are

$$x = \frac{-b \pm \sqrt{b^2 - 4ac}}{2a}.$$

Natural Logarithms

The natural logarithm of a positive real number x is denoted by $\ln x$. It is defined to be the number such that

$$e^{\ln x} = x,$$

where $e = 2.7182\ldots$ is the base of natural logarithms.

Logarithms have the following properties:

$$\ln(xy) = \ln x + \ln y,$$
$$\ln(x/y) = \ln x - \ln y,$$
$$\ln y^x = x \ln y.$$

A.2 Trigonometry

The trigonometric functions for a right triangle are

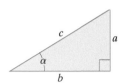

$$\sin\alpha = \frac{1}{\csc\alpha} = \frac{a}{c}, \quad \cos\alpha = \frac{1}{\sec\alpha} = \frac{b}{c}, \quad \tan\alpha = \frac{1}{\cot\alpha} = \frac{a}{b}.$$

The sine and cosine satisfy the relation

$$\sin^2\alpha + \cos^2\alpha = 1,$$

and the sine and cosine of the sum and difference of two angles satisfy

$$\sin(\alpha + \beta) = \sin\alpha\cos\beta + \cos\alpha\sin\beta,$$
$$\sin(\alpha - \beta) = \sin\alpha\cos\beta - \cos\alpha\sin\beta,$$
$$\cos(\alpha + \beta) = \cos\alpha\cos\beta - \sin\alpha\sin\beta,$$
$$\cos(\alpha - \beta) = \cos\alpha\cos\beta + \sin\alpha\sin\beta.$$

The **law of cosines** for an arbitrary triangle is

$$c^2 = a^2 + b^2 - 2ab\cos\alpha_c,$$

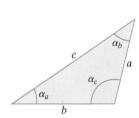

and the **law of sines** is

$$\frac{\sin\alpha_a}{a} = \frac{\sin\alpha_b}{b} = \frac{\sin\alpha_c}{c}.$$

A.3 Derivatives

$$\frac{d}{dx}x^n = nx^{n-1} \qquad \frac{d}{dx}\sin x = \cos x \qquad \frac{d}{dx}\sinh x = \cosh x$$

$$\frac{d}{dx}e^x = e^x \qquad \frac{d}{dx}\cos x = -\sin x \qquad \frac{d}{dx}\cosh x = \sinh x$$

$$\frac{d}{dx}\ln x = \frac{1}{x} \qquad \frac{d}{dx}\tan x = \frac{1}{\cos^2 x} \qquad \frac{d}{dx}\tanh x = \frac{1}{\cosh^2 x}$$

A.4 Integrals

$$\int x^n \, dx = \frac{x^{n+1}}{n+1} \quad (n \neq -1)$$

$$\int \frac{dx}{(1 - a^2x^2)^{1/2}} = \frac{1}{a} \arcsin ax \quad \text{or} \quad -\frac{1}{a} \arccos ax$$

$$\int x^{-1} \, dx = \ln x$$

$$\int \sin x \, dx = -\cos x$$

$$\int (a + bx)^{1/2} \, dx = \frac{2}{3b} (a + bx)^{3/2}$$

$$\int \cos x \, dx = \sin x$$

$$\int x(a + bx)^{1/2} \, dx = -\frac{2(2a - 3bx)(a + bx)^{3/2}}{15b^2}$$

$$\int \sin^2 x \, dx = -\frac{1}{2} \sin x \cos x + \frac{1}{2} x$$

$$\int (1 + a^2x^2)^{1/2} \, dx = \frac{1}{2} \left\{ x(1 + a^2x^2)^{1/2} \right.$$

$$\int \cos^2 x \, dx = \frac{1}{2} \sin x \cos x + \frac{1}{2} x$$

$$\left. + \frac{1}{a} \ln \left[x + \left(\frac{1}{a^2} + x^2 \right)^{1/2} \right] \right\}$$

$$\int \sin^3 x \, dx = -\frac{1}{3} \cos x (\sin^2 x + 2)$$

$$\int x(1 + a^2x^2)^{1/2} \, dx = \frac{a}{3} \left(\frac{1}{a^2} + x^2 \right)^{3/2}$$

$$\int \cos^3 x \, dx = \frac{1}{3} \sin x (\cos^2 x + 2)$$

$$\int x^2(1 + a^2x^2)^{1/2} \, dx = \frac{1}{4} ax \left(\frac{1}{a^2} + x^2 \right)^{3/2}$$

$$\int \cos^4 x \, dx = \frac{3}{8} x + \frac{1}{4} \sin 2x + \frac{1}{32} \sin 4x$$

$$- \frac{1}{8a^2} x(1 + a^2x^2)^{1/2} - \frac{1}{8a^3} \ln \left[x + \left(\frac{1}{a^2} + x^2 \right)^{1/2} \right]$$

$$\int \sin^n x \cos x \, dx = \frac{(\sin x)^{n+1}}{n+1} \quad (n \neq -1)$$

$$\int (1 - a^2x^2)^{1/2} \, dx = \frac{1}{2} \left[x(1 - a^2x^2)^{1/2} + \frac{1}{a} \arcsin ax \right]$$

$$\int \sinh x \, dx = \cosh x$$

$$\int x(1 - a^2x^2)^{1/2} \, dx = -\frac{a}{3} \left(\frac{1}{a^2} - x^2 \right)^{3/2}$$

$$\int \cosh x \, dx = \sinh x$$

$$\int x^2(a^2 - x^2)^{1/2} \, dx = -\frac{1}{4} x(a^2 - x^2)^{3/2}$$

$$\int \tanh x \, dx = \ln \cosh x$$

$$+ \frac{1}{8} a^2 \left[x(a^2 - x^2)^{1/2} + a^2 \arcsin \frac{x}{a} \right]$$

$$\int e^{ax} \, dx = \frac{e^{ax}}{a}$$

$$\int \frac{dx}{(1 + a^2x^2)^{1/2}} = \frac{1}{a} \ln \left[x + \left(\frac{1}{a^2} + x^2 \right)^{1/2} \right]$$

$$\int xe^{ax} \, dx = \frac{e^{ax}}{a^2} (ax - 1)$$

A.5 Taylor Series

The Taylor series of a function $f(x)$ is

$$f(a + x) = f(a) + f'(a)x + \frac{1}{2!}f''(a)x^2 + \frac{1}{3!}f'''(a)x^3 + \cdots,$$

where the primes indicate derivatives.

Some useful Taylor series are

$$e^x = 1 + x + \frac{x^2}{2!} + \frac{x^3}{3!} + \cdots,$$

$$\sin(a + x) = \sin a + (\cos a)x - \frac{1}{2}(\sin a)x^2 - \frac{1}{6}(\cos a)x^3 + \cdots,$$

$$\cos(a + x) = \cos a - (\sin a)x - \frac{1}{2}(\cos a)x^2 + \frac{1}{6}(\sin a)x^3 + \cdots,$$

$$\tan(a + x) = \tan a + \left(\frac{1}{\cos^2 a}\right)x + \left(\frac{\sin a}{\cos^3 a}\right)x^2$$

$$+ \left(\frac{\sin^2 a}{\cos^4 a} + \frac{1}{3\cos^2 a}\right)x^3 + \cdots.$$

APPENDIX
B
Properties of Areas and Lines

B.1 Areas

The coordinates of the centroid of the area A are

$$\bar{x} = \frac{\int_A x \, dA}{\int_A dA}, \qquad \bar{y} = \frac{\int_A y \, dA}{\int_A dA}.$$

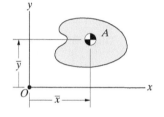

The moment of inertia about the x axis I_x, the moment of inertia about the y axis I_y, and the product of inertia I_{xy} are

$$I_x = \int_A y^2 \, dA, \qquad I_y = \int_A x^2 \, dA, \qquad I_{xy} = \int_A xy \, dA.$$

The polar moment of inertia about O is

$$J_O = \int_A r^2 \, dA = \int_A (x^2 + y^2) \, dA = I_x + I_y.$$

Area $= bh$

$$I_x = \frac{1}{3} bh^3, \qquad I_y = \frac{1}{3} hb^3, \qquad I_{xy} = \frac{1}{4} b^2 h^2$$

$$I_{x'} = \frac{1}{12} bh^3, \qquad I_{y'} = \frac{1}{12} hb^3, \qquad I_{x'y'} = 0$$

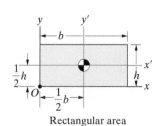

Rectangular area

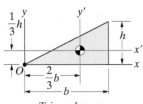

Triangular area

$$\text{Area} = \frac{1}{2}bh$$

$$I_x = \frac{1}{12}bh^3, \qquad I_y = \frac{1}{4}hb^3, \qquad I_{xy} = \frac{1}{8}b^2h^2$$

$$I_{x'} = \frac{1}{36}bh^3, \qquad I_{y'} = \frac{1}{36}hb^3, \qquad I_{x'y'} = \frac{1}{72}b^2h^2$$

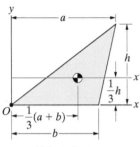

Triangular area

$$\text{Area} = \frac{1}{2}bh \qquad I_x = \frac{1}{12}bh^3, \qquad I_{x'} = \frac{1}{36}bh^3$$

Circular area

$$\text{Area} = \pi R^2 \qquad I_{x'} = I_{y'} = \frac{1}{4}\pi R^4, \qquad I_{x'y'} = 0$$

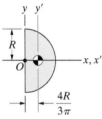

Semicircular area

$$\text{Area} = \frac{1}{2}\pi R^2 \qquad I_x = I_y = \frac{1}{8}\pi R^4, \qquad I_{xy} = 0$$

$$I_{x'} = \frac{1}{8}\pi R^4, \qquad I_{y'} = \left(\frac{\pi}{8} - \frac{8}{9\pi}\right)R^4, \qquad I_{x'y'} = 0$$

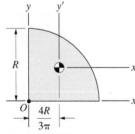

Quarter-circular area

$$\text{Area} = \frac{1}{4}\pi R^2 \qquad I_x = I_y = \frac{1}{16}\pi R^4, \qquad I_{xy} = \frac{1}{8}R^4$$

$$I_{x'} = I_{y'} = \left(\frac{\pi}{16} - \frac{4}{9\pi}\right)R^4, \qquad I_{x'y'} = \left(\frac{1}{8} - \frac{4}{9\pi}\right)R^4$$

$\text{Area} = \alpha R^2$

$$I_x = \frac{1}{4}R^4\left(\alpha - \frac{1}{2}\sin 2\alpha\right), \qquad I_y = \frac{1}{4}R^4\left(\alpha + \frac{1}{2}\sin 2\alpha\right),$$

$$I_{xy} = 0$$

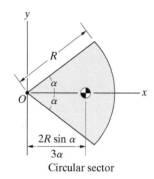

Circular sector

$\text{Area} = \frac{1}{4}\pi ab$

$$I_x = \frac{1}{16}\pi ab^3, \qquad I_y = \frac{1}{16}\pi a^3 b, \qquad I_{xy} = \frac{1}{8}a^2b^2$$

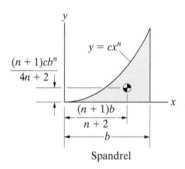

Quarter-elliptical area

$\text{Area} = \dfrac{cb^{n+1}}{n+1}$

$$I_x = \frac{c^3 b^{3n+1}}{9n+3}, \qquad I_y = \frac{cb^{n+3}}{n+3}, \qquad I_{xy} = \frac{c^2 b^{2n+2}}{4n+4}$$

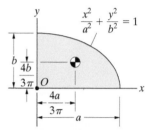

Spandrel

B.2 Lines

The coordinates of the centroid of the line L are

$$\bar{x} = \frac{\displaystyle\int_L x\,dL}{\displaystyle\int_L dL}, \qquad \bar{y} = \frac{\displaystyle\int_L y\,dL}{\displaystyle\int_L dL}, \qquad \bar{z} = \frac{\displaystyle\int_L z\,dL}{\displaystyle\int_L dL}.$$

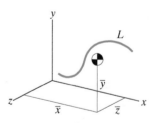

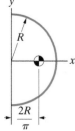

Semicircular arc

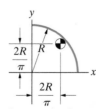

Quarter-circular arc

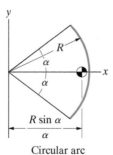

Circular arc

APPENDIX

C

Properties of Volumes and Homogeneous Objects

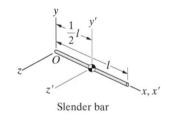

The coordinates of the centroid of the volume V are

$$\bar{x} = \frac{\int_V x \, dV}{\int_V dV}, \qquad \bar{y} = \frac{\int_V y \, dV}{\int_V dV}, \qquad \bar{z} = \frac{\int_V z \, dV}{\int_V dV}.$$

The center of mass of a homogeneous object coincides with the centroid of its volume.

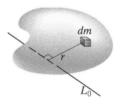

The moment of inertia of the object about the axis L_0 is

$$I_0 = \int_m r^2 \, dm.$$

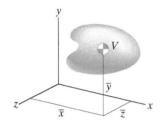

Slender bar

$$I_{x \text{ axis}} = 0, \qquad I_{y \text{ axis}} = I_{z \text{ axis}} = \frac{1}{3} m l^2$$

$$I_{x' \text{ axis}} = 0, \qquad I_{y' \text{ axis}} = I_{z' \text{ axis}} = \frac{1}{12} m l^2$$

Thin circular plate

$$I_{x' \text{ axis}} = I_{y' \text{ axis}} = \frac{1}{4} m R^2, \qquad I_{z' \text{ axis}} = \frac{1}{2} m R^2$$

$$I_{x \text{ axis}} = \frac{1}{3}mh^2, \qquad I_{y \text{ axis}} = \frac{1}{3}mb^2, \qquad I_{z \text{ axis}} = \frac{1}{3}m(b^2 + h^2)$$

$$I_{x' \text{ axis}} = \frac{1}{12}mh^2, \qquad I_{y' \text{ axis}} = \frac{1}{12}mb^2, \qquad I_{z' \text{ axis}} = \frac{1}{12}m(b^2 + h^2)$$

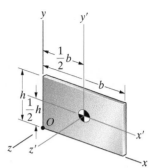

Thin rectangular plate

$$I_{x \text{ axis}} = \frac{m}{A}I_x, \qquad I_{y \text{ axis}} = \frac{m}{A}I_y, \qquad I_{z \text{ axis}} = I_{x \text{ axis}} + I_{y \text{ axis}}$$

The terms I_x and I_y are the moments of inertia of the plate's cross-sectional area A about the x and y axes.

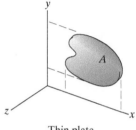

Thin plate

Volume $= abc$

$$I_{x' \text{ axis}} = \frac{1}{12}m(a^2 + b^2), \qquad I_{y' \text{ axis}} = \frac{1}{12}m(a^2 + c^2),$$

$$I_{z' \text{ axis}} = \frac{1}{12}m(b^2 + c^2)$$

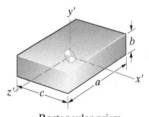

Rectangular prism

Volume $= \pi R^2 l$

$$I_{x \text{ axis}} = I_{y \text{ axis}} = m\left(\frac{1}{3}l^2 + \frac{1}{4}R^2\right), \qquad I_{z \text{ axis}} = \frac{1}{2}mR^2$$

$$I_{x' \text{ axis}} = I_{y' \text{ axis}} = m\left(\frac{1}{12}l^2 + \frac{1}{4}R^2\right), \qquad I_{z' \text{ axis}} = \frac{1}{2}mR^2$$

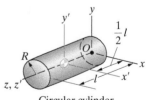

Circular cylinder

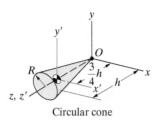

$$\text{Volume} = \frac{1}{3}\pi R^2 h$$

$$I_{x \text{ axis}} = I_{y \text{ axis}} = m\left(\frac{3}{5}h^2 + \frac{3}{20}R^2\right), \qquad I_{z \text{ axis}} = \frac{3}{10}mR^2$$

$$I_{x' \text{ axis}} = I_{y' \text{ axis}} = m\left(\frac{3}{80}h^2 + \frac{3}{20}R^2\right), \qquad I_{z' \text{ axis}} = \frac{3}{10}mR^2$$

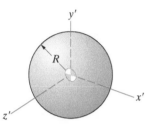

Circular cone

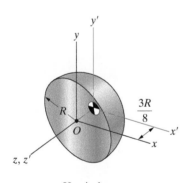

Sphere

$$\text{Volume} = \frac{4}{3}\pi R^3$$

$$I_{x' \text{ axis}} = I_{y' \text{ axis}} = I_{z' \text{ axis}} = \frac{2}{5}mR^2$$

Hemisphere

$$\text{Volume} = \frac{2}{3}\pi R^3$$

$$I_{x \text{ axis}} = I_{y \text{ axis}} = I_{z \text{ axis}} = \frac{2}{5}mR^2$$

$$I_{x' \text{ axis}} = I_{y' \text{ axis}} = \frac{83}{320}mR^2, \quad I_{z' \text{ axis}} = \frac{2}{5}mR^2$$

Solutions to Practice Problems

Active Example 1.1

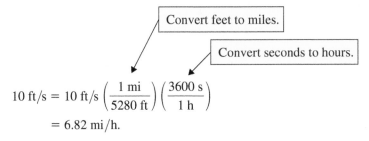

Convert feet to miles.

Convert seconds to hours.

$$10 \text{ ft/s} = 10 \text{ ft/s} \left(\frac{1 \text{ mi}}{5280 \text{ ft}} \right) \left(\frac{3600 \text{ s}}{1 \text{ h}} \right)$$
$$= 6.82 \text{ mi/h}.$$

Active Example 1.4

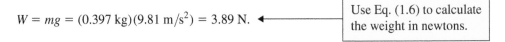

$$W = mg = (0.397 \text{ kg})(9.81 \text{ m/s}^2) = 3.89 \text{ N.}$$

Use Eq. (1.6) to calculate the weight in newtons.

Active Example 2.1

Drawing the vectors **U** and 2**V** to scale, place them head to tail.

The measured value of $|\mathbf{U} - 2\mathbf{V}|$ is 5.7.

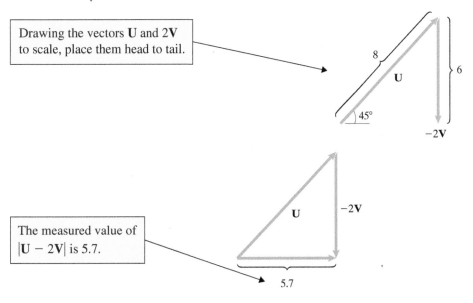

Active Example 2.3

$|F_y| = 3|F_x|.$

The magnitude of $\mathbf{F}$ is

$$900 \text{ N} = \sqrt{F_x^2 + F_y^2}$$

$$= \sqrt{F_x^2 + (3F_x)^2}.$$

Solving yields $F_x = 285$ N. The vector $\mathbf{F}$ in terms of its components is

$$\mathbf{F} = 285\mathbf{i} - 3(285)\mathbf{j} \text{ (N)}$$

$$= 285\mathbf{i} - 854\mathbf{j} \text{ (N)}.$$

Required the magnitude of the y component of $\mathbf{F}$ to be three times the magnitude of the x component.

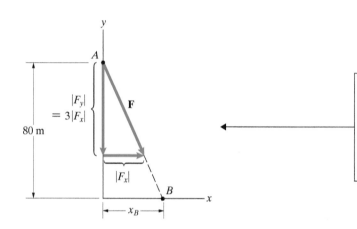

Use similar triangles to determine the location of point B:

$$\frac{x_B}{80 \text{ m}} = \frac{|F_x|}{3|F_x|}:$$

$$x_B = 26.7 \text{ m}.$$

Active Example 2.6

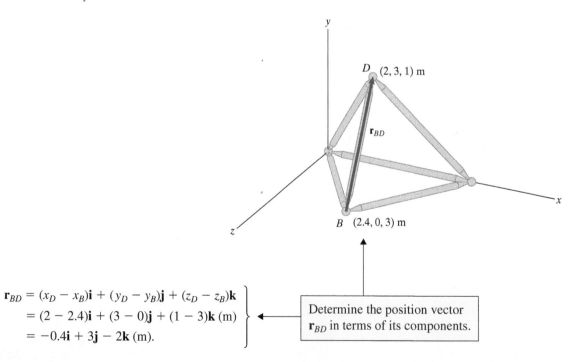

$$\mathbf{r}_{BD} = (x_D - x_B)\mathbf{i} + (y_D - y_B)\mathbf{j} + (z_D - z_B)\mathbf{k}$$

$$= (2 - 2.4)\mathbf{i} + (3 - 0)\mathbf{j} + (1 - 3)\mathbf{k} \text{ (m)}$$

$$= -0.4\mathbf{i} + 3\mathbf{j} - 2\mathbf{k} \text{ (m)}.$$

Determine the position vector $\mathbf{r}_{BD}$ in terms of its components.

$$|\mathbf{r}_{BD}| = \sqrt{r^2_{BDx} + r^2_{BDy} + r^2_{BDz}}$$
$$= \sqrt{(-0.4 \text{ m})^2 + (3 \text{ m})^2 + (-2 \text{ m})^2}$$
$$= 3.63 \text{ m}.$$

Calculate the magnitude of $\mathbf{r}_{BD}$.

$$\mathbf{e}_{BD} = \frac{\mathbf{r}_{BD}}{|\mathbf{r}_{BD}|}$$
$$= \frac{-0.4\mathbf{i} + 3\mathbf{j} - 2\mathbf{k} \text{ (m)}}{3.63 \text{ (m)}}$$
$$= -0.110\mathbf{i} + 0.827\mathbf{j} - 0.551\mathbf{k}.$$

Divide $\mathbf{r}_{BD}$ by its magnitude to obtain $\mathbf{e}_{BD}$ in terms of its components.

Active Example 2.11

The vectors $\mathbf{U}$ and $\mathbf{V}$ are perpendicular if $\mathbf{U} \cdot \mathbf{V} = 0$. Use this condition to determine V_x.

$$\mathbf{U} \cdot \mathbf{V} = U_x V_x + U_y V_y + U_z V_z$$
$$= (6)V_x + (-5)(2) + (-3)(2)$$
$$= 6V_x - 16.$$

Calculate $\mathbf{U} \cdot \mathbf{V}$ in terms of the components of the vectors.

$$\mathbf{U} \cdot \mathbf{V} = 6V_x - 16 = 0,$$
$$V_x = 2.67.$$

Equate $\mathbf{U} \cdot \mathbf{V}$ to zero and solve for V_x.

Active Example 2.14

The cross product $\mathbf{U} \times \mathbf{V}$ is perpendicular to $\mathbf{U}$ and perpendicular to $\mathbf{V}$. By determining the vector $\mathbf{U} \times \mathbf{V}$ in terms of its components and dividing it by its magnitude $|\mathbf{U} \times \mathbf{V}|$, we can obtain the components of a unit vector that is perpendicular to $\mathbf{U}$ and perpendicular to $\mathbf{V}$.

$$\mathbf{U} \times \mathbf{V} = (U_y V_z - U_z V_y)\mathbf{i} - (U_x V_z - U_z V_x)\mathbf{j}$$
$$+ (U_x V_y - U_y V_x)\mathbf{k}$$
$$= [(2)(-4) - (-1)(-3)]\mathbf{i} - [(3)(-4) - (-1)(5)]\mathbf{j}$$
$$+ [(3)(-3) - (2)(5)]\mathbf{k}$$
$$= -11\mathbf{i} + 7\mathbf{j} - 19\mathbf{k}.$$

Calculate $\mathbf{U} \times \mathbf{V}$ in terms of the components of the vectors.

$$|\mathbf{U} \times \mathbf{V}| = \sqrt{(-11)^2 + (7)^2 + (-19)^2}$$
$$= 23.0.$$
$$\frac{\mathbf{U} \times \mathbf{V}}{|\mathbf{U} \times \mathbf{V}|} = \frac{-11\mathbf{i} + 7\mathbf{j} - 19\mathbf{k}}{23.0}$$
$$= -0.477\mathbf{i} + 0.304\mathbf{j} - 0.825\mathbf{k}.$$

Divide the vector $\mathbf{U} \times \mathbf{V}$ by its magnitude.

Active Example 3.1

Draw the Free-Body Diagram of the Car

Draw a sketch of the isolated car.

Complete the free-body diagram by showing the forces exerted on the car by its weight, the cable, and the ramp.

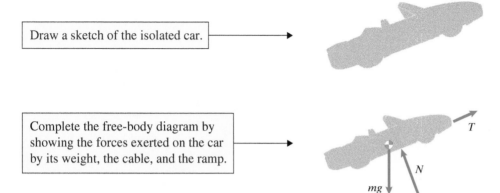

Apply the Equilibrium Equations

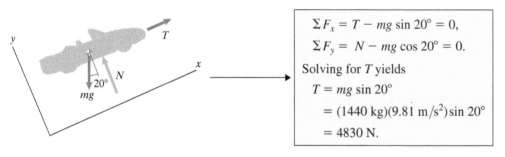

$$\Sigma F_x = T - mg \sin 20° = 0,$$
$$\Sigma F_y = N - mg \cos 20° = 0.$$

Solving for T yields

$$T = mg \sin 20°$$
$$= (1440 \text{ kg})(9.81 \text{ m/s}^2) \sin 20°$$
$$= 4830 \text{ N}.$$

Active Example 3.5

Draw the Free-Body Diagram and Apply Equilibrium

Isolate part of the cable system near point A and show the forces exerted due to the tensions in the cables. The sum of the forces must equal zero:

$$\Sigma \mathbf{F} = \mathbf{T}_{AB} + \mathbf{T}_{AC} + \mathbf{T}_{AD} - (981 \text{ N})\mathbf{j} = \mathbf{0}.$$

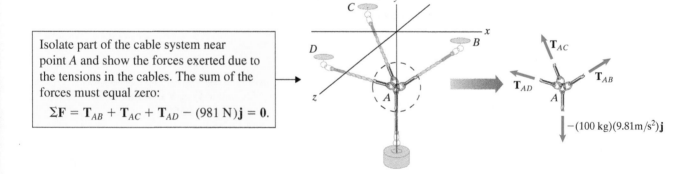

Write the Forces in Terms of Their Components

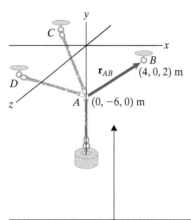

$$\mathbf{r}_{AB} = (x_B - x_A)\mathbf{i} + (y_B - y_A)\mathbf{j} + (z_B - z_A)\mathbf{k}$$
$$= 4\mathbf{i} + 6\mathbf{j} + 2\mathbf{k} \text{ (m).}$$
$$\mathbf{e}_{AB} = \frac{\mathbf{r}_{AB}}{|\mathbf{r}_{AB}|} = 0.535\mathbf{i} + 0.802\mathbf{j} + 0.267\mathbf{k}.$$

> Obtain a unit vector that has the same direction as the force $\mathbf{T}_{AB}$ by dividing the position vector $\mathbf{r}_{AB}$ from point A to point B by its magnitude.

$$\mathbf{T}_{AB} = T_{AB}\mathbf{e}_{AB}$$
$$= T_{AB}(0.535\mathbf{i} + 0.802\mathbf{j} + 0.267\mathbf{k}),$$
$$\mathbf{T}_{AC} = T_{AC}(-0.302\mathbf{i} + 0.905\mathbf{j} - 0.302\mathbf{k}),$$
$$\mathbf{T}_{AD} = T_{AD}(-0.408\mathbf{i} + 0.817\mathbf{j} + 0.408\mathbf{k}).$$

> Express the force $\mathbf{T}_{AB}$ in terms of its components by writing it as the product of the tension T_{AB} in cable AB and the unit vector $\mathbf{e}_{AB}$. Express the forces $\mathbf{T}_{AC}$ and $\mathbf{T}_{AD}$ in terms of their components using the same procedure.

> Substitute these expressions into the equilibrium equation
> $$\mathbf{T}_{AB} + \mathbf{T}_{AC} + \mathbf{T}_{AD} - (981 \text{ N})\mathbf{j} = \mathbf{0}.$$
> Because the $\mathbf{i}$, $\mathbf{j}$, and $\mathbf{k}$ components must each equal zero, this results in three equations:

$$0.535T_{AB} - 0.302T_{AC} - 0.408T_{AD} = 0,$$
$$0.802T_{AB} + 0.905T_{AC} + 0.817T_{AD} - 981 \text{ N} = 0,$$
$$0.267T_{AB} - 0.302T_{AC} + 0.408T_{AD} = 0.$$

Solving these three equations yields $T_{AB} = 432$ N, $T_{AC} = 574$ N, and $T_{AD} = 141$ N.

Active Example 4.1

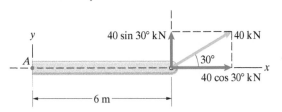

The magnitude of the moment of the horizontal component about A is zero. The magnitude of the moment of the vertical component is $(6\ \text{m})(40 \sin 30° \ \text{N}) = 120$ kN-m. Its direction is counterclockwise, so the sum of the moments is $M_A = 120$ kN-m.

Resolve the 40-kN force into horizontal and vertical components.

Calculate the sum of the moments of the components about A.

Active Example 4.4

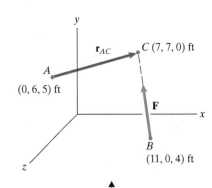

$$\mathbf{r}_{AC} = (x_C - x_A)\mathbf{i} + (y_C - y_A)\mathbf{j} + (z_C - z_A)\mathbf{k}$$
$$= 7\mathbf{i} + \mathbf{j} - 5\mathbf{k} \ (\text{ft}).$$
$$\mathbf{M}_A = \mathbf{r}_{AC} \times \mathbf{F}$$
$$= \begin{vmatrix} \mathbf{i} & \mathbf{j} & \mathbf{k} \\ 7 & 1 & -5 \\ -40 & 70 & -40 \end{vmatrix}$$
$$= 310\mathbf{i} + 480\mathbf{j} + 530\mathbf{k} \ (\text{ft-lb}).$$

(a) Apply Eq. (4.2) to determine the moment of $\mathbf{F}$ about point A.

$$D = \frac{|\mathbf{M}_A|}{|\mathbf{F}|}$$
$$= \frac{\sqrt{(310)^2 + (480)^2 + (530)^2} \ \text{ft-lb}}{90 \ \text{lb}}$$
$$= 8.66 \ \text{ft}.$$

(b) Use the relation $|\mathbf{M}_A| = D|\mathbf{F}|$, where D is the perpendicular distance from A to the line of action of $\mathbf{F}$.

Active Example 4.6

$$\mathbf{r} = (x_A - x_C)\mathbf{i} + (y_A - y_C)\mathbf{j} + (z_A - z_C)\mathbf{k}$$
$$\quad = 4\mathbf{i} - 2\mathbf{j} + 2\mathbf{k} \text{ (m)}.$$

> Determine the components of the vector from point C to the point of application of $\mathbf{F}$.

$$\mathbf{M}_C = \mathbf{r} \times \mathbf{F}$$

$$= \begin{vmatrix} \mathbf{i} & \mathbf{j} & \mathbf{k} \\ 4 & -2 & 2 \\ -2 & 6 & 3 \end{vmatrix}$$

$$= -18\mathbf{i} - 16\mathbf{j} + 20\mathbf{k} \text{ (kN-m)}.$$

> Calculate the moment of $\mathbf{F}$ about point C.

$$\mathbf{M}_{BC} = (\mathbf{e}_{BC} \cdot \mathbf{M}_C)\mathbf{e}_{BC}$$
$$\quad = [(0)(-18) + (0.8)(-16) + (-0.6)(20)]\mathbf{e}_{BC}$$
$$\quad = -24.8\mathbf{e}_{BC} \text{ (kN-m)}.$$

> Apply Eq. (4.4) to determine the moment of $\mathbf{F}$ about the axis BC. Although the moment of $\mathbf{F}$ about point C is not the same as the moment of $\mathbf{F}$ about point B, their components parallel to the axis BC are the same.

Active Example 4.9

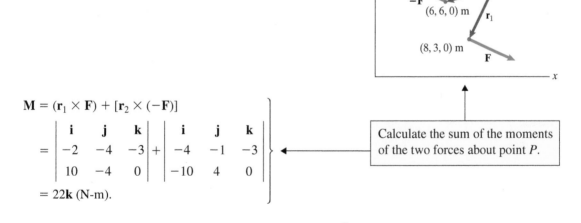

$$\mathbf{M} = (\mathbf{r}_1 \times \mathbf{F}) + [\mathbf{r}_2 \times (-\mathbf{F})]$$

$$= \begin{vmatrix} \mathbf{i} & \mathbf{j} & \mathbf{k} \\ -2 & -4 & -3 \\ 10 & -4 & 0 \end{vmatrix} + \begin{vmatrix} \mathbf{i} & \mathbf{j} & \mathbf{k} \\ -4 & -1 & -3 \\ -10 & 4 & 0 \end{vmatrix}$$

$$= 22\mathbf{k} \text{ (N-m)}.$$

> Calculate the sum of the moments of the two forces about point P.

> The magnitude of the moment is 22 N-m. Pointing the thumb of the right hand in the direction of the unit vector $\mathbf{k}$, the direction of the moment in the x–y plane is counterclockwise.

Active Example 4.12

$$\mathbf{F}' = \mathbf{F}$$
$$= 20\mathbf{i} + 15\mathbf{j} - 5\mathbf{k} \text{ (kN)}.$$

> The force $\mathbf{F}'$ must equal the sum of the forces in system 2.

$$\mathbf{M}' = \begin{vmatrix} \mathbf{i} & \mathbf{j} & \mathbf{k} \\ 4 & 3 & -2 \\ 20 & 15 & -5 \end{vmatrix} + (-105\mathbf{i} + 110\mathbf{j} + 90\mathbf{k})$$

$$= -90\mathbf{i} + 90\mathbf{j} + 90\mathbf{k} \text{ (kN-m)}.$$

> The couple $\mathbf{M}'$ must equal the sum of the moments about the origin due to the forces and moments in system 2.

Active Example 5.1

> (a) Draw a diagram of the beam isolated from its pin and roller supports and show the reactions due to the support.

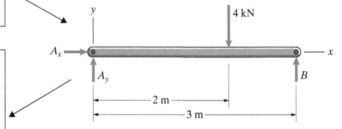

> (b) Write the equilibrium equations,
> $$\Sigma F_x = A_x = 0,$$
> $$\Sigma F_y = A_y + B - 4 \text{ kN} = 0,$$
> $$\Sigma M_{\text{left end}} = (3 \text{ m})B - (2 \text{ m})(4 \text{ kN}) = 0,$$
> and solve them, obtaining
> $$A_x = 0, \; A_y = 1.33 \text{ kN}, \; B = 2.67 \text{ kN}.$$

Active Example 5.5

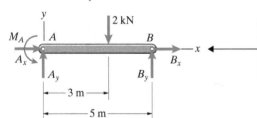

> Draw the free-body diagram of the beam. There are five unknown reactions.

$$\Sigma F_x = A_x + B_x = 0,$$
$$\Sigma F_y = A_y + B_y - 2 \text{ kN} = 0,$$
$$\Sigma M_{\text{point } A} = M_A + (5 \text{ m})B_y - (3 \text{ m})(2 \text{ kN}) = 0.$$

> Write the equilibrium equations.

There are three independent equilibrium equations, so the beam is statically indeterminate and the degree of redundancy is $5 - 3 = 2$. We cannot determine any of the reactions from the equilibrium equations.

Active Example 5.7

Draw the Free-Body Diagram of the Bar

Isolate the bar and show the reactions exerted by the cables and the ball and socket support.

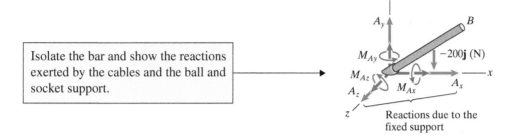

Reactions due to the
fixed support

Apply the Equilibrium Equations

$$\Sigma F_x = A_x = 0,$$
$$\Sigma F_y = A_y - 200 \text{ N} = 0,$$
$$\Sigma F_z = A_z = 0.$$

The sums of the forces in each coordinate direction equal zero.

$$\Sigma \mathbf{M}_{\text{point } A} = M_{Ax}\mathbf{i} + M_{Ay}\mathbf{j} + M_{Az}\mathbf{k} + \left[\frac{1}{2}\,\mathbf{r}_{AB} \times (-200\mathbf{j}) \right]$$

$$= M_{Ax}\mathbf{i} + M_{Ay}\mathbf{j} + M_{Az}\mathbf{k} + \begin{vmatrix} \mathbf{i} & \mathbf{j} & \mathbf{k} \\ 0.5 & 0.3 & 0.2 \\ 0 & -200 & 0 \end{vmatrix}$$

$$= (M_{Ax} + 40)\mathbf{i} + M_{Ay}\mathbf{j} + (M_{Az} - 100)\mathbf{k}.$$

The sum of the moments about any point equals zero.

The components of this vector (the sums of the moments about the three coordinate axes) must each equal zero.

$$\Sigma M_x = M_{Ax} + 40 \text{ N-m} = 0,$$
$$\Sigma M_y = M_{Ay} = 0,$$
$$\Sigma M_z = M_{Az} - 100 \text{ N-m} = 0.$$

Solving the six scalar equilibrium equations yields $A_x = 0$, $A_y = 200$ N, $A_z = 0$, $M_{Ax} = -40$ N-m, $M_{Ay} = 0$, and $M_{Az} = 100$ N-m.

Active Example 5.10

The force exerted on the plate by the bar AB must be directed along the line between A and B, and the line of action of the weight of the plate is vertical, so the three forces on the plate are not parallel. Therefore they must be concurrent.

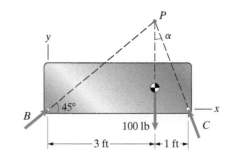

The angle $\alpha = \arctan(1/3) = 18.4°$.

$\Sigma F_x = B \sin 45° - C \sin \alpha = 0$,

$\Sigma F_y = B \cos 45° + C \cos \alpha - 100 \text{ lb} = 0$.

Solving yields the reactions $B = 35.4$ lb, $C = 79.1$ lb.

Apply the equilibrium equations.

Active Example 6.1

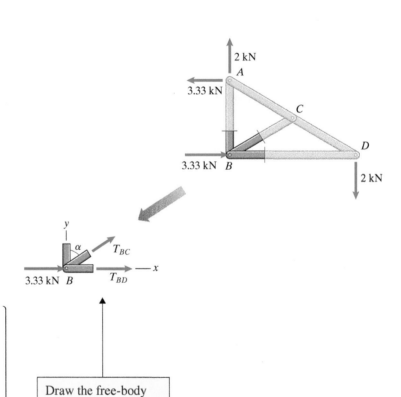

The angle $\alpha = \arctan(5/3) = 59.0°$.

$\Sigma F_x = T_{BC} \sin \alpha + T_{BD} + 3.33 \text{ kN} = 0$,

$\Sigma F_y = T_{BC} \cos \alpha = 0$.

Solving yields $T_{BC} = 0$ and $T_{BD} = -3.33$ kN. The axial force in member BC is zero and the axial force in member BD is 3.33 kN in compression, or

BC: zero, BD: 3.33 kN (C).

(Notice that joint C is one of the "special joints" we discussed. We could have determined by observation that $T_{BC} = 0$.)

Draw the free-body diagram of joint B and apply the equilibrium equations.

Active Example 6.3

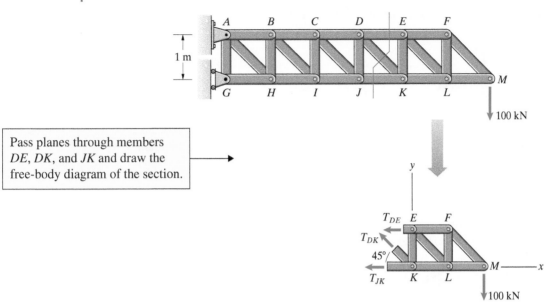

Pass planes through members *DE*, *DK*, and *JK* and draw the free-body diagram of the section.

$$\Sigma F_x = -T_{DE} - T_{DK} \cos 45° - T_{JK} = 0,$$

$$\Sigma F_y = T_{DK} \sin 45° - 100 \text{ kN} = 0,$$

$$\Sigma M_{\text{point } K} = (1 \text{ m})T_{DE} - (2 \text{ m})(100 \text{ kN}) = 0.$$

Solving yields $T_{DE} = 200$ kN, $T_{DK} = 141$ kN, and $T_{JK} = -300$ kN. The axial loads are

DE: 200 kN (T), *DK*: 141 kN (T),

JK: 300 kN (C).

Apply the equilibrium equations.

Active Example 6.5

We can determine the axial forces in members AB and AC by analyzing joint A.

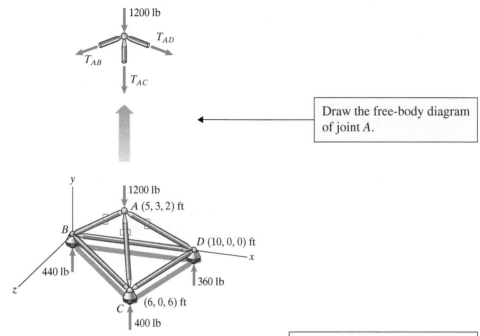

Draw the free-body diagram of joint A.

Divide the position vector from A to B by its magnitude to obtain a unit vector $\mathbf{e}_{AB}$ that points from A toward B. Express the axial force in member AB in terms of its components by writing it as $T_{AB}\mathbf{e}_{AB}$. Express the axial forces in members AC and AD in terms of their components in the same way.

$$\mathbf{r}_{AB} = -5\mathbf{i} - 3\mathbf{j} - 2\mathbf{k} \text{ (ft)}.$$

$$\mathbf{e}_{AB} = \frac{\mathbf{r}_{AB}}{|\mathbf{r}_{AB}|} = -0.811\mathbf{i} - 0.487\mathbf{j} - 0.324\mathbf{k}.$$

$$T_{AB}\mathbf{e}_{AB} = -T_{AB}(0.811\mathbf{i} + 0.487\mathbf{j} + 0.324\mathbf{k}),$$

$$T_{AC}\mathbf{e}_{AC} = T_{AC}(0.196\mathbf{i} - 0.588\mathbf{j} + 0.784\mathbf{k}),$$

$$T_{AD}\mathbf{e}_{AD} = T_{AD}(0.811\mathbf{i} - 0.487\mathbf{j} - 0.324\mathbf{k}).$$

$$T_{AB}\mathbf{e}_{AB} + T_{AC}\mathbf{e}_{AC} + T_{AD}\mathbf{e}_{AC} - (1200 \text{ lb})\mathbf{j} = 0.$$

The $\mathbf{i}$, $\mathbf{j}$, and $\mathbf{k}$ components of this equation must each equal zero, resulting in the three equations

$$-0.811\,T_{AB} + 0.196\,T_{AC} + 0.811\,T_{AD} = 0,$$

$$0.487\,T_{AB} + 0.588\,T_{AC} + 0.487\,T_{AD} + 1200 \text{ lb} = 0,$$

$$-0.324\,T_{AB} + 0.784\,T_{AC} - 0.324\,T_{AD} = 0.$$

Apply equilibrium.

Solving yields $T_{AB} = -904$ lb, $T_{AC} = -680$ lb, and $T_{AD} = -740$ lb. The axial forces are

AB: 904 lb (C), AC: 680 lb (C).

Active Example 6.6

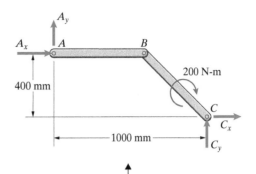

$\Sigma F_x = A_x + C_x = 0,$

$\Sigma F_y = A_y + C_y = 0,$

$\Sigma M_{\text{point } A} = -200 \text{ N-m} + (0.4 \text{ m})C_x + (1 \text{ m})C_y = 0.$

We can't determine any reactions from these equations. The free-body diagram of the entire frame is statically indeterminate.

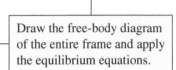

Draw the free-body diagram of the entire frame and apply the equilibrium equations.

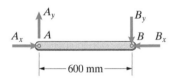

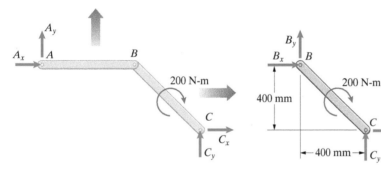

Draw the free-body diagrams of the individual members.

$\Sigma F_x = A_x - B_x = 0,$

$\Sigma F_y = A_y - B_y = 0,$

$\Sigma M_{\text{point } A} = -(0.6 \text{ m})B_y = 0.$

Solving yields $A_y = 0$, $B_y = 0$, and $A_x = B_x$. (Notice that AB is a two-force member. We could have obtained these results by observation.)

Apply equilibrium to member AB.

$\Sigma F_x = B_x + C_x = 0,$

$\Sigma F_y = B_y + C_y = 0,$

$\Sigma M_{\text{point } B} = -200 \text{ N-m} + (0.4 \text{ m})C_x + (0.4 \text{ m})C_y = 0.$

Because it has already been determined that $B_y = 0$, these equations can be solved for B_x, C_x, and C_y. The results are $B_x = -500 \text{ N}$, $C_x = 500 \text{ N}$, and $C_y = 0$, which completes the solution.

Apply equilibrium to member BC.

Active Example 7.1

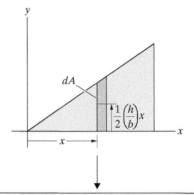

$$\bar{y} = \frac{\displaystyle\int_A y\,dA}{\displaystyle\int_A dA} = \frac{\displaystyle\int_0^b \frac{1}{2}\left(\frac{h}{b}x\right)\left(\frac{h}{b}x\,dx\right)}{\displaystyle\int_0^b \frac{h}{b}x\,dx} = \frac{\dfrac{1}{2}\left(\dfrac{h}{b}\right)^2\left[\dfrac{x^3}{3}\right]_0^b}{\dfrac{h}{b}\left[\dfrac{x^2}{2}\right]_0^b} = \frac{1}{3}h. \;\longleftarrow$$

> The area of the strip is $dA = (h/b)x\,dx$. The height of the midpoint of the strip is $y = (1/2)(h/b)x$. Use these expressions to evaluate Eq. (7.7).

Active Example 7.3

> **Choose the Parts**
> Divide the area into simple parts. The y coordinates of the centroids of the parts are shown.

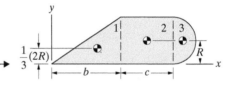

> **Determine the Values for the Parts**
> Tabulate the terms needed to apply Eq. (7.9)$_2$.

	$\bar{y}_i$	A_i	$\bar{y}_i A_i$
Part 1 (triangle)	$\dfrac{1}{3}(2R)$	$\dfrac{1}{2}b(2R)$	$\left[\dfrac{1}{3}(2R)\right]\left[\dfrac{1}{2}b(2R)\right]$
Part 2 (rectangle)	R	$c(2R)$	$R[c(2R)]$
Part 3 (semicircle)	R	$\dfrac{1}{2}\pi R^2$	$R\left(\dfrac{1}{2}\pi R^2\right)$

$$\bar{y} = \frac{\bar{y}_1 A_1 + \bar{y}_2 A_2 + \bar{y}_3 A_3}{A_1 + A_2 + A_3}$$

$$= \frac{\left[\frac{1}{3}(2R)\right]\left[\frac{1}{2}b(2R)\right] + R[c(2R)] + R\left(\frac{1}{2}\pi R^2\right)}{\frac{1}{2}b(2R) + c(2R) + \frac{1}{2}\pi R^2}.$$

Calculate the Centroid
Use Eq. $(7.9)_2$ to determine the y component of the centroid.

Active Example 7.5

(a)

$$w = ax + b.$$

Write w as an arbitrary *linear* function of x.

$$0 = a(0) + b,$$
$$100\ \text{N/m} = a(12\ \text{m}) + b.$$

Solving yields $a = (100/12)\ \text{N/m}^2$ and $b = 0$. Therefore

$$w = \frac{100}{12}\, x\ \text{N/m}.$$

Use the known values of w at $x = 0$ and at $x = 12$ m to determine the constants a and b.

(b)

$$F = \int_L w\, dx$$
$$= \int_0^{12} \frac{100}{12}\, x\, dx$$
$$= 600\ \text{N}.$$

Apply Eq. (7.10) to determine the downward force exerted by the distributed load.

$$M = \int_L xw\, dx$$
$$= \int_0^{12} \frac{100}{12}\, x^2\, dx$$
$$= 4800\ \text{N-m}.$$

Apply Eq. (7.11) to determine the clockwise moment about the origin exerted by the distributed load.

Active Example 7.8

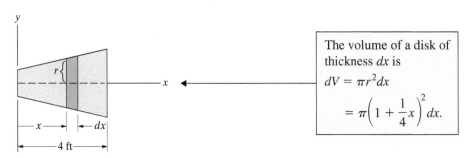

$$\bar{x} = \frac{\int_V x \, dV}{\int_V dV} = \frac{\int_0^4 x\pi\left(1 + \frac{1}{4}x\right)^2 dx}{\int_0^4 \pi\left(1 + \frac{1}{4}x\right)^2 dx} = 2.43 \text{ ft.} \quad \longleftarrow \quad \boxed{\text{Apply Eq. (7.15)}_1.}$$

Active Example 7.11

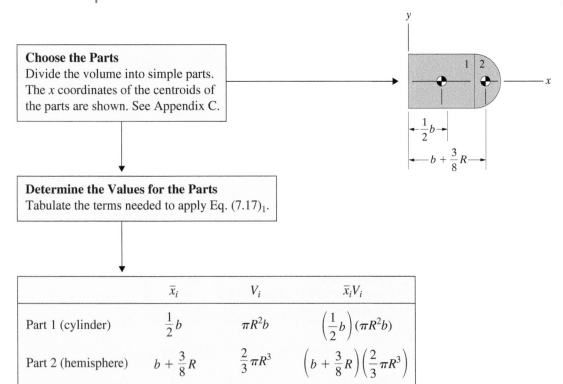

Choose the Parts
Divide the volume into simple parts.
The x coordinates of the centroids of
the parts are shown. See Appendix C.

Determine the Values for the Parts
Tabulate the terms needed to apply Eq. $(7.17)_1$.

	$\bar{x}_i$	V_i	$\bar{x}_i V_i$
Part 1 (cylinder)	$\dfrac{1}{2}b$	$\pi R^2 b$	$\left(\dfrac{1}{2}b\right)(\pi R^2 b)$
Part 2 (hemisphere)	$b + \dfrac{3}{8}R$	$\dfrac{2}{3}\pi R^3$	$\left(b + \dfrac{3}{8}R\right)\left(\dfrac{2}{3}\pi R^3\right)$

$$\bar{x} = \frac{\bar{x}_1 V_1 + \bar{x}_2 V_2}{V_1 + V_2}$$

$$= \frac{\left(\frac{1}{2}b\right)\left(\pi R^2 b\right) + \left(b + \frac{3}{8}R\right)\left(\frac{2}{3}\pi R^3\right)}{\pi R^2 b + \frac{2}{3}\pi R^3}.$$

Calculate the Centroid
Use Eq. (7.17)$_1$ to determine the x component of the centroid.

Active Example 7.14

Revolving this triangle area about the x axis generates the volume of the cone. The y coordinate of the centroid of the area is shown. The area of the triangle is

$$A = \frac{1}{2}hR.$$ The volume of the cone is

$$V = 2\pi \bar{y}_T A = \frac{1}{3}\pi hR^2.$$

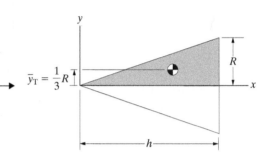

Active Example 7.16

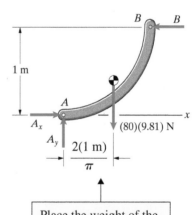

$$\Sigma F_x = A_x - B = 0,$$

$$\Sigma F_y = A_y - (80)(9.81)\ \text{N} = 0,$$

$$\Sigma M_{\text{point } A} = (1\text{m})B - \frac{2(1\ \text{m})}{\pi}[(80)(9.81)\ \text{N}] = 0.$$

Solving yields $A_x = 500\ \text{N}$, $A_y = 785\ \text{N}$, and $B = 500\ \text{N}$.

Place the weight of the bar at its center of mass (the centroid of its axis; see Appendix B.2) and apply equilibrium.

Active Example 7.18

The center of mass coincides
with the centroid of the volume
of the bar, so

$$\bar{y}_1 = \frac{1}{2}(240 \text{ mm}) = 120 \text{ mm}.$$

Center of mass of bar 1.

The y coordinate of the centroid of the
volume is

$$\bar{y}_2 = \frac{1}{2}(80 \text{ mm}) = 40 \text{ mm}.$$

Center of mass of bar 2.

$$\bar{y} = \frac{\bar{y}_1 m_1 + \bar{y}_2 m_2}{m_1 + m_2}$$

$$= \frac{(120 \text{ mm})(10.8 \text{ kg}) + (40 \text{ mm})(5.99 \text{ kg})}{10.8 \text{ kg} + 5.99 \text{ kg}}$$

$$= 91.4 \text{ mm}.$$

Apply Eq. (7.27)$_2$.

Active Example 9.1

Draw the free-body diagram of the crate. It is assumed that slip of the crate *up* the ramp is impending, so the direction of the friction force on the crate is *down* the ramp and its magnitude is $\mu_s N$.

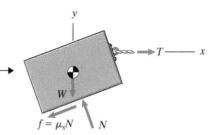

$$\Sigma F_x = T - N \sin 20° - \mu_s N \cos 20° = 0,$$
$$\Sigma F_y = N \cos 20° - \mu_s N \sin 20° - W = 0.$$

Solving these equations yields $T = 161$ lb.

Apply equilibrium.

Active Example 9.4

Draw the free-body diagram of the wedge assuming that $F = 0$ and that slip of the wedge out of the log is impending.

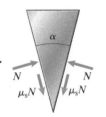

The sum of the forces in the vertical direction is

$$2N \sin\left(\frac{\alpha}{2}\right) - 2\mu_s N \cos\left(\frac{\alpha}{2}\right) = 0.$$

The wedge is in equilibrium if

$$\mu_s = \tan\left(\frac{\alpha}{2}\right) = \tan\left(\frac{10°}{2}\right) = 0.0875.$$

This is the *minimum* static coefficient of friction necessary for the wedge to remain in place in the log, so it will not slip out.

Apply equilibrium.

Active Example 9.5

The force $F = 200$ lb, the slope of the thread is $\alpha = 1.14°$, and the angle of friction is

$$\theta_k = \arctan \mu_k = \arctan (0.22) = 12.4°.$$

Substituting these values into Eq. (9.11),

$$M = rF \tan(\theta_k - \alpha)$$
$$= (1.6 \text{ in})(200 \text{ lb}) \tan(12.4° - 1.14°)$$
$$= 63.8 \text{ in-lb}.$$

Apply Eq. (9.11).

Active Example 9.6

$M = (6\text{ in})(W - T).$ ◄————— The pulley moves in the counterclockwise direction. Express the counterclockwise couple on the pulley in terms of T and W.

The angle of kinetic friction is

$\quad \theta_k = \arctan \mu_k = \arctan(0.2) = 11.3°.$

Equation (9.12) is

$\quad M = rF \sin \theta_k:$

$\quad (6\text{ in})(W - T) = (0.5\text{ in})\sqrt{(W + T \sin 45°)^2 + (T \cos 45°)^2}\, \sin 11.3°.$ ◄————— Apply Eq. (9.12).

Setting $W = 1000$ lb and solving yields

$\quad T = 970$ lb.

Active Example 9.7

The radii $r_o = 1.75$ in and $r_i = 0.5$ in.

$\quad \alpha = \arctan[b/(r_o - r_i)] = \arctan[5/(1.75 - 0.5)] = 76.0°.$ ◄————— Determine the angle α.

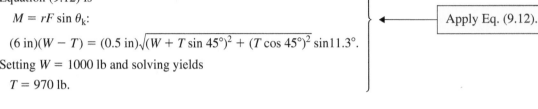

$$M = \frac{2\mu_k F}{3 \cos \alpha} \frac{r_o^3 - r_i^3}{r_o^2 - r_i^2}$$

$$= \frac{2(0.18)(200\text{ lb})}{3 \cos 76.0°} \left[\frac{(1.75\text{ in})^3 - (0.5\text{ in})^3}{(1.75\text{ in})^2 - (0.5\text{ in})^2}\right]$$ ◄————— Apply Eq. (9.13).

$$= 184 \text{ in-lb}.$$

Active Example 9.9

$T = We^{\mu_s \beta} = (100\text{ lb})e^{(0.2)(\pi/2)} = 137$ lb.   ◄————— Apply Eq. (9.17) to the left cylinder. Assume that slip of the rope in the direction of the force T is impending.

$F = Te^{(0.4)(\pi/2)} = (137\text{ lb})e^{(0.4)(\pi/2)} = 257$ lb.   ◄————— Apply Eq. (9.17) to the right cylinder. Assume that slip of the rope in the direction of the force F is impending.

Answers to Even-Numbered Problems

Chapter 1

1.2	(a) $e = 2.7183$; (b) $e^2 = 7.3891$; (c) $e^2 = 7.3892$.
1.4	17.8 m^2.
1.6	The 1-in wrench fits the 25-mm nut.
1.8	(a) 267 mi/h; (b) 392 ft/s.
1.10	310 N-m.
1.12	$g = 32.2 \text{ ft/s}^2$.
1.14	(a) 0.0208 m^2; (b) 32.2 in^2.
1.16	2.07×10^6 Pa.
1.18	27.4 lb/ft.
1.20	(a) kg-m/s; (b) 2.70 slug-ft/s.
1.22	(a) 0.397 kg; (b) 0.643 N.
1.24	(a) 4.60×10^{19} slugs; (b) 6.71×10^{20} kg.
1.26	163 lb.
1.28	32.1 km.
1.30	345,000 km.

Chapter 2

2.2	$|\mathbf{F}_{AB} + \mathbf{F}_{AC}| = 146$ kN, direction is $32°$ above the horizontal.
2.4	$|\mathbf{F}_A + \mathbf{F}_B + \mathbf{F}_C| = 83$ N.
2.6	$|\mathbf{r}_{AC}| = 181$ mm.
2.8	$|\mathbf{F}_B| = 86.6$ N, $|\mathbf{F}_C| = 50.0$ N.
2.10	$|\mathbf{L}| = 453$ lb, $|\mathbf{D}| = 211$ lb.
2.12	$|\mathbf{F}_{BA}| = 174$ lb.
2.14	$|\mathbf{r}_{BC}| = 390$ m, $\alpha = 21.2°$.
2.18	$F_y = -102$ MN.
2.20	$|\mathbf{F}| = 447$ kip.
2.22	$V_x = 16$, $V_y = 12$ or $V_x = -16$, $V_y = -12$.
2.24	(a) $\mathbf{F} = 56.4\mathbf{i} + 20.5\mathbf{j}$ (lb); (b) 97.4 lb.
2.26	$\mathbf{r}_{AD} = -1.8\mathbf{i} - 0.3\mathbf{j}$ (m), $|\mathbf{r}_{AD}| = 1.825$ m.
2.28	$\mathbf{r}_{AB} - \mathbf{r}_{BC} = \mathbf{i} - 1.73\mathbf{j}$ (m).
2.30	(a) $\mathbf{r}_{AB} = 48\mathbf{i} + 15\mathbf{j}$ (in);
	(b) $\mathbf{r}_{BC} = -53\mathbf{i} + 5\mathbf{j}$ (in);
	(c) $|\mathbf{r}_{AB} + \mathbf{r}_{BC}| = 20.6$ in.
2.32	(a) $\mathbf{r}_{AB} = 52.0\mathbf{i} + 30\mathbf{j}$ (mm);
	(b) $\mathbf{r}_{AB} = -42.4\mathbf{i} - 42.4\mathbf{j}$ (mm).
2.34	$x_B = 785$ m, $y_B = 907$ m or $x_B = 255$ m, $y_B = 1173$ m.
2.36	$\mathbf{e}_{CA} = 0.458\mathbf{i} - 0.889\mathbf{j}$.
2.38	$\mathbf{e} = 0.806\mathbf{i} + 0.593\mathbf{j}$.
2.40	$\mathbf{F} = -937\mathbf{i} + 750\mathbf{j}$ (N).
2.42	14,500 lb.
2.44	$|\mathbf{F}_{BA}| = 802$ N.
2.46	$|\mathbf{F}_A| = 1720$ lb, $\alpha = 33.3°$.
2.48	$57.9° \leq \alpha \leq 90°$.
2.50	$|\mathbf{F}_A| = 10$ kN, $|\mathbf{F}_D| = 8.66$ kN.
2.52	$|\mathbf{L}| = 214$ lb, $|\mathbf{D}| = 85.4$ lb.

2.54	$|\mathbf{F}_A| = 68.2$ kN.
2.56	$|\mathbf{F}_{AC}| = 2.11$ kN, $|\mathbf{F}_{AD}| = 2.76$ kN.
2.58	$x = 75 - 0.880s$, $y = 12 + 0.476s$.
2.60	$\mathbf{r} = (0.814s - 6)\mathbf{i} + (0.581s + 1)\mathbf{j}$ (m).
2.62	$e_z = \dfrac{2}{3}$ or $e_z = -\dfrac{2}{3}$.
2.64	$U_x = 3.61$, $U_y = -7.22$, $U_z = -28.89$ or $U_x = -3.61$, $U_y = 7.22$, $U_z = 28.89$.
2.66	(a) $|\mathbf{U}| = 7$, $|\mathbf{V}| = 13$;
	(b) $|3\mathbf{U} + 2\mathbf{V}| = 27.5$.
2.68	(a) $\cos\theta_x = 0.333$, $\cos\theta_y = -0.667$, $\cos\theta_z = -0.667$;
	(b) $\mathbf{e} = 0.333\mathbf{i} - 0.667\mathbf{j} - 0.667\mathbf{k}$.
2.70	$\mathbf{F} = -0.5\mathbf{i} + 0.2\mathbf{j} + 0.843\mathbf{k}$.
2.72	$\mathbf{r}_{BD} = -\mathbf{i} + 3\mathbf{j} - 2\mathbf{k}$ (m), $|\mathbf{r}_{BD}| = 3.74$ m.
2.74	$\mathbf{e}_{CD} = -0.535\mathbf{i} + 0.802\mathbf{j} + 0.267\mathbf{k}$.
2.76	$\mathbf{F} = 300\mathbf{i} + 477\mathbf{j} + 205\mathbf{k}$ (lb).
2.78	(a) $|\mathbf{r}_{AB}| = 16.2$ m;
	(b) $\cos\theta_x = 0.615$, $\cos\theta_y = -0.492$, $\cos\theta_z = -0.615$.
2.80	$\mathbf{r}_{AR}$: $\cos\theta_x = 0.667$, $\cos\theta_y = 0.667$, $\cos\theta_z = 0.333$. $\mathbf{r}_{BR}$: $\cos\theta_x = -0.242$, $\cos\theta_y = 0.970$, $\cos\theta_z = 0$.
2.82	$h = 8848$ m (29,030 ft).
2.84	$|\mathbf{F}_A + \mathbf{F}_B| = 217$ lb.
2.86	$\mathbf{F} = 474\mathbf{i} + 516\mathbf{j} + 565\mathbf{k}$ (N).
2.88	(a) $\mathbf{e}_{BC} = -0.286\mathbf{i} - 0.857\mathbf{j} + 0.429\mathbf{k}$;
	(b) $\mathbf{F} = -2.29\mathbf{i} - 6.86\mathbf{j} + 3.43\mathbf{k}$ (kN).
2.90	$|\mathbf{F}| = 424$ lb.
2.92	259 lb.
2.94	$|\mathbf{F}_{AC}| = 1116$ N, $|\mathbf{F}_{AD}| = 910$ N.
2.96	$\mathbf{T} = -15.4\mathbf{i} + 27.0\mathbf{j} + 7.7\mathbf{k}$ (lb).
2.98	$\mathbf{T} = -41.1\mathbf{i} + 28.8\mathbf{j} + 32.8\mathbf{k}$ (N).
2.100	$32.4°$.
2.102	Either $|\mathbf{V}| = 0$ or $\mathbf{V}$ is perpendicular to $\mathbf{U}$.
2.104	$U_x = 2.857$, $V_y = 0.857$, $W_z = -3.143$.
2.108	$\theta = 62.3°$.
2.110	$\theta = 53.5°$.
2.112	$14.0\mathbf{i} + 11.2\mathbf{j} - 8.40\mathbf{k}$ (N).
2.114	(a) $42.5°$; (b) $-423\mathbf{j} + 604\mathbf{k}$ (lb).
2.116	$\mathbf{F}_p = 5.54\mathbf{j} + 3.69\mathbf{k}$ (N), $\mathbf{F}_n = 10\mathbf{i} + 6.46\mathbf{j} - 9.69\mathbf{k}$ (N).
2.118	$\mathbf{T}_n = -37.1\mathbf{i} + 31.6\mathbf{j} + 8.2\mathbf{k}$ (N).
2.120	$\mathbf{F}_p = -0.1231\mathbf{i} + 0.0304\mathbf{j} - 0.1216\mathbf{k}$ (lb).
2.122	$\mathbf{v}_p = -1.30\mathbf{i} - 1.68\mathbf{j} - 3.36\mathbf{k}$ (m/s).
2.124	(a) $\mathbf{U} \times \mathbf{V} = 44\mathbf{i} + 56\mathbf{j} - 16\mathbf{k}$.
2.126	$2180\mathbf{i} + 1530\mathbf{j} - 1750\mathbf{k}$ (ft-lb).
2.128	Either $|\mathbf{V}| = 0$ or $\mathbf{V}$ is parallel to $\mathbf{U}$.
2.130	(a), (c) $\mathbf{U} \times \mathbf{V} = -51.8\mathbf{k}$; (b), (d) $\mathbf{V} \times \mathbf{U} = 51.8\mathbf{k}$.

613

2.134   (a) $\mathbf{r}_{OA} \times \mathbf{r}_{OB} = -4\mathbf{i} + 36\mathbf{j} + 32\mathbf{k}$ (m^2);
      (b) $-0.083\mathbf{i} + 0.745\mathbf{j} + 0.662\mathbf{k}$
      or $0.083\mathbf{i} - 0.745\mathbf{j} - 0.662\mathbf{k}$.

2.136 $\mathbf{r}_{AB} \times \mathbf{F} = -2400\mathbf{i} + 9600\mathbf{j} + 7200\mathbf{k}$ (ft-lb).

2.138 $\mathbf{r}_{CA} \times \mathbf{T} = -4.72\mathbf{i} - 3.48\mathbf{j} - 7.96\mathbf{k}$ (N-m).

2.140 $x_B = 2.81$ m, $y_B = 6.75$ m, $z_B = 3.75$ m.

2.144 1.8×10^6 mm^2.

2.146 $U_y = -2$.

2.148 $|\mathbf{A}| = 1110$ lb, $\alpha = 29.7°$.

2.150 $|\mathbf{E}| = 313$ lb, $|\mathbf{F}| = 140$ lb.

2.152 $\mathbf{e}_{AB} = 0.625\mathbf{i} - 0.469\mathbf{j} - 0.625\mathbf{k}$.

2.154 $\mathbf{F}_p = 8.78\mathbf{i} - 6.59\mathbf{j} - 8.78\mathbf{k}$ (lb).

2.156 $\mathbf{r}_{BA} \times \mathbf{F} = -70\mathbf{i} + 40\mathbf{j} - 100\mathbf{k}$ (ft-lb).

2.158   (a), (b) $686\mathbf{i} - 486\mathbf{j} - 514\mathbf{k}$ (ft-lb).

2.160   (a) $\mathbf{F} = 139\mathbf{i} + 58.2\mathbf{j} + 80\mathbf{k}$ (lb);   (b) $\theta_x = 35.5°$,
      $\theta_y = 70°$, $\theta_z = 62.0°$.

2.162 $\mathbf{F}_p = 1.29\mathbf{i} - 3.86\mathbf{j} + 2.57\mathbf{k}$ (kN),
      $\mathbf{F}_n = -1.29\mathbf{i} - 2.14\mathbf{j} - 2.57\mathbf{k}$ (kN).

2.164 $\mathbf{r}_{AG} \times \mathbf{W} = -16.4\mathbf{i} - 82.4\mathbf{k}$ (N-m).

2.166 $\mathbf{r}_{BC} \times \mathbf{T} = 33.3\mathbf{i} - 125\mathbf{j} - 183\mathbf{k}$ (N-m).

Chapter 3

3.2 $F_2 = 4.77$ lb, $\alpha = 35.2°$.

3.4 $T_{AB} = T_{AC} = 1.53$ kN.

3.6 $T = 785$ N, $P = 823$ N.

3.8 $k = 1960$ N/m, $m_A = 4$ kg, $m_B = 6$ kg.

3.10   (a) $|N_{\text{crane}}| = 197$ kN, $|f_{\text{crane}}| = 0.707$ kN;
      (b) $|N_{\text{caisson}}| = 3.22$ kN, $|f_{\text{caisson}}| = 0.707$ kN.

3.12   (a) $|N| = 11.06$ kN, $|f| = 4.03$ kN;
      (b) $\alpha = 31.0°$.

3.14   (a) 254 lb;   (b) 41.8°.

3.16   5.91 kN.

3.18   (a) 128 N;   (b) 98.1 N.

3.20 $T_{\text{left}} = 299$ lb, $T_{\text{right}} = 300$ lb.

3.22   188 lb.

3.24   (a) 66.1 lb;   (b) 12.3 lb.

3.26 $T_{AB} = 2.75$ kN, $T_{BC} = 2.06$ kN.

3.28   Upper cable tension is $0.828W$, lower cable tension is
      $0.132W$.

3.30 $T_{AB} = 1.21$ N, $T_{AD} = 2.76$ N.

3.32 $m = 12.2$ kg.

3.34 $F_B = 3680$ lb, $F_C = 2330$ lb.

3.36 $h = b$.

3.38 $T_{AB} = 688$ lb.

3.40 $T_{AB} = 64.0$ kN, $T_{BC} = 61.0$ kN.

3.44 $\alpha = 79.7°$, $T_{AB} = 120$ N,
      $T_{BC} = 21.4$ N, $T_{CD} = 62.6$ N.

3.46 $W_1 = 133$ lb.

3.48   (b) Left surface: 36.6 lb;   right surface: 25.9 lb.

3.50 $k = 1420$ N/m.

3.52 $T = mgL/(h + R)$.

3.56 $m_2 = 12.5$ kg.

3.58   (a) $T = W/2$;   (b) $T = W/4$;   (c) $T = W/8$.

3.60 $L = 131.1$ kN, $D = 36.0$ kN.

3.62   (a) $\gamma = -14.0°$;   (b) 4 km.

3.64 $T_{AB} = 405$ lb, $T_{AC} = 395$ lb, $T_{AD} = 103$ lb.

3.66 $T_{AB} = 1.54$ lb, $T_{AC} = 1.85$ lb.

3.68   Two at B,   three at C,   and three at D.

3.70 $T_{AB} = 9390$ lb, $T_{AC} = 5390$ lb, $T_{AD} = 10{,}980$ lb.

3.72 $D = 1176$ N, $T_{OA} = 6774$ N.

3.74 $T_{BC} = 1.61$ kN, $T_{BD} = 1.01$ kN.

3.76 $T_{EF} = T_{EG} = 738$ kN.

3.78   (a) The tension $= 2.70$ kN;
      (b) The force exerted by the bar $= 1.31\mathbf{i} - 1.31\mathbf{k}$ (kN).

3.80 $T_{AB} = 357$ N.

3.82 $F = 36.6$ N.

3.84 $W = 25.0$ lb.

3.86   (a) 83.9 lb;   (b) 230.5 lb.

3.88 $T = mg/26$.

3.90 $F = 162.0$ N.

3.92 $T_{AB} = 420$ N, $T_{AC} = 533$ N, $|\mathbf{F}_S| = 969$ N.

3.94 $N = 2580$ lb, $f = 995$ lb.

3.96 $T_{AC} = 16.7$ lb, $T_{AD} = 17.2$ lb, $T_{AE} = 9.21$ lb.

3.98   Normal force $= 12.15$ kN,   friction force $= 4.03$ kN.

Chapter 4

4.2   134 N-m.

4.4 $F = 36.2$ N.

4.6   25.0 kN-m clockwise.

4.8 $L = 2.4$ m.

4.10 $15.8° \le \alpha \le 37.3°$.

4.12   0.961 kN-m counterclockwise.

4.14 $M_S = 611$ in-lb.

4.16 $M_P = 298$ N-m.

4.18   410 N-m counterclockwise.

4.20   (a) $F_B = 37.5$ lb, $F_C = 22.5$ lb, $F_D = 26.0$ lb;
      (b) Zero.

4.22   (a) $A = 56.6$ lb, $B = 24.4$ lb, $C = 12.2$ lb;
      (b) Zero.

4.24   640 lb.

4.26 $M = 2.39$ kN-m.

4.28   (a) $A_x = 18.1$ kN, $A_y = -29.8$ kN, $B = -20.4$ kN;
      (b) Zero.

4.30   (a) $A_x = 300$ lb, $A_y = 240$ lb, $B = 280$ lb;
      (b) Zero.

4.32   60.4 ft-lb.

4.34 -22.3 ft-lb.

4.36 $M = -2340$ N-m.

4.38 $T_{AB} = T_{AC} = 223$ kN.

4.40   617 N-m.

4.42 $M_A = -3.00$ kN-m, $M_D = 7.50$ kN-m.

4.44   796 N.

4.46   (a), (b) $480\mathbf{k}$ (N-m).

4.48   (a) $800\mathbf{k}$ (kN-m);
      (b) $-400\mathbf{k}$ (kN-m).

4.50 $\mathbf{F} = 20\mathbf{i} + 40\mathbf{j}$ (N).

4.52 $\mathbf{M}_O = -5600\mathbf{k}$ (ft-lb).

4.54   (a), (b) 1270 N-m.

4.56   128 ft-lb.

4.58   985 ft-lb.

4.60   58.0 kN.

4.62 (a) $|\mathbf{F}| = 1586$ N;
(b) $|\mathbf{F}| = 1584$ N.

4.64 $-16.4\mathbf{i} - 111.9\mathbf{k}$ (N-m).

4.66 $\mathbf{F} = 4\mathbf{i} - 4\mathbf{j} + 2\mathbf{k}$ (kN) or
$\mathbf{F} = 4\mathbf{i} - 3.38\mathbf{j} + 2.92\mathbf{k}$ (kN).

4.68 $\mathbf{M}_D = 1.25\mathbf{i} + 1.25\mathbf{j} - 6.25\mathbf{k}$ (kN-m).

4.70 $T_{AC} = 2.23$ kN, $T_{AD} = 2.43$ kN.

4.72 $T_{AB} = 1.60$ kN, $T_{AC} = 1.17$ kN.

4.74 $T_{BC} = 886$ N, $T_{BD} = 555$ N.

4.76 $\mathbf{M} = 482\mathbf{k}$ (kN-m).

4.78 (a) $\mathbf{M}_{x\,axis} = 80\mathbf{i}$ (N-m);
(b) $\mathbf{M}_{y\,axis} = -140\mathbf{j}$ (N-m);
(c) $\mathbf{M}_{z\,axis} = \mathbf{0}$.

4.80 (a) Zero; (b) $2.7\,\mathbf{k}$ (kN-m).

4.82 (a) $\mathbf{M}_{x\,axis} = -16\mathbf{i}$ (kN-m);
(b) $\mathbf{M}_{z\,axis} = 15\mathbf{k}$ (kN-m).

4.84 $\mathbf{F} = 80\mathbf{i} + 80\mathbf{j} + 40\mathbf{k}$ (lb).

4.86 $-16.4\mathbf{i}$ (N-m).

4.88 (a), (b) $\mathbf{M}_{AB} = -76.1\mathbf{i} - 95.1\mathbf{j}$ (N-m).

4.90 $\mathbf{M}_{AO} = 119.1\mathbf{j} + 79.4\mathbf{k}$ (N-m).

4.92 $\mathbf{M}_{AB} = 77.1\mathbf{j} - 211.9\mathbf{k}$ (ft-lb).

4.94 $\mathbf{M}_{y\,axis} = 215\mathbf{j}$ (N-m).

4.96 $\mathbf{M}_{x\,axis} = 44\mathbf{i}$ (N-m).

4.98 $-338\mathbf{j}$ (ft-lb).

4.100 $|\mathbf{F}| = 13$ lb.

4.102 $\mathbf{M}_{axis} = -478\mathbf{i} - 174\mathbf{k}$ (N-m).

4.104 1 N-m.

4.106 $124\mathbf{k}$ (ft-lb).

4.108 28 N-m clockwise.

4.110 $\alpha = 30.9°$ or $\alpha = 71.8°$.

4.112 (b) $FL\cos 30°$.

4.114 40 ft-lb clockwise, or $-40\mathbf{k}$ (ft-lb).

4.116 2200 ft-lb clockwise.

4.118 (a) $C = 26$ kN-m; (b) Zero.

4.120 (a) $\mathbf{M} = -14\mathbf{i} - 10\mathbf{j} - 8\mathbf{k}$ (kN-m); (b) $D = 6.32$ m.

4.122 356 ft-lb.

4.124 $|\mathbf{M}| = 6.13$ kN-m.

4.126 $M_{Cy} = 7$ kN-m, $M_{Cz} = -2$ kN-m.

4.128 Yes.

4.130 Systems 1, 2, and 4 are equivalent.

4.134 $F = 265$ N.

4.136 $F = 70$ lb, $M = 130$ in-lb.

4.138 (a) $\mathbf{F} = -10\mathbf{j}$ (lb), $M = -10$ ft-lb; (b) $D = 1$ ft.

4.140 $\mathbf{F} = 200\mathbf{i} + 180\mathbf{j}$ (N), $d = 0.317$ m.

4.142 (a) $A_x = 12$ kip, $A_y = 10$ kip, $B = -10$ kip;
(b) $\mathbf{F} = -12\mathbf{i}$ (kip), intersects at $y = 5$ ft;
(c) They are both zero.

4.144 $\mathbf{F} = 104\mathbf{j}$ (kN), $M = 13.2$ kN-m counterclockwise.

4.146 $\mathbf{F} = 100\mathbf{j}$ (lb), $\mathbf{M} = \mathbf{0}$.

4.148 (a) $\mathbf{F} = 920\mathbf{i} - 390\mathbf{j}$ (N), $M = -419$ N-m;
(b) intersects at $y = 456$ mm.

4.150 $\mathbf{F} = 800\mathbf{j}$ (lb), intersects at $x = 7.5$ in.

4.152 (a) $-360\mathbf{k}$ (in-lb);
(b) $-36\mathbf{j}$ (in-lb);
(c) $\mathbf{F} = 10\mathbf{i} - 30\mathbf{j} + 3\mathbf{k}$ (lb),
$\mathbf{M} = -36\mathbf{j} - 360\mathbf{k}$ (in-lb).

4.154 $x = 2.00$ ft, $z = -0.857$ ft.

4.156 $\mathbf{F} = 100\mathbf{j} + 80\mathbf{k}$ (N), $\mathbf{M} = 240\mathbf{j} - 300\mathbf{k}$ (N-m).

4.158 (a) $\mathbf{F} = \mathbf{0}$, $\mathbf{M} = rA\mathbf{i}$;
(b) $\mathbf{F}' = \mathbf{0}$, $\mathbf{M}' = rA\mathbf{i}$.

4.160 (a) $\mathbf{F} = \mathbf{0}$, $\mathbf{M} = 4.60\mathbf{i} + 1.86\mathbf{j} - 3.46\mathbf{k}$ (kN-m);
(b) 6.05 kN-m.

4.162 $\mathbf{F} = -20\mathbf{i} + 20\mathbf{j} + 10\mathbf{k}$ (lb),
$\mathbf{M} = 50\mathbf{i} + 250\mathbf{j} + 100\mathbf{k}$ (in-lb).

4.164 (a) $\mathbf{F} = 28\mathbf{k}$ (kip), $\mathbf{M} = 96\mathbf{i} - 192\mathbf{j}$ (ft-kip);
(b) $x = 6.86$ ft, $y = 3.43$ ft.

4.166 $\mathbf{F} = 100\mathbf{i} + 20\mathbf{j} - 20\mathbf{k}$ (N),
$\mathbf{M} = -143\mathbf{i} + 406\mathbf{j} - 280\mathbf{k}$ (N-m).

4.168 $\mathbf{M}_p = 0$, line of action intersects at $y = 0$, $z = 2$ ft.

4.170 $x = 2.41$ m, $y = 3.80$ m.

4.172 $\mathbf{F} = 40.8\mathbf{i} + 40.8\mathbf{j} + 81.6\mathbf{k}$ (N),
$\mathbf{M} = -179.6\mathbf{i} + 391.9\mathbf{j} - 32.7\mathbf{k}$ (N-m).

4.174 (a) $320\mathbf{i}$ (in-lb);
(b) $\mathbf{F} = -20\mathbf{k}$ (lb), $\mathbf{M} = 320\mathbf{i} + 660\mathbf{j}$ (in-lb);
(c) $\mathbf{M}_t = 0$, $x = 33$ in, $y = -16$ in.

4.176 $|\mathbf{M}_P| = 244$ N-m.

4.178 (a) -76.2 N-m;
(b) -66.3 N-m.

4.180 $|\mathbf{F}| = 224$ lb, $|\mathbf{M}| = 1600$ ft-lb.

4.182 501 lb.

4.184 $-228.1\mathbf{i} - 68.4\mathbf{k}$ (N-m).

4.186 $\mathbf{M}_{x\,axis} = -153\mathbf{i}$ (ft-lb).

4.188 $\mathbf{M}_{CD} = -173\mathbf{i} + 1038\mathbf{k}$ (ft-lb).

4.190 (a) $\mathbf{T}_{AB} = \mathbf{T}_{CD} = 173.2$ lb;
(b) $\mathbf{F} = 300\mathbf{j}$ (lb) at $x = 4$ ft.

4.192 $\mathbf{F} = -20\mathbf{i} + 70\mathbf{j}$ (N), $M = 22$ N-m.

4.194 $\mathbf{F}' = -100\mathbf{i} + 40\mathbf{j} + 30\mathbf{k}$ (lb),
$\mathbf{M} = -80\mathbf{i} + 200\mathbf{k}$ (in-lb).

4.196 $\mathbf{F} = 1166\mathbf{i} + 566\mathbf{j}$ (N), $y = 13.9$ m.

4.198 $\mathbf{F} = 190\mathbf{j}$ (N), $\mathbf{M} = -98\mathbf{i} + 184\mathbf{k}$ (N-m).

4.200 $\mathbf{F} = -0.364\mathbf{i} + 4.908\mathbf{j} + 1.090\mathbf{k}$ (kN),
$\mathbf{M} = -0.131\mathbf{i} - 0.044\mathbf{j} + 1.112\mathbf{k}$ (kN-m).

Chapter 5

5.2 $A_x = -1$ kN, $A_y = -5.73$ kN,
$M_A = -22.9$ kN-m.

5.4 Tension is 386 lb, $B_x = 493$ lb, $B_y = 186$ lb.

5.6 (b) $A_x = 0$, $A_y = -1.85$ kN, $B_y = 2.74$ kN.

5.8 (b) $A_x = 0$, $A_y = -5$ kN, $B_y = 15$ kN.

5.10 (b) $A = 100$ lb, $B = 200$ lb.

5.12 (b) $A_x = 502$ N, $A_y = 870$ N.

5.14 (b) $A_x = 4$ kN, $A_y = -2.8$ kN, $B_y = 2.8$ kN.

5.16 On each hand, 66.3 lb. On each foot, 23.7 lb.

5.18 $A_x = -100$ lb, $A_y = -225$ lb, $E = 625$ lb.

5.20 $k = 3380$ N/m, $B_x = -188.0$ N, $B_y = 98.7$ N.

5.22 5.93 kN.

5.24 $R = 12.5$ lb, $B_x = 11.3$ lb, $B_y = 15.3$ lb.

5.26 (a) 21.2 lb; (b) 30 lb.

5.28 $W_L = 1125$ lb.

5.30 6.23 lb.

5.32 $T = 3.68$ lb.

5.34 $T_{AE} = 31.0$ lb, $D_x = -29.9$ lb, $D_y = 34.0$ lb.

5.36 $A_x = -1.83$ kN, $A_y = 2.10$ kN, $B_y = 2.46$ kN.

5.38 $A_x = -200$ lb, $A_y = -100$ lb, $M_A = 1600$ ft-lb.

5.40 $k = 3.21$ lb/ft.

5.42 $A_x = 3.46$ kN, $A_y = -2$ kN,
$B_x = -3.46$ kN, $B_y = 2$ kN.

5.44 $\mathbf{F} = 28.3\mathbf{i} + 58.3\mathbf{j}$ (lb), $D = 7.03$ ft, $A_x = -28.3$ lb,
$A_y = -58.3$ lb, $M_A = -410$ ft-lb.

5.46 $A_x = -1.57$ kN, $A_y = 1.57$ kN, $E_x = 1.57$ kN.

5.48 $A_x = 0$, $A_y = 200$ lb, $M_A = 900$ ft-lb.

5.50 $A_x = 57.7$ lb, $A_y = -13.3$ lb, $B = 15.3$ lb.

5.52 $W = 15$ kN.

5.54 (b) $C_x = 500$ N, $C_y = -200$ N.

5.56 $T_{BC} = 5.45$ lb, $A_x = 5.03$ lb, $A_y = 7.90$ lb.

5.58 20.3 kN.

5.60 $W_2 = 2484$ lb, $A_x = -2034$ lb, $A_y = 2425$ lb.

5.62 $W = 46.2$ N, $A_x = 22.3$ N, $A_y = 61.7$ N.

5.64 $F = 44.5$ lb, $A_x = 25.3$ lb, $A_y = -1.9$ lb.

5.66 $W = 132$ lb.

5.68

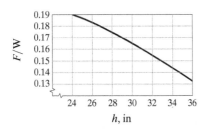

5.76 (1) and (2) are improperly supported. For (3), reactions
are $A = F/2$, $B = F/2$, $C = F$.

5.78 (b) $A_x = -6.53$ kN, $A_y = -3.27$ kN,
$A_z = 3.27$ kN, $M_{Ax} = 0$, $M_{Ay} = -6.53$ kN-m,
$M_{Az} = -6.53$ kN-m.

5.80 374 lb.

5.82 $C_x = -349$ lb, $C_y = 698$ lb,
$C_z = 175$ lb, $M_{Cx} = -3490$ ft-lb,
$M_{Cy} = -2440$ ft-lb, $M_{Cz} = 2790$ ft-lb.

5.84 (a) $-17.8\mathbf{i} - 62.8\mathbf{k}$ (N-m);
(b) $A_x = 0$, $A_y = 360$ N, $A_z = 0$,
$M_{Ax} = 17.8$ N-m, $M_{Ay} = 0$, $M_{Az} = 62.8$ N-m.

5.86 $A_x = 166.7$ N, $A_y = 200$ N, $A_z = 66.7$ N,
$T_{BC} = 100$ N, $T_{BD} = 170$ N.

5.88 $|\mathbf{F}| = 10.9$ kN.

5.90 $T_{AB} = 553$ lb, $T_{AC} = 289$ lb,
$O_x = 632$ lb, $O_y = 574$ lb, $O_z = 0$.

5.92 $x = 0.1$ m, $z = 0.133$ m.

5.94 $T_{BD} = 50.2$ lb, $A_x = -34.4$ lb,
$A_y = 17.5$ lb, $A_z = -24.1$ lb,
$M_{Ax} = 0$, $M_{Ay} = 192.5$ in-lb.

5.96 $\mathbf{F} = 4\mathbf{j}$ (kN) at $x = 0$, $z = 0.15$ m.

5.98 (b) $A_x = -0.74$ kN, $A_y = 1$ kN, $A_z = -0.64$ kN,
$B_x = 0.74$ kN, $B_z = 0.64$ kN.

5.100 $F_y = 34.5$ lb.

5.102 $T_{BD} = 1.47$ kN, $T_{BE} = 1.87$ kN,
$A_x = 0$, $A_y = 4.24$ kN, $A_z = 0$.

5.104 $T = 139$ lb, $A_x = 46.4$ lb, $A_y = -26.8$ lb,
$A_z = 31.7$ lb, $M_{Ax} = -63.4$ ft-lb,
$M_{Ay} = -110$ ft-lb.

5.106 Tension is 60 N, $B_x = -10$ N, $B_y = 90$ N,
$B_z = 10$ N, $M_{By} = 1$ N-m, $M_{Bz} = -3$ N-m.

5.108 Tension is 60 N, $B_x = -10$ N, $B_y = 75$ N,
$B_z = 15$ N, $C_y = 15$ N, $C_z = -5$ N.

5.110 $A_x = -2.86$ kip, $A_y = 17.86$ kip, $A_z = -8.10$ kip,
$B_y = 3.57$ kip, $B_z = 12.38$ kip.

5.112 $A_x = 0$, $A_y = 400$ N, $B_x = 1000$ N,
$B_y = -400$ N, $B_z = 0$, $T = 1080$ N.

5.114 $|\mathbf{A}| = 8.54$ kN, $|\mathbf{B}| = 10.75$ kN.

5.116 $A_x = 3.62$ kN, $A_y = 5.89$ kN, $A_z = 5.43$ kN,
$C_x = 8.15$ kN, $C_y = 0$, $C_z = 0.453$ kN.

5.118 $T_{AB} = 488$ lb, $T_{CD} = 373$ lb, reaction is
$31\mathbf{i} + 823\mathbf{j} - 87\mathbf{k}$ (lb).

5.120 $A_x = -76.7$ N, $A_y = 97.0$ N, $A_z = -54.3$ N,
$M_{Ax} = -2.67$ N-m, $M_{Ay} = 6.39$ N-m,
$M_{Az} = 2.13$ N-m.

5.122 (a) 60 lb;
(b) $A_x = 38.1$ lb, $A_y = 46.3$ lb or $A_x = -38.1$ lb,
$A_y = -46.3$ lb.

5.124 Tension is 33.3 lb; magnitude of reaction is 44.1 lb.

5.126 $\alpha = 10.9°$, $F_A = 1.96$ kN, $F_B = 2.27$ kN.

5.128 (a) No, because of the 3 kN-m couple; (b) magnitude at
A is 7.88 kN; magnitude at B is 6.66 kN; (c) no.

5.130 (b) $A_x = -8$ kN, $A_y = 2$ kN, $C_x = 8$ kN.

5.134 (b) $T_A = 7.79$ lb, $T_B = 10.28$ lb;   (c) 6.61 lb.

5.136 (a) There are four unknown reactions and three equilibrium equations;   (b) $A_x = -50$ lb, $B_x = 50$ lb.

5.138 (b) Force on nail = 55 lb, normal force = 50.77 lb,
friction force = 9.06 lb.

5.140 $k = 13,500$ N/m.

5.142 $A_y = 727$ lb, $H_x = 225$ lb, $H_y = 113$ lb.

5.144 $\alpha = 0$ and $\alpha = 59.4°$.

5.146 The force is 800 N upward; its line of action passes
through the midpoint of the plate.

5.148 $m = 67.2$ kg.

5.150 $\alpha = 90°$, $T_{BC} = W/2$, $A = W/2$.

Chapter 6

6.2 AB: 915 N (C); AC: 600 N (C); BC: 521 N (T).

6.4 BC: 800 lb (T); CD: 600 lb (C).

6.6 (a) Tension: 2.43 kN in AB and BD.
Compression: 2.88 kN in CD.
(b) Tension: 1.74 kN in BD.
Compression: 1.60 kN in CD.

6.8 Tension, 31.9 kip in AC, CE, EG, and GH. Compression, 42.5 kip in BD and DF.

6.10 BD: zero; CD: 10 kN (T); CE: 16 kN (C).

6.12 (a) Tension: 5540 lb in BD. Compression: 7910 lb in CE.
(b) Tension: 2770 lb in BD. Compression: 3760 lb in CE.

6.14 $F = 8.33$ kN.

6.16 DE: 3.66 kN (C); DF: 1.45 kN (C); DG: 3.36 kN (T).

6.18 AB: 10.56 kN (T); AC: 17.58 kN (C); BC: 6.76 kN (T);
BD: 1.81 kN (T); CD: 16.23 kN (C).

6.20 *AB*: 375 lb (C); *AC*: 625 lb (T); *BC*: 300 lb (T).

6.22 *BC*: 90.1 kN (T); *CD*: 90.1 kN (C); *CE*: 300 kN (T).

6.24 *BC*: 1200 kN (C); *BI*: 300 kN (T); *BJ*: 636 kN (T).

6.26 *AB*: 2520 lb (C); *BC*: 2160 lb (C); *CD*: 1680 lb (C).

6.32 *BC*: 400 kN (T), *BI*: 141 kN (T), *HI*: 500 kN (C).

6.34 (a), (b) 141 kN (C).

6.36 *AB*: 1.33*F* (C); *BC*: 1.33*F* (C); *CE*: 1.33*F* (T).

6.38 *BD*: 95.6 kip (C); *BE*: 41.1 kip (T); *CE*: 58.4 kip (T).

6.40 *DF*: 69.1 kip (C); *DG*: 29.4 kip (C); *EG*: 95.6 kip (T).

6.42 96.2 kN (T).

6.44 *AC*: 2000 lb (C); *BC*: 800 lb (T); *BD*: 1000 lb (T).

6.46 *DF*: 16 kN (T); *DG*: 6.67 kN (C); *EG*: 26.7 kN (C).

6.48 2.50 kN (C).

6.50 *CE*: 680 kN (T); *CF*: 374 kN (C); *DF*: 375 kN (C).

6.52 (a) 1160 lb (C).

6.54 *IL*: 16 kN (C); *KM*: 24 kN (T).

6.58 *AD*: 4.72 kN (C); *BD*: 4.16 kN *CD* (C); *CD*: 4.85 kN (C).

6.60 *AB*, *AC*, *AD*: 0.408*F* (C).

6.62 *AB*: 379 lb (C); *AC*: 665 lb (C); *AD*: 160 lb (C).

6.64 *BC*: 32.7 kN (T); *BD*: 45.2 kN (T); *BE*: 112.1 kN (C).

6.66 $P_3 = -315$ kN.

6.68 5.59 kN (C) in each member.

6.70 $A_x = 400$ N, $A_y = -900$ N, $B_x = -400$ N, $B_y = 900$ N, $M_A = -540$ N-m.

6.72 $C_x = 736$ N, $C_y = 2450$ N, $E_x = 245$ N, $E_y = -1720$ N.

6.74 $C_x = 66.7$ lb, $C_y = 24$ lb.

6.76 $A_x = 0$, $A_y = -400$ N, $C_x = -600$ N, $C_y = -300$ N, $D_x = 0$, $D_y = 1000$ N.

6.78 $D_x = -1475$ N, $D_y = -516$ N, $E_x = 0$, $E_y = -516$ N, $M_E = 619$ N-m.

6.80 $A_x = -2.35$ kN, $A_y = 2.35$ kN, $B_x = 0$, $B_y = -4.71$ kN, $C_x = 2.35$ kN, $C_y = 2.35$ kN.

6.82 Tension = 62.5 lb, $F_x = -75$ lb, $F_y = 25$ lb.

6.84 $B_x = -400$ lb, $B_y = -300$ lb, $C_x = 400$ lb, $C_y = 200$ lb, $D_x = 0$, $D_y = 100$ lb.

6.86 $A_x = -150$ lb, $A_y = 120$ lb, $B_x = 180$ lb, $B_y = -30$ lb, $D_x = -30$ lb, $D_y = -90$ lb.

6.88 $A_x = -310$ lb, $A_y = -35$ lb, $B_x = 80$ lb, $B_y = -80$ lb, $C_x = 310$ lb, $C_y = 195$ lb, $D_x = -80$ lb, $D_y = -80$ lb.

6.90 $A_x = 170$ lb, $A_y = 129$ lb, $B_x = -170$ lb, $B_y = -209$ lb.

6.94 $A_x = -22$ lb, $A_y = 15$ lb, $C_x = -14$ lb, $C_y = 3$ lb.

6.96 300 lb (C).

6.98 *B*: 73.5 N; *C*: 88.8 N.

6.100 $T_{BC} = 1410$ N, $T_{DF} = 625$ N.

6.102 $A_x = 2$ kN, $A_y = -1.52$ kN, $B_x = -2$ kN, $B_y = 1.52$ kN.

6.104 $E_x = 604$ lb, $E_y = 179$ lb, axial force is 616 lb.

6.106 100 N.

6.108 At *B*: 1750 N. *DE*: 1320 N (C).

6.110 742 lb.

6.112 1150 lb.

6.114 $K_x = 847$ N, $K_y = 363$ N.

6.116 $T_{AB} = 7.14$ kN (C), $T_{AC} = 5.71$ kN (T), $T_{BC} = 10$ kN (T).

6.118 *BC*: 120 kN (C); *BG*: 42.4 kN (T); *FG*: 90 kN (T).

6.120 *AB*: 125 lb (C); *AC*: zero; *BC*: 188 lb (T); *BD*: 225 lb (C); *CD*: 125 lb (C); *CE*: 225 lb (T).

6.122 $T_{BD} = 13.3$ kN (T), $T_{CD} = 11.7$ kN (T), $T_{CE} = 28.3$ kN (C).

6.124 *AC*: 480 N (T); *CD*: 240 N (C); *CF*: 300 N (T).

6.126 Tension: member *AC*, 480 lb (T); Compression: member *BD*, 633 lb (C).

6.128 *CD*: 11.42 kN (C); *CJ*: 4.17 kN (C); *IJ*: 12.00 kN (T).

6.130 *AB*: 7.20 kN (C); *AC*: 4.56 kN (C).

6.132 $A_x = -1.57$ kN, $A_y = 1.18$ kN, $B_x = 0$, $B_y = -2.35$ kN, $C_x = 1.57$ kN, $C_y = 1.18$ kN.

6.134 $B_x = 3820$ lb, $B_y = 6690$ lb, $C = 9020$ lb, $D_x = -1390$ lb, $D_y = -1930$ lb.

6.136 973 N.

6.138 $A_x = -52.33$ kN, $A_y = -43.09$ kN, $E_x = 0.81$ kN, $E_y = -14.86$ kN.

Chapter 7

7.2 $\bar{x} = 3/8$.

7.4 $\bar{x} = 1.25$, $\bar{y} = 0.825$.

7.8 $\bar{x} = 0.711$ ft, $y = 0.584$ ft.

7.10 $\bar{x} = 0$, $y = 1.6$ ft.

7.12 $\bar{x} = 8$, $\bar{y} = 3.6$.

7.14 $\bar{x} = 0.533$.

7.16 $\bar{x} = 1$.

7.18 $\bar{y} = -7.6$.

7.20 $\bar{y} = 2.53$.

7.22 $a = 0.656$, $b = 6.56 \times 10^{-5}\,\text{m}^{-2}$.

7.24 $\bar{x} = \bar{y} = 4R/3\pi$.

7.26 $\bar{x} = 3.31$.

7.28 $\bar{x} = 116$ mm.

7.30 $\bar{x} = 9.90$ in, $\bar{y} = 0$.

7.32 $\bar{x} = 23.9$ in, $\bar{y} = 33.3$ in.

7.34 $\bar{x} = 2.88$ ft, $\bar{y} = 3.20$ ft.

7.36 $\bar{x} = 3.67$ mm, $\bar{y} = 21.52$ mm.

7.38 $b = 39.6$ mm, $h = 18.2$ mm.

7.40 $\bar{x} = 9.64$ m, $\bar{y} = 4.60$ m.

7.44 $\bar{x} = 6.47$ ft, $\bar{y} = 10.60$ ft.

7.46 $A_x = 0$, $A_y = 160$ N, $B = 200$ N.

7.48 $A_x = -1200$ N, $A_y = 800$ N, $B = 2200$ N.

7.50 $A_x = 0$, $A_y = 10$ kN, $M_A = -31.3$ kN-m.

7.52 $A_x = 0$, $A_y = 4.17$ kN, $B_y = 8.83$ kN.

7.54 $A_y = 3267$ lb, $B_x = -800$ lb, $B_y = -1267$ lb.

7.56 *BD*: 21.3 kN (C); *CD*: 3.77 kN (C); *CE*: 24 kN (T).

7.58 $A_x = -18$ kN, $A_y = 20$ kN, $B_x = 0$, $B_y = -4$ kN, $C_x = 18$ kN, $C_y = -16$ kN.

7.60 $V = 275$ m^3, height = 2.33 m.

7.62 $V = 4.16$ m^3, $\bar{x} = 1.41$ m.

7.64 $\bar{x} = 0.675R$, $\bar{y} = 0$, $\bar{z} = 0$.

7.66 $\bar{y} = 0.410$.

7.68 $\bar{x} = 3.24$.

7.70 $\bar{x} = R \sin \alpha / \alpha$, $\bar{y} = R(1 - \cos \alpha)/\alpha$.

7.72 $\bar{x} = 38.3$ mm.

7.74 $\bar{x} = -128$ mm, $\bar{y} = \bar{z} = 0$.

7.76 $\bar{x} = 0$, $\bar{y} = 43.7$ mm, $\bar{z} = 38.2$ mm.

7.78 $\bar{x} = 229.5$ mm, $\bar{y} = \bar{z} = 0$.

7.80 $\bar{x} = 23.65$ mm, $\bar{y} = 36.63$ mm, $\bar{z} = 3.52$ mm.

7.82 $\bar{x} = 6$ m, $\bar{y} = 1.83$ m.

7.84 $\bar{x} = 65.9$ mm, $\bar{y} = 21.7$ mm, $\bar{z} = 68.0$ mm.

7.86 $A = \frac{3}{4} \pi R \sqrt{h^2 + R^2}$.

7.88 $\bar{y}_s = 4R/3\pi$.

7.90 $\bar{y} = 0.410$.

7.92 $A = 138$ ft^2.

7.94 $V = 0.0377$ m^3.

7.96 $V = 2.48 \times 10^6$ mm^3.

7.98 Volume $= 0.0266$ m^3.

7.100 $A_x = 0$, $A_y = 294$ N, $B_y = 196$ N.

7.102 $A_x = 0$, $A_y = 316$ N, $B = 469$ N.

7.104 $\bar{x} = 6.59$ in, $\bar{y} = 2.17$ in, $\bar{z} = 6.80$ in.

7.106 $A_x = 0$, $A_y = 3.16$ kN, $M_A = 1.94$ kN-m.

7.108 $\bar{x} = 121$ mm, $\bar{y} = 0$, $\bar{z} = 0$.

7.110 $\bar{x}_3 = 82$ mm, $\bar{y}_3 = 122$ mm, $\bar{z}_3 = 16$ mm.

7.112 (a) $\bar{x} = 5.17$ m; (b) $A_x = -50$ kN, $A_y = -25.0$ kN, $G = 33.8$ kN.

7.114 Mass $= 408$ kg, $\bar{x} = 2.5$ m, $\bar{y} = -1.5$ m.

7.116 $\bar{x} = 20.10$ in, $\bar{y} = 8.03$ in, $\bar{z} = 15.35$ in.

7.118 $\bar{x} = 3/8$, $\bar{y} = 3/5$.

7.120 $\bar{x} = 87.3$ mm, $\bar{y} = 55.3$ mm.

7.122 917 N (T).

7.124 $A_x = 7$ kN, $A_y = -6$ kN, $D_x = 4$ kN, $D_y = 0$.

7.126 $\bar{x} = 1.87$ m.

7.128 $A = 682$ in^2.

7.130 $\bar{x} = 110$ mm.

7.132 $\bar{x} = 1.70$ m.

7.134 $\bar{x} = 25.24$ mm, $\bar{y} = 8.02$ mm, $\bar{z} = 27.99$ mm.

7.136 (a) $\bar{x} = 1.511$ m; (b) $\bar{x} = 1.611$ m.

7.138 $A = 80.7$ kN, $B = 171.6$ kN.

9.52 $F/2$.

9.54 333 N.

9.56 $F = 74.3$ lb.

9.58 (a) $f = 24.5$ N;   (b) $\mu_s = 0.503$.

9.60 (a) $f = 8$ kN;   (b) $\mu_s = 0.533$.

9.62 $\mu_s = 0.432$.

9.64 $\mu_s = 0.901$.

9.66 $F = 139$ lb.

9.68 $F = 102$ lb.

9.70 $F = 1360$ lb.

9.72 $F = 156$ N.

9.74 343 kg.

9.76 No. The minimum value of μ_s required is 0.176.

9.78 $F = 1160$ N.

9.80 1.84 N-m.

9.82 (a) 0.967 in-lb;   (b) 0.566 in-lb.

9.84 (a) 2.39 ft-lb;   (b) 1.20 ft-lb.

9.86 11.8 ft-lb.

9.88 108 in-lb.

9.90 27.4 in-lb.

9.92 4.18 N-m.

9.94 4.88 N-m.

9.96 17.4 N-m.

9.98 $W = 1.55$ lb.

9.100 106 N.

9.102 51.9 lb.

9.104 $T = 40.9$ N.

9.106 $F_B = 207$ N.

9.108 $M = 1.92$ ft-lb.

9.110 $T = 346$ N.

9.112 $M = 160$ in-lb.

9.114 $M = 12.7$ N-m.

9.116 $M = 7.81$ N-m.

9.118 $M = 5.20$ N-m.

9.120 (a) $M = 93.5$ N-m;   (b) 8.17 percent.

9.122 9.51 ft-lb.

9.124 80.1 lb.

9.126 $T_C = 107$ N.

9.128 $M = rW(e^{\pi\mu_k} - 1)$.

9.130 (a) 14.2 lb;   (b) 128.3 lb.

9.132 13.1 lb.

9.134 $M_A = 65.2$ N-m, $M_B = 32.6$ N-m.

9.136 (a) $f = 10.3$ lb.

9.138 $F = 290$ lb.

9.140 $\alpha = 65.7°$.

9.142 $\alpha = 24.2°$.

9.144 $b = (h/\mu_s - t)/2$.

9.146 $h = 5.82$ in.

9.148 286 lb.

9.150 1130 kg, torque $= 2.67$ kN-m.

9.152 $f = 2.63$ N.

9.154 $\mu_s = 0.272$.

9.156 $M = 1.13$ N-m.

9.158 $P = 43.5$ N.

9.160 146 lb.

9.162 (a) $W = 106$ lb;   (b) $W = 273$ lb.

Chapter 9

9.2 1.04 lb.

9.4 (a) $\alpha = 38.7°$;   (b) $\alpha = 11.3°$.

9.6 (a) No;   (b) 20.4 lb.

9.8 177 N.

9.10 20 lb.

9.12 $\alpha = 14.0°$.

9.14 (a) $T = 56.5$ N.

9.16 (a) Yes. The force is $\mu_s W$;   (b) $3\mu_s W$.

9.18 $89.6 \leq T \leq 110.4$ lb.

9.20 $F = 267$ N.

9.22 $M = hrF\mu_k/[2(h + b\mu_k)]$.

9.24 9.40 ft-lb.

9.26 $\alpha = 33.4°$.

9.28 $\alpha = 28.3°$.

9.30 (a) $M = 162$ in-lb;   (b) $M = 135$ in-lb.

9.32 $M = \mu_s RW[\sin\alpha + \mu_s(1 - \cos\alpha)]/[(1 + \mu_s^2)\sin\alpha]$.

9.34 $\alpha = 39.6°$.

9.36 (a) $T = 9.42$ lb;   (b) $T = 33.3$ lb.

9.40 $y = 234$ mm.

9.42 $\alpha = 9.27°$.

9.44 $F = 44$ lb.

9.48 $\alpha = 1.54°$, $P = 202$ N.

9.50 (a) $F = \mu_s W$;

   (b) $F = (W/2)(\mu_{sA} + \mu_{sB})/[1 + (h/b)(\mu_{sA} - \mu_{sB})]$.

Index

Taken from *Statics and Mechanics of Materials*, Third Edition by R.C. Hibbeler

Stress and Strain

7

CHAPTER OBJECTIVES

- To show how to use the method of sections for determining the internal loadings in a member.

- To introduce the concepts of normal and shear stress, and to use them in the analysis and design of members subject to axial load and direct shear.

- To define normal and shear strain, and show how they can be determined for various types of problems.

7.1 Introduction

It was stated in Chapter 1 that **Mechanics of materials** is a branch of mechanics that studies the relationships between the *external* loads applied to a deformable body and the intensity of *internal* forces acting within the body. This subject also involves computing the *deformations* of the body, and it provides a study of the body's *stability* when the body is subjected to external forces.

In the design of any structure or machine, it is *first* necessary to use the principles of statics to determine the forces acting both on and within its various members. The size of the members, their deflection, and their stability depend not only on the internal loadings, but also on the type of material from which the members are made. Consequently, an accurate determination and fundamental understanding of *material behavior* will be of vital importance for developing the necessary equations used in mechanics of materials. Realize that many formulas and rules for design, as defined in engineering codes and used in practice, are based on the fundamentals of mechanics of materials, and for this reason an understanding of the principles of this subject is very important.

7.2 Internal Resultant Loadings

In mechanics of materials, statics is primarily used to determine the resultant loadings that act within a body. For example, consider the body shown in Fig. 7–1a, which is held in equilibrium by the four external forces.* In order to obtain the internal loadings acting on a specific region within the body, it is necessary to pass an imaginary section or "cut" through the region where the internal loadings are to be determined. The two parts of the body are then separated, and a free-body diagram of one of the parts is drawn, Fig. 7–1b. Notice that there is actually a distribution of internal force acting on the "exposed" area of the section. These forces represent the effects of the material of the top part of the body acting on the adjacent material of the bottom part.

Although the exact distribution of this internal loading may be *unknown*, we can use the equations of equilibrium to relate the external forces on the bottom part of the body to the distribution's *resultant force and moment*, $\mathbf{F}_R$ and $\mathbf{M}_{R_O}$, *at any specific point O* on the sectioned area, Fig. 7–1c. It will be shown in later portions of the text that point O is most often chosen at the *centroid* of the sectioned area, and so we will always choose this location for O, unless otherwise stated. Also, if a member is long and slender, as in the case of a rod or beam, the section to be considered is generally taken *perpendicular* to the longitudinal axis of the member. This section is referred to as the **cross section**.

In order to design the horizontal members of this building frame, it is first necessary to find the internal loadings at various points along their length.

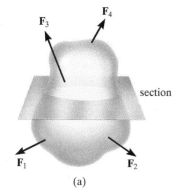

(a)

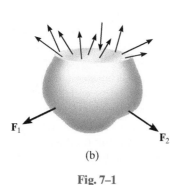

(b)

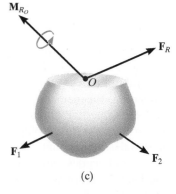

(c)

Fig. 7–1

---

*The body's weight is not shown, since it is assumed to be quite small, and therefore negligible compared with the other loads.

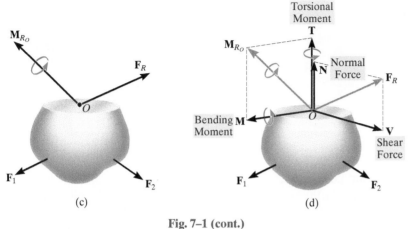

Fig. 7–1 (cont.)

Three Dimensions.   Later in this text we will show how to relate the resultant loadings, $\mathbf{F}_R$ and $\mathbf{M}_{R_O}$, to the *distribution of force* on the sectioned area, and thereby develop equations that can be used for analysis and design. To do this, however, the components of $\mathbf{F}_R$ and $\mathbf{M}_{R_O}$ acting both normal and perpendicular to the sectioned area must be considered, Fig. 7–1d. Four different types of resultant loadings can then be defined as follows:

Normal force, N.   This force acts perpendicular to the area. It is developed whenever the external loads tend to push or pull on the two segments of the body.

Shear force, V.   The shear force lies in the plane of the area and it is developed when the external loads tend to cause the two segments of the body to slide over one another.

Torsional moment or torque, T.   This effect is developed when the external loads tend to twist one segment of the body with respect to the other about an axis perpendicular to the area.

Bending moment, M.   The bending moment is caused by the external loads that tend to bend the body about an axis lying within the plane of the area.

In this text, note that graphical representation of a moment or torque is shown in three dimensions as a vector with an associated curl. By the *right-hand rule*, the thumb gives the arrowhead sense of this vector and the fingers or curl indicate the tendency for rotation (twisting or bending).

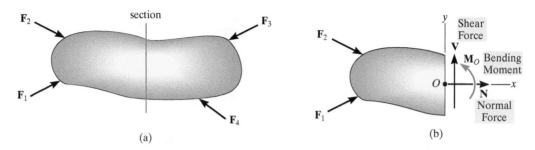

Fig. 7–2

Coplanar Loadings.   If the body is subjected to a *coplanar system of forces*, Fig. 7–2a, then only normal-force, shear-force, and bending- moment components will exist at the section, Fig. 7–2b. If we use the x, y, z coordinate axes, as shown on the left segment, then **N** can be obtained by applying $\Sigma F_x = 0$, and **V** can be obtained from $\Sigma F_y = 0$. Finally, the bending moment **M**$_O$ can be determined by summing moments about point O (the z axis), $\Sigma M_O = 0$, in order to eliminate the moments caused by the unknowns **N** and **V**.

Important Points

- *Mechanics of materials* is a study of the relationship between the external loads applied to a body and the stress and strain caused by the internal loads within the body.

- External forces can be applied to a body as *distributed* or *concentrated surface loadings*, or as *body forces* that act throughout the volume of the body.

- Linear distributed loadings produce a *resultant force* having a *magnitude* equal to the *area* under the load diagram, and having a *location* that passes through the *centroid* of this area.

- A support produces a *force* in a particular direction on its attached member if it *prevents translation* of the member in that direction, and it produces a *couple moment* on the member if it *prevents rotation*.

- The equations of equilibrium $\Sigma \mathbf{F} = \mathbf{0}$ and $\Sigma \mathbf{M} = \mathbf{0}$ must be satisfied in order to prevent a body from translating with accelerated motion and from rotating.

- When applying the equations of equilibrium, it is important to first draw the free-body diagram for the body in order to account for all the terms in the equations.

- The method of sections is used to determine the internal resultant loadings acting on the surface of the sectioned body. In general, these resultants consist of a normal force, shear force, torsional moment, and bending moment.

Procedure for Analysis

The resultant *internal* loadings at a point located on the section of a body can be obtained using the method of sections. This requires the following steps.

Support Reactions.

- First decide which segment of the body is to be considered. If the segment has a support or connection to another body, then *before* the body is sectioned, it will be necessary to determine the reactions acting on the chosen segment. To do this draw the free-body diagram of the *entire body* and then apply the necessary equations of equilibrium to obtain these reactions.

Free-Body Diagram.

- Keep all external distributed loadings, couple moments, torques, and forces in their *exact locations*, before passing an imaginary section through the body at the point where the resultant internal loadings are to be determined.

- Draw a free-body diagram of one of the "cut" segments and indicate the unknown resultants **N**, **V**, **M**, and **T** at the section. These resultants are normally placed at the point representing the geometric center or *centroid* of the sectioned area.

- If the member is subjected to a *coplanar* system of forces, only **N**, **V**, and **M** act at the centroid.

- Establish the x, y, z coordinate axes with origin at the centroid and show the resultant internal loadings acting along the axes.

Equations of Equilibrium.

- Moments should be summed at the section, about each of the coordinate axes where the resultants act. Doing this eliminates the unknown forces **N** and **V** and allows a direct solution for **M** (and **T**).

- If the solution of the equilibrium equations yields a negative value for a resultant, the assumed *directional sense* of the resultant is *opposite* to that shown on the free-body diagram.

The following examples illustrate this procedure numerically and also provide a review of some of the important principles of statics.

EXAMPLE 7.1

Determine the resultant internal loadings acting on the cross section at C of the cantilevered beam shown in Fig. 7–3a.

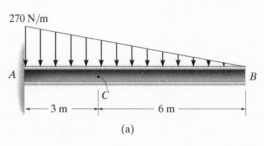

(a)

Fig. 7–3

SOLUTION

Support Reactions.   The support reactions at A do not have to be determined if segment CB is considered.

Free-Body Diagram.   The free-body diagram of segment CB is shown in Fig. 7–3b. It is important to keep the distributed loading on the segment until *after* the section is made. Only then should this loading be replaced by a single resultant force. Notice that the intensity of the distributed loading at C is found by proportion, i.e., from Fig. 7–3a, $w/6\text{ m} = (270\text{ N/m})/9\text{ m}$, $w = 180\text{ N/m}$. The magnitude of the resultant of the distributed load is equal to the area under the loading curve (triangle) and acts through the centroid of this area. Thus, $F = \frac{1}{2}(180\text{ N/m})(6\text{ m}) = 540\text{ N}$, which acts $\frac{1}{3}(6\text{ m}) = 2\text{ m}$ from C as shown in Fig. 7–3b.

Equations of Equilibrium.   Applying the equations of equilibrium we have

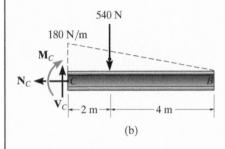

(b)

$$\xrightarrow{+} \Sigma F_x = 0; \qquad\qquad -N_C = 0$$
$$N_C = 0 \qquad\qquad Ans.$$

$$+\uparrow \Sigma F_y = 0; \qquad\qquad V_C - 540\text{ N} = 0$$
$$V_C = 540\text{ N} \qquad\qquad Ans.$$

$$\zeta + \Sigma M_C = 0; \qquad -M_C - 540\text{ N}(2\text{ m}) = 0$$
$$M_C = -1080\text{ N} \cdot \text{m} \qquad Ans.$$

NOTE: The negative sign indicates that $\mathbf{M}_C$ acts in the opposite direction to that shown on the free-body diagram. Try solving this problem using segment AC, by first obtaining the support reactions at A, which are given in Fig. 7–3c.

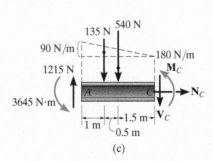

(c)

EXAMPLE 7.2

Determine the resultant internal loadings acting on the cross section at
C of the machine shaft shown in Fig. 7–4a. The shaft is supported by
journal bearings at A and B, which only exert vertical forces on the shaft.

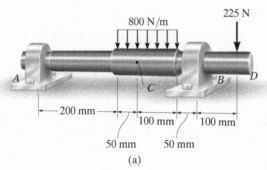

(a)

$$(800 \text{ N/m})(0.150 \text{ m}) = 120 \text{ N}$$

(b)

Fig. 7–4

SOLUTION

We will solve this problem using segment AC of the shaft.

Support Reactions.   The free-body diagram of the entire shaft is
shown in Fig. 7–4b. Since segment AC is to be considered, only the
reaction at A has to be determined. Why?

$$\zeta+ \Sigma M_B = 0; \quad -A_y(0.400 \text{ m}) + 120 \text{ N}(0.125 \text{ m}) - 225 \text{ N}(0.100 \text{ m}) = 0$$

$$A_y = -18.75 \text{ N}$$

The negative sign indicates that $\mathbf{A}_y$ acts in the *opposite sense* to that
shown on the free-body diagram.

Free-Body Diagram.   The free-body diagram of segment AC is
shown in Fig. 7–4c.

Equations of Equilibrium.

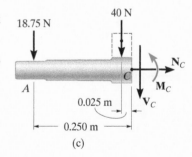

(c)

$$\xrightarrow{+} \Sigma F_x = 0; \qquad\qquad N_C = 0 \qquad\qquad Ans.$$

$$+\uparrow \Sigma F_y = 0; \qquad -18.75 \text{ N} - 40 \text{ N} - V_C = 0$$

$$V_C = -58.8 \text{ N} \qquad\qquad Ans.$$

$$\zeta+ \Sigma M_C = 0; \quad M_C + 40 \text{ N}(0.025 \text{ m}) + 18.75 \text{ N}(0.250 \text{ m}) = 0$$

$$M_C = -5.69 \text{ N} \cdot \text{m} \qquad\qquad Ans.$$

NOTE: The negative signs for V_C and M_C indicate they act in the
opposite directions on the free-body diagram. As an exercise,
calculate the reaction at B and try to obtain the same results using
segment CBD of the shaft.

EXAMPLE 7.3

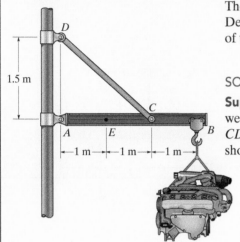

(a)

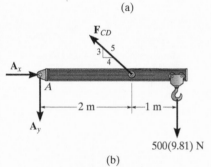

(b)

9810 N

A E $\mathbf{M}_E$ $\mathbf{N}_E$

$\mathbf{V}_E$

$\leftarrow$ 1 m $\rightarrow$

2452.5 N

(c)

Fig. 7–5

The 500-kg engine is suspended from the crane boom in Fig. 7–5a. Determine the resultant internal loadings acting on the cross section of the boom at point E.

SOLUTION

Support Reactions.   We will consider segment AE of the boom so we must first determine the pin reactions at A. Notice that member CD is a two-force member. The free-body diagram of the boom is shown in Fig. 7–5b. Applying the equations of equilibrium,

$$\downarrow + \Sigma M_A = 0; \qquad F_{CD}\left(\tfrac{3}{5}\right)(2 \text{ m}) - [500(9.81) \text{ N}](3 \text{ m}) = 0$$

$$F_{CD} = 12\,262.5 \text{ N}$$

$$\xrightarrow{+} \Sigma F_x = 0; \qquad A_x - (12\,262.5 \text{ N})\left(\tfrac{4}{5}\right) = 0$$

$$A_x = 9810 \text{ N}$$

$$+\uparrow \Sigma F_y = 0; \qquad -A_y + (12\,262.5 \text{ N})\left(\tfrac{3}{5}\right) - 500(9.81) \text{ N} = 0$$

$$A_y = 2452.5 \text{ N}$$

Free-Body Diagram.   The free-body diagram of segment AE is shown in Fig. 7–5c.

Equations of Equilibrium.

$$\xrightarrow{+} \Sigma F_x = 0; \qquad N_E + 9810 \text{ N} = 0$$

$$N_E = -9810 \text{ N} = -9.81 \text{ kN} \qquad Ans.$$

$$+\uparrow \Sigma F_y = 0; \qquad -V_E - 2452.5 \text{ N} = 0$$

$$V_E = -2452.5 \text{ N} = -2.45 \text{ kN} \qquad Ans.$$

$$\downarrow + \Sigma M_E = 0; \qquad M_E + (2452.5 \text{ N})(1 \text{ m}) = 0$$

$$M_E = -2452.5 \text{ N} \cdot \text{m} = -2.45 \text{ kN} \cdot \text{m} \qquad Ans.$$

EXAMPLE 7.4

Determine the resultant internal loadings acting on the cross section at B of the pipe shown in Fig. 7–6a. The pipe has a mass of 2 kg/m and is subjected to both a vertical force of 50 N and a couple moment of 70 N·m at its end A. It is fixed to the wall at C.

SOLUTION

The problem can be solved by considering segment AB, so we do not need to calculate the support reactions at C.

Free-Body Diagram. The x, y, z axes are established at B and the free-body diagram of segment AB is shown in Fig. 7–6b. The resultant force and moment components at the section are assumed to act in the positive coordinate directions and to pass through the *centroid* of the cross-sectional area at B. The weight of each segment of pipe is calculated as follows:

$$W_{BD} = (2 \text{ kg/m})(0.5 \text{ m})(9.81 \text{ N/kg}) = 9.81 \text{ N}$$

$$W_{AD} = (2 \text{ kg/m})(1.25 \text{ m})(9.81 \text{ N/kg}) = 24.525 \text{ N}$$

These forces act through the center of gravity of each segment.

Equations of Equilibrium. Applying the six scalar equations of equilibrium, we have*

$\Sigma F_x = 0;$ $\qquad (F_B)_x = 0$ $\qquad$ *Ans.*

$\Sigma F_y = 0;$ $\qquad (F_B)_y = 0$ $\qquad$ *Ans.*

$\Sigma F_z = 0;$ $\quad (F_B)_z - 9.81 \text{ N} - 24.525 \text{ N} - 50 \text{ N} = 0$

$\qquad (F_B)_z = 84.3 \text{ N}$ $\qquad$ *Ans.*

$\Sigma(M_B)_x = 0;$ $\quad (M_B)_x + 70 \text{ N·m} - 50 \text{ N} (0.5 \text{ m})$

$\qquad - 24.525 \text{ N} (0.5 \text{ m}) - 9.81 \text{ N} (0.25 \text{ m}) = 0$

$\qquad (M_B)_x = -30.3 \text{ N·m}$ $\qquad$ *Ans.*

$\Sigma(M_B)_y = 0;$ $(M_B)_y + 24.525 \text{ N} (0.625 \text{ m}) + 50 \text{ N} (1.25 \text{ m}) = 0$

$\qquad (M_B)_y = -77.8 \text{ N·m}$ $\qquad$ *Ans.*

$\Sigma(M_B)_z = 0;$ $\qquad (M_B)_z = 0$ $\qquad$ *Ans.*

NOTE: What do the negative signs for $(M_B)_x$ and $(M_B)_y$ indicate? Note that the normal force $N_B = (F_B)_y = 0$, whereas the shear force is $V_B = \sqrt{(0)^2 + (84.3)^2} = 84.3 \text{ N}$. Also, the torsional moment is $T_B = (M_B)_y = 77.8 \text{ N·m}$ and the bending moment is $M_B = \sqrt{(30.3)^2 + (0)^2} = 30.3 \text{ N·m}$.

*The *magnitude* of each moment about an axis is equal to the magnitude of each force times the perpendicular distance from the axis to the line of action of the force. The *direction* of each moment is determined using the right-hand rule, with positive moments (thumb) directed along the positive coordinate axes.

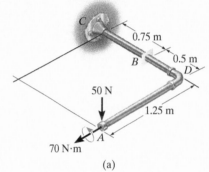

(a)

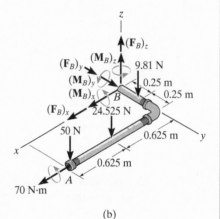

(b)

Fig. 7–6

FUNDAMENTAL PROBLEMS

F7–1. Determine the internal normal force, shear force, and bending moment at point C in the beam.

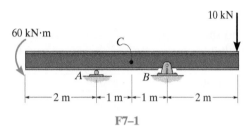

F7–1

F7–2. Determine the internal normal force, shear force, and bending moment at point C in the beam.

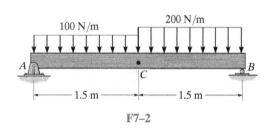

F7–2

F7–3. Determine the internal normal force, shear force, and bending moment at point C in the beam.

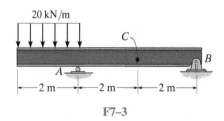

F7–3

F7–4. Determine the internal normal force, shear force, and bending moment at point C in the beam.

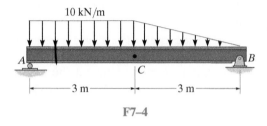

F7–4

F7–5. Determine the internal normal force, shear force, and bending moment at point C in the beam.

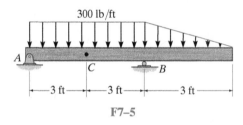

F7–5

F7–6. Determine the internal normal force, shear force, and bending moment at point C in the beam.

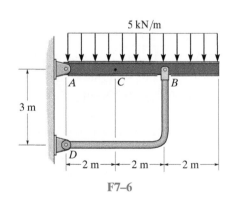

F7–6

PROBLEMS

7–1. Determine the resultant internal normal force acting on the cross section through point A in each column. In (a), segment BC weighs 180 lb/ft and segment CD weighs 250 lb/ft. In (b), the column has a mass of 200 kg/m.

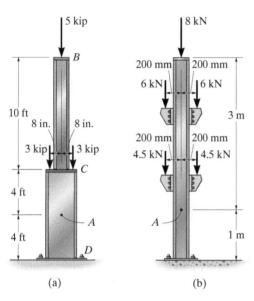

(a)   (b)

Prob. 7–1

7–2. Determine the resultant internal torque acting on the cross sections through points C and D. The support bearings at A and B allow free turning of the shaft.

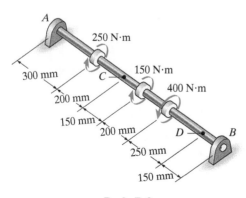

Prob. 7–2

7–3. Determine the resultant internal torque acting on the cross sections through points B and C.

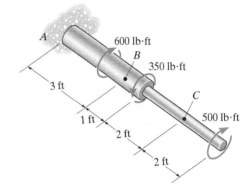

Prob. 7–3

*7–4. A force of 80 N is supported by the bracket as shown. Determine the resultant internal loadings acting on the section through point A.

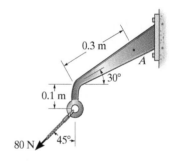

Prob. 7–4

•7–5. Determine the resultant internal loadings in the beam at cross sections through points D and E. Point E is just to the right of the 3-kip load.

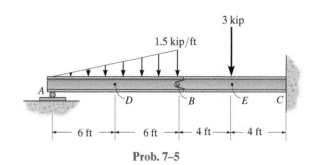

Prob. 7–5

7–6. Determine the normal force, shear force, and moment at a section through point C. Take P = 8 kN.

7–7. The cable will fail when subjected to a tension of 2 kN. Determine the largest vertical load P the frame will support and calculate the internal normal force, shear force, and moment at the cross section through point C for this loading.

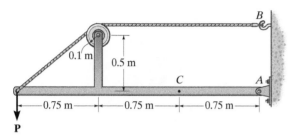

Probs. 7–6/7

*7–8. Determine the resultant internal loadings on the cross section through point C. Assume the reactions at the supports A and B are vertical.

•7–9. Determine the resultant internal loadings on the cross section through point D. Assume the reactions at the supports A and B are vertical.

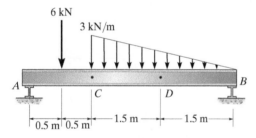

Probs. 7–8/9

7–10. The boom DF of the jib crane and the column DE have a uniform weight of 50 lb/ft. If the hoist and load weigh 300 lb, determine the resultant internal loadings in the crane on cross sections through points A, B, and C.

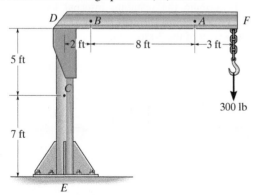

Prob. 7–10

7–11. The force F = 80 lb acts on the gear tooth. Determine the resultant internal loadings on the root of the tooth, i.e., at the centroid point A of section a–a.

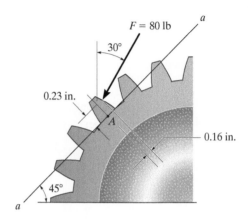

Prob. 7–11

*7–12. The sky hook is used to support the cable of a scaffold over the side of a building. If it consists of a smooth rod that contacts the parapet of a wall at points A, B, and C, determine the normal force, shear force, and moment on the cross section at points D and E.

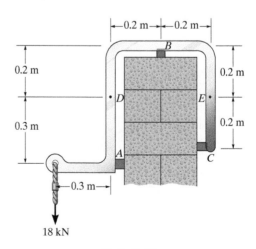

Prob. 7–12

•**7–13.** The 800-lb load is being hoisted at a constant speed using the motor M, which has a weight of 90 lb. Determine the resultant internal loadings acting on the cross section through point B in the beam. The beam has a weight of 40 lb/ft and is fixed to the wall at A.

7–14. Determine the resultant internal loadings acting on the cross section through points C and D of the beam in Prob. 7–13.

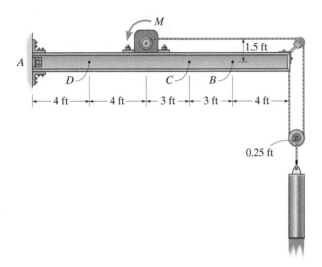

Probs. 7–13/14

7–15. Determine the resultant internal loading on the cross section through point C of the pliers. There is a pin at A, and the jaws at B are smooth.

*7–16.** Determine the resultant internal loading on the cross section through point D of the pliers.

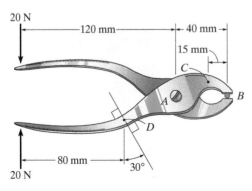

Probs. 7–15/16

•**7–17.** Determine resultant internal loadings acting on section $a–a$ and section $b–b$. Each section passes through the centerline at point C.

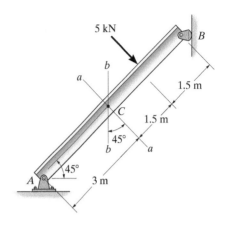

Prob. 7–17

7–18. The bolt shank is subjected to a tension of 80 lb. Determine the resultant internal loadings acting on the cross section at point C.

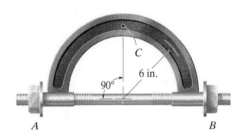

Prob. 7–18

7–19. Determine the resultant internal loadings acting on the cross section through point C. Assume the reactions at the supports A and B are vertical.

*7–20.** Determine the resultant internal loadings acting on the cross section through point D. Assume the reactions at the supports A and B are vertical.

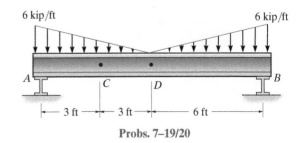

Probs. 7–19/20

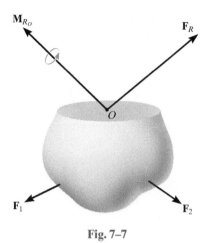

Fig. 7–7

7.3 Stress

It was stated in Section 7.2 that the force and moment acting at a specified point O on the sectioned area of the body, Fig. 7–7, represents the resultant effects of the actual *distribution of loading* acting over the sectioned area, Fig. 7–8a. Obtaining this *distribution* is of primary importance in mechanics of materials. To solve this problem it is necessary to establish the concept of stress.

We begin by considering the sectioned area to be subdivided into small areas, such as ΔA shown in Fig. 7–8a. As we reduce ΔA to a smaller and smaller size, we must make two assumptions regarding the properties of the material. We will consider the material to be **continuous**, that is, to consist of a *continuum* or uniform distribution of matter having no voids. Also, the material must be **cohesive**, meaning that all portions of it are connected together, without having breaks, cracks, or separations. A typical finite yet very small force $\Delta \mathbf{F}$, acting on ΔA, is shown in Fig. 7–8a. This force, like all the others, will have a unique direction, but for further discussion we will replace it by its *three components*, namely, $\Delta \mathbf{F}_x$, $\Delta \mathbf{F}_y$, and $\Delta \mathbf{F}_z$, which are taken tangent, tangent, and normal to the area, respectively. As ΔA approaches zero, so do $\Delta \mathbf{F}$ and its components; however, the quotient of the force and area will, in general, approach a finite limit. This quotient is called *stress*, and as noted, it describes the *intensity of the internal force* acting on a *specific plane* (area) passing through a point.

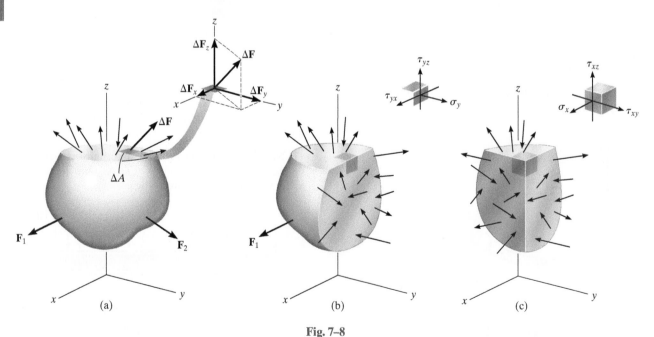

Fig. 7–8

Normal Stress.

The *intensity* of the force acting normal to ΔA is defined as the **normal stress**, σ (sigma). Since $\Delta \mathbf{F}_z$ is normal to the area then

$$\sigma_z = \lim_{\Delta A \to 0} \frac{\Delta F_z}{\Delta A} \tag{7–1}$$

If the normal force or stress "pulls" on ΔA as shown in Fig. 7–8a, it is referred to as *tensile stress*, whereas if it "pushes" on ΔA it is called *compressive stress*.

Shear Stress.

The intensity of force acting tangent to ΔA is called the **shear stress**, τ (tau). Here we have shear stress components,

$$\tau_{zx} = \lim_{\Delta A \to 0} \frac{\Delta F_x}{\Delta A}$$
$$\tau_{zy} = \lim_{\Delta A \to 0} \frac{\Delta F_y}{\Delta A} \tag{7–2}$$

Note that in this subscript notation z specifies the orientation of the area ΔA, Fig. 7–9, and x and y indicate the axes along which each shear stress acts.

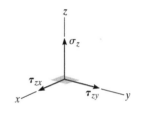

Fig. 7–9

General State of Stress.

If the body is further sectioned by planes parallel to the $x-z$ plane, Fig. 7–8b, and the $y-z$ plane, Fig. 7–8c, we can then "cut out" a cubic volume element of material that represents the **state of stress** acting around the chosen point in the body. This state of stress is then characterized by three components acting on each face of the element, Fig. 7–10.

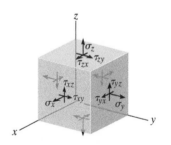

Fig. 7–10

Units.

Since stress represents a force per unit area, in the International Standard or SI system, the magnitudes of both normal and shear stress are specified in the basic units of newtons per square meter (N/m^2). This unit, called a pascal $(1 \text{ Pa} = 1 \text{ N/m}^2)$ is rather small, and in engineering work prefixes such as kilo- (10^3), symbolized by k, mega- (10^6), symbolized by M, or giga- (10^9), symbolized by G, are used to represent larger, more realistic values of stress.* Likewise, in the Foot-Pound-Second system of units, engineers usually express stress in pounds per square inch (psi) or kilopounds per square inch (ksi), where 1 kilopound (kip) = 1000 lb.

---

*Sometimes stress is expressed in units of N/mm^2, where $1 \text{ mm} = 10^{-3}$ m. However, in the SI system, prefixes are not allowed in the denominator of a fraction and therefore it is better to use the equivalent $1 \text{ N/mm}^2 = 1 \text{ MN/m}^2 = 1 \text{ MPa}$.

7.4 Average Normal Stress in an Axially Loaded Bar

In this section we will determine the average stress distribution acting on the cross-sectional area of an axially loaded bar such as the one shown in Fig. 7–11a. This bar is **prismatic** since all cross sections are the same throughout its length. When the load P is applied to the bar through the centroid of its cross-sectional area, then the bar will deform uniformly throughout the central region of its length, as shown in Fig. 7–11b, provided the material of the bar is both homogeneous and isotropic.

Homogeneous material has the same physical and mechanical properties throughout its volume, and *isotropic material* has these same properties in all directions. Many engineering materials may be approximated as being both homogeneous and isotropic as assumed here. Steel, for example, contains thousands of randomly oriented crystals in each cubic millimeter of its volume, and since most problems involving this material have a physical size that is very much larger than a single crystal, the above assumption regarding its material composition is quite realistic.

Note that anisotropic materials such as wood have different properties in different directions, and although this is the case, like wood if the anisotropy is oriented along the bar's axis, then the bar will also deform uniformly when subjected to the axial load P.

Average Normal Stress Distribution. If we pass a section through the bar, and separate it into two parts, then equilibrium requires the resultant normal force at the section to be P, Fig. 7–11c. Due to the *uniform* deformation of the material, it is necessary that the cross section be subjected to a *constant normal stress distribution*, Fig. 7–11d.

Region of uniform deformation of bar

(a)   (b)

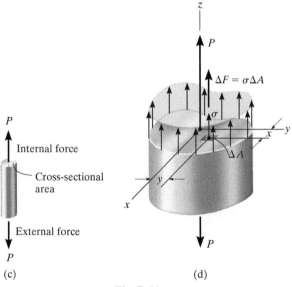

Internal force

Cross-sectional area

External force

(c)

$\Delta F = \sigma \Delta A$

(d)

Fig. 7–11

As a result, each small area ΔA on the cross section is subjected to a force $\Delta F = \sigma \, \Delta A$, and the *sum* of these forces acting over the entire cross-sectional area must be equivalent to the internal resultant force **P** at the section. If we let $\Delta A \rightarrow dA$ and therefore $\Delta F \rightarrow dF$, then, recognizing σ is *constant*, we have

$$+\uparrow F_{Rz} = \Sigma F_z; \qquad \int dF = \int_A \sigma \, dA$$

$$P = \sigma A$$

$$\boxed{\sigma = \frac{P}{A}} \qquad (7\text{–}3)$$

Here

σ = average normal stress at any point on the cross-sectional area

P = *internal resultant normal force*, which acts through the *centroid* of the cross-sectional area. P is determined using the method of sections and the equations of equilibrium

A = cross-sectional area of the bar where σ is determined

Since the internal load P passes through the centroid of the cross-section, the uniform stress distribution will produce zero moments about the x and y axes passing through this point, Fig. 7–11d. To show this, we require the moment of P about each axis to be equal to the moment of the stress distribution about the axes, namely,

$$(M_R)_x = \Sigma M_x; \quad 0 = \int_A y \, dF = \int_A y\sigma \, dA = \sigma \int_A y \, dA$$

$$(M_R)_y = \Sigma M_y; \quad 0 = -\int_A x \, dF = -\int_A x\sigma \, dA = -\sigma \int_A x \, dA$$

These equations are indeed satisfied, since by definition of the centroid, $\int y \, dA = 0$ and $\int x \, dA = 0$.

Equilibrium.   It should be apparent that only a normal stress exists on any small volume element of material located at each point on the cross section of an axially loaded bar. If we consider vertical equilibrium of the element, Fig. 7–12, then apply the equation of force equilibrium,

$$\Sigma F_z = 0; \qquad \sigma(\Delta A) - \sigma'(\Delta A) = 0$$

$$\sigma = \sigma'$$

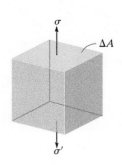

Fig. 7–12

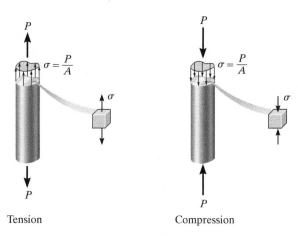

Tension   Compression

Fig. 7–13

In other words, the two normal stress components on the element must be equal in magnitude but opposite in direction. This is referred to as *uniaxial stress*.

The previous analysis applies to members subjected to either tension or compression, as shown in Fig. 7–13. As a graphical interpretation, the *magnitude* of the internal resultant force **P** is *equivalent* to the *volume* under the stress diagram; that is, $P = \sigma A$ (volume = height × base). Furthermore, as a consequence of the balance of moments, *this resultant passes through the centroid of this volume*.

Although we have developed this analysis for *prismatic* bars, this assumption can be relaxed somewhat to include bars that have a *slight taper*. For example, it can be shown, using the more exact analysis of the theory of elasticity, that for a tapered bar of rectangular cross section, for which the angle between two adjacent sides is 15°, the average normal stress, as calculated by $\sigma = P/A$, is only 2.2% *less* than its value found from the theory of elasticity.

Maximum Average Normal Stress.

In our analysis both the internal force P and the cross-sectional area A were *constant* along the longitudinal axis of the bar, and as a result the normal stress $\sigma = P/A$ is also *constant* throughout the bar's length. Occasionally, however, the bar may be subjected to *several* external loads along its axis, or a change in its cross-sectional area may occur. As a result, the normal stress within the bar could be different from one section to the next, and, if the *maximum* average normal stress is to be determined, then it becomes important to find the location where the ratio P/A is a *maximum*. To do this it is necessary to determine the internal force P at various sections along the bar. Here it may be helpful to show this variation by drawing an *axial or normal force diagram*. Specifically, this diagram is a plot of the normal force P versus its position x along the bar's length. As a sign convention, P will be positive if it causes tension in the member, and negative if it causes compression. Once the internal loading throughout the bar is known, the maximum ratio of P/A can then be identified.

This steel tie rod is used as a hanger to suspend a portion of a staircase, and as a result it is subjected to tensile stress.

Important Points

- When a body subjected to external loads is sectioned, there is a distribution of force acting over the sectioned area which holds each segment of the body in equilibrium. The intensity of this internal force at a point in the body is referred to as *stress*.

- Stress is the limiting value of force per unit area, as the area approaches zero. For this definition, the material is considered to be continuous and cohesive.

- The magnitude of the stress components at a point depends upon the type of loading acting on the body, and the orientation of the element at the point.

- When a prismatic bar is made from homogeneous and isotropic material, and is subjected to an axial force acting through the centroid of the cross-sectional area, then the center region of the bar will deform uniformly. As a result, the material will be subjected *only to normal stress*. This stress is uniform or *averaged* over the cross-sectional area.

Procedure for Analysis

The equation $\sigma = P/A$ gives the *average* normal stress on the cross-sectional area of a member when the section is subjected to an internal resultant normal force $\mathbf{P}$. For axially loaded members, application of this equation requires the following steps.

Internal Loading.

- Section the member *perpendicular* to its longitudinal axis at the point where the normal stress is to be determined and use the necessary free-body diagram and force equation of equilibrium to obtain the *internal axial force* $\mathbf{P}$ at the section.

Average Normal Stress.

- Determine the member's cross-sectional area at the section and calculate the average normal stress $\sigma = P/A$.

- It is suggested that σ be shown acting on a small volume element of the material located at a point on the section where stress is calculated. To do this, first draw σ on the face of the element coincident with the sectioned area A. Here σ acts in the *same direction* as the internal force $\mathbf{P}$ since all the normal stresses on the cross section develop this resultant. The normal stress σ on the other face of the element acts in the opposite direction.

7

EXAMPLE | 7.5

The bar in Fig. 7–14a has a constant width of 35 mm and a thickness of 10 mm. Determine the maximum average normal stress in the bar when it is subjected to the loading shown.

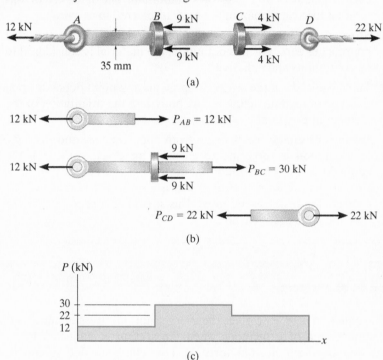

(a)

(b)

(c)

SOLUTION

Internal Loading.   By inspection, the internal axial forces in regions AB, BC, and CD are all constant yet have different magnitudes. Using the method of sections, these loadings are determined in Fig. 7–14b; and the normal force diagram which represents these results graphically is shown in Fig. 7–14c. The largest loading is in region BC, where $P_{BC} = 30$ kN. Since the cross-sectional area of the bar is *constant*, the largest average normal stress also occurs within this region of the bar.

Average Normal Stress.   Applying Eq. 7–3, we have

$$\sigma_{BC} = \frac{P_{BC}}{A} = \frac{30(10^3)\,\text{N}}{(0.035\,\text{m})(0.010\,\text{m})} = 85.7\,\text{MPa} \qquad Ans.$$

NOTE: The stress distribution acting on an arbitrary cross section of the bar within region BC is shown in Fig. 7–14d. Graphically the *volume* (or "block") represented by this distribution of stress is equivalent to the load of 30 kN; that is, $30\,\text{kN} = (85.7\,\text{MPa})(35\,\text{mm})(10\,\text{mm})$.

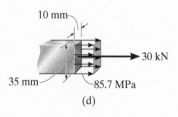

(d)

Fig. 7–14

EXAMPLE 7.6

The 80-kg lamp is supported by two rods AB and BC as shown in Fig. 7–15a. If AB has a diameter of 10 mm and BC has a diameter of 8 mm, determine the average normal stress in each rod.

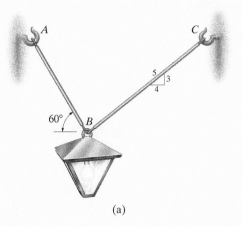

(a)

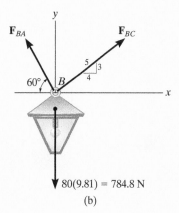

(b)

Fig. 7–15

SOLUTION

Internal Loading.   We must first determine the axial force in each rod. A free-body diagram of the lamp is shown in Fig. 7–15b. Applying the equations of force equilibrium,

$$\xrightarrow{+}\Sigma F_x = 0; \qquad F_{BC}\left(\tfrac{4}{5}\right) - F_{BA}\cos 60° = 0$$

$$+\uparrow\Sigma F_y = 0; \quad F_{BC}\left(\tfrac{3}{5}\right) + F_{BA}\sin 60° - 784.8\text{ N} = 0$$

$$F_{BC} = 395.2\text{ N}, \qquad F_{BA} = 632.4\text{ N}$$

By Newton's third law of action, equal but opposite reaction, these forces subject the rods to tension throughout their length.

Average Normal Stress.   Applying Eq. 7–3,

$$\sigma_{BC} = \frac{F_{BC}}{A_{BC}} = \frac{395.2\text{ N}}{\pi(0.004\text{ m})^2} = 7.86\text{ MPa} \qquad Ans.$$

$$\sigma_{BA} = \frac{F_{BA}}{A_{BA}} = \frac{632.4\text{ N}}{\pi(0.005\text{ m})^2} = 8.05\text{ MPa} \qquad Ans.$$

NOTE: The average normal stress distribution acting over a cross section of rod AB is shown in Fig. 7–15c, and at a point on this cross section, an element of material is stressed as shown in Fig. 7–15d.

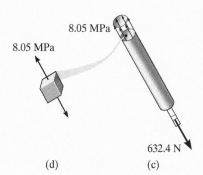

8.05 MPa

8.05 MPa

632.4 N

(d)

(c)

EXAMPLE 7.7

Member AC shown in Fig. 7–16a is subjected to a vertical force of 3 kN. Determine the position x of this force so that the average compressive stress at the smooth support C is equal to the average tensile stress in the tie rod AB. The rod has a cross-sectional area of 400 mm^2 and the contact area at C is 650 mm^2.

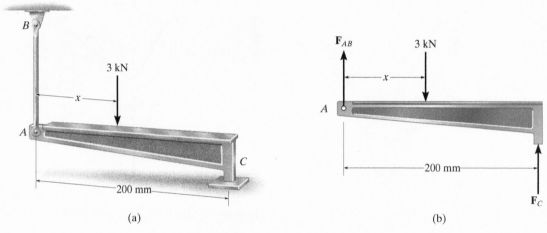

(a)   (b)

Fig. 7–16

SOLUTION

Internal Loading. The forces at A and C can be related by considering the free-body diagram for member AC, Fig. 7–16b. There are three unknowns, namely, F_{AB}, F_C, and x. To solve this problem we will work in units of newtons and millimeters.

$$+\uparrow \Sigma F_y = 0; \qquad F_{AB} + F_C - 3000 \text{ N} = 0 \qquad (1)$$

$$\downarrow+\Sigma M_A = 0; \qquad -3000 \text{ N}(x) + F_C(200 \text{ mm}) = 0 \qquad (2)$$

Average Normal Stress. A necessary third equation can be written that requires the tensile stress in the bar AB and the compressive stress at C to be equivalent, i.e.,

$$\sigma = \frac{F_{AB}}{400 \text{ mm}^2} = \frac{F_C}{650 \text{ mm}^2}$$
$$F_C = 1.625 F_{AB}$$

Substituting this into Eq. 1, solving for F_{AB}, then solving for F_C, we obtain

$$F_{AB} = 1143 \text{ N}$$
$$F_C = 1857 \text{ N}$$

The position of the applied load is determined from Eq. 2,

$$x = 124 \text{ mm} \qquad \qquad \textit{Ans.}$$

NOTE: $0 < x < 200$ mm, as required.

7.5 Average Shear Stress

Shear stress has been defined in Section 7.3 as the stress component that acts *in the plane* of the sectioned area. To show how this stress can develop, consider the effect of applying a force $\mathbf{F}$ to the bar in Fig. 7–17a. If the supports are considered rigid, and $\mathbf{F}$ is large enough, it will cause the material of the bar to deform and fail along the planes identified by AB and CD. A free-body diagram of the unsupported center segment of the bar, Fig. 7–17b, indicates that the shear force $V = F/2$ must be applied at each section to hold the segment in equilibrium. The *average shear stress* distributed over each sectioned area that develops this shear force is defined by

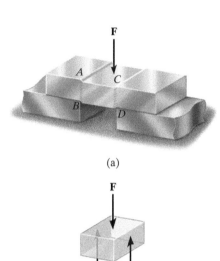

(a)

$$\tau_{avg} = \frac{V}{A} \qquad\qquad (7\text{–}4)$$

Here

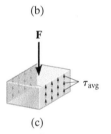

τ_{avg} = average shear stress at the section, which is assumed to be the *same* at each point located on the section
V = internal resultant shear force on the section determined from the equations of equilibrium
A = area at the section

(b)

(c)

Fig. 7–17

The distribution of average shear stress acting over the sections is shown in Fig. 7–17c. Notice that τ_{avg} is in the *same direction* as $\mathbf{V}$, since the shear stress must create associated forces all of which contribute to the internal resultant force $\mathbf{V}$ at the section.

The loading case discussed here is an example of **simple or direct shear**, since the shear is caused by the *direct action* of the applied load $\mathbf{F}$. This type of shear often occurs in various types of simple connections that use bolts, pins, welding material, etc. In all these cases, however, application of Eq. 7–4 is *only approximate*. A more precise investigation of the shear-stress distribution over the section often reveals that much larger shear stresses occur in the material than those predicted by this equation. Although this may be the case, application of Eq. 7–4 is generally acceptable for many problems in engineering design and analysis. For example, engineering codes allow its use when considering design sizes for fasteners such as bolts and for obtaining the bonding strength of glued joints subjected to shear loadings.

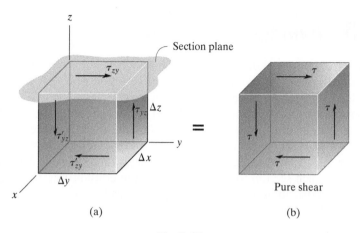

Fig. 7–18

Shear Stress Equilibrium.

Figure 7–18*a* shows a volume element of material taken at a point located on the surface of a sectioned area which is subjected to a shear stress τ_{zy}. Force and moment equilibrium requires the shear stress acting on this face of the element to be accompanied by shear stress acting on three other faces. To show this we will first consider force equilibrium in the *y* direction. Then

$$\Sigma F_y = 0; \qquad \tau_{zy}(\Delta x\,\Delta y) - \tau'_{zy}\,\Delta x\,\Delta y = 0$$
$$\tau_{zy} = \tau'_{zy}$$

In a similar manner, force equilibrium in the *z* direction yields $\tau_{yz} = \tau'_{yz}$. Finally, taking moments about the *x* axis,

$$\Sigma M_x = 0; \qquad -\tau_{zy}(\Delta x\,\Delta y)\,\Delta z + \tau_{yz}(\Delta x\,\Delta z)\,\Delta y = 0$$
$$\tau_{zy} = \tau_{yz}$$

so that

$$\tau_{zy} = \tau'_{zy} = \tau_{yz} = \tau'_{yz} = \tau$$

In other words, ***all four shear stresses must have equal magnitude and be directed either toward or away from each other at opposite edges of the element***, Fig. 7–18*b*. This is referred to as the *complementary property of shear*, and under the conditions shown in Fig. 7–18, the material is subjected to *pure shear*.

Important Points

- If two parts are *thin or small* when joined together, the applied loads may cause shearing of the material with negligible bending. If this is the case, it is generally assumed that an *average shear stress* acts over the cross-sectional area.

- When shear stress τ acts on a plane, then equilibrium of a volume element of material at a point on the plane requires associated shear stress of the same magnitude act on three adjacent sides of the element.

Procedure for Analysis

The equation $\tau_{\text{avg}} = V/A$ is used to determine the *average shear stress* in the material. Application requires the following steps.

Internal Shear.

- Section the member at the point where the average shear stress is to be determined.

- Draw the necessary free-body diagram, and calculate the internal shear force **V** acting at the section that is necessary to hold the part in equilibrium.

Average Shear Stress.

- Determine the sectioned area A, and determine the average shear stress $\tau_{\text{avg}} = V/A$.

- It is suggested that τ_{avg} be shown on a small volume element of material located at a point on the section where it is determined. To do this, first draw τ_{avg} on the face of the element, coincident with the sectioned area A. This stress acts in the *same direction* as **V**. The shear stresses acting on the three adjacent planes can then be drawn in their appropriate directions following the scheme shown in Fig. 7–18.

EXAMPLE 7.8

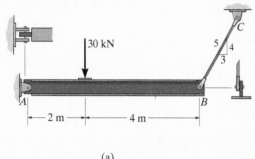

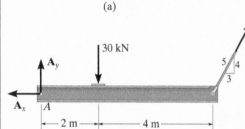

30 kN

5 / 4 / 3

A

B

|← 2 m →|← 4 m →|

(a)

Determine the average shear stress in the 20-mm-diameter pin at A and the 30-mm-diameter pin at B that support the beam in Fig. 7–19a.

SOLUTION

Internal Loadings. The forces on the pins can be obtained by considering the equilibrium of the beam, Fig. 7–19b.

$$\zeta + \Sigma M_A = 0; \quad F_B\left(\frac{4}{5}\right)(6 \text{ m}) - 30 \text{ kN}(2 \text{ m}) = 0 \quad F_B = 12.5 \text{ kN}$$

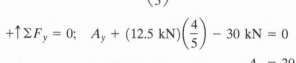

$$\xrightarrow{+} \Sigma F_x = 0; \quad (12.5 \text{ kN})\left(\frac{3}{5}\right) - A_x = 0 \quad A_x = 7.50 \text{ kN}$$

$$+\uparrow \Sigma F_y = 0; \quad A_y + (12.5 \text{ kN})\left(\frac{4}{5}\right) - 30 \text{ kN} = 0$$

$$A_y = 20 \text{ kN}$$

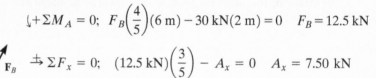

30 kN

A_y

5 / 4 / 3

A_x A

|← 2 m →|← 4 m →|

(b)

Thus, the resultant force acting on pin A is

$$F_A = \sqrt{A_x^2 + A_y^2} = \sqrt{(7.50 \text{ kN})^2 + (20 \text{ kN})^2} = 21.36 \text{ kN}$$

The pin at A is supported by two fixed "leaves" and so the free-body diagram of the center segment of the pin shown in Fig. 7–19c has *two* shearing surfaces between the beam and each leaf. The force of the beam (21.36 kN) acting on the pin is therefore supported by shear force on each of these surfaces. This case is called *double shear*. Thus,

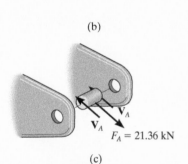

V_A
V_A
$F_A = 21.36$ kN

(c)

$$V_A = \frac{F_A}{2} = \frac{21.36 \text{ kN}}{2} = 10.68 \text{ kN}$$

In Fig. 7–19a, note that pin B is subjected to *single shear*, which occurs on the section between the cable and beam, Fig. 7–19d. For this pin segment,

$$V_B = F_B = 12.5 \text{ kN}$$

Average Shear Stress.

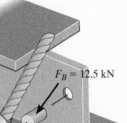

$F_B = 12.5$ kN

V_B

(d)

Fig. 7–19

$$(\tau_A)_{\text{avg}} = \frac{V_A}{A_A} = \frac{10.68(10^3) \text{ N}}{\frac{\pi}{4}(0.02 \text{ m})^2} = 34.0 \text{ MPa} \qquad \qquad \textit{Ans.}$$

$$(\tau_B)_{\text{avg}} = \frac{V_B}{A_B} = \frac{12.5(10^3) \text{ N}}{\frac{\pi}{4}(0.03 \text{ m})^2} = 17.7 \text{ MPa} \qquad \qquad \textit{Ans.}$$

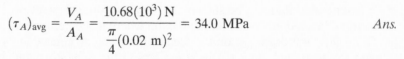

7

EXAMPLE | 7.9

If the wood joint in Fig. 7–20a has a width of 150 mm, determine the average shear stress developed along shear planes a–a and b–b. For each plane, represent the state of stress on an element of the material.

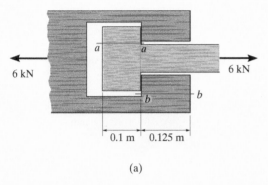

(a)

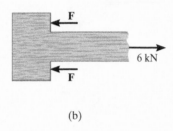

(b)

Fig. 7–20

SOLUTION

Internal Loadings. Referring to the free-body diagram of the member, Fig. 7–20b,

$$\xrightarrow{+}\ \Sigma F_x = 0; \qquad 6\ \text{kN} - F - F = 0 \qquad F = 3\ \text{kN}$$

Now consider the equilibrium of segments cut across shear planes a–a and b–b, shown in Figs. 7–20c and 7–20d.

$$\xrightarrow{+}\ \Sigma F_x = 0; \qquad V_a - 3\ \text{kN} = 0 \qquad V_a = 3\ \text{kN}$$

$$\xrightarrow{+}\ \Sigma F_x = 0; \qquad 3\ \text{kN} - V_b = 0 \qquad V_b = 3\ \text{kN}$$

Average Shear Stress.

$$(\tau_a)_{\text{avg}} = \frac{V_a}{A_a} = \frac{3(10^3)\ \text{N}}{(0.1\ \text{m})(0.15\ \text{m})} = 200\ \text{kPa} \qquad Ans.$$

$$(\tau_b)_{\text{avg}} = \frac{V_b}{A_b} = \frac{3(10^3)\ \text{N}}{(0.125\ \text{m})(0.15\ \text{m})} = 160\ \text{kPa} \qquad Ans.$$

The state of stress on elements located on sections a–a and b–b is shown in Figs. 7–20c and 7–20d, respectively.

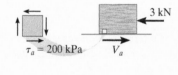

(c)

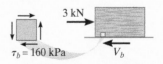

(d)

FUNDAMENTAL PROBLEMS

F7–7. The uniform beam is supported by two rods AB and CD that have cross-sectional areas of 10 mm² and 15 mm², respectively. Determine the intensity w of the distributed load so that the average normal stress in each rod does not exceed 300 kPa.

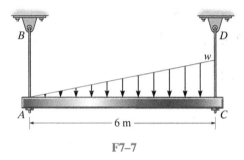

F7–7

F7–8. Determine the average normal stress developed on the cross section. Sketch the normal stress distribution over the cross section.

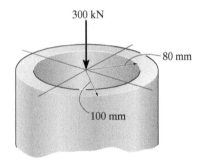

F7–8

F7–9. Determine the average normal stress developed on the cross section. Sketch the normal stress distribution over the cross section.

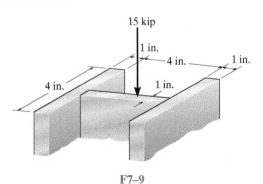

F7–9

F7–10. If the 600-kN force acts through the centroid of the cross section, determine the location $\bar{y}$ of the centroid and the average normal stress developed on the cross section. Also, sketch the normal stress distribution over the cross section.

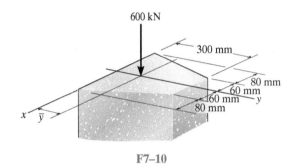

F7–10

F7–11. Determine the average normal stress developed at points A, B, and C. The diameter of each segment is indicated in the figure.

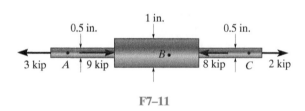

F7–11

F7–12. Determine the average normal stress developed in rod AB if the load has a mass of 50 kg. The diameter of rod AB is 8 mm.

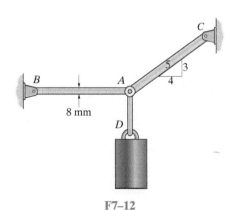

F7–12

PROBLEMS

7–21. The column is subjected to an axial force of 8 kN, which is applied through the centroid of the cross-sectional area. Determine the average normal stress acting at section *a–a*. Show this distribution of stress acting over the area's cross section.

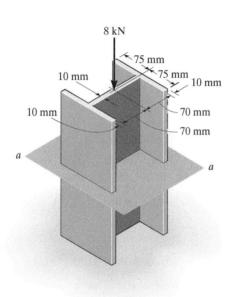

Prob. 7–21

7–22. The lever is held to the fixed shaft using a tapered pin *AB*, which has a mean diameter of 6 mm. If a couple is applied to the lever, determine the average shear stress in the pin between the pin and lever.

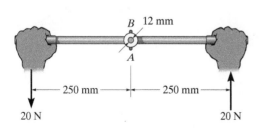

Prob. 7–22

•7–23. The bar has a cross-sectional area *A* and is subjected to the axial load *P*. Determine the average normal and average shear stresses acting over the shaded section, which is oriented at θ from the horizontal. Plot the variation of these stresses as a function of θ ($0 \le \theta \le 90°$).

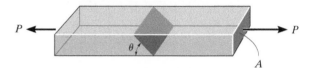

Prob. 7–23

*7–24. The built-up shaft consists of a pipe *AB* and solid rod *BC*. The pipe has an inner diameter of 20 mm and outer diameter of 28 mm. The rod has a diameter of 12 mm. Determine the average normal stress at points *D* and *E* and represent the stress on a volume element located at each of these points.

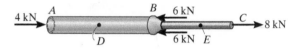

Prob. 7–24

7–25. The bars of the truss each have a cross-sectional area of 1.25 in². Determine the average normal stress in each member due to the loading *P* = 8 kip. State whether the stress is tensile or compressive.

7–26. The bars of the truss each have a cross-sectional area of 1.25 in². If the maximum average normal stress in any bar is not to exceed 20 ksi, determine the maximum magnitude *P* of the loads that can be applied to the truss.

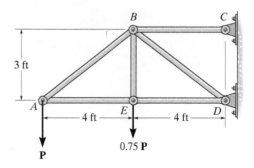

Probs. 7–25/26

•7–27.   The plate has a width of 0.5 m. If the stress distribution at the support varies as shown, determine the force **P** applied to the plate and the distance d to where it is applied.

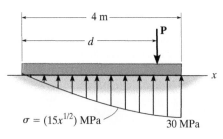

$\sigma = (15x^{1/2})$ MPa

30 MPa

Prob. 7–27

*7–28.   The two members used in the construction of an aircraft fuselage are joined together using a 30° fish-mouth weld. Determine the average normal and average shear stress on the plane of each weld. Assume each inclined plane supports a horizontal force of 400 lb.

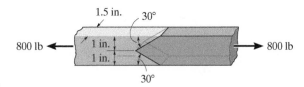

Prob. 7–28

7–29.   If the block is subjected to the centrally applied force of 600 kN, determine the average normal stress in the material. Show the stress acting on a differential volume element of the material.

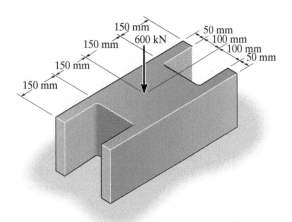

Prob. 7–29

7–30.   The pins on the frame at B and C each have a diameter of 0.25 in. If these pins are subjected to *double shear*, determine the average shear stress in each pin.

•7–31.   Solve Prob. 7–30 assuming that pins B and C are subjected to *single shear*.

*7–32.   The pins on the frame at D and E each have a diameter of 0.25 in. If these pins are subjected to *double shear*, determine the average shear stress in each pin.

7–33.   Solve Prob. 7–32 assuming that pins D and E are subjected to *single shear*.

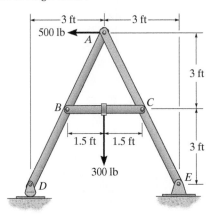

Probs. 7–30/31/32/33

7–34.   A 175-lb woman stands on a vinyl floor wearing stiletto high-heel shoes. If the heel has the dimensions shown, determine the average normal stress she exerts on the floor and compare it with the average normal stress developed when a man having the same weight is wearing flat-heeled shoes. Assume the load is applied slowly, so that dynamic effects can be ignored. Also, assume the entire weight is supported only by the heel of one shoe.

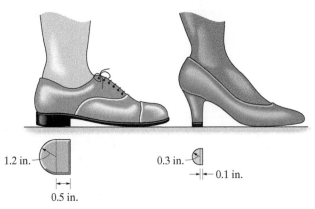

Prob. 7–34

•**7–35.** The truss is made from three pin-connected members having the cross-sectional areas shown in the figure. Determine the average normal stress developed in each member when the truss is subjected to the load shown. State whether the stress is tensile or compressive.

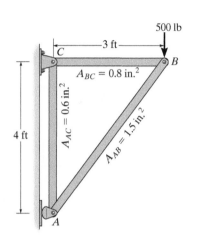

Prob. 7–35

*__7–36.__ Determine the average normal stress developed in links AB and CD of the smooth two-tine grapple that supports the log having a mass of 3 Mg. The cross-sectional area of each link is 400 mm².

7–37. Determine the average shear stress developed in pins A and B of the smooth two-tine grapple that supports the log having a mass of 3 Mg. Each pin has a diameter of 25 mm and is subjected to double shear.

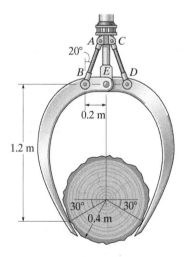

Probs. 7–36/37

7–38. The beam is supported by a pin at A and a short link BC. If $P = 15$ kN, determine the average shear stress developed in the pins at A, B, and C. All pins are in double shear as shown, and each has a diameter of 18 mm.

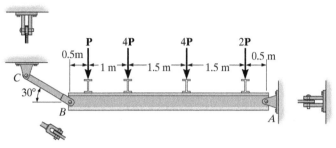

Prob. 7–38

•**7–39.** The beam is supported by a pin at A and a short link BC. Determine the maximum magnitude P of the loads the beam will support if the average shear stress in each pin is not to exceed 80 MPa. All pins are in double shear as shown, and each has a diameter of 18 mm.

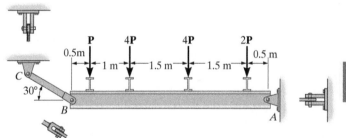

Prob. 7–39

*__7–40.__ The block is subjected to a compressive force of 2 kN. Determine the average normal and average shear stress developed in the wood fibers that are oriented along section a–a at 30° with the axis of the block.

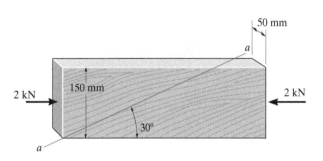

Prob. 7–40

7–41. During the tension test, the wooden specimen is subjected to an average normal stress of 2 ksi. Determine the axial force **P** applied to the specimen. Also, find the average shear stress developed along section *a–a* of the specimen.

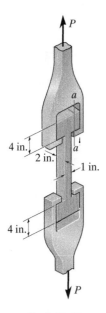

Prob. 7–41

7–42. If the joint is subjected to an axial force of $P = 9$ kN, determine the average shear stress developed in each of the 6-mm diameter bolts between the plates and the members and along each of the four shaded shear planes.

•7–43. The average shear stress in each of the 6-mm diameter bolts and along each of the four shaded shear planes is not allowed to exceed 80 MPa and 500 kPa, respectively. Determine the maximum axial force **P** that can be applied to the joint.

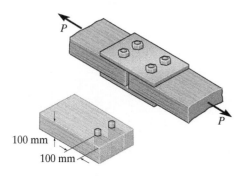

Probs. 7–42/43

*7–44.** The shaft is subjected to the axial force of 40 kN. Determine the average bearing stress acting on the collar *C* and the normal stress in the shaft.

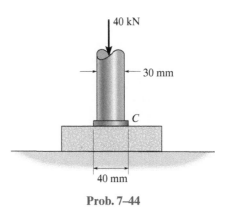

Prob. 7–44

7–45. Rods *AB* and *BC* each have a diameter of 5 mm. If the load of $P = 2$ kN is applied to the ring, determine the average normal stress in each rod if $\theta = 60°$.

7–46. Rods *AB* and *BC* each have a diameter of 5 mm. Determine the angle θ of rod *BC* so that the average normal stress in rod *AB* is 1.5 times that in rod *BC*. What is the load **P** that will cause this to happen if the average normal stress in each rod is not allowed to exceed 100 MPa?

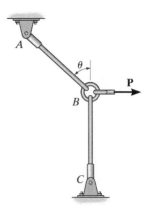

Probs. 7–45/46

•7–47. The specimen failed in a tension test at an angle of 52° when the axial load was 19.80 kip. If the diameter of the specimen is 0.5 in., determine the average normal and average shear stress acting on the area of the inclined failure plane. Also, what is the average normal stress acting on the *cross section* when failure occurs?

Prob. 7–47

*7–48. The anchor bolt was pulled out of the concrete wall and the failure surface formed part of a frustum and cylinder. This indicates a shear failure occurred along the cylinder BC and tension failure along the frustum AB. If the shear and normal stresses along these surfaces have the magnitudes shown, determine the force **P** that must have been applied to the bolt.

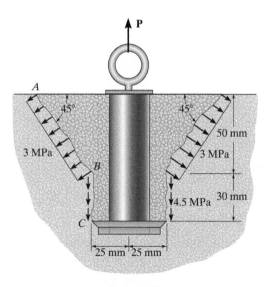

Prob. 7–48

7–49. The open square butt joint is used to transmit a force of 50 kip from one plate to the other. Determine the average normal and average shear stress components that this loading creates on the face of the weld, section AB.

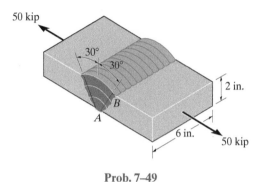

Prob. 7–49

7–50. If $P = 20$ kN, determine the average shear stress developed in the pins at A and C. The pins are subjected to double shear as shown, and each has a diameter of 18 mm.

•7–51. Determine the maximum magnitude P of the load the beam will support if the average shear stress in each pin is not allowed to exceed 60 MPa. All pins are subjected to double shear as shown, and each has a diameter of 18 mm.

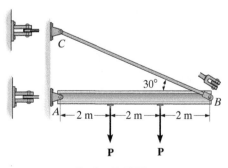

Probs. 7–50/51

7.6   Allowable Stress

To properly *design* a structural member or mechanical element it is necessary to restrict the stress in the material to a level that will be safe. To ensure this safety, it is therefore necessary to choose an allowable stress that restricts the applied load to one that is *less* than the load the member can fully support. There are many reasons for doing this. For example, the load for which the member is designed may be different from actual loadings placed on it. The intended measurements of a structure or machine may not be exact, due to errors in fabrication or in the assembly of its component parts. Unknown vibrations, impact, or accidental loadings can occur that may not be accounted for in the design. Atmospheric corrosion, decay, or weathering tend to cause materials to deteriorate during service. And lastly, some materials, such as wood, concrete, or fiber-reinforced composites, can show high variability in mechanical properties.

One method of specifying the allowable load for a member is to use a number called the factor of safety. The ***factor of safety*** (F.S.) is a ratio of the failure load F_{fail} to the allowable load F_{allow}. Here F_{fail} is found from experimental testing of the material, and the factor of safety is selected based on experience so that the above mentioned uncertainties are accounted for when the member is used under similar conditions of loading and geometry. Stated mathematically,

$$\boxed{\text{F.S.} = \frac{F_{\text{fail}}}{F_{\text{allow}}}} \tag{7-5}$$

If the load applied to the member is *linearly related* to the stress developed within the member, as in the case of using $\sigma = P/A$ and $\tau_{\text{avg}} = V/A$, then we can also express the factor of safety as a ratio of the failure stress σ_{fail} (or τ_{fail}) to the allowable stress σ_{allow} (or τ_{allow});* that is,

$$\text{F.S.} = \frac{\sigma_{\text{fail}}}{\sigma_{\text{allow}}} \tag{7-6}$$

or

$$\text{F.S.} = \frac{\tau_{\text{fail}}}{\tau_{\text{allow}}} \tag{7-7}$$

---

*In some cases, such as columns, the applied load is not linearly related to stress and therefore only Eq. 7–5 can be used to determine the factor of safety. See Chapter 17.

In any of these equations, the factor of safety must be *greater* than 1 in order to avoid the potential for failure. Specific values depend on the types of materials to be used and the intended purpose of the structure or machine. For example, the F.S. used in the design of aircraft or space-vehicle components may be close to 1 in order to reduce the weight of the vehicle. Or, in the case of a nuclear power plant, the factor of safety for some of its components may be as high as 3 due to uncertainties in loading or material behavior. In many cases, the factor of safety for a specific case can be found in design codes and engineering handbooks. These values are intended to form a balance of ensuring public and environmental safety and providing a reasonable economic solution to design.

7.7   Design of Simple Connections

By making simplifying assumptions regarding the behavior of the material, the equations $\sigma = P/A$ and $\tau_{avg} = V/A$ can often be used to analyze or design a simple connection or mechanical element. In particular, if a member is subjected to *normal force* at a section, its required area at the section is determined from

$$A = \frac{P}{\sigma_{allow}} \qquad (7\text{–}8)$$

On the other hand, if the section is subjected to an average *shear force*, then the required area at the section is

$$A = \frac{V}{\tau_{allow}} \qquad (7\text{–}9)$$

As discussed in Sec. 7.6, the allowable stress used in each of these equations is determined either by applying a factor of safety to the material's normal or shear failure stress or by finding these stresses directly from an appropriate design code.

Three examples of where the above equations apply are shown in Fig. 7–21.

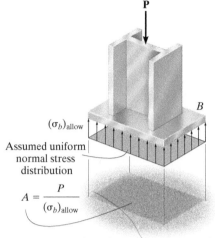

$$A = \frac{P}{(\sigma_b)_{allow}}$$

The area of the column base plate B is determined from the allowable bearing stress for the concrete.

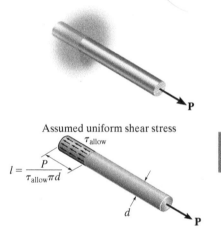

$$l = \frac{P}{\tau_{allow} \pi d}$$

The embedded length l of this rod in concrete can be determined using the allowable shear stress of the bonding glue.

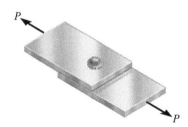

The area of the bolt for this lap joint is determined from the shear stress which is largest between the plates.

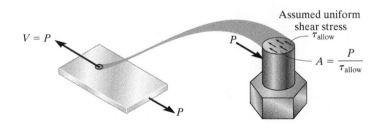

$$A = \frac{P}{\tau_{allow}}$$

Fig. 7–21

Important Point

- Design of a member for strength is based on selecting an allowable stress that will enable it to safely support its intended load. Since there are many unknown factors that can influence the actual stress in a member, then depending upon the intended use of the member, a *factor of safety* is applied to obtain the allowable load the member can support.

Procedure for Analysis

When solving problems using the average normal and shear stress equations, a careful consideration should first be made as to choose the section over which the critical stress is acting. Once this section is determined, the member must then be designed to have a sufficient area at the section to resist the stress that acts on it. This area is determined using the following steps.

Internal Loading.

- Section the member through the area and draw a free-body diagram of a segment of the member. The internal resultant force at the section is then determined using the equations of equilibrium.

Required Area.

- Provided the allowable stress is known or can be determined, the required area needed to sustain the load at the section is then determined from $A = P/\sigma_{\text{allow}}$ or $A = V/\tau_{\text{allow}}$.

Appropriate factors of safety must be considered when designing cranes and cables used to transfer heavy loads.

EXAMPLE | 7.10

The control arm is subjected to the loading shown in Fig. 7–22a. Determine to the nearest $\frac{1}{4}$ in. the required diameter of the steel pin at C if the allowable shear stress for the steel is $\tau_{\text{allow}} = 8$ ksi.

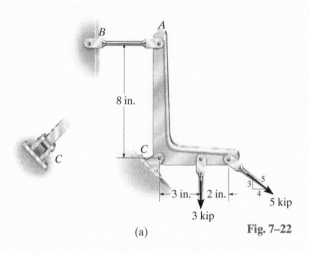

(a)   Fig. 7–22

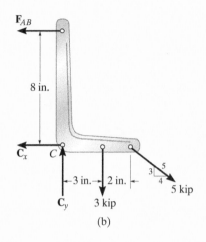

(b)

SOLUTION

Internal Shear Force.   A free-body diagram of the arm is shown in Fig. 7–22b. For equilibrium we have

$$\curvearrowleft + \Sigma M_C = 0; \qquad F_{AB}(8 \text{ in.}) - 3 \text{ kip } (3 \text{ in.}) - 5 \text{ kip } \left(\tfrac{3}{5}\right)(5 \text{ in.}) = 0$$

$$F_{AB} = 3 \text{ kip}$$

$$\xrightarrow{+} \Sigma F_x = 0; \qquad -3 \text{ kip} - C_x + 5 \text{ kip } \left(\tfrac{4}{5}\right) = 0 \qquad C_x = 1 \text{ kip}$$

$$+\uparrow \Sigma F_y = 0; \qquad C_y - 3 \text{ kip} - 5 \text{ kip } \left(\tfrac{3}{5}\right) = 0 \qquad C_y = 6 \text{ kip}$$

The pin at C resists the resultant force at C, which is

$$F_C = \sqrt{(1 \text{ kip})^2 + (6 \text{ kip})^2} = 6.082 \text{ kip}$$

Since the pin is subjected to double shear, a shear force of 3.041 kip acts over its cross-sectional area *between* the arm and each supporting leaf for the pin, Fig. 7–22c.

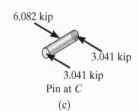

Pin at C

(c)

Required Area.   We have

$$A = \frac{V}{\tau_{\text{allow}}} = \frac{3.041 \text{ kip}}{8 \text{ kip/in}^2} = 0.3802 \text{ in}^2$$

$$\pi \left(\frac{d}{2}\right)^2 = 0.3802 \text{ in}^2$$

$$d = 0.696 \text{ in.}$$

Use a pin having a diameter of

$$d = \tfrac{3}{4} \text{ in.} = 0.750 \text{ in.} \qquad\qquad Ans.$$

EXAMPLE | 7.11

The suspender rod is supported at its end by a fixed-connected circular disk as shown in Fig. 7–23a. If the rod passes through a 40-mm-diameter hole, determine the minimum required diameter of the rod and the minimum thickness of the disk needed to support the 20-kN load. The allowable normal stress for the rod is $\sigma_{\text{allow}} = 60$ MPa, and the allowable shear stress for the disk is $\tau_{\text{allow}} = 35$ MPa.

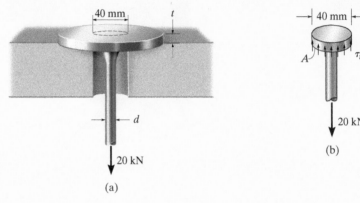

Fig. 7–23

SOLUTION

Diameter of Rod.   By inspection, the axial force in the rod is 20 kN. Thus the required cross-sectional area of the rod is

$$A = \frac{P}{\sigma_{\text{allow}}}; \qquad \frac{\pi}{4}d^2 = \frac{20(10^3) \text{ N}}{60(10^6) \text{ N/m}^2}$$

so that

$$d = 0.0206 \text{ m} = 20.6 \text{ mm} \qquad \textit{Ans.}$$

Thickness of Disk.   As shown on the free-body diagram in Fig. 7–23b, the material at the sectioned area of the disk must resist *shear stress* to prevent movement of the disk through the hole. If this shear stress is *assumed* to be uniformly distributed over the sectioned area, then, since $V = 20$ kN, we have

$$A = \frac{V}{\tau_{\text{allow}}}; \qquad 2\pi(0.02 \text{ m})(t) = \frac{20(10^3) \text{ N}}{35(10^6) \text{ N/m}^2}$$

$$t = 4.55(10^{-3}) \text{ m} = 4.55 \text{ mm} \qquad \textit{Ans.}$$

EXAMPLE | 7.12

The shaft shown in Fig. 7–24a is supported by the collar at C, which is attached to the shaft and located on the right side of the bearing at B. Determine the largest value of P for the axial forces at E and F so that the bearing stress on the collar does not exceed an allowable stress of $(\sigma_b)_{\text{allow}} = 75$ MPa and the average normal stress in the shaft does not exceed an allowable stress of $(\sigma_t)_{\text{allow}} = 55$ MPa.

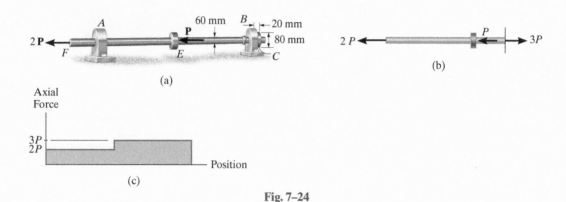

(a)

(b)

(c)

Fig. 7–24

SOLUTION

To solve the problem we will determine P for each possible failure condition. Then we will choose the *smallest* value. Why?

Normal Stress.   Using the method of sections, the axial load within region FE of the shaft is 2P, whereas the *largest* axial force, 3P, occurs within region EC, Fig. 7–24b. The variation of the internal loading is clearly shown on the normal-force diagram, Fig. 7–24c. Since the cross-sectional area of the entire shaft is constant, region EC is subjected to the maximum average normal stress. Applying Eq. 7–8, we have

$$A = \frac{P}{\sigma_{\text{allow}}}; \qquad \pi(0.03 \text{ m})^2 = \frac{3P}{55(10^6) \text{ N/m}^2}$$

$$P = 51.8 \text{ kN} \qquad\qquad Ans.$$

Bearing Stress.   As shown on the free-body diagram in Fig. 7–24d, the collar at C must resist the load of 3P, which acts over a bearing area of $A_b = [\pi(0.04 \text{ m})^2 - \pi(0.03 \text{ m})^2] = 2.199(10^{-3}) \text{ m}^2$. Thus,

$$A = \frac{P}{\sigma_{\text{allow}}}; \qquad 2.199(10^{-3}) \text{ m}^2 = \frac{3P}{75(10^6) \text{ N/m}^2}$$

$$P = 55.0 \text{ kN}$$

(d)

By comparison, the largest load that can be applied to the shaft is $P = 51.8$ kN, since any load larger than this will cause the allowable normal stress in the shaft to be exceeded.

NOTE: Here we have not considered a possible shear failure of the collar as in Example 7.11.

FUNDAMENTAL PROBLEMS

F7–13. Rods AC and BC are used to suspend the 200-kg mass. If each rod is made of a material for which the average normal stress can not exceed 150 MPa, determine the minimum required diameter of each rod to the nearest mm.

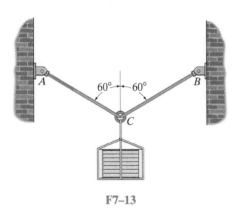

F7–13

F7–14. The frame supports the loading shown. The pin at A has a diameter of 0.25 in. If it is subjected to double shear, determine the average shear stress in the pin.

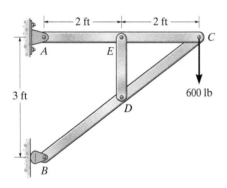

F7–14

F7–15. Determine the maximum average shear stress developed in each 3/4-in.-diameter bolt.

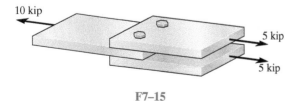

F7–15

F7–16. If each of the three nails has a diameter of 4 mm and can withstand an average shear stress of 60 MPa, determine the maximum allowable force **P** that can be applied to the board.

F7–16

F7–17. The strut is glued to the horizontal member at surface AB. If the strut has a thickness of 25 mm and the glue can withstand an average shear stress of 600 kPa, determine the maximum force **P** that can be applied to the strut.

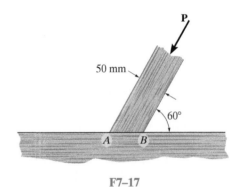

F7–17

F7–18. Determine the maximum average shear stress developed in the 30-mm-diameter pin.

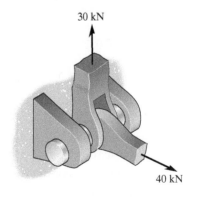

F7–18

F7–19. If the eyebolt is made of a material having a yield stress of $\sigma_Y = 250$ MPa, determine the minimum required diameter d of its shank. Apply a factor of safety F.S. = 1.5 against yielding.

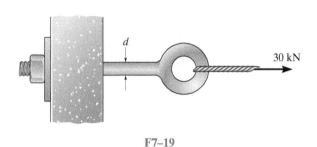

F7–19

F7–20. If the bar assembly is made of a material having a yield stress of $\sigma_Y = 50$ ksi, determine the minimum required dimensions h_1 and h_2 to the nearest 1/8 in. Apply a factor of safety F.S. = 1.5 against yielding. Each bar has a thickness of 0.5 in.

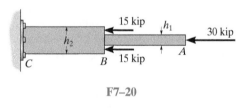

F7–20

F7–21. Determine the maximum force **P** that can be applied to the rod if it is made of material having a yield stress of $\sigma_Y = 250$ MPa. Consider the possibility that failure occurs in the rod and at section a–a. Apply a factor of safety F.S. = 2 against yielding.

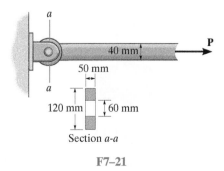

F7–21

F7–22. The pin is made of a material having a failure shear stress of $\tau_{fail} = 100$ MPa. Determine the minimum required diameter of the pin to the nearest mm. Apply a factor of safety F.S. = 2.5 against shear failure.

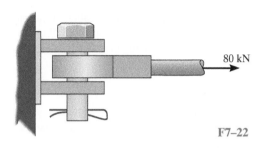

F7–22

F7–23. If the bolt head and the supporting bracket are made of the same material having a failure shear stress of $\tau_{fail} = 120$ MPa, determine the maximum allowable force **P** that can be applied to the bolt so that it does not pull through the plate. Apply a factor of safety F.S. = 2.5 against shear failure.

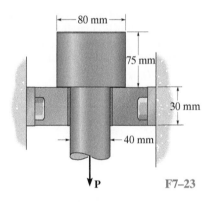

F7–23

F7–24. Six nails are used to hold the hanger at A against the column. Determine the minimum required diameter of each nail to the nearest 1/16 in. if it is made of material having $\tau_{fail} = 16$ ksi. Apply a factor of safety F.S. = 2 against shear failure.

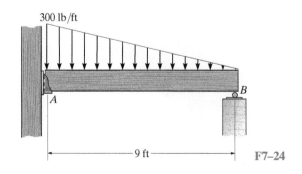

F7–24

7

PROBLEMS

*7–52. Member B is subjected to a compressive force of 800 lb. If A and B are both made of wood and are $\frac{3}{8}$ in. thick, determine to the nearest $\frac{1}{4}$ in. the smallest dimension h of the horizontal segment so that it does not fail in shear. The average shear stress for the segment is $\tau_{\text{allow}} = 300$ psi.

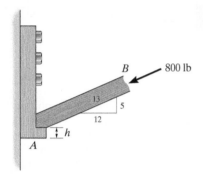

Prob. 7–52

7–53. The lever is attached to the shaft A using a key that has a width d and length of 25 mm. If the shaft is fixed and a vertical force of 200 N is applied perpendicular to the handle, determine the dimension d if the allowable shear stress for the key is $\tau_{\text{allow}} = 35$ MPa.

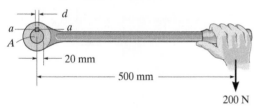

Prob. 7–53

7–54. The joint is fastened together using two bolts. Determine the required diameter of the bolts if the failure shear stress for the bolts is $\tau_{\text{fail}} = 350$ MPa. Use a factor of safety for shear of F.S. = 2.5.

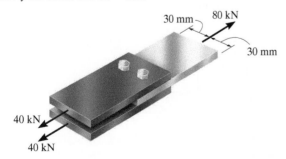

Prob. 7–54

7–55. The lapbelt assembly is to be subjected to a force of 800 N. Determine (a) the required thickness t of the belt if the allowable tensile stress for the material is $(\sigma_t)_{\text{allow}} = 10$ MPa, (b) the required lap length d_l if the glue can sustain an allowable shear stress of $(\tau_{\text{allow}})_g = 0.75$ MPa, and (c) the required diameter d_r of the pin if the allowable shear stress for the pin is $(\tau_{\text{allow}})_p = 30$ MPa.

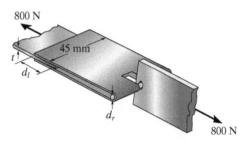

Prob. 7–55

*7–56. The wood specimen is subjected to the pull of 10 kN in a tension testing machine. If the allowable normal stress for the wood is $(\sigma_t)_{\text{allow}} = 12$ MPa and the allowable shear stress is $\tau_{\text{allow}} = 1.2$ MPa, determine the required dimensions b and t so that the specimen reaches these stresses simultaneously. The specimen has a width of 25 mm.

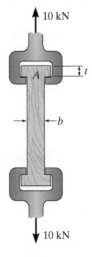

Prob. 7–56

7–57. Member B is subjected to a compressive force of 600 lb. If A and B are both made of wood and are 1.5 in. thick, determine to the nearest 1/8 in. the smallest dimension a of the support so that the average shear stress along the blue line does not exceed $\tau_{allow} = 50$ psi. Neglect friction.

*7–60. The tension member is fastened together using *two* bolts, one on each side of the member as shown. Each bolt has a diameter of 0.3 in. Determine the maximum load P that can be applied to the member if the allowable shear stress for the bolts is $\tau_{allow} = 12$ ksi and the allowable average normal stress is $\sigma_{allow} = 20$ ksi.

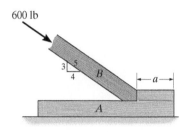

Prob. 7–57

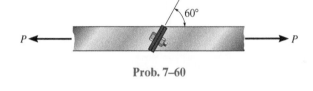

Prob. 7–60

7–58. The joint is used to transmit a torque of $T = 3$ kN $\cdot$ m. Determine the required minimum diameter of the shear pin A if it is made from a material having a shear failure stress of $\tau_{fail} = 150$ MPa. Apply a factor of safety of 3 against failure.

7–59. Determine the maximum allowable torque $\mathbf{T}$ that can be transmitted by the joint. The shear pin A has a diameter of 25 mm, and it is made from a material having a failure shear stress of $\tau_{fail} = 150$ MPa. Apply a factor of safety of 3 against failure.

7–61. The three steel wires are used to support the load. If the wires have an allowable tensile stress of $\sigma_{allow} = 165$ MPa, determine the required diameter of each wire if the applied load is $P = 6$ kN.

7–62. The three steel wires are used to support the load. If the wires have an allowable tensile stress of $\sigma_{allow} = 165$ MPa, and wire AB has a diameter of 6 mm, BC has a diameter of 5 mm, and BD has a diameter of 7 mm, determine the greatest force P that can be applied before one of the wires fails.

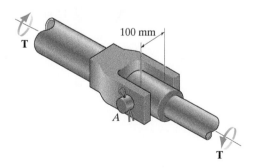

Probs. 7–58/59

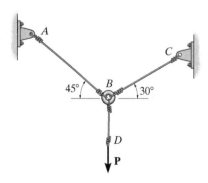

Probs. 7–61/62

7–63. The assembly consists of three disks A, B, and C that are used to support the load of 140 kN. Determine the smallest diameter d_1 of the top disk, the diameter d_2 within the support space, and the diameter d_3 of the hole in the bottom disk. The allowable bearing stress for the material is $(\sigma_{\text{allow}})_b = 350$ MPa and allowable shear stress is $\tau_{\text{allow}} = 125$ MPa.

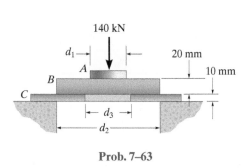

Prob. 7–63

7–66. The 60 mm × 60 mm oak post is supported on the pine block. If the allowable bearing stresses for these materials are $\sigma_{\text{oak}} = 43$ MPa and $\sigma_{\text{pine}} = 25$ MPa, determine the greatest load P that can be supported. If a rigid bearing plate is used between these materials, determine its required area so that the maximum load P can be supported. What is this load?

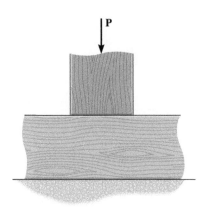

Prob. 7–66

*7–64. The boom is supported by the winch cable that has a diameter of 0.25 in. and an allowable normal stress of $\sigma_{\text{allow}} = 24$ ksi. Determine the greatest load that can be supported without causing the cable to fail when $\theta = 30°$ and $\phi = 45°$. Neglect the size of the winch.

7–65. The boom is supported by the winch cable that has an allowable normal stress of $\sigma_{\text{allow}} = 24$ ksi. If it is required that it be able to slowly lift 5000 lb, from $\theta = 20°$ to $\theta = 50°$, determine the smallest diameter of the cable to the nearest $\frac{1}{16}$ in. The boom AB has a length of 20 ft. Neglect the size of the winch. Set $d = 12$ ft.

7–67. The frame is subjected to the load of 4 kN which acts on member ABD at D. Determine the required diameter of the pins at D and C if the allowable shear stress for the material is $\tau_{\text{allow}} = 40$ MPa. Pin C is subjected to double shear, whereas pin D is subjected to single shear.

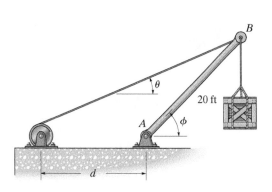

Probs. 7–64/65

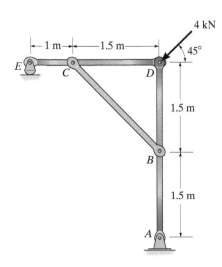

Prob. 7–67

*7–68. The eye bolt is used to support the load of 5 kip. Determine its diameter d to the nearest $\frac{1}{8}$ in. and the required thickness h to the nearest $\frac{1}{8}$ in. of the support so that the washer will not penetrate or shear through it. The allowable normal stress for the bolt is $\sigma_{\text{allow}} = 21$ ksi and the allowable shear stress for the supporting material is $\tau_{\text{allow}} = 5$ ksi.

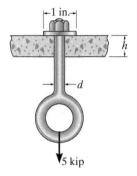

Prob. 7–68

7–69. The soft-ride suspension system of the mountain bike is pinned at C and supported by the shock absorber BD. If it is designed to support a load $P = 1500$ N, determine the required minimum diameter of pins B and C. Use a factor of safety of 2 against failure. The pins are made of material having a failure shear stress of $\tau_{\text{fail}} = 150$ MPa, and each pin is subjected to double shear.

7–70. The soft-ride suspension system of the mountain bike is pinned at C and supported by the shock absorber BD. If it is designed to support a load of $P = 1500$ N, determine the factor of safety of pins B and C against failure if they are made of a material having a shear failure stress of $\tau_{\text{fail}} = 150$ MPa. Pin B has a diameter of 7.5 mm, and pin C has a diameter of 6.5 mm. Both pins are subjected to double shear.

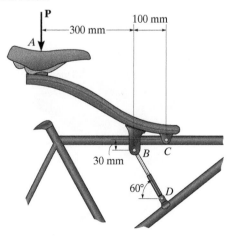

Probs. 7–69/70

7–71. The compound wooden beam is connected together by a bolt at B. Assuming that the connections at $A, B, C,$ and D exert only vertical forces on the beam, determine the required diameter of the bolt at B and the required outer diameter of its washers if the allowable tensile stress for the bolt is $(\sigma_t)_{\text{allow}} = 150$ MPa and the allowable bearing stress for the wood is $(\sigma_b)_{\text{allow}} = 28$ MPa. Assume that the hole in the washers has the same diameter as the bolt.

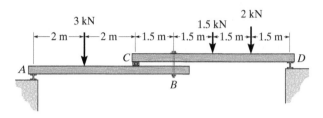

Prob. 7–71

*7–72. The assembly is used to support the distributed loading of $w = 500$ lb/ft. Determine the factor of safety with respect to yielding for the steel rod BC and the pins at B and C if the yield stress for the steel in tension is $\sigma_y = 36$ ksi and in shear $\tau_y = 18$ ksi. The rod has a diameter of 0.40 in., and the pins each have a diameter of 0.30 in.

7–73. If the allowable shear stress for each of the 0.30- in.-diameter steel pins at $A, B,$ and C is $\tau_{\text{allow}} = 12.5$ ksi, and the allowable normal stress for the 0.40-in.-diameter rod is $\sigma_{\text{allow}} = 22$ ksi, determine the largest intensity w of the uniform distributed load that can be suspended from the beam.

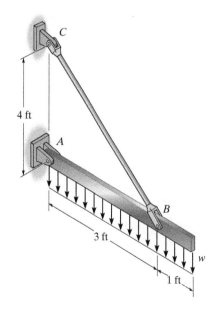

Probs. 7–72/73

7–74. If the allowable bearing stress for the material under the supports at A and B is $(\sigma_b)_{\text{allow}} = 1.5$ MPa, determine the size of *square* bearing plates A' and B' required to support the load. Dimension the plates to the nearest mm. The reactions at the supports are vertical. Take $P = 100$ kN.

7–75. If the allowable bearing stress for the material under the supports at A and B is $(\sigma_b)_{\text{allow}} = 1.5$ MPa, determine the maximum load P that can be applied to the beam. The bearing plates A' and B' have square cross sections of 150 mm $\times$ 150 mm and 250 mm $\times$ 250 mm, respectively.

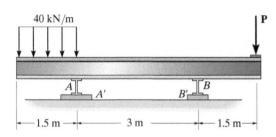

Probs. 7–74/75

*7–76. The rods AB and CD are made of steel having a failure tensile stress of $\sigma_{\text{fail}} = 510$ MPa. Using a factor of safety of F.S. = 1.75 for tension, determine their smallest diameter so that they can support the load shown. The beam is assumed to be pin connected at A and C.

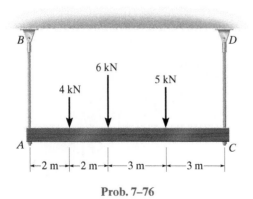

Prob. 7–76

7–77. The aluminum bracket A is used to support the centrally applied load of 8 kip. If it has a constant thickness of 0.5 in., determine the smallest height h in order to prevent a shear failure. The failure shear stress is $\tau_{\text{fail}} = 23$ ksi. Use a factor of safety for shear of F.S. = 2.5.

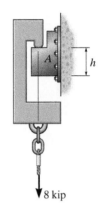

Prob. 7–77

7–78. The hanger is supported using the rectangular pin. Determine the magnitude of the allowable suspended load $\mathbf{P}$ if the allowable bearing stress is $(\sigma_b)_{\text{allow}} = 220$ MPa, the allowable tensile stress is $(\sigma_t)_{\text{allow}} = 150$ MPa, and the allowable shear stress is $\tau_{\text{allow}} = 130$ MPa. Take $t = 6$ mm, $a = 5$ mm, and $b = 25$ mm.

7–79. The hanger is supported using the rectangular pin. Determine the required thickness t of the hanger, and dimensions a and b if the suspended load is $P = 60$ kN. The allowable tensile stress is $(\sigma_t)_{\text{allow}} = 150$ MPa, the allowable bearing stress is $(\sigma_b)_{\text{allow}} = 290$ MPa, and the allowable shear stress is $\tau_{\text{allow}} = 125$ MPa.

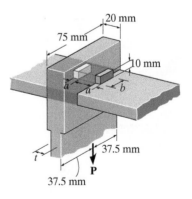

Probs. 7–78/79

7.8   Deformation

Whenever a force is applied to a body, it will tend to change the body's shape and size. These changes are referred to as **deformation**, and they may be either highly visible or practically unnoticeable. For example, a rubber band will undergo a very large deformation when stretched, whereas only slight deformations of structural members occur when a building is occupied by people walking about. Deformation of a body can also occur when the temperature of the body is changed. A typical example is the thermal expansion or contraction of a roof caused by the weather.

   In a general sense, the deformation of a body will not be uniform throughout its volume, and so the change in geometry of any line segment within the body may vary substantially along its length. Hence, to study deformational changes in a more uniform manner, we will consider line segments that are very short and located in the neighborhood of a point. Realize, however, that these changes will also depend on the orientation of the line segment at the point. For example, a line segment may elongate if it is oriented in one direction, whereas it may contract if it is oriented in another direction.

Note the before and after positions of three different line segments on this rubber membrane which is subjected to tension. The vertical line is lengthened, the horizontal line is shortened, and the inclined line changes its length and rotates.

7.9 Strain

In order to describe the deformation of a body by changes in length of line segments and the changes in the angles between them, we will develop the concept of strain. Strain is actually measured by experiments, and once the strain is obtained, it will be shown in the next chapter how it can be related to the stress acting within the body.

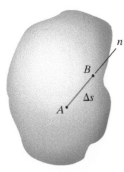

Undeformed body
(a)

Normal Strain. If we define the normal strain as the change in length of a line per unit length, then we will not have to specify the *actual length* of any particular line segment. Consider, for example, the line AB, which is contained within the undeformed body shown in Fig. 7–25a. This line lies along the n axis and has an original length of Δs. After deformation, points A and B are displaced to A' and B', and the line becomes a curve having a length of $\Delta s'$, Fig. 7–25b. The change in length of the line is therefore $\Delta s' - \Delta s$. If we define the *average normal strain* using the symbol ϵ_{avg} (epsilon), then

$$\epsilon_{avg} = \frac{\Delta s' - \Delta s}{\Delta s} \qquad (7\text{--}10)$$

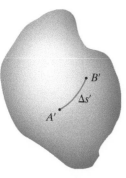

Deformed body
(b)

Fig. 7–25

As point B is chosen closer and closer to point A, the length of the line will become shorter and shorter, such that $\Delta s \to 0$. Also, this causes B' to approach A', such that $\Delta s' \to 0$. Consequently, in the limit the normal strain at point A and in the direction of n is

$$\epsilon = \lim_{B \to A \text{ along } n} \frac{\Delta s' - \Delta s}{\Delta s} \qquad (7\text{--}11)$$

Hence, when ϵ (or ϵ_{avg}) is positive the initial line will elongate, whereas if ϵ is negative the line contracts.

Note that normal strain is a *dimensionless quantity*, since it is a ratio of two lengths. Although this is the case, it is sometimes stated in terms of a ratio of length units. If the SI system is used, then the basic unit for length is the meter (m). Ordinarily, for most engineering applications ϵ will be very small, so measurements of strain are in micrometers per meter (μm/m), where $1\,\mu$m $= 10^{-6}$ m. In the Foot-Pound-Second system, strain is often stated in units of inches per inch (in./in.). Sometimes for experimental work, strain is expressed as a percent, e.g., $0.001 \text{ m/m} = 0.1\%$. As an example, a normal strain of $480(10^{-6})$ can be reported as $480(10^{-6})$ in./in., $480 \mu\text{m/m}$, or 0.0480%. Also, one can state this answer as simply 480μ (480 "micros").

Shear Strain.   Deformations not only cause line segments to elongate or contract, but they also cause them to change direction. If we select two line segments that are originally perpendicular to one another, then the change in angle that occurs between these two line segments is referred to as **shear strain**. This angle is denoted by γ (gamma) and is always measured in radians (rad), which are dimensionless. For example, consider the line segments AB and AC originating from the same point A in a body, and directed along the perpendicular n and t axes, Fig. 7–26a. After deformation, the ends of both lines are displaced, and the lines themselves become curves, such that the angle between them at A is θ', Fig. 7–26b. Hence the shear strain at point A associated with the n and t axes becomes

$$\gamma_{nt} = \frac{\pi}{2} - \lim_{\substack{B \to A \text{ along } n \\ C \to A \text{ along } t}} \theta' \qquad (7\text{–}12)$$

Notice that if θ' is smaller than $\pi/2$ the shear strain is positive, whereas if θ' is larger than $\pi/2$ the shear strain is negative.

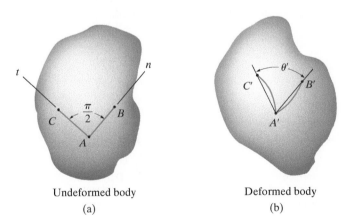

Undeformed body   Deformed body
(a)   (b)

Fig. 7–26

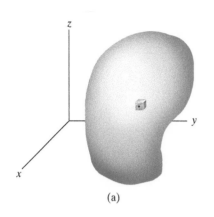

(a)

Cartesian Strain Components.

Using the definitions of normal and shear strain, we will now show how they can be used to describe the deformation of the body in Fig. 7–27a. To do so, imagine the body is subdivided into small elements such as the one shown in Fig. 7–27b. This element is rectangular, has undeformed dimensions Δx, Δy, and Δz, and is located in the neighborhood of a point in the body, Fig. 7–27a. If the element's dimensions are very small, then its deformed shape will be a parallelepiped, Fig. 7–27c, since very small line segments will remain approximately straight after the body is deformed. In order to achieve this deformed shape, we will first consider how the normal strain changes the lengths of the sides of the rectangular element, and then how the shear strain changes the angles of each side. For example, Δx elongates $\epsilon_x \Delta x$, so its new length is $\Delta x + \epsilon_x \Delta x$. Therefore, the approximate lengths of the three sides of the parallelepiped are

$$(1 + \epsilon_x)\,\Delta x \qquad (1 + \epsilon_y)\,\Delta y \qquad (1 + \epsilon_z)\,\Delta z$$

And the approximate angles between these sides are

$$\frac{\pi}{2} - \gamma_{xy} \qquad \frac{\pi}{2} - \gamma_{yz} \qquad \frac{\pi}{2} - \gamma_{xz}$$

Notice that the ***normal strains cause a change in volume*** of the element, whereas the ***shear strains cause a change in its shape***. Of course, both of these effects occur simultaneously during the deformation.

In summary, then, the *state of strain* at a point in a body requires specifying three normal strains, ϵ_x, ϵ_y, ϵ_z, and three shear strains, γ_{xy}, γ_{yz}, γ_{xz}. These strains completely describe the deformation of a rectangular volume element of material located at the point and oriented so that its sides are originally parallel to the x, y, z axes. Provided these strains are defined at all points in the body, then the deformed shape of the body can be determined.

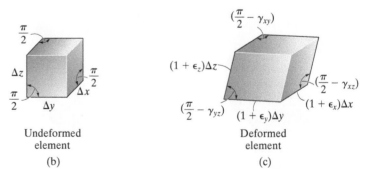

Undeformed element

(b)

Deformed element

(c)

Fig. 7–27

Small Strain Analysis. Most engineering design involves applications for which only *small deformations* are allowed. In this text, therefore, we will assume that the deformations that take place within a body are almost infinitesimal. In particular, the *normal strains* occurring within the material are *very small* compared to 1, so that $\epsilon \ll 1$. This assumption has wide practical application in engineering, and it is often referred to as a *small strain analysis*. It can be used, for example, to approximate $\sin \theta = \theta$, $\cos \theta = 1$, and $\tan \theta = \theta$, provided θ is very small.

The rubber bearing support under this concrete bridge girder is subjected to both normal and shear strain. The normal strain is caused by the weight and bridge loads on the girder, and the shear strain is caused by the horizontal movement of the girder due to temperature changes.

Important Points

- Loads will cause all material bodies to deform and, as a result, points in a body will undergo *displacements or changes in position.*

- *Normal strain* is a measure per unit length of the elongation or contraction of a small line segment in the body, whereas *shear strain* is a measure of the change in angle that occurs between two small line segments that are originally perpendicular to one another.

- The state of strain at a point is characterized by six strain components: three normal strains ϵ_x, ϵ_y, ϵ_z and three shear strains γ_{xy}, γ_{yz}, γ_{xz}. These components depend upon the original orientation of the line segments and their location in the body.

- Strain is the geometrical quantity that is measured using experimental techniques. Once obtained, the stress in the body can then be determined from material property relations, as discussed in the next chapter.

- Most engineering materials undergo very small deformations, and so the normal strain $\epsilon \ll 1$. This assumption of "small strain analysis" allows the calculations for normal strain to be simplified, since first-order approximations can be made about their size.

7

EXAMPLE | 7.13

When force **P** is applied to the rigid lever arm ABC in Fig. 7–28a, the arm rotates counterclockwise about pin A through an angle of $0.05°$. Determine the normal strain developed in wire BD.

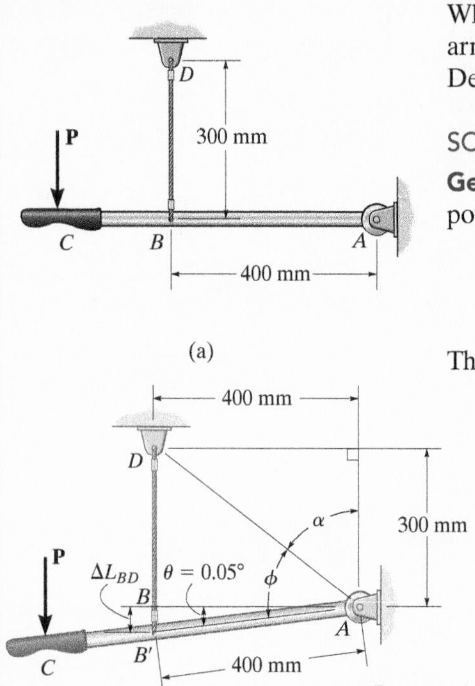

SOLUTION I

Geometry. The orientation of the lever arm after it rotates about point A is shown in Fig. 7–28b. From the geometry of this figure,

$$\alpha = \tan^{-1}\left(\frac{400 \text{ mm}}{300 \text{ mm}}\right) = 53.1301°$$

Then

$$\phi = 90° - \alpha + 0.05° = 90° - 53.1301° + 0.05° = 36.92°$$

For triangle ABD the Pythagorean theorem gives

$$L_{AD} = \sqrt{(300 \text{ mm})^2 + (400 \text{ mm})^2} = 500 \text{ mm}$$

Using this result and applying the law of cosines to triangle $AB'D$,

$$L_{B'D} = \sqrt{L_{AD}^2 + L_{AB'}^2 - 2(L_{AD})(L_{AB'})\cos\phi}$$
$$= \sqrt{(500 \text{ mm})^2 + (400 \text{ mm})^2 - 2(500 \text{ mm})(400 \text{ mm})\cos 36.92°}$$
$$= 300.3491 \text{ mm}$$

Normal Strain.

$$\epsilon_{BD} = \frac{L_{B'D} - L_{BD}}{L_{BD}} = \frac{300.3491 \text{ mm} - 300 \text{ mm}}{300 \text{ mm}} = 0.00116 \text{ mm/mm} \quad \textit{Ans.}$$

SOLUTION II

Since the strain is small, this same result can be obtained by approximating the elongation of wire BD as ΔL_{BD}, shown in Fig. 7–28b. Here,

$$\Delta L_{BD} = \theta L_{AB} = \left[\left(\frac{0.05°}{180°}\right)(\pi \text{ rad})\right](400 \text{ mm}) = 0.3491 \text{ mm}$$

Therefore,

$$\epsilon_{BD} = \frac{\Delta L_{BD}}{L_{BD}} = \frac{0.3491 \text{ mm}}{300 \text{ mm}} = 0.00116 \text{ mm/mm} \quad \textit{Ans.}$$

(a)

(b)

Fig. 7–28

P

D

300 mm

C B A

400 mm

400 mm

D

α

300 mm

P ΔL_{BD} $\theta = 0.05°$ ϕ

B

C B'

400 mm

A

7

EXAMPLE | 7.14

Due to a loading, the plate is deformed into the dashed shape shown in Fig. 7–29a. Determine (a) the average normal strain along the side *AB*, and (b) the average shear strain in the plate at *A* relative to the *x* and *y* axes.

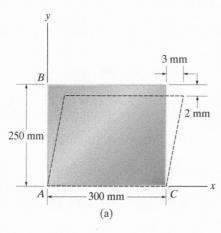

(a)

Fig. 7–29

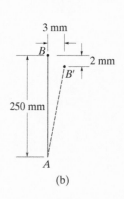

(b)

SOLUTION

Part (a). Line *AB*, coincident with the *y* axis, becomes line *AB'* after deformation, as shown in Fig. 7–29b. The length of *AB'* is

$$AB' = \sqrt{(250 \text{ mm} - 2 \text{ mm})^2 + (3 \text{ mm})^2} = 248.018 \text{ mm}$$

The average normal strain for *AB* is therefore

$$(\epsilon_{AB})_{\text{avg}} = \frac{AB' - AB}{AB} = \frac{248.018 \text{ mm} - 250 \text{ mm}}{250 \text{ mm}}$$

$$= -7.93(10^{-3}) \text{ mm/mm} \qquad \textit{Ans.}$$

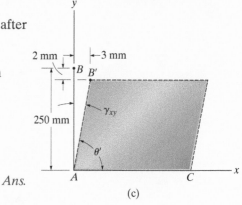

(c)

The negative sign indicates the strain causes a contraction of *AB*.

Part (b). As noted in Fig. 7–29c, the once 90° angle *BAC* between the sides of the plate at *A* changes to θ' due to the displacement of *B* to *B'*. Since $\gamma_{xy} = \pi/2 - \theta'$, then γ_{xy} is the angle shown in the figure. Thus,

$$\gamma_{xy} = \tan^{-1}\left(\frac{3 \text{ mm}}{250 \text{ mm} - 2 \text{ mm}}\right) = 0.0121 \text{ rad} \qquad \textit{Ans.}$$

7

EXAMPLE | 7.15

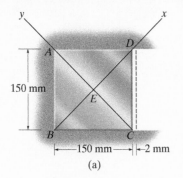

(a)

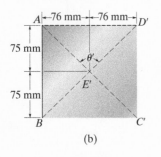

(b)

Fig. 7–30

The plate shown in Fig. 7–30a is fixed connected along AB and held in the horizontal guides at its top and bottom, AD and BC. If its right side CD is given a uniform horizontal displacement of 2 mm, determine (a) the average normal strain along the diagonal AC, and (b) the shear strain at E relative to the x, y axes.

SOLUTION

Part (a). When the plate is deformed, the diagonal AC becomes AC', Fig. 7–30b. The length of diagonals AC and AC' can be found from the Pythagorean theorem. We have

$$AC = \sqrt{(0.150 \text{ m})^2 + (0.150 \text{ m})^2} = 0.21213 \text{ m}$$

$$AC' = \sqrt{(0.150 \text{ m})^2 + (0.152 \text{ m})^2} = 0.21355 \text{ m}$$

Therefore the average normal strain along the diagonal is

$$(\epsilon_{AC})_{\text{avg}} = \frac{AC' - AC}{AC} = \frac{0.21355 \text{ m} - 0.21213 \text{ m}}{0.21213 \text{ m}}$$

$$= 0.00669 \text{ mm/mm} \qquad \textit{Ans.}$$

Part (b). To find the shear strain at E relative to the x and y axes, it is first necessary to find the angle θ' after deformation, Fig. 7–30b. We have

$$\tan\left(\frac{\theta'}{2}\right) = \frac{76 \text{ mm}}{75 \text{ mm}}$$

$$\theta' = 90.759° = \left(\frac{\pi}{180°}\right)(90.759°) = 1.58404 \text{ rad}$$

Applying Eq. 7–12, the shear strain at E is therefore

$$\gamma_{xy} = \frac{\pi}{2} - 1.58404 \text{ rad} = -0.0132 \text{ rad} \qquad \textit{Ans.}$$

The *negative sign* indicates that the angle θ' is *greater than* 90°.

NOTE: If the x and y axes were horizontal and vertical at point E, then the 90° angle between these axes would not change due to the deformation, and so $\gamma_{xy} = 0$ at point E.

FUNDAMENTAL PROBLEMS

F7–25. When force **P** is applied to the rigid arm *ABC*, point *B* displaces vertically downward through a distance of 0.2 mm. Determine the normal strain developed in wire *CD*.

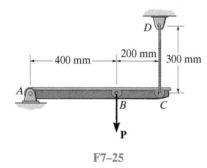

F7–25

F7–26. If the applied force **P** causes the rigid arm *ABC* to rotate clockwise about pin *A* through an angle of 0.02°, determine the normal strain developed in wires *BD* and *CE*.

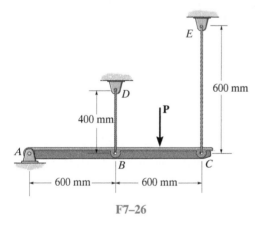

F7–26

F7–27. The rectangular plate is deformed into the shape of a rhombus shown by the dashed line. Determine the average shear strain at corner *A* with respect to the *x* and *y* axes.

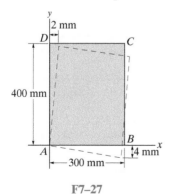

F7–27

F7–28. The triangular plate is deformed into the shape shown by the dashed line. Determine the normal strain developed along edge *BC* and the average shear strain at corner *A* with respect to the *x* and *y* axes.

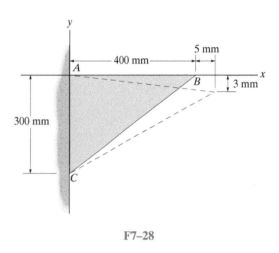

F7–28

F7–29. The square plate is deformed into the shape shown by the dashed line. Determine the average normal strain along diagonal *AC* and the shear strain of point *E* with respect to the *x* and *y* axes.

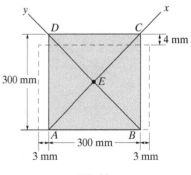

F7–29

PROBLEMS

*7–80.   An air-filled rubber ball has a diameter of 6 in. If the air pressure within it is increased until the ball's diameter becomes 7 in., determine the average normal strain in the rubber.

7–81.   A thin strip of rubber has an unstretched length of 15 in. If it is stretched around a pipe having an outer diameter of 5 in., determine the average normal strain in the strip.

7–82.   The rigid beam is supported by a pin at A and wires BD and CE. If the load $\mathbf{P}$ on the beam causes the end C to be displaced 10 mm downward, determine the normal strain developed in wires CE and BD.

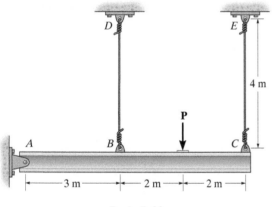

Prob. 7–82

7–83.   The two wires are connected together at A. If the force $\mathbf{P}$ causes point A to be displaced horizontally 2 mm, determine the normal strain developed in each wire.

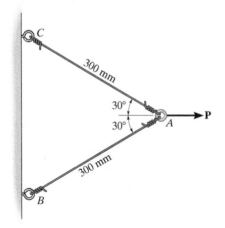

Prob. 7–83

*7–84.   The rigid beam is supported by a pin at A and wires BD and CE. If the distributed load causes the end C to be displaced 10 mm downward, determine the normal strain developed in wires CE and BD.

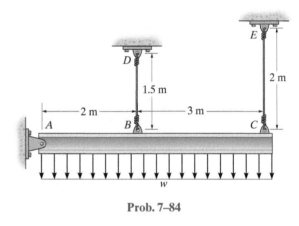

Prob. 7–84

7–85.   Nylon strips are fused to glass plates. When moderately heated the nylon will become soft while the glass stays approximately rigid. Determine the average shear strain in the nylon due to the load $\mathbf{P}$ when the assembly deforms as indicated.

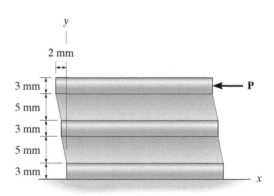

Prob. 7–85

7–86. If the unstretched length of the bowstring is 35.5 in., determine the average normal strain in the string when it is stretched to the position shown.

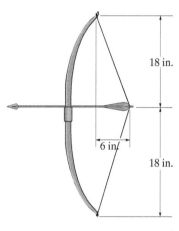

18 in.

6 in.

18 in.

Prob. 7–86

7–87. Part of a control linkage for an airplane consists of a rigid member *CBD* and a flexible cable *AB*. If a force is applied to the end *D* of the member and causes it to rotate by $\theta = 0.3°$, determine the normal strain in the cable. Originally the cable is unstretched.

*7–88. Part of a control linkage for an airplane consists of a rigid member *CBD* and a flexible cable *AB*. If a force is applied to the end *D* of the member and causes a normal strain in the cable of 0.0035 mm/mm, determine the displacement of point *D*. Originally the cable is unstretched.

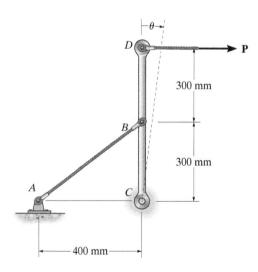

θ

D ▸ **P**

300 mm

B

300 mm

A

C

400 mm

Probs. 7–87/88

7–89. The corners *B* and *D* of the square plate are given the displacements indicated. Determine the shear strains at *A* and *B*.

7–90. The corners *B* and *D* of the square plate are given the displacements indicated. Determine the average normal strains along side *AB* and diagonal *DB*.

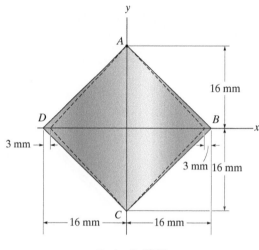

y

A

16 mm

D   *B*   → *x*

3 mm →

3 mm 16 mm

16 mm   *C*   16 mm

Probs. 7–89/90

7–91. The piece of rubber is originally rectangular. Determine the average shear strain γ_{xy} at *A* if the corners *B* and *D* are subjected to the displacements that cause the rubber to distort as shown by the dashed lines.

*7–92. The piece of rubber is originally rectangular and subjected to the deformation shown by the dashed lines. Determine the average normal strain along the diagonal *DB* and side *AD*.

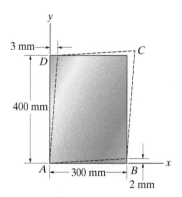

y

3 mm

D   *C*

400 mm

A 300 mm *B* → *x*

2 mm

Probs. 7–91/92

7–93. Two bars are used to support a load. When unloaded, AB is 5 in. long, AC is 8 in. long, and the ring at A has coordinates $(0, 0)$. If a load **P** acts on the ring at A, the normal strain in AB becomes $\epsilon_{AB} = 0.02$ in./in., and the normal strain in AC becomes $\epsilon_{AC} = 0.035$ in./in. Determine the coordinate position of the ring due to the load.

7–94. Two bars are used to support a load **P**. When unloaded, AB is 5 in. long, AC is 8 in. long, and the ring at A has coordinates $(0, 0)$. If a load is applied to the ring at A, so that it moves it to the coordinate position $(0.25$ in., -0.73 in.$)$, determine the normal strain in each bar.

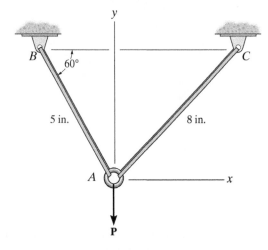

Probs. 7–93/94

7–95. The square deforms into the position shown by the dashed lines. Determine the average normal strain along each diagonal, AB and CD. Side $D'B'$ remains horizontal.

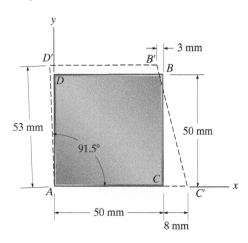

Prob. 7–95

***7–96.** The three cords are attached to the ring at B. When a force is applied to the ring it moves it to point B', such that the normal strain in AB is ϵ_{AB} and the normal strain in CB is ϵ_{CB}. Provided these strains are small, determine the normal strain in DB. Note that AB and CB remain horizontal and vertical, respectively, due to the roller guides at A and C.

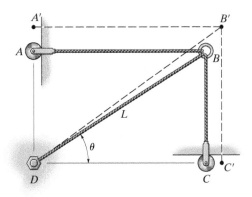

Prob. 7–96

7–97. The piece of plastic is originally rectangular. Determine the shear strain γ_{xy} at corners A and B if the plastic distorts as shown by the dashed lines.

7–98. The piece of plastic is originally rectangular. Determine the shear strain γ_{xy} at corners D and C if the plastic distorts as shown by the dashed lines.

7–99. The piece of plastic is originally rectangular. Determine the average normal strain that occurs along the diagonals AC and DB.

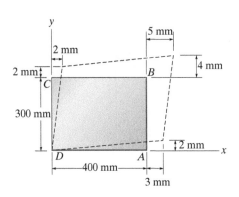

Probs. 7–97/98/99

CONCEPTUAL PROBLEMS

P7–1. Here hurricane winds caused the failure of this highway sign. Assuming the wind creates a uniform pressure on the sign of 2 kPa, use reasonable dimensions for the sign and determine the resultant shear and moment at the two connections where the failure occurred.

P7–1

P7–2. The two structural tubes are connected by the pin which passes through them. If the vertical load being supported is 100 kN, draw a free-body diagram of the pin and then use the method of sections to find the maximum average shear force in the pin. If the pin has a diameter of 50 mm, what is the maximum average shear stress in the pin?

P7–2

P7–3. The hydraulic cylinder H applies a horizontal force F on the pin at A. Draw the free-body diagram of the pin and show the forces acting on it. Using the method of sections, explain why the average shear stress in the pin is largest at sections through the gaps D and E and not at some intermediate section.

P7–3

P7–4. The vertical load on the hook is 1000 lb. Draw the appropriate free-body diagrams and determine the maximum average shear force on the pins at A, B, and C. Note that due to symmetry four wheels are used to support the loading on the railing.

P7–4

7

CHAPTER REVIEW

The internal loadings in a body consist of a normal force, shear force, bending moment, and torsional moment. They represent the resultants of both a normal and shear stress distribution that acts over the cross section. To obtain these resultants, use the method of sections and the equations of equilibrium.	$\Sigma F_x = 0$ $\Sigma F_y = 0$ $\Sigma F_z = 0$ $\Sigma M_x = 0$ $\Sigma M_y = 0$ $\Sigma M_z = 0$	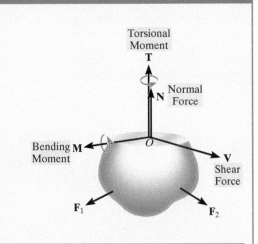
If a bar is made from homogeneous isotropic material and it is subjected to a series of external axial loads that pass through the centroid of the cross section, then a uniform normal stress distribution will act over the cross section. This average normal stress can be determined from $\sigma = P/A$, where P is the internal axial load at the section.	$\sigma = \dfrac{P}{A}$	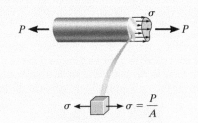
The average shear stress can be determined using $\tau_{\text{avg}} = V/A$, where V is the shear force acting on the cross-sectional area A. This formula is often used to find the average shear stress in fasteners or in parts used for connections.	$\tau_{\text{avg}} = \dfrac{V}{A}$	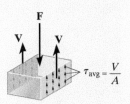

The design of any simple connection requires that the average stress along any cross section not exceed an allowable stress of σ_{allow} or τ_{allow}. These values are reported in codes and are considered safe on the basis of experiments or through experience. Sometimes a factor of safety is reported provided the ultimate stress is known.	$$\text{F.S.} = \frac{\sigma_{fail}}{\sigma_{allow}} = \frac{\tau_{fail}}{\tau_{allow}}$$	
Deformation is defined as the change in the shape and size of a body. It causes line segments to change length and orientation.		
Normal strain ϵ is the change in length per unit length of a line segment. If ϵ is positive, the line segment elongates. If it is negative, the line segment contracts.	$$\epsilon_{avg} = \frac{\Delta s' - \Delta s}{\Delta s}$$	
Shear strain γ is a measure of the change in angle made between two line segments that are originally perpendicular to one another.	$$\gamma = \frac{\pi}{2} - \theta$$	
Strain is dimensionless, however, ϵ is sometimes reported in in-/in., mm/mm, and γ is in radians.		

REVIEW PROBLEMS

*7–100. The 200-mm-diameter aluminum cylinder supports a compressive load of 300 kN. Determine the average normal and shear stress acting on section *a–a*. Show the results on a differential element located on the section.

7–102. Determine the required thickness of member *BC* and the diameter of the pins at *A* and *B* if the allowable normal stress for member *BC* is σ_{allow} = 29 ksi and the allowable shear stress for the pins is τ_{allow} = 10 ksi.

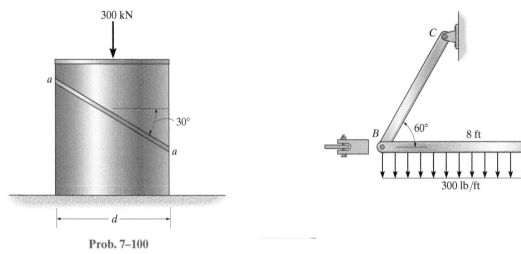

Prob. 7–100

Prob. 7–102

7–101. The long bolt passes through the 30-mm-thick plate. If the force in the bolt shank is 8 kN, determine the average normal stress in the shank, the average shear stress along the cylindrical area of the plate defined by the section lines *a–a*, and the average shear stress in the bolt head along the cylindrical area defined by the section lines *b–b*.

7–103. Determine the resultant internal loadings acting on the cross sections located through points *D* and *E* of the frame.

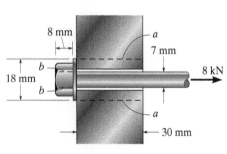

Prob. 7–101

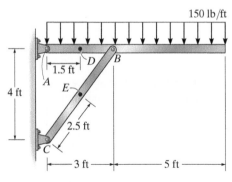

Prob. 7–103

*7–104. The pulley is held fixed to the 20-mm-diameter shaft using a key that fits within a groove cut into the pulley and shaft. If the suspended load has a mass of 50 kg, determine the average shear stress in the key along section *a–a*. The key is 5 mm by 5 mm square and 12 mm long.

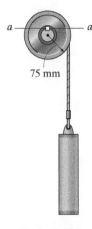

75 mm

Prob. 7–104

7–105. The bearing pad consists of a 150 mm by 150 mm block of aluminum that supports a compressive load of 6 kN. Determine the average normal and shear stress acting on the plane through section *a–a*. Show the results on a differential volume element located on the plane.

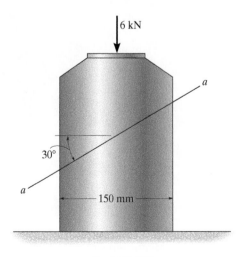

6 kN

30°

150 mm

Prob. 7–105

7–106. The material distorts into the dashed position shown. Determine (a) the average normal strains along sides *AC* and *CD* and the shear strain γ_{xy} at *F*, and (b) the average normal strain along line *BE*.

7–107. The material distorts into the dashed position shown. Determine the average normal strain that occurs along the diagonals *AD* and *CF*.

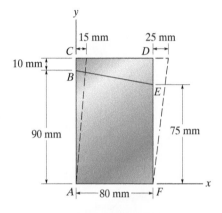

Probs. 7–106/107

*7–108. The cable has a specific weight γ (weight/volume) and cross-sectional area *A*. If the sag *s* is small, so that its length is approximately *L* and its weight can be distributed uniformly along the horizontal axis, determine the average normal stress in the cable at its lowest point *C*.

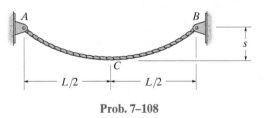

Prob. 7–108

7

Mechanics of Materials

Horizontal ground displacements caused by an earthquake produced excessive strains in these bridge piers until they fractured. The material properties of the concrete and steel reinforcement must be known so that engineers can properly design this structure and thereby avoid such failures.

Mechanical Properties of Materials

8

CHAPTER OBJECTIVES

- To show how stress can be related to strain by using experimental methods to determine the stress–strain diagram for a particular material.

- To discuss the properties of the stress–strain diagram for materials commonly used in engineering.

- To discuss other mechanical properties and tests related to the development of the mechanics of materials.

8.1 The Tension and Compression Test

The strength of a material depends on its ability to sustain a load without undue deformation or failure. This property is inherent in the material itself and must be determined by *experiment*. One of the most important tests to perform in this regard is the ***tension or compression test***. Although several important mechanical properties of a material can be determined from this test, it is used primarily to determine the relationship between the average normal stress and average normal strain in many engineering materials such as metals, ceramics, polymers, and composites.

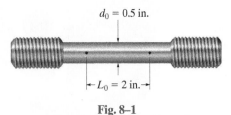

$d_0 = 0.5$ in.

$L_0 = 2$ in.

Fig. 8–1

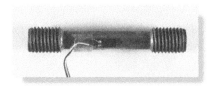

Typical steel specimen with attached strain gauge.

To perform a tension or compression test a specimen of the material is made into a "standard" shape and size. It has a constant circular cross section with enlarged ends, so that failure will not occur at the grips. Before testing, two small punch marks are placed along the specimen's uniform length. Measurements are taken of both the specimen's initial cross-sectional area, A_0, and the ***gauge-length*** distance L_0 between the punch marks. For example, when a metal specimen is used in a tension test it generally has an initial diameter of $d_0 = 0.5$ in. (13 mm) and a gauge length of $L_0 = 2$ in. (50 mm), Fig. 8–1. In order to apply an axial load with no bending of the specimen, the ends are usually seated into ball-and-socket joints. A testing machine like the one shown in Fig. 8–2 is then used to stretch the specimen at a very slow, constant rate until it fails. The machine is designed to read the load required to maintain this uniform stretching.

At frequent intervals during the test, data is recorded of the applied load P, as read on the dial of the machine or taken from a digital readout. Also, the elongation $\delta = L - L_0$ between the punch marks on the specimen may be measured using either a caliper or a mechanical or optical device called an ***extensometer***. This value of δ (delta) is then used to calculate the average normal strain in the specimen. Sometimes, however, this measurement is not taken, since it is also possible to read the strain *directly* by using an ***electrical-resistance strain gauge***, which looks like the one shown in Fig. 8–3. The operation of this gauge is based on the change in electrical resistance of a very thin wire or piece of metal foil under strain. Essentially the gauge is cemented to the specimen along its length. If the cement is very strong in comparison to the gauge, then the gauge is in effect an integral part of the specimen, so that when the specimen is strained in the direction of the gauge, the wire and specimen will experience the same strain. By measuring the electrical resistance of the wire, the gauge may be calibrated to read values of normal strain directly.

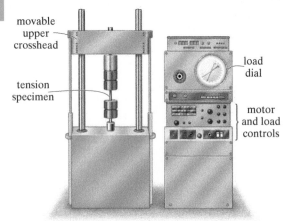

movable upper crosshead

tension specimen

load dial

motor and load controls

Fig. 8–2

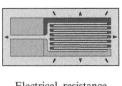

Electrical–resistance strain gauge

Fig. 8–3

8.2 The Stress–Strain Diagram

It is not feasible to prepare a test specimen to match the size, A_0 and L_0, of each structural member. Rather, the test results must be reported so they apply to a member of *any size*. To achieve this, the load and corresponding deformation data are used to calculate various values of the stress and corresponding strain in the specimen. A plot of the results produces a curve called the ***stress–strain diagram***. There are two ways in which it is normally described.

Conventional Stress–Strain Diagram.   We can determine the ***nominal*** or ***engineering stress*** by dividing the applied load P by the specimen's *original* cross-sectional area A_0. This calculation assumes that the stress is *constant* over the cross section and throughout the gauge length. We have

$$\sigma = \frac{P}{A_0} \qquad\qquad (8\text{–}1)$$

Likewise, the ***nominal*** or ***engineering strain*** is found directly from the strain gauge reading, or by dividing the change in the specimen's gauge length, δ, by the specimen's original gauge length L_0. Here the strain is assumed to be constant throughout the region between the gauge points. Thus,

$$\epsilon = \frac{\delta}{L_0} \qquad\qquad (8\text{–}2)$$

If the corresponding values of σ and ϵ are plotted so that the vertical axis is the stress and the horizontal axis is the strain, the resulting curve is called a ***conventional stress–strain diagram***. Realize, however, that two stress–strain diagrams for a particular material will be quite similar, but will never be exactly the same. This is because the results actually depend on variables such as the material's composition, microscopic imperfections, the way it is manufactured, the rate of loading, and the temperature during the time of the test.

We will now discuss the characteristics of the conventional stress–strain curve as it pertains to *steel*, a commonly used material for fabricating both structural members and mechanical elements. Using the method described above, the characteristic stress–strain diagram for a steel specimen is shown in Fig. 8–4. From this curve we can identify four different ways in which the material behaves, depending on the amount of strain induced in the material.

8

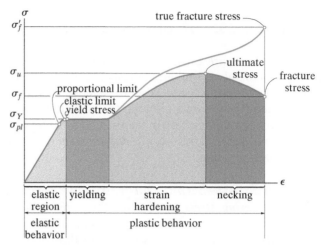

Conventional and true stress-strain diagrams
for ductile material (steel) (not to scale)

Fig. 8–4

Elastic Behavior.   Elastic behavior of the material occurs when the strains in the specimen are within the light orange region shown in Fig. 8–4. Here the curve is actually a *straight line* throughout most of this region, so that the stress is *proportional* to the strain. The material in this region is said to be *linear elastic*. The upper stress limit to this linear relationship is called the ***proportional limit***, σ_{pl}. If the stress slightly exceeds the proportional limit, the curve tends to bend and flatten out as shown. This continues until the stress reaches the ***elastic limit***. Upon reaching this point, if the load is removed the specimen will still return back to its original shape. Normally for steel, however, the elastic limit is seldom determined, since it is very close to the proportional limit and therefore rather difficult to detect.

Yielding.   A slight increase in stress above the elastic limit will result in a breakdown of the material and cause it to *deform permanently*. This behavior is called ***yielding***, and it is indicated by the rectangular dark orange region of the curve. The stress that causes yielding is called the ***yield stress*** or ***yield point***, σ_Y, and the deformation that occurs is called ***plastic deformation***. Although not shown in Fig. 8–4, for low-carbon steels or those that are hot rolled, the yield point is often distinguished by two values. The ***upper yield point*** occurs first, followed by a sudden decrease in load-carrying capacity to a ***lower yield point***. Notice that once the yield point is reached, then as shown in Fig. 8–4, the specimen will continue to elongate (strain) *without any increase in load*. When the material is in this state, it is often referred to as being ***perfectly plastic***.

Strain Hardening.   When yielding has ended, an increase in load can be supported by the specimen, resulting in a curve that rises continuously but becomes flatter until it reaches a maximum stress referred to as the *ultimate stress*, σ_u. The rise in the curve in this manner is called *strain hardening*, and it is identified in Fig. 8–4 as the region in light green.

Necking.   Up to the ultimate stress, as the specimen elongates, its cross-sectional area will decrease. This decrease is fairly *uniform* over the specimen's entire gauge length; however, just after, at the ultimate stress, the cross-sectional area will begin to decrease in a *localized* region of the specimen. As a result, a constriction or "neck" tends to form in this region as the specimen elongates further, Fig. 8–5a. This region of the curve due to necking is indicated in dark green in Fig. 8–4. Here the stress–strain diagram tends to curve downward until the specimen breaks at the *fracture stress*, σ_f, Fig. 8–5b.

True Stress–Strain Diagram.   Instead of always using the *original* cross-sectional area and specimen length to calculate the (engineering) stress and strain, we could have used the *actual* cross-sectional area and specimen length at the *instant* the load is measured. The values of stress and strain found from these measurements are called *true stress* and *true strain*, and a plot of their values is called the *true stress–strain diagram*. When this diagram is plotted, it has a form shown by the light-blue curve in Fig. 8–4. Note that the conventional and true σ–ϵ diagrams are practically coincident when the strain is small. The differences between the diagrams begin to appear in the strain-hardening range, where the magnitude of strain becomes more significant. In particular, there is a large divergence within the necking region. Here it can be seen from the conventional σ–ϵ diagram that the specimen *actually* supports a *decreasing load*, since A_0 is constant when calculating engineering stress, $\sigma = P/A_0$. However, from the true σ–ϵ diagram, the actual area A within the necking region is always decreasing until fracture, σ'_f, and so the material actually sustains *increasing stress*, since $\sigma = P/A$.

Typical necking pattern which has occurred on this steel specimen just before fracture.

This steel specimen clearly shows the necking that occurred just before the specimen failed. This resulted in the formation of a "cup-cone" shape at the fracture location, which is characteristic of ductile materials.

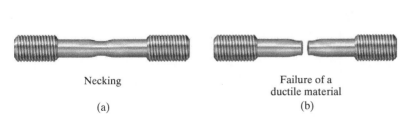

Necking

(a)

Failure of a
ductile material

(b)

Fig. 8–5

Although the true and conventional stress–strain diagrams are different, most engineering design is done so that the material supports a stress within the elastic range. This is because the deformation of the material is generally not severe and the material will restore itself when the load is removed. The true strain up to the elastic limit will remain small enough so that the error in using the engineering values of σ and ϵ is very small (about 0.1%) compared with their true values. This is one of the primary reasons for using conventional stress–strain diagrams.

The above concepts can be summarized with reference to Fig. 8–6, which shows an actual conventional stress–strain diagram for a mild steel specimen. In order to enhance the details, the elastic region of the curve has been shown in light blue color using an exaggerated strain scale, also shown in light blue. Tracing the behavior, the proportional limit is reached at $\sigma_{pl} = 35$ ksi (241 MPa), where $\epsilon_{pl} = 0.0012$ in./in. This is followed by an upper yield point of $(\sigma_Y)_u = 38$ ksi (262 MPa), then suddenly a lower yield point of $(\sigma_Y)_l = 36$ ksi (248 MPa). The end of yielding occurs at a strain of $\epsilon_Y = 0.030$ in./in., which is 25 times greater than the strain at the proportional limit! Continuing, the specimen undergoes strain hardening until it reaches the ultimate stress of $\sigma_u = 63$ ksi (434 MPa), then it begins to neck down until a fracture occurs, $\sigma_f = 47$ ksi (324 MPa). By comparison, the strain at failure, $\epsilon_f = 0.380$ in./in., is 317 times greater than ϵ_{pl}!

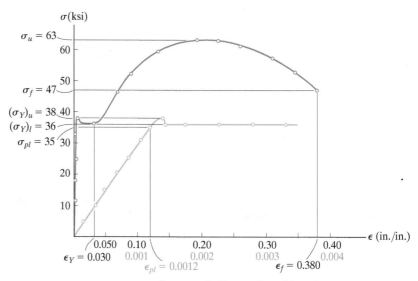

Stress-strain diagram for mild steel

Fig. 8–6

8.3 Stress–Strain Behavior of Ductile and Brittle Materials

Materials can be classified as either being ductile or brittle, depending on their stress–strain characteristics.

Ductile Materials. Any material that can be subjected to large strains before it fractures is called a ***ductile material***. Mild steel, as discussed previously, is a typical example. Engineers often choose ductile materials for design because these materials are capable of absorbing shock or energy, and if they become overloaded, they will usually exhibit large deformation before failing.

One way to specify the ductility of a material is to report its percent elongation or percent reduction in area at the time of fracture. The ***percent elongation*** is the specimen's fracture strain expressed as a percent. Thus, if the specimen's original gauge length is L_0 and its length at fracture is L_f, then

$$\text{Percent elongation} = \frac{L_f - L_0}{L_0}(100\%) \qquad (8\text{–}3)$$

As seen in Fig. 8–6, since $\epsilon_f = 0.380$, this value would be 38% for a mild steel specimen.

The ***percent reduction in area*** is another way to specify ductility. It is defined within the region of necking as follows:

$$\text{Percent reduction of area} = \frac{A_0 - A_f}{A_0}(100\%) \qquad (8\text{–}4)$$

Here A_0 is the specimen's original cross-sectional area and A_f is the area of the neck at fracture. Mild steel has a typical value of 60%.

Besides steel, other metals such as brass, molybdenum, and zinc may also exhibit ductile stress–strain characteristics similar to steel, whereby they undergo elastic stress–strain behavior, yielding at constant stress, strain hardening, and finally necking until fracture. In most metals, however, constant yielding will *not occur* beyond the elastic range. One metal for which this is the case is aluminum. Actually, this metal often does not have a well-defined *yield point*, and consequently it is standard practice to define a ***yield strength*** using a graphical procedure called the ***offset method***. Normally a 0.2% strain (0.002 in./in.) is chosen, and from this point on the ϵ axis, a line parallel to the initial straight-line portion of the stress–strain diagram is drawn. The point where this line intersects the curve defines the yield strength. An example of the construction for determining the yield strength for an aluminum alloy is shown in Fig. 8–7. From the graph, the yield strength is $\sigma_{YS} = 51$ ksi (352 MPa).

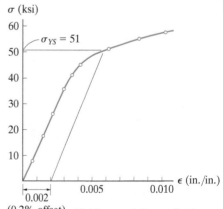

Yield strength for an aluminum alloy

Fig. 8–7

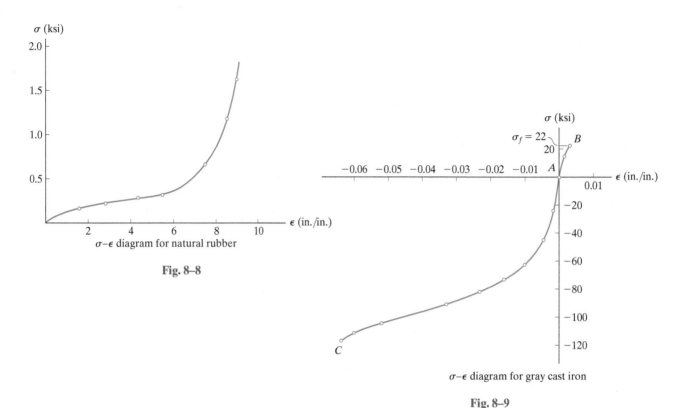

$\sigma-\epsilon$ diagram for natural rubber

Fig. 8–8

$\sigma-\epsilon$ diagram for gray cast iron

Fig. 8–9

Concrete used for structural purposes must be routinely tested in compression to be sure it provides the necessary design strength for this bridge deck. The concrete cylinders shown are compression tested for ultimate stress after curing for 30 days.

Realize that the yield strength is not a physical property of the material, since it is a stress that causes a *specified* permanent strain in the material. In this text, however, we will assume that the yield strength, yield point, elastic limit, and proportional limit all *coincide* unless otherwise stated. An exception would be natural rubber, which in fact does not even have a proportional limit, since stress and strain are *not* linearly related. Instead, as shown in Fig. 8–8, this material, which is known as a polymer, exhibits *nonlinear elastic behavior*.

Wood is a material that is often moderately ductile, and as a result it is usually designed to respond only to elastic loadings. The strength characteristics of wood vary greatly from one species to another, and for each species they depend on the moisture content, age, and the size and arrangement of knots in the wood. Since wood is a fibrous material, its tensile or compressive characteristics will differ greatly when it is loaded either parallel or perpendicular to its grain. Specifically, wood splits easily when it is loaded in tension perpendicular to its grain, and consequently tensile loads are almost always intended to be applied parallel to the grain of wood members.

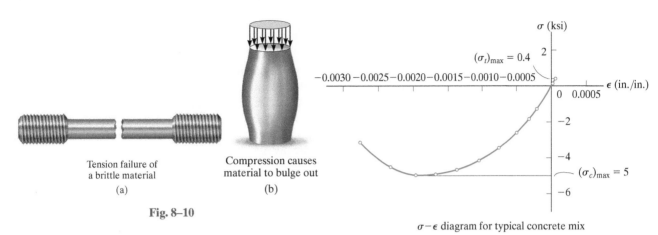

Tension failure of
a brittle material
(a)

Compression causes
material to bulge out
(b)

Fig. 8–10

$\sigma-\epsilon$ diagram for typical concrete mix

Fig. 8–11

Brittle Materials.

Materials that exhibit little or no yielding before failure are referred to as ***brittle materials***. Gray cast iron is an example, having a stress–strain diagram in tension as shown by portion AB of the curve in Fig. 8–9. Here fracture at $\sigma_f = 22$ ksi (152 MPa) took place initially at an imperfection or microscopic crack and then spread rapidly across the specimen, causing complete fracture. Since the appearance of initial cracks in a specimen is quite random, brittle materials do not have a well-defined tensile fracture stress. Instead the *average* fracture stress from a set of observed tests is generally reported. A typical failed specimen is shown in Fig. 8–10a.

Compared with their behavior in tension, brittle materials, such as gray cast iron, exhibit a much higher resistance to axial compression, as evidenced by portion AC of the curve in Fig. 8–9. For this case any cracks or imperfections in the specimen tend to close up, and as the load increases the material will generally bulge or become barrel shaped as the strains become larger, Fig. 8–10b.

Like gray cast iron, concrete is classified as a brittle material, and it also has a low strength capacity in tension. The characteristics of its stress–strain diagram depend primarily on the mix of concrete (water, sand, gravel, and cement) and the time and temperature of curing. A typical example of a "complete" stress–strain diagram for concrete is given in Fig. 8–11. By inspection, its maximum compressive strength is almost 12.5 times greater than its tensile strength, $(\sigma_c)_{max} = 5$ ksi (34.5 MPa) versus $(\sigma_t)_{max} = 0.40$ ksi (2.76 MPa). For this reason, concrete is almost always reinforced with steel bars or rods whenever it is designed to support tensile loads.

It can generally be stated that most materials exhibit both ductile and brittle behavior. For example, steel has brittle behavior when it contains a high carbon content, and it is ductile when the carbon content is reduced. Also, at low temperatures materials become harder and more brittle, whereas when the temperature rises they become softer and more ductile. This effect is shown in Fig. 8–12 for a methacrylate plastic.

Steel rapidly loses its strength when heated. For this reason engineers often require main structural members to be insulated in case of fire.

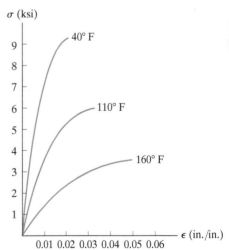

$\sigma-\epsilon$ diagrams for a methacrylate plastic

Fig. 8–12

8.4 Hooke's Law

As noted in the previous section, the stress–strain diagrams for most engineering materials exhibit a *linear relationship* between stress and strain within the elastic region. Consequently, an increase in stress causes a proportionate increase in strain. This fact was discovered by Robert Hooke in 1676 using springs and is known as *Hooke's law*. It may be expressed mathematically as

$$\sigma = E\epsilon \tag{8–5}$$

Here E represents the constant of proportionality, which is called the **modulus of elasticity** or **Young's modulus**, named after Thomas Young, who published an account of it in 1807.

Equation 8–5 actually represents the equation of the *initial straight-lined portion* of the stress–strain diagram up to the proportional limit. Furthermore, the modulus of elasticity represents the *slope* of this line. Since strain is dimensionless, from Eq. 8–5, E will have the same units as stress, such as psi, ksi, or pascals. As an example of its calculation, consider the stress–strain diagram for steel shown in Fig. 8–6. Here $\sigma_{pl} = 35$ ksi and $\epsilon_{pl} = 0.0012$ in./in., so that

$$E = \frac{\sigma_{pl}}{\epsilon_{pl}} = \frac{35 \text{ ksi}}{0.0012 \text{ in./in.}} = 29(10^3) \text{ ksi}$$

As shown in Fig. 8–13, the proportional limit for a particular type of steel alloy depends on its carbon content; however, most grades of steel, from the softest rolled steel to the hardest tool steel, have about the

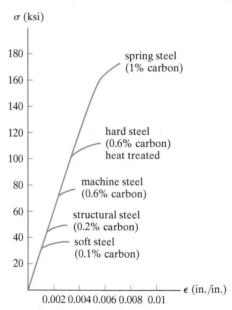

Fig. 8–13

same modulus of elasticity, generally accepted to be $E_{st} = 29(10^3)$ ksi or 200 GPa. Values of E for other commonly used engineering materials are often tabulated in engineering codes and reference books. Representative values are also listed on the inside back cover of this book. It should be noted that the modulus of elasticity is a mechanical property that indicates the *stiffness* of a material. Materials that are very stiff, such as steel, have large values of E [$E_{st} = 29(10^3)$ ksi or 200 GPa], whereas spongy materials such as vulcanized rubber may have low values [$E_r = 0.10$ ksi or 0.70 MPa].

The modulus of elasticity is one of the most important mechanical properties used in the development of equations presented in this text. It must always be remembered, though, that E can be used only if a material has *linear elastic behavior*. Also, if the stress in the material is *greater* than the proportional limit, the stress–strain diagram ceases to be a straight line and so Eq. 8–5 is no longer valid.

Strain Hardening.

If a specimen of ductile material, such as steel, is loaded into the *plastic region* and then unloaded, *elastic strain is recovered* as the material returns to its equilibrium state. The *plastic strain remains*, however, and as a result the material is subjected to a ***permanent set***. For example, a wire when bent (plastically) will spring back a little (elastically) when the load is removed; however, it will not fully return to its original position. This behavior can be illustrated on the stress–strain diagram shown in Fig. 8–14a. Here the specimen is first loaded beyond its yield point A to point A'. Since interatomic forces have to be overcome to elongate the specimen *elastically*, then these same forces pull the atoms back together when the load is removed, Fig. 8–14a. Consequently, the modulus of elasticity, E, is the same, and therefore the slope of line $O'A'$ is the same as line OA.

If the load is reapplied, the atoms in the material will again be displaced until yielding occurs at or near the stress A', and the stress–strain diagram continues along the same path as before, Fig. 8–14b. It should be noted, however, that this new stress–strain diagram, defined by $O'A'B$, now has a *higher* yield point (A'), a consequence of strain-hardening. In other words, the material now has a *greater elastic region*; however, it has *less ductility*, a smaller plastic region, than when it was in its original state.

This pin was made from a hardened steel alloy, that is, one having a high carbon content. It failed due to brittle fracture.

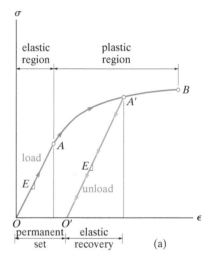

(a)

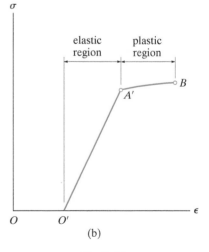

(b)

Fig. 8–14

8.5 Strain Energy

As a material is deformed by an external loading, it tends to store energy *internally* throughout its volume. Since this energy is related to the strains in the material, it is referred to as **strain energy**. To obtain this strain energy consider a volume element of material from a tension test specimen. It is subjected to uniaxial stress as shown in Fig. 8–15. This stress develops a force $\Delta F = \sigma \, \Delta A = \sigma(\Delta x \, \Delta y)$ on the top and bottom faces of the element *after* the element of length Δz undergoes a vertical displacement $\epsilon \, \Delta z$. By definition, *work* is determined by the product of the force and displacement in the direction of the force. Since the force is increased uniformly from zero to its final magnitude ΔF when the displacement $\epsilon \, \Delta z$ is attained, the work done on the element by the force is equal to the *average* force magnitude $(\Delta F/2)$ times the displacement $\epsilon \, \Delta z$. This "external work" on the element is equivalent to the "internal work" or strain energy stored in the element—assuming that no energy is lost in the form of heat. Consequently, the strain energy ΔU is $\Delta U = (\frac{1}{2} \Delta F) \, \epsilon \, \Delta z = (\frac{1}{2} \sigma \, \Delta x \, \Delta y) \, \epsilon \, \Delta z$. Since the volume of the element is $\Delta V = \Delta x \, \Delta y \, \Delta z$, then $\Delta U = \frac{1}{2} \sigma \epsilon \, \Delta V$.

For applications, it is sometimes convenient to specify the strain energy per unit volume of material. This is called the **strain-energy density**, and it can be expressed as

$$u = \frac{\Delta U}{\Delta V} = \frac{1}{2} \sigma \epsilon \qquad (8\text{–}6)$$

If the material behavior is *linear elastic*, then Hooke's law applies, $\sigma = E\epsilon$, and therefore we can express the elastic strain-energy density in terms of the uniaxial stress as

$$u = \frac{1}{2} \frac{\sigma^2}{E} \qquad (8\text{–}7)$$

Modulus of Resilience.   In particular, when the stress σ reaches the proportional limit, the strain-energy density, as calculated by Eq. 8–6 or 8–7, is referred to as the **modulus of resilience**, i.e.,

$$\boxed{u_r = \frac{1}{2} \sigma_{pl} \epsilon_{pl} = \frac{1}{2} \frac{\sigma_{pl}^2}{E}} \qquad (8\text{–}8)$$

From the elastic region of the stress–strain diagram, Fig. 8–16a, notice that u_r is equivalent to the shaded *triangular area* under the diagram. Physically a material's resilience represents the ability of the material to absorb energy without any permanent damage to the material.

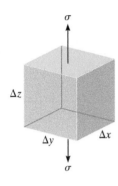

σ

Δz

Δy Δx

σ

Fig. 8–15

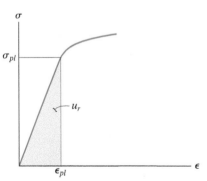

Modulus of resilience, u_r

(a)

Fig. 8–16

Modulus of Toughness. Another important property of a material is the **modulus of toughness**, u_t. This quantity represents the *entire area* under the stress–strain diagram, Fig. 8–16b, and therefore it indicates the strain-energy density of the material just before it fractures. This property becomes important when designing members that may be accidentally overloaded. Alloying metals can also change their resilience and toughness. For example, by changing the percentage of carbon in steel, the resulting stress–strain diagrams in Fig. 8–17 show how the degrees of resilience and toughness can be changed.

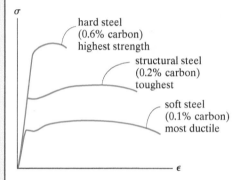

Modulus of toughness, u_t

(b)

Fig. 8–16 (cont.)

Important Points

- A *conventional stress–strain diagram* is important in engineering since it provides a means for obtaining data about a material's tensile or compressive strength without regard for the material's physical size or shape.

- *Engineering stress and strain* are calculated using the *original* cross-sectional area and gauge length of the specimen.

- A *ductile material*, such as mild steel, has four distinct behaviors as it is loaded. They are *elastic behavior, yielding, strain hardening,* and *necking*.

- A material is *linear elastic* if the stress is proportional to the strain within the elastic region. This behavior is described by *Hooke's law*, $\sigma = E\epsilon$, where the *modulus of elasticity E* is the slope of the line.

- Important points on the stress–strain diagram are the *proportional limit, elastic limit, yield stress, ultimate stress,* and *fracture stress*.

- The *ductility* of a material can be specified by the specimen's *percent elongation* or the *percent reduction in area*.

- If a material does not have a distinct yield point, a *yield strength* can be specified using a graphical procedure such as the *offset method*.

- *Brittle materials*, such as gray cast iron, have very little or no yielding and so they can fracture suddenly.

- *Strain hardening* is used to establish a higher yield point for a material. This is done by straining the material beyond the elastic limit, then releasing the load. The modulus of elasticity remains the same; however, the material's ductility *decreases*.

- *Strain energy* is energy stored in a material due to its deformation. This energy per unit volume is called *strain-energy density*. If it is measured up to the proportional limit, it is referred to as the *modulus of resilience*, and if it is measured up to the point of fracture, it is called the *modulus of toughness*. It can be determined from the area under the $\sigma-\epsilon$ diagram.

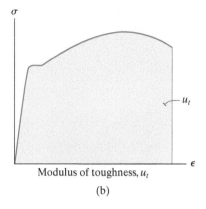

Fig. 8–17

This nylon specimen exhibits a high degree of toughness as noted by the large amount of necking that has occurred just before fracture.

EXAMPLE 8.1

A tension test for a steel alloy results in the stress–strain diagram shown in Fig. 8–18. Calculate the modulus of elasticity and the yield strength based on a 0.2% offset. Identify on the graph the ultimate stress and the fracture stress.

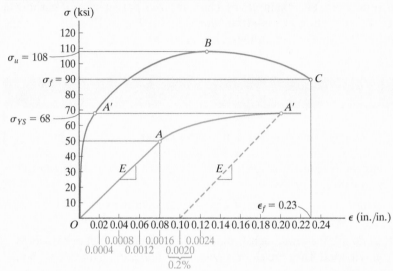

Fig. 8–18

SOLUTION

Modulus of Elasticity.   We must calculate the *slope* of the initial straight-line portion of the graph. Using the magnified curve and scale shown in blue, this line extends from point O to an estimated point A, which has coordinates of approximately (0.0016 in./in., 50 ksi). Therefore,

$$E = \frac{50 \text{ ksi}}{0.0016 \text{ in./in.}} = 31.2(10^3) \text{ ksi} \qquad \textit{Ans.}$$

Note that the equation of line OA is thus $\sigma = 31.2(10^3)\epsilon$.

Yield Strength.   For a 0.2% offset, we begin at a strain of 0.2% or 0.0020 in./in. and graphically extend a (dashed) line parallel to OA until it intersects the σ–ϵ curve at A'. The yield strength is approximately

$$\sigma_{YS} = 68 \text{ ksi} \qquad \textit{Ans.}$$

Ultimate Stress.   This is defined by the peak of the σ–ϵ graph, point B in Fig. 8–18.

$$\sigma_u = 108 \text{ ksi} \qquad \textit{Ans.}$$

Fracture Stress.   When the specimen is strained to its maximum of $\epsilon_f = 0.23$ in./in., it fractures at point C. Thus,

$$\sigma_f = 90 \text{ ksi} \qquad \textit{Ans.}$$

EXAMPLE | 8.2

The stress–strain diagram for an aluminum alloy that is used for making aircraft parts is shown in Fig. 8–19. If a specimen of this material is stressed to 600 MPa, determine the permanent strain that remains in the specimen when the load is released. Also, find the modulus of resilience both before and after the load application.

SOLUTION

Permanent Strain. When the specimen is subjected to the load, it strain-hardens until point B is reached on the σ–ϵ diagram. The strain at this point is approximately 0.023 mm/mm. When the load is released, the material behaves by following the straight line BC, which is parallel to line OA. Since both lines have the same slope, the strain at point C can be determined analytically. The slope of line OA is the modulus of elasticity, i.e.,

$$E = \frac{450 \text{ MPa}}{0.006 \text{ mm/mm}} = 75.0 \text{ GPa}$$

From triangle CBD, we require

$$E = \frac{BD}{CD}; \qquad 75.0(10^9) \text{ Pa} = \frac{600(10^6) \text{ Pa}}{CD}$$
$$CD = 0.008 \text{ mm/mm}$$

This strain represents the amount of *recovered elastic strain*. The permanent strain, ϵ_{OC}, is thus

$$\epsilon_{OC} = 0.023 \text{ mm/mm} - 0.008 \text{ mm/mm}$$
$$= 0.0150 \text{ mm/mm} \qquad\qquad Ans.$$

Note: If gauge marks on the specimen were originally 50 mm apart, then after the load is *released* these marks will be 50 mm + (0.0150)(50 mm) = 50.75 mm apart.

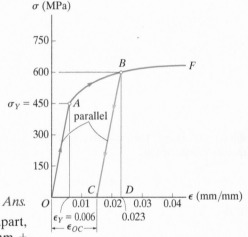

Fig. 8–19

Modulus of Resilience. Applying Eq. 8–8, we have*

$$(u_r)_{\text{initial}} = \frac{1}{2}\sigma_{pl}\epsilon_{pl} = \frac{1}{2}(450 \text{ MPa})(0.006 \text{ mm/mm})$$
$$= 1.35 \text{ MJ/m}^3 \qquad\qquad Ans.$$

$$(u_r)_{\text{final}} = \frac{1}{2}\sigma_{pl}\epsilon_{pl} = \frac{1}{2}(600 \text{ MPa})(0.008 \text{ mm/mm})$$
$$= 2.40 \text{ MJ/m}^3 \qquad\qquad Ans.$$

NOTE: By comparison, the effect of strain-hardening the material has caused an increase in the modulus of resilience; however, note that the modulus of toughness for the material has decreased since the area under the original curve, $OABF$, is larger than the area under curve CBF.

*Work in the SI system of units is measured in joules, where 1 J = 1 N · m.

8

FUNDAMENTAL PROBLEMS

F8–1. Define homogeneous material.

F8–2. Indicate the points on the stress-strain diagram which represent the proportional limit and the ultimate stress.

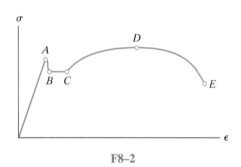

F8–2

F8–3. Define the modulus of elasticity E.

F8–4. At room temperature, mild steel is a ductile material. True or false?

F8–5. Engineering stress and strain are calculated using the *actual* cross-sectional area and length of the specimen. True or false?

F8–6. As the temperature increases the modulus of elasticity will increase. True or false?

F8–7. A 100-mm long rod has a diameter of 15 mm. If an axial tensile load of 100 kN is applied, determine its change is length. $E = 200$ GPa.

F8–8. A bar has a length of 8 in. and cross-sectional area of 12 in^2. Determine the modulus of elasticity of the material if it is subjected to an axial tensile load of 10 kip and stretches 0.003 in. The material has linear-elastic behavior.

F8–9. A 10-mm-diameter brass rod has a modulus of elasticity of $E = 100$ GPa. If it is 4 m long and subjected to an axial tensile load of 6 kN, determine its elongation.

F8–10. The material for the 50-mm-long specimen has the stress–strain diagram shown. If $P = 100$ kN, determine the elongation of the specimen.

F8–11. The material for the 50-mm-long specimen has the stress–strain diagram shown. If $P = 150$ kN is applied and then released, determine the permanent elongation of the specimen.

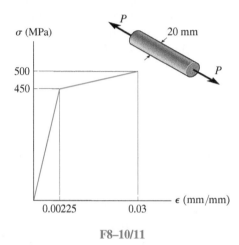

F8–10/11

F8–12. If the elongation of wire BC is 0.2 mm after the force **P** is applied, determine the magnitude of **P**. The wire is A-36 steel and has a diameter of 3 mm.

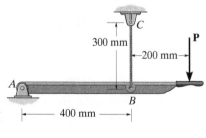

F8–12

PROBLEMS

•8–1. A concrete cylinder having a diameter of 6.00 in. and gauge length of 12 in. is tested in compression. The results of the test are reported in the table as load versus contraction. Draw the stress–strain diagram using scales of 1 in. = 0.5 ksi and 1 in. = $0.2(10^{-3})$ in./in. From the diagram, determine approximately the modulus of elasticity.

Load (kip)	Contraction (in.)
0	0
5.0	0.0006
9.5	0.0012
16.5	0.0020
20.5	0.0026
25.5	0.0034
30.0	0.0040
34.5	0.0045
38.5	0.0050
46.5	0.0062
50.0	0.0070
53.0	0.0075

Prob. 8–1

8–2. Data taken from a stress–strain test for a ceramic are given in the table. The curve is linear between the origin and the first point. Plot the diagram, and determine the modulus of elasticity and the modulus of resilience.

8–3. Data taken from a stress–strain test for a ceramic are given in the table. The curve is linear between the origin and the first point. Plot the diagram, and determine approximately the modulus of toughness. The rupture stress is $\sigma_r = 53.4$ ksi.

σ (ksi)	ϵ (in./in.)
0	0
33.2	0.0006
45.5	0.0010
49.4	0.0014
51.5	0.0018
53.4	0.0022

Probs. 8–2/3

*8–4. A tension test was performed on a specimen having an original diameter of 12.5 mm and a gauge length of 50 mm. The data are listed in the table. Plot the stress–strain diagram, and determine approximately the modulus of elasticity, the ultimate stress, and the fracture stress. Use a scale of 20 mm = 50 MPa and 20 mm = 0.05 mm/mm. Redraw the linear-elastic region, using the same stress scale but a strain scale of 20 mm = 0.001 mm/mm.

•8–5. A tension test was performed on a steel specimen having an original diameter of 12.5 mm and gauge length of 50 mm. Using the data listed in the table, plot the stress–strain diagram, and determine approximately the modulus of toughness. Use a scale of 20 mm = 50 MPa and 20 mm = 0.05 mm/mm.

Load (kN)	Elongation (mm)
0	0
11.1	0.0175
31.9	0.0600
37.8	0.1020
40.9	0.1650
43.6	0.2490
53.4	1.0160
62.3	3.0480
64.5	6.3500
62.3	8.8900
58.8	11.9380

Probs. 8–4/5

8–6. A specimen is originally 1 ft long, has a diameter of 0.5 in., and is subjected to a force of 500 lb. When the force is increased from 500 lb to 1800 lb, the specimen elongates 0.009 in. Determine the modulus of elasticity for the material if it remains linear elastic.

8–7. A structural member in a nuclear reactor is made of a zirconium alloy. If an axial load of 4 kip is to be supported by the member, determine its required cross-sectional area. Use a factor of safety of 3 relative to yielding. What is the load on the member if it is 3 ft long and its elongation is 0.02 in.? $E_{zr} = 14(10^3)$ ksi, $\sigma_Y = 57.5$ ksi. The material has elastic behavior.

*8–8. The strut is supported by a pin at C and an A-36 steel guy wire AB. If the wire has a diameter of 0.2 in., determine how much it stretches when the distributed load acts on the strut.

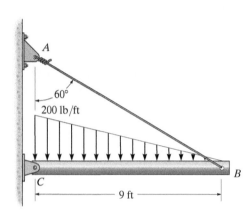

Prob. 8–8

•8–9. The $\sigma-\epsilon$ diagram for a collagen fiber bundle from which a human tendon is composed is shown. If a segment of the Achilles tendon at A has a length of 6.5 in. and an approximate cross-sectional area of 0.229 in², determine its elongation if the foot supports a load of 125 lb, which causes a tension in the tendon of 343.75 lb.

8–10. The stress–strain diagram for a metal alloy having an original diameter of 0.5 in. and a gauge length of 2 in. is given in the figure. Determine approximately the modulus of elasticity for the material, the load on the specimen that causes yielding, and the ultimate load the specimen will support.

8–11. The stress–strain diagram for a steel alloy having an original diameter of 0.5 in. and a gauge length of 2 in. is given in the figure. If the specimen is loaded until it is stressed to 90 ksi, determine the approximate amount of elastic recovery and the increase in the gauge length after it is unloaded.

*8–12. The stress–strain diagram for a steel alloy having an original diameter of 0.5 in. and a gauge length of 2 in. is given in the figure. Determine approximately the modulus of resilience and the modulus of toughness for the material.

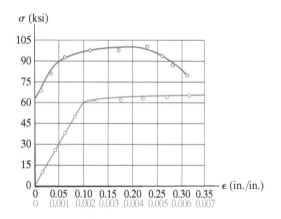

Probs. 8–10/11/12

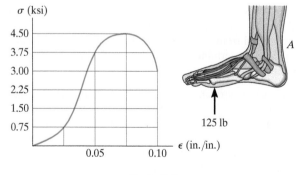

Prob. 8–9

•8–13. A bar having a length of 5 in. and cross-sectional area of 0.7 in² is subjected to an axial force of 8000 lb. If the bar stretches 0.002 in., determine the modulus of elasticity of the material. The material has linear-elastic behavior.

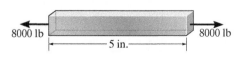

Prob. 8–13

8–14. The rigid pipe is supported by a pin at A and an A-36 steel guy wire BD. If the wire has a diameter of 0.25 in., determine how much it stretches when a load of $P = 600$ lb acts on the pipe.

8–15. The rigid pipe is supported by a pin at A and an A-36 guy wire BD. If the wire has a diameter of 0.25 in., determine the load P if the end C is displaced 0.075 in. downward.

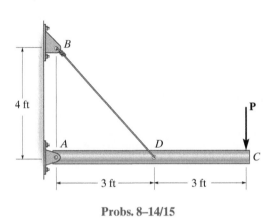

Probs. 8–14/15

*8–16.** Determine the elongation of the square hollow bar when it is subjected to the axial force $P = 100$ kN. If this axial force is increased to $P = 360$ kN and released, find the permanent elongation of the bar. The bar is made of a metal alloy having a stress–strain diagram which can be approximated as shown.

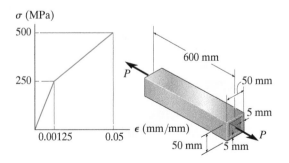

Prob. 8–16

•**8–17.** A tension test was performed on an aluminum 2014-T6 alloy specimen. The resulting stress–strain diagram is shown in the figure. Estimate (a) the proportional limit, (b) the modulus of elasticity, and (c) the yield strength based on a 0.2% strain offset method.

8–18. A tension test was performed on an aluminum 2014-T6 alloy specimen. The resulting stress–strain diagram is shown in the figure. Estimate (a) the modulus of resilience; and (b) modulus of toughness.

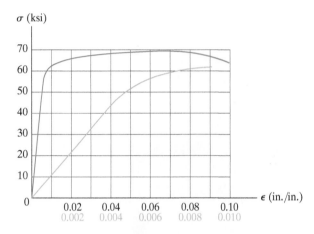

Probs. 8–17/18

8–19. The stress–strain diagram for a bone is shown, and can be described by the equation $\epsilon = 0.45(10^{-6})\,\sigma + 0.36(10^{-12})\,\sigma^3$, where σ is in kPa. Determine the yield strength assuming a 0.3% offset.

*8–20.** The stress–strain diagram for a bone is shown and can be described by the equation $\epsilon = 0.45(10^{-6})\,\sigma + 0.36(10^{-12})\,\sigma^3$, where σ is in kPa. Determine the modulus of toughness and the amount of elongation of a 200-mm-long region just before it fractures if failure occurs at $\epsilon = 0.12$ mm/mm.

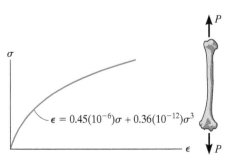

Probs. 8–19/20

When the rubber block is compressed (negative strain) its sides will expand (positive strain). The ratio of these strains remains constant.

8.6 Poisson's Ratio

When a deformable body is subjected to an axial tensile force, not only does it elongate but it also contracts laterally. For example, if a rubber band is stretched, it can be noted that both the thickness and width of the band are decreased. Likewise, a compressive force acting on a body causes it to contract in the direction of the force and yet its sides expand laterally.

Consider a bar having an original radius r and length L and subjected to the tensile force P in Fig. 8–20. This force elongates the bar by an amount δ, and its radius contracts by an amount δ'. Strains in the longitudinal or axial direction and in the lateral or radial direction are, respectively,

$$\epsilon_{long} = \frac{\delta}{L} \quad \text{and} \quad \epsilon_{lat} = \frac{\delta'}{r}$$

In the early 1800s, the French scientist S. D. Poisson realized that within the *elastic range* the *ratio* of these strains is a *constant*, since the deformations δ and δ' are proportional. This constant is referred to as **Poisson's ratio**, ν (nu), and it has a numerical value that is unique for a particular material that is both *homogeneous and isotropic*. Stated mathematically it is

$$\nu = -\frac{\epsilon_{lat}}{\epsilon_{long}} \tag{8–9}$$

The negative sign is included here since *longitudinal elongation* (positive strain) causes *lateral contraction* (negative strain), and vice versa. Notice that these strains are caused only by the axial or longitudinal force P; i.e., no force or stress acts in a lateral direction in order to strain the material in this direction.

Poisson's ratio is a *dimensionless* quantity, and for most nonporous solids it has a value that is generally between $\frac{1}{4}$ and $\frac{1}{3}$. Typical values of ν for common engineering materials are listed on the inside back cover. For an "ideal material" having no lateral deformation when it is stretched or compressed Poisson's ratio will be 0. Furthermore, it will be shown in Sec. 14.10 that the *maximum* possible value for Poisson's ratio is 0.5. Therefore, $0 \le \nu \le 0.5$.

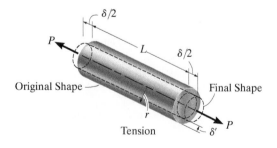

Fig. 8–20

EXAMPLE | 8.3

A bar made of A-36 steel has the dimensions shown in Fig. 8–21. If an axial force of $P = 80$ kN is applied to the bar, determine the change in its length and the change in the dimensions of its cross section after applying the load. The material behaves elastically.

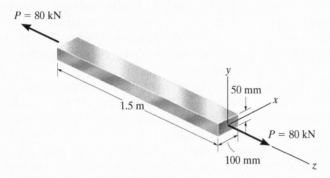

Fig. 8–21

SOLUTION

The normal stress in the bar is

$$\sigma_z = \frac{P}{A} = \frac{80(10^3)\ \text{N}}{(0.1\ \text{m})(0.05\ \text{m})} = 16.0(10^6)\ \text{Pa}$$

From the table on the inside back cover for A-36 steel $E_{st} = 200$ GPa, and so the strain in the z direction is

$$\epsilon_z = \frac{\sigma_z}{E_{st}} = \frac{16.0(10^6)\ \text{Pa}}{200(10^9)\ \text{Pa}} = 80(10^{-6})\ \text{mm/mm}$$

The axial elongation of the bar is therefore

$$\delta_z = \epsilon_z L_z = [80(10^{-6})](1.5\ \text{m}) = 120\ \mu\text{m} \qquad \textit{Ans.}$$

Using Eq. 8–9, where $\nu_{st} = 0.32$ as found from the inside back cover, the lateral contraction strains in *both* the x and y directions are

$$\epsilon_x = \epsilon_y = -\nu_{st}\epsilon_z = -0.32[80(10^{-6})] = -25.6\ \mu\text{m/m}$$

Thus the changes in the dimensions of the cross section are

$$\delta_x = \epsilon_x L_x = -[25.6(10^{-6})](0.1\ \text{m}) = -2.56\ \mu\text{m} \qquad \textit{Ans.}$$

$$\delta_y = \epsilon_y L_y = -[25.6(10^{-6})](0.05\ \text{m}) = -1.28\ \mu\text{m} \qquad \textit{Ans.}$$

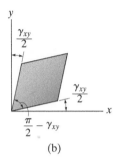

(a)

(b)

Fig. 8–22

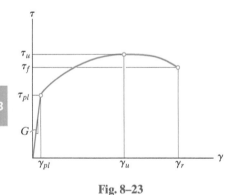

Fig. 8–23

8.7 The Shear Stress–Strain Diagram

In Sec. 7.5 it was shown that when a small element of material is subjected to *pure shear*, equilibrium requires that equal shear stresses must be developed on four faces of the element. These stresses τ_{xy} must be directed toward or away from diagonally opposite corners of the element, as shown in Fig. 8–22a. Furthermore, if the material is *homogeneous* and *isotropic*, then this shear stress will distort the element uniformly, Fig. 8–22b. As mentioned in Sec. 7.9, the shear strain γ_{xy} measures the angular distortion of the element relative to the sides originally along the x and y axes.

The behavior of a material subjected to pure shear can be studied in a laboratory using specimens in the shape of thin tubes and subjecting them to a torsional loading. If measurements are made of the applied torque and the resulting angle of twist, then by the methods to be explained in Chapter 10, the data can be used to determine the shear stress and shear strain, and a shear stress–strain diagram plotted. An example of such a diagram for a ductile material is shown in Fig. 8–23. Like the tension test, this material when subjected to shear will exhibit linear-elastic behavior and it will have a defined *proportional limit* τ_{pl}. Also, strain hardening will occur until an *ultimate shear stress* τ_u is reached. And finally, the material will begin to lose its shear strength until it reaches a point where it fractures, τ_f.

For most engineering materials, like the one just described, the elastic behavior is *linear*, and so Hooke's law for shear can be written as

$$\tau = G\gamma \tag{8–10}$$

Here G is called the **shear modulus of elasticity** or the **modulus of rigidity**. Its value represents the slope of the line on the τ–γ diagram, that is, $G = \tau_{pl}/\gamma_{pl}$. Typical values for common engineering materials are listed on the inside back cover. Notice that the units of measurement for G will be the *same* as those for τ (Pa or psi), since γ is measured in radians, a dimensionless quantity.

It will be shown in Sec. 14.10 that the three material constants, E, ν, and G are actually *related* by the equation

$$G = \frac{E}{2(1 + \nu)} \tag{8–11}$$

Provided E and G are known, the value of ν can then be determined from this equation rather than through experimental measurement. For example, in the case of A-36 steel, $E_{st} = 29(10^3)$ ksi and $G_{st} = 11.0(10^3)$ ksi, so that, from Eq. 8–11, $\nu_{st} = 0.32$.

8

EXAMPLE 8.4

A specimen of titanium alloy is tested in torsion and the shear stress–strain diagram is shown in Fig. 8–24a. Determine the shear modulus G, the proportional limit, and the ultimate shear stress. Also, determine the maximum distance d that the top of a block of this material, shown in Fig. 8–24b, could be displaced horizontally if the material behaves elastically when acted upon by a shear force $\mathbf{V}$. What is the magnitude of $\mathbf{V}$ necessary to cause this displacement?

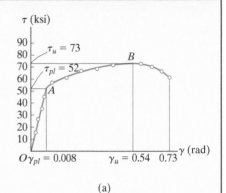

(a)

SOLUTION

Shear Modulus.   This value represents the slope of the straight-line portion OA of the τ–γ diagram. The coordinates of point A are (0.008 rad, 52 ksi). Thus,

$$G = \frac{52 \text{ ksi}}{0.008 \text{ rad}} = 6500 \text{ ksi} \qquad \textit{Ans.}$$

the equation of line OA is therefore $\tau = G\gamma = 6500\gamma$, which is Hooke's law for shear.

Proportional Limit.   By inspection, the graph ceases to be linear at point A. Thus,

$$\tau_{pl} = 52 \text{ ksi} \qquad \textit{Ans.}$$

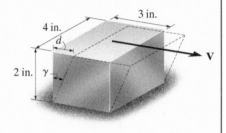

(b)

Fig. 8–24

Ultimate Stress.   This value represents the maximum shear stress, point B. From the graph,

$$\tau_u = 73 \text{ ksi} \qquad \textit{Ans.}$$

Maximum Elastic Displacement and Shear Force.   Since the maximum elastic shear strain is 0.008 rad, a very small angle, the top of the block in Fig. 8–24b will be displaced horizontally:

$$\tan(0.008 \text{ rad}) \approx 0.008 \text{ rad} = \frac{d}{2 \text{ in.}}$$

$$d = 0.016 \text{ in.} \qquad \textit{Ans.}$$

The corresponding *average* shear stress in the block is $\tau_{pl} = 52$ ksi. Thus, the shear force V needed to cause the displacement is

$$\tau_{avg} = \frac{V}{A}; \qquad 52 \text{ ksi} = \frac{V}{(3 \text{ in.})(4 \text{ in.})}$$

$$V = 624 \text{ kip} \qquad \textit{Ans.}$$

8

EXAMPLE | 8.5

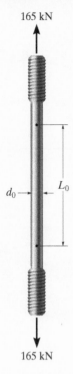

165 kN

d_0 → ← L_0

165 kN

Fig. 8–25

An aluminum specimen shown in Fig. 8–25 has a diameter of $d_0 = 25$ mm and a gauge length of $L_0 = 250$ mm. If a force of 165 kN elongates the gauge length 1.20 mm, determine the modulus of elasticity. Also, determine by how much the force causes the diameter of the specimen to contract. Take $G_{al} = 26$ GPa and $\sigma_Y = 440$ MPa.

SOLUTION

Modulus of Elasticity. The average normal stress in the specimen is

$$\sigma = \frac{P}{A} = \frac{165(10^3)\ \text{N}}{(\pi/4)(0.025\ \text{m})^2} = 336.1\ \text{MPa}$$

and the average normal strain is

$$\epsilon = \frac{\delta}{L} = \frac{1.20\ \text{mm}}{250\ \text{mm}} = 0.00480\ \text{mm/mm}$$

Since $\sigma < \sigma_Y = 440$ MPa, the material behaves elastically. The modulus of elasticity is therefore

$$E_{al} = \frac{\sigma}{\epsilon} = \frac{336.1(10^6)\ \text{Pa}}{0.00480} = 70.0\ \text{GPa} \qquad Ans.$$

Contraction of Diameter. First we will determine Poisson's ratio for the material using Eq. 8–11.

$$G = \frac{E}{2(1+\nu)}$$

$$26\ \text{GPa} = \frac{70.0\ \text{GPa}}{2(1+\nu)}$$

$$\nu = 0.347$$

Since $\epsilon_{long} = 0.00480$ mm/mm, then by Eq. 8–9,

$$\nu = -\frac{\epsilon_{lat}}{\epsilon_{long}}$$

$$0.347 = -\frac{\epsilon_{lat}}{0.00480\ \text{mm/mm}}$$

$$\epsilon_{lat} = -0.00166\ \text{mm/mm}$$

The contraction of the diameter is therefore

$$\delta' = (0.00166)(25\ \text{mm})$$

$$= 0.0416\ \text{mm} \qquad Ans.$$

Important Points

- *Poisson's ratio*, ν, is a ratio of the lateral strain of a homogeneous and isotropic material to its longitudinal strain. Generally these strains are of opposite signs, that is, if one is an elongation, the other will be a contraction.
- The *shear stress-strain diagram*, is a plot of the shear stress versus the shear strain. If the material is homogeneous and isotropic, and is also linear elastic, the slope of the straight line within the elastic region is called the modulus of rigidity or the shear modulus, G.
- There is a mathematical relationship between G, E, and ν.

FUNDAMENTAL PROBLEMS

F8–13. A 100-mm long rod has a diameter of 15 mm. If an axial tensile load of 10 kN is applied to it, determine the change in its diameter. $E = 70$ GPa, $\nu = 0.35$.

F8–14. A solid circular rod that is 600 mm long and 20 mm in diameter is subjected to an axial force of $P = 50$ kN. The elongation of the rod is $\delta = 1.40$ mm, and its diameter becomes $d' = 19.9837$ mm. Determine the modulus of elasticity and the modulus of rigidity of the material. Assume that the material does not yield.

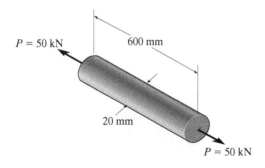

F8–14

F8–15. A 20-mm-wide block is firmly bonded to rigid plates at its top and bottom. When the force **P** is applied the block deforms into the shape shown by the dashed line. Determine the magnitude of **P**. The block's material has a modulus of rigidity of $G = 26$ GPa. Assume that the material does not yield and use small angle analysis.

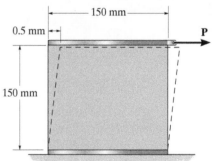

F8–15

F8–16. A 20-mm-wide block is bonded to rigid plates at its top and bottom. When the force **P** is applied the block deforms into the shape shown by the dashed line. If $a = 3$ mm and **P** is released, determine the permanent shear strain in the block.

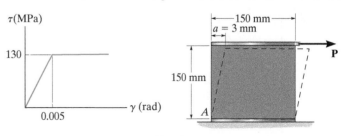

F8–16

PROBLEMS

•8–21.   The acrylic plastic rod is 200 mm long and 15 mm in diameter. If an axial load of 300 N is applied to it, determine the change in its length and the change in its diameter. $E_p = 2.70$ GPa, $\nu_p = 0.4$.

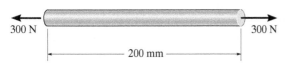

300 N   300 N

|← 200 mm →|

Prob. 8–21

8–22.   The short cylindrical block of 2014-T6 aluminum, having an original diameter of 0.5 in. and a length of 1.5 in., is placed in the smooth jaws of a vise and squeezed until the axial load applied is 800 lb. Determine (a) the decrease in its length and (b) its new diameter.

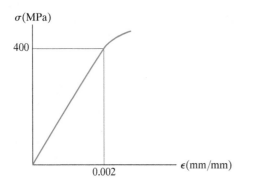

800 lb   800 lb

Prob. 8–22

8–23.   The elastic portion of the stress–strain diagram for a steel alloy is shown in the figure. The specimen from which it was obtained had an original diameter of 13 mm and a gauge length of 50 mm. When the applied load on the specimen is 50 kN, the diameter is 12.99265 mm. Determine Poisson's ratio for the material.

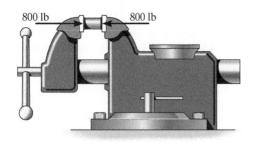

σ(MPa)

400

0.002 ϵ(mm/mm)

Prob. 8–23

*8–24.   The elastic portion of the stress–strain diagram for a steel alloy is shown in the figure. The specimen from which it was obtained had an original diameter of 13 mm and a gauge length of 50 mm. If a load of $P = 20$ kN is applied to the specimen, determine its diameter and gauge length. Take $\nu = 0.4$.

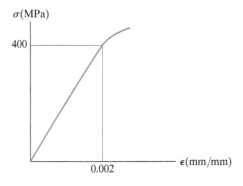

σ(MPa)

400

0.002 ϵ(mm/mm)

Prob. 8–24

•8–25.   The aluminum block has a rectangular cross section and is subjected to an axial compressive force of 8 kip. If the 1.5-in. side changed its length to 1.500132 in., determine Poisson's ratio and the new length of the 2-in. side. $E_{al} = 10(10^3)$ ksi.

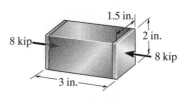

1.5 in.
2 in.
8 kip
8 kip
3 in.

Prob. 8–25

8–26. The block is made of titanium Ti-6A1-4V and is subjected to a compression of 0.06 in. along the y axis, and its shape is given a tilt of $\theta = 89.7°$. Determine ϵ_x, ϵ_y, and γ_{xy}.

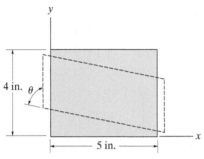

4 in. θ

5 in.

Prob. 8–26

8–27. The shear stress–strain diagram for a steel alloy is shown in the figure. If a bolt having a diameter of 0.75 in. is made of this material and used in the double lap joint, determine the modulus of elasticity E and the force P required to cause the material to yield. Take $\nu = 0.3$.

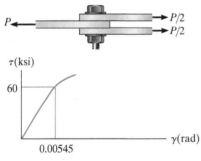

P $P/2$
    $P/2$

$\tau(\text{ksi})$

60

0.00545 $\gamma(\text{rad})$

Prob. 8–27

*8–28. A shear spring is made by bonding the rubber annulus to a rigid fixed ring and a plug. When an axial load P is placed on the plug, show that the slope at point y in the rubber is $dy/dr = -\tan\gamma = -\tan(P/(2\pi hGr))$. For small angles we can write $dy/dr = -P/(2\pi hGr)$. Integrate this expression and evaluate the constant of integration using the condition that $y = 0$ at $r = r_o$. From the result compute the deflection $y = \delta$ of the plug.

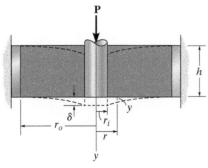

P

h

r_o δ r_i
r
y

y

Prob. 8–28

•8–29. The support consists of three rigid plates, which are connected together using two symmetrically placed rubber pads. If a vertical force of 5 N is applied to plate A, determine the approximate vertical displacement of this plate due to shear strains in the rubber. Each pad has cross-sectional dimensions of 30 mm and 20 mm. $G_r = 0.20$ MPa.

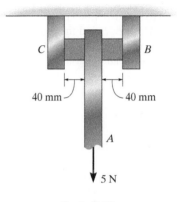

C B

40 mm   40 mm

A

5 N

Prob. 8–29

8–30. A shear spring is made from two blocks of rubber, each having a height h, width b, and thickness a. The blocks are bonded to three plates as shown. If the plates are rigid and the shear modulus of the rubber is G, determine the displacement of plate A if a vertical load P is applied to this plate. Assume that the displacement is small so that $\delta = a \tan\gamma \approx a\gamma$.

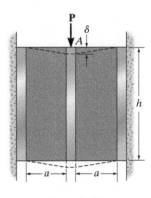

P
δ
A

h

a a

Prob. 8–30

8

CHAPTER REVIEW

One of the most important tests for material strength is the tension test. The results, found from stretching a specimen of known size, are plotted as normal stress on the vertical axis and normal strain on the horizontal axis.

Many engineering materials exhibit initial linear elastic behavior, whereby stress is proportional to strain, defined by Hooke's law, $\sigma = E\epsilon$. Here E, called the modulus of elasticity, is the slope of this straight line on the stress–strain diagram.	$$\sigma = E\epsilon$$	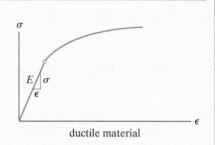 ductile material

When the material is stressed beyond the yield point, permanent deformation will occur. In particular, steel has a region of yielding, whereby the material will exhibit an increase in strain with no increase in stress. The region of strain hardening causes further yielding of the material with a corresponding increase in stress. Finally, at the ultimate stress, a localized region on the specimen will begin to constrict, forming a neck. It is after this that the fracture occurs.

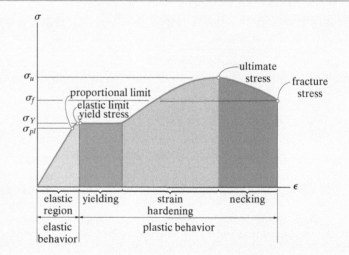

Ductile materials, such as most metals, exhibit both elastic and plastic behavior. Wood is moderately ductile. Ductility is usually specified by the permanent elongation to failure or by the percent reduction in the cross-sectional area.	Percent elongation $= \dfrac{L_f - L_0}{L_0}(100\%)$ Percent reduction of area $= \dfrac{A_0 - A_f}{A_0}(100\%)$	

Brittle materials exhibit little or no yielding before failure. Cast iron, concrete, and glass are typical examples.		

The yield point of a material at A can be increased by strain hardening. This is accomplished by applying a load that causes the stress to be greater than the yield stress, then releasing the load. The larger stress A' becomes the new yield point for the material.

When a load is applied to a member, the deformations cause strain energy to be stored in the material. The strain energy per unit volume or strain energy density is equivalent to the area under the stress–strain curve. This area up to the yield point is called the modulus of resilience. The entire area under the stress–strain diagram is called the modulus of toughness.

Poisson's ratio ν is a dimensionless material property that relates the lateral strain to the longitudinal strain. Its range of values is $0 \leq \nu \leq 0.5$.

$$\nu = -\frac{\epsilon_{\text{lat}}}{\epsilon_{\text{long}}}$$

Shear stress versus shear strain diagrams can also be established for a material. Within the elastic region, $\tau = G\gamma$, where G is the shear modulus, found from the slope of the line. The value of ν can be obtained from the relationship that exists between G, E and ν.

$$G = \frac{E}{2(1 + \nu)}$$

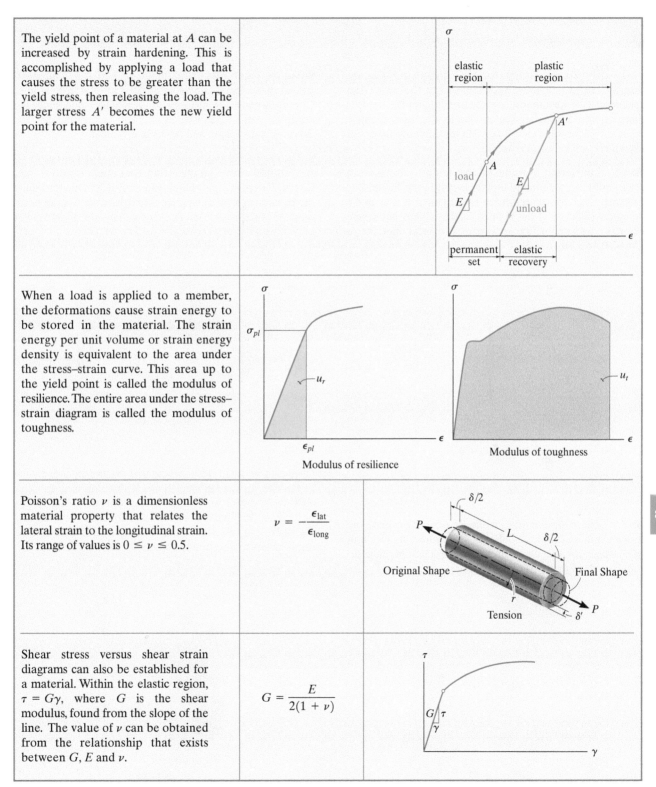

REVIEW PROBLEMS

8–31. The elastic portion of the tension stress–strain diagram for an aluminum alloy is shown in the figure. The specimen used for the test has a gauge length of 2 in. and a diameter of 0.5 in. When the applied load is 9 kip, the new diameter of the specimen is 0.49935 in. Compute the shear modulus G_{al} for the aluminum.

*8–32. The elastic portion of the tension stress–strain diagram for an aluminum alloy is shown in the figure. The specimen used for the test has a gauge length of 2 in. and a diameter of 0.5 in. If the applied load is 10 kip, determine the new diameter of the specimen. The shear modulus is $G_{al} = 3.8(10^3)$ ksi.

8–34. A short cylindrical block of 6061-T6 aluminum, having an original diameter of 20 mm and a length of 75 mm, is placed in a compression machine and squeezed until the axial load applied is 5 kN. Determine (a) the decrease in its length and (b) its new diameter.

8–35. The rigid beam rests in the horizontal position on two 2014-T6 aluminum cylinders having the *unloaded* lengths shown. If each cylinder has a diameter of 30 mm, determine the placement x of the applied 80-kN load so that the beam remains horizontal. What is the new diameter of cylinder A after the load is applied? $\nu_{al} = 0.35$.

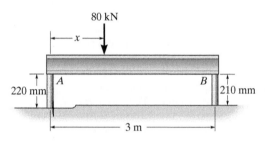

Prob. 8–35

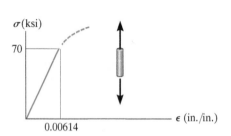

Probs. 8–31/32

•8–33. The σ–ϵ diagram for elastic fibers that make up human skin and muscle is shown. Determine the modulus of elasticity of the fibers and estimate their modulus of toughness and modulus of resilience.

*8–36. The head H is connected to the cylinder of a compressor using six steel bolts. If the clamping force in each bolt is 800 lb, determine the normal strain in the bolts. Each bolt has a diameter of $\frac{3}{16}$ in. If $\sigma_Y = 40$ ksi and $E_{st} = 29(10^3)$ ksi, what is the strain in each bolt when the nut is unscrewed so that the clamping force is released?

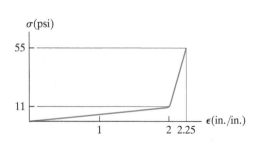

Prob. 8–33

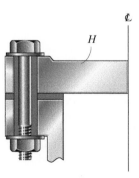

Prob. 8–36

•8–37.   The stone has a mass of 800 kg and center of gravity at G. It rests on a pad at A and a roller at B. The pad is fixed to the ground and has a compressed height of 30 mm, a width of 140 mm, and a length of 150 mm. If the coefficient of static friction between the pad and the stone is $\mu_s = 0.8$, determine the approximate horizontal displacement of the stone, caused by the shear strains in the pad, before the stone begins to slip. Assume the normal force at A acts 1.5 m from G as shown. The pad is made from a material having $E = 4$ MPa and $\nu = 0.35$.

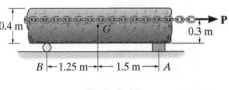

Prob. 8–37

8–38.   The bar DA is rigid and is originally held in the horizontal position when the weight W is supported from C. If the weight causes B to be displaced downward 0.025 in., determine the strain in wires DE and BC. Also, if the wires are made of A-36 steel and have a cross-sectional area of 0.002 in^2, determine the weight W.

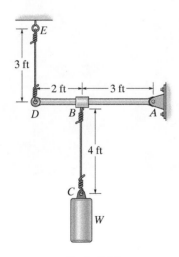

Prob. 8–38

8–39.   The 8-mm-diameter bolt is made of an aluminum alloy. It fits through a magnesium sleeve that has an inner diameter of 12 mm and an outer diameter of 20 mm. If the original lengths of the bolt and sleeve are 80 mm and 50 mm, respectively, determine the strains in the sleeve and the bolt if the nut on the bolt is tightened so that the tension in the bolt is 8 kN. Assume the material at A is rigid. $E_{al} = 70$ GPa, $E_{mg} = 45$ GPa.

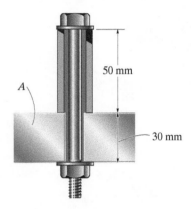

Prob. 8–39

*8–40.   The A-36 steel wire AB has a cross-sectional area of 10 mm^2 and is unstretched when $\theta = 45.0°$. Determine the applied load P needed to cause $\theta = 44.9°$.

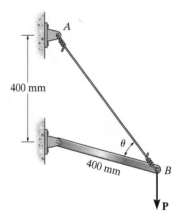

Prob. 8–40

8

The string of drill pipe suspended from this traveling block on an oil rig is subjected to extremely large loadings and axial deformations.

Axial Load

9

CHAPTER OBJECTIVES

In Chapter 8 we developed the method for finding the normal stress in axially loaded members. In this chapter, our objectives are:

- To determine the deformation of axially loaded members.
- To determine the support reactions when these reactions cannot be determined solely from the equations of equilibrium.
- To analyze the effects of thermal stresses.

9.1 Saint-Venant's Principle

In the previous chapters, we have developed the concept of *stress* as a means of measuring the force distribution within a body and *strain* as a means of measuring a body's deformation. We have also shown that the mathematical relationship between stress and strain depends on the type of material from which the body is made. In particular, if the material behaves in a linear elastic manner, then Hooke's law applies, and there is a proportional relationship between stress and strain.

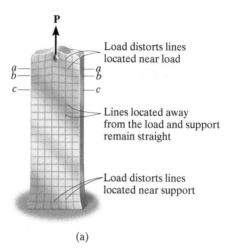

Load distorts lines
located near load

a ——————— a
b ——————— b
c ——————— c

Lines located away
from the load and support
remain straight

Load distorts lines
located near support

(a)

Fig. 9–1

Using this idea, consider the manner in which a rectangular bar will deform elastically when the bar is subjected to a force **P** applied along its centroidal axis, Fig. 9–1a. Here the bar is fixed connected at one end, with the force applied through a hole at its other end. Due to the loading, the bar deforms as indicated by the once horizontal and vertical grid lines drawn on the bar. Notice how the *localized deformation* that occurs at each end tends to even out and become uniform throughout the midsection of the bar.

If the material remains elastic then the strains caused by this deformation are directly related to the stress in the bar. As a result, the stress will be distributed more uniformly throughout the cross-sectional area when the section is taken farther and farther from the point where any external load is applied. For example, consider a profile of the variation of the stress distribution acting at sections *a–a*, *b–b*, and *c–c*, each of which is shown in Fig. 9–1b. By comparison, the stress tends to reach a uniform value at section *c–c*, which is sufficiently removed from the end since the localized deformation caused by **P** *vanishes*. The minimum distance from the bar's end where this occurs can be determined using a mathematical analysis based on the theory of elasticity.

It has been found that this distance should at least be equal to the *largest dimension* of the loaded cross section. Hence, section *c–c* should be located at a distance at least equal to the width (not the thickness) of the bar.*

---

*When section *c–c* is so located, the theory of elasticity predicts the maximum stress to be $\sigma_{max} = 1.02\sigma_{avg}$.

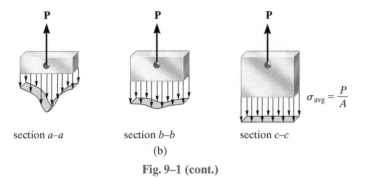

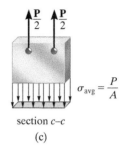

$$\sigma_{avg} = \frac{P}{A}$$

section a–a section b–b section c–c section c–c

(b)   (c)

Fig. 9–1 (cont.)

In the same way, the stress distribution at the support will also even out and become uniform over the cross section located the same distance away from the support.

The fact that stress and deformation behave in this manner is referred to as *Saint-Venant's principle*, since it was first noticed by the French scientist Barré de Saint-Venant in 1855. Essentially it states that the *stress and strain produced at points in a body sufficiently removed from the region of load application will be the same as the stress and strain produced by any applied loadings that have the same statically equivalent resultant, and are applied to the body within the same region.* For example, if two symmetrically applied forces $P/2$ act on the bar, Fig. 9–1c, the stress distribution at section c–c will be uniform and therefore equivalent to $\sigma_{avg} = P/A$ as in Fig. 9–1b.

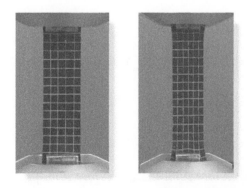

Notice how the lines on this rubber membrane distort after it is stretched. The localized distortions at the grips smooth out as stated by Saint-Venant's principle.

9.2   Elastic Deformation of an Axially Loaded Member

Using Hooke's law and the definitions of stress and strain, we will now develop an equation that can be used to determine the *elastic* displacement of a member subjected to axial loads. To generalize the development, consider the bar shown in Fig. 9–2a, which has a cross-sectional area that *gradually* varies along its length L. The bar is subjected to concentrated loads at its ends and a variable external load distributed along its length. This distributed load could, for example, represent the weight of the bar if it does not remain horizontal, or friction forces acting on the bar's surface. Here we wish to find the **relative displacement** δ (delta) of one end of the bar with respect to the other end as caused by this loading. We will *neglect* the localized deformations that occur at points of concentrated loading and where the cross section suddenly changes. From Saint-Venant's principle, these effects occur within small regions of the bar's length and will therefore have only a slight effect on the final result. For the most part, the bar will deform uniformly, so the normal stress will be uniformly distributed over the cross section.

Using the method of sections, a differential element (or wafer) of length *dx* and cross-sectional area A(x) is isolated from the bar at the arbitrary position x. The free-body diagram of this element is shown in Fig. 9–2b. The resultant internal axial force will be a function of x since the external distributed loading will cause it to vary along the length of the bar. This load, P(x), will deform the element into the shape indicated by the dashed outline, and therefore the displacement of one end of the element with respect to the other end is *dδ*. The stress and strain in the element are

$$\sigma = \frac{P(x)}{A(x)} \quad \text{and} \quad \epsilon = \frac{d\delta}{dx}$$

Provided the stress does not exceed the proportional limit, we can apply Hooke's law; i.e.,

$$\sigma = E\epsilon$$

$$\frac{P(x)}{A(x)} = E\left(\frac{d\delta}{dx}\right)$$

$$d\delta = \frac{P(x)\,dx}{A(x)E}$$

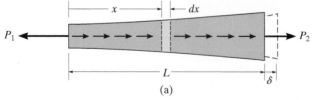

(a)

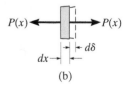

(b)

Fig. 9–2

For the entire length L of the bar, we must integrate this expression to find δ. This yields

$$\delta = \int_0^L \frac{P(x)\, dx}{A(x)E} \qquad (9\text{--}1)$$

where

δ = displacement of one point on the bar relative to the other point

L = original length of bar

$P(x)$ = internal axial force at the section, located a distance x from one end

$A(x)$ = cross-sectional area of the bar, expressed as a function of x

E = modulus of elasticity for the material

Constant Load and Cross-Sectional Area.   In many cases the bar will have a constant cross-sectional area A; and the material will be homogeneous, so E is constant. Furthermore, if a constant external force is applied at each end, Fig. 9–3, then the internal force P throughout the length of the bar is also constant. As a result, Eq. 9–1 can be integrated to yield

$$\delta = \frac{PL}{AE} \qquad (9\text{--}2)$$

If the bar is subjected to several different axial forces along its length, or the cross-sectional area or modulus of elasticity changes abruptly from one region of the bar to the next, the above equation can be applied to each *segment* of the bar where these quantities remain *constant*. The displacement of one end of the bar with respect to the other is then found from the *algebraic addition* of the relative displacements of the ends of each segment. For this general case,

The vertical displacement at the top of these building columns depends upon the loading applied on the roof and to the floor attached to their midpoint.

$$\delta = \sum \frac{PL}{AE} \qquad (9\text{--}3)$$

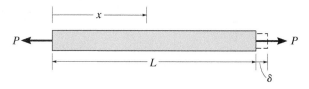

Fig. 9–3

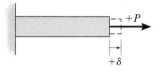

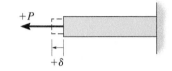

Positive sign convention for P and δ

Fig. 9–4

Sign Convention.

In order to apply Eq. 9–3, we must develop a sign convention for the internal axial force and the displacement of one end of the bar with respect to the other end. To do so, we will consider both the force and displacement to be *positive* if they cause *tension and elongation*, respectively, Fig. 9–4; whereas a *negative* force and displacement will cause *compression* and *contraction*, respectively.

For example, consider the bar shown in Fig. 9–5*a*. The *internal axial forces "P,"* are determined by the method of sections for each segment, Fig. 9–5*b*. They are $P_{AB} = +5$ kN, $P_{BC} = -3$ kN, $P_{CD} = -7$ kN. This variation in axial load is shown on the axial or *normal force diagram* for the bar, Fig. 9–5*c*. Since we now know how the *internal* force varies throughout the bar's length, the displacement of end A relative to end D is determined from

$$\delta_{A/D} = \sum \frac{PL}{AE} = \frac{(5 \text{ kN})L_{AB}}{AE} + \frac{(-3 \text{ kN})L_{BC}}{AE} + \frac{(-7 \text{ kN})L_{CD}}{AE}$$

If the other data are substituted and a positive answer is calculated, it means that end A will move away from end D (the bar elongates), whereas a negative result would indicate that end A moves toward end D (the bar shortens). The double subscript notation is used to indicate this relative displacement ($\delta_{A/D}$); however, if the displacement is to be determined relative to a *fixed point*, then only a single subscript will be used. For example, if D is located at a *fixed* support, then the displacement will be denoted as simply δ_A.

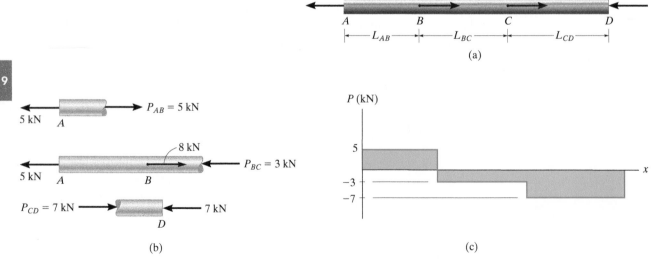

Fig. 9–5

Important Points

- *Saint-Venant's principle* states that both the localized deformation and stress which occur within the regions of load application or at the supports tend to "even out" at a distance sufficiently removed from these regions.

- The displacement of one end of an axially loaded member relative to the other end is determined by relating the applied *internal* load to the stress using $\sigma = P/A$ and relating the displacement to the strain using $\epsilon = d\delta/dx$. Finally, these two equations are combined using Hooke's law, $\sigma = E\epsilon$, which yields Eq. 9–1.

- Since Hooke's law has been used in the development of the displacement equation, it is important that no internal load causes yielding of the material, and that the material is homogeneous and behaves in a linear elastic manner.

Procedure for Analysis

The relative displacement between any two points A and B on an axially loaded member can be determined by applying Eq. 9–1 (or Eq. 9–2). Application requires the following steps.

Internal Force.

- Use the method of sections to determine the internal axial force P within the member.

- If this force varies along the member's length due to an *external distributed loading*, a section should be made at the arbitrary location x from one end of the member and the force represented as a function of x, i.e., $P(x)$.

- If several *constant external forces* act on the member, the internal force in each *segment* of the member, between any two external forces, must be determined.

- For any segment, an internal *tensile force* is *positive* and an internal *compressive force* is *negative*. For convenience, the results of the internal loading can be shown graphically by constructing the normal-force diagram.

Displacement.

- When the member's cross-sectional area *varies* along its length, the area must be expressed as a function of its position x, i.e., $A(x)$.

- If the cross-sectional area, the modulus of elasticity, or the internal loading *suddenly changes*, then Eq. 9–2 should be applied to each segment for which these quantities are constant.

- When substituting the data into Eqs. 9–1 through 9–3, be sure to account for the proper sign for the internal force **P**. Tensile loadings are positive and compressive loadings are negative. Also, use a consistent set of units. For any segment, if the result is a *positive* numerical quantity, it indicates *elongation*; if it is *negative*, it indicates a *contraction*.

EXAMPLE | 9.1

The A-36 steel bar shown in Fig. 9–6a is made from two segments having cross-sectional areas of $A_{AB} = 1 \text{ in}^2$ and $A_{BD} = 2 \text{ in}^2$. Determine the vertical displacement of end A and the displacement of B relative to C.

(a)

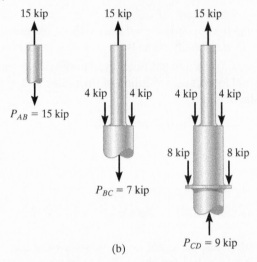

(b)

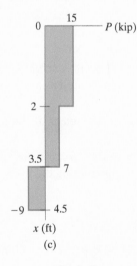

(c)

Fig. 9–6

SOLUTION

Internal Force.   Due to the application of the external loadings, the internal axial forces in regions AB, BC, and CD will all be different. These forces are obtained by applying the method of sections and the equation of vertical force equilibrium as shown in Fig. 9–6b. This variation is plotted in Fig. 9–6c.

Displacement.   From the inside back cover, $E_{st} = 29(10^3)$ ksi. Using the sign convention, i.e., internal tensile forces are positive and compressive forces are negative, the vertical displacement of A relative to the *fixed* support D is

$$\delta_A = \sum \frac{PL}{AE} = \frac{[+15 \text{ kip}](2 \text{ ft})(12 \text{ in./ft})}{(1 \text{ in}^2)[29(10^3) \text{ kip/in}^2]} + \frac{[+7 \text{ kip}](1.5 \text{ ft})(12 \text{ in./ft})}{(2 \text{ in}^2)[29(10^3) \text{ kip/in}^2]}$$

$$+ \frac{[-9 \text{ kip}](1 \text{ ft})(12 \text{ in./ft})}{(2 \text{ in}^2)[29(10^3) \text{ kip/in}^2]}$$

$$= +0.0127 \text{ in.} \hspace{3cm} Ans.$$

Since the result is *positive*, the bar *elongates* and so the displacement at A is upward.

Applying Eq. 9–2 between points B and C, we obtain,

$$\delta_{B/C} = \frac{P_{BC}L_{BC}}{A_{BC}E} = \frac{[+7 \text{ kip}](1.5 \text{ ft})(12 \text{ in./ft})}{(2 \text{ in}^2)[29(10^3) \text{ kip/in}^2]} = +0.00217 \text{ in.} \quad Ans.$$

Here B moves away from C, since the segment elongates.

EXAMPLE | 9.2

The assembly shown in Fig. 9–7a consists of an aluminum tube AB having a cross-sectional area of 400 mm². A steel rod having a diameter of 10 mm is attached to a rigid collar and passes through the tube. If a tensile load of 80 kN is applied to the rod, determine the displacement of the end C of the rod. Take $E_{st} = 200$ GPa, $E_{al} = 70$ GPa.

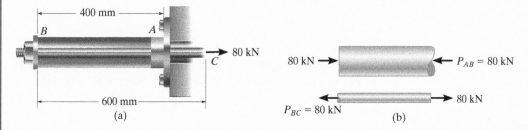

Fig. 9–7

SOLUTION

Internal Force. The free-body diagram of the tube and rod segments in Fig. 9–7b, shows that the rod is subjected to a tension of 80 kN and the tube is subjected to a compression of 80 kN.

Displacement. We will first determine the displacement of end C with respect to end B. Working in units of newtons and meters, we have

$$\delta_{C/B} = \frac{PL}{AE} = \frac{[+80(10^3) \text{ N}](0.6 \text{ m})}{\pi(0.005 \text{ m})^2[200(10^9) \text{ N/m}^2]} = +0.003056 \text{ m} \rightarrow$$

The positive sign indicates that end C moves *to the right* relative to end B, since the bar elongates.

The displacement of end B with respect to the *fixed* end A is

$$\delta_B = \frac{PL}{AE} = \frac{[-80(10^3) \text{ N}](0.4 \text{ m})}{[400 \text{ mm}^2(10^{-6}) \text{ m}^2/\text{mm}^2][70(10^9) \text{ N/m}^2]}$$
$$= -0.001143 \text{ m} = 0.001143 \text{ m} \rightarrow$$

Here the negative sign indicates that the tube shortens, and so B moves to the *right* relative to A.

Since both displacements are to the right, the displacement of C relative to the fixed end A is therefore

$$(\overset{+}{\rightarrow}) \qquad \delta_C = \delta_B + \delta_{C/B} = 0.001143 \text{ m} + 0.003056 \text{ m}$$

$$= 0.00420 \text{ m} = 4.20 \text{ mm} \rightarrow \qquad \qquad Ans.$$

EXAMPLE 9.3

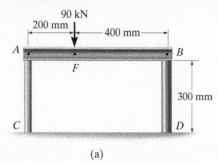

(a)

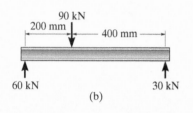

(b)

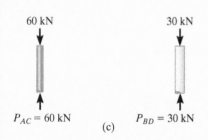

(c)

Rigid beam AB rests on the two short posts shown in Fig. 9–8a. AC is made of steel and has a diameter of 20 mm, and BD is made of aluminum and has a diameter of 40 mm. Determine the displacement of point F on AB if a vertical load of 90 kN is applied over this point. Take $E_{st} = 200$ GPa, $E_{al} = 70$ GPa.

SOLUTION

Internal Force. The compressive forces acting at the top of each post are determined from the equilibrium of member AB, Fig. 9–8b. These forces are equal to the internal forces in each post, Fig. 9–8c.

Displacement. The displacement of the top of each post is

Post AC:

$$\delta_A = \frac{P_{AC}L_{AC}}{A_{AC}E_{st}} = \frac{[-60(10^3)\ N](0.300\ m)}{\pi(0.010\ m)^2[200(10^9)\ N/m^2]} = -286(10^{-6})\ m$$

$$= 0.286\ mm\ \downarrow$$

Post BD:

$$\delta_B = \frac{P_{BD}L_{BD}}{A_{BD}E_{al}} = \frac{[-30(10^3)\ N](0.300\ m)}{\pi(0.020\ m)^2[70(10^9)\ N/m^2]} = -102(10^{-6})\ m$$

$$= 0.102\ mm\ \downarrow$$

A diagram showing the centerline displacements at A, B, and F on the beam is shown in Fig. 9–8d. By proportion of the blue shaded triangle, the displacement of point F is therefore

$$\delta_F = 0.102\ mm + (0.184\ mm)\left(\frac{400\ mm}{600\ mm}\right) = 0.225\ mm\ \downarrow \quad Ans.$$

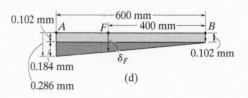

(d)

Fig. 9–8

EXAMPLE 9.4

A member is made from a material that has a specific weight γ and modulus of elasticity E. If it is in the form of a *cone* having the dimensions shown in Fig. 9–9a, determine how far its end is displaced due to gravity when it is suspended in the vertical position.

(a)

SOLUTION

Internal Force. The internal axial force varies along the member since it is dependent on the weight $W(y)$ of a segment of the member below any section, Fig. 9–9b. Hence, to calculate the displacement, we must use Eq. 9–1. At the section located a distance y from its free end, the radius x of the cone as a function of y is determined by proportion; i.e.,

$$\frac{x}{y} = \frac{r_0}{L}; \qquad x = \frac{r_0}{L}y$$

The volume of a cone having a base of radius x and height y is

$$V = \frac{1}{3}\pi y x^2 = \frac{\pi r_0^2}{3L^2}y^3$$

Since $W = \gamma V$, the internal force at the section becomes

$$+\uparrow\Sigma F_y = 0; \qquad P(y) = \frac{\gamma\pi r_0^2}{3L^2}y^3$$

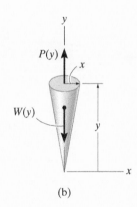

(b)

Fig. 9–9

Displacement. The area of the cross section is also a function of position y, Fig. 9–9b. We have

$$A(y) = \pi x^2 = \frac{\pi r_0^2}{L^2}y^2$$

Applying Eq. 9–1 between the limits of $y = 0$ and $y = L$ yields

$$\delta = \int_0^L \frac{P(y)\,dy}{A(y)E} = \int_0^L \frac{\left[(\gamma\pi r_0^2/3L^2)\,y^3\right]dy}{\left[(\pi r_0^2/L^2)\,y^2\right]E}$$

$$= \frac{\gamma}{3E}\int_0^L y\,dy$$

$$= \frac{\gamma L^2}{6E} \qquad\qquad\qquad Ans.$$

NOTE: As a partial check of this result, notice how the units of the terms, when canceled, give the displacement in units of length as expected.

FUNDAMENTAL PROBLEMS

F9–1. The 20-mm-diameter A-36 steel rod is subjected to the axial forces shown. Determine the displacement of end C with respect to the fixed support at A.

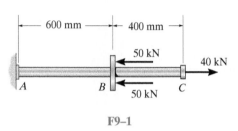

F9–1

F9–2. Segments AB and CD of the assembly are solid circular rods, and segment BC is a tube. If the assembly is made of 6061-T6 aluminum, determine the displacement of end D with respect to end A.

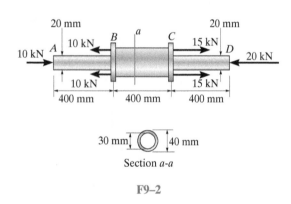

Section a-a

F9–2

F9–3. The 30-mm-diameter A-36 steel rod is subjected to the loading shown. Determine the displacement of end A with respect to end C.

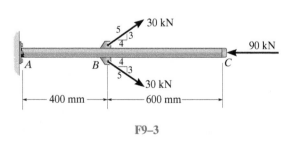

F9–3

F9–4. If the 20-mm-diameter rod is made of A-36 steel and the stiffness of the spring is $k = 50$ MN/m, determine the displacement of end A when the 60-kN force is applied.

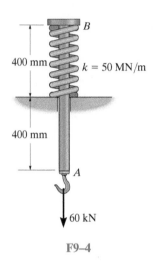

F9–4

F9–5. The 20-mm-diameter 2014-T6 aluminum rod is subjected to the uniform distributed axial load. Determine the displacement of end A.

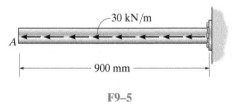

F9–5

F9–6. The 20-mm-diameter 2014-T6 aluminum rod is subjected to the triangular distributed axial load. Determine the displacement of end A.

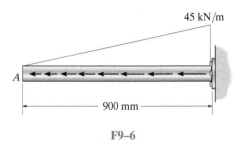

F9–6

PROBLEMS

•9–1. The ship is pushed through the water using an A-36 steel propeller shaft that is 8 m long, measured from the propeller to the thrust bearing D at the engine. If it has an outer diameter of 400 mm and a wall thickness of 50 mm, determine the amount of axial contraction of the shaft when the propeller exerts a force on the shaft of 5 kN. The bearings at B and C are journal bearings.

9–3. The A-36 steel rod is subjected to the loading shown. If the cross-sectional area of the rod is 50 mm^2, determine the displacement of its end D. Neglect the size of the couplings at B, C, and D.

*9–4. The A-36 steel rod is subjected to the loading shown. If the cross-sectional area of the rod is 50 mm^2, determine the displacement of C. Neglect the size of the couplings at B, C, and D.

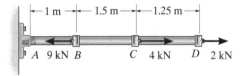

Probs. 9–3/4

•9–5. The assembly consists of a steel rod CB and an aluminum rod BA, each having a diameter of 12 mm. If the rod is subjected to the axial loadings at A and at the coupling B, determine the displacement of the coupling B and the end A. The unstretched length of each segment is shown in the figure. Neglect the size of the connections at B and C, and assume that they are rigid. E_{st} = 200 GPa, E_{al} = 70 GPa.

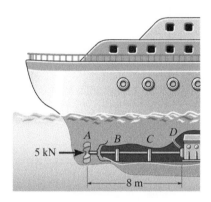

Prob. 9–1

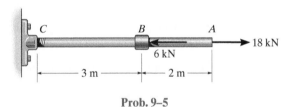

Prob. 9–5

9–2. The copper shaft is subjected to the axial loads shown. Determine the displacement of end A with respect to end D. The diameters of each segment are d_{AB} = 3 in., d_{BC} = 2 in., and d_{CD} = 1 in. Take E_{cu} = 18(10^3) ksi.

9–6. The bar has a cross-sectional area of 3 in^2, and E = 35(10^3) ksi. Determine the displacement of its end A when it is subjected to the distributed loading.

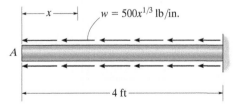

Prob. 9–6

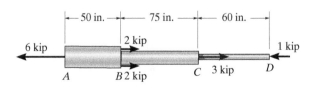

Prob. 9–2

9–7. The load of 800 lb is supported by the four 304 stainless steel wires that are connected to the rigid members AB and DC. Determine the vertical displacement of the load if the members were horizontal before the load was applied. Each wire has a cross-sectional area of 0.05 in².

***9–8.** The load of 800 lb is supported by the four 304 stainless steel wires that are connected to the rigid members AB and DC. Determine the angle of tilt of each member after the load is applied. The members were originally horizontal, and each wire has a cross-sectional area of 0.05 in².

9–11. The load is supported by the four 304 stainless steel wires that are connected to the rigid members AB and DC. Determine the vertical displacement of the 500-lb load if the members were originally horizontal when the load was applied. Each wire has a cross-sectional area of 0.025 in².

***9–12.** The load is supported by the four 304 stainless steel wires that are connected to the rigid members AB and DC. Determine the angle of tilt of each member after the 500-lb load is applied. The members were originally horizontal, and each wire has a cross-sectional area of 0.025 in².

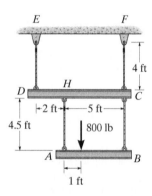

Probs. 9–7/8

Probs. 9–11/12

•9–9. The assembly consists of three titanium (Ti-6A1-4V) rods and a rigid bar AC. The cross-sectional area of each rod is given in the figure. If a force of 6 kip is applied to the ring F, determine the horizontal displacement of point F.

9–10. The assembly consists of three titanium (Ti-6A1-4V) rods and a rigid bar AC. The cross-sectional area of each rod is given in the figure. If a force of 6 kip is applied to the ring F, determine the angle of tilt of bar AC.

•9–13. The bar has a length L and cross-sectional area A. Determine its elongation due to the force **P** and its own weight. The material has a specific weight γ (weight/volume) and a modulus of elasticity E.

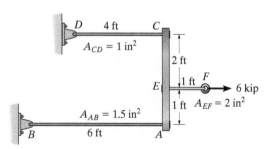

Probs. 9–9/10

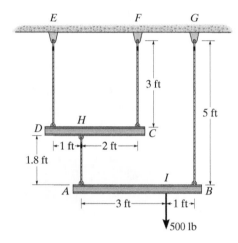

Prob. 9–13

9–14. The post is made of Douglas fir and has a diameter of 60 mm. If it is subjected to the load of 20 kN and the soil provides a frictional resistance that is uniformly distributed along its sides of $w = 4$ kN/m, determine the force **F** at its bottom needed for equilibrium. Also, what is the displacement of the top of the post A with respect to its bottom B? Neglect the weight of the post.

9–15. The post is made of Douglas fir and has a diameter of 60 mm. If it is subjected to the load of 20 kN and the soil provides a frictional resistance that is distributed along its length and varies linearly from $w = 0$ at $y = 0$ to $w = 3$ kN/m at $y = 2$ m, determine the force **F** at its bottom needed for equilibrium. Also, what is the displacement of the top of the post A with respect to its bottom B? Neglect the weight of the post.

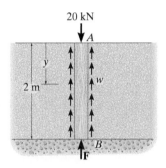

Probs. 9–14/15

*9–16. The linkage is made of two pin-connected A-36 steel members, each having a cross-sectional area of 1.5 in². If a vertical force of $P = 50$ kip is applied to point A, determine its vertical displacement at A.

•9–17. The linkage is made of two pin-connected A-36 steel members, each having a cross-sectional area of 1.5 in². Determine the magnitude of the force **P** needed to displace point A 0.025 in. downward.

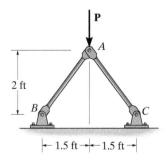

Probs. 9–16/17

9–18. The assembly consists of two A-36 steel rods and a rigid bar BD. Each rod has a diameter of 0.75 in. If a force of 10 kip is applied to the bar as shown, determine the vertical displacement of the load.

9–19. The assembly consists of two A-36 steel rods and a rigid bar BD. Each rod has a diameter of 0.75 in. If a force of 10 kip is applied to the bar, determine the angle of tilt of the bar.

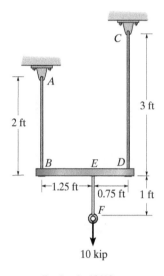

Probs. 9–18/19

*9–20. The rigid bar is supported by the pin-connected rod CB that has a cross-sectional area of 500 mm² and is made of A-36 steel. Determine the vertical displacement of the bar at B when the load is applied.

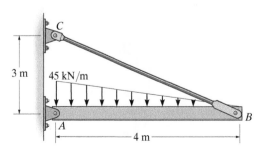

Prob. 9–20

•9–21.   A spring-supported pipe hanger consists of two springs which are originally unstretched and have a stiffness of $k = 60$ kN/m, three 304 stainless steel rods, AB and CD, which have a diameter of 5 mm, and EF, which has a diameter of 12 mm, and a rigid beam GH. If the pipe and the fluid it carries have a total weight of 4 kN, determine the displacement of the pipe when it is attached to the support.

9–22.   A spring-supported pipe hanger consists of two springs, which are originally unstretched and have a stiffness of $k = 60$ kN/m, three 304 stainless steel rods, AB and CD, which have a diameter of 5 mm, and EF, which has a diameter of 12 mm, and a rigid beam GH. If the pipe is displaced 82 mm when it is filled with fluid, determine the weight of the fluid.

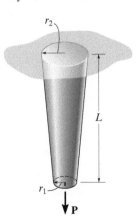

Probs. 9–21/22

9–23.   The rod has a slight taper and length L. It is suspended from the ceiling and supports a load $\mathbf{P}$ at its end. Show that the displacement of its end due to this load is $\delta = PL/(\pi E r_2 r_1)$. Neglect the weight of the material. The modulus of elasticity is E.

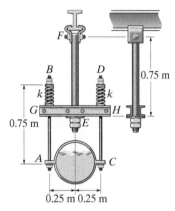

Prob. 9–23

*9–24.   Determine the relative displacement of one end of the tapered plate with respect to the other end when it is subjected to an axial load P.

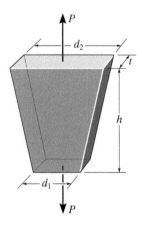

Prob. 9–24

•9–25.   Determine the elongation of the A-36 steel member when it is subjected to an axial force of 30 kN. The member is 10 mm thick. Use the result of Prob. 9–24.

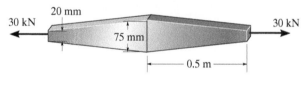

Prob. 9–25

9–26.   The casting is made of a material that has a specific weight γ and modulus of elasticity E. If it is formed into a pyramid having the dimensions shown, determine how far its end is displaced due to gravity when it is suspended in the vertical position.

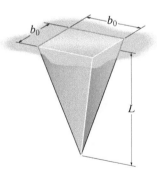

Prob. 9–26

9.3 Principle of Superposition

The principle of superposition is often used to determine the stress or displacement at a point in a member when the member is subjected to a complicated loading. By subdividing the loading into components, the *principle of superposition* states that the resultant stress or displacement at the point can be determined by algebraically summing the stress or displacement caused by each load component applied separately to the member.

The following two conditions must be satisfied if the principle of superposition is to be applied.

1. ***The loading must be linearly related to the stress or displacement that is to be determined.*** For example, the equations $\sigma = P/A$ and $\delta = PL/AE$ involve a linear relationship between P and σ or δ.

2. ***The loading must not significantly change the original geometry or configuration of the member.*** If significant changes do occur, the direction and location of the applied forces and their moment arms will change. For example, consider the slender rod shown in Fig. 9–10a, which is subjected to the load **P**. In Fig. 9–10b, **P** is replaced by two of its components, $\mathbf{P} = \mathbf{P}_1 + \mathbf{P}_2$. If **P** causes the rod to deflect a large amount, as shown, the moment of the load about its support, Pd, will not equal the sum of the moments of its component loads, $Pd \neq P_1 d_1 + P_2 d_2$, because $d_1 \neq d_2 \neq d$.

This principle will be used throughout this text whenever we assume Hooke's law applies and also, the bodies that are considered will be such that the loading will produce deformations that are so small that the change in position and direction of the loading will be insignificant and can be neglected.

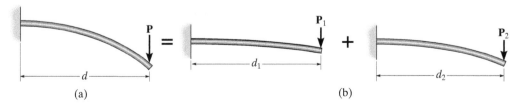

(a)   (b)

Fig. 9–10

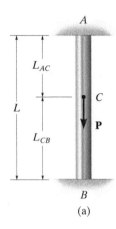

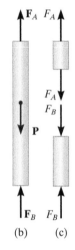

(b)   (c)

Fig. 9–11

9.4 Statically Indeterminate Axially Loaded Member

Consider the bar shown in Fig. 9–11a which is fixed supported at both of its ends. From the free-body diagram, Fig. 9–11b, equilibrium requires

$$+\uparrow \Sigma F = 0; \qquad\qquad F_B + F_A - P = 0$$

This type of problem is called **statically indeterminate**, since the equilibrium equation(s) are not sufficient to determine the two reactions on the bar.

In order to establish an additional equation needed for solution, it is necessary to consider how points on the bar displace. Specifically, an equation that specifies the conditions for displacement is referred to as a **compatibility** or **kinematic condition**. In this case, a suitable compatibility condition would require the displacement of one end of the bar with respect to the other end to be equal to zero, since the end supports are fixed. Hence, the compatibility condition becomes

$$\delta_{A/B} = 0$$

This equation can be expressed in terms of the applied loads by using a *load–displacement relationship*, which depends on the material behavior. For example, if linear-elastic behavior occurs, $\delta = PL/AE$ can be used. Realizing that the internal force in segment AC is $+F_A$, and in segment CB the internal force is $-F_B$, Fig. 9–11c, the above equation can be written as

$$\frac{F_A L_{AC}}{AE} - \frac{F_B L_{CB}}{AE} = 0$$

Assuming that AE is constant, then $F_A = F_B(L_{CB}/L_{AC})$, so that using the equilibrium equation, the equations for the reactions become

$$F_A = P\left(\frac{L_{CB}}{L}\right) \quad \text{and} \quad F_B = P\left(\frac{L_{AC}}{L}\right)$$

Since both of these results are positive, the direction of the reactions is shown correctly on the free-body diagram.

Important Points

- The *principle of superposition* is sometimes used to simplify stress and displacement problems having complicated loadings. This is done by subdividing the loading into components, then algebraically adding the results.

- Superposition requires that the loading be linearly related to the stress or displacement, and the loading does not significantly change the original geometry of the member.

- A problem is *statically indeterminate* if the equations of equilibrium are not sufficient to determine all the reactions on a member.

- *Compatibility conditions* specify the displacement constraints that occur at the supports or other points on a member.

Procedure for Analysis

The support reactions for statically indeterminate problems are determined by satisfying equilibrium, compatibility, and force-displacement requirements for the member.

Equilibrium.

- Draw a free-body diagram of the member in order to identify all the forces that act on it.

- The problem can be classified as statically indeterminate if the number of unknown reactions on the free-body diagram is greater than the number of available equations of equilibrium.

- Write the equations of equilibrium for the member.

Compatibility.

- Consider drawing a displacement diagram in order to investigate the way the member will elongate or contract when subjected to the external loads.

- Express the compatibility conditions in terms of the displacements caused by the loading.

- Use a load–displacement relation, such as $\delta = PL/AE$, to relate the unknown displacements to the reactions.

- Solve the equilibrium and compatibility equations for the reactions. If any of the results has a negative numerical value, it indicates that this force acts in the opposite sense of direction to that indicated on the free-body diagram.

Most concrete columns are reinforced with steel rods; and since these two materials work together in supporting the applied load, the forces in each material become statically indeterminate.

9

EXAMPLE 9.5

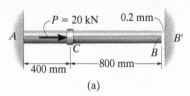

(a)

The steel rod shown in Fig. 9–12a has a diameter of 10 mm. It is fixed to the wall at A, and before it is loaded, there is a gap of 0.2 mm between the wall at B' and the rod. Determine the reactions at A and B' if the rod is subjected to an axial force of $P = 20$ kN as shown. Neglect the size of the collar at C. Take $E_{st} = 200$ GPa.

SOLUTION

Equilibrium. As shown on the free-body diagram, Fig. 9–12b, we will *assume* that force P is large enough to cause the rod's end B to contact the wall at B'. The problem is statically indeterminate since there are two unknowns and only one equation of equilibrium.

$$\xrightarrow{+} \Sigma F_x = 0; \qquad -F_A - F_B + 20(10^3)\ \text{N} = 0 \qquad (1)$$

Compatibility. The force P causes point B to move to B', with no further displacement. Therefore the compatibility condition for the rod is

$$\delta_{B/A} = 0.0002\ \text{m}$$

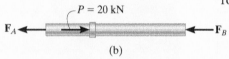

(b)

This displacement can be expressed in terms of the unknown reactions using the load–displacement relationship, Eq. 9–2, applied to segments AC and CB, Fig. 9–12c. Working in units of newtons and meters, we have

$$\delta_{B/A} = 0.0002\ \text{m} = \frac{F_A L_{AC}}{AE} - \frac{F_B L_{CB}}{AE}$$

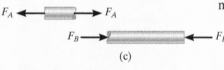

(c)

Fig. 9–12

$$0.0002\ \text{m} = \frac{F_A(0.4\ \text{m})}{\pi(0.005\ \text{m})^2[200(10^9)\ \text{N/m}^2]}$$

$$- \frac{F_B(0.8\ \text{m})}{\pi(0.005\ \text{m})^2[200(10^9)\ \text{N/m}^2]}$$

or

$$F_A(0.4\ \text{m}) - F_B(0.8\ \text{m}) = 3141.59\ \text{N} \cdot \text{m} \qquad (2)$$

Solving Eqs. 1 and 2 yields

$$F_A = 16.0\ \text{kN} \qquad F_B = 4.05\ \text{kN} \qquad \qquad Ans.$$

Since the answer for F_B is *positive*, indeed end B contacts the wall at B' as originally assumed.

NOTE: If F_B were a negative quantity, the problem would be statically determinate, so that $F_B = 0$ and $F_A = 20$ kN.

9

EXAMPLE | 9.6

The aluminum post shown in Fig. 9–13a is reinforced with a brass core. If this assembly supports an axial compressive load of $P = 9$ kip, applied to the rigid cap, determine the average normal stress in the aluminum and the brass. Take $E_{al} = 10(10^3)$ ksi and $E_{br} = 15(10^3)$ ksi.

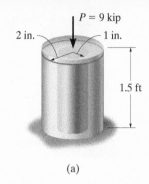

(a)

SOLUTION

Equilibrium. The free-body diagram of the post is shown in Fig. 9–13b. Here the resultant axial force at the base is represented by the unknown components carried by the aluminum, $\mathbf{F}_{al}$, and brass, $\mathbf{F}_{br}$. The problem is statically indeterminate. Why?

Vertical force equilibrium requires

$$+\uparrow \Sigma F_y = 0; \qquad -9 \text{ kip} + F_{al} + F_{br} = 0 \qquad (1)$$

Compatibility. The rigid cap at the top of the post causes both the aluminum and brass to displace the same amount. Therefore,

$$\delta_{al} = \delta_{br}$$

Using the load–displacement relationships,

$$\frac{F_{al}L}{A_{al}E_{al}} = \frac{F_{br}L}{A_{br}E_{br}}$$

$$F_{al} = F_{br}\left(\frac{A_{al}}{A_{br}}\right)\left(\frac{E_{al}}{E_{br}}\right)$$

$$F_{al} = F_{br}\left[\frac{\pi[(2 \text{ in.})^2 - (1 \text{ in.})^2]}{\pi(1 \text{ in.})^2}\right]\left[\frac{10(10^3) \text{ ksi}}{15(10^3) \text{ ksi}}\right]$$

$$F_{al} = 2F_{br} \qquad (2)$$

(b)

Solving Eqs. 1 and 2 simultaneously yields

$$F_{al} = 6 \text{ kip} \qquad F_{br} = 3 \text{ kip}$$

Since the results are positive, indeed the stress will be compressive.

The average normal stress in the aluminum and brass is therefore

$$\sigma_{al} = \frac{6 \text{ kip}}{\pi[(2 \text{ in.})^2 - (1 \text{ in.})^2]} = 0.637 \text{ ksi} \qquad \textit{Ans.}$$

$$\sigma_{br} = \frac{3 \text{ kip}}{\pi(1 \text{ in.})^2} = 0.955 \text{ ksi} \qquad \textit{Ans.}$$

NOTE: Using these results, the stress distributions are shown in Fig. 9–13c.

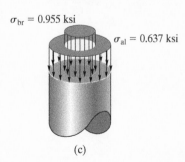

(c)

Fig. 9–13

EXAMPLE | 9.7

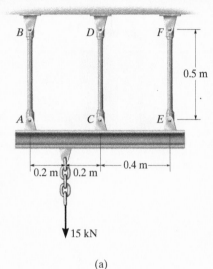

(a)

The three A-36 steel bars shown in Fig. 9–14a are pin connected to a *rigid* member. If the applied load on the member is 15 kN, determine the force developed in each bar. Bars *AB* and *EF* each have a cross-sectional area of 50 mm², and bar *CD* has a cross-sectional area of 30 mm².

SOLUTION

Equilibrium. The free-body diagram of the rigid member is shown in Fig. 9–14b. This problem is statically indeterminate since there are three unknowns and only two available equilibrium equations.

$$+\uparrow \Sigma F_y = 0; \qquad F_A + F_C + F_E - 15\text{ kN} = 0 \qquad (1)$$

$$\downarrow + \Sigma M_C = 0; \quad -F_A(0.4\text{ m}) + 15\text{ kN}(0.2\text{ m}) + F_E(0.4\text{ m}) = 0 \quad (2)$$

Compatibility. The applied load will cause the horizontal line *ACE* shown in Fig. 9–14c to move to the inclined line *A′C′E′*. The displacements of points *A*, *C*, and *E* can be related by similar triangles. Thus the compatibility equation that relates these displacements is

$$\frac{\delta_A - \delta_E}{0.8\text{ m}} = \frac{\delta_C - \delta_E}{0.4\text{ m}}$$

$$\delta_C = \frac{1}{2}\delta_A + \frac{1}{2}\delta_E$$

(b)

Using the load–displacement relationship, Eq. 9–2, we have

$$\frac{F_C L}{(30\text{ mm}^2)E_{st}} = \frac{1}{2}\left[\frac{F_A L}{(50\text{ mm}^2)E_{st}}\right] + \frac{1}{2}\left[\frac{F_E L}{(50\text{ mm}^2)E_{st}}\right]$$

$$F_C = 0.3F_A + 0.3F_E \qquad (3)$$

(c)

Fig. 9–14

Solving Eqs. 1–3 simultaneously yields

$$F_A = 9.52\text{ kN} \qquad\qquad Ans.$$
$$F_C = 3.46\text{ kN} \qquad\qquad Ans.$$
$$F_E = 2.02\text{ kN} \qquad\qquad Ans.$$

EXAMPLE 9.8

The bolt shown in Fig. 9–15*a* is made of 2014-T6 aluminum alloy and is tightened so it compresses a cylindrical tube made of Am 1004-T61 magnesium alloy. The tube has an outer radius of $\frac{1}{2}$ in., and it is assumed that both the inner radius of the tube and the radius of the bolt are $\frac{1}{4}$ in. The washers at the top and bottom of the tube are considered to be rigid and have a negligible thickness. Initially the nut is hand tightened snugly; then, using a wrench, the nut is further tightened one-half turn. If the bolt has 20 threads per inch, determine the stress in the bolt.

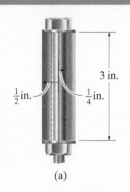

3 in.

$\frac{1}{2}$in. $\frac{1}{4}$in.

(a)

SOLUTION

Equilibrium. The free-body diagram of a section of the bolt and the tube, Fig. 9–15*b*, is considered in order to relate the force in the bolt F_b to that in the tube, F_t. Equilibrium requires

$$+\uparrow\Sigma F_y = 0; \qquad F_b - F_t = 0 \qquad (1)$$

Compatibility. When the nut is tightened on the bolt, the tube will shorten δ_t, and the bolt will *elongate* δ_b, Fig. 9–15*c*. Since the nut undergoes one-half turn, it advances a distance of $(\frac{1}{2})(\frac{1}{20}$ in.$) =$ 0.025 in. along the bolt. Thus, the compatibility of these displacements requires

$$(+\uparrow) \qquad\qquad \delta_t = 0.025 \text{ in.} - \delta_b$$

Taking the moduli of elasticity from the table on the inside back cover, and applying Eq. 9–2, yields

$$\frac{F_t(3 \text{ in.})}{\pi[(0.5 \text{ in.})^2 - (0.25 \text{ in.})^2][6.48(10^3) \text{ ksi}]} =$$

$$0.025 \text{ in.} - \frac{F_b(3 \text{ in.})}{\pi(0.25 \text{ in.})^2[10.6(10^3) \text{ ksi}]}$$

$$0.78595F_t = 25 - 1.4414F_b \qquad (2)$$

Solving Eqs. 1 and 2 simultaneously, we get

$$F_b = F_t = 11.22 \text{ kip}$$

The stresses in the bolt and tube are therefore

$$\sigma_b = \frac{F_b}{A_b} = \frac{11.22 \text{ kip}}{\pi(0.25 \text{ in.})^2} = 57.2 \text{ ksi} \qquad\qquad Ans.$$

$$\sigma_t = \frac{F_t}{A_t} = \frac{11.22 \text{ kip}}{\pi[(0.5 \text{ in.})^2 - (0.25 \text{ in.})^2]} = 19.1 \text{ ksi}$$

These stresses are less than the reported yield stress for each material, $(\sigma_Y)_{al} = 60$ ksi and $(\sigma_Y)_{mg} = 22$ ksi (see the inside back cover), and therefore this "elastic" analysis is valid.

F$_t$

F$_b$

(b)

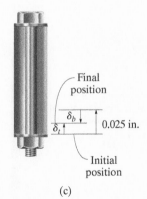

Final position

δ_b

δ_t 0.025 in.

Initial position

(c)

Fig. 9–15

9.5 The Force Method of Analysis for Axially Loaded Members

It is also possible to solve statically indeterminate problems by writing the compatibility equation using the principle of superposition. This method of solution is often referred to as the *flexibility or force method of analysis*. To show how it is applied, consider again the bar in Fig. 9–16a. If we choose the support at B as "redundant" and *temporarily* remove its effect on the bar, then the bar will become statically determinate as in Fig. 9–16b. By using the principle of superposition, we must add back the unknown redundant load $\mathbf{F}_B$, as shown in Fig. 9–16c.

If load $\mathbf{P}$ causes B to be displaced *downward* by an amount δ_P, the reaction $\mathbf{F}_B$ must displace end B of the bar *upward* by an amount δ_B, such that no displacement occurs at B when the two loadings are superimposed. Thus,

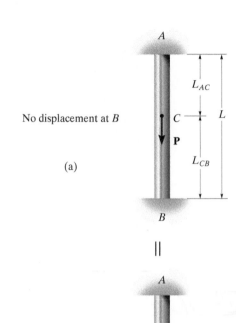

No displacement at B

(a)

$$(+\downarrow) \qquad\qquad 0 = \delta_P - \delta_B$$

This equation represents the compatibility equation for displacements at point B, for which we have assumed that displacements are positive downward.

Applying the load–displacement relationship to each case, we have $\delta_P = PL_{AC}/AE$ and $\delta_B = F_B L/AE$. Consequently,

$$0 = \frac{PL_{AC}}{AE} - \frac{F_B L}{AE}$$

$$F_B = P\left(\frac{L_{AC}}{L}\right)$$

Displacement at B when redundant force at B is removed

(b)

$\parallel$

$+$

From the free-body diagram of the bar, Fig. 9–11b, the reaction at A can now be determined from the equation of equilibrium,

$$+\uparrow \Sigma F_y = 0; \qquad P\left(\frac{L_{AC}}{L}\right) + F_A - P = 0$$

Since $L_{CB} = L - L_{AC}$, then

$$F_A = P\left(\frac{L_{CB}}{L}\right)$$

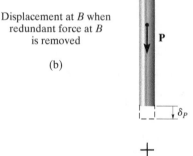

Displacement at B when only the redundant force at B is applied

(c)

Fig. 9–16

These results are the same as those obtained in Sec. 9.4, except that here we have applied the condition of compatibility to obtain one reaction *and then* the equilibrium condition to obtain the other.

Procedure for Analysis

The force method of analysis requires the following steps.

Compatibility.

- Choose one of the supports as redundant and write the equation of compatibility. To do this, the known displacement at the redundant support, which is usually zero, is equated to the displacement at the support caused *only* by the external loads acting on the member *plus* (vectorially) the displacement at this support caused *only* by the redundant reaction acting on the member.
- Express the external load and redundant displacements in terms of the loadings by using a load–displacement relationship, such as $\delta = PL/AE$.
- Once established, the compatibility equation can then be solved for the magnitude of the redundant force.

Equilibrium.

- Draw a free-body diagram and write the appropriate equations of equilibrium for the member using the calculated result for the redundant. Solve these equations for any other reactions.

EXAMPLE | 9.9

The A-36 steel rod shown in Fig. 9–17a has a diameter of 10 mm. It is fixed to the wall at A, and before it is loaded there is a gap between the wall at B' and the rod of 0.2 mm. Determine the reactions at A and B'. Neglect the size of the collar at C. Take $E_{st} = 200$ GPa.

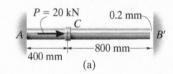

(a)

SOLUTION

Compatibility. Here we will consider the support at B' as redundant. Using the principle of superposition, Fig. 9–17b, we have

$$(\overset{+}{\rightarrow}) \qquad\qquad 0.0002 \text{ m} = \delta_P - \delta_B \qquad\qquad (1)$$

The deflections δ_P and δ_B are determined from Eq. 9–2.

$$\delta_P = \frac{PL_{AC}}{AE} = \frac{[20(10^3) \text{ N}](0.4 \text{ m})}{\pi(0.005 \text{ m})^2[200(10^9) \text{ N/m}^2]} = 0.5093(10^{-3}) \text{ m}$$

$$\delta_B = \frac{F_B L_{AB}}{AE} = \frac{F_B(1.20 \text{ m})}{\pi(0.005 \text{ m})^2[200(10^9) \text{ N/m}^2]} = 76.3944(10^{-9})F_B$$

Substituting into Eq. 1, we get

$$0.0002 \text{ m} = 0.5093(10^{-3}) \text{ m} - 76.3944(10^{-9})F_B$$

$$F_B = 4.05(10^3) \text{ N} = 4.05 \text{ kN} \qquad\qquad Ans.$$

Equilibrium. From the free-body diagram, Fig. 9–17c,

$$\overset{+}{\rightarrow} \Sigma F_x = 0; \quad -F_A + 20 \text{ kN} - 4.05 \text{ kN} = 0 \quad F_A = 16.0 \text{ kN} \quad Ans.$$

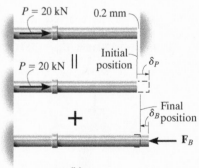

(b)

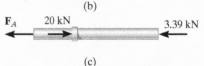

(c)

Fig. 9–17

PROBLEMS

9–27. The column is constructed from high-strength concrete and six A-36 steel reinforcing rods. If it is subjected to an axial force of 30 kip, determine the average normal stress in the concrete and in each rod. Each rod has a diameter of 0.75 in.

*9–28. The column is constructed from high-strength concrete and six A-36 steel reinforcing rods. If it is subjected to an axial force of 30 kip, determine the required diameter of each rod so that one-fourth of the load is carried by the concrete and three-fourths by the steel.

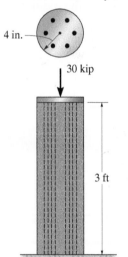

Probs. 9–27/28

•9–29. The steel pipe is filled with concrete and subjected to a compressive force of 80 kN. Determine the average normal stress in the concrete and the steel due to this loading. The pipe has an outer diameter of 80 mm and an inner diameter of 70 mm. E_{st} = 200 GPa, E_c = 24 GPa.

Prob. 9–29

9–30. The 304 stainless steel post A has a diameter of d = 2 in. and is surrounded by a red brass C83400 tube B. Both rest on the rigid surface. If a force of 5 kip is applied to the rigid cap, determine the average normal stress developed in the post and the tube.

9–31. The 304 stainless steel post A is surrounded by a red brass C83400 tube B. Both rest on the rigid surface. If a force of 5 kip is applied to the rigid cap, determine the required diameter d of the steel post so that the load is shared equally between the post and tube.

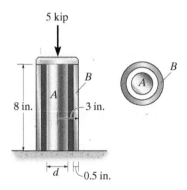

Probs. 9–30/31

*9–32. The composite bar consists of a 20-mm-diameter A-36 steel segment AB and 50-mm-diameter red brass C83400 end segments DA and CB. Determine the average normal stress in each segment due to the applied load.

•9–33. The composite bar consists of a 20-mm-diameter A-36 steel segment AB and 50-mm-diameter red brass C83400 end segments DA and CB. Determine the displacement of A with respect to B due to the applied load.

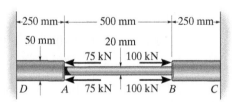

Probs. 9–32/33

9–34. The A-36 steel column, having a cross-sectional area of 18 in², is encased in high-strength concrete as shown. If an axial force of 60 kip is applied to the column, determine the average compressive stress in the concrete and in the steel. How far does the column shorten? It has an original length of 8 ft.

9–35. The A-36 steel column is encased in high-strength concrete as shown. If an axial force of 60 kip is applied to the column, determine the required area of the steel so that the force is shared equally between the steel and concrete. How far does the column shorten? It has an original length of 8 ft.

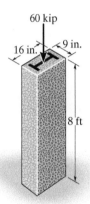

Probs. 9–34/35

*9–36. The rigid member is held in the position shown by three A-36 steel tie rods. Each rod has an unstretched length of 0.75 m and a cross-sectional area of 125 mm². Determine the forces in the rods if a turnbuckle on rod *EF* undergoes one full turn. The lead of the screw is 1.5 mm. Neglect the size of the turnbuckle and assume that it is rigid. *Note:* The lead would cause the rod, when *unloaded*, to shorten 1.5 mm when the turnbuckle is rotated one revolution.

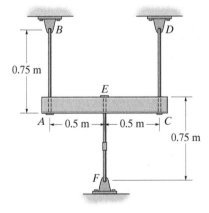

Prob. 9–36

•9–37. The concrete post is reinforced using six steel reinforcing rods, each having a diameter of 20 mm. Determine the stress in the concrete and the steel if the post is subjected to an axial load of 900 kN. $E_{st} = 200$ GPa, $E_c = 25$ GPa.

9–38. The post is constructed from concrete and six A-36 steel reinforcing rods. If it is subjected to an axial force of 900 kN, determine the required diameter of each rod so that one-fifth of the load is carried by the steel and four-fifths by the concrete. $E_{st} = 200$ GPa, $E_c = 25$ GPa.

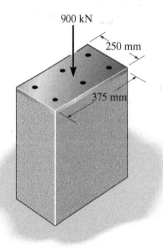

Probs. 9–37/38

9–39. The assembly consists of two red brass C83400 copper alloy rods *AB* and *CD* of diameter 30 mm, a stainless 304 steel alloy rod *EF* of diameter 40 mm, and a rigid cap *G*. If the supports at *A*, *C* and *F* are rigid, determine the average normal stress developed in rods *AB*, *CD* and *EF*.

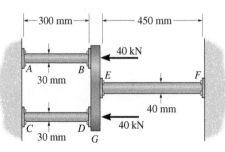

Prob. 9–39

*9–40. The two pipes are made of the same material and are connected as shown. If the cross-sectional area of BC is A and that of CD is $2A$, determine the reactions at B and D when a force **P** is applied at the junction C.

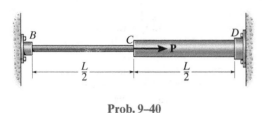

Prob. 9–40

•9–41. The bolt has a diameter of 20 mm and passes through a tube that has an inner diameter of 50 mm and an outer diameter of 60 mm. If the bolt and tube are made of A-36 steel, determine the normal stress in the tube and bolt when a force of 40 kN is applied to the bolt. Assume the end caps are rigid.

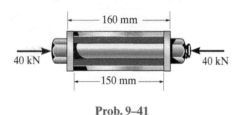

Prob. 9–41

9–42. If the gap between C and the rigid wall at D is initially 0.15 mm, determine the support reactions at A and D when the force **P** = 200 kN is applied. The assembly is made of A36 steel.

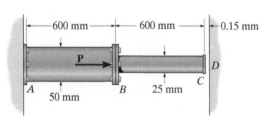

Prob. 9–42

9–43. Two A-36 steel wires are used to support the 650-lb engine. Originally, AB is 32 in. long and $A'B'$ is 32.008 in. long. Determine the force supported by each wire when the engine is suspended from them. Each wire has a cross-sectional area of 0.01 in^2.

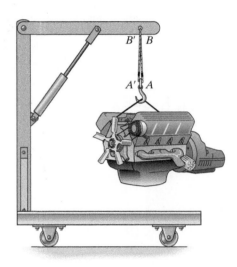

Prob. 9–43

*9–44. Rod AB has a diameter d and fits snugly between the rigid supports at A and B when it is unloaded. The modulus of elasticity is E. Determine the support reactions at A and B if the rod is subjected to the linearly distributed axial load.

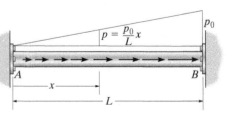

Prob. 9–44

•9–45. The tapered member is fixed connected at its ends *A* and *B* and is subjected to a load $P = 7$ kip at $x = 30$ in. Determine the reactions at the supports. The material is 2 in. thick and is made from 2014-T6 aluminum.

9–46. The tapered member is fixed connected at its ends *A* and *B* and is subjected to a load **P**. Determine the location *x* of the load and its greatest magnitude so that the average normal stress in the bar does not exceed $\sigma_{allow} = 4$ ksi. The member is 2 in. thick.

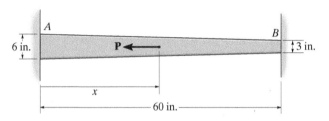

Probs. 9–45/46

9–47. The rigid bar supports the uniform distributed load of 6 kip/ft. Determine the force in each cable if each cable has a cross-sectional area of 0.05 in^2, and $E = 31(10^3)$ ksi.

*9–48. The rigid bar is originally horizontal and is supported by two cables each having a cross-sectional area of 0.05 in^2, and $E = 31(10^3)$ ksi. Determine the slight rotation of the bar when the uniform load is applied.

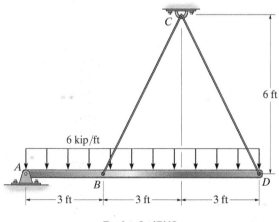

Probs. 9–47/48

•9–49. The press consists of two rigid heads that are held together by the two A-36 steel $\frac{1}{2}$-in.-diameter rods. A 6061-T6-solid-aluminum cylinder is placed in the press and the screw is adjusted so that it just presses up against the cylinder. If it is then tightened one-half turn, determine the average normal stress in the rods and in the cylinder. The single-threaded screw on the bolt has a lead of 0.01 in. *Note:* The lead represents the distance the screw advances along its axis for one complete turn of the screw.

9–50. The press consists of two rigid heads that are held together by the two A-36 steel $\frac{1}{2}$-in.-diameter rods. A 6061-T6-solid-aluminum cylinder is placed in the press and the screw is adjusted so that it just presses up against the cylinder. Determine the angle through which the screw can be turned before the rods or the specimen begin to yield. The single-threaded screw on the bolt has a lead of 0.01 in. *Note:* The lead represents the distance the screw advances along its axis for one complete turn of the screw.

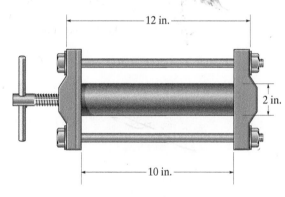

Probs. 9–49/50

9–51. The three suspender bars are made of A-36 steel and have equal cross-sectional areas of 450 mm^2. Determine the average normal stress in each bar if the rigid beam is subjected to the loading shown.

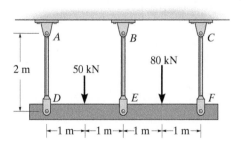

Prob. 9–51

9

9.6 Thermal Stress

A change in temperature can cause a body to change its dimensions. Generally, if the temperature increases, the body will expand, whereas if the temperature decreases, it will contract. Ordinarily this expansion or contraction is *linearly* related to the temperature increase or decrease that occurs. If this is the case, and the material is homogeneous and isotropic, it has been found from experiment that the displacement of a member having a length L can be calculated using the formula

$$\delta_T = \alpha \,\Delta T L \qquad\qquad (9\text{–}4)$$

where

α = a property of the material, referred to as the ***linear coefficient of thermal expansion***. The units measure strain per degree of temperature. They are $1/°F$ (Fahrenheit) in the FPS system, and $1/°C$ (Celsius) or $1/K$ (Kelvin) in the SI system. Typical values are given on the inside back cover

ΔT = the algebraic change in temperature of the member

L = the original length of the member

δ_T = the algebraic change in the length of the member

The change in length of a *statically determinate* member can easily be calculated using Eq. 9–4, since the member is free to expand or contract when it undergoes a temperature change. However, in a *statically indeterminate* member, these thermal displacements will be constrained by the supports, thereby producing ***thermal stresses*** that must be considered in design. Determining these thermal stresses is possible using the methods outlined in the previous sections. The following examples illustrate some applications.

Most traffic bridges are designed with expansion joints to accommodate the thermal movement of the deck and thus avoid any thermal stress.

Long extensions of ducts and pipes that carry fluids are subjected to variations in climate that will cause them to expand and contract. Expansion joints, such as the one shown, are used to mitigate thermal stress in the material.

EXAMPLE | 9.10

The A-36 steel bar shown in Fig. 9–18a is constrained to just fit between two fixed supports when $T_1 = 60°F$. If the temperature is raised to $T_2 = 120°F$, determine the average normal thermal stress developed in the bar.

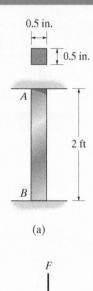

0.5 in.

0.5 in.

A

2 ft

B

(a)

SOLUTION

Equilibrium. The free-body diagram of the bar is shown in Fig. 9–18b. Since there is no external load, the force at A is equal but opposite to the force at B; that is,

$$+\uparrow \Sigma F_y = 0; \qquad\qquad F_A = F_B = F$$

The problem is statically indeterminate since this force cannot be determined from equilibrium.

Compatibility. Since $\delta_{A/B} = 0$, the thermal displacement δ_T at A that occurs, Fig. 9–18c, is counteracted by the force **F** that is required to push the bar δ_F back to its original position. The compatibility condition at A becomes

$$(+\uparrow) \qquad\qquad \delta_{A/B} = 0 = \delta_T - \delta_F$$

Applying the thermal and load–displacement relationships, we have

$$0 = \alpha \Delta T L - \frac{FL}{AE}$$

Thus, from the data on the inside back cover,

$$F = \alpha \Delta T AE$$
$$= [6.60(10^{-6})/°F](120°F - 60°F)(0.5 \text{ in.})^2[29(10^3) \text{ kip/in}^2]$$
$$= 2.871 \text{ kip}$$

Since **F** also represents the internal axial force within the bar, the average normal compressive stress is thus

$$\sigma = \frac{F}{A} = \frac{2.871 \text{ kip}}{(0.5 \text{ in.})^2} = 11.5 \text{ ksi} \qquad\qquad Ans.$$

F

F

(b)

NOTE: From the magnitude of **F**, it should be apparent that changes in temperature can cause large reaction forces in statically indeterminate members.

δ_T

δ_F

(c)

Fig. 9–18

9

EXAMPLE 9.11

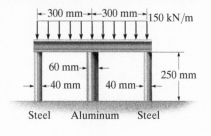

(a)

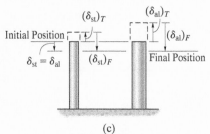

(b)

(c)

Fig. 9–19

The rigid beam shown in Fig. 9–19a is fixed to the top of the three posts made of A-36 steel and 2014-T6 aluminum. The posts each have a length of 250 mm when no load is applied to the beam, and the temperature is $T_1 = 20°C$. Determine the force supported by each post if the bar is subjected to a uniform distributed load of 150 kN/m and the temperature is raised to $T_2 = 80°C$.

SOLUTION

Equilibrium. The free-body diagram of the beam is shown in Fig. 9–19b. Moment equilibrium about the beam's center requires the forces in the steel posts to be equal. Summing forces on the free-body diagram, we have

$$+\uparrow \Sigma F_y = 0; \qquad 2F_{st} + F_{al} - 90(10^3)\text{ N} = 0 \qquad (1)$$

Compatibility. Due to load, geometry, and material symmetry, the top of each post is displaced by an equal amount. Hence,

$$(+\downarrow) \qquad\qquad\qquad \delta_{st} = \delta_{al} \qquad\qquad\qquad (2)$$

The final position of the top of each post is equal to its displacement caused by the temperature increase, plus its displacement caused by the internal axial compressive force, Fig. 9–19c. Thus, for the steel and aluminum post, we have

$$(+\downarrow) \qquad\qquad \delta_{st} = -(\delta_{st})_T + (\delta_{st})_F$$

$$(+\downarrow) \qquad\qquad \delta_{al} = -(\delta_{al})_T + (\delta_{al})_F$$

Applying Eq. 2 gives

$$-(\delta_{st})_T + (\delta_{st})_F = -(\delta_{al})_T + (\delta_{al})_F$$

Using Eqs. 9–2 and 9–4 and the material properties on the inside back cover, we get

$$-[12(10^{-6})/°C](80°C - 20°C)(0.250\text{ m}) + \frac{F_{st}(0.250\text{ m})}{\pi(0.020\text{ m})^2[200(10^9)\text{ N/m}^2]}$$

$$= -[23(10^{-6})/°C](80°C - 20°C)(0.250\text{ m}) + \frac{F_{al}(0.250\text{ m})}{\pi(0.030\text{ m})^2[73.1(10^9)\text{ N/m}^2]}$$

$$F_{st} = 1.216F_{al} - 165.9(10^3) \qquad (3)$$

To be *consistent*, all numerical data has been expressed in terms of newtons, meters, and degrees Celsius. Solving Eqs. 1 and 3 simultaneously yields

$$F_{st} = -16.4\text{ kN} \quad F_{al} = 123\text{ kN} \qquad\qquad Ans.$$

The negative value for F_{st} indicates that this force acts opposite to that shown in Fig. 9–19b. In other words, the steel posts are in tension and the aluminum post is in compression.

EXAMPLE | 9.12

A 2014-T6 aluminum tube having a cross-sectional area of 600 mm² is used as a sleeve for an A-36 steel bolt having a cross-sectional area of 400 mm², Fig. 9–20a. When the temperature is $T_1 = 15°C$, the nut holds the assembly in a snug position such that the axial force in the bolt is negligible. If the temperature increases to $T_2 = 80°C$, determine the force in the bolt and sleeve.

150 mm

(a)

SOLUTION

Equilibrium.   The free-body diagram of a top segment of the assembly is shown in Fig. 9–20b. The forces F_b and F_s are produced since the sleeve has a higher coefficient of thermal expansion than the bolt, and therefore the sleeve will expand more when the temperature is increased. It is required that

$$+\uparrow \Sigma F_y = 0; \qquad\qquad F_s = F_b \qquad\qquad (1)$$

Compatibility.   The temperature increase causes the sleeve and bolt to expand $(\delta_s)_T$ and $(\delta_b)_T$, Fig. 9–20c. However, the redundant forces F_b and F_s elongate the bolt and shorten the sleeve. Consequently, the end of the assembly reaches a final position, which is not the same as its initial position. Hence, the compatibility condition becomes

$$(+\downarrow) \qquad \delta = (\delta_b)_T + (\delta_b)_F = (\delta_s)_T - (\delta_s)_F$$

F_s

F_b

(b)

Applying Eqs. 9–2 and 9–4, and using the mechanical properties from the table on the inside back cover, we have

$$[12(10^{-6})/°C](80°C - 15°C)(0.150\text{ m})$$
$$+ \frac{F_b(0.150\text{ m})}{(400\text{ mm}^2)(10^{-6}\text{ m}^2/\text{mm}^2)[200(10^9)\text{ N/m}^2]}$$
$$= [23(10^{-6})/°C](80°C - 15°C)(0.150\text{ m})$$
$$- \frac{F_s(0.150\text{ m})}{(600\text{ mm}^2)(10^{-6}\text{ m}^2/\text{mm}^2)[73.1(10^9)\text{ N/m}^2]}$$

Using Eq. 1 and solving gives

$$F_s = F_b = 20.3\text{ kN} \qquad\qquad Ans.$$

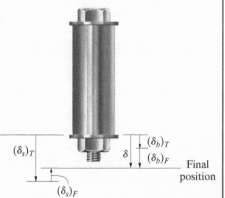

Initial position

$(\delta_s)_T$

$(\delta_b)_T$

$(\delta_b)_F$

δ

Final position

$(\delta_s)_F$

(c)

Fig. 9–20

NOTE: Since linear elastic material behavior was assumed in this analysis, the average normal stresses should be checked to make sure that they do not exceed the proportional limits for the material.

PROBLEMS

*9–52. A steel surveyor's tape is to be used to measure the length of a line. The tape has a rectangular cross section of 0.05 in. by 0.2 in. and a length of 100 ft when $T_1 = 60°F$ and the tension or pull on the tape is 20 lb. Determine the true length of the line if the tape shows the reading to be 463.25 ft when used with a pull of 35 lb at $T_2 = 90°F$. The ground on which it is placed is flat. $\alpha_{st} = 9.60(10^{-6})/°F$, $E_{st} = 29(10^3)$ ksi.

Prob. 9–52

•9–53. Three bars each made of different materials are connected together and placed between two walls when the temperature is $T_1 = 12°C$. Determine the force exerted on the (rigid) supports when the temperature becomes $T_2 = 18°C$. The material properties and cross-sectional area of each bar are given in the figure.

Steel	Brass	Copper
$E_{st} = 200$ GPa	$E_{br} = 100$ GPa	$E_{cu} = 120$ GPa
$\alpha_{st} = 12(10^{-6})/°C$	$\alpha_{br} = 21(10^{-6})/°C$	$\alpha_{cu} = 17(10^{-6})/°C$

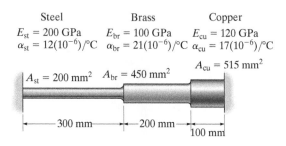

Prob. 9–53

9–54. The rod is made of A-36 steel and has a diameter of 0.25 in. If the rod is 4 ft long when the springs are compressed 0.5 in. and the temperature of the rod is $T = 40°F$, determine the force in the rod when its temperature is $T = 160°F$.

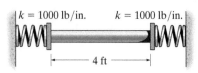

Prob. 9–54

9–55. A 6-ft-long steam pipe is made of A-36 steel with $\sigma_Y = 40$ ksi. It is connected directly to two turbines A and B as shown. The pipe has an outer diameter of 4 in. and a wall thickness of 0.25 in. The connection was made at $T_1 = 70°F$. If the turbines' points of attachment are assumed rigid, determine the force the pipe exerts on the turbines when the steam and thus the pipe reach a temperature of $T_2 = 275°F$.

*9–56. A 6-ft-long steam pipe is made of A-36 steel with $\sigma_Y = 40$ ksi. It is connected directly to two turbines A and B as shown. The pipe has an outer diameter of 4 in. and a wall thickness of 0.25 in. The connection was made at $T_1 = 70°F$. If the turbines' points of attachment are assumed to have a stiffness of $k = 80(10^3)$ kip/in., determine the force the pipe exerts on the turbines when the steam and thus the pipe reach a temperature of $T_2 = 275°F$.

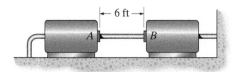

Probs. 9–55/56

•9–57. The pipe is made of A-36 steel and is connected to the collars at A and B. When the temperature is 60°F, there is no axial load in the pipe. If hot gas traveling through the pipe causes its temperature to rise by $\Delta T = (40 + 15x)°F$, where x is in feet, determine the average normal stress in the pipe. The inner diameter is 2 in., the wall thickness is 0.15 in.

9–58. The bronze C86100 pipe has an inner radius of 0.5 in. and a wall thickness of 0.2 in. If the gas flowing through it changes the temperature of the pipe uniformly from $T_A = 200°F$ at A to $T_B = 60°F$ at B, determine the axial force it exerts on the walls. The pipe was fitted between the walls when $T = 60°F$.

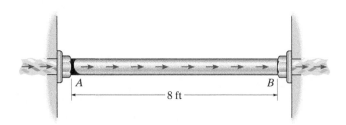

Probs. 9–57/58

9–59. The 40-ft-long A-36 steel rails on a train track are laid with a small gap between them to allow for thermal expansion. Determine the required gap δ so that the rails just touch one another when the temperature is increased from $T_1 = -20°F$ to $T_2 = 90°F$. Using this gap, what would be the axial force in the rails if the temperature were to rise to $T_3 = 110°F$? The cross-sectional area of each rail is 5.10 in^2.

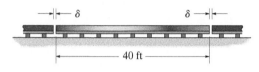

Prob. 9–59

*9–60. The device is used to measure a change in temperature. Bars AB and CD are made of A-36 steel and 2014-T6 aluminum alloy, respectively. When the temperature is at 75°F, ACE is in the horizontal position. Determine the vertical displacement of the pointer at E when the temperature rises to 150°F.

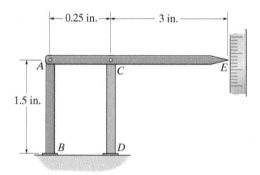

Prob. 9–60

•9–61. The bar has a cross-sectional area A, length L, modulus of elasticity E, and coefficient of thermal expansion α. The temperature of the bar changes uniformly along its length from T_A at A to T_B at B so that at any point x along the bar $T = T_A + x(T_B - T_A)/L$. Determine the force the bar exerts on the rigid walls. Initially no axial force is in the bar and the bar has a temperature of T_A.

Prob. 9–61

9–62. The A-36 steel rod has a diameter of 50 mm and is lightly attached to the rigid supports at A and B when $T_1 = 80°C$. If the temperature becomes $T_2 = 20°C$ and an axial force of $P = 200$ kN is applied to its center, determine the reactions at A and B.

9–63. The A-36 steel rod has a diameter of 50 mm and is lightly attached to the rigid supports at A and B when $T_1 = 50°C$. Determine the force P that must be applied to the collar at its midpoint so that, when $T_2 = 30°C$, the reaction at B is zero.

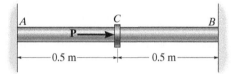

Probs. 9–62/63

*9–64. The rigid block has a weight of 80 kip and is to be supported by posts A and B, which are made of A-36 steel, and the post C, which is made of C83400 red brass. If all the posts have the same original length before they are loaded, determine the average normal stress developed in each post when post C is heated so that its temperature is increased by 20°F. Each post has a cross-sectional area of 8 in^2.

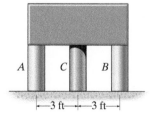

Prob. 9–64

9.7   Stress Concentrations

In Sec. 9.1, it was pointed out that when an axial force is applied to a member, it creates a complex stress distribution within the localized region of the point of load application. Not only do complex stress distributions arise just under a concentrated loading, they can also arise at sections where the member's cross-sectional area changes. For example, consider the bar in Fig. 9–21a, which is subjected to an axial force P. Here the once horizontal and vertical grid lines deflect into an irregular pattern around the hole centered in the bar. The maximum normal stress in the bar occurs on section a–a, which is taken through the bar's *smallest* cross-sectional area. Provided the material behaves in a linear-elastic manner, the stress distribution acting on this section can be determined either from a mathematical analysis, using the theory of elasticity, or experimentally by measuring the strain normal to section a–a and then calculating the stress using Hooke's law, $\sigma = E\epsilon$. Regardless of the method used, the general shape of the stress distribution will be like that shown in Fig. 9–21b. In a similar manner, if the bar has a reduction in its cross section, achieved using shoulder fillets as in Fig. 9–22a, then again the maximum normal stress in the bar will occur at the *smallest* cross-sectional area, section a–a, and the stress distribution will look like that shown in Fig. 9–22b.

This saw blade has grooves cut into it in order to relieve both the dynamic stress that develops within it as it rotates and the thermal stress that develops as it heats up. Note the small circles at the end of each groove. These serve to reduce the stress concentrations that develop at the end of each groove.

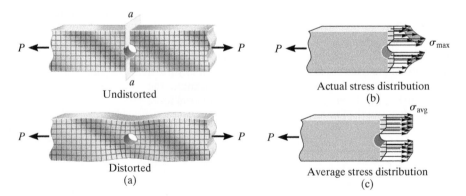

Undistorted

Distorted
(a)

Actual stress distribution
(b)

Average stress distribution
(c)

Fig. 9–21

In both of these cases, *force equilibrium* requires the magnitude of the *resultant force* developed by the stress distribution to be equal to *P*. In other words,

$$P = \int_A \sigma \, dA \qquad (9\text{--}5)$$

This integral *graphically* represents the total *volume* under each of the stress-distribution diagrams shown in Fig. 9–21*b* or Fig. 9–22*b*. The resultant **P** must act through the *centroid* of each *volume*.

In engineering practice, the actual stress distributions in Fig. 9–21*b* and Fig. 9–22*b* do *not* have to be determined. Instead, only the *maximum stress* at these sections must be known, and the member is then designed to resist this stress when the axial load **P** is applied. Specific values of this maximum normal stress can be determined by experimental methods or by advanced mathematical techniques using the theory of elasticity. The results of these investigations are usually reported in graphical form using a ***stress-concentration factor*** *K*. We define *K* as a ratio of the maximum stress to the average normal stress acting at the cross section; i.e.,

$$\boxed{K = \frac{\sigma_{\max}}{\sigma_{\mathrm{avg}}}} \qquad (9\text{--}6)$$

Provided *K* is known, and the average normal stress has been calculated from $\sigma_{\mathrm{avg}} = P/A$, where *A* is the *smallest* cross-sectional area, Figs. 9–21*c* and 9–22*c*, then the maximum normal stress at the cross section is $\sigma_{\max} = K(P/A)$.

Stress concentrations often arise at sharp corners on heavy machinery. Engineers can mitigate this effect by using stiffeners welded to the corners.

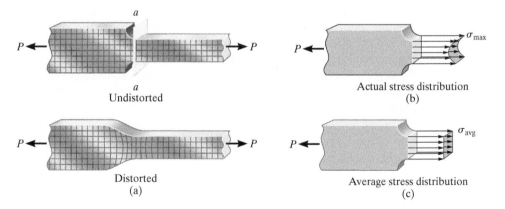

a

a

Undistorted

Distorted

(a)

$\sigma_{\max}$

Actual stress distribution

(b)

σ_{avg}

Average stress distribution

(c)

Fig. 9–22

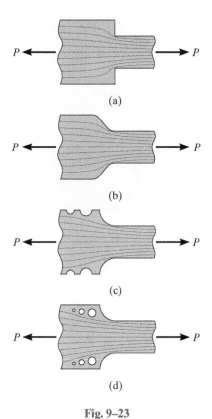

(a)

(b)

(c)

(d)

Fig. 9–23

Specific values of K are generally reported in handbooks related to stress analysis.* Examples are given in Figs. 9–24 and 9–25. Note that K is independent of the bar's material properties; rather, it *depends only* on the bar's *geometry* and the type of discontinuity. As the size r of the discontinuity is *decreased*, the stress concentration is increased. For example, if a bar requires a change in cross section, it has been determined that a sharp corner, Fig. 9–23*a*, produces a stress-concentration factor greater than 3. In other words, the maximum normal stress will be three times greater than the average normal stress on the smallest cross section. However, this can be reduced to, say, 1.5 by introducing a fillet, Fig. 9–23*b*. A further reduction can be made by means of small grooves or holes placed at the transition, Fig. 9–23*c* and 9–23*d*. In all of these cases these designs help to reduce the rigidity of the material surrounding the corners, so that both the strain and the stress are more evenly spread throughout the bar.

The stress-concentration factors given in Figs. 9–24 and 9–25 were determined on the basis of a static loading, with the assumption that the stress in the material does not exceed the proportional limit. If the material is *very brittle*, the proportional limit may be at the fracture stress, and so for this material, failure will begin *at* the point of stress concentration. Essentially a crack begins to form at this point, and a higher stress concentration will develop at the *tip* of this crack. This, in turn, causes the crack to propagate over the cross section, resulting in sudden fracture. For this reason, it is very important to use stress-concentration factors in design when using brittle materials. On the other hand, if the material is ductile and subjected to a static load, it is often not necessary to use stress-concentration factors since any stress that exceeds the proportional limit will not result in a crack. Instead, the material will have reserve strength due to yielding and strain-hardening. In the next section we will discuss the effects caused by this phenomenon.

Stress concentrations are also responsible for many failures of structural members or mechanical elements subjected to *fatigue loadings*. For these cases, a stress concentration will cause the material to crack if the stress exceeds the material's endurance limit, whether or not the material is ductile or brittle. Here, the material *localized* at the tip of the crack remains in a *brittle state*, and so the crack continues to grow, leading to a progressive fracture. As a result, one must seek ways to limit the amount of damage that can be caused by fatigue.

*See Lipson, C. and R. C. Juvinall, *Handbook of Stress and Strength,* Macmillan.

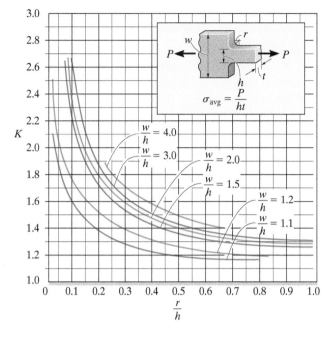

$$\sigma_{avg} = \frac{P}{ht}$$

$\dfrac{w}{h} = 4.0$

$\dfrac{w}{h} = 3.0$

$\dfrac{w}{h} = 2.0$

$\dfrac{w}{h} = 1.5$

$\dfrac{w}{h} = 1.2$

$\dfrac{w}{h} = 1.1$

K

$\dfrac{r}{h}$

Fig. 9–24

$$\sigma_{avg} = \frac{P}{(w - 2r)t}$$

K

$\dfrac{r}{w}$

Fig. 9–25

Important Points

- *Stress concentrations* occur at sections where the cross-sectional area suddenly changes. The more severe the change, the larger the stress concentration.

- For design or analysis, it is only necessary to determine the maximum stress acting on the smallest cross-sectional area. This is done using a *stress concentration factor*, K, that has been determined through experiment and is only a function of the geometry of the specimen.

- Normally the stress concentration in a ductile specimen that is subjected to a static loading will *not* have to be considered in design; however, if the material is *brittle*, or subjected to *fatigue* loadings, then stress concentrations become important.

Failure of this steel pipe in tension occurred at its smallest cross-sectional area, which is through the hole. Notice how the material yielded around the fractured surface.

EXAMPLE | **9.13**

The bar in Fig. 9–26a is made of steel that is assumed to be elastic perfectly plastic, with $\sigma_Y = 250$ MPa. Determine (a) the maximum value of the applied load P that can be applied without causing the steel to yield and (b) the maximum value of P that the bar can support. Sketch the stress distribution at the critical section for each case.

SOLUTION

Part (a). When the material behaves elastically, we must use a stress-concentration factor determined from Fig. 9–24 that is unique for the bar's geometry. Here

$$\frac{r}{h} = \frac{4\text{ mm}}{(40\text{ mm} - 8\text{ mm})} = 0.125$$

$$\frac{w}{h} = \frac{40\text{ mm}}{(40\text{ mm} - 8\text{ mm})} = 1.25$$

From the figure $K \approx 1.75$. The maximum load, without causing yielding, occurs when $\sigma_{max} = \sigma_Y$. The average normal stress is $\sigma_{avg} = P/A$. Using Eq. 9–6, we have

$$\sigma_{max} = K\sigma_{avg}; \qquad \sigma_Y = K\left(\frac{P_Y}{A}\right)$$

$$250(10^6)\text{ Pa} = 1.75\left[\frac{P_Y}{(0.002\text{ m})(0.032\text{ m})}\right]$$

$$P_Y = 9.14\text{ kN} \qquad\qquad Ans.$$

This load has been calculated using the *smallest* cross section. The resulting stress distribution is shown in Fig. 9–26b. For equilibrium, the "volume" contained within this distribution must equal 9.14 kN.

Part (b). The maximum load sustained by the bar will cause *all the material* at the smallest cross section to yield. Therefore, as P is increased to the *plastic load* P_p, it gradually changes the stress distribution from the elastic state shown in Fig. 9–26b to the plastic state shown in Fig. 9–26c. We require

$$\sigma_Y = \frac{P_p}{A}$$

$$250(10^6)\text{ Pa} = \frac{P_p}{(0.002\text{ m})(0.032\text{ m})}$$

$$P_p = 16.0\text{ kN} \qquad\qquad Ans.$$

Here P_p equals the "volume" contained within the stress distribution, which in this case is $P_p = \sigma_Y A$.

(a)

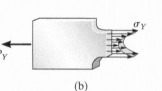

(b)

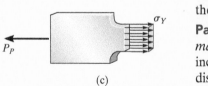

(c)

Fig. 9–26

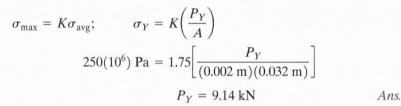

PROBLEMS

9–65. Determine the maximum normal stress developed in the bar when it is subjected to a tension of $P = 8$ kN.

9–66. If the allowable normal stress for the bar is $\sigma_{allow} = 120$ MPa, determine the maximum axial force P that can be applied to the bar.

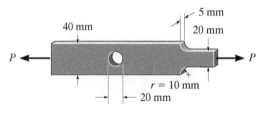

Probs. 9–65/66

•9–67. The member is to be made from a steel plate that is 0.25 in. thick. If a 1-in. hole is drilled through its center, determine the approximate width w of the plate so that it can support an axial force of 3350 lb. The allowable stress is $\sigma_{allow} = 22$ ksi.

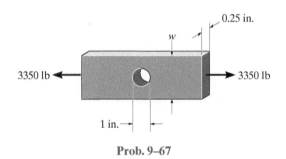

Prob. 9–67

*9–68. The A-36 steel plate has a thickness of 12 mm. If there are shoulder fillets at B and C, and $\sigma_{allow} = 150$ MPa, determine the maximum axial load P that it can support. Calculate its elongation, neglecting the effect of the fillets.

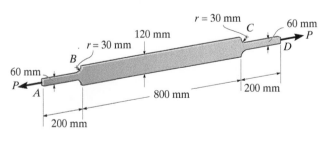

Prob. 9–68

9–69. Determine the maximum axial force P that can be applied to the bar. The bar is made from steel and has an allowable stress of $\sigma_{allow} = 21$ ksi.

9–70. Determine the maximum normal stress developed in the bar when it is subjected to a tension of $P = 2$ kip.

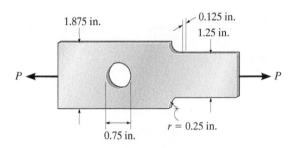

Probs. 9–69/70

•9–71. Determine the maximum normal stress developed in the bar when it is subjected to a tension of $P = 8$ kN.

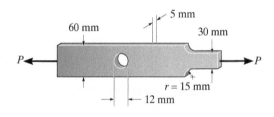

Prob. 9–71

*9–72. The resulting stress distribution along section AB for the bar is shown. From this distribution, determine the approximate resultant axial force P applied to the bar. Also, what is the stress-concentration factor for this geometry?

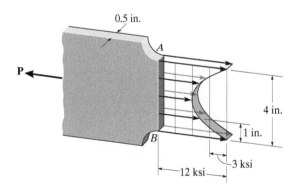

Prob. 9–72

CONCEPTUAL PROBLEMS

P9–1. The concrete footing A was poured when this column was put in place. Later the rest of the foundation slab was poured. Can you explain why the 45° cracks occurred at each corner? Can you think of a better design that would avoid such cracks?

P9–2. The row of bricks, along with mortar and an internal steel reinforcing rod, was intended to serve as a lintel beam to support the bricks above this ventilation opening on an exterior wall of a building. Explain what may have caused the bricks to fail in the manner shown.

P9–1

P9–2

CHAPTER REVIEW

When a loading is applied at a point on a body, it tends to create a stress distribution within the body that becomes more uniformly distributed at regions removed from the point of application of the load. This is called Saint-Venant's principle.

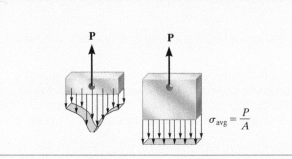

$$\sigma_{avg} = \frac{P}{A}$$

The relative displacement at the end of an axially loaded member relative to the other end is determined from

$$\delta = \int_0^L \frac{P(x)\,dx}{AE}$$

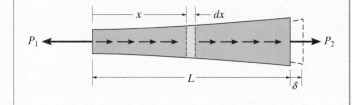

If a series of concentrated external axial forces are applied to a member and AE is also constant for the member, then

$$\delta = \Sigma \frac{PL}{AE}$$

For application, it is necessary to use a sign convention for the internal load P and displacement δ. We considered tension and elongation as positive values. Also, the material must not yield, but rather it must remain linear elastic.

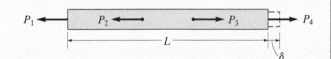

Superposition of load and displacement is possible provided the material remains linear elastic and no significant changes in the geometry of the member occur after loading.

The reactions on a statically indeterminate bar can be determined using the equilibrium equations and compatibility conditions that specify the displacement at the supports. These displacements are related to the loads using a load–displacement relationship such as $\delta = PL/AE$.

A change in temperature can cause a member made of homogeneous isotropic material to change its length by

$$\delta = \alpha \Delta T L$$

If the member is confined, this change will produce thermal stress in the member.

Holes and sharp transitions at a cross section will create stress concentrations. For the design of a member made of brittle material one obtains the stress concentration factor K from a graph, which has been determined from experiment. This value is then multiplied by the average stress to obtain the maximum stress at the cross section.

$$\sigma_{max} = K\sigma_{avg}$$

9

REVIEW PROBLEMS

9–73. The 2014-T6 aluminum rod has a diameter of 0.5 in. and is lightly attached to the rigid supports at A and B when $T_1 = 70°F$. If the temperature becomes $T_2 = -10°F$, and an axial force of $P = 16$ lb is applied to the rigid collar as shown, determine the reactions at A and B.

9–74. The 2014-T6 aluminum rod has a diameter of 0.5 in. and is lightly attached to the rigid supports at A and B when $T_1 = 70°F$. Determine the force P that must be applied to the collar so that, when $T = 0°F$, the reaction at B is zero.

*9–76. Two A-36 steel pipes, each having a cross-sectional area of 0.32 in². are screwed together using a union at B as shown. Originally the assembly is adjusted so that no load is on the pipe. If the union is then tightened so that its screw, having a lead of 0.15 in., undergoes two full turns, determine the average normal stress developed in the pipe. Assume that the union at B and couplings at A and C are rigid. Neglect the size of the union. *Note:* The lead would cause the pipe, when *unloaded*, to shorten 0.15 in. when the union is rotated one revolution.

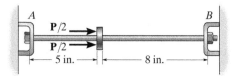

Probs. 9–73/74

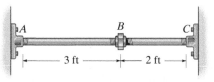

Prob. 9–76

9–75. The rods each have the same 25-mm diameter and 600-mm length. If they are made of A-36 steel, determine the forces developed in each rod when the temperature increases to 50°C.

9–77. The brass plug is force-fitted into the rigid casting. The uniform normal bearing pressure on the plug is estimated to be 15 MPa. If the coefficient of static friction between the plug and casting is $\mu_s = 0.3$, determine the axial force P needed to pull the plug out. Also, calculate the displacement of end B relative to end A just before the plug starts to slip out. $E_{br} = 98$ GPa.

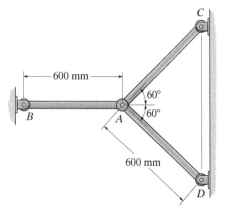

Prob. 9–75

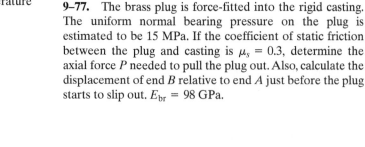

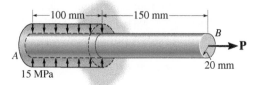

Prob. 9–77

9–78. The assembly consists of two bars AB and CD of the same material having a modulus of elasticity E_1 and coefficient of thermal expansion α_1, and a bar EF having a modulus of elasticity E_2 and coefficient of thermal expansion α_2. All the bars have the same length L and cross-sectional area A. If the rigid beam is originally horizontal at temperature T_1, determine the angle it makes with the horizontal when the temperature is increased to T_2.

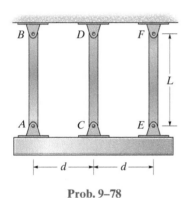

Prob. 9–78

9–79. The circular bar has a variable radius of $r = r_0 e^{ax}$ and is made of a material having a modulus of elasticity of E. Determine the displacement of end A when it is subjected to the axial force $\mathbf{P}$.

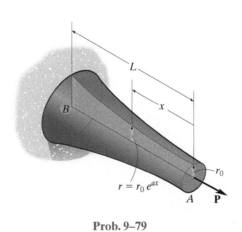

Prob. 9–79

*9–80. The rigid link is supported by a pin at A and two A-36 steel wires, each having an unstretched length of 12 in. and cross-sectional area of $0.0125 \, \text{in}^2$. Determine the force developed in the wires when the link supports the vertical load of 350 lb.

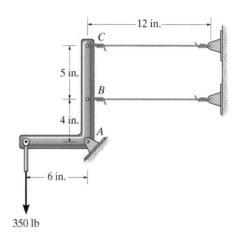

Prob. 9–80

9–81. The weight of the kentledge exerts an axial force of $P = 1500$ kN on the 300-mm diameter high strength concrete bore pile. If the distribution of the resisting skin friction developed from the interaction between the soil and the surface of the pile is approximated as shown, and the resisting bearing force $\mathbf{F}$ is required to be zero, determine the maximum intensity p_0 kN/m for equilibrium. Also, find the corresponding elastic shortening of the pile. Neglect the weight of the pile.

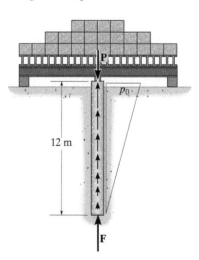

Prob. 9–81

Answers to Selected Problems

Chapter 7

7–1.   **a.** $F_A = 13.8$ kip,   **b.** $F_A = 34.9$ kN

7–2. $T_C = 250$ N $\cdot$ m, $T_D = 0$

7–3. $T_B = 150$ lb $\cdot$ ft, $T_C = 500$ lb $\cdot$ ft

7–5. $9.00(4) - A_y(12) = 0$, $A_y = 3.00$ kip,
$B_y = 6.00$ kip, $N_D = 0$, $V_D = 0.750$ kip,
$M_D = 13.5$ kip $\cdot$ ft, $N_E = 0$, $V_E = -9.00$ kip,
$M_E = -24.0$ kip $\cdot$ ft

7–6. $N_C = -30.0$ kN, $V_C = -8.00$ kN,
$M_C = 6.00$ kN $\cdot$ m

7–7. $P = 0.533$ kN, $N_C = -2.00$ kN,
$V_C = -0.533$ kN, $M_C = 0.400$ kN $\cdot$ m

7–9. $B_y = 3.00$ kN, $N_D = 0$, $V_D = -1.875$ kN,
$M_D = 3.94$ kN $\cdot$ m

7–10. $N_A = 0$, $V_A = 450$ lb, $M_A = -1.125$ kip $\cdot$ ft,
$N_B = 0$, $V_B = 850$ lb, $M_B = -6.325$ kip $\cdot$ ft,
$V_C = 0$, $N_C = -1.20$ kip, $M_C = -8.125$ kip $\cdot$ ft

7–11. $V_A = 77.3$ lb, $N_A = 20.7$ lb, $M_A = 14.5$ lb $\cdot$ in.

7–13. $N_B = -0.4$ kip, $V_B = 0.960$ kip,
$-M_B - 0.16(2) - 0.8(4.25) + 0.4(1.5) = 0$,
$M_B = -3.12$ kip $\cdot$ ft

7–14. $N_C = -0.4$ kip, $V_C = 1.08$ kip,
$M_C = -6.18$ kip $\cdot$ ft, $N_D = 0$, $V_D = 1.45$ kip,
$M_D = -15.7$ kip $\cdot$ ft

7–15. $V_C = 60$ N, $N_C = 0$, $M_C = 0.9$ N $\cdot$ m

7–17. $N_B = 5.303$ kN, $N_{a-a} = -3.75$ kN,
$V_{a-a} = 1.25$ kN, $M_{a-a} = 3.75$ kN $\cdot$ m,
$N_{b-b} = -1.77$ kN, $V_{b-b} = 3.54$ kN,
$M_{b-b} = 3.75$ kN $\cdot$ m

7–18. $N_C = -80$ lb, $V_C = 0$, $M_C = -480$ lb $\cdot$ in.

7–19. $N_C = 0$, $V_C = 4.50$ kip, $M_C = 31.5$ kip $\cdot$ ft

7–21. $\sigma = 1.82$ MPa

7–22. $\tau_{avg} = 29.5$ MPa

7–23. $V = P \cos \theta$, $N = P \sin \theta$,
$$\sigma = \frac{P}{A} \sin^2 \theta, \tau_{avg} = \frac{P}{2A} \sin 2\theta$$

7–25.   Joint A: $\sigma_{AB} = 10.7$ ksi   (T),
$\sigma_{AE} = 8.53$ ksi   (C),
Joint E: $\sigma_{ED} = 8.53$ ksi   (C),
$\sigma_{EB} = 4.80$ ksi   (T),

Joint B: $\sigma_{BC} = 23.5$ ksi   (T),
$\sigma_{BD} = 18.7$ ksi   (C)

7–26. $P = 6.82$ kip

7–27. $dF = 7.5(10^6) \, x^{1/2} \, dx$,
$P = 40$ MN, $d = 2.40$ m

7–29. $\sigma_{avg} = 5$ MPa

7–30. $(\tau_B)_{avg} = 6.05$ ksi

7–31. $D_y = 650$ lb, $E_x = 500$ lb, $E_y = 350$ lb,
$C_y = 150$ lb, $B_y = 150$ lb,
$F_B = F_C = 594.24$ lb,
$(\tau_B)_{avg} = (\tau_C)_{avg} = 12.1$ ksi

7–33. $(\tau_D)_{avg} = 13.2$ ksi, $(\tau_E)_{avg} = 12.4$ ksi

7–34. $\sigma = 869$ psi;
$\sigma = 50.5$ psi

7–35.   Joint B: $\sigma_{AB} = \dfrac{F_{AB}}{A_{AB}} = \dfrac{625}{1.5} = 417$ psi   (C),
$\sigma_{BC} = 469$ psi   (T)
Joint A: $\sigma_{AC} = 833$ psi   (T)

7–37. $\tau_A = \tau_B = 138$ MPa

7–38. $\tau_B = \tau_C = 324$ MPa
$\tau_A = 324$ MPa

7–39. $A_x = 9.5263P$, $A_y = 5.5P$, $F_A = 11P$,
$P = 3.70$ kN

7–41. $P = 4$ kip, $(\tau_{a-a})_{avg} = 250$ psi

7–42. $(\tau_{avg})_b = 79.6$ MPa
$(\tau_{avg})_p = 225$ kPa

7–43. $V_b = P/4$, $V_p = P/4$, $P = 9.05$ kN

7–45. $(\sigma_{avg})_{AB} = 118$ MPa, $(\sigma_{avg})_{BC} = 58.8$ MPa

7–46. $\theta = 48.2°$
$P = 1.46$ kN

7–47. $V = 12.19$ kip, $N = 15.603$ kip,
Inclined plane: $\sigma' = 62.6$ ksi, $\tau'_{avg} = 48.9$ ksi,
Cross section: $\sigma = 101$ ksi, $\tau_{avg} = 0$

7–49. $\sigma = 3.125$ ksi, $\tau_{avg} = 1.80$ ksi

7–50. $\tau_A = 78.6$ MPa
$\tau_C = 78.6$ MPa

7–51. $A_x = 1.732P$, $A_y = P$, $F_A = 2P$,
$P = 15.3$ kN

7–53. $d = 5.71$ mm

7–54. $d = 13.5$ mm

7–55. $t = 1.78$ mm

$d_t = 11.9$ mm

$d_r = 4.12$ mm

7–57. $a = 6\dfrac{1}{2}$ in.

7–58. $d_A = 27.6$ mm

7–59. $T = 2.45$ kN $\cdot$ m

7–61. $d_{BD} = 7.00$ mm, $d_{AB} = 6.50$ mm,

$d_{BC} = 6.00$ mm

7–62. $P = 4.43$ kN

7–63. $d_2 = 35.7$ mm

$d_3 = 27.6$ mm

$d_1 = 22.6$ mm

7–65. $d = 1\dfrac{1}{16}$ in.

7–66. $P = 90$ kN, $A = 6.19(10^{-3})$ m^2,

$P_{\max} = 155$ kN

7–67. Use $d_C = 12$ mm

Use $d_D = 14$ mm

7–69. $d_B = 7.08$ mm, $d_C = 6.29$ mm

7–70. $(\text{F.S.})_B = 2.24$, $(\text{F.S.})_C = 2.13$

7–71. $d_B = 6.11$ mm

$d_w = 15.4$ mm

7–73. $w = 0.530$ kip/ft

7–74. $a_{A'} = 130$ mm, $a_{B'} = 300$ mm

7–75. $P = 72.5$ kN

7–77. $h = 1.74$ in.

7–78. $P = 55.0$ kN

7–79. $t = 5.33$ mm

$b = 24.0$ mm

$a = 4.31$ mm

7–81. $\epsilon = 0.0472$ in./in.

7–82. $\epsilon_{CE} = 0.00250$ mm/mm, $\epsilon_{BD} = 0.00107$ mm/mm

7–83. $\epsilon_{AC} = \epsilon_{AB} = 0.00578$ mm/mm

7–85. $\gamma = 0.197$ rad

7–86. $\epsilon_{\text{avg}} = 0.0689$ in./in.

7–87. $\epsilon_{AB} = 0.00251$ mm/mm

7–89. $(\gamma_{xy})_A = 0.206$ rad, $(\gamma_{xy})_B = -0.206$ rad

7–90. $(\epsilon_{\text{avg}})_{AB} = -0.0889$ mm/mm,

$(\epsilon_{\text{avg}})_{BD} = -0.1875$ mm/mm

7–91. $\gamma_{xy} = 0.0142$ rad

7–93. $x = -0.192$ in., $y = -0.218$ in.

7–94. $\epsilon_{AB} = 0.152$ in./in., $\epsilon_{AC} = 0.0274$ in./in.

7–95. $\epsilon_{AB} = 1.61(10^{-3})$ mm/mm

$\epsilon_{CD} = 126(10^{-3})$ mm/mm

7–97. $(\gamma_B)_{xy} = 11.6(10^{-3})$ rad,

$(\gamma_A)_{xy} = -11.6(10^{-3})$ rad

7–98. $(\gamma_C)_{xy} = -11.6(10^{-3})$ rad,

$(\gamma_D)_{xy} = 11.6(10^{-3})$ rad

7–99. $\epsilon_{AC} = 1.60(10^{-3})$ mm/mm

$\epsilon_{DB} = 12.8(10^{-3})$ mm/mm

7–101. $\sigma_s = 208$ MPa, $(\tau_{\text{avg}})_a = 4.72$ MPa,

$(\tau_{\text{avg}})_b = 45.5$ MPa

7–102. $t = \dfrac{1}{4}$ in., $d_A = 1\dfrac{1}{8}$ in., $d_B = \dfrac{13}{16}$ in.

7–103. $N_D = 1.20$ kip

$V_D = -0.625$ kip

$M_D = -0.769$ kip $\cdot$ ft

$N_E = -2.00$ kip

$V_E = 0$

$M_E = 0$

7–105. $\sigma_{a-a} = 200$ kPa, $\tau_{a-a} = 115$ kPa

7–106. $(\epsilon_{\text{avg}})_{AC} = 0.0112$ mm/mm,

$(\epsilon_{\text{avg}})_{CD} = 0.125$ mm/mm,

$(\gamma_{xy})_F = 0.245$ rad,

$(\epsilon_{\text{avg}})_{BE} = 0.0635$ mm/mm

7–107. $(\epsilon_{\text{avg}})_{AD} = 0.132$ mm/mm,

$(\epsilon_{\text{avg}})_{CF} = -0.0687$ mm/mm

Chapter 8

8–1. $E_{\text{approx}} = \dfrac{1.31 - 0}{0.0004 - 0} = 3.275(10^3)$ ksi

8–2. $E = 55.3(10^3)$ ksi, $u_r = 9.96\,\dfrac{\text{in} \cdot \text{lb}}{\text{in}^3}$

8–3. $(u_r)_{\text{approx}} = 85.0\,\dfrac{\text{in} \cdot \text{lb}}{\text{in}^3}$

8–5. $(u_t)_{\text{approx}} = 117$ MJ/m^3

8–6. $E = 8.83(10^3)$ ksi

8–7. $A = 0.209$ in^2, $P = 1.62$ kip

8–9. $\sigma = 1.50$ ksi, $\epsilon = 0.035$ in./in., $\delta = 0.228$ in.

8–10. $E = 30.0(10^3)$ ksi, $P_Y = 11.8$ kip, $P_{\text{ult}} = 19.6$ kip

8–11. Elastic Recovery $= 0.003$ in./in.,

$\Delta L = 0.094$ in.

8–13. $\sigma = 11.43$ ksi, $\epsilon = 0.000400$ in./in.,

$E = 28.6(10^3)$ ksi

8–14. $\delta_{BD} = 0.0632$ in.

8–15. $P = 570$ lb

8–17. $\sigma_{pl} = 44$ ksi, $\sigma_Y = 60$ ksi, $E = 11.0(10^3)$ ksi

8–18. $(U_i)_r = 88\,\dfrac{\text{in} \cdot \text{lb}}{\text{in}^3}$, $[(U_i)_t]_{\text{approx}} = 6.50(10^3)\,\dfrac{\text{in} \cdot \text{lb}}{\text{in}^3}$

8–19. $\sigma = 2.22$ MPa

8–21. $\sigma = 1.697$ MPa,
$\delta = 0.126$ mm, $\Delta d = -0.00377$ mm

8–22. **a.** $\delta = -0.577(10^{-3})$ in.
b. $d' = 0.5000673$ in.

8–23. $\nu = 0.300$

8–25. $\epsilon_{\text{long}} = -0.0002667$, $\epsilon_{\text{lat}} = 0.0000880$, $\nu = 0.330$,
$h' = 2.000176$ in.

8–26. $\epsilon_y = -0.0150$ in./in., $\epsilon_x = 0.00540$ in./in.,
$\gamma_{xy} = -0.00524$ rad

8–27. $P = 53.0$ kip, $E = 28.6(10^3)$ ksi

8–29. $\tau_{\text{avg}} = 4166.67$ Pa, $\gamma = 0.02083$ rad,
$\delta = 0.833$ mm

8–30. $\delta = \dfrac{Pa}{2bhG}$

8–31. $G_{\text{al}} = 4.31(10^3)$ ksi

8–33. $E = 5.5$ psi, $u_t = 19.25$ psi, $u_r = 11$ psi

8–34. $\delta = -0.0173$ mm, $d' = 20.0016$ mm

8–35. $x = 1.53$ m, $d'_A = 30.008$ mm

8–37. $\tau = 148.89$ kPa, $G = 1.481$ MPa, $\delta_h = 3.02$ mm

8–38. $\epsilon_{DE} = 0.00116$ in./in., $W = 112$ lb,
$\epsilon_{BC} = 0.00193$ in./in.

8–39. $\epsilon_b = 0.00227$ mm/mm,
$\epsilon_r = 0.000884$ mm/mm

Chapter 9

9–1. $\delta_A = \dfrac{-5.00(10^3)(8)}{\frac{\pi}{4}(0.4^2 - 0.3^2)200(10^9)} = -3.64(10^{-3})$ mm

9–2. $\delta_{A/D} = 0.766(10^{-3})$ in.

9–3. $\delta_D = 0.850$ mm

9–5. $\delta_A = 6.14$ mm

9–6. $\delta_A = 0.0128$ in.

9–7. $\delta_P = 0.0350$ in. $\downarrow$

9–9. $\delta_C = 0.0055172$ in., $\delta_A = 0.0110344$ in.,
$\delta_{F/E} = 0.0020690$ in., $\delta'_E = 0.0036782$ in.,
$\delta_F = 0.0113$ in.

9–10. $\theta = 0.00878°$

9–11. $\delta_t = 0.0260$ in.

9–13. $\delta = \dfrac{1}{AE}\displaystyle\int_0^L (\gamma Ax + P)\,dx = \dfrac{\gamma L^2}{2E} + \dfrac{PL}{AE}$

9–14. $\delta_{A/B} = -0.864$ mm

9–15. $\delta_{A/B} = -1.03$ mm

9–17. $\delta = -0.4310(10^{-3})P$, $P = 46.4$ kip

9–18. $\delta_F = 0.0230$ in. $\downarrow$

9–19. $\theta = 0.439(10^{-3})$ rad

9–21. $\delta_D = 0.1374$ mm, $\delta_{A/B} = 0.3958$ mm,
$\delta_C = 0.5332$ mm, $\delta_{\text{tot}} = 33.9$ mm

9–22. $W = 9.69$ kN

9–25. $\delta = 0.360$ mm

9–26. $\delta = \dfrac{\gamma L^2}{6E}$

9–27. $\sigma_{\text{st}} = 3.14$ ksi, $\sigma_{\text{con}} = 0.455$ ksi

9–29. $P_{\text{st}} = 57.47$ kN, $P_{\text{con}} = 22.53$ kN,
$\sigma_{\text{st}} = 48.8$ MPa, $\sigma_{\text{con}} = 5.85$ MPa

9–30. $\sigma_{\text{br}} = 0.341$ ksi, $\sigma_{\text{st}} = 0.654$ ksi

9–31. $d = 2.39$ in.

9–33. $F_D = 107.89$ kN, $\delta_{A/B} = 0.335$ mm

9–34. $\sigma_{\text{st}} = 1.66$ ksi, $\sigma_{\text{con}} = 0.240$ ksi,
$\delta = 0.0055$ in.

9–35. $A_{\text{st}} = 18.2$ in^2, $\delta = 0.00545$ in.

9–37. $P_{\text{con}} = 36.552\,P_{\text{st}}$,
$\sigma_{\text{con}} = 8.42$ MPa, $\sigma_{\text{st}} = 67.3$ MPa

9–38. $d = 24.6$ mm

9–39. $\sigma_{AB} = 26.5$ MPa, $\sigma_{EF} = 33.8$ MPa

9–41. $F_b = 10.17\,(10^3)$ N, $F_t = 29.83\,(10^3)$ N,
$\sigma_b = 32.4$ MPa, $\sigma_t = 34.5$ MPa

9–42. $F_D = 20.4$ kN, $F_A = 180$ kN

9–43. $T_{AB} = 361$ lb, $T_{A'B'} = 289$ lb

9–45. $y = 3 - 0.025x$, $F_A = 4.09$ kip, $F_B = 2.91$ kip

9–46. $x = 28.9$ in., $P = 60.4$ kip

9–47. $T_{CD} = 27.2$ kip, $T_{CD} = 9.06$ kip

9–49. $F_{\text{st}} = 1.822$ kip, $F_{\text{al}} = 3.644$ kip,
$\sigma_{\text{rod}} = 9.28$ ksi, $\sigma_{\text{cyl}} = 1.16$ ksi

9–50. $\theta = 698°$

9–51. $\sigma_{BE} = 96.3$ MPa, $\sigma_{AD} = 79.6$ MPa,
$\sigma_{CF} = 113$ MPa

9–53. $0 = \Delta_T - \delta$, $F = 4.20$ kN

9–54. $F = 0.509$ kip

9–55. $F = 116$ kip

9–57. $0 = \delta_T - \delta_F$, $F = 19.14A$, $\sigma = 19.1$ ksi

9–58. $F = 7.60$ kip

9–59. $\delta = 0.348$ in., $F = 19.5$ kip

9–61. $0 = \Delta_T - \delta_F$, $F = \dfrac{\alpha AE}{2}(T_B - T_A)$

9–62. $F_B = 183$ kN, $F_A = 383$ kN

9–63. $P = 188$ kN

9–65. $\sigma_{\text{max}} = 190$ MPa

9–66. $P = 5.05$ kN

9–67. $K = 2.45$, $w = 2.49$ in.

9–69. $P = 1.21$ kip

9–70. $\sigma_{max} = 34.8$ ksi

9–71. Maximum normal stress at fillet: $K = 1.4$,
Maximum normal stress at the hole: $K = 2.65$,
$\sigma_{max} = 88.3$ MPa

9–73. $F_B = 2.13$ kip, $F_A = 2.14$ kip

9–74. $P = 4.85$ kip

9–75. $F_{AB} = F_{AC} = F_{AD} = 58.9$ kN

9–77. $P = 56.5$ kN, $\delta_{B/A} = 0.0918$ mm

9–78. $\theta = \dfrac{3E_2 L(T_2 - T_1)(\alpha_2 - \alpha_1)}{d(5E_2 + E_1)}$

9–79. $\delta = -\dfrac{P}{2a\pi r_0^2 E}\left(1 - e^{-2aL}\right)$

9–81. $p_0 = 250$ kN/m, $\delta = 2.93$ mm

Average Mechanical Properties of Typical Engineering Materials[a]
(U.S. Customary Units)

Materials	Specific Weight γ (lb/in³)	Modulus of Elasticity E (10³) ksi	Modulus of Rigidity G (10³) ksi	Yield Strength (ksi) σ_Y Tens.	Comp.[b]	Shear	Ultimate Strength (ksi) σ_u Tens.	Comp.[b]	Shear	% Elongation in 2 in. specimen	Poisson's Ratio ν	Coef. of Therm. Expansion α (10⁻⁶)/°F
Metallic												
Aluminum Wrought Alloys — 2014-T6	0.101	10.6	3.9	60	60	25	68	68	42	10	0.35	12.8
Aluminum Wrought Alloys — 6061-T6	0.098	10.0	3.7	37	37	19	42	42	27	12	0.35	13.1
Cast Iron Alloys — Gray ASTM 20	0.260	10.0	3.9	–	–	–	26	97	–	0.6	0.28	6.70
Cast Iron Alloys — Malleable ASTM A-197	0.263	25.0	9.8	–	–	–	40	83	–	5	0.28	6.60
Copper Alloys — Red Brass C83400	0.316	14.6	5.4	11.4	11.4	–	35	35	–	35	0.35	9.80
Copper Alloys — Bronze C86100	0.319	15.0	5.6	50	50	–	95	95	–	20	0.34	9.60
Magnesium Alloy [Am 1004-T61]	0.066	6.48	2.5	22	22	–	40	40	22	1	0.30	14.3
Steel Alloys — Structural A36	0.284	29.0	11.0	36	36	–	58	58	–	30	0.32	6.60
Steel Alloys — Stainless 304	0.284	28.0	11.0	30	30	–	75	75	–	40	0.27	9.60
Steel Alloys — Tool L2	0.295	29.0	11.0	102	102	–	116	116	–	22	0.32	6.50
Titanium Alloy [Ti-6Al-4V]	0.160	17.4	6.4	134	134	–	145	145	–	16	0.36	5.20
Nonmetallic												
Concrete — Low Strength	0.086	3.20	–	–	–	1.8	–	–	–	–	0.15	6.0
Concrete — High Strength	0.086	4.20	–	–	–	5.5	–	–	–	–	0.15	6.0
Plastic Reinforced — Kevlar 49	0.0524	19.0	–	–	–	–	104	70	10.2	2.8	0.34	–
Plastic Reinforced — 30% Glass	0.0524	10.5	–	–	–	–	13	19	–	–	0.34	–
Wood Select Structural Grade — Douglas Fir	0.017	1.90	–	–	–	–	0.30[c]	3.78[d]	0.90[d]	–	0.29[e]	–
Wood Select Structural Grade — White Spruce	0.130	1.40	–	–	–	–	0.36[c]	5.18[d]	0.97[d]	–	0.31[e]	–

[a] Specific values may vary for a particular material due to alloy or mineral composition, mechanical working of the specimen, or heat treatment. For a more exact value reference books for the material should be consulted.

[b] The yield and ultimate strengths for ductile materials can be assumed equal for both tension and compression.

[c] Measured perpendicular to the grain.

[d] Measured parallel to the grain.

[e] Deformation measured perpendicular to the grain when the load is applied along the grain.

Average Mechanical Properties of Typical Engineering Materials[a]

(SI Units)

Materials	Density ρ (Mg/m³)	Modulus of Elasticity E (GPa)	Modulus of Rigidity G (GPa)	Yield Strength (MPa) σ_Y[b]			Ultimate Strength (MPa) σ_u			% Elongation in 50 mm specimen	Poisson's Ratio ν	Coef. of Therm. Expansion α (10⁻⁶)/°C
				Tens.	Comp.[b]	Shear	Tens.	Comp.[b]	Shear			
Metallic												
Aluminum Wrought Alloys — 2014-T6	2.79	73.1	27	414	414	172	469	469	290	10	0.35	23
Aluminum Wrought Alloys — 6061-T6	2.71	68.9	26	255	255	131	290	290	186	12	0.35	24
Cast Iron Alloys — Gray ASTM 20	7.19	67.0	27	–	–	–	179	669	–	0.6	0.28	12
Cast Iron Alloys — Malleable ASTM A-197	7.28	172	68	–	–	–	276	572	–	5	0.28	12
Copper Alloys — Red Brass C83400	8.74	101	37	70.0	70.0	–	241	241	–	35	0.35	18
Copper Alloys — Bronze C86100	8.83	103	38	345	345	–	655	655	–	20	0.34	17
Magnesium Alloy [Am 1004-T61]	1.83	44.7	18	152	152	–	276	276	152	1	0.30	26
Steel Alloys — Structural A36	7.85	200	75	250	250	–	400	400	–	30	0.32	12
Steel Alloys — Stainless 304	7.86	193	75	207	207	–	517	517	–	40	0.27	17
Steel Alloys — Tool L2	8.16	200	75	703	703	–	800	800	–	22	0.32	12
Titanium Alloy [Ti-6Al-4V]	4.43	120	44	924	924	–	1,000	1,000	–	16	0.36	9.4
Nonmetallic												
Concrete — Low Strength	2.38	22.1	–	–	–	12	–	–	–	–	0.15	11
Concrete — High Strength	2.38	29.0	–	–	–	38	–	–	–	–	0.15	11
Plastic Reinforced — Kevlar 49	1.45	131	–	–	–	–	717	483	20.3	2.8	0.34	–
Plastic Reinforced — 30% Glass	1.45	72.4	–	–	–	–	90	131	–	–	0.34	–
Wood Select Structural Grade — Douglas Fir	0.47	13.1	–	–	–	–	2.1[c]	26[d]	6.2[d]	–	0.29[e]	–
Wood Select Structural Grade — White Spruce	3.60	9.65	–	–	–	–	2.5[c]	36[d]	6.7[d]	–	0.31[e]	–

[a] Specific values may vary for a particular material due to alloy or mineral composition, mechanical working of the specimen, or heat treatment. For a more exact value reference books for the material should be consulted.

[b] The yield and ultimate strengths for ductile materials can be assumed equal for both tension and compression.

[c] Measured perpendicular to the grain.

[d] Measured parallel to the grain.

[e] Deformation measured perpendicular to the grain when the load is applied along the grain.

Engineering Mechanics
DYNAMICS

Taken from: *Engineering Mechanics: Statics and Dynamics*, Fifth Edition
by Anthony Bedford and Wallace Fowler.

Introduction

How do engineers design and construct the devices we use, from simple objects such as chairs and pencil sharpeners to complicated ones such as dams, cars, airplanes, and spacecraft? They must have a deep understanding of the physics underlying the design of such devices and must be able to use mathematical models to predict their behavior. Students of engineering begin to learn how to analyze and predict the behaviors of physical systems by studying mechanics.

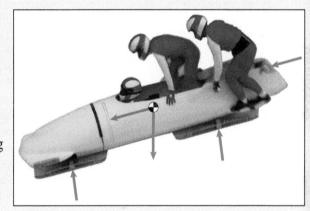

◄ The motions of the bobsled and its crew—their positions, velocities, and accelerations—can be analyzed using the equations of dynamics. Engineers use dynamics to predict the motions of objects.

12.1 Engineering and Mechanics

BACKGROUND

How can engineers design complex systems and predict their characteristics before they are constructed? Engineers have always relied on their knowledge of previous designs, experiments, ingenuity, and creativity to develop new designs. Modern engineers add a powerful technique: They develop mathematical equations based on the physical characteristics of the devices they design. With these mathematical models, engineers predict the behavior of their designs, modify them, and test them prior to their actual construction. Aerospace engineers use mathematical models to predict the paths the space shuttle will follow in flight. Civil engineers use mathematical models to analyze the effects of loads on buildings and foundations.

At its most basic level, mechanics is the study of forces and their effects. Elementary mechanics is divided into *statics*, the study of objects in equilibrium, and *dynamics*, the study of objects in motion. The results obtained in elementary mechanics apply directly to many fields of engineering. Mechanical and civil engineers designing structures use the equilibrium equations derived in statics. Civil engineers analyzing the responses of buildings to earthquakes and aerospace engineers determining the trajectories of satellites use the equations of motion derived in dynamics.

Mechanics was the first analytical science. As a result, fundamental concepts, analytical methods, and analogies from mechanics are found in virtually every field of engineering. Students of chemical and electrical engineering gain a deeper appreciation for basic concepts in their fields, such as equilibrium, energy, and stability, by learning them in their original mechanical contexts. By studying mechanics, they retrace the historical development of these ideas.

Mechanics consists of broad principles that govern the behavior of objects. In this book we describe these principles and provide examples that demonstrate some of their applications. Although it is essential that you practice working problems similar to these examples, and we include many problems of this kind, our objective is to help you understand the principles well enough to apply them to situations that are new to you. Each generation of engineers confronts new problems.

Problem Solving

In the study of mechanics, you learn problem-solving procedures that you will use in succeeding courses and throughout your career. Although different types of problems require different approaches, the following steps apply to many of them:

- Identify the information that is given and the information, or answer, you must determine. It's often helpful to restate the problem in your own words. When appropriate, make sure you understand the physical system or model involved.

- Develop a *strategy* for the problem. This means identifying the principles and equations that apply and deciding how you will use them to solve the problem. Whenever possible, draw diagrams to help visualize and solve the problem.

- Whenever you can, try to predict the answer. This will develop your intuition and will often help you recognize an incorrect answer.

- Solve the equations and, whenever possible, interpret your results and compare them with your prediction. This last step is a *reality check*. Is your answer reasonable?

Numbers

Engineering measurements, calculations, and results are expressed in numbers. You need to know how we express numbers in the examples and problems and how to express the results of your own calculations.

Significant Digits   This term refers to the number of meaningful (that is, accurate) digits in a number, counting to the right starting with the first non-zero digit. The two numbers 7.630 and 0.007630 are each stated to four significant digits. If only the first four digits in the number 7,630,000 are known to be accurate, this can be indicated by writing the number in scientific notation as 7.630×10^6.

If a number is the result of a measurement, the significant digits it contains are limited by the accuracy of the measurement. If the result of a measurement is stated to be 2.43, this means that the actual value is believed to be closer to 2.43 than to 2.42 or 2.44.

Numbers may be rounded off to a certain number of significant digits. For example, we can express the value of π to three significant digits, 3.14, or we can express it to six significant digits, 3.14159. When you use a calculator or computer, the number of significant digits is limited by the number of digits the machine is designed to carry.

Use of Numbers in This Book   You should treat numbers given in problems as exact values and not be concerned about how many significant digits they contain. If a problem states that a quantity equals 32.2, you can assume its value is 32.200. . . . We generally express intermediate results and answers in the examples and the answers to the problems to at least three significant digits. If you use a calculator, your results should be that accurate. Be sure to avoid round-off errors that occur if you round off intermediate results when making a series of calculations. Instead, carry through your calculations with as much accuracy as you can by retaining values in your calculator.

Space and Time

Space simply refers to the three-dimensional universe in which we live. Our daily experiences give us an intuitive notion of space and the locations, or positions, of points in space. The distance between two points in space is the length of the straight line joining them.

Measuring the distance between points in space requires a unit of length. We use both the International System of units, or SI units, and U.S. Customary units. In SI units, the unit of length is the meter (m). In U.S. Customary units, the unit of length is the foot (ft).

Time is, of course, familiar—our lives are measured by it. The daily cycles of light and darkness and the hours, minutes, and seconds measured by our clocks and watches give us an intuitive notion of time. Time is measured by the intervals between repeatable events, such as the swings of a clock pendulum or the vibrations of a quartz crystal in a watch. In both SI units and U.S. Customary units, the unit of time is the second (s). The minute (min), hour (h), and day are also frequently used.

If the position of a point in space relative to some reference point changes with time, the rate of change of its position is called its *velocity*, and the rate of change of its velocity is called its *acceleration*. In SI units, the velocity is expressed in meters per second (m/s) and the acceleration is expressed in meters per second per second, or meters per second squared (m/s^2). In U.S.

Customary units, the velocity is expressed in feet per second (ft/s) and the acceleration is expressed in feet per second squared (ft/s^2).

Newton's Laws

Elementary mechanics was established on a firm basis with the publication in 1687 of *Philosophiae Naturalis Principia Mathematica*, by Isaac Newton. Although highly original, it built on fundamental concepts developed by many others during a long and difficult struggle toward understanding (Fig. 12.1).

Figure 12.1
Chronology of developments in mechanics up to the publication of Newton's *Principia* in relation to other events in history.

Newton stated three "laws" of motion, which we express in modern terms:

1. *When the sum of the forces acting on a particle is zero, its velocity is constant. In particular, if the particle is initially stationary, it will remain stationary.*

2. *When the sum of the forces acting on a particle is not zero, the sum of the forces is equal to the rate of change of the linear momentum of the particle. If the mass is constant, the sum of the forces is equal to the product of the mass of the particle and its acceleration.*

3. *The forces exerted by two particles on each other are equal in magnitude and opposite in direction.*

Notice that we did not define force and mass before stating Newton's laws. The modern view is that these terms are defined by the second law. To demonstrate, suppose that we choose an arbitrary object and define it to have unit mass. Then we define a unit of force to be the force that gives our unit mass an acceleration of unit magnitude. In principle, we can then determine the mass of any object: We apply a unit force to it, measure the resulting acceleration, and use the second law to determine the mass. We can also determine the magnitude of any force: We apply it to our unit mass, measure the resulting acceleration, and use the second law to determine the force.

Thus Newton's second law gives precise meanings to the terms *mass* and *force*. In SI units, the unit of mass is the kilogram (kg). The unit of force is the newton (N), which is the force required to give a mass of one kilogram an acceleration of one meter per second squared. In U.S. Customary units, the unit of force is the pound (lb). The unit of mass is the slug, which is the amount of mass accelerated at one foot per second squared by a force of one pound.

Although the results we discuss in this book are applicable to many of the problems met in engineering practice, there are limits to the validity of Newton's laws. For example, they don't give accurate results if a problem involves velocities that are not small compared to the velocity of light (3×10^8 m/s). Einstein's special theory of relativity applies to such problems. Elementary mechanics also fails in problems involving dimensions that are not large compared to atomic dimensions. Quantum mechanics must be used to describe phenomena on the atomic scale.

International System of Units

In SI units, length is measured in meters (m) and mass in kilograms (kg). Time is measured in seconds (s), although other familiar measures such as minutes (min), hours (h), and days are also used when convenient. Meters, kilograms, and seconds are called the *base units* of the SI system. Force is measured in newtons (N). Recall that these units are related by Newton's second law: One newton is the force required to give an object of one kilogram mass an acceleration of one meter per second squared:

$$1 \text{ N} = (1 \text{ kg})(1 \text{ m/s}^2) = 1 \text{ kg-m/s}^2.$$

Because the newton can be expressed in terms of the base units, it is called a *derived unit*.

To express quantities by numbers of convenient size, multiples of units are indicated by prefixes. The most common prefixes, their abbreviations, and the multiples they represent are shown in Table 12.1. For example, 1 km is 1 kilometer, which is 1000 m, and 1 Mg is 1 megagram, which is 10^6 g, or 1000 kg. We frequently use kilonewtons (kN).

Table 12.1 The common prefixes used in SI units and the multiples they represent.

Prefix	Abbreviation	Multiple
nano-	n	10^{-9}
micro-	μ	10^{-6}
milli-	m	10^{-3}
kilo-	k	10^3
mega-	M	10^6
giga-	G	10^9

U.S. Customary Units

In U.S. Customary units, length is measured in feet (ft) and force is measured in pounds (lb). Time is measured in seconds (s). These are the base units of the U.S. Customary system. In this system of units, mass is a derived unit. The unit of mass is the slug, which is the mass of material accelerated at one foot per second squared by a force of one pound. Newton's second law states that

$$1 \text{ lb} = (1 \text{ slug})(1 \text{ ft/s}^2).$$

From this expression we obtain

$$1 \text{ slug} = 1 \text{ lb-s}^2/\text{ft}.$$

We use other U.S. Customary units such as the mile (1 mi = 5280 ft) and the inch (1 ft = 12 in). We also use the kilopound (kip), which is 1000 lb.

Angular Units

In both SI and U.S. Customary units, angles are normally expressed in radians (rad). We show the value of an angle θ in radians in Fig. 12.2. It is defined to be the ratio of the part of the circumference subtended by θ to the radius of the circle. Angles are also expressed in degrees. Since there are 360 degrees (360°) in a complete circle, and the complete circumference of the circle is $2\pi R$, 360° equals 2π rad.

Equations containing angles are nearly always derived under the assumption that angles are expressed in radians. Therefore, when you want to substitute the value of an angle expressed in degrees into an equation, you should first convert it into radians. A notable exception to this rule is that many calculators are designed to accept angles expressed in either degrees or radians when you use them to evaluate functions such as sin θ.

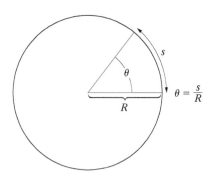

Figure 12.2
Definition of an angle in radians.

Conversion of Units

Many situations arise in engineering practice that require values expressed in one kind of unit to be converted into values in other units. For example, if some of the data to be used in an equation are given in SI units and some are given in U.S. Customary units, they must all be expressed in terms of one system of units before they are substituted into the equation. Converting units is straightforward, although it must be done with care.

Suppose that we want to express 1 mile per hour (mi/h) in terms of feet per second (ft/s). Because 1 mile equals 5280 feet and 1 hour equals 3600 seconds, we can treat the expressions

$$\left(\frac{5280 \text{ ft}}{1 \text{ mi}}\right) \quad \text{and} \quad \left(\frac{1 \text{ h}}{3600 \text{ s}}\right)$$

as ratios whose values are 1. In this way, we obtain

$$1 \text{ mi/h} = (1 \text{ mi/h})\left(\frac{5280 \text{ ft}}{1 \text{ mi}}\right)\left(\frac{1 \text{ h}}{3600 \text{ s}}\right) = 1.47 \text{ ft/s}.$$

Some useful unit conversions are given in Table 12.2.

Table 12.2   Unit conversions.

Time	1 minute	=	60 seconds
	1 hour	=	60 minutes
	1 day	=	24 hours
Length	1 foot	=	12 inches
	1 mile	=	5280 feet
	1 inch	=	25.4 millimeters
	1 foot	=	0.3048 meters
Angle	2π radians	=	360 degrees
Mass	1 slug	=	14.59 kilograms
Force	1 pound	=	4.448 newtons

RESULTS

- Identify the given information and the answer that must be determined.
- Develop a strategy; identify principles and equations that apply and how they will be used.
- Try to predict the answer whenever possible.
- Obtain the answer and, whenever possible, interpret it and compare it with the prediction.

> Problem Solving: These steps apply to many types of problems.

SI Units—The *base units* are time in seconds (s), length in meters (m), and mass in kilograms (kg). The unit of force is the newton (N), which is the force required to accelerate a mass of one kilogram at one meter per second squared.

U.S. Customary Units—The base units are time in seconds (s), length in feet (ft), and force in pounds (lb). The unit of mass is the slug, which is the mass accelerated at one foot per second squared by a force of one pound.

> Systems of units.

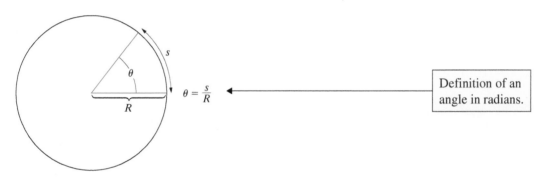

$$\theta = \frac{s}{R}$$

> Definition of an angle in radians.

Equivalent quantities, such as 1 hour = 60 minutes, can be written as ratios whose values are 1:

$$\left(\frac{1\ \text{h}}{60\ \text{min}}\right) = 1,$$

and used to convert units. For example,

$$15\ \text{min} = 15\ \text{min}\left(\frac{1\ \text{h}}{60\ \text{min}}\right) = 0.25\ \text{h}.$$

> Conversion of units.

A comprehensive resource on units has been compiled by Russ Rowlett of the University of North Carolina at Chapel Hill and made available online at www.unc.edu/~rowlett/units.

Active Example 12.1 | Converting Units (▶ *Related Problem 12.11*)

A man is riding a bicycle at a speed of 6 meters per second (m/s). How fast is he going in kilometers per hour (km/h)?

Strategy
One kilometer is 1000 meters and one hour is 60 minutes × 60 seconds = 3600 seconds. We can use these unit conversions to determine his speed in km/h.

Solution

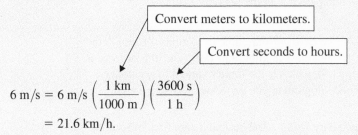

Convert meters to kilometers.

Convert seconds to hours.

$$6 \, \text{m/s} = 6 \, \text{m/s} \left(\frac{1 \, \text{km}}{1000 \, \text{m}} \right) \left(\frac{3600 \, \text{s}}{1 \, \text{h}} \right)$$

$$= 21.6 \, \text{km/h}.$$

Practice Problem A man is riding a bicycle at a speed of 10 feet per second (ft/s). How fast is he going in miles per hour (mi/h)?

Answer: 6.82 mi/h.

Example 12.2 | Converting Units of Pressure (▶ *Related Problem 12.16*)

Deep Submersible Vehicle.

The pressure exerted at a point of the hull of the deep submersible vehicle is 3.00×10^6 Pa (pascals). A pascal is 1 newton per square meter. Determine the pressure in pounds per square foot.

Strategy
From Table 12.2, 1 pound = 4.448 newtons and 1 foot = 0.3048 meters. With these unit conversions we can calculate the pressure in pounds per square foot.

Solution
The pressure (to three significant digits) is

$$3.00 \times 10^6 \, \text{N/m}^2 = (3.00 \times 10^6 \, \text{N/m}^2) \left(\frac{1 \, \text{lb}}{4.448 \, \text{N}} \right) \left(\frac{0.3048 \, \text{m}}{1 \, \text{ft}} \right)^2$$

$$= 62{,}700 \, \text{lb/ft}^2.$$

Critical Thinking
How could we have obtained this result in a more direct way? Notice from the table of unit conversions in the inside front cover that 1 Pa = 0.0209 lb/ft^2. Therefore,

$$3.00 \times 10^6 \, \text{N/m}^2 = (3.00 \times 10^6 \, \text{N/m}^2) \left(\frac{0.0209 \, \text{lb/ft}^2}{1 \, \text{N/m}^2} \right)$$

$$= 62{,}700 \, \text{lb/ft}^2.$$

| **Example 12.3** | **Determining Units from an Equation** (▶ *Related Problem 12.20*) |

Suppose that in Einstein's equation

$$E = mc^2,$$

the mass m is in kilograms and the velocity of light c is in meters per second.

(a) What are the SI units of E?

(b) If the value of E in SI units is 20, what is its value in U.S. Customary base units?

Strategy

(a) Since we know the units of the terms m and c, we can deduce the units of E from the given equation.

(b) We can use the unit conversions for mass and length from Table 12.2 to convert E from SI units to U.S. Customary units.

Solution

(a) From the equation for E,

$$E = (m\,\text{kg})(c\,\text{m/s})^2,$$

the SI units of E are kg-m^2/s^2.

(b) From Table 12.2, 1 slug $= 14.59$ kg and 1 ft $= 0.3048$ m. Therefore,

$$1\,\text{kg-m}^2/\text{s}^2 = (1\,\text{kg-m}^2/\text{s}^2)\left(\frac{1\,\text{slug}}{14.59\,\text{kg}}\right)\left(\frac{1\,\text{ft}}{0.3048\,\text{m}}\right)^2$$

$$= 0.738\,\text{slug-ft}^2/\text{s}^2.$$

The value of E in U.S. Customary units is

$$E = (20)(0.738) = 14.8\,\text{slug-ft}^2/\text{s}^2.$$

Critical Thinking

In part (a), how did we know that we could determine the units of E by determining the units of mc^2? The dimensions, or units, of each term in an equation must be the same. For example, in the equation $a + b = c$, the dimensions of each of the terms a, b, and c must be the same. The equation is said to be *dimensionally homogeneous*. This requirement is expressed by the colloquial phrase "Don't compare apples and oranges."

Problems

12.1 The value of π is 3.14159265. . . . If C is the circumference of a circle and r is its radius, determine the value of r/C to four significant digits.

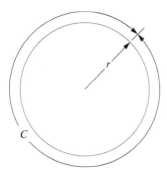

Problem 12.1

12.2 The base of natural logarithms is $e = 2.718281828\ldots$.

(a) Express e to five significant digits.

(b) Determine the value of e^2 to five significant digits.

(c) Use the value of e you obtained in part (a) to determine the value of e^2 to five significant digits.
[Part (c) demonstrates the hazard of using rounded-off values in calculations.]

12.3 A machinist drills a circular hole in a panel with a nominal radius $r = 5$ mm. The actual radius of the hole is in the range $r = 5 \pm 0.01$ mm.

(a) To what number of significant digits can you express the radius?

(b) To what number of significant digits can you express the area of the hole?

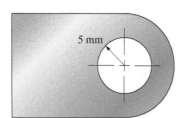

Problem 12.3

12.4 The opening in the soccer goal is 24 ft wide and 8 ft high, so its area is 24 ft $\times$ 8 ft $= 192\ \text{ft}^2$. What is its area in m^2 to three significant digits?

Problem 12.4

12.5 The Burj Dubai, scheduled for completion in 2008, will be the world's tallest building with a height of 705 m. The area of its ground footprint will be 8000 m^2. Convert its height and footprint area to U.S. Customary units to three significant digits.

Problem 12.5

12.6 Suppose that you have just purchased a Ferrari F355 coupe and you want to know whether you can use your set of SAE (U.S. Customary unit) wrenches to work on it. You have wrenches with widths $w = 1/4$ in, $1/2$ in, $3/4$ in, and 1 in, and the car has nuts with dimensions $n = 5$ mm, 10 mm, 15 mm, 20 mm, and 25 mm. Defining a wrench to fit if w is no more than 2% larger than n, which of your wrenches can you use?

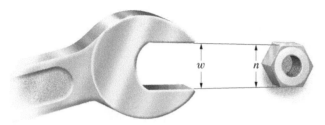

Problem 12.6

12.7 Suppose that the height of Mt. Everest is known to be between 29,032 ft and 29,034 ft. Based on this information, to how many significant digits can you express the height (a) in feet? (b) in meters?

12.8 The maglev (magnetic levitation) train from Shanghai to the airport at Pudong reaches a speed of 430 km/h. Determine its speed (a) in mi/h; (b) in ft/s.

Problem 12.8

12.9 In the 2006 Winter Olympics, the men's 15-km cross-country skiing race was won by Andrus Veerpalu of Estonia in a time of 38 minutes, 1.3 seconds. Determine his average speed (the distance traveled divided by the time required) to three significant digits (a) in km/h; (b) in mi/h.

12.10 The Porsche's engine exerts 229 ft-lb (foot-pounds) of torque at 4600 rpm. Determine the value of the torque in N-m (newton-meters).

Problem 12.10

▶ **12.11** The *kinetic energy* of the man in Active Example 12.1 is defined by $\frac{1}{2}mv^2$, where m is his mass and v is his velocity. The man's mass is 68 kg and he is moving at 6 m/s, so his kinetic energy is $\frac{1}{2}(68 \text{ kg})(6 \text{ m/s})^2 = 1224 \text{ kg-m}^2/\text{s}^2$. What is his kinetic energy in U.S. Customary units?

12.12 The acceleration due to gravity at sea level in SI units is $g = 9.81 \text{ m/s}^2$. By converting units, use this value to determine the acceleration due to gravity at sea level in U.S. Customary units.

12.13 A *furlong per fortnight* is a facetious unit of velocity, perhaps made up by a student as a satirical comment on the bewildering variety of units engineers must deal with. A furlong is 660 ft (1/8 mile). A fortnight is 2 weeks (14 nights). If you walk to class at 2 m/s, what is your speed in furlongs per fortnight to three significant digits?

12.14 Determine the cross-sectional area of the beam (a) in m^2; (b) in in^2.

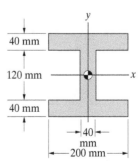

Problem 12.14

12.15 The cross-sectional area of the C12×30 American Standard Channel steel beam is $A = 8.81$ in². What is its cross-sectional area in mm²?

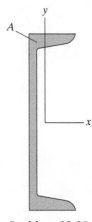

Problem 12.15

▶ **12.16** A pressure transducer measures a value of 300 lb/in². Determine the value of the pressure in pascals. A pascal (Pa) is one newton per square meter.

12.17 A horsepower is 550 ft-lb/s. A watt is 1 N-m/s. Determine how many watts are generated by the engines of the passenger jet if they are producing 7000 horsepower.

Problem 12.17

12.18 Distributed loads on beams are expressed in units of force per unit length. If the value of a distributed load is 400 N/m, what is its value in lb/ft?

12.19 The moment of inertia of the rectangular area about the x axis is given by the equation

$$I = \tfrac{1}{3}bh^3.$$

The dimensions of the area are $b = 200$ mm and $h = 100$ mm. Determine the value of I to four significant digits in terms of (a) mm⁴, (b) m⁴, and (c) in⁴.

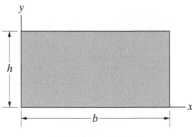

Problem 12.19

▶ **12.20** In Example 12.3, instead of Einstein's equation consider the equation $L = mc$, where the mass m is in kilograms and the velocity of light c is in meters per second. (a) What are the SI units of L? (b) If the value of L in SI units is 12, what is its value in U.S. Customary base units?

12.21 The equation

$$\sigma = \frac{My}{I}$$

is used in the mechanics of materials to determine normal stresses in beams.

(a) When this equation is expressed in terms of SI base units, M is in newton-meters (N-m), y is in meters (m), and I is in meters to the fourth power (m⁴). What are the SI units of σ?
(b) If $M = 2000$ N-m, $y = 0.1$ m, and $I = 7 \times 10^{-5}$ m⁴, what is the value of σ in U.S. Customary base units?

12.2 Newtonian Gravitation

Newton postulated that the gravitational force between two particles of mass m_1 and m_2 that are separated by a distance r (Fig. 12.3) is

$$F = \frac{Gm_1m_2}{r^2},$$

(12.1)

where G is called the universal gravitational constant. The value of G in SI units is 6.67×10^{-11} N-m^2/kg^2. Based on this postulate, he calculated the gravitational force between a particle of mass m_1 and a homogeneous sphere of mass m_2 and found that it is also given by Eq. (12.1), with r denoting the distance from the particle to the center of the sphere. Although the earth is not a homogeneous sphere, we can use this result to approximate the weight of an object of mass m due to the gravitational attraction of the earth. We have

$$W = \frac{Gmm_E}{r^2},$$

(12.2)

where m_E is the mass of the earth and r is the distance from the center of the earth to the object. Notice that the weight of an object depends on its location relative to the center of the earth, whereas the mass of the object is a measure of the amount of matter it contains and doesn't depend on its position.

When an object's weight is the only force acting on it, the resulting acceleration is called the acceleration due to gravity. In this case, Newton's second law states that $W = ma$, and from Eq. (12.2) we see that the acceleration due to gravity is

$$a = \frac{Gm_E}{r^2}.$$

(12.3)

The *acceleration due to gravity at sea level* is denoted by g. Denoting the radius of the earth by R_E, we see from Eq. (12.3) that $Gm_E = gR_E^2$. Substituting this result into Eq. (12.3), we obtain an expression for the acceleration due to gravity at a distance r from the center of the earth in terms of the acceleration due to gravity at sea level:

$$a = g\frac{R_E^2}{r^2}.$$

(12.4)

Since the weight of the object $W = ma$, the weight of an object at a distance r from the center of the earth is

$$W = mg\frac{R_E^2}{r^2}.$$

(12.5)

At sea level $(r = R_E)$, the weight of an object is given in terms of its mass by the simple relation

$$W = mg.$$

(12.6)

The value of g varies from location to location on the surface of the earth. The values we use in examples and problems are $g = 9.81$ m/s^2 in SI units and $g = 32.2$ ft/s^2 in U.S. Customary units.

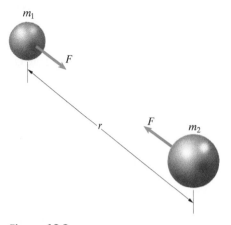

Figure 12.3
The gravitational forces between two particles are equal in magnitude and directed along the line between them.

RESULTS

The gravitational force between two particles of mass m_1 and m_2 that are separated by a distance r is

$$F = \frac{Gm_1m_2}{r^2}, \tag{12.1}$$

where G is the universal gravitational constant. The value of G in SI units is

$$6.67 \times 10^{-11} \text{ N-m}^2/\text{kg}^2.$$

Newtonian gravitation.

When the earth is modeled as a homogeneous sphere of radius R_E, the acceleration due to gravity at a distance r from the center is

$$a = g\frac{R_E^2}{r^2}, \tag{12.4}$$

where g is the acceleration due to gravity at sea level.

Acceleration due to gravity of the earth.

$$W = mg, \tag{12.6}$$

where m is the mass of the object and g is the acceleration due to gravity at sea level.

Weight of an object at sea level.

Active Example 12.4   **Weight and Mass** (▶ *Related Problem 12.22*)

The C-clamp weighs 14 oz at sea level. [16 oz (ounces) = 1 lb.] The acceleration due to gravity at sea level is $g = 32.2 \text{ ft/s}^2$. What is the mass of the C-clamp in slugs?

Strategy
We must first determine the weight of the C-clamp in pounds. Then we can use Eq. (12.6) to determine the mass in slugs.

Solution

$$14 \text{ oz} = 14 \text{ oz} \left(\frac{1 \text{ lb}}{16 \text{ oz}}\right) = 0.875 \text{ lb}.$$

Convert the weight from ounces to pounds.

$$m = \frac{W}{g} = \frac{0.875 \text{ lb}}{32.2 \text{ ft/s}^2} = 0.0272 \text{ slug}.$$

Use Eq. (12.6) to calculate the mass in slugs.

Practice Problem The mass of the C-clamp is 0.397 kg. The acceleration due to gravity at sea level is $g = 9.81 \text{ m/s}^2$. What is the weight of the C-clamp at sea level in newtons?

Answer: 3.89 N.

Example 12.5   Determining an Object's Weight (▶ *Related Problem 12.27*)

When the Mars Exploration Rover was fully assembled, its mass was 180 kg. The acceleration due to gravity at the surface of Mars is 3.68 m/s^2 and the radius of Mars is 3390 km.

(a) What was the rover's weight when it was at sea level on Earth?

(b) What is the rover's weight on the surface of Mars?

(c) The entry phase began when the spacecraft reached the Mars atmospheric entry interface point at 3522 km from the center of Mars. What was the rover's weight at that point?

Mars Exploration Rover being assembled.

Strategy

The rover's weight at sea level on Earth is given by Eq. (12.6) with $g = 9.81$ m/s^2.

We can determine the weight on the surface of Mars by using Eq. (12.6) with the acceleration due to gravity equal to 3.68 m/s^2.

To determine the rover's weight as it began the entry phase, we can write an equation for Mars equivalent to Eq. (12.5).

Solution

(a) The weight at sea level on Earth is

$$W = mg$$
$$= (180 \text{ kg})(9.81 \text{ m/s}^2)$$
$$= 1770 \text{ N } (397 \text{ lb}).$$

(b) Let $g_M = 3.68$ m/s^2 be the acceleration due to gravity at the surface of Mars. Then the weight of the rover on the surface of Mars is

$$W = mg_M$$
$$= (180 \text{ kg})(3.68 \text{ m/s}^2)$$
$$= 662 \text{ N } (149 \text{ lb}).$$

(c) Let $R_M = 3390$ km be the radius of Mars. From Eq. (12.5), the rover's weight when it is 3522 km above the center of Mars is

$$W = mg_M \frac{R_M^2}{r^2}$$
$$= (180 \text{ kg})(3.68 \text{ m/s}^2) \frac{(3{,}390{,}000 \text{ m})^2}{(3{,}522{,}000 \text{ m})^2}$$
$$= 614 \text{ N } (138 \text{ lb}).$$

Critical Thinking

In part (c), how did we know that we could apply Eq. (12.5) to Mars? Equation (12.5) is applied to Earth based on modeling it as a homogeneous sphere. It can be applied to other celestial objects under the same assumption. The accuracy of the results depends on how aspherical and inhomogeneous the object is.

Problems

▶ **12.22** The acceleration due to gravity on the surface of the moon is 1.62 m/s². (a) What would the mass of the C-clamp in Active Example 12.4 be on the surface of the moon? (b) What would the weight of the C-clamp in newtons be on the surface of the moon?

12.23 The 1 ft × 1 ft × 1 ft cube of iron weighs 490 lb at sea level. Determine the weight in newtons of a 1 m × 1 m × 1 m cube of the same material at sea level.

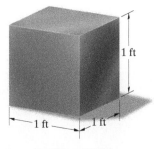

Problem 12.23

12.24 The area of the Pacific Ocean is 64,186,000 square miles and its average depth is 12,925 ft. Assume that the weight per unit volume of ocean water is 64 lb/ft³. Determine the mass of the Pacific Ocean (a) in slugs; (b) in kilograms.

12.25 The acceleration due to gravity at sea level is $g = 9.81$ m/s². The radius of the earth is 6370 km. The universal gravitational constant is $G = 6.67 \times 10^{-11}$ N-m²/kg². Use this information to determine the mass of the earth.

12.26 A person weighs 180 lb at sea level. The radius of the earth is 3960 mi. What force is exerted on the person by the gravitational attraction of the earth if he is in a space station in orbit 200 mi above the surface of the earth?

▶ **12.27** The acceleration due to gravity on the surface of the moon is 1.62 m/s². The moon's radius is $R_M = 1738$ km. (See Example 12.5.)

(a) What is the weight in newtons on the surface of the moon of an object that has a mass of 10 kg?

(b) Using the approach described in Example 12.5, determine the force exerted on the object by the gravity of the moon if the object is located 1738 km above the moon's surface.

12.28 If an object is near the surface of the earth, the variation of its weight with distance from the center of the earth can often be neglected. The acceleration due to gravity at sea level is $g = 9.81$ m/s². The radius of the earth is 6370 km. The weight of an object at sea level is mg, where m is its mass. At what height above the surface of the earth does the weight of the object decrease to $0.99mg$?

12.29 The planet Neptune has an equatorial diameter of 49,532 km and its mass is 1.0247×10^{26} kg. If the planet is modeled as a homogeneous sphere, what is the acceleration due to gravity at its surface? (The universal gravitational constant is $G = 6.67 \times 10^{-11}$ N-m²/kg².)

Problem 12.29

12.30 At a point between the earth and the moon, the magnitude of the force exerted on an object by the earth's gravity equals the magnitude of the force exerted on the object by the moon's gravity. What is the distance from the center of the earth to that point to three significant digits? The distance from the center of the earth to the center of the moon is 383,000 km, and the radius of the earth is 6370 km. The radius of the moon is 1738 km, and the acceleration due to gravity at its surface is 1.62 m/s².

CHAPTER
13

Motion of a Point

In this chapter we begin the study of motion. We are not yet concerned with the properties of objects or the causes of their motions—our objective is simply to describe and analyze the motion of a point in space. After defining the position, velocity, and acceleration of a point, we consider the simplest case, motion along a straight line. We then show how motion of a point along an arbitrary path, or *trajectory*, is expressed and analyzed using various coordinate systems.

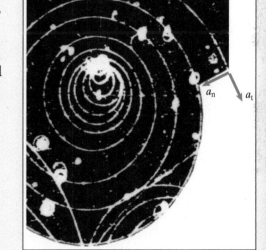

◀ The lines show the paths followed by subatomic particles moving in a magnetic field. The particles with curved paths have both tangential and normal components of acceleration.

13.1 Position, Velocity, and Acceleration

BACKGROUND

If you observe people in a room, such as a group at a party, you perceive their positions relative to the room. For example, some people may be in the back of the room, some in the middle of the room, and so forth. The room is your "frame of reference." To make this idea precise, we can introduce a cartesian coordinate system with its axes aligned with the walls of the room as in Fig. 13.1a and specify the position of a person (actually, the position of some point of the person, such as his or her center of mass) by specifying the components of the position vector **r** relative to the origin of the coordinate system. This coordinate system is a convenient reference frame for objects in the room. If you are sitting in an airplane, you perceive the positions of objects within the airplane relative to the airplane. In this case, the interior of the airplane is your frame of reference. To precisely specify the position of a person within the airplane, we can introduce a cartesian coordinate system that is fixed relative to the airplane and measure the position of the person's center of mass by specifying the components of the position vector **r** relative to the origin (Fig. 13.1b). A *reference frame* is simply a coordinate system that is suitable for specifying positions of points. You may be familiar only with cartesian coordinates. We discuss other examples in this chapter and continue our discussion of reference frames throughout the book.

We can describe the position of a point P relative to a given reference frame with origin O by the *position vector* **r** from O to P (Fig. 13.2a). Suppose that P is in motion relative to the chosen reference frame, so that **r** is a function of time t (Fig. 13.2b). We express this by the notation

$$\mathbf{r} = \mathbf{r}(t).$$

The *velocity* of P relative to the given reference frame at time t is defined by

$$\mathbf{v} = \frac{d\mathbf{r}}{dt} = \lim_{\Delta t \to 0} \frac{\mathbf{r}(t + \Delta t) - \mathbf{r}(t)}{\Delta t}, \tag{13.1}$$

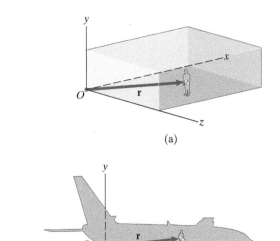

(a)

(b)

Figure 13.1
Convenient reference frames for specifying positions of objects
(**a**) in a room;
(**b**) in an airplane.

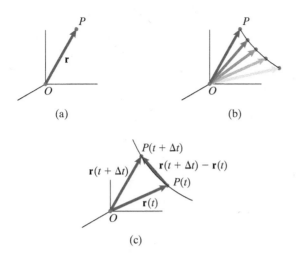

(a)   (b)

(c)

Figure 13.2
(a) The position vector **r** of *P* relative to *O*.
(b) Motion of *P* relative to the reference frame.
(c) Change in position of *P* from *t* to *t* + Δ*t*.

where the vector $\mathbf{r}(t + \Delta t) - \mathbf{r}(t)$ is the change in position, or *displacement*, of *P* during the interval of time Δ*t* (Fig. 13.2c). Thus, the velocity is the rate of change of the position of *P*.

The dimensions of a derivative are determined just as if it is a ratio, so the dimensions of **v** are (distance)/(time). The reference frame being used is often obvious, and we simply call **v** the velocity of *P*. However, remember that the position and velocity of a point can be specified only relative to some reference frame.

Notice in Eq. (13.1) that the derivative of a vector with respect to time is defined in exactly the same way as is the derivative of a scalar function. As a result, the derivative of a vector shares some of the properties of the derivative of a scalar function. We will use two of these properties: the derivative with re-spect to time, or time derivative, of the sum of two vector functions **u** and **w** is

$$\frac{d}{dt}(\mathbf{u} + \mathbf{w}) = \frac{d\mathbf{u}}{dt} + \frac{d\mathbf{w}}{dt},$$

and the time derivative of the product of a scalar function *f* and a vector function **u** is

$$\frac{d(f\mathbf{u})}{dt} = \frac{df}{dt}\mathbf{u} + f\frac{d\mathbf{u}}{dt}.$$

The *acceleration* of *P* relative to the given reference frame at time *t* is defined by

$$\mathbf{a} = \frac{d\mathbf{v}}{dt} = \lim_{\Delta t \to 0} \frac{\mathbf{v}(t + \Delta t) - \mathbf{v}(t)}{\Delta t}, \qquad (13.2)$$

where $\mathbf{v}(t + \Delta t) - \mathbf{v}(t)$ is the change in the velocity of *P* during the inter-val of time Δ*t* (Fig. 13.3). The acceleration is the rate of change of the veloc-ity of *P* at time *t* (the second time derivative of the displacement), and its dimensions are (distance)/(time)^2.

We have defined the velocity and acceleration of *P* relative to the origin *O* of the reference frame. We can show that *a point has the same velocity and ac-celeration relative to any fixed point in a given reference frame.* Let *O'* be an arbitrary fixed point, and let **r'** be the position vector from *O'* to *P* (Fig. 13.4a). The velocity of *P* relative to *O'* is $\mathbf{v'} = d\mathbf{r'}/dt$. The velocity of *P* relative to the

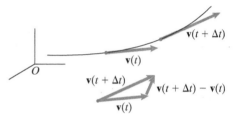

Figure 13.3
Change in the velocity of *P* from *t* to *t* + Δ*t*.

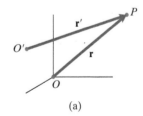

(a)

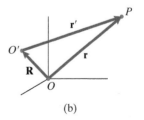

(b)

Figure 13.4
(a) Position vectors of *P* relative to *O* and *O'*.
(b) Position vector of *O'* relative to *O*.

origin O is $\mathbf{v} = d\mathbf{r}/dt$. We wish to show that $\mathbf{v}' = \mathbf{v}$. Let $\mathbf{R}$ be the vector from O to O' (Fig. 13.4b), so that

$$\mathbf{r}' = \mathbf{r} - \mathbf{R}.$$

Since the vector $\mathbf{R}$ is constant, the velocity of P relative to O' is

$$\mathbf{v}' = \frac{d\mathbf{r}'}{dt} = \frac{d\mathbf{r}}{dt} - \frac{d\mathbf{R}}{dt} = \frac{d\mathbf{r}}{dt} = \mathbf{v}.$$

The acceleration of P relative to O' is $\mathbf{a}' = d\mathbf{v}'/dt$, and the acceleration of P relative to O is $\mathbf{a} = d\mathbf{v}/dt$. Since $\mathbf{v}' = \mathbf{v}$, $\mathbf{a}' = \mathbf{a}$. Thus, the velocity and acceleration of a point P relative to a given reference frame do not depend on the location of the fixed reference point used to specify the position of P.

RESULTS

Position
The position of a point P relative to a given coordinate system, or *reference frame*, with origin O can be described by the *position vector* $\mathbf{r}$ from O to P.

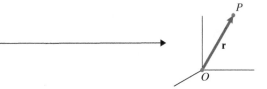

Velocity
The *velocity* of P relative to O at a time t is the derivative of the position $\mathbf{r}$ with respect to t (the rate of change of $\mathbf{r}$).

$$\mathbf{v} = \frac{d\mathbf{r}}{dt}. \qquad (13.1)$$

Acceleration
The *acceleration* of P relative to O at a time t is the derivative of the velocity $\mathbf{v}$ with respect to t (the rate of change of $\mathbf{v}$).

$$\mathbf{a} = \frac{d\mathbf{v}}{dt}. \qquad (13.2)$$

A point has the same velocity and acceleration relative to any fixed point in a given reference frame.

13.2 Straight-Line Motion

BACKGROUND

We discuss this simple type of motion primarily so that you can gain experience and insight before proceeding to the general case of the motion of a point. But engineers must analyze straight-line motions in many practical situations, such as the motion of a vehicle on a straight road or the motion of a piston in an internal combustion engine.

Description of the Motion

Consider a straight line through the origin O of a given reference frame. We assume that the direction of the line relative to the reference frame is fixed.

(For example, the x axis of a cartesian coordinate system passes through the origin and has fixed direction relative to the reference frame.) We can specify the position of a point P on such a line relative to O by a coordinate s measured along the line from O to P. In Fig. 13.5a we define s to be positive to the right, so s is positive when P is to the right of O and negative when P is to the left of O. The *displacement* of P during an interval of time from t_0 to t is the change in the position $s(t) - s(t_0)$, where $s(t)$ denotes the position at time t.

By introducing a unit vector $\mathbf{e}$ that is parallel to the line and points in the positive s direction (Fig. 13.5b), we can write the position vector of P relative to O as

$$\mathbf{r} = s\mathbf{e}.$$

Because the magnitude and direction of $\mathbf{e}$ are constant, $d\mathbf{e}/dt = \mathbf{0}$, and so the velocity of P relative to O is

$$\mathbf{v} = \frac{d\mathbf{r}}{dt} = \frac{ds}{dt}\mathbf{e}.$$

We can write the velocity vector as $\mathbf{v} = v\mathbf{e}$, obtaining the scalar equation

$$v = \frac{ds}{dt}.$$

The velocity v of point P along the straight line is the rate of change of the position s. Notice that v is equal to the slope at time t of the line tangent to the graph of s as a function of time (Fig. 13.6).

The acceleration of P relative to O is

$$\mathbf{a} = \frac{d\mathbf{v}}{dt} = \frac{d}{dt}(v\mathbf{e}) = \frac{dv}{dt}\mathbf{e}.$$

Writing the acceleration vector as $\mathbf{a} = a\mathbf{e}$, we obtain the scalar equation

$$a = \frac{dv}{dt} = \frac{d^2s}{dt^2}.$$

The acceleration a is equal to the slope at time t of the line tangent to the graph of v as a function of time (Fig. 13.7).

By introducing the unit vector $\mathbf{e}$, we have obtained scalar equations describing the motion of P. The position is specified by the coordinate s, and the velocity and acceleration are governed by the equations

$$v = \frac{ds}{dt} \tag{13.3}$$

and

$$a = \frac{dv}{dt}. \tag{13.4}$$

Applying the *chain rule* of differential calculus, we can write the derivative of the velocity with respect to time as

$$\frac{dv}{dt} = \frac{dv}{ds}\frac{ds}{dt},$$

obtaining an alternative expression for the acceleration that is often useful:

$$a = \frac{dv}{ds}v. \tag{13.5}$$

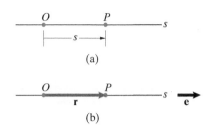

Figure 13.5
(a) The coordinate s from O to P.
(b) The unit vector $\mathbf{e}$ and position vector $\mathbf{r}$.

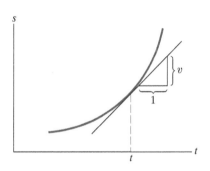

Figure 13.6
The slope of the straight line tangent to the graph of s versus t is the velocity at time t.

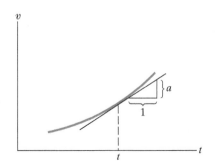

Figure 13.7
The slope of the straight line tangent to the graph of v versus t is the acceleration at time t.

Figure 13.8
The coordinate s measures the position of the center of mass of the truck relative to a reference point.

Analysis of the Motion

In some situations, the position s of a point of an object is known as a function of time. Engineers use methods such as radar and laser-Doppler interferometry to measure positions as functions of time. In this case, we can obtain the velocity and acceleration as functions of time from Eqs. (13.3) and (13.4) by differentiation. For example, if the position of the truck in Fig. 13.8 during the interval of time from $t = 2$ s to $t = 4$ s is given by the equation

$$s = 6 + \frac{1}{3}t^3 \text{ m},$$

then the velocity and acceleration of the truck during that interval of time are

$$v = \frac{ds}{dt} = t^2 \text{ m/s}$$

and

$$a = \frac{dv}{dt} = 2t \text{ m/s}^2.$$

However, it is more common to know an object's acceleration than to know its position, because the acceleration of an object can be determined by Newton's second law when the forces acting on it are known. When the acceleration is known, we can determine the velocity and position from Eqs. (13.3)–(13.5) by integration.

Acceleration Specified as a Function of Time   If the acceleration is a known function of time, we can integrate the relation

$$\frac{dv}{dt} = a \tag{13.6}$$

with respect to time to determine the velocity as a function of time. We obtain

$$v = \int a \, dt + A,$$

where A is an integration constant. Then we can integrate the relation

$$\frac{ds}{dt} = v \tag{13.7}$$

to determine the position as a function of time,

$$s = \int v \, dt + B,$$

where B is another integration constant. We would need additional information about the motion, such as the values of v and s at a given time, to determine the constants A and B.

Instead of using indefinite integrals, we can write Eq. (13.6) as

$$dv = a \, dt$$

and integrate in terms of definite integrals:

$$\int_{v_0}^{v} dv = \int_{t_0}^{t} a\,dt. \tag{13.8}$$

The lower limit v_0 is the velocity at time t_0, and the upper limit v is the velocity at an arbitrary time t. Evaluating the integral on the left side of Eq. (13.8), we obtain an expression for the velocity as a function of time:

$$v = v_0 + \int_{t_0}^{t} a\,dt. \tag{13.9}$$

We can then write Eq. (13.7) as

$$ds = v\,dt$$

and integrate in terms of definite integrals to obtain

$$\int_{s_0}^{s} ds = \int_{t_0}^{t} v\,dt,$$

where the lower limit s_0 is the position at time t_0 and the upper limit s is the position at an arbitrary time t. Evaluating the integral on the left side, we obtain the position as a function of time:

$$s = s_0 + \int_{t_0}^{t} v\,dt. \tag{13.10}$$

Although we have shown how to determine the velocity and position when the acceleration is known as a function of time, don't try to remember results such as Eqs. (13.9) and (13.10). As we will demonstrate in the examples, we recommend that straight-line motion problems be solved by using Eqs. (13.3)–(13.5).

We can make some useful observations from Eqs. (13.9) and (13.10):

- The area defined by the graph of the acceleration of P as a function of time from t_0 to t is equal to the change in the velocity from t_0 to t (Fig. 13.9a).
- The area defined by the graph of the velocity of P as a function of time from t_0 to t is equal to the change in position from t_0 to t (Fig. 13.9b).

These relationships can often be used to obtain a qualitative understanding of an object's motion, and in some cases can even be used to determine the object's motion quantitatively.

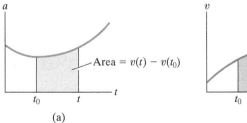
(a)

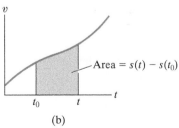
(b)

Figure 13.9
Relations between areas defined by the graphs of the acceleration and velocity of P and changes in its velocity and position.

Constant Acceleration   In some situations, the acceleration of an object is constant or nearly constant. For example, if a dense object such as a golf ball or a rock is dropped and doesn't fall too far, the object's acceleration is approximately equal to the acceleration due to gravity at sea level.

Let the acceleration be a known constant a_0. From Eqs. (13.9) and (13.10), the velocity and position as functions of time are

$$v = v_0 + a_0(t - t_0) \tag{13.11}$$

and

$$s = s_0 + v_0(t - t_0) + \frac{1}{2}a_0(t - t_0)^2, \tag{13.12}$$

where s_0 and v_0 are the position and velocity, respectively, at time t_0. Notice that *if the acceleration is constant, the velocity is a linear function of time.*

From Eq. (13.5), we can write the acceleration as

$$a_0 = \frac{dv}{ds}v.$$

Writing this expression as $v\,dv = a_0\,ds$ and integrating,

$$\int_{v_0}^{v} v\,dv = \int_{s_0}^{s} a_0\,ds,$$

we obtain an equation for the velocity as a function of position:

$$v^2 = v_0^2 + 2a_0(s - s_0). \tag{13.13}$$

Although Eqs. (13.11)–(13.13) can be useful *when the acceleration is constant,* they must not be used otherwise.

RESULTS

Position
The position of a point P on a straight line relative to a reference point O can be described by the coordinate s measured along the line from O to P. The *displacement* of P during an interval of time from t_0 to t is the change in position $s(t) - s(t_0)$, where $s(t)$ denotes the position at time t.

Velocity
The *velocity* of P relative to O at a time t is the derivative of the position s with respect to t (the rate of change of s).

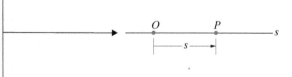

$$v = \frac{ds}{dt}. \tag{13.3}$$

Acceleration
The *acceleration* of P relative to O at a time t is the derivative of the velocity v with respect to t (the rate of change of v).

$$a = \frac{dv}{dt}. \qquad (13.4)$$

Applying the chain rule

$$a = \frac{dv}{dt} = \frac{dv}{ds}\frac{ds}{dt}$$

results in an alternative expression for the acceleration that is often useful.

$$a = \frac{dv}{ds}v. \qquad (13.5)$$

When the Acceleration is Known as a Function of Time

The acceleration can be integrated with respect to time to determine the velocity as a function of time. A is an integration constant.

$$\begin{cases} \dfrac{dv}{dt} = a, \\[2mm] v = \displaystyle\int a\,dt + A. \end{cases}$$

Alternatively, definite integrals can be used to determine the velocity. Here v_0 is the velocity at time t_0, and v is the velocity at time t. This result shows that the change in the velocity from time t_0 to time t is equal to the area defined by the graph of the acceleration from time t_0 to time t.

$$\begin{cases} \displaystyle\int_{v_0}^{v} dv = \int_{t_0}^{t} a\,dt, \\[3mm] v = v_0 + \displaystyle\int_{t_0}^{t} a\,dt. \end{cases}$$

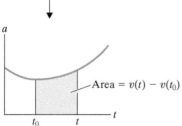

When the Velocity is Known as a Function of Time

The velocity can be integrated with respect to time to determine the position as a function of time. B is an integration constant.

$$\begin{cases} \dfrac{ds}{dt} = v, \\[2mm] s = \displaystyle\int v\,dt + B. \end{cases}$$

Definite integrals can be used to determine the position. Here s_0 is the velocity at time t_0, and s is the velocity at time t. This result shows that the change in the position from time t_0 to time t is equal to the area defined by the graph of the velocity from time t_0 to time t.

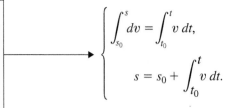

$$\begin{cases} \displaystyle\int_{s_0}^{s} dv = \int_{t_0}^{t} v\, dt, \\[2mm] \displaystyle s = s_0 + \int_{t_0}^{t} v\, dt. \end{cases}$$

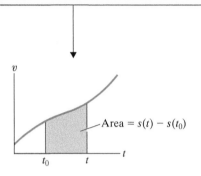

When the Acceleration is Constant

Suppose that *the acceleration is a constant* $a = a_0$. Equations (13.3)–(13.5) can be integrated to obtain these convenient results for the velocity v and position s at time t. Here v_0 is the velocity at time t_0, and s_0 is the position at time t_0.

$$\begin{cases} v = v_0 + a_0(t - t_0), & (13.11) \\[2mm] s = s_0 + v_0(t - t_0) + \dfrac{1}{2}a_0(t - t_0)^2, & (13.12) \\[2mm] v^2 = v_0^2 + 2a_0(s - s_0). & (13.13) \end{cases}$$

Active Example 13.1   **Acceleration that is a Function of Time (▶ *Related Problem 13.12*)**

The acceleration (in m/s^2) of point P relative to point O is given as a function of time by $a = 3t^2$, where t is in seconds. At $t = 1$ s, the position of P is $s = 3$ m, and at $t = 2$ s, the position of P is $s = 7.5$ m. What is the position of P at $t = 3$ s?

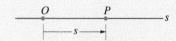

Strategy
Because the acceleration is given as a function of time, we can integrate it to obtain an equation for the velocity as a function of time. Then we can integrate the velocity to obtain an equation for the position as a function of time. The resulting equations will contain two unknown integration constants. We can evaluate them by using the given values of the position at $t = 1$ s and $t = 2$ s.

Solution

Integrate the acceleration to determine the velocity as a function of time. *A* is an integration constant.	→	$\begin{cases} a = \dfrac{dv}{dt} = 3t^2, \\[2mm] v = t^3 + A. \end{cases}$

Integrate the velocity to determine the position as a function of time. *B* is an integration constant.	→	$\begin{cases} v = \dfrac{ds}{dt} = t^3 + A, \\[2mm] s = \dfrac{1}{4}t^4 + At + B. \end{cases}$

Use the known positions at $t = 1$ s and at $t = 2$ s to determine *A* and *B*, obtaining $A = 0.75$ and $B = 2$.	→	$\begin{cases} s\big|_{t=1\,\text{s}} = 3 = \dfrac{1}{4}(1)^4 + A(1) + B, \\[2mm] s\big|_{t=2\,\text{s}} = 7.5 = \dfrac{1}{4}(2)^4 + A(2) + B. \end{cases}$

Determine the position at $t = 3$ s.	→	$\begin{cases} s = \dfrac{1}{4}t^4 + 0.75t + 2 : \\[2mm] s\big|_{t=3\,\text{s}} = \dfrac{1}{4}(3)^4 + 0.75(3) + 2 = 24.5 \text{ m}. \end{cases}$

Practice Problem The acceleration (in ft/s^2) of point P relative to point O is given as a function of time by $a = 2t$, where t is in seconds. At $t = 3$ s, the position and velocity of P are $s = 30$ ft and $v = 14$ ft/s. What are the position and velocity of P at $t = 10$ s?

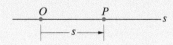

Answer: $s = 389$ ft, $v = 105$ ft/s.

Example 13.2	Straight-Line Motion with Constant Acceleration (▶ *Related Problem 13.1*)

Engineers testing a vehicle that will be dropped by parachute estimate that the vertical velocity of the vehicle when it reaches the ground will be 6 m/s. If they drop the vehicle from the test rig shown, from what height h should they drop it to match the impact velocity of the parachute drop?

Strategy

If the only significant force acting on an object near the earth's surface is its weight, the acceleration of the object is approximately constant and equal to the acceleration due to gravity at sea level. Therefore, we can assume that the vehicle's acceleration during its short fall is $g = 9.81$ m/s^2. We can integrate Eqs. (13.3) and (13.4) to obtain the vehicle's velocity and position as functions of time and then use them to determine the position of the vehicle when its velocity is 6 m/s.

Solution

Let $t = 0$ be the time at which the vehicle is dropped, and let s be the position of the bottom of the cushioning material beneath the vehicle relative to its position at $t = 0$ (Fig. a). The vehicle's acceleration is $a = 9.81$ m/s^2.

From Eq. (13.4),

$$\frac{dv}{dt} = a = 9.81 \text{ m/s}^2.$$

Integrating, we obtain

$$v = 9.81t + A,$$

where A is an integration constant. Because the vehicle is at rest when it is released, $v = 0$ at $t = 0$. Therefore, $A = 0$, and the vehicle's velocity as a function of time is

$$v = 9.81t \text{ m/s}.$$

(a) The coordinate s measures the position of the bottom of the platform relative to its initial position.

We substitute this result into Eq. (13.3) to get

$$\frac{ds}{dt} = v = 9.81t$$

and integrate, obtaining

$$s = 4.91t^2 + B.$$

The position $s = 0$ when $t = 0$, so the integration constant $B = 0$, and the position as a function of time is

$$s = 4.91t^2.$$

From our equation for the velocity as a function of time, the time necessary for the vehicle to reach 6 m/s as it falls is

$$t = \frac{v}{9.81 \text{ m/s}^2} = \frac{6 \text{ m/s}}{9.81 \text{ m/s}^2} = 0.612 \text{ s}.$$

Substituting this time into our equation for the position as a function of time yields the required height h:

$$h = 4.91t^2 = 4.91(0.612)^2 = 1.83 \text{ m}.$$

Critical Thinking

Notice that we could have determined the height h from which the vehicle should be dropped in a simpler way by using Eq. (13.13), which relates the velocity to the position.

$$v^2 = v_0^2 + 2a_0(s - s_0):$$

$$(6 \text{ m/s})^2 = 0 + 2(9.81 \text{ m/s}^2)(h - 0).$$

Solving, we obtain $h = 1.83$ m. But it is essential to remember that Eqs. (13.11)–(13.13) apply *only when the acceleration is constant*, as it is in this example.

Example 13.3 Graphical Solution of Straight-Line Motion (▶ *Related Problem 13.26*)

The cheetah, *Acinonyx jubatus*, can run as fast as 75 mi/h. If you assume that the animal's acceleration is constant and that it reaches top speed in 4 s, what distance can the cheetah cover in 10 s?

Strategy

The acceleration has a constant value for the first 4 s and is then zero. We can determine the distance traveled during each of these "phases" of the motion and sum them to obtain the total distance covered. We do so both analytically and graphically.

Solution

The top speed in terms of feet per second is

$$75 \text{ mi/h} = (75 \text{ mi/h})\left(\frac{5280 \text{ ft}}{1 \text{ mi}}\right)\left(\frac{1 \text{ h}}{3600 \text{ s}}\right) = 110 \text{ ft/s}.$$

First Method Let a_0 be the acceleration during the first 4 s. We integrate Eq. (13.4) to get

$$\int_0^v dv = \int_0^t a_0 \, dt,$$

$$\left[v \right]_0^v = a_0 \left[t \right]_0^t,$$

$$v - 0 = a_0(t - 0),$$

obtaining the velocity as a function of time during the first 4 s:

$$v = a_0 t \text{ ft/s}.$$

When $t = 4$ s, $v = 110$ ft/s; so $a_0 = 110/4 = 27.5$ ft/s^2. Therefore, the velocity during the first 4 s is $v = 27.5t$ ft/s. Now we integrate Eq. (13.3),

$$\int_0^s ds = \int_0^t 27.5t \, dt,$$

$$\left[s \right]_0^s = 27.5\left[\frac{t^2}{2}\right]_0^t,$$

$$s - 0 = 27.5\left(\frac{t^2}{2} - 0\right),$$

obtaining the position as a function of time during the first 4 s:

$$s = 13.75t^2 \text{ ft}.$$

At $t = 4$ s, the position is $s = 13.75(4)^2 = 220$ ft.

From $t = 4$ s to $t = 10$ s, the velocity $v = 110$ ft/s. We write Eq. (13.3) as

$$ds = v \, dt = 110 \, dt$$

and integrate to determine the distance traveled during the second phase of the motion,

$$\int_0^s ds = \int_4^{10} 110 \, dt,$$

$$\left[s \right]_0^s = 110 \left[t \right]_4^{10},$$

$$s - 0 = 110(10 - 4),$$

obtaining $s = 660$ ft. The total distance the cheetah travels is 220 ft $+$ 660 ft $= 880$ ft, or 293 yd, in 10 s.

Second Method We draw a graph of the cheetah's velocity as a function of time in Fig. a. The acceleration is constant during the first 4 s of motion, so the velocity is a linear function of time from $v = 0$ at $t = 0$ to $v = 110$ ft/s at $t = 4$ s. The velocity is constant during the last 6 s. The total distance covered is the sum of the areas during the two phases of motion:

$$\tfrac{1}{2}(4 \text{ s})(110 \text{ ft/s}) + (6 \text{ s})(110 \text{ ft/s}) = 220 \text{ ft} + 660 \text{ ft} = 880 \text{ ft}.$$

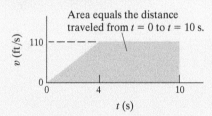

(a) The cheetah's velocity as a function of time.

Critical Thinking

Notice that in the first method we used definite, rather than indefinite, integrals to determine the cheetah's velocity and position as functions of time. You should rework the example using indefinite integrals and compare your results with ours. Whether to use definite or indefinite integrals is primarily a matter of taste, but you need to be familiar with both procedures.

Problems

The problems that follow involve straight-line motion. The time *t* is in seconds unless otherwise stated.

▶ **13.1** In Example 13.2, suppose that the vehicle is dropped from a height $h = 6$ m. (a) What is its downward velocity 1 s after it is released? (b) What is its downward velocity just before it reaches the ground?

13.2 The milling machine is programmed so that during the interval of time from $t = 0$ to $t = 2$ s, the position of its head (in inches) is given as a function of time by $s = 4t - 2t^2$. What are the velocity (in in/s) and acceleration (in in/s^2) of the head at $t = 1$ s?

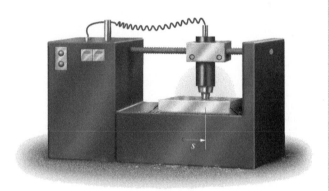

Problem 13.2

13.3 In an experiment to estimate the acceleration due to gravity, a student drops a ball at a distance of 1 m above the floor. His lab partner measures the time it takes to fall and obtains an estimate of 0.46 s.

(a) What do they estimate the acceleration due to gravity to be?

(b) Let *s* be the ball's position relative to the floor. Using the value of the acceleration due to gravity that they obtained, and assuming that the ball is released at $t = 0$, determine *s* (in m) as a function of time.

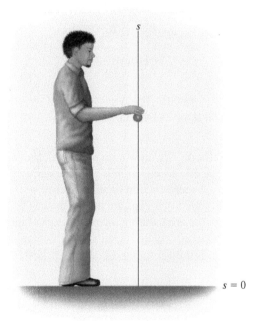

Problem 13.3

13.4 The boat's position during the interval of time from $t = 2$ s to $t = 10$ s is given by $s = 4t + 1.6t^2 - 0.08t^3$ m.

(a) Determine the boat's velocity and acceleration at $t = 4$ s.

(b) What is the boat's maximum velocity during this interval of time, and when does it occur?

Problem 13.4

13.5 The rocket starts from rest at $t = 0$ and travels straight up. Its height above the ground as a function of time can be approximated by $s = bt^2 + ct^3$, where b and c are constants. At $t = 10$ s, the rocket's velocity and acceleration are $v = 229$ m/s and $a = 28.2$ m/s². Determine the time at which the rocket reaches supersonic speed (325 m/s). What is its altitude when that occurs?

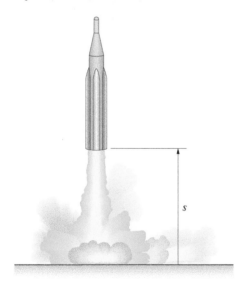

Problem 13.5

13.6 The position of a point during the interval of time from $t = 0$ to $t = 6$ s is given by $s = -\frac{1}{2}t^3 + 6t^2 + 4t$ m.

(a) What is the maximum velocity during this interval of time, and at what time does it occur?

(b) What is the acceleration when the velocity is a maximum?

13.7 The position of a point during the interval of time from $t = 0$ to $t = 3$ s is $s = 12 + 5t^2 - t^3$ ft.

(a) What is the maximum velocity during this interval of time, and at what time does it occur?

(b) What is the acceleration when the velocity is a maximum?

13.8 The rotating crank causes the position of point P as a function of time to be $s = 0.4 \sin(2\pi t)$ m.

(a) Determine the velocity and acceleration of P at $t = 0.375$ s.

(b) What is the maximum magnitude of the velocity of P?

(c) When the magnitude of the velocity of P is a maximum, what is the acceleration of P?

13.9 For the mechanism in Problem 13.8, draw graphs of the position s, velocity v, and acceleration a of point P as functions of time for $0 \le t \le 2$ s. Using your graphs, confirm that the slope of the graph of s is zero at times for which v is zero and that the slope of the graph of v is zero at times for which a is zero.

Problems 13.8/13.9

13.10 A seismograph measures the horizontal motion of the ground during an earthquake. An engineer analyzing the data determines that for a 10-s interval of time beginning at $t = 0$ the position is approximated by $s = 100 \cos(2\pi t)$ mm. What are (a) the maximum velocity and (b) the maximum acceleration of the ground during the 10-s interval?

13.11 In an assembly operation, the robot's arm moves along a straight horizontal line. During an interval of time from $t = 0$ to $t = 1$ s, the position of the arm is given by $s = 30t^2 - 20t^3$ mm.

(a) Determine the maximum velocity during this interval of time.

(b) What are the position and acceleration when the velocity is a maximum?

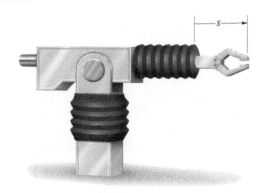

Problem 13.11

▶ **13.12** In Active Example 13.1, the acceleration (in m/s^2) of point P relative to point O is given as a function of time by $a = 3t^2$. Suppose that at $t = 0$ the position and velocity of P are $s = 5$ m and $v = 2$ m/s. Determine the position and velocity of P at $t = 4$ s.

13.13 The Porsche starts from rest at time $t = 0$. During the first 10 seconds of its motion, its velocity in km/h is given as a function of time by $v = 22.8t - 0.88t^2$, where t is in seconds. (a) What is the car's maximum acceleration in m/s^2, and when does it occur? (b) What distance in km does the car travel during the 10 seconds?

Problem 13.13

13.14 The acceleration of a point is $a = 20t$ m/s^2. When $t = 0$, $s = 40$ m and $v = -10$ m/s. What are the position and velocity at $t = 3$ s?

13.15 The acceleration of a point is $a = 60t - 36t^2$ ft/s^2. When $t = 0$, $s = 0$ and $v = 20$ ft/s. What are the position and velocity as functions of time?

13.16 As a first approximation, a bioengineer studying the mechanics of bird flight assumes that the snow petrel takes off with constant acceleration. Video measurements indicate that a bird requires a distance of 4.3 m to take off and is moving at 6.1 m/s when it does. What is its acceleration?

13.17 Progressively developing a more realistic model, the bioengineer next models the acceleration of the snow petrel by an equation of the form $a = C(1 + \sin \omega t)$, where C and ω are constants. From video measurements of a bird taking off, he estimates that $\omega = 18$ and determines that the bird requires 1.42 s to take off and is moving at 6.1 m/s when it does. What is the constant C?

Problems 13.16/13.17

13.18 Missiles designed for defense against ballistic missiles have attained accelerations in excess of 100 g's, or 100 times the acceleration due to gravity. Suppose that the missile shown lifts off from the ground and has a constant acceleration of 100 g's. How long does it take to reach an altitude of 3000 m? How fast is it going when it reaches that altitude?

13.19 Suppose that the missile shown lifts off from the ground and, because it becomes lighter as its fuel is expended, its acceleration (in g's) is given as a function of time in seconds by

$$a = \frac{100}{1 - 0.2t}.$$

What is the missile's velocity in miles per hour 1 s after liftoff?

Problems 13.18/13.19

13.20 The airplane releases its drag parachute at time $t = 0$. Its velocity is given as a function of time by

$$v = \frac{80}{1 + 0.32t} \text{ m/s.}$$

What is the airplane's acceleration at $t = 3$ s?

13.21 How far does the airplane in Problem 13.20 travel during the interval of time from $t = 0$ to $t = 10$ s?

Problems 13.20/13.21

13.22 The velocity of a bobsled is $v = 10t$ ft/s. When $t = 2$ s, the position of the sled is $s = 25$ ft. What is its position when $t = 10$ s?

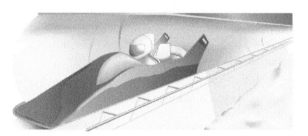

Problem 13.22

13.23 In September 2003, Tony Schumacher started from rest and drove a quarter mile (1320 ft) in 4.498 s in a National Hot Rod Association race. His speed as he crossed the finish line was 328.54 mi/h. Assume that the car's acceleration can be expressed by a linear function of time $a = b + ct$.

(a) Determine the constants b and c.

(b) What was the car's speed 2 s after the start of the race?

13.24 The velocity of an object is $v = 200 - 2t^2$ m/s. When $t = 3$ s, the position of the object is $s = 600$ m. What are the position and acceleration of the object at $t = 6$ s?

13.25 An inertial navigation system measures the acceleration of a vehicle from $t = 0$ to $t = 6$ s and determines it to be $a = 2 + 0.1t$ m/s^2. At $t = 0$, the vehicle's position and velocity are $s = 240$ m and $v = 42$ m/s, respectively. What are the vehicle's position and velocity at $t = 6$ s?

▶ **13.26** In Example 13.3, suppose that the cheetah's acceleration is constant and it reaches its top speed of 75 mi/h in 5 s. What distance can it cover in 10 s?

13.27 The graph shows the airplane's acceleration during take-off. What is the airplane's velocity when it rotates (lifts off) at $t = 30$ s?

13.28 The graph shows the airplane's acceleration during take-off. What distance has the airplane traveled when it lifts off at $t = 30$ s?

Problems 13.27/13.28

13.29 The car is traveling at 30 mi/h when the traffic light 295 ft ahead turns yellow. The driver takes 1 s to react before he applies the brakes.

(a) After he applies the brakes, what constant rate of deceleration will cause the car to come to a stop just as it reaches the light?

(b) How long does it take the car to travel the 295 ft to the light?

13.30 The car is traveling at 30 mi/h when the traffic light 295 ft ahead turns yellow. The driver takes 1 s to react before he applies the accelerator. If the car has a constant acceleration of 5 ft/s² and the light remains yellow for 5 s, will the car reach the light before it turns red? How fast is the car moving when it reaches the light?

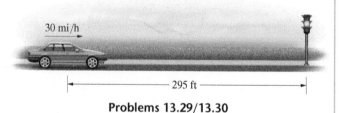

Problems 13.29/13.30

13.31 A high-speed rail transportation system has a top speed of 100 m/s. For the comfort of the passengers, the magnitude of the acceleration and deceleration is limited to 2 m/s². Determine the minimum time required for a trip of 100 km.

Strategy: A graphical approach can help you solve this problem. Recall that the change in the position from an initial time t_0 to a time t is equal to the area defined by the graph of the velocity as a function of time from t_0 to t.

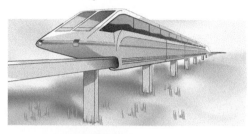

Problem 13.31

13.32 The nearest star, Proxima Centauri, is 4.22 light years from the Earth. Ignoring relative motion between the solar system and Proxima Centauri, suppose that a spacecraft accelerates from the vicinity of the Earth at $0.01g$ (0.01 times the acceleration due to gravity at sea level) until it reaches one-tenth the speed of light, coasts until it is time to decelerate, and then decelerates at $0.01g$ until it comes to rest in the vicinity of Proxima Centauri. How long does the trip take? (Light travels at 3×10^8 m/s.)

13.33 A race car starts from rest and accelerates at $a = 5 + 2t$ ft/s² for 10 s. The brakes are then applied, and the car has a constant acceleration $a = -30$ ft/s² until it comes to rest. Determine (a) the maximum velocity, (b) the total distance traveled, and (c) the total time of travel.

13.34 When $t = 0$, the position of a point is $s = 6$ m, and its velocity is $v = 2$ m/s. From $t = 0$ to $t = 6$ s, the acceleration of the point is $a = 2 + 2t^2$ m/s². From $t = 6$ s until it comes to rest, its acceleration is $a = -4$ m/s².

(a) What is the total time of travel?

(b) What total distance does the point move?

13.35 Zoologists studying the ecology of the Serengeti Plain estimate that the average adult cheetah can run 100 km/h and the average springbok can run 65 km/h. If the animals run along the same straight line, start at the same time, are each assumed to have constant acceleration, and reach top speed in 4 s, how close must a cheetah be when the chase begins to catch a springbok in 15 s?

13.36 Suppose that a person unwisely drives 75 mi/h in a 55 mi/h zone and passes a police car going 55 mi/h in the same direction. If the police officers begin constant acceleration at the instant they are passed and increase their velocity to 80 mi/h in 4 s, how long does it take them to be even with the pursued car?

13.37 If $\theta = 1$ rad and $d\theta/dt = 1$ rad/s, what is the velocity of P relative to O?

   Strategy: You can write the position of P relative to O as

$$s = (2 \text{ ft}) \cos \theta + (2 \text{ ft}) \cos \theta$$

and then take the derivative of this expression with respect to time to determine the velocity.

13.38 If $\theta = 1$ rad, $d\theta/dt = -2$ rad/s, and $d^2\theta/dt^2 = 0$, what are the velocity and acceleration of P relative to O?

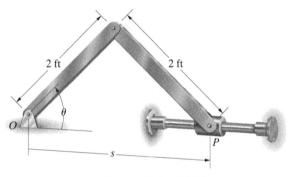

Problems 13.37/13.38

13.39* If $\theta = 1$ rad and $d\theta/dt = 1$ rad/s, what is the velocity of P relative to O?

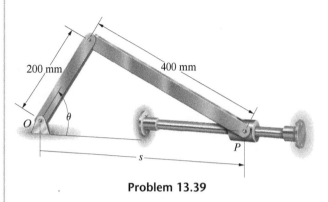

Problem 13.39

13.3 Straight-Line Motion When the Acceleration Depends on Velocity or Position

BACKGROUND

Acceleration Specified as a Function of Velocity Aerodynamic and hydrodynamic forces can cause an object's acceleration to depend on its velocity (Fig. 13.10). Suppose that the acceleration is a known function of velocity—that is,

$$\frac{dv}{dt} = a(v). \tag{13.14}$$

We cannot integrate this equation with respect to time to determine the velocity, because $a(v)$ is not known as a function of time. But we can *separate variables*, putting terms involving v on one side of the equation and terms involving t on the other side:

$$\frac{dv}{a(v)} = dt. \tag{13.15}$$

We can now integrate, obtaining

$$\int_{v_0}^{v} \frac{dv}{a(v)} = \int_{t_0}^{t} dt, \tag{13.16}$$

Figure 13.10
Aerodynamic and hydrodynamic forces depend on an object's velocity. As the bullet slows, the aerodynamic drag force resisting its motion decreases.

where v_0 is the velocity at time t_0. In principle, we can solve this equation for the velocity as a function of time and then integrate the relation

$$\frac{ds}{dt} = v$$

to determine the position as a function of time.

By using the chain rule, we can also determine the velocity as a function of the position. Writing the acceleration as

$$\frac{dv}{dt} = \frac{dv}{ds}\frac{ds}{dt} = \frac{dv}{ds}v$$

and substituting it into Eq. (13.14), we obtain

$$\frac{dv}{ds}v = a(v).$$

Separating variables yields

$$\frac{v\,dv}{a(v)} = ds.$$

Integrating,

$$\int_{v_0}^{v} \frac{v\,dv}{a(v)} = \int_{s_0}^{s} ds,$$

we can obtain a relation between the velocity and the position.

Acceleration Specified as a Function of Position   Gravitational forces and forces exerted by springs can cause an object's acceleration to depend on its position. If the acceleration is a known function of position—that is,

$$\frac{dv}{dt} = a(s), \tag{13.17}$$

we cannot integrate with respect to time to determine the velocity, because $a(s)$ is not known as a function of time. Moreover, we cannot separate variables, because the equation contains three variables: v, t, and s. However, by using the chain rule

$$\frac{dv}{dt} = \frac{dv}{ds}\frac{ds}{dt} = \frac{dv}{ds}v,$$

we can write Eq. (13.17) as

$$\frac{dv}{ds}v = a(s).$$

Now we can separate variables,

$$v\,dv = a(s)\,ds, \tag{13.18}$$

and we integrate:

$$\int_{v_0}^{v} v\, dv = \int_{s_0}^{s} a(s)\, ds. \qquad (13.19)$$

In principle, we can solve this equation for the velocity as a function of the position:

$$v = \frac{ds}{dt} = v(s). \qquad (13.20)$$

Then we can separate variables in this equation and integrate to determine the position as a function of time:

$$\int_{s_0}^{s} \frac{ds}{v(s)} = \int_{t_0}^{t} dt.$$

RESULTS

When the acceleration is known as a function of velocity, $a = a(v)$.

$\Rightarrow$

Separate variables,

$$\frac{dv}{dt} = a(v):$$

$$\frac{dv}{a(v)} = dt,$$

and integrate to determine the velocity as a function of time.

Or, first apply the chain rule,

$$\frac{dv}{dt} = \frac{dv}{ds}\frac{ds}{dt} = \frac{dv}{ds}v = a(v),$$

then separate variables,

$$\frac{v\, dv}{a(v)} = ds,$$

and integrate to determine the velocity as a function of position.

When the acceleration is known as a function of position, $a = a(s)$.

$\Rightarrow$

Apply the chain rule,

$$\frac{dv}{dt} = \frac{dv}{ds}\frac{ds}{dt} = \frac{dv}{ds}v = a(s),$$

then separate variables,

$$v\, dv = a(s)\, ds,$$

and integrate to determine the velocity as a function of position.

Active Example 13.4 | **Acceleration that is a Function of Velocity** (▶ *Related Problem 13.40*)

After deploying its drag parachute, the airplane's acceleration (in m/s²) is $a = -0.004v^2$, where v is the velocity in m/s. Determine the time required for the plane's velocity to decrease from 80 m/s to 10 m/s.

Strategy

The airplane's acceleration is known as a function of its velocity. Writing the acceleration as $a = dv/dt$, we can separate variables and integrate to determine the velocity as a function of time.

Solution

Separate variables.

$$\begin{cases} \dfrac{dv}{dt} = -0.004v^2 : \\[2mm] \dfrac{dv}{v^2} = -0.004 \, dt. \end{cases}$$

Integrate, defining $t = 0$ to be the time at which the velocity is 80 m/s. Here v is the velocity at time t.

$$\begin{cases} \displaystyle\int_{80}^{v} \dfrac{dv}{v^2} = -0.004 \int_0^t dt, \\[3mm] \left[-\dfrac{1}{v} \right]_{80}^{v} = -0.004 \Big[t \Big]_0^t, \\[3mm] -\dfrac{1}{v} + \dfrac{1}{80} = -0.004t. \end{cases}$$

Solve for t in terms of the velocity. From this equation, we find that the time required for the velocity to decrease to 10 m/s is 21.9 s. The graph shows the airplane's velocity as a function of time.

$$t = 250 \left(\dfrac{1}{v} - \dfrac{1}{80} \right).$$

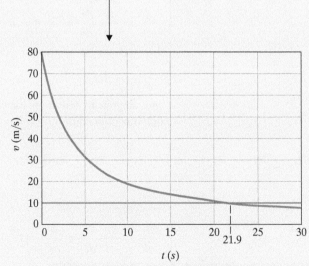

Practice Problem What distance does the airplane travel as its velocity decreases from 80 m/s to 10 m/s?

Answer: 520 m.

Example 13.5	**Gravitational (Position-Dependent) Acceleration** (▶ *Related Problem 13.62*)

In terms of the distance s from the center of the earth, the magnitude of the acceleration due to gravity is gR_E^2/s^2, where R_E is the radius of the earth. (See the discussion of gravity in Section 12.2.) If a spacecraft is a distance s_0 from the center of the earth, what outward velocity v_0 must it be given to reach a specified distance h from the earth's center?

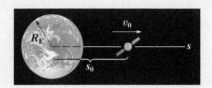

Strategy

The acceleration is known as a function of the position s. We can apply the chain rule and separate variables, then integrate to determine the velocity as a function of s.

Solution

The acceleration due to gravity is *toward* the center of the earth:

$$a = -\frac{gR_E^2}{s^2}.$$

Applying the chain rule results in

$$a = \frac{dv}{dt} = \frac{dv}{ds}\frac{ds}{dt} = \frac{dv}{ds}v = -\frac{gR_E^2}{s^2}.$$

Separating variables, we obtain

$$v\,dv = -\frac{gR_E^2}{s^2}\,ds.$$

We integrate this equation using the initial condition ($v = v_0$ when $s = s_0$) as the lower limits and the final condition ($v = 0$ when $s = h$) as the upper limits:

$$\int_{v_0}^{0} v\,dv = -\int_{s_0}^{h}\frac{gR_E^2}{s^2}\,ds,$$

$$\left[\frac{v^2}{2}\right]_{v_0}^{0} = gR_E^2\left[\frac{1}{s}\right]_{s_0}^{h},$$

$$0 - \frac{v_0^2}{2} = gR_E^2\left(\frac{1}{h} - \frac{1}{s_0}\right).$$

Solving for v_0, we obtain the initial velocity necessary for the spacecraft to reach a distance h:

$$v_0 = \sqrt{2gR_E^2\left(\frac{1}{s_0} - \frac{1}{h}\right)}.$$

Critical Thinking

We can make an interesting and important observation from the result of this example. Notice that as the distance h increases, the necessary initial velocity v_0 approaches a finite limit. This limit,

$$v_{esc} = \lim_{h\to\infty} v_0 = \sqrt{\frac{2gR_E^2}{s_0}},$$

is called the *escape velocity*. In the absence of other effects, an object with this initial velocity will continue moving outward indefinitely. The existence of an escape velocity makes it feasible to send spacecraft to other planets. Once escape velocity is attained, it isn't necessary to expend additional fuel to keep going.

Problems

▶ 13.40 In Active Example 13.4, determine the time required for the plane's velocity to decrease from 50 m/s to 10 m/s.

13.41 An engineer designing a system to control a router for a machining process models the system so that the router's acceleration (in in/s^2) during an interval of time is given by $a = -0.4v$, where v is the velocity of the router in in/s. When $t = 0$, the position is $s = 0$ and the velocity is $v = 2$ in/s. What is the position at $t = 3$ s?

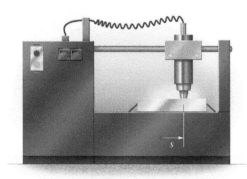

Problem 13.41

13.42 The boat is moving at 10 m/s when its engine is shut down. Due to hydrodynamic drag, its subsequent acceleration is $a = -0.05v^2$ m/s^2, where v is the velocity of the boat in m/s. What is the boat's velocity 4 s after the engine is shut down?

13.43 In Problem 13.42, what distance does the boat move in the 4 s following the shutdown of its engine?

Problems 13.42/13.43

13.44 A steel ball is released from rest in a container of oil. Its downward acceleration is $a = 2.4 - 0.6v$ in/s^2, where v is the ball's velocity in in/s. What is the ball's downward velocity 2 s after it is released?

13.45 In Problem 13.44, what distance does the ball fall in the first 2 s after its release?

Problems 13.44/13.45

13.46 The greatest ocean depth yet discovered is the Marianas Trench in the western Pacific Ocean. A steel ball released at the surface requires 64 min to reach the bottom. The ball's downward acceleration is $a = 0.9g - cv$, where $g = 9.81$ m/s^2 and the constant $c = 3.02$ s^{-1}. What is the depth of the Marianas Trench in kilometers?

13.47 The acceleration of a regional airliner during its takeoff run is $a = 14 - 0.0003v^2$ ft/s^2, where v is its velocity in ft/s. How long does it take the airliner to reach its takeoff speed of 200 ft/s?

13.48 In Problem 13.47, what distance does the airliner require to take off?

13.49 A sky diver jumps from a helicopter and is falling straight down at 30 m/s when her parachute opens. From then on, her downward acceleration is approximately $a = g - cv^2$, where $g = 9.81$ m/s^2 and c is a constant. After an initial "transient" period, she descends at a nearly constant velocity of 5 m/s.

(a) What is the value of c, and what are its SI units?

(b) What maximum deceleration is the sky diver subjected to?

(c) What is her downward velocity when she has fallen 2 m from the point at which her parachute opens?

Problem 13.49

13.50 The rocket sled starts from rest and accelerates at $a = 30 + 2t$ m/s^2 until its velocity is 400 m/s. It then hits a water brake and its acceleration is $a = -0.003v^2$ m/s^2 until its velocity decreases to 100 m/s. What total distance does the sled travel?

13.51 In Problem 13.50, what is the sled's total time of travel?

Problems 13.50/13.51

13.52 A car's acceleration is related to its position by $a = 0.01s$ m/s^2. When $s = 100$ m, the car is moving at 12 m/s. How fast is the car moving when $s = 420$ m?

13.53 Engineers analyzing the motion of a linkage determine that the velocity of an attachment point is given by $v = A + 4s^2$ ft/s, where A is a constant. When $s = 2$ ft, the acceleration of the point is measured and determined to be $a = 320$ ft/s^2. What is the velocity of the point when $s = 2$ ft?

13.54 The acceleration of an object is given as a function of its position in feet by $a = 2s^2$ ft/s^2. When $s = 0$, its velocity is $v = 1$ ft/s. What is the velocity of the object when $s = 2$ ft?

13.55 Gas guns are used to investigate the properties of materials subjected to high-velocity impacts. A projectile is accelerated through the barrel of the gun by gas at high pressure. Assume that the acceleration of the projectile in m/s^2 is given by $a = c/s$, where s is the position of the projectile in the barrel in meters and c is a constant that depends on the initial gas pressure behind the projectile. The projectile starts from rest at $s = 1.5$ m and accelerates until it reaches the end of the barrel at $s = 3$ m. Determine the value of the constant c necessary for the projectile to leave the barrel with a velocity of 200 m/s.

13.56 If the propelling gas in the gas gun described in Problem 13.55 is air, a more accurate modeling of the acceleration of the projectile is obtained by assuming that the acceleration of the projectile is given by $a = c/s^\gamma$, where $\gamma = 1.4$ is the ratio of specific heat for air. (This means that an isentropic expansion process is assumed instead of the isothermal process assumed in Problem 13.55.) Determine the value of the constant c necessary for the projectile to leave the barrel with a velocity of 200 m/s.

Problems 13.55/13.56

13.57 A spring–mass oscillator consists of a mass and a spring connected as shown. The coordinate s measures the displacement of the mass relative to its position when the spring is unstretched. If the spring is linear, the mass is subjected to a deceleration proportional to s. Suppose that $a = -4s$ m/s^2 and that you give the mass a velocity $v = 1$ m/s in the position $s = 0$.

(a) How far will the mass move to the right before the spring brings it to a stop?

(b) What will be the velocity of the mass when it has returned to the position $s = 0$?

13.58 In Problem 13.57, suppose that at $t = 0$ you release the mass from rest in the position $s = 1$ m. Determine the velocity of the mass as a function of s as it moves from the initial position to $s = 0$.

13.59 A spring–mass oscillator consists of a mass and a spring connected as shown. The coordinate s measures the displacement of the mass relative to its position when the spring is unstretched. Suppose that the nonlinear spring subjects the mass to an acceleration $a = -4s - 2s^3$ m/s^2 and that you give the mass a velocity $v = 1$ m/s in the position $s = 0$.

(a) How far will the mass move to the right before the spring brings it to a stop?

(b) What will be the velocity of the mass when it has returned to the position $s = 0$?

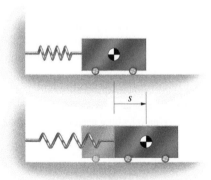

Problems 13.57–13.59

13.60 The mass is released from rest with the springs unstretched. Its downward acceleration is $a = 32.2 - 50s$ ft/s^2, where s is the position of the mass measured from the position in which it is released.

(a) How far does the mass fall?

(b) What is the maximum velocity of the mass as it falls?

13.61 Suppose that the mass in Problem 13.60 is in the position $s = 0$ and is given a downward velocity of 10 ft/s.

(a) How far does the mass fall?

(b) What is the maximum velocity of the mass as it falls?

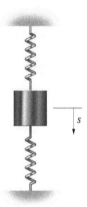

Problems 13.60/13.61

▶ **13.62** If a spacecraft is 100 mi above the surface of the earth, what initial velocity v_0 straight away from the earth would be required for the vehicle to reach the moon's orbit, 238,000 mi from the center of the earth? The radius of the earth is 3960 mi. Neglect the effect of the moon's gravity. (See Example 13.5.)

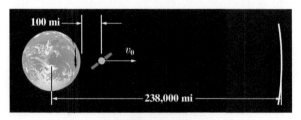

Problem 13.62

13.63 The moon's radius is 1738 km. The magnitude of the acceleration due to gravity of the moon at a distance s from the center of the moon is

$$\frac{4.89 \times 10^{12}}{s^2} \text{ m/s}^2.$$

Suppose that a spacecraft is launched straight up from the moon's surface with a velocity of 2000 m/s.

(a) What will the magnitude of its velocity be when it is 1000 km above the surface of the moon?

(b) What maximum height above the moon's surface will it reach?

13.64* The velocity of an object subjected only to the earth's gravitational field is

$$v = \left[v_0^2 + 2gR_E^2 \left(\frac{1}{s} - \frac{1}{s_0} \right) \right]^{1/2},$$

where s is the object's position relative to the center of the earth, v_0 is the object's velocity at position s_0, and R_E is the earth's radius. Using this equation, show that the object's acceleration is given as a function of s by $a = -gR_E^2/s^2$.

13.65 Suppose that a tunnel could be drilled straight through the earth from the North Pole to the South Pole and the air was evacuated. An object dropped from the surface would fall with acceleration $a = -gs/R_E$, where g is the acceleration of gravity at sea level, R_E is the radius of the earth, and s is the distance of the object from the center of the earth. (The acceleration due to gravity is equal to zero at the center of the earth and increases linearly with distance from the center.) What is the magnitude of the velocity of the dropped object when it reaches the center of the earth?

13.66* Determine the time in seconds required for the object in Problem 13.65 to fall from the surface of the earth to the center. The earth's radius is 6370 km.

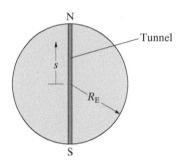

Problems 13.65/13.66

13.4 Curvilinear Motion—Cartesian Coordinates

BACKGROUND

The motion of a point along a straight line can be described by the scalars s, v, and a. But if a point describes a *curvilinear* path relative to some reference frame, we must specify its motion in terms of its position, velocity, and acceleration vectors. In many cases, the motion of the point can be analyzed conveniently by expressing the vectors in terms of cartesian coordinates.

Let $\mathbf{r}$ be the position vector of a point P relative to the origin O of a cartesian reference frame (Fig. 13.11). The components of $\mathbf{r}$ are the x, y, and z coordinates of P:

$$\mathbf{r} = x\mathbf{i} + y\mathbf{j} + z\mathbf{k}.$$

The unit vectors $\mathbf{i}$, $\mathbf{j}$, and $\mathbf{k}$ each have constant magnitude and constant direction relative to the reference frame, so the velocity of P relative to the reference frame is

$$\mathbf{v} = \frac{d\mathbf{r}}{dt} = \frac{dx}{dt}\mathbf{i} + \frac{dy}{dt}\mathbf{j} + \frac{dz}{dt}\mathbf{k}. \tag{13.21}$$

Expressing the velocity in terms of scalar components yields

$$\mathbf{v} = v_x\mathbf{i} + v_y\mathbf{j} + v_z\mathbf{k}, \tag{13.22}$$

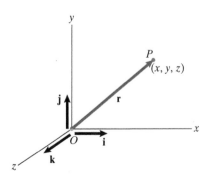

Figure 13.11
A cartesian coordinate system with origin O.

from which we obtain scalar equations relating the components of the velocity to the coordinates of P:

$$v_x = \frac{dx}{dt}, \quad v_y = \frac{dy}{dt}, \quad v_z = \frac{dz}{dt}. \tag{13.23}$$

The acceleration of P is

$$\mathbf{a} = \frac{d\mathbf{v}}{dt} = \frac{dv_x}{dt}\mathbf{i} + \frac{dv_y}{dt}\mathbf{j} + \frac{dv_z}{dt}\mathbf{k}.$$

By expressing the acceleration in terms of scalar components as

$$\mathbf{a} = a_x\mathbf{i} + a_y\mathbf{j} + a_z\mathbf{k}, \tag{13.24}$$

we obtain the scalar equations

$$a_x = \frac{dv_x}{dt}, \quad a_y = \frac{dv_y}{dt}, \quad a_z = \frac{dv_z}{dt}. \tag{13.25}$$

Equations (13.23) and (13.25) describe the motion of a point relative to a cartesian coordinate system. Notice that the equations describing the motion in each coordinate direction are identical in form to the equations that describe the motion of a point along a straight line. As a consequence, the motion in each coordinate direction can often be analyzed using the methods we applied to straight-line motion.

The *projectile problem* is the classic example of this kind. If an object is thrown through the air and aerodynamic drag is negligible, the object accelerates downward with the acceleration due to gravity. In terms of a fixed cartesian coordinate system with its y axis upward, the acceleration is given by $a_x = 0$, $a_y = -g$, and $a_z = 0$. Suppose that at $t = 0$ the projectile is located at the origin and has velocity v_0 in the x–y plane at an angle θ_0 above the horizontal (Fig. 13.12). At $t = 0$, $x = 0$ and $v_x = v_0 \cos \theta_0$. The acceleration in the x direction is zero—that is,

$$a_x = \frac{dv_x}{dt} = 0.$$

Therefore v_x is constant and remains equal to its initial value:

$$v_x = \frac{dx}{dt} = v_0 \cos \theta_0. \tag{13.26}$$

(This result may seem unrealistic. The reason is that your intuition, based upon everyday experience, accounts for drag, whereas the analysis presented here does not.) Integrating Eq. (13.26) yields

$$\int_0^x dx = \int_0^t v_0 \cos \theta_0 \, dt,$$

whereupon we obtain the x coordinate of the object as a function of time:

$$x = (v_0 \cos \theta_0)t. \tag{13.27}$$

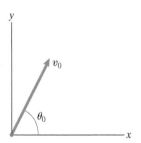

Figure 13.12
Initial conditions for a projectile problem.

Thus we have determined the position and velocity of the projectile in the x direction as functions of time without considering the projectile's motion in the y or z direction.

At $t = 0$, $y = 0$ and $v_y = v_0 \sin \theta_0$. The acceleration in the y direction is

$$a_y = \frac{dv_y}{dt} = -g.$$

Integrating, we obtain

$$\int_{v_0 \sin \theta_0}^{v_y} dv_y = \int_0^t -g \, dt,$$

from which it follows that

$$v_y = \frac{dy}{dt} = v_0 \sin \theta_0 - gt. \tag{13.28}$$

Integrating this equation yields

$$\int_0^y dy = \int_0^t (v_0 \sin \theta_0 - gt) \, dt,$$

and we find that the y coordinate as a function of time is

$$y = (v_0 \sin \theta_0)t - \tfrac{1}{2}gt^2. \tag{13.29}$$

Notice from this analysis that the same vertical velocity and position are obtained by throwing the projectile straight up with initial velocity $v_0 \sin \theta_0$ (Figs. 13.13a, b). The vertical motion is completely independent of the horizontal motion.

By solving Eq. (13.27) for t and substituting the result into Eq. (13.29), we obtain an equation describing the parabolic trajectory of the projectile:

$$y = (\tan \theta_0)x - \frac{g}{2v_0^2 \cos^2 \theta_0}x^2. \tag{13.30}$$

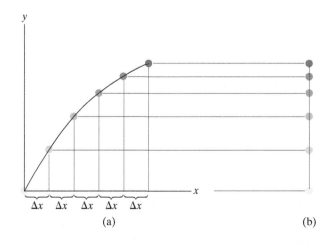

(a)   (b)

Figure 13.13
(a) Positions of the projectile at equal time intervals Δt. The distance $\Delta x = v_0(\cos \theta_0) \, \Delta t$.
(b) Positions at equal time intervals Δt of a projectile given an initial vertical velocity equal to $v_0 \sin \theta_0$.

RESULTS

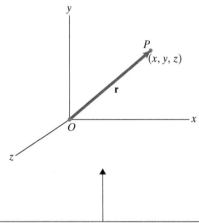

The components of the position vector of a point P relative to the origin O of a cartesian coordinate system are the x, y, z coordinates of P.	$\mathbf{r} = x\mathbf{i} + y\mathbf{j} + z\mathbf{k}.$

Cartesian components of the velocity of P relative to the reference frame.	$v_x = \dfrac{dx}{dt}, \ \ v_y = \dfrac{dy}{dt}, \ \ v_z = \dfrac{dz}{dt}.$	(13.23)

Cartesian components of the acceleration of P relative to the reference frame.	$a_x = \dfrac{dv_x}{dt}, \ \ a_y = \dfrac{dv_y}{dt}, \ \ a_z = \dfrac{dv_z}{dt}.$	(13.25)

The equations describing the motion in each coordinate direction are identical in form to the equations that describe the motion of a point along a straight line. As a consequence, the motion in each coordinate direction can often be analyzed using the methods for straight-line motion.

Active Example 13.6	**Analysis of Motion in Terms of Cartesian Components**

(▶ *Related Problem 13.67*)

During a test flight in which a helicopter starts from rest at $t = 0$ at the origin of the coordinate system shown and moves in the x–y plane, onboard accelerometers indicate that its components of acceleration (in m/s^2) during the interval of time from $t = 0$ to $t = 10$ s are

$$a_x = 0.6t,$$

$$a_y = 1.8 - 0.36t,$$

What is the magnitude of the helicopter's velocity at $t = 6$ s?

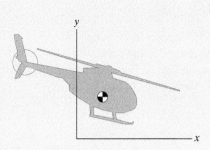

Strategy

We can analyze the motion in each coordinate direction independently, integrating each component of the acceleration to determine each component of the velocity as a function of time.

Solution

Integrate the x component of the acceleration to determine the x component of the velocity as a function of time.

$$\begin{cases} a_x = \dfrac{dv_x}{dt} = 0.6t, \\[2mm] \displaystyle\int_0^{v_x} dv_x = 0.6\int_0^t t\, dt, \\[2mm] v_x = 0.3t^2. \end{cases}$$

Evaluate the x component of the velocity at $t = 6$ s.

$$v_x\big|_{t=6\,s} = 0.3(6)^2 = 10.8 \text{ m/s.}$$

Integrate the y component of the acceleration to determine the y component of the velocity as a function of time.

$$\begin{cases} a_y = \dfrac{dv_y}{dt} = 1.8 - 0.36t, \\[2mm] \displaystyle\int_0^{v_y} dv_y = \int_0^t (1.8 - 0.36t)\, dt, \\[2mm] v_y = 1.8t - 0.18t^2. \end{cases}$$

Evaluate the y component of the velocity at $t = 6$ s.

$$v_y\big|_{t=6\,s} = 1.8(6) - 0.18(6)^2 = 4.32 \text{ m/s.}$$

Calculate the magnitude of the velocity at $t = 6$ s.

$$\begin{cases} |\mathbf{v}|_{t=6\,s} = \sqrt{v_x^2 + v_y^2} \\[2mm] = \sqrt{(10.8 \text{ m/s})^2 + (4.32 \text{ m/s})^2} \\[2mm] = 11.6 \text{ m/s} \end{cases}$$

Practice Problem Determine the position vector of the helicopter at $t = 6$ s relative to its position at $t = 0$.

Answer: $\mathbf{r}|_{t=6\,s} = 21.6\mathbf{i} + 19.4\mathbf{j}$ (m).

Example 13.7	**A Projectile Problem** (▶ *Related Problem 13.69*)

The skier leaves the 20° surface at 10 m/s.
(a) Determine the distance d to the point where he lands.
(b) What are the magnitudes of his components of velocity parallel and perpendicular to the 45° surface just before he lands?

Strategy

(a) By neglecting aerodynamic drag and treating the skier as a projectile, we can determine his velocity and position as functions of time. Using the equation describing the straight surface on which he lands, we can relate his horizontal and vertical coordinates at impact and thereby obtain an equation for the time at which he lands. Knowing the time, we can determine his position and velocity. (b) We can determine his velocity parallel and perpendicular to the 45° surface by using the result that the component of a vector $\mathbf{U}$ in the direction of a unit vector $\mathbf{e}$ is $(\mathbf{e} \cdot \mathbf{U})\mathbf{e}$.

Solution

(a) In Fig. a, we introduce a coordinate system with its origin where the skier leaves the surface. His components of velocity at that instant $(t = 0)$ are

$$v_x = 10 \cos 20° = 9.40 \text{ m/s}$$

and

$$v_y = -10 \sin 20° = -3.42 \text{ m/s}.$$

The x component of acceleration is zero, so v_x is constant and the skier's x coordinate as a function of time is

$$x = 9.40t \text{ m}.$$

The y component of acceleration is

$$a_y = \frac{dv_y}{dt} = -9.81 \text{ m/s}^2.$$

Integrating to determine v_y as a function of time, we obtain

$$\int_{-3.42}^{v_y} dv_y = \int_0^t -9.81 \, dt,$$

from which it follows that

$$v_y = \frac{dy}{dt} = -3.42 - 9.81t \text{ m/s}.$$

We integrate this equation to determine the y coordinate as a function of time. We have

$$\int_0^y dy = \int_0^t (-3.42 - 9.81t) \, dt,$$

yielding

$$y = -3.42t - 4.905t^2 \text{ m}.$$

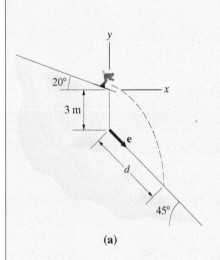

(a)

The slope of the surface on which the skier lands is -1, so the linear equation describing it is $y = (-1)x + A$, where A is a constant. At $x = 0$, the y coordinate of the surface is -3 m, so $A = -3$ m and the equation describing the $45°$ surface is

$$y = -x - 3 \text{ m}.$$

Substituting our equations for x and y as functions of time into this equation, we obtain an equation for the time at which the skier lands:

$$-3.42t - 4.905t^2 = -9.40t - 3.$$

Solving for t, we get $t = 1.60$ s. Therefore, his coordinates when he lands are

$$x = 9.40(1.60) = 15.0 \text{ m}$$

and

$$y = -3.42(1.60) - 4.905(1.60)^2 = -18.0 \text{ m},$$

and the distance d is

$$d = \sqrt{(15.0)^2 + (18.0 - 3)^2} = 21.3 \text{ m}.$$

(b) The components of the skier's velocity just before he lands are

$$v_x = 9.40 \text{ m/s}$$

and

$$v_y = -3.42 - 9.81(1.60) = -19.1 \text{ m/s},$$

and the magnitude of his velocity is $|\mathbf{v}| = \sqrt{(9.40)^2 + (-19.1)^2} = 21.3$ m/s. Let $\mathbf{e}$ be a unit vector that is parallel to the slope on which he lands (Fig. a):

$$\mathbf{e} = \cos 45°\mathbf{i} - \sin 45°\mathbf{j}.$$

The component of the velocity parallel to the surface is

$$(\mathbf{e} \cdot \mathbf{v})\mathbf{e} = [(\cos 45°\mathbf{i} - \sin 45°\mathbf{j}) \cdot (9.40\mathbf{i} - 19.1\mathbf{j})]\mathbf{e}$$

$$= 20.2\mathbf{e} \text{ (m/s)}.$$

The magnitude of the skier's velocity parallel to the surface is 20.2 m/s. Therefore, the magnitude of his velocity perpendicular to the surface is

$$\sqrt{|\mathbf{v}|^2 - (20.2)^2} = 6.88 \text{ m/s}.$$

Critical Thinking

The key to solving this problem was that we knew the skier's acceleration. Knowing the acceleration, we were able to determine the components of his velocity and position as functions of time. Notice how we determined the position at which he landed on the slope. We knew that at the instant he landed, his x and y coordinates specified a point on the straight line defining the surface of the slope. By substituting his x and y coordinates as functions of time into the equation for the straight line defining the slope, we were able to solve for the time at which he landed. Knowing the time, we could determine his velocity and position at that instant.

Problems

▶ **13.67** In a second test, the coordinates of the position (in m) of the helicopter in Active Example 13.6 are given as functions of time by

$$x = 4 + 2t,$$
$$y = 4 + 4t + t^2.$$

(a) What is the magnitude of the helicopter's velocity at $t = 3$ s?

(b) What is the magnitude of the helicopter's acceleration at $t = 3$ s?

13.68 In terms of a particular reference frame, the position of the center of mass of the F-14 at the time shown ($t = 0$) is $\mathbf{r} = 10\mathbf{i} + 6\mathbf{j} + 22\mathbf{k}$ (m). The velocity from $t = 0$ to $t = 4$ s is $\mathbf{v} = (52 + 6t)\mathbf{i} + (12 + t^2)\mathbf{j} - (4 + 2t^2)\mathbf{k}$ (m/s). What is the position of the center of mass of the plane at $t = 4$ s?

Problem 13.68

▶ **13.69** In Example 13.7, suppose that the angle between the horizontal and the slope on which the skier lands is 30° instead of 45°. Determine the distance d to the point where he lands.

13.70 A projectile is launched from ground level with initial velocity $v_0 = 20$ m/s. Determine its range R if (a) $\theta_0 = 30°$, (b) $\theta_0 = 45°$, and (c) $\theta_0 = 60°$.

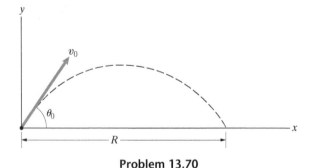

Problem 13.70

13.71 Immediately after the bouncing golf ball leaves the floor, its components of velocity are $v_x = 0.662$ m/s and $v_y = 3.66$ m/s.

(a) Determine the horizontal distance from the point where the ball left the floor to the point where it hits the floor again.

(b) The ball leaves the floor at $x = 0$, $y = 0$. Determine the ball's y coordinate as a function of x. (The parabolic function you obtain is shown superimposed on the photograph of the ball.)

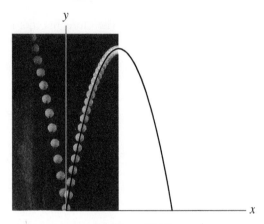

Problem 13.71

13.72 Suppose that you are designing a mortar to launch a rescue line from coast guard vessels to ships in distress. The light line is attached to a weight fired by the mortar. Neglect aerodynamic drag and the weight of the line for your preliminary analysis. If you want the line to be able to reach a ship 300 ft away when the mortar is fired at 45° above the horizontal, what muzzle velocity is required?

13.73 In Problem 13.72, what maximum height above the point from which it was fired is reached by the weight?

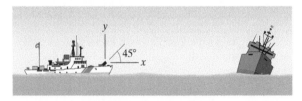

Problems 13.72/13.73

13.74 When the athlete releases the shot, it is 1.82 m above the ground and its initial velocity is $v_0 = 13.6$ m/s. Determine the horizontal distance the shot travels from the point of release to the point where it hits the ground.

Problem 13.74

13.75 A pilot wants to drop survey markers at remote locations in the Australian outback. If he flies at a constant velocity $v_0 = 40$ m/s at altitude $h = 30$ m and the marker is released with zero velocity relative to the plane, at what horizontal distance d from the desired impact point should the marker be released?

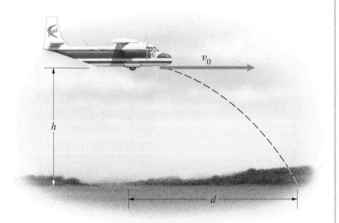

Problem 13.75

13.76 If the pitching wedge the golfer is using gives the ball an initial angle $\theta_0 = 50°$, what range of velocities v_0 will cause the ball to land within 3 ft of the hole? (Assume that the hole lies in the plane of the ball's trajectory.)

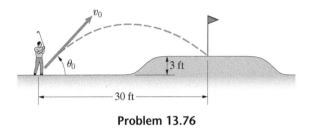

Problem 13.76

13.77 A batter strikes a baseball 3 ft above home plate and pops it up. The second baseman catches it 6 ft above second base 3.68 s after it was hit. What was the ball's initial velocity, and what was the angle between the ball's initial velocity vector and the horizontal?

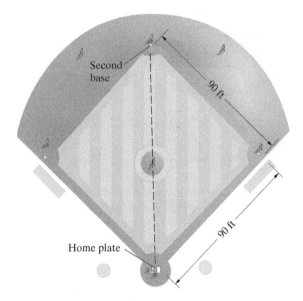

Problem 13.77

13.78 A baseball pitcher releases a fastball with an initial velocity $v_0 = 90$ mi/h. Let θ be the initial angle of the ball's velocity vector above the horizontal. When it is released, the ball is 6 ft above the ground and 58 ft from the batter's plate. The batter's strike zone extends from 1 ft 10 in above the ground to 4 ft 6 in above the ground. Neglecting aerodynamic effects, determine whether the ball will hit the strike zone (a) if $\theta = 1°$ and (b) if $\theta = 2°$.

13.79 In Problem 13.78, assume that the pitcher releases the ball at an angle $\theta = 1°$ above the horizontal, and determine the range of velocities v_0 (in ft/s) within which he must release the ball to hit the strike zone.

Problems 13.78/13.79

13.80 A zoology graduate student is provided with a bow and an arrow tipped with a syringe of sedative and is assigned to measure the temperature of a black rhinoceros (*Diceros bicornis*). The range of his bow when it is fully drawn and aimed 45° above the horizontal is 100 m. A truculent rhino suddenly charges straight toward him at 30 km/h. If he fully draws his bow and aims 20° above the horizontal, how far away should the rhino be when the student releases the arrow?

Problem 13.80

13.81 The crossbar of the goalposts in American football is $y_c = 10$ ft above the ground. To kick a field goal, the kicker must make the ball go between the two uprights supporting the crossbar, and the ball must be above the crossbar when it does so. Suppose that the kicker attempts a 40-yd field goal $(x_c = 120$ ft) and kicks the ball with initial velocity $v_0 = 70$ ft/s and angle $\theta_0 = 40°$. By what vertical distance does the ball clear the crossbar?

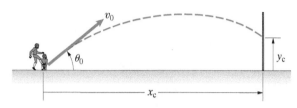

Problem 13.81

13.82* An American football quarterback stands at A. At the instant the quarterback throws the football, the receiver is at B running at 20 ft/s toward C, where he catches the ball. The ball is thrown at an angle of 45° above the horizontal, and it is thrown and caught at the same height above the ground. Determine the magnitude of the ball's initial velocity and the length of time it is in the air.

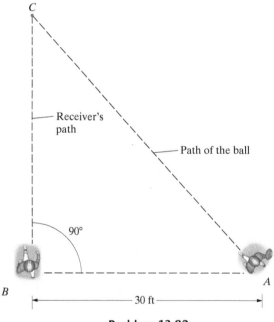

Problem 13.82

13.83 The cliff divers of Acapulco, Mexico, must time their dives so that they enter the water at the crest (high point) of a wave. The crests of the waves are 1 m above the mean water depth $h = 4$ m. The horizontal velocity of the waves is equal to $\sqrt{gh}$. The diver's aiming point is 2 m out from the base of the cliff. Assume that his velocity is horizontal when he begins the dive.

(a) What is the magnitude of the diver's velocity when he enters the water?

(b) How far from his aiming point must a wave crest be when he dives in order for him to enter the water at the crest?

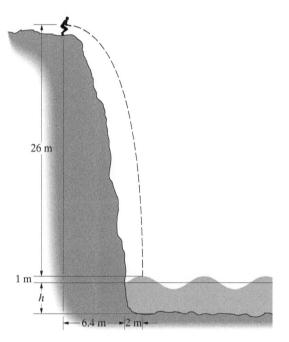

Problem 13.83

13.84 A projectile is launched at 10 m/s from a sloping surface. The angle $\alpha = 80°$. Determine the range R.

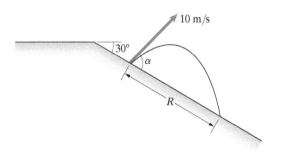

Problem 13.84

13.85 A projectile is launched at 100 ft/s at 60° above the horizontal. The surface on which it lands is described by the equation shown. Determine the x coordinate of the point of impact.

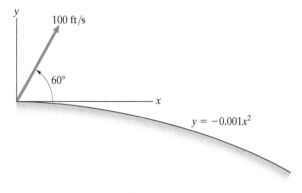

Problem 13.85

13.86 At $t = 0$, a steel ball in a tank of oil is given a horizontal velocity $\mathbf{v} = 2\mathbf{i}$ (m/s). The components of the ball's acceleration, in m/s², are $a_x = -1.2v_x$, $a_y = -8 - 1.2v_y$, and $a_z = -1.2v_z$. What is the velocity of the ball at $t = 1$ s?

13.87 In Problem 13.86, what is the position of the ball at $t = 1$ s relative to its position at $t = 0$?

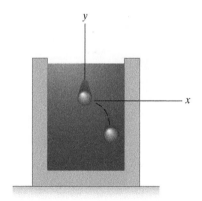

Problems 13.86/13.87

13.88 The point P moves along a circular path with radius R. Show that the magnitude of its velocity is $|\mathbf{v}| = R|d\theta/dt|$.

Strategy: Use Eqs. (13.23).

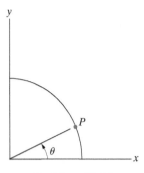

Problem 13.88

13.89 If $y = 150$ mm, $dy/dt = 300$ mm/s, and $d^2y/dt^2 = 0$, what are the magnitudes of the velocity and acceleration of point P?

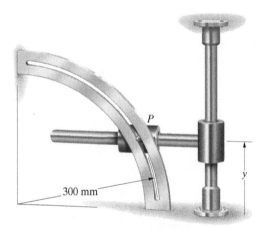

Problem 13.89

13.90* A car travels at a constant speed of 100 km/h on a straight road of increasing grade whose vertical profile can be approximated by the equation shown. When the car's horizontal coordinate is $x = 400$ m, what is the car's acceleration?

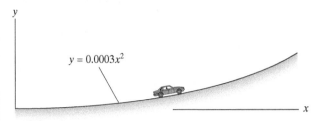

$y = 0.0003x^2$

Problem 13.90

13.91* Suppose that a projectile has the initial conditions shown in Fig. 13.12. Show that in terms of the $x'y'$ coordinate system with its origin at the highest point of the trajectory, the equation describing the trajectory is

$$y' = -\frac{g}{2v_0^2 \cos^2 \theta_0}(x')^2.$$

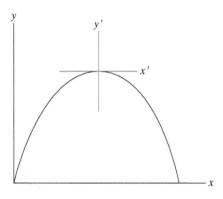

Problem 13.91

13.92* The acceleration components of a point are $a_x = -4 \cos 2t$, $a_y = -4 \sin 2t$, and $a_z = 0$. At $t = 0$, the position and velocity of the point are $\mathbf{r} = \mathbf{i}$ and $\mathbf{v} = 2\mathbf{j}$. Show that (a) the magnitude of the velocity is constant, (b) the velocity and acceleration vectors are perpendicular, (c) the magnitude of the acceleration is constant and points toward the origin, and (d) the trajectory of the point is a circle with its center at the origin.

13.5 Angular Motion

BACKGROUND

We have seen that in some cases the curvilinear motion of a point can be analyzed by using cartesian coordinates. In the sections that follow, we describe problems that can be analyzed more simply in terms of other coordinate systems. To help you understand our discussion of these alternative coordinate systems, we introduce two preliminary topics in this section: the angular motion of a line in a plane and the time derivative of a unit vector rotating in a plane.

Angular Motion of a Line

We can specify the angular position of a line L in a particular plane relative to a reference line L_0 in the plane by an angle θ (Fig. 13.14). The *angular velocity* of L relative to L_0 is defined by

$$\omega = \frac{d\theta}{dt}, \tag{13.31}$$

and the *angular acceleration* of L relative to L_0 is defined by

$$\alpha = \frac{d\omega}{dt} = \frac{d^2\theta}{dt^2}. \tag{13.32}$$

The dimensions of the angular position, angular velocity, and angular acceleration are rad, rad/s, and rad/s^2, respectively. Although these quantities are often expressed in terms of degrees or revolutions instead of radians, convert them into radians before using them in calculations.

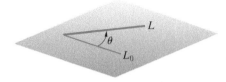

Figure 13.14
A line L and a reference line L_0 in a plane.

Rotating Unit Vector

The directions of the unit vectors **i**, **j**, and **k** relative to the cartesian reference frame are constant. However, in other coordinate systems, the unit vectors used to describe the motion of a point rotate as the point moves. To obtain expressions for the velocity and acceleration in such coordinate systems, we must know the time derivative of a rotating unit vector.

We can describe the angular motion of a unit vector **e** in a plane just as we described the angular motion of a line. The direction of **e** relative to a reference line L_0 is specified by the angle θ in Fig. 13.15a, and the rate of rotation of **e** relative to L_0 is specified by the angular velocity

$$\omega = \frac{d\theta}{dt}.$$

The time derivative of **e** is defined by

$$\frac{d\mathbf{e}}{dt} = \lim_{\Delta t \to 0} \frac{\mathbf{e}(t + \Delta t) - \mathbf{e}(t)}{\Delta t}.$$

Figure 13.15b shows the vector **e** at time t and at time $t + \Delta t$. The change in **e** during this interval is $\Delta\mathbf{e} = \mathbf{e}(t + \Delta t) - \mathbf{e}(t)$, and the angle through which **e** rotates is $\Delta\theta = \theta(t + \Delta t) - \theta(t)$. The triangle in Fig. 13.15b is isosceles, so

$$|\Delta\mathbf{e}| = 2|\mathbf{e}| \sin(\Delta\theta/2) = 2 \sin(\Delta\theta/2).$$

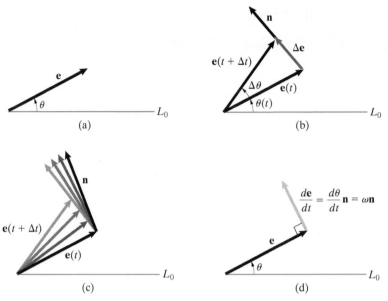

Figure 13.15
(a) A unit vector **e** and reference line L_0.
(b) The change $\Delta\mathbf{e}$ in **e** from t to $t + \Delta t$.
(c) As Δt goes to zero, **n** becomes perpendicular to **e**(t).
(d) The time derivative of **e**.

To write the vector $\Delta\mathbf{e}$ in terms of this expression, we introduce a unit vector **n** that points in the direction of $\Delta\mathbf{e}$ (Fig. 13.15b):

$$\Delta\mathbf{e} = |\Delta\mathbf{e}|\mathbf{n} = 2\sin(\Delta\theta/2)\mathbf{n}.$$

In terms of this expression, the time derivative of **e** is

$$\frac{d\mathbf{e}}{dt} = \lim_{\Delta t \to 0} \frac{\Delta\mathbf{e}}{\Delta t} = \lim_{\Delta t \to 0} \frac{2\sin(\Delta\theta/2)\mathbf{n}}{\Delta t}.$$

To evaluate the limit, we write it in the form

$$\frac{d\mathbf{e}}{dt} = \lim_{\Delta t \to 0} \frac{\sin(\Delta\theta/2)}{\Delta\theta/2} \frac{\Delta\theta}{\Delta t}\mathbf{n}.$$

In the limit as Δt approaches zero, $\sin(\Delta\theta/2)/(\Delta\theta/2) = 1$, $\Delta\theta/\Delta t = d\theta/dt$, and the unit vector **n** is perpendicular to **e**(t) (Fig. 13.15c). Therefore, the time derivative of **e** is

$$\frac{d\mathbf{e}}{dt} = \frac{d\theta}{dt}\mathbf{n} = \omega\mathbf{n}, \tag{13.33}$$

where **n** is a unit vector that is perpendicular to **e** and points in the positive θ direction (Fig. 13.15d). In the sections that follow, we use this result in deriving expressions for the velocity and acceleration of a point in different coordinate systems.

RESULTS

Angular Motion of a Line

Angular Position
The angular position of a line L in a plane relative to a reference line L_0 in the plane can be described by an angle θ.

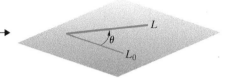

Angular Velocity
The *angular velocity* of L relative to L_0 at a time t is the derivative of the angular position θ with respect to t (the rate of change of θ).

$$\omega = \frac{d\theta}{dt}. \qquad (13.31)$$

Angular Acceleration
The *angular acceleration* of L relative to L_0 at a time t is the derivative of the angular velocity ω with respect to t (the rate of change of ω).

$$\alpha = \frac{d\omega}{dt} = \frac{d^2\theta}{dt^2}. \qquad (13.32)$$

The equations relating the angular position θ, the angular velocity ω, and the angular acceleration α are identical in form to the equations that relate the position s, the velocity v, and the acceleration a in the motion of a point along a straight line. As a consequence, problems involving angular motion can be solved using the same methods that were applied to straight-line motion.

Straight-Line Motion	Angular Motion
$v = \dfrac{ds}{dt}$	$\omega = \dfrac{d\theta}{dt}$
$a = \dfrac{dv}{dt} = \dfrac{d^2s}{dt^2}$	$\alpha = \dfrac{d\omega}{dt} = \dfrac{d^2\theta}{dt^2}$

Rotating Unit Vector

Let $\mathbf{e}$ be a unit vector that rotates in a plane relative to a reference line L_0 in the plane.

The derivative of $\mathbf{e}$ with respect to time is

$$\frac{d\mathbf{e}}{dt} = \frac{d\theta}{dt}\mathbf{n} = \omega\mathbf{n}, \qquad (13.33)$$

where $\mathbf{n}$ is a unit vector that is perpendicular to $\mathbf{e}$ and points in the positive θ direction.

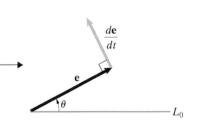

Active Example 13.8 Analysis of Angular Motion (▶ *Related Problem 13.96*)

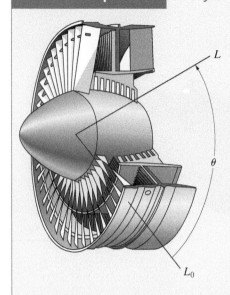

The rotor of a jet engine is rotating at 10,000 rpm (revolutions per minute) when the fuel is shut off. The ensuing angular acceleration (in rad/s²) is $\alpha = -0.02\omega$, where ω is the rotor's angular velocity in rad/s. How long does it take the rotor to slow to 1000 rpm?

Strategy

To analyze the angular motion of the rotor, we define a line L that is fixed to the rotor and perpendicular to its axis. Then we examine the angular motion of L relative to a reference line L_0. The rotor's angular acceleration is known in terms of its angular velocity. Just as in the case of straight-line motion, we can separate variables and integrate to obtain a relationship between the angular velocity and the time.

Solution

Determine the conversion from rpm to rad/s.
$$1 \text{ rpm} = (1 \text{ revolution/min})\left(\frac{2\pi \text{ rad}}{1 \text{ revolution}}\right)\left(\frac{1 \text{ min}}{60 \text{ s}}\right)$$
$$= \frac{\pi}{30} \text{rad/s}.$$

Write the angular acceleration as $\alpha = d\omega/dt$ and separate variables.
$$\alpha = \frac{d\omega}{dt} = -0.02\omega,$$
$$\frac{d\omega}{\omega} = -0.02dt.$$

Integrate, defining $t = 0$ to be the time at which the angular velocity is 10,000 rpm $= 10{,}000\pi/30$ rad/s.
$$\int_{10{,}000\pi/30}^{1000\pi/30} \frac{d\omega}{\omega} = -0.02 \int_0^t dt,$$
$$\left[\ln \omega\right]_{10{,}000\pi/30}^{1000\pi/30} = -0.02 \left[t\right]_0^t,$$
$$\ln(10) = 0.02t.$$

Solve for t.
$$t = \frac{\ln(10)}{0.02} = 115 \text{ s}.$$

Practice Problem Determine the number of revolutions the rotor turns as it decelerates from 10,000 rpm to 1000 rpm. Begin by applying the chain rule to the angular acceleration:

$$\alpha = \frac{d\omega}{dt} = \frac{d\omega}{d\theta}\frac{d\theta}{dt} = \frac{d\omega}{d\theta}\omega.$$

Answer: 7500 revolutions.

Problems

13.93 When an airplane touches down at $t = 0$, a stationary wheel is subjected to a constant angular acceleration $\alpha = 110$ rad/s^2 until $t = 1$ s.

(a) What is the wheel's angular velocity at $t = 1$ s?

(b) At $t = 0$, the angle $\theta = 0$. Determine θ in radians and in revolutions at $t = 1$ s.

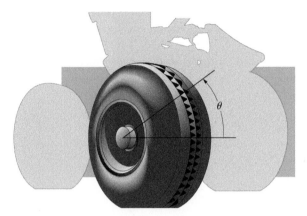

Problem 13.93

13.94 Let L be a line from the center of the earth to a fixed point on the equator, and let L_0 be a fixed reference direction. The figure views the earth from above the north pole.

(a) Is $d\theta/dt$ positive or negative? (Remember that the sun rises in the east.)

(b) Determine the approximate value of $d\theta/dt$ in rad/s and use it to calculate the angle through which the earth rotates in one hour.

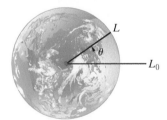

Problem 13.94

13.95 The angular acceleration of the line L relative to the line L_0 is given as a function of time by $\alpha = 2.5 - 1.2t$ rad/s^2. At $t = 0$, $\theta = 0$ and the angular velocity of L relative to L_0 is $\omega = 5$ rad/s. Determine θ and ω at $t = 3$ s.

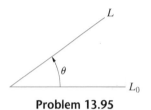

Problem 13.95

▶ **13.96** In Active Example 13.8, suppose that the angular acceleration of the rotor is $\alpha = -0.00002\omega^2$, where ω is the angular velocity of the rotor in rad/s. How long does it take the rotor to slow from 10,000 rpm to 1000 rpm?

13.97 The astronaut is not rotating. He has an orientation control system that can subject him to a constant angular acceleration of 0.1 rad/s^2 about the vertical axis in either direction. If he wants to rotate 180° about the vertical axis (that is, rotate so that he is facing toward the left) and not be rotating in his new orientation, what is the minimum time in which he could achieve the new orientation?

13.98 The astronaut is not rotating. He has an orientation control system that can subject him to a constant angular acceleration of 0.1 rad/s^2 about the vertical axis in either direction. Refer to Problem 13.97. For safety, the control system will not allow his angular velocity to exceed 15° per second. If he wants to rotate 180° about the vertical axis (that is, rotate so that he is facing toward the left) and not be rotating in his new orientation, what is the minimum time in which he could achieve the new orientation?

Problems 13.97/13.98

13.99 The rotor of an electric generator is rotating at 200 rpm when the motor is turned off. Due to frictional effects, the angular acceleration of the rotor after the motor is turned off is $\alpha = -0.01\omega$ rad/s^2, where ω is the angular velocity in rad/s.

(a) What is the rotor's angular velocity one minute after the motor is turned off?

(b) After the motor is turned off, how many revolutions does the rotor turn before it comes to rest?

Strategy: To do part (b), use the chain rule to write the angular acceleration as

$$\alpha = \frac{d\omega}{dt} = \frac{d\omega}{d\theta}\frac{d\theta}{dt} = \frac{d\omega}{d\theta}\omega.$$

13.100 The needle of a measuring instrument is connected to a *torsional spring* that gives it an angular acceleration $\alpha = -4\theta$ rad/s^2, where θ is the needle's angular position in radians relative to a reference direction. The needle is given an angular velocity $\omega = 2$ rad/s in the position $\theta = 0$.

(a) What is the magnitude of the needle's angular velocity when $\theta = 30°$?

(b) What maximum angle θ does the needle reach before it rebounds?

Problem 13.100

13.101 The angle θ measures the direction of the unit vector **e** relative to the x axis. The angular velocity of **e** is $\omega = d\theta/dt = 2$ rad/s, a constant. Determine the derivative $d\mathbf{e}/dt$ when $\theta = 90°$ in two ways:

(a) Use Eq. (13.33).

(b) Express the vector **e** in terms of its x and y components and take the time derivative of **e**.

13.102 The angle θ measures the direction of the unit vector **e** relative to the x axis. The angle θ is given as a function of time by $\theta = 2t^2$ rad. What is the vector $d\mathbf{e}/dt$ at $t = 4$ s?

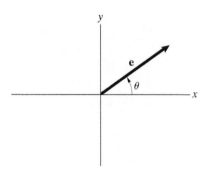

Problems 13.101/13.102

13.103 The line OP is of constant length R. The angle $\theta = \omega_0 t$, where ω_0 is a constant.

(a) Use the relations

$$v_x = \frac{dx}{dt} \quad \text{and} \quad v_y = \frac{dy}{dt}$$

to determine the velocity of point P relative to O.

(b) Use Eq. (13.33) to determine the velocity of point P relative to O, and confirm that your result agrees with the result of part (a).

Strategy: In part (b), write the position vector of P relative to O as $\mathbf{r} = R\mathbf{e}$, where **e** is a unit vector that points from O toward P.

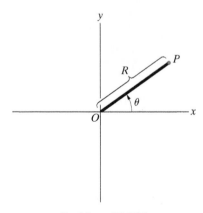

Problem 13.103

13.6 Curvilinear Motion—Normal and Tangential Components

BACKGROUND

In this method of describing curvilinear motion, we specify the position of a point by a coordinate measured *along its path* and express the velocity and acceleration in terms of their components tangential and normal (perpendicular) to the path. Normal and tangential components are particularly useful when a point moves along a circular path. Furthermore, they give us unique insight into the character of the velocity and acceleration in curvilinear motion. We first discuss motion in a planar path because of its conceptual simplicity.

Planar Motion

Consider a point P moving along a plane curvilinear path relative to some reference frame (Fig. 13.16a). The position vector $\mathbf{r}$ specifies the position of P relative to the reference point O, and the coordinate s measures P's position along the path relative to a point O' on the path. The velocity of P relative to O is

$$\mathbf{v} = \frac{d\mathbf{r}}{dt} = \lim_{\Delta t \to 0} \frac{\mathbf{r}(t + \Delta t) - \mathbf{r}(t)}{\Delta t} = \lim_{\Delta t \to 0} \frac{\Delta \mathbf{r}}{\Delta t}, \qquad (13.34)$$

where $\Delta \mathbf{r} = \mathbf{r}(t + \Delta t) - \mathbf{r}(t)$ (Fig. 13.16b). We denote the distance traveled along the path from t to $t + \Delta t$ by Δs. By introducing a unit vector $\mathbf{e}$ defined to point in the direction of $\Delta \mathbf{r}$, we can write Eq. (13.34) as

$$\mathbf{v} = \lim_{\Delta t \to 0} \frac{\Delta s}{\Delta t} \mathbf{e}.$$

As Δt approaches zero, $\Delta s / \Delta t$ becomes ds/dt and $\mathbf{e}$ becomes a unit vector tangent to the path at the position of P at time t, which we denote by $\mathbf{e}_t$ (Fig. 13.16c):

$$\mathbf{v} = v\mathbf{e}_t = \frac{ds}{dt} \mathbf{e}_t. \qquad (13.35)$$

The velocity of a point in curvilinear motion is a vector whose magnitude equals the rate of change of distance traveled along the path and whose direction is tangent to the path.

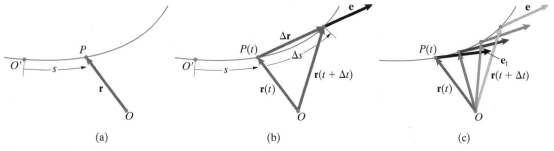

(a)   (b)   (c)

Figure 13.16
(a) The position of P along its path is specified by the coordinate s.
(b) Position of P at time t and at time $t + \Delta t$.
(c) The limit of $\mathbf{e}$ as $\Delta t \to 0$ is a unit vector tangent to the path.

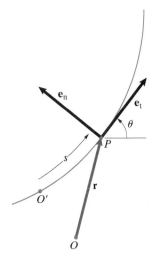

Figure 13.17
The path angle θ.

To determine the acceleration of P, we take the time derivative of Eq. (13.35):

$$\mathbf{a} = \frac{d\mathbf{v}}{dt} = \frac{dv}{dt}\mathbf{e}_t + v\frac{d\mathbf{e}_t}{dt}. \tag{13.36}$$

If the path is not a straight line, the unit vector $\mathbf{e}_t$ rotates as P moves. As a consequence, the time derivative of $\mathbf{e}_t$ is not zero. In the previous section, we derived an expression for the time derivative of a rotating unit vector in terms of the unit vector's angular velocity [Eq. (13.33)]. To use that result, we define the *path angle* θ specifying the direction of $\mathbf{e}_t$ relative to a reference line (Fig. 13.17). Then, from Eq. (13.33), the time derivative of $\mathbf{e}_t$ is

$$\frac{d\mathbf{e}_t}{dt} = \frac{d\theta}{dt}\mathbf{e}_n,$$

where $\mathbf{e}_n$ is a unit vector that is normal to $\mathbf{e}_t$ and points in the positive θ direction if $d\theta/dt$ is positive. Substituting this expression into Eq. (13.36), we obtain the acceleration of P:

$$\mathbf{a} = \frac{dv}{dt}\mathbf{e}_t + v\frac{d\theta}{dt}\mathbf{e}_n. \tag{13.37}$$

We can derive this result in another way that is less rigorous, but that gives additional insight into the meanings of the tangential and normal components of the acceleration. Figure 13.18a shows the velocity of P at times t and $t + \Delta t$. In Fig. 13.18b, you can see that the change in the velocity, $\mathbf{v}(t + \Delta t) - \mathbf{v}(t)$, consists of two components. The component Δv, which is tangent to the path at time t, is due to the change in the magnitude of the velocity. The component $v\Delta\theta$, which is perpendicular to the path at time t, is due to the change in the direction of the velocity vector. Thus, the change in the velocity is (approximately)

$$\mathbf{v}(t + \Delta t) - \mathbf{v}(t) = \Delta v\,\mathbf{e}_t + v\Delta\theta\,\mathbf{e}_n.$$

To obtain the acceleration, we divide this expression by Δt and take the limit as $\Delta t \to 0$:

$$\mathbf{a} = \lim_{\Delta t \to 0}\frac{\Delta\mathbf{v}}{\Delta t} = \lim_{\Delta t \to 0}\left(\frac{\Delta v}{\Delta t}\mathbf{e}_t + v\frac{\Delta\theta}{\Delta t}\mathbf{e}_n\right)$$

$$= \frac{dv}{dt}\mathbf{e}_t + v\frac{d\theta}{dt}\mathbf{e}_n.$$

Figure 13.18
(a) Velocity of P at t and at $t + \Delta t$.
(b) The tangential and normal components of the change in the velocity.

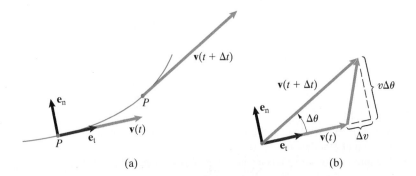

(a)   (b)

Thus, we again obtain Eq. (13.37). However, this derivation clearly points out that the tangential component of the acceleration arises from the rate of change of the magnitude of the velocity, whereas the normal component arises from the rate of change in the direction of the velocity vector. Notice that if the path is a straight line at time t, the normal component of the acceleration equals zero, because in that case $d\theta/dt$ is zero.

We can express the acceleration in another form that often is more convenient to use. Figure 13.19 shows the positions on the path reached by P at times t and $t + dt$. If the path is curved, straight lines extended from these points perpendicular to the path will intersect as shown. The distance ρ from the path to the point where these two lines intersect is called the *instantaneous radius of curvature* of the path. (If the path is circular, ρ is simply the radius of the path.) The angle $d\theta$ is the change in the path angle, and ds is the distance traveled from t to $t + \Delta t$. You can see from the figure that ρ is related to ds by

$$ds = \rho \, d\theta.$$

Dividing by dt, we obtain

$$\frac{ds}{dt} = v = \rho\frac{d\theta}{dt}.$$

Using this relation, we can write Eq. (13.37) as

$$\mathbf{a} = \frac{dv}{dt}\mathbf{e}_{t} + \frac{v^2}{\rho}\mathbf{e}_{n}.$$

For a given value of v, the normal component of the acceleration depends on the instantaneous radius of curvature. The greater the curvature of the path, the greater is the normal component of acceleration. When the acceleration is expressed in this way, the unit vector $\mathbf{e}_{n}$ must be defined to point toward the *concave* side of the path (Fig. 13.20).

Thus, the velocity and acceleration in terms of normal and tangential components are (Fig. 13.21)

$$\mathbf{v} = v\mathbf{e}_{t} = \frac{ds}{dt}\mathbf{e}_{t} \qquad (13.38)$$

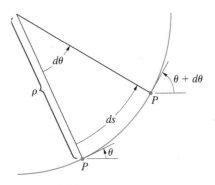

Figure 13.19
The instantaneous radius of curvature, ρ.

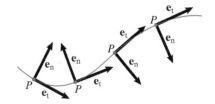

Figure 13.20
The unit vector normal to the path points toward the concave side.

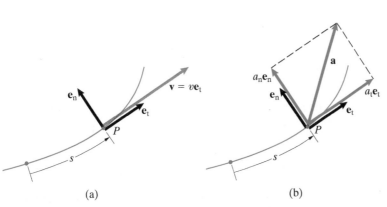

(a) (b)

Figure 13.21
Normal and tangential components of the velocity (a) and acceleration (b).

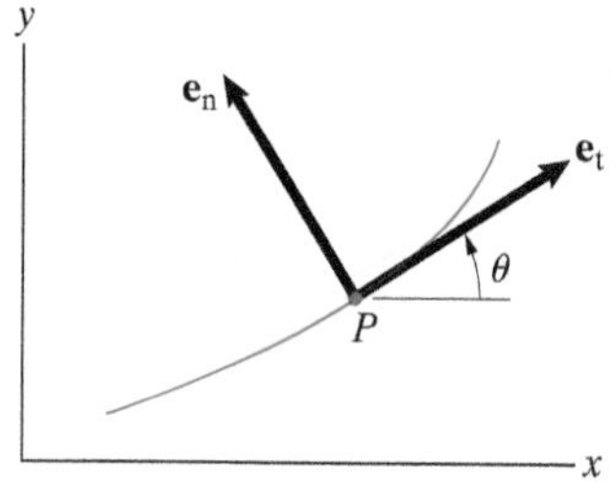

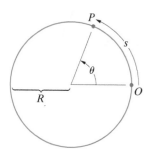

Figure 13.22
A point P moving in the x–y plane.

and

$$\mathbf{a} = a_t \mathbf{e}_t + a_n \mathbf{e}_n, \tag{13.39}$$

where

$$a_t = \frac{dv}{dt} \quad \text{and} \quad a_n = v\frac{d\theta}{dt} = \frac{v^2}{\rho}. \tag{13.40}$$

If the motion occurs in the x–y plane of a cartesian reference frame (Fig. 13.22) and θ is the angle between the x axis and the unit vector $\mathbf{e}_t$, the unit vectors $\mathbf{e}_t$ and $\mathbf{e}_n$ are related to the cartesian unit vectors by

$$\mathbf{e}_t = \cos\theta\,\mathbf{i} + \sin\theta\,\mathbf{j}$$

and

$$\mathbf{e}_n = -\sin\theta\,\mathbf{i} + \cos\theta\,\mathbf{j}. \tag{13.41}$$

If the path in the x–y plane is described by a function $y = y(x)$, it can be shown that the instantaneous radius of curvature is given by

$$\rho = \frac{\left[1 + \left(\dfrac{dy}{dx}\right)^2\right]^{3/2}}{\left|\dfrac{d^2y}{dx^2}\right|}. \tag{13.42}$$

Circular Motion

If a point P moves in a plane circular path of radius R (Fig. 13.23), the distance s is related to the angle θ by

$$s = R\theta \qquad \text{(circular path)}.$$

Using this relation, then, we can specify the position of P along the circular path by either s or θ. Taking the time derivative of the equation, we obtain a relation between $v = ds/dt$ and the angular velocity of the line from the center of the path to P:

$$v = R\frac{d\theta}{dt} = R\omega \qquad \text{(circular path)}. \tag{13.43}$$

Taking another time derivative, we obtain a relation between the tangential component of the acceleration $a_t = dv/dt$ and the angular acceleration:

$$a_t = R\frac{d\omega}{dt} = R\alpha \qquad \text{(circular path)}. \tag{13.44}$$

For this circular path, the instantaneous radius of curvature $\rho = R$, so the normal component of the acceleration is

$$a_n = \frac{v^2}{R} = R\omega^2 \qquad \text{(circular path)}. \tag{13.45}$$

Because problems involving circular motion of a point are so common, these relations are worth remembering. But you must be careful to use them *only* when the path is circular.

Figure 13.23
A point moving in a circular path.

Three-Dimensional Motion

Although most applications of normal and tangential components involve the motion of a point in a plane, we briefly discuss three-dimensional motion for the insight it provides into the nature of the velocity and acceleration. If we consider the motion of a point along a three-dimensional path relative to some reference frame, the steps leading to Eq. (13.38) are unaltered. The velocity is

$$\mathbf{v} = v\mathbf{e}_t = \frac{ds}{dt}\mathbf{e}_t, \tag{13.46}$$

where $v = ds/dt$ is the rate of change of distance along the path and the unit vector $\mathbf{e}_t$ is tangent to the path and points in the direction of motion. We take the time derivative of this equation to obtain the acceleration:

$$\mathbf{a} = \frac{d\mathbf{v}}{dt} = \frac{dv}{dt}\mathbf{e}_t + v\frac{d\mathbf{e}_t}{dt}.$$

As the point moves along its three-dimensional path, the direction of the unit vector $\mathbf{e}_t$ changes. In the case of motion of a point in a plane, this unit vector rotates in the plane, but in three-dimensional motion, the picture is more complicated. Figure 13.24a shows the path seen from a viewpoint perpendicular to the plane containing the vector $\mathbf{e}_t$ at times t and $t + dt$. This plane is called the *osculating plane*. It can be thought of as the instantaneous plane of rotation of the unit vector $\mathbf{e}_t$, and its orientation will generally change as P moves along its path. Since $\mathbf{e}_t$ is rotating in the osculating plane at time t, its time derivative is

$$\frac{d\mathbf{e}_t}{dt} = \frac{d\theta}{dt}\mathbf{e}_n, \tag{13.47}$$

where $d\theta/dt$ is the angular velocity of $\mathbf{e}_t$ in the osculating plane and the unit vector $\mathbf{e}_n$ is defined as shown in Fig. 13.24b. The vector $\mathbf{e}_n$ is perpendicular to $\mathbf{e}_t$, parallel to the osculating plane, and directed toward the concave side of the path. Therefore the acceleration is

$$\mathbf{a} = \frac{dv}{dt}\mathbf{e}_t + v\frac{d\theta}{dt}\mathbf{e}_n. \tag{13.48}$$

In the same way as in the case of motion in a plane, we can also express the acceleration in terms of the instantaneous radius of curvature of the path (Fig. 13.24c):

$$\mathbf{a} = \frac{dv}{dt}\mathbf{e}_t + \frac{v^2}{\rho}\mathbf{e}_n. \tag{13.49}$$

We see that the expressions for the velocity and acceleration in normal and tangential components for three-dimensional motion are identical in form to the expressions for planar motion. The velocity is a vector whose magnitude equals the rate of change of distance traveled along the path and whose direction is tangent to the path. The acceleration has a component tangential to the path equal to the rate of change of the magnitude of the velocity and a component perpendicular to the path that depends on the magnitude of the velocity and the instantaneous radius of curvature of the path. In planar motion, the unit vector $\mathbf{e}_n$ is parallel to the plane of the motion. In three-dimensional motion,

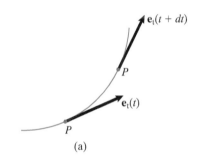

(a)

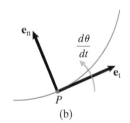

(b)

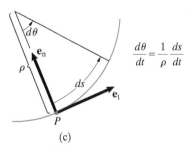

$$\frac{d\theta}{dt} = \frac{1}{\rho}\frac{ds}{dt}$$

(c)

Figure 13.24
(a) Defining the osculating plane.
(b) Definition of the unit vector $\mathbf{e}_n$.
(c) The instantaneous radius of curvature.

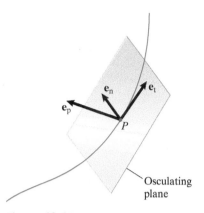

Figure 13.25
Defining the third unit vector $\mathbf{e}_p$.

$\mathbf{e}_n$ is parallel to the osculating plane, whose orientation depends on the nature of the path. Notice from Eq. (13.47) that $\mathbf{e}_n$ can be expressed in terms of $\mathbf{e}_t$ by

$$\mathbf{e}_n = \frac{\dfrac{d\mathbf{e}_t}{dt}}{\left|\dfrac{d\mathbf{e}_t}{dt}\right|}. \tag{13.50}$$

As the final step necessary to establish a three-dimensional coordinate system, we introduce a third unit vector that is perpendicular to both $\mathbf{e}_t$ and $\mathbf{e}_n$ by the definition

$$\mathbf{e}_p = \mathbf{e}_t \times \mathbf{e}_n. \tag{13.51}$$

The unit vector $\mathbf{e}_p$ is perpendicular to the osculating plane (Fig. 13.25).

RESULTS

Normal and Tangential Components in Planar Motion

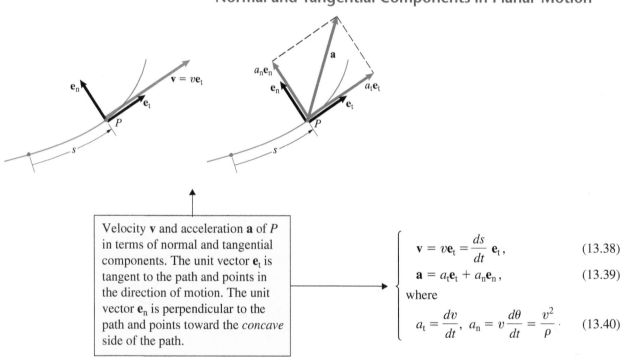

Velocity $\mathbf{v}$ and acceleration $\mathbf{a}$ of P in terms of normal and tangential components. The unit vector $\mathbf{e}_t$ is tangent to the path and points in the direction of motion. The unit vector $\mathbf{e}_n$ is perpendicular to the path and points toward the *concave* side of the path.

$$\mathbf{v} = v\mathbf{e}_t = \frac{ds}{dt}\,\mathbf{e}_t, \tag{13.38}$$

$$\mathbf{a} = a_t\mathbf{e}_t + a_n\mathbf{e}_n, \tag{13.39}$$

where

$$a_t = \frac{dv}{dt},\quad a_n = v\frac{d\theta}{dt} = \frac{v^2}{\rho}. \tag{13.40}$$

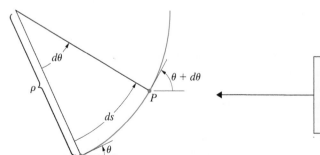

The parameter ρ is the *instantaneous radius of curvature* of the path. θ is the angle between a fixed reference direction and the path.

Motion in the *x–y* Plane of a Cartesian Reference Frame

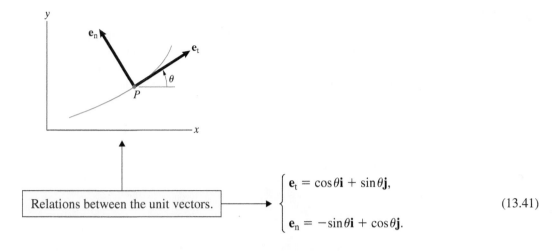

Relations between the unit vectors.

$$\begin{cases} \mathbf{e}_t = \cos\theta\mathbf{i} + \sin\theta\mathbf{j}, \\ \\ \mathbf{e}_n = -\sin\theta\mathbf{i} + \cos\theta\mathbf{j}. \end{cases}$$

(13.41)

Expression for the instantaneous radius of curvature when the path is described by a function $y = y(x)$.

$$\rho = \frac{\left[1 + \left(\dfrac{dy}{dx}\right)^2\right]^{3/2}}{\left|\dfrac{d^2y}{dx^2}\right|}.$$

(13.42)

Motion in a Circular Path

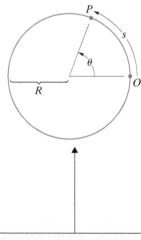

If a point moves in a circular path of radius R, the velocity and the normal and tangential components of the acceleration can be expressed in terms of the angular velocity and angular acceleration.

$$\begin{cases} v = R\dfrac{d\theta}{dt} = R\omega, \quad \text{(circular motion)} \quad (13.43) \\ \\ a_t = R\dfrac{d\omega}{dt} = R\alpha, \quad \text{(circular motion)} \quad (13.44) \\ \\ a_n = \dfrac{v^2}{R} = R\omega^2. \quad \text{(circular motion)} \quad (13.45) \end{cases}$$

Active Example 13.9   Motion in Terms of Normal and Tangential Components
(▶ *Related Problem 13.104*)

The motorcycle starts from rest at $t = 0$ on a circular track with a 400-m radius. The tangential component of the motorcycle's acceleration (in m/s^2) is given as a function of time by $a_t = 2 + 0.2t$. What is the motorcycle's velocity in terms of normal and tangential components at $t = 10$ s? What distance s has the motorcycle moved along the track at $t = 10$ s?

Strategy

Let s be the distance along the track from the initial position O of the motorcycle to its position at time t. Knowing the tangential acceleration as a function of time, we can integrate to determine the velocity v and position s as functions of time.

Solution

Integrate the tangential acceleration to determine the velocity as a function of time.

$$\begin{cases} a_t = \dfrac{dv}{dt} = 2 + 0.2t, \\[2mm] \displaystyle\int_0^v dv = \int_0^t (2 + 0.2t)dt, \\[2mm] v = 2t + 0.1t^2 \,\text{m/s}. \end{cases}$$

Evaluate the velocity at $t = 10$ s.

$$\begin{cases} v|_{t=10\,\text{s}} = 2(10) + 0.1(10)^2 \\[2mm] \qquad\quad = 30 \text{ m/s}. \end{cases}$$

Express the velocity at $t = 10$ s as a vector in terms of normal and tangential components.

$$\begin{cases} \mathbf{v} = v\mathbf{e}_t \\[2mm] \quad = 30\mathbf{e}_t \,(\text{m/s}). \end{cases}$$

Integrate $v = ds/dt$ to determine the position as a function of time.

$$\begin{cases} v = \dfrac{ds}{dt} = 2t + 0.1t^2, \\[2mm] \displaystyle\int_0^S ds = \int_0^t (2t + 0.1t^2)dt, \\[2mm] s = t^2 + \dfrac{0.1}{3}t^3 \,\text{m}. \end{cases}$$

| Evaluate the position at $t = 10$ s. | $\longrightarrow$ | $\begin{cases} s\big|_{t=10\,\text{s}} = (10)^2 + \dfrac{0.1}{3}(10)^3 \\ \qquad\qquad = 133 \text{ m.} \end{cases}$ |

Practice Problem Determine the motorcycle's acceleration in terms of normal and tangential components at $t = 10$ s.

Answer: $\mathbf{a} = 4\mathbf{e}_t + 2.25\mathbf{e}_n \ (\text{m/s}^2)$.

Example 13.10 The Circular-Orbit Problem (▶ *Related Problem 13.114*)

A satellite is in a circular orbit of radius R around the earth. What is its velocity?

Strategy
The acceleration due to gravity at a distance R from the center of the earth is gR_E^2/R^2, where R_E is the radius of the earth. (See Eq. 12.4.) By using this expression together with the equation for the acceleration in terms of normal and tangential components, we can obtain an equation for the satellite's velocity.

Solution
In terms of normal and tangential components (Fig. a), the acceleration of the satellite is

$$\mathbf{a} = \frac{dv}{dt}\mathbf{e}_t + \frac{v^2}{R}\mathbf{e}_n.$$

This expression must equal the acceleration due to gravity toward the center of the earth:

$$\frac{dv}{dt}\mathbf{e}_t + \frac{v^2}{R}\mathbf{e}_n = \frac{gR_E^2}{R^2}\mathbf{e}_n. \tag{1}$$

Because there is no $\mathbf{e}_t$ component on the right side of Eq. (1), we conclude that the magnitude of the satellite's velocity is constant:

$$\frac{dv}{dt} = 0.$$

Equating the $\mathbf{e}_n$ components in Eq. (1) and solving for v, we obtain

$$v = \sqrt{\frac{gR_E^2}{R}}.$$

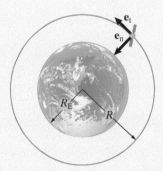

(a) Describing the satellite's motion in terms of normal and tangential components.

Critical Thinking
In Example 13.5 we determined the escape velocity of an object traveling straight away from the earth in terms of its initial distance from the center of the earth. The escape velocity for an object at a distance R from the center of the earth, $v_{\text{esc}} = \sqrt{2gR_E^2/R}$, is only $\sqrt{2}$ times the velocity of an object in a circular orbit of radius R. This explains why it was possible to begin launching probes to other planets not long after the first satellites were placed in earth orbit.

Example 13.11 Relating Cartesian Components to Normal and Tangential Components
(▶ *Related Problem 13.122*)

During a flight in which a helicopter starts from rest at $t = 0$, the cartesian components of its acceleration are

$$a_x = 0.6t \text{ m/s}^2$$

and

$$a_y = 1.8 - 0.36t \text{ m/s}^2.$$

What are the normal and tangential components of the helicopter's acceleration and the instantaneous radius of curvature of its path at $t = 4$ s?

Strategy
We can integrate the cartesian components of acceleration to determine the cartesian components of the velocity at $t = 4$ s, and then we can determine the components of the tangential unit vector $\mathbf{e}_t$ by dividing the velocity vector by its magnitude: $\mathbf{e}_t = \mathbf{v}/|\mathbf{v}|$. Next, we can determine the tangential component of the acceleration by evaluating the dot product of the acceleration vector with $\mathbf{e}_t$. Knowing the tangential component of the acceleration, we can then evaluate the normal component and determine the radius of curvature of the path from the relation $a_n = v^2/\rho$.

Solution
Integrating the components of acceleration with respect to time (see Active Example 13.6), we find that the cartesian components of the velocity are

$$v_x = 0.3t^2 \text{ m/s}$$

and

$$v_y = 1.8t - 0.18t^2 \text{ m/s}.$$

At $t = 4$ s, $v_x = 4.80$ m/s and $v_y = 4.32$ m/s. The tangential unit vector $\mathbf{e}_t$ at $t = 4$ s is (Fig. a)

$$\mathbf{e}_t = \frac{\mathbf{v}}{|\mathbf{v}|} = \frac{4.80\mathbf{i} + 4.32\mathbf{j}}{\sqrt{(4.80)^2 + (4.32)^2}} = 0.743\mathbf{i} + 0.669\mathbf{j}.$$

The components of the acceleration at $t = 4$ s are

$$a_x = 0.6(4) = 2.4 \text{ m/s}^2$$

and

$$a_y = 1.8 - 0.36(4) = 0.36 \text{ m/s}^2,$$

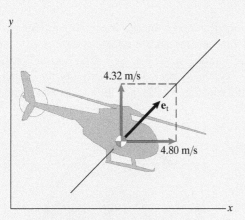

(a) Cartesian components of the velocity and the vector $\mathbf{e}_t$.

so the tangential component of the acceleration at $t = 4$ s is

$$a_t = \mathbf{e}_t \cdot \mathbf{a}$$

$$= (0.743\mathbf{i} + 0.669\mathbf{j}) \cdot (2.4\mathbf{i} + 0.36\mathbf{j})$$

$$= 2.02 \text{ m/s}^2.$$

The magnitude of the acceleration is $\sqrt{(2.4)^2 + (0.36)^2} = 2.43 \text{ m/s}^2$, so the magnitude of the normal component of the acceleration is

$$a_n = \sqrt{|\mathbf{a}|^2 - a_t^2} = \sqrt{(2.43)^2 - (2.02)^2} = 1.34 \text{ m/s}^2.$$

The radius of curvature of the path is thus

$$\rho = \frac{|\mathbf{v}|^2}{a_n} = \frac{(4.80)^2 + (4.32)^2}{1.34} = 31.2 \text{ m}.$$

Critical Thinking

The cartesian components of a vector are parallel to the axes of the cartesian coordinate system, whereas the normal and tangential components are normal and tangential to the *path*. In this example, the cartesian components of the acceleration of the helicopter were given as functions of time. How could we determine the normal and tangential components of the acceleration at $t = 4$ s without knowing the path? Notice that we used the fact that *the velocity vector is tangent to the path*. We integrated the cartesian components of the acceleration to determine the cartesian components of the velocity at $t = 4$ s. That told us the direction of the path. By dividing the velocity vector by its magnitude, we obtained a unit vector tangent to the path that pointed in the direction of the motion, which is the vector $\mathbf{e}_t$.

Example 13.12 Centrifuge (▶ *Related Problem 13.128*)

The distance from the center of the medical centrifuge to its samples is 300 mm. When the centrifuge is turned on, its motor and control system give it an angular acceleration $\alpha = A - B\omega^2$. Choose the constants A and B so that the samples will be subjected to a maximum horizontal acceleration of 12,000 g's and the centrifuge will reach 90% of its maximum operating speed in 2 min.

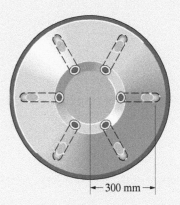

← 300 mm →

Strategy

Since we know both the radius of the circular path in which the samples move and the horizontal acceleration to which they are to be subjected, we can solve for the operating angular velocity of the centrifuge. We will use the given angular acceleration to determine the centrifuge's angular velocity as a function of time in terms of the constants A and B. We can then use the operating angular velocity and the condition that the centrifuge reach 90% of the operating angular velocity in 2 min to determine the constants A and B.

Solution

From Eq. (13.45), the samples are subjected to a normal acceleration

$$a_n = R\omega^2.$$

Setting $a_n = (12{,}000)(9.81)$ m/s^2 and $R = 0.3$ m and solving for the angular velocity, we find that the desired maximum operating speed is $\omega_{max} = 626$ rad/s.

The angular acceleration is

$$\alpha = \frac{d\omega}{dt} = A - B\omega^2.$$

We separate variables to get

$$\frac{d\omega}{A - B\omega^2} = dt.$$

Then we integrate to determine ω as a function of time, assuming that the centrifuge starts from rest at $t = 0$:

$$\int_0^{\omega} \frac{d\omega}{A - B\omega^2} = \int_0^t dt.$$

Evaluating the integrals, we obtain

$$\frac{1}{2\sqrt{AB}} \ln\left(\frac{A + \sqrt{AB}\omega}{A - \sqrt{AB}\omega}\right) = t.$$

The solution of this equation for ω is

$$\omega = \sqrt{\frac{A}{B}}\left(\frac{e^{2\sqrt{AB}t} - 1}{e^{2\sqrt{AB}t} + 1}\right).$$

As t becomes large, ω approaches $\sqrt{A/B}$, so we have the condition that

$$\sqrt{\frac{A}{B}} = \omega_{\text{max}} = 626 \text{ rad/s}, \qquad (1)$$

and we can write the equation for ω as

$$\omega = \omega_{\text{max}}\left(\frac{e^{2\sqrt{AB}t} - 1}{e^{2\sqrt{AB}t} + 1}\right). \qquad (2)$$

We also have the condition that $\omega = 0.9\omega_{\text{max}}$ after 2 min. Setting $\omega = 0.9\omega_{\text{max}}$ and $t = 120$ s in Eq. (2) and solving for $\sqrt{AB}$, we obtain

$$\sqrt{AB} = \frac{\ln(19)}{240}.$$

We solve this equation together with Eq. (1), obtaining $A = 7.69 \text{ rad/s}^2$ and $B = 1.96 \times 10^{-5} \text{ rad}^{-1}$. The graph shows the angular velocity of the centrifuge as a function of time.

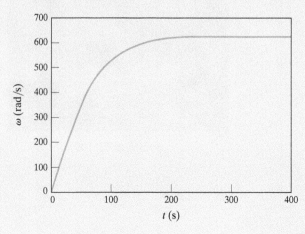

Problems

▶ **13.104** In Active Example 13.9, determine the motorcycle's velocity and acceleration in terms of normal and tangential components at $t = 5$ s.

13.105 The armature starts from rest at $t = 0$ and has constant angular acceleration $\alpha = 2$ rad/s^2. At $t = 4$ s, what are the velocity and acceleration of point P relative to point O in terms of normal and tangential components?

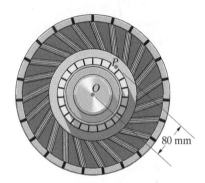

80 mm

Problem 13.105

13.106 Suppose that you want to design a medical centrifuge to subject samples to normal accelerations of 1000 g's.

(a) If the distance from the center of the centrifuge to the sample is 300 mm, what speed of rotation in rpm is necessary?

(b) If you want the centrifuge to reach its design rpm in 1 min, what constant angular acceleration is necessary?

13.107 The medical centrifuge starts from rest at $t = 0$ and is subjected to a constant angular acceleration $\alpha = 3$ rad/s^2. What is the magnitude of the total acceleration to which the samples are subjected at $t = 1$ s?

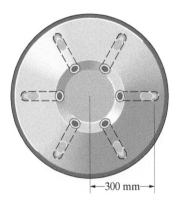

←300 mm→

Problems 13.106/13.107

13.108 A centrifuge used to subject engineering components to high acceleration has a radius of 8 m. It starts from rest at $t = 0$, and during its two-minute acceleration phase it is programmed so that its angular acceleration is given as a function of time in seconds by $\alpha = 0.192 - 0.0016t$ rad/s^2. At $t = 120$ s, what is the magnitude of the acceleration a component is subjected to?

Problem 13.108

13.109 A powerboat being tested for maneuverability is started from rest at $t = 0$ and driven in a circular path 12 m in radius. The tangential component of the boat's acceleration as a function of time is $a_t = 0.4t$ m/s^2.

(a) What are the boat's velocity and acceleration in terms of normal and tangential components at $t = 4$ s?

(b) What distance does the boat move along its circular path from $t = 0$ to $t = 4$ s?

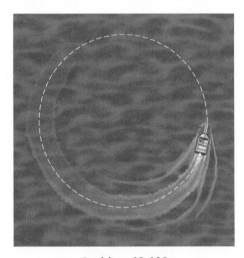

Problem 13.109

13.110 The angle $\theta = 2t^2$ rad.

(a) What are the velocity and acceleration of point P in terms of normal and tangential components at $t = 1$ s?

(b) What distance along the circular path does point P move from $t = 0$ to $t = 1$ s?

13.111 The angle $\theta = 2t^2$ rad. What are the velocity and acceleration of point P in terms of normal and tangential components when P has gone one revolution around the circular path starting at $t = 0$?

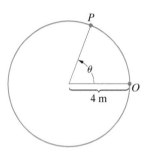

Problems 13.110/13.111

13.112 At the instant shown, the crank AB is rotating with a counterclockwise angular velocity of 5000 rpm. Determine the velocity of point B (a) in terms of normal and tangential components and (b) in terms of cartesian components.

13.113 The crank AB is rotating with a constant counterclockwise angular velocity of 5000 rpm. Determine the acceleration of point B (a) in terms of normal and tangential components and (b) in terms of cartesian components.

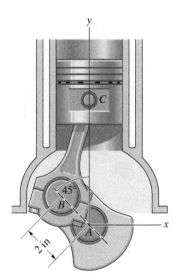

Problems 13.112/13.113

▶ **13.114** Suppose that a circular tunnel of radius R could be dug beneath the equator. In principle, a satellite could be placed in orbit about the center of the earth within the tunnel. The acceleration due to gravity in the tunnel would be gR/R_E, where g is the acceleration due to gravity at sea level and R_E is the earth's radius. Determine the velocity of the satellite and show that the time required to complete one orbit is independent of the radius R. (See Example 13.10.)

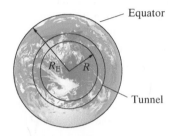

Problem 13.114

13.115 At the instant shown, the magnitude of the airplane's velocity is 130 m/s, its tangential component of acceleration is $a_t = -4$ m/s^2, and the rate of change of its path angle is $d\theta/dt = 5°/$s.

(a) What are the airplane's velocity and acceleration in terms of normal and tangential components?

(b) What is the instantaneous radius of curvature of the airplane's path?

Problem 13.115

13.116 In the preliminary design of a sun-powered car, a group of engineering students estimates that the car's acceleration will be 0.6 m/s². Suppose that the car starts from rest at A, and the tangential component of its acceleration is $a_t = 0.6$ m/s². What are the car's velocity and acceleration in terms of normal and tangential components when it reaches B?

13.117 After subjecting a car design to wind-tunnel testing, the students estimate that the tangential component of the car's acceleration will be $a_t = 0.6 - 0.002v^2$ m/s², where v is the car's velocity in m/s. If the car starts from rest at A, what are its velocity and acceleration in terms of normal and tangential components when it reaches B?

13.118 Suppose that the tangential component of acceleration of a car is given in terms of the car's position by $a_t = 0.4 - 0.001s$ m/s², where s is the distance the car travels along the track from point A. What are the car's velocity and acceleration in terms of normal and tangential components at point B?

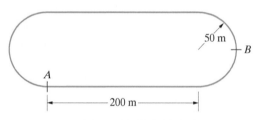

Problems 13.116–13.118

13.119 The car increases its speed at a constant rate from 40 mi/h at A to 60 mi/h at B. What is the magnitude of its acceleration 2 s after it passes point A?

13.120 The car increases its speed at a constant rate from 40 mi/h at A to 60 mi/h at B. Determine the magnitude of its acceleration when it has traveled along the road a distance (a) 120 ft from A and (b) 160 ft from A.

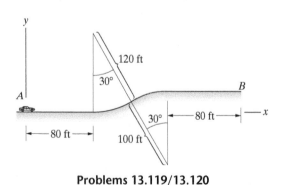

Problems 13.119/13.120

13.121 Astronaut candidates are to be tested in a centrifuge with 10-m radius that rotates in the horizontal plane. Test engineers want to subject the candidates to an acceleration of 5 g's, or five times the acceleration due to gravity. Earth's gravity effectively exerts an acceleration of 1 g in the vertical direction. Determine the angular velocity of the centrifuge in revolutions per second so that the magnitude of the total acceleration is 5 g's.

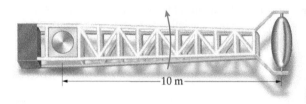

Problem 13.121

▶ **13.122** In Example 13.11, what is the helicopter's velocity in terms of normal and tangential components at $t = 4$ s?

13.123 The athlete releases the shot with velocity $v = 16$ m/s.

(a) What are the velocity and acceleration of the shot in terms of normal and tangential components when it is at the highest point of its trajectory?

(b) What is the instantaneous radius of curvature of the shot's path when it is at the highest point of its trajectory?

13.124 At $t = 0$, the athlete releases the shot with velocity $v = 16$ m/s.

(a) What are the velocity and acceleration of the shot in terms of normal and tangential components at $t = 0.3$ s?

(b) Use the relation $a_n = v^2/\rho$ to determine the instantaneous radius of curvature of the shot's path at $t = 0.3$ s.

13.125 At $t = 0$, the athlete releases the shot with velocity $v = 16$ m/s. Use Eq. (13.42) to determine the instantaneous radius of curvature of the shot's path at $t = 0.3$ s.

Problems 13.123–13.125

13.126 The cartesian coordinates of a point moving in the x–y plane are

$$x = 20 + 4t^2 \text{ m} \quad \text{and} \quad y = 10 - t^3 \text{ m}.$$

What is the instantaneous radius of curvature of the path of the point at $t = 3$ s?

13.127 The helicopter starts from rest at $t = 0$. The cartesian components of its acceleration are $a_x = 0.6t$ m/s^2 and $a_y = 1.8 - 0.36t$ m/s^2. Determine the tangential and normal components of the acceleration at $t = 6$ s.

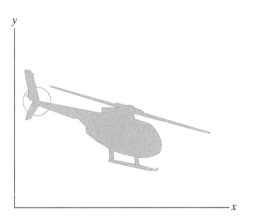

Problem 13.127

▶ **13.128** Suppose that when the centrifuge in Example 13.12 is turned on, its motor and control system give it an angular acceleration (in rad/s^2) $\alpha = 12 - 0.02\omega$, where ω is the centrifuge's angular velocity. Determine the tangential and normal components of the acceleration of the samples at $t = 0.2$ s.

13.129* For astronaut training, the airplane shown is to achieve "weightlessness" for a short period of time by flying along a path such that its acceleration is $a_x = 0$ and $a_y = -g$. If the velocity of the plane at O at time $t = 0$ is $\mathbf{v} = v_0\mathbf{i}$, show that the autopilot must fly the airplane so that its tangential component of acceleration as a function of time is

$$a_t = g \frac{gt/v_0}{\sqrt{1 + (gt/v_0)^2}}.$$

13.130* In Problem 13.129, what is the airplane's normal component of acceleration as a function of time?

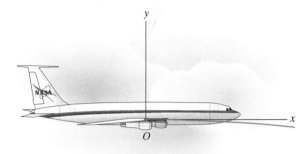

Problems 13.129/13.130

13.131 If $y = 100$ mm, $dy/dt = 200$ mm/s, and $d^2y/dt^2 = 0$, what are the velocity and acceleration of P in terms of normal and tangential components?

13.132* Suppose that the point P moves upward in the slot with velocity $\mathbf{v} = 300\mathbf{e}_t$ (mm/s). When $y = 150$ mm, what are dy/dt and d^2y/dt^2?

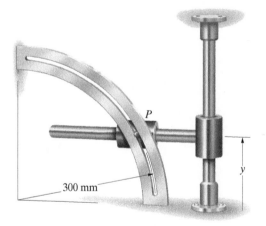

Problems 13.131/13.132

13.133* A car travels at 100 km/h on a straight road of increasing grade whose vertical profile can be approximated by the equation shown. When the car's horizontal coordinate is $x = 400$ m, what are the tangential and normal components of the car's acceleration?

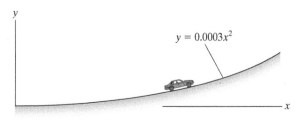

$y = 0.0003x^2$

Problem 13.133

13.134 A boy rides a skateboard on the concrete surface of an empty drainage canal described by the equation shown. He starts at $y = 20$ ft, and the magnitude of his velocity is approximated by $v = \sqrt{2(32.2)(20 - y)}$ ft/s.

(a) Use Eq. (13.42) to determine the instantaneous radius of curvature of the boy's path when he reaches the bottom.

(b) What is the normal component of his acceleration when he reaches the bottom?

13.135 In Problem 13.134, what is the normal component of the boy's acceleration when he has passed the bottom and reached $y = 10$ ft?

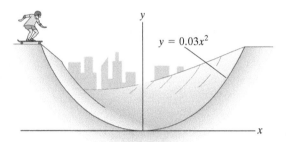

Problems 13.134/13.135

13.136* By using Eqs. (13.41): (a) show that the relations between the cartesian unit vectors and the unit vectors $\mathbf{e}_t$ and $\mathbf{e}_n$ are

$$\mathbf{i} = \cos\theta\,\mathbf{e}_t - \sin\theta\,\mathbf{e}_n$$

$$\mathbf{j} = \sin\theta\,\mathbf{e}_t + \cos\theta\,\mathbf{e}_n.$$

(b) Show that

$$\frac{d\mathbf{e}_t}{dt} = \frac{d\theta}{dt}\mathbf{e}_n \quad \text{and} \quad \frac{d\mathbf{e}_n}{dt} = -\frac{d\theta}{dt}\mathbf{e}_t.$$

13.7 Curvilinear Motion—Polar and Cylindrical Coordinates

BACKGROUND

Polar coordinates are often used to describe the curvilinear motion of a point. Circular motion, certain orbit problems, and, more generally, *central-force* problems, in which the acceleration of a point is directed toward a given point, can be expressed conveniently in polar coordinates.

Consider a point P in the x–y plane of a cartesian coordinate system. We can specify the position of P relative to the origin O either by its cartesian coordinates x, y or by its polar coordinates r, θ (Fig. 13.26a). To express vectors in terms of polar coordinates, we define a unit vector $\mathbf{e}_r$ that points in the direction of the radial line from the origin to P and a unit vector $\mathbf{e}_\theta$ that is perpendicular to $\mathbf{e}_r$ and points in the direction of increasing θ (Fig. 13.26b). In terms of these vectors, the position vector $\mathbf{r}$ from O to P is

$$\mathbf{r} = r\mathbf{e}_r. \tag{13.52}$$

(Notice that $\mathbf{r}$ has no component in the direction of $\mathbf{e}_\theta$.)

We can determine the velocity of P in terms of polar coordinates by taking the time derivative of Eq. (13.52):

$$\mathbf{v} = \frac{d\mathbf{r}}{dt} = \frac{dr}{dt}\mathbf{e}_r + r\frac{d\mathbf{e}_r}{dt}. \tag{13.53}$$

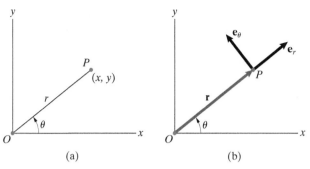

Figure 13.26
(a) The polar coordinates of P.
(b) The unit vectors $\mathbf{e}_r$ and $\mathbf{e}_\theta$ and the position vector $\mathbf{r}$.

As P moves along a curvilinear path, the unit vector $\mathbf{e}_r$ rotates with angular velocity $\omega = d\theta/dt$. Therefore, from Eq. (13.33), we can express the time derivative of $\mathbf{e}_r$ in terms of $\mathbf{e}_\theta$ as

$$\frac{d\mathbf{e}_r}{dt} = \frac{d\theta}{dt}\mathbf{e}_\theta. \tag{13.54}$$

Substituting this result into Eq. (13.53), we obtain the velocity of P:

$$\mathbf{v} = \frac{dr}{dt}\mathbf{e}_r + r\frac{d\theta}{dt}\mathbf{e}_\theta = \frac{dr}{dt}\mathbf{e}_r + r\omega\mathbf{e}_\theta. \tag{13.55}$$

We can get this result in another way that is less rigorous, but more direct and intuitive. Figure 13.27 shows the position vector of P at times t and $t + \Delta t$. The change in the position vector, $\mathbf{r}(t + \Delta t) - \mathbf{r}(t)$, consists of two components. The component Δr is due to the change in the radial position r and is in the $\mathbf{e}_r$ direction. The component $r\Delta\theta$ is due to the change in θ and is in the $\mathbf{e}_\theta$ direction. Thus, the change in the position of P is (approximately)

$$\mathbf{r}(t + \Delta t) - \mathbf{r}(t) = \Delta r\mathbf{e}_r + r\Delta\theta\mathbf{e}_\theta.$$

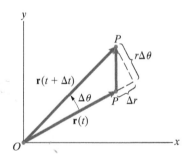

Figure 13.27
The position vector of P at t and $t + \Delta t$.

Dividing this expression by Δt and taking the limit as $\Delta t \to 0$, we obtain the velocity of P:

$$\mathbf{v} = \lim_{\Delta t \to 0}\left(\frac{\Delta r}{\Delta t}\mathbf{e}_r + r\frac{\Delta\theta}{\Delta t}\mathbf{e}_\theta\right)$$
$$= \frac{dr}{dt}\mathbf{e}_r + r\omega\mathbf{e}_\theta.$$

One component of the velocity is in the radial direction and is equal to the rate of change of the radial position r. The other component is normal, or *transverse*, to the radial direction and is proportional to the radial distance and to the rate of change of θ.

We obtain the acceleration of P by taking the time derivative of Eq. (13.55):

$$\mathbf{a} = \frac{d\mathbf{v}}{dt} = \frac{d^2r}{dt^2}\mathbf{e}_r + \frac{dr}{dt}\frac{d\mathbf{e}_r}{dt} + \frac{dr}{dt}\frac{d\theta}{dt}\mathbf{e}_\theta + r\frac{d^2\theta}{dt^2}\mathbf{e}_\theta + r\frac{d\theta}{dt}\frac{d\mathbf{e}_\theta}{dt}. \tag{13.56}$$

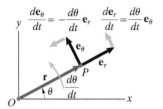

Figure 13.28
Time derivatives of $\mathbf{e}_r$ and $\mathbf{e}_\theta$.

The time derivative of the unit vector $\mathbf{e}_r$ due to the rate of change of θ is given by Eq. (13.54). As P moves, $\mathbf{e}_\theta$ also rotates with angular velocity $d\theta/dt$ (Fig. 13.28). You can see from this figure that the time derivative of $\mathbf{e}_\theta$ is in the $-\mathbf{e}_r$ direction if $d\theta/dt$ is positive:

$$\frac{d\mathbf{e}_\theta}{dt} = -\frac{d\theta}{dt}\mathbf{e}_r.$$

Substituting this expression and Eq. (13.54) into Eq. (13.56), we obtain the acceleration of P:

$$\mathbf{a} = \left[\frac{d^2r}{dt^2} - r\left(\frac{d\theta}{dt}\right)^2\right]\mathbf{e}_r + \left[r\frac{d^2\theta}{dt^2} + 2\frac{dr}{dt}\frac{d\theta}{dt}\right]\mathbf{e}_\theta.$$

Thus, the velocity and acceleration are respectively (Fig. 13.29)

$$\mathbf{v} = v_r\mathbf{e}_r + v_\theta\mathbf{e}_\theta = \frac{dr}{dt}\mathbf{e}_r + r\omega\mathbf{e}_\theta \tag{13.57}$$

and

$$\mathbf{a} = a_r\mathbf{e}_r + a_\theta\mathbf{e}_\theta, \tag{13.58}$$

where

$$a_r = \frac{d^2r}{dt^2} - r\left(\frac{d\theta}{dt}\right)^2 = \frac{d^2r}{dt^2} - r\omega^2 \tag{13.59}$$

$$a_\theta = r\frac{d^2\theta}{dt^2} + 2\frac{dr}{dt}\frac{d\theta}{dt} = r\alpha + 2\frac{dr}{dt}\omega.$$

The term $-r\omega^2$ in the radial component of the acceleration is called the *centripetal acceleration*, and the term $2(dr/dt)\omega$ in the transverse component is called the *Coriolis acceleration*.

The unit vectors $\mathbf{e}_r$ and $\mathbf{e}_\theta$ are related to the cartesian unit vectors by

$$\mathbf{e}_r = \cos\theta\mathbf{i} + \sin\theta\mathbf{j}$$

and

$$\mathbf{e}_\theta = -\sin\theta\mathbf{i} + \cos\theta\mathbf{j}. \tag{13.60}$$

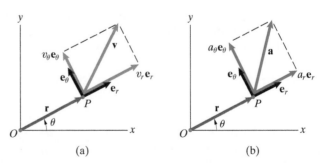

Figure 13.29
Radial and transverse components of the velocity (a) and acceleration (b).

Circular Motion Circular motion can be conveniently described using either radial and transverse or normal and tangential components. Let us compare these two methods of expressing the velocity and acceleration of a point P moving in a circular path of radius R (Fig. 13.30). Because the polar coordinate $r = R$ is constant, Eq. (13.57) for the velocity reduces to

$$\mathbf{v} = R\omega\mathbf{e}_\theta.$$

In terms of normal and tangential components, the velocity is

$$\mathbf{v} = v\mathbf{e}_t.$$

Notice in Fig. 13.30 that $\mathbf{e}_\theta = \mathbf{e}_t$. Comparing these two expressions for the velocity, we obtain the relation between the velocity and the angular velocity in circular motion:

$$v = R\omega.$$

From Eqs. (13.58) and (13.59), the acceleration for a circular path of radius R in terms of polar coordinates is

$$\mathbf{a} = -R\omega^2\mathbf{e}_r + R\alpha\mathbf{e}_\theta,$$

and the acceleration in terms of normal and tangential components is

$$\mathbf{a} = \frac{dv}{dt}\mathbf{e}_t + \frac{v^2}{R}\mathbf{e}_n.$$

The unit vector $\mathbf{e}_r = -\mathbf{e}_n$. Because of the relation $v = R\omega$, the normal components of acceleration are equal: $v^2/R = R\omega^2$. Equating the transverse and tangential components, we obtain the relation

$$\frac{dv}{dt} = a_t = R\alpha.$$

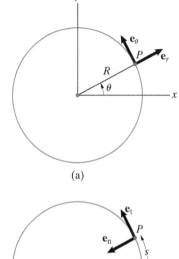

(a)

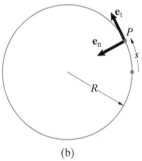

(b)

Figure 13.30
A point P moving in a circular path.
(**a**) Polar coordinates.
(**b**) Normal and tangential components.

Cylindrical Coordinates Polar coordinates describe the motion of a point P in the x–y plane. We can describe three-dimensional motion by using *cylindrical coordinates* r, θ, and z (Fig. 13.31). The cylindrical coordinates r and θ are the polar coordinates of P, measured in the plane parallel to the x–y plane, and the

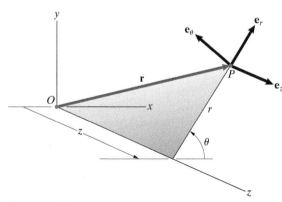

Figure 13.31
Cylindrical coordinates r, θ, and z of point P and the unit vectors $\mathbf{e}_r$, $\mathbf{e}_\theta$, and $\mathbf{e}_z$.

definitions of the unit vectors $\mathbf{e}_r$ and $\mathbf{e}_\theta$ are unchanged. The position of P perpendicular to the x–y plane is measured by the coordinate z, and the unit vector $\mathbf{e}_z$ points in the positive z axis direction.

In terms of cylindrical coordinates, the position vector $\mathbf{r}$ is the sum of the expression for the position vector in polar coordinates and the z component:

$$\mathbf{r} = r\mathbf{e}_r + z\mathbf{e}_z. \tag{13.61}$$

(The polar coordinate r is not the magnitude of $\mathbf{r}$, except when P lies in the x–y plane.) By taking time derivatives, we obtain the velocity

$$\mathbf{v} = \frac{d\mathbf{r}}{dt} = v_r\mathbf{e}_r + v_\theta\mathbf{e}_\theta + v_z\mathbf{e}_z$$

$$= \frac{dr}{dt}\mathbf{e}_r + r\omega\,\mathbf{e}_\theta + \frac{dz}{dt}\mathbf{e}_z \tag{13.62}$$

and acceleration

$$\mathbf{a} = \frac{d\mathbf{v}}{dt} = a_r\mathbf{e}_r + a_\theta\,\mathbf{e}_\theta + a_z\mathbf{e}_z, \tag{13.63}$$

where

$$a_r = \frac{d^2r}{dt^2} - r\omega^2, \quad a_\theta = r\alpha + 2\frac{dr}{dt}\omega, \quad \text{and} \quad a_z = \frac{d^2z}{dt^2}. \tag{13.64}$$

Notice that Eqs. (13.62) and (13.63) reduce to the polar coordinate expressions for the velocity and acceleration, Eqs. (13.57) and (13.58), when P moves along a path in the x–y plane.

RESULTS

Polar Coordinates

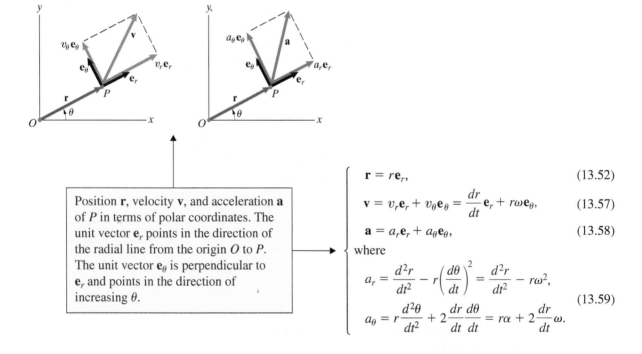

Position $\mathbf{r}$, velocity $\mathbf{v}$, and acceleration $\mathbf{a}$ of P in terms of polar coordinates. The unit vector $\mathbf{e}_r$ points in the direction of the radial line from the origin O to P. The unit vector $\mathbf{e}_\theta$ is perpendicular to $\mathbf{e}_r$ and points in the direction of increasing θ.

$$\mathbf{r} = r\mathbf{e}_r, \tag{13.52}$$

$$\mathbf{v} = v_r\mathbf{e}_r + v_\theta\mathbf{e}_\theta = \frac{dr}{dt}\mathbf{e}_r + r\omega\mathbf{e}_\theta, \tag{13.57}$$

$$\mathbf{a} = a_r\mathbf{e}_r + a_\theta\mathbf{e}_\theta, \tag{13.58}$$

where

$$a_r = \frac{d^2r}{dt^2} - r\left(\frac{d\theta}{dt}\right)^2 = \frac{d^2r}{dt^2} - r\omega^2,$$

$$a_\theta = r\frac{d^2\theta}{dt^2} + 2\frac{dr}{dt}\frac{d\theta}{dt} = r\alpha + 2\frac{dr}{dt}\omega. \tag{13.59}$$

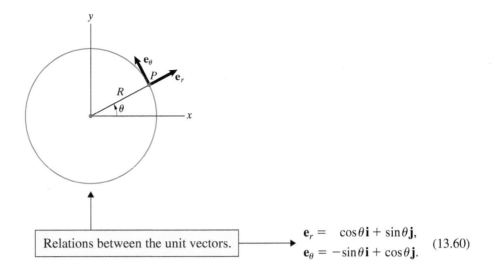

| Relations between the unit vectors. | $\begin{aligned} \mathbf{e}_r &= \quad\cos\theta\,\mathbf{i} + \sin\theta\,\mathbf{j}, \\ \mathbf{e}_\theta &= -\sin\theta\,\mathbf{i} + \cos\theta\,\mathbf{j}. \end{aligned}$ | (13.60) |

Cylindrical Coordinates

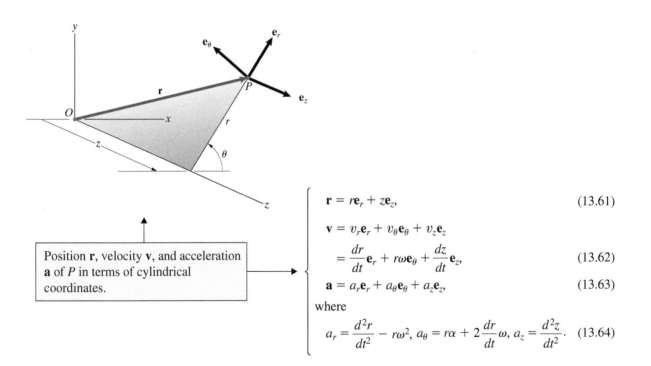

| Position **r**, velocity **v**, and acceleration **a** of P in terms of cylindrical coordinates. | $\mathbf{r} = r\mathbf{e}_r + z\mathbf{e}_z,$ | (13.61) |

$$\mathbf{v} = v_r\mathbf{e}_r + v_\theta\mathbf{e}_\theta + v_z\mathbf{e}_z$$

$$= \frac{dr}{dt}\mathbf{e}_r + r\omega\mathbf{e}_\theta + \frac{dz}{dt}\mathbf{e}_z, \qquad (13.62)$$

$$\mathbf{a} = a_r\mathbf{e}_r + a_\theta\mathbf{e}_\theta + a_z\mathbf{e}_z, \qquad (13.63)$$

where

$$a_r = \frac{d^2r}{dt^2} - r\omega^2, \; a_\theta = r\alpha + 2\frac{dr}{dt}\omega, \; a_z = \frac{d^2z}{dt^2}. \quad (13.64)$$

Active Example 13.13 Analyzing Motion in Terms of Polar Coordinates (▶ *Related Problem 13.138*)

The robot arm is programmed so that the point P traverses the path described by

$$r = 1 - 0.5 \cos 2\pi t \text{ m},$$
$$\theta = 0.5 - 0.2 \sin 2\pi t \text{ rad}.$$

What is the velocity of P in terms of polar coordinates at $t = 0.8$ s?

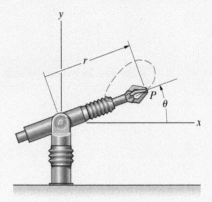

Strategy
The polar coordinates r and θ of P are known as functions of time, so we can determine the derivatives in the expression for the velocity in terms of polar coordinates and evaluate the velocity at $t = 0.8$ s.

Solution

Determine the derivatives in the expression for the velocity. ⟶

$$\begin{cases} \dfrac{dr}{dt} = \pi \sin 2\pi t, \\[2mm] \dfrac{d\theta}{dt} = -0.4\pi \cos 2\pi t. \end{cases}$$

Determine the velocity as a function of time. ⟶

$$\begin{cases} \mathbf{v} = \dfrac{dr}{dt}\mathbf{e}_r + r\dfrac{d\theta}{dt}\mathbf{e}_\theta \\[2mm] \quad = \pi \sin 2\pi t\, \mathbf{e}_r + (1 - 0.5\cos 2\pi t)(-0.4\pi \cos 2\pi t)\mathbf{e}_\theta. \end{cases}$$

Evaluate the velocity at $t = 0.8$ s. ⟶ $\mathbf{v} = -2.99\mathbf{e}_r - 0.328\mathbf{e}_\theta$ (m/s).

Practice Problem What is the acceleration of P in terms of polar coordinates at $t = 0.8$ s?

Answer: $\mathbf{a} = 5.97\mathbf{e}_r - 4.03\mathbf{e}_\theta$ (m/s^2).

Example 13.14 Expressing Motion in Terms of Polar Coordinates (▶ *Related Problem 13.141*)

Suppose that you are standing on a large disk (say, a merry-go-round) rotating with constant angular velocity ω_0 and you start walking at constant speed v_0 along a straight radial line painted on the disk. What are your velocity and acceleration when you are a distance r from the center of the disk?

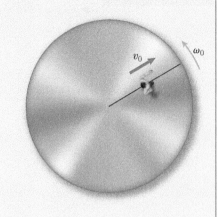

Strategy

We can describe your motion in terms of polar coordinates (Fig. a). By using the information given about your motion and the motion of the disk, we can evaluate the terms in the expressions for the velocity and acceleration in terms of polar coordinates.

Solution

The speed with which you walk along the radial line is the rate of change of r, $dr/dt = v_0$, and the angular velocity of the disk is the rate of change of θ, $\omega = \omega_0$. Your velocity is

$$\mathbf{v} = \frac{dr}{dt}\mathbf{e}_r + r\omega\mathbf{e}_\theta = v_0\mathbf{e}_r + r\omega_0\mathbf{e}_\theta.$$

Your velocity consists of two components: a radial component due to the speed at which you are walking and a transverse component due to the disk's rate of rotation. The transverse component increases as your distance from the center of the disk increases.

Your walking speed $v_0 = dr/dt$ is constant, so $d^2r/dt^2 = 0$. Also, the disk's angular velocity $\omega_0 = d\theta/dt$ is constant, so $d^2\theta/dt^2 = 0$. The radial component of your acceleration is

$$a_r = \frac{d^2r}{dt^2} - r\omega^2 = -r\omega_0^2,$$

and the transverse component is

$$a_\theta = r\alpha + 2\frac{dr}{dt}\omega = 2v_0\omega_0.$$

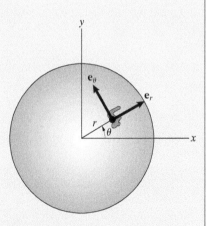

(a) Your position in terms of polar coordinates.

Critical Thinking

Why didn't we use normal and tangential components to determine your velocity and acceleration? The reason they would not be convenient in this example is that the path is not known, and normal and tangential components are defined in terms of the path.

If you have ever tried walking on a merry-go-round, you know that it is a difficult proposition. This example indicates why. Subjectively, you are walking along a straight line with constant velocity, but you are actually experiencing the centripetal acceleration a_r and the Coriolis acceleration a_θ due to the disk's rotation.

Example 13.15 | **Velocity in Terms of Polar and Cartesian Components**
(▶ *Related Problems 13.155 and 13.156*)

In the cam–follower mechanism shown, the slotted bar rotates with constant angular velocity $\omega = 4$ rad/s, and the radial position of the follower is determined by the elliptic profile of the stationary cam. The path of the follower is described by the polar equation

$$r = \frac{0.15}{1 + 0.5 \cos \theta} \text{ m.}$$

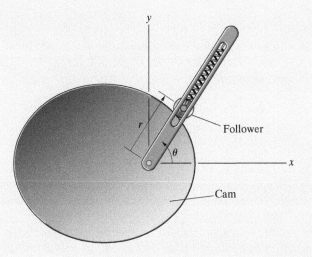

Determine the velocity of the follower when $\theta = 45°$ in terms of (a) polar coordinates and (b) cartesian coordinates.

Strategy
By taking the time derivative of the polar equation for the profile of the cam, we can obtain a relation between the known angular velocity and the radial component of velocity that permits us to evaluate the velocity in terms of polar coordinates. Then, by using Eqs. (13.60), we can obtain the velocity in terms of cartesian coordinates.

Solution
(a) The polar equation for the cam profile is of the form $r = r(\theta)$. Taking its derivative with respect to time, we obtain

$$\frac{dr}{dt} = \frac{dr(\theta)}{d\theta} \frac{d\theta}{dt}$$

$$= \frac{d}{d\theta}\left(\frac{0.15}{1 + 0.5 \cos \theta}\right) \frac{d\theta}{dt}$$

$$= \left[\frac{0.075 \sin \theta}{(1 + 0.5 \cos \theta)^2}\right] \frac{d\theta}{dt}.$$

The velocity of the follower in polar coordinates is therefore

$$\mathbf{v} = \frac{dr}{dt}\mathbf{e}_r + r\frac{d\theta}{dt}\mathbf{e}_\theta$$

$$= \left[\frac{0.075 \sin \theta}{(1 + 0.5 \cos \theta)^2}\right]\frac{d\theta}{dt}\mathbf{e}_r + \left(\frac{0.15}{1 + 0.5 \cos \theta}\right)\frac{d\theta}{dt}\mathbf{e}_\theta.$$

The angular velocity $\omega = d\theta/dt = 4$ rad/s, so we can evaluate the polar components of the velocity when $\theta = 45°$, obtaining

$$\mathbf{v} = 0.116\mathbf{e}_r + 0.443\mathbf{e}_\theta \ (\text{m/s}).$$

(b) Substituting Eqs. (13.60) with $\theta = 45°$ into the polar coordinate expression for the velocity, we obtain the velocity in terms of cartesian coordinates:

$$\mathbf{v} = 0.116\mathbf{e}_r + 0.443\mathbf{e}_\theta$$

$$= 0.116(\cos 45°\mathbf{i} + \sin 45°\mathbf{j}) + 0.443(-\sin 45°\mathbf{i} + \cos 45°\mathbf{j})$$

$$= -0.232\mathbf{i} + 0.395\mathbf{j} \ (\text{m/s}).$$

Critical Thinking

Notice that, in determining the velocity of the follower, we made the tacit assumption that it stays in contact with the surface of the cam as the bar rotates. Designers of cam mechanisms must insure that the spring is sufficiently strong so that the follower does not lose contact with the surface. In Chapter 14 we introduce the concepts needed to analyze such problems.

Problems

13.137 The polar coordinates of the collar A are given as functions of time in seconds by $r = 1 + 0.2t^2$ ft and $\theta = 2t$ rad. What are the magnitudes of the velocity and acceleration of the collar at $t = 2$ s?

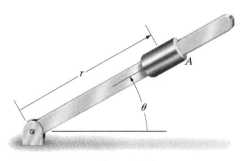

Problem 13.137

▶ **13.138** In Active Example 13.13, suppose that the robot arm is reprogrammed so that the point P traverses the path described by

$$r = 1 - 0.5 \sin 2\pi t \ \text{m},$$

$$\theta = 0.5 - 0.2 \cos 2\pi t \ \text{rad}.$$

What is the velocity of P in terms of polar coordinates at $t = 0.8$ s?

13.139 At the instant shown, $r = 3$ m and $\theta = 30°$. The cartesian components of the velocity of point A are $v_x = 2$ m/s and $v_y = 8$ m/s.

(a) Determine the velocity of point A in terms of polar coordinates.

(b) What is the angular velocity $d\theta/dt$ of the crane at the instant shown?

13.140 The polar coordinates of point A of the crane are given as functions of time in seconds by $r = 3 + 0.2t^2$ m and $\theta = 0.02t^2$ rad. Determine the acceleration of point A in terms of polar coordinates at $t = 3$ s.

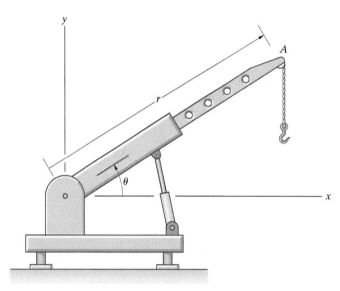

Problems 13.139/13.140

▶ **13.141** The radial line rotates with a constant angular velocity of 2 rad/s. Point P moves along the line at a constant speed of 4 m/s. Determine the magnitudes of the velocity and acceleration of P when $r = 2$ m. (See Example 13.14.)

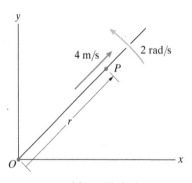

Problem 13.141

13.142 At the instant shown, the coordinates of the collar A are $x = 2.3$ ft, $y = 1.9$ ft. The collar is sliding on the bar from B toward C at a constant speed of 4 ft/s.

(a) What is the velocity of the collar in terms of polar coordinates?

(b) Use the answer to part (a) to determine the angular velocity of the radial line from the origin to the collar A at the instant shown.

13.143 At the instant shown, the coordinates of the collar A are $x = 2.3$ ft, $y = 1.9$ ft. The collar is sliding on the bar from B toward C at a constant speed of 4 ft/s.

(a) What is the acceleration of the collar in terms of polar coordinates?

(b) Use the answer to part (a) to determine the angular acceleration of the radial line from the origin to the collar A at the instant shown.

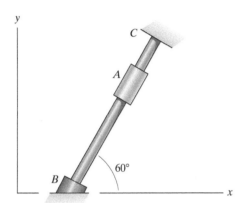

Problems 13.142/13.143

13.144* A boat searching for underwater archaeological sites in the Aegean Sea moves at 4 knots and follows the path $r = 10\theta$ m, where θ is in radians. (A knot is one nautical mile, or 1852 meters, per hour.) When $\theta = 2\pi$ rad, determine the boat's velocity (a) in terms of polar coordinates and (b) in terms of cartesian coordinates.

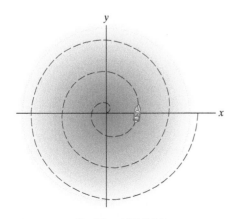

Problem 13.144

13.145 The collar A slides on the circular bar. The radial position of A (in meters) is given as a function of θ by $r = 2 \cos \theta$. At the instant shown, $\theta = 25°$ and $d\theta/dt = 4$ rad/s. Determine the velocity of A in terms of polar coordinates.

13.146 In Problem 13.145, $d^2\theta/dt^2 = 0$ at the instant shown. Determine the acceleration of A in terms of polar coordinates.

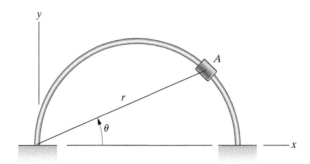

Problems 13.145/13.146

13.147 The radial coordinate of the earth satellite is related to its angular position θ by

$$r = \frac{1.91 \times 10^7}{1 + 0.5 \cos \theta} \text{ m.}$$

The product of the radial position and the transverse component of the velocity is

$$rv_\theta = 8.72 \times 10^{10} \text{ m}^2/\text{s.}$$

What is the satellite's velocity in terms of polar coordinates when $\theta = 90°$?

13.148* In Problem 13.147, what is the satellite's acceleration in terms of polar coordinates when $\theta = 90°$?

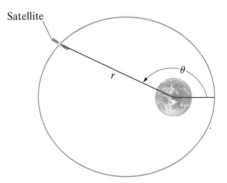

Problems 13.147/13.148

13.149 A bead slides along a wire that rotates in the x–y plane with constant angular velocity ω_0. The radial component of the bead's acceleration is zero. The radial component of its velocity is v_0 when $r = r_0$. Determine the polar components of the bead's velocity as a function of r.

Strategy: The radial component of the bead's velocity is

$$v_r = \frac{dr}{dt},$$

and the radial component of its acceleration is

$$a_r = \frac{d^2r}{dt^2} - r\left(\frac{d\theta}{dt}\right)^2 = \frac{dv_r}{dt} - r\omega_0^2.$$

By using the chain rule,

$$\frac{dv_r}{dt} = \frac{dv_r}{dr}\frac{dr}{dt} = \frac{dv_r}{dr}v_r,$$

you can express the radial component of the acceleration in the form

$$a_r = \frac{dv_r}{dr}v_r - r\omega_0^2.$$

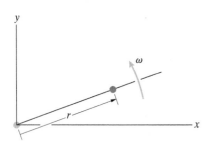

Problem 13.149

13.150 If the motion of a point in the x–y plane is such that its transverse component of acceleration a_θ is zero, show that the product of its radial position and its transverse velocity is constant: $rv_\theta = $ constant.

13.151* From astronomical data, Johannes Kepler deduced that the line from the sun to a planet traces out equal areas in equal times (Fig. a). Show that this result follows from the fact that the transverse component a_θ of the planet's acceleration is zero. [When r changes by an amount dr and θ changes by an amount $d\theta$ (Fig. b), the resulting differential element of area is $dA = \frac{1}{2}r(r\,d\theta)$.]

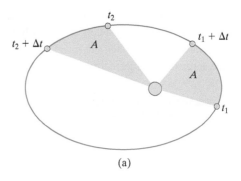

(a)

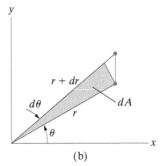

(b)

Problem 13.151

13.152 The bar rotates in the x–y plane with constant angular velocity $\omega_0 = 12$ rad/s. The radial component of acceleration of the collar C (in m/s²) is given as a function of the radial position in meters by $a_r = -8r$. When $r = 1$ m, the radial component of velocity of C is $v_r = 2$ m/s. Determine the velocity of C in terms of polar coordinates when $r = 1.5$ m.

Strategy: Use the chain rule to write the first term in the radial component of the acceleration as

$$\frac{d^2r}{dt^2} = \frac{dv_r}{dt} = \frac{dv_r}{dr}\frac{dr}{dt} = \frac{dv_r}{dr}v_r.$$

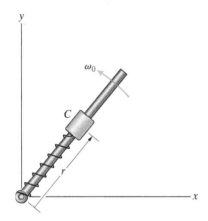

Problem 13.152

13.153 The hydraulic actuator moves the pin P upward with velocity $\mathbf{v} = 2\mathbf{j}$ (m/s). Determine the velocity of the pin in terms of polar coordinates and the angular velocity of the slotted bar when $\theta = 35°$.

13.154 The hydraulic actuator moves the pin P upward with constant velocity $\mathbf{v} = 2\mathbf{j}$ (m/s). Determine the acceleration of the pin in terms of polar coordinates and the angular acceleration of the slotted bar when $\theta = 35°$.

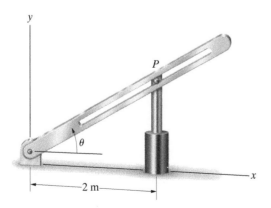

Problems 13.153/13.154

▶ **13.155** In Example 13.15, determine the velocity of the cam follower when $\theta = 135°$ (a) in terms of polar coordinates and (b) in terms of cartesian coordinates.

▶ **13.156*** In Example 13.15, determine the acceleration of the cam follower when $\theta = 135°$ (a) in terms of polar coordinates and (b) in terms of cartesian coordinates.

13.157 In the cam–follower mechanism, the slotted bar rotates with constant angular velocity $\omega = 10$ rad/s and the radial position of the follower A is determined by the profile of the stationary cam. The path of the follower is described by the polar equation

$$r = 1 + 0.5 \cos 2\theta \text{ ft.}$$

Determine the velocity of the cam follower when $\theta = 30°$ (a) in terms of polar coordinates and (b) in terms of cartesian coordinates.

13.158* In Problem 13.157, determine the acceleration of the cam follower when $\theta = 30°$ (a) in terms of polar coordinates and (b) in terms of cartesian coordinates.

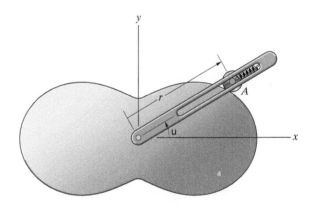

Problems 13.157/13.158

13.159* The cartesian coordinates of a point P in the x–y plane are related to the polar coordinates of the point by the equations $x = r\cos\theta$ and $y = r\sin\theta$.

(a) Show that the unit vectors $\mathbf{i}$ and $\mathbf{j}$ are related to the unit vectors $\mathbf{e}_r$ and $\mathbf{e}_\theta$ by

$$\mathbf{i} = \cos\theta\,\mathbf{e}_r - \sin\theta\,\mathbf{e}_\theta$$

and

$$\mathbf{j} = \sin\theta\,\mathbf{e}_r + \cos\theta\,\mathbf{e}_\theta.$$

(b) Beginning with the expression for the position vector of P in terms of cartesian coordinates, $\mathbf{r} = x\mathbf{i} + y\mathbf{j}$, derive Eq. (13.52) for the position vector in terms of polar coordinates.

(c) By taking the time derivative of the position vector of point P expressed in terms of cartesian coordinates, derive Eq. (13.55) for the velocity in terms of polar coordinates.

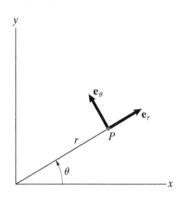

Problem 13.159

13.160 The airplane flies in a straight line at 400 mi/h. The radius of its propeller is 5 ft, and the propeller turns at 2000 rpm in the counterclockwise direction when seen from the front of the airplane. Determine the velocity and acceleration of a point on the tip of the propeller in terms of cylindrical coordinates. (Let the z axis be oriented as shown in the figure.)

Problem 13.160

13.161 A charged particle P in a magnetic field moves along the spiral path described by $r = 1$ m, $\theta = 2z$ rad, where z is in meters. The particle moves along the path in the direction shown with constant speed $|\mathbf{v}| = 1$ km/s. What is the velocity of the particle in terms of cylindrical coordinates?

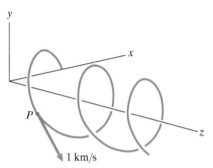

Problem 13.161

13.8 Relative Motion

BACKGROUND

We have discussed the curvilinear motion of a point relative to a given reference frame. In many applications, it is necessary to analyze the motions of two or more points relative to a reference frame and also their motions relative to each other. As a simple example, consider a passenger on a moving bus. If he walks down the aisle, the position and velocity that are important to him are his position in the bus and how fast he is moving down the aisle. His subjective motion is relative to the bus. But he also has a position and velocity relative to the earth. It would be convenient to have a framework for analyzing the bus's motion relative to the earth, the passenger's motion relative to the bus, and his motion relative to the earth. We develop such a framework in this section, introducing concepts and terminology that will be used in many contexts throughout the book.

Let A and B be two points whose motions we want to describe relative to a reference frame with origin O. We denote the positions of A and B relative to O by $\mathbf{r}_A$ and $\mathbf{r}_B$ (Fig. 13.32). We also want to describe the motion of point A relative to point B, and denote the position of A relative to B by $\mathbf{r}_{A/B}$. These vectors are related by

$$\mathbf{r}_A = \mathbf{r}_B + \mathbf{r}_{A/B}. \tag{13.65}$$

Stated in words, *the position of A is equal to the position of B plus the position of A relative to B*. Notice that when we simply say the "position of A" or "position of B," we mean their positions relative to O. The derivative of Eq. (13.65) with respect to time is

$$\frac{d\mathbf{r}_A}{dt} = \frac{d\mathbf{r}_B}{dt} + \frac{d\mathbf{r}_{A/B}}{dt}.$$

We write this equation as

$$\mathbf{v}_A = \mathbf{v}_B + \mathbf{v}_{A/B}, \tag{13.66}$$

where $\mathbf{v}_A$ is the velocity of A relative to O, $\mathbf{v}_B$ is the velocity of B relative to O, and $\mathbf{v}_{A/B} = d\mathbf{r}_{A/B}/dt$ is the velocity of A relative to B. *The velocity of A is equal to the velocity of B plus the velocity of A relative to B*. We now take the derivative of Eq. (13.66) with respect to time,

$$\frac{d\mathbf{v}_A}{dt} = \frac{d\mathbf{v}_B}{dt} + \frac{d\mathbf{v}_{A/B}}{dt},$$

and write this equation as

$$\mathbf{a}_A = \mathbf{a}_B + \mathbf{a}_{A/B}. \tag{13.67}$$

The term $\mathbf{a}_A$ is the acceleration of A relative to O, $\mathbf{a}_B$ is the acceleration of B relative to O, and $\mathbf{a}_{A/B} = d\mathbf{v}_{A/B}/dt$ is the acceleration of A relative to B. *The acceleration of A is equal to the acceleration of B plus the acceleration of A relative to B*.

Although they are simple in form, Eqs. (13.65)–(13.67) and the underlying concepts are extremely useful, and we apply them in a variety of contexts throughout the book.

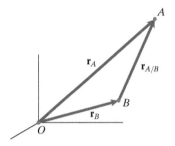

Figure 13.32

RESULTS

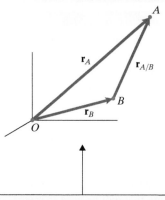

Let $\mathbf{r}_A$ and $\mathbf{r}_B$ be the positions of two points A and B relative to the origin O of a given reference frame. The position of A is equal to the position of B plus the position $\mathbf{r}_{A/B}$ of A relative to B.

$$\mathbf{r}_A = \mathbf{r}_B + \mathbf{r}_{A/B}. \quad (13.65)$$

The velocity of A relative to O is equal to the velocity of B relative to O plus the velocity $\mathbf{v}_{A/B}$ of A relative to B.

$$\mathbf{v}_A = \mathbf{v}_B + \mathbf{v}_{A/B}. \quad (13.66)$$

The acceleration of A relative to O is equal to the acceleration of B relative to O plus the acceleration $\mathbf{a}_{A/B}$ of A relative to B.

$$\mathbf{a}_A = \mathbf{a}_B + \mathbf{a}_{A/B}. \quad (13.67)$$

Active Example 13.16 **Motion of a Ship in a Current** (▶ *Related Problem 13.167*)

A ship moving at 5 knots (nautical miles per hour) relative to the water is in a uniform current flowing east at 2 knots. If the helmsman wants to travel northwest relative to the earth, what direction must he point the ship? What is the resulting magnitude of the ship's velocity relative to the earth?

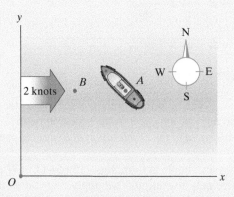

Strategy

Let the reference frame shown be stationary with respect to the earth. We denote the ship by A and define B to be a point that is stationary *relative to the water*. That is, point B is moving toward the east at 2 knots. By applying Eq. (13.66), we can determine the direction of the ship's motion relative to the water and the magnitude of the ship's velocity relative to the earth.

Solution

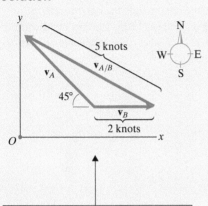

The ship's velocity relative to the earth is equal to the water's velocity relative to the earth plus the ship's velocity relative to the water.

$$\mathbf{v}_A = \mathbf{v}_B + \mathbf{v}_{A/B}.$$

Let v_A be the unknown magnitude of the ship's velocity $\mathbf{v}_A$ relative to the earth, which points northwest.

$$\mathbf{v}_A = -v_A\cos 45°\mathbf{i} + v_A\sin 45°\mathbf{j}.$$

Use the fact that the magnitude of the ship's velocity relative to the water is known, $|v_{A/B}| = 5$ knots, to determine v_A.

$$\begin{cases} \mathbf{v}_{A/B} = \mathbf{v}_A - \mathbf{v}_B = -(v_A\cos 45° + 2 \text{ knots})\mathbf{i} + v_A\sin 45°\mathbf{j}, \\ |\mathbf{v}_{A/B}| = \sqrt{(v_A\cos 45° + 2 \text{ knots})^2 + (v_A\sin 45°)^2} = 5 \text{ knots.} \\ \text{Solving yields } v_A = 3.38 \text{ knots.} \end{cases}$$

Use the solution for v_A to determine the components of the ship's velocity relative to the water. They indicate that the helmsman must point the ship at arctan $(4.39/2.39) = 61.4°$ west of north to travel northwest relative to the earth.

$$\begin{cases} \mathbf{v}_{A/B} = -(v_A\cos 45° + 2 \text{ knots})\mathbf{i} + v_A\sin 45°\mathbf{j}, \\ = -4.39\mathbf{i} + 2.39\mathbf{j} \text{ (knots).} \end{cases}$$

Practice Problem If the helmsman wants to travel due north relative to the earth, what direction must he point the ship? What is the resulting magnitude of the ship's velocity relative to the earth?

Answer: 23.6° west of north, 4.58 knots.

Problems

13.162 At $t = 0$, two projectiles A and B are simultaneously launched from O with the initial velocities and elevation angles shown. Determine the velocity of projectile A relative to projectile B (a) at $t = 0.5$ s and (b) at $t = 1$ s.

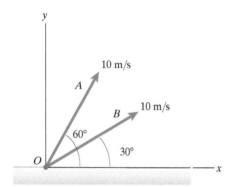

Problem 13.162

13.163 Relative to the earth-fixed coordinate system, the disk rotates about the fixed point O at 10 rad/s. What is the velocity of point A relative to point B at the instant shown?

13.164 Relative to the earth-fixed coordinate system, the disk rotates about the fixed point O with a constant angular velocity of 10 rad/s. What is the acceleration of point A relative to point B at the instant shown?

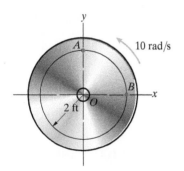

Problems 13.163/13.164

13.165 The train on the circular track is traveling at 50 ft/s. The train on the straight track is traveling at 20 ft/s. In terms of the earth-fixed coordinate system shown, what is the velocity of passenger A relative to passenger B?

13.166 The train on the circular track is traveling at a constant speed of 50 ft/s. The train on the straight track is traveling at 20 ft/s and is increasing its speed at 2 ft/s². In terms of the earth-fixed coordinate system shown, what is the acceleration of passenger A relative to passenger B?

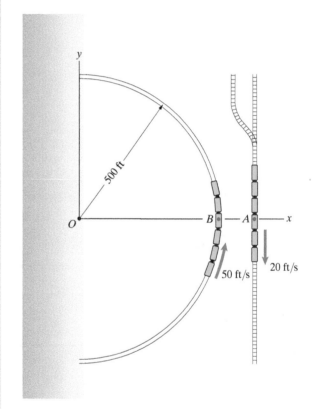

Problems 13.165/13.166

▶ **13.167** In Active Example 13.16, suppose that the velocity of the current increases to 3 knots flowing east. If the helmsman wants to travel northwest relative to the earth, what direction must he point the ship? What is the resulting magnitude of the ship's velocity relative to the earth?

13.168 A private pilot wishes to fly from a city P to a city Q that is 200 km directly north of city P. The airplane will fly with an airspeed of 290 km/h. At the altitude at which the airplane will be flying, there is an east wind (that is, the wind's direction is west) with a speed of 50 km/h. What direction should the pilot point the airplane to fly directly from city P to city Q? How long will the trip take?

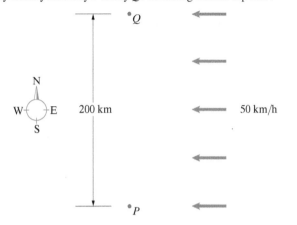

Problem 13.168

13.169 The river flows north at 3 m/s. (Assume that the current is uniform.) If you want to travel in a straight line from point C to point D in a boat that moves at a constant speed of 10 m/s relative to the water, in what direction should you point the boat? How long does it take to make the crossing?

13.170 The river flows north at 3 m/s. (Assume that the current is uniform.) What minimum speed must a boat have relative to the water in order to travel in a straight line from point C to point D? How long does it take to make the crossing?

Strategy: Draw a vector diagram showing the relationships of the velocity of the river relative to the earth, the velocity of the boat relative to the river, and the velocity of the boat relative to the earth. See which direction of the velocity of the boat relative to the river causes its magnitude to be a minimum.

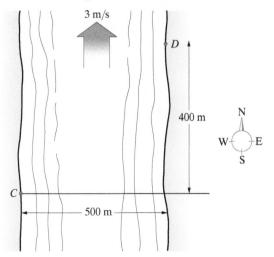

Problems 13.169/13.170

13.171* Relative to the earth, the sailboat sails north with speed $v_0 = 6$ knots (nautical miles per hour) and then sails east at the same speed. The telltale indicates the direction of the wind *relative to the boat*. Determine the direction and magnitude of the wind's velocity (in knots) relative to the earth.

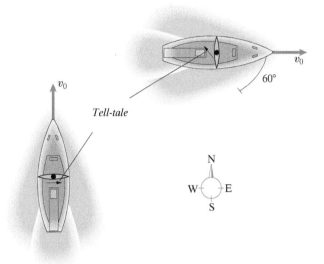

Problem 13.171

Review Problems

13.172 Suppose that you throw a ball straight up at 10 m/s and release it at 2 m above the ground.

(a) What maximum height above the ground does the ball reach?

(b) How long after you release it does the ball hit the ground?

(c) What is the magnitude of its velocity just before it hits the ground?

13.173 Suppose that you must determine the duration of the yellow light at a highway intersection. Assume that cars will be approaching the intersection traveling as fast as 65 mi/h, that drivers' reaction times are as long as 0.5 s, and that cars can safely achieve a deceleration of at least 0.4 g.

(a) How long must the light remain yellow to allow drivers to come to a stop safely before the light turns red?

(b) What is the minimum distance cars must be from the intersection when the light turns yellow to come to a stop safely at the intersection?

13.174 The acceleration of a point moving along a straight line is $a = 4t + 2$ m/s^2. When $t = 2$ s, the position of the point is $s = 36$ m, and when $t = 4$ s, its position is $s = 90$ m. What is the velocity of the point when $t = 4$ s?

13.175 A model rocket takes off straight up. Its acceleration during the 2 s its motor burns is 25 m/s^2. Neglect aerodynamic drag, and determine

(a) the maximum velocity of the rocket during the flight and

(b) the maximum altitude the rocket reaches.

13.176 In Problem 13.175, if the rocket's parachute fails to open, what is the total time of flight from takeoff until the rocket hits the ground?

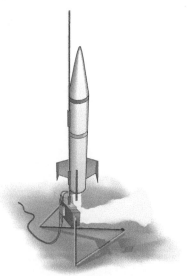

Problems 13.175/13.176

13.177 The acceleration of a point moving along a straight line is $a = -cv^3$, where c is a constant. If the velocity of the point is v_0, what distance does the point move before its velocity decreases to $v_0/2$?

13.178 Water leaves the nozzle at 20° above the horizontal and strikes the wall at the point indicated. What is the velocity of the water as it leaves the nozzle?

Strategy: Determine the motion of the water by treating each particle of water as a projectile.

Problem 13.178

13.179 In practice, the quarterback throws the football with velocity v_0 at 45° above the horizontal. At the same instant, the receiver standing 20 ft in front of him starts running straight downfield at 10 ft/s and catches the ball. Assume that the ball is thrown and caught at the same height above the ground. What is the velocity v_0?

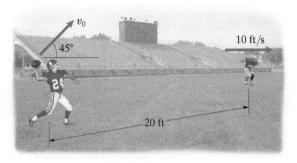

Problem 13.179

13.180 The constant velocity $v = 2$ m/s. What are the magnitudes of the velocity and acceleration of point P when $x = 0.25$ m?

13.181 The constant velocity $v = 2$ m/s. What is the acceleration of point P in terms of normal and tangential components when $x = 0.25$ m?

13.182 The constant velocity $v = 2$ m/s. What is the acceleration of point P in terms of polar coordinates when $x = 0.25$ m?

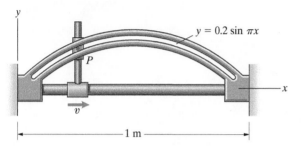

$$y = 0.2 \sin \pi x$$

1 m

Problems 13.180–13.182

13.183 A point P moves along the spiral path $r = (0.1)\theta$ ft, where θ is in radians. The angular position $\theta = 2t$ rad, where t is in seconds, and $r = 0$ at $t = 0$. Determine the magnitudes of the velocity and acceleration of P at $t = 1$ s.

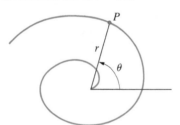

Problem 13.183

13.184 In the cam–follower mechanism, the slotted bar rotates with constant angular velocity $\omega = 12$ rad/s, and the radial position of the follower A is determined by the profile of the stationary cam. The slotted bar is pinned a distance $h = 0.2$ m to the left of the center of the circular cam. The follower moves in a circular path 0.42 m in radius. Determine the velocity of the follower when $\theta = 40°$ (a) in terms of polar coordinates and (b) in terms of cartesian coordinates.

13.185* In Problem 13.184, determine the acceleration of the follower when $\theta = 40°$ (a) in terms of polar coordinates and (b) in terms of cartesian coordinates.

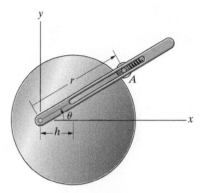

Problems 13.184/13.185

Design Project

Design and carry out experiments to measure the acceleration due to gravity. Galileo (1564–1642) did so by measuring the motions of falling objects. Use his method, but also try to devise other approaches that may result in improved accuracy. Investigate the repeatability of your measurements. Write a brief report describing your experiments, discussing possible sources of error, and presenting your results.

Force, Mass, and Acceleration

Until now, we have analyzed motions of objects without considering the forces that cause them. In this chapter we relate cause and effect: By drawing the free-body diagram of an object to identify the forces acting on it, we can use Newton's second law to determine the acceleration of the object. Alternatively, when we know an object's acceleration, we can use Newton's second law to obtain information about the forces acting on it.

◄ The normal force exerted on his skies by the snow gives the skier a normal component of acceleration, resulting in his curved path.

14.1 Newton's Second Law

BACKGROUND

Newton stated that the total force on a particle is equal to the rate of change of its *linear momentum*, which is the product of its mass and velocity:

$$\mathbf{f} = \frac{d}{dt}(m\mathbf{v}).$$

If the particle's mass is constant, the total force equals the product of its mass and acceleration:

$$\mathbf{f} = m\frac{d\mathbf{v}}{dt} = m\mathbf{a}. \tag{14.1}$$

We pointed out in Chapter 12 that the second law gives precise meanings to the terms *force* and *mass*. Once a unit of mass is chosen, a unit of force is defined to be the force necessary to give one unit of mass an acceleration of unit magnitude. For example, the unit of force in SI units, the newton, is the force necessary to give a mass of one kilogram an acceleration of one meter per second squared. In principle, the second law then gives the value of any force and the mass of any object. By subjecting a one-kilogram mass to an arbitrary force and measuring the acceleration of the mass, we can solve the second law for the direction of the force and its magnitude in newtons. By subjecting an arbitrary mass to a one-newton force and again measuring the acceleration, we can solve the second law for the value of the mass in kilograms.

If the mass of a particle and the total force acting on it are known, Newton's second law determines its acceleration. In Chapter 13, we described how to determine the velocity, position, and trajectory of a point whose acceleration is known. Therefore, with the second law, a particle's motion can be determined when the total force acting on it is known, or the total force can be determined when the motion is known.

Equation of Motion for the Center of Mass

Newton's second law is postulated for a particle, or small element of matter, but an equation of precisely the same form describes the motion of the center of mass of an arbitrary object. We can show that the total external force on an arbitrary object is equal to the product of its mass and the acceleration of its center of mass.

To do so, we consider an arbitrary system of N particles. Let m_i be the mass of the ith particle, and let $\mathbf{r}_i$ be its position vector (Fig. 14.1a). Let m be the total mass of the particles; that is,

$$m = \sum_i m_i,$$

where the summation sign with subscript i means "the sum over i from 1 to N." The position of the center of mass of the system is

$$\mathbf{r} = \frac{\sum_i m_i \mathbf{r}_i}{m}.$$

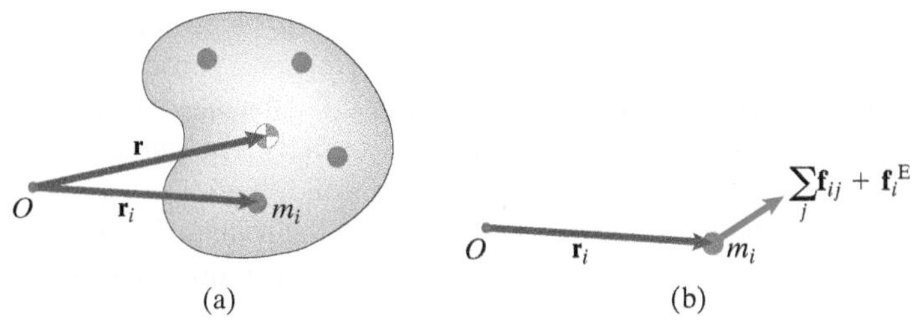

Figure 14.1
(a) Dividing an object into particles. The vector $\mathbf{r}_i$ is the position vector of the ith particle, and $\mathbf{r}$ is the position vector of the object's center of mass.
(b) Forces on the ith particle.

By taking two time derivatives of this expression, we obtain

$$\sum_i m_i \frac{d^2 \mathbf{r}_i}{dt^2} = m \frac{d^2 \mathbf{r}}{dt^2} = m\mathbf{a}, \tag{14.2}$$

where $\mathbf{a}$ is the acceleration of the center of mass.

The ith particle of the system may be acted upon by forces exerted by the other particles. Let $\mathbf{f}_{ij}$ be the force exerted on the ith particle by the jth particle. Then Newton's third law states that the ith particle exerts a force on the jth particle of equal magnitude and opposite direction: $\mathbf{f}_{ji} = -\mathbf{f}_{ij}$. If the external force on the ith particle (i.e., the total force exerted on the ith particle by objects other than the object we are considering) is denoted by $\mathbf{f}_i^{\mathrm{E}}$, Newton's second law for the ith particle is (Fig. 14.1b)

$$\sum_j \mathbf{f}_{ij} + \mathbf{f}_i^{\mathrm{E}} = m_i \frac{d^2 \mathbf{r}_i}{dt^2}.$$

We can write this equation for each particle of the system. Summing the resulting equations from $i = 1$ to N, we obtain

$$\sum_i \sum_j \mathbf{f}_{ij} + \sum_i \mathbf{f}_i^{\mathrm{E}} = \sum_i m_i \frac{d^2 \mathbf{r}_i}{dt^2}. \tag{14.3}$$

The first term on the left side, the sum of the internal forces on the system, is zero due to Newton's third law:

$$\sum_i \sum_j \mathbf{f}_{ij} = \mathbf{f}_{12} + \mathbf{f}_{21} + \mathbf{f}_{13} + \mathbf{f}_{31} + \cdots = \mathbf{0}.$$

The second term on the left side of Eq. (14.3) is the sum of the external forces on the system. Denoting this sum by $\Sigma \mathbf{F}$ and using Eq. (14.2), we conclude that *the sum of the external forces equals the product of the total mass and the acceleration of the center of mass:*

$$\Sigma \mathbf{F} = m\mathbf{a}. \tag{14.4}$$

Because this equation is identical in form to Newton's postulate for a single particle, for convenience we also refer to it as Newton's second law.

Notice that we made no assumptions restricting the nature of the system of particles or its state of motion in obtaining Eq. (14.4). The sum of the external forces on any object or collection of objects, solid, liquid, or gas, equals the product of the total mass and the acceleration of the center of mass.

For example, suppose that the space shuttle is in orbit and has fuel remaining in its tanks. If its engines are turned on, the fuel sloshes in a complicated manner, affecting the shuttle's motion due to internal forces between the fuel and the shuttle. Nevertheless, we can use Eq. (14.4) to determine the exact acceleration of the center of mass of the shuttle, including the fuel it contains, and thereby determine the velocity, position, and trajectory of the center of mass.

Inertial Reference Frames

When we discussed the motion of a point in Chapter 13, we specified the position, velocity, and acceleration of the point relative to an arbitrary reference frame. But Newton's second law cannot be expressed in terms of just any reference frame. Suppose that no force acts on a particle and that we measure the particle's motion relative to a particular reference frame and determine that its acceleration is zero. In terms of this reference frame, Newton's second law agrees with our observation. But if we then measure the particle's motion relative to a second reference frame that is accelerating or rotating with respect to the first one, we would find that the particle's acceleration is *not* zero. In terms of the second reference frame, Newton's second law, at least in the form given by Eq. (14.4), does not predict the correct result.

A well-known example is a person riding in an elevator. Suppose that you conduct an experiment in which you ride in an elevator while standing on a set of scales that measure your weight (Fig. 14.2a). The forces acting on you are your weight W and the force N exerted on you by the scales (Fig. 14.2b). You exert an equal and opposite force N on the scales, which is the force they measure. If the elevator is stationary, you observe that the scales read your weight, $N = W$. The sum of the forces on you is zero, and Newton's second law correctly states that your acceleration relative to the elevator is zero. If the elevator has an upward acceleration a (Fig. 14.2c), you know you will feel heavier, and indeed, you observe that the scales read a force greater than your weight, $N > W$. In terms of an earth-fixed reference frame, Newton's second law correctly relates the forces acting on you to your acceleration: $\Sigma F = N - W = ma$. But suppose that you use the elevator as your frame of reference. Then the sum of the forces acting on you is not zero, so Newton's second law states that you are accelerating relative to the elevator. But you are stationary relative to the elevator. Thus, expressed in terms of this accelerating reference frame, *Newton's second law gives an erroneous result.*

Newton stated that the second law should be expressed in terms of a reference frame at rest with respect to the "fixed stars." Even if the stars were fixed that would not be practical advice, because virtually every convenient reference frame accelerates, rotates, or both. Newton's second law *can* be applied rigorously using reference frames that accelerate and rotate by properly accounting for the acceleration and rotation. We explain how to do this in

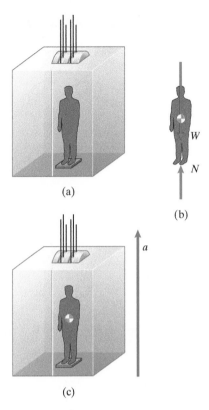

Figure 14.2
(**a**) Riding in an elevator while standing on scales.
(**b**) Your free-body diagram.
(**c**) Upward acceleration of the elevator.

Chapter 17, but for now, we need to give some guidance on when Newton's second law can be applied.

Fortunately, in nearly all "down-to-earth" situations, applying Eq. (14.4) in terms of a reference frame that is fixed relative to the earth results in sufficiently accurate answers. For example, if a piece of chalk is thrown across a room, a reference frame that is fixed relative to the room can be used to predict the chalk's motion. While the chalk is in motion, the earth rotates, and therefore the reference frame rotates. But *because the chalk's flight is brief*, the effect on the prediction is very small. (The earth rotates slowly—its angular velocity is one-half that of a clock's hour hand.) Equation (14.4) can usually be applied using a reference frame that translates (moves without rotating) at constant velocity relative to the earth. For example, if two people play tennis on the deck of a cruise ship moving with constant velocity relative to the earth, Eq. (14.4) can be expressed in terms of a reference frame fixed relative to the ship to analyze the ball's motion. But such a "ship-fixed" reference frame cannot be used if the ship is turning or changing its speed.

A reference frame in which Eq. (14.4) can be applied is said to be *Newtonian*, or *inertial*. We discuss inertial reference frames in greater detail in Chapter 17. For now, it should be assumed examples and problems are expressed in terms of inertial reference frames.

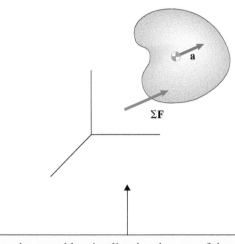

Newton's second law implies that the sum of the external forces on any object equals the product of its mass and the acceleration of its center of mass relative to an inertial reference frame. In many situations, a reference frame (coordinate system) that is fixed with respect to the earth can be assumed to be inertial.

$$\Sigma \mathbf{F} = m\mathbf{a}. \qquad (14.4)$$

In SI units, force is usually expressed in newtons, mass in kilograms, and acceleration in meters per second squared. In U.S. Customary units, force is usually expressed in pounds, mass in slugs, and acceleration in feet per second squared.

14.2 Applications—Cartesian Coordinates and Straight-Line Motion

By drawing the free-body diagram of an object, the external forces acting on it can be identified and Newton's second law used to determine the object's acceleration. Conversely, if the motion of an object is known, Newton's second law can be used to determine the total external force on the object. In particular, if an object's acceleration in a particular direction is known to be zero, the sum of the external forces in that direction must equal zero.

If we express the sum of the forces acting on an object of mass m and the acceleration of its center of mass in terms of their components in a cartesian reference frame (Fig. 14.3), Newton's second law states that

$$\Sigma \mathbf{F} = m\mathbf{a},$$

or

$$(\Sigma F_x \mathbf{i} + \Sigma F_y \mathbf{j} + \Sigma F_z \mathbf{k}) = m(a_x \mathbf{i} + a_y \mathbf{j} + a_z \mathbf{k}).$$

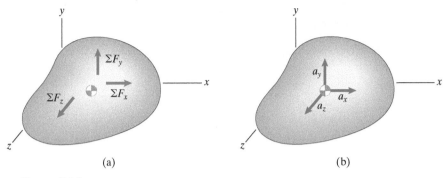

Figure 14.3
(a) Cartesian components of the sum of the forces
   on an object.
(b) Components of the acceleration of the center of
   mass of the object.

Equating x, y, and z components, we obtain three scalar equations of motion:

$$\Sigma F_x = ma_x, \qquad \Sigma F_y = ma_y, \qquad \Sigma F_z = ma_z. \qquad (14.5)$$

The total force in each coordinate direction equals the product of the mass and
the component of the acceleration in that direction.

If an object's motion is confined to the x–y plane, $a_z = 0$, so the sum of the
forces in the z direction is zero. Thus, when the motion is confined to a fixed
plane, the component of the total force normal to that plane equals zero. For
straight-line motion along the x axis (Fig. 14.4a), Eqs. (14.5) are

$$\Sigma F_x = ma_x, \qquad \Sigma F_y = 0, \quad \text{and} \quad \Sigma F_z = 0.$$

We see that in straight-line motion, the components of the total force perpendicular to the line equal zero, and the component of the total force tangent
to the line equals the product of the mass and the acceleration along the line
(Fig. 14.4b).

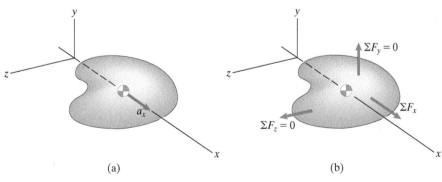

Figure 14.4
(a) Acceleration of an object in straight-line motion
   along the x axis.
(b) The y and z components of the total force acting on
   the object equal zero.

Active Example 14.1 | Straight-Line Motion (▶ *Related Problem 14.1*)

The 100-lb crate is released from rest on the inclined surface at time $t = 0$. The coefficients of friction between the crate and the inclined surface are $\mu_s = 0.2$ and $\mu_k = 0.15$. How fast is the crate moving at $t = 1$ s?

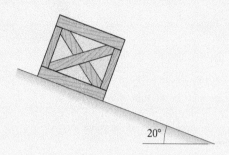

Strategy

We must first determine whether the crate slips when it is released. By assuming that it remains stationary, we can solve for the friction force necessary to keep the crate in equilibrium and see if it exceeds the maximum static friction force the surfaces will support. If the crate slips, we can use Newton's second law to determine its acceleration down the inclined surface. Once the acceleration is known, we can integrate it to determine the velocity of the crate as a function of time.

Solution

> Draw the free-body diagram of the crate. The external forces are the weight of the crate and the normal and friction forces exerted by the inclined surface.

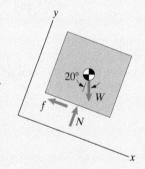

> Assuming that the crate is stationary, use the equilibrium equations to determine the friction force necessary for equilibrium and the normal force.

$$\left\{ \begin{array}{l} \Sigma F_x = W \sin 20° - f = 0, \\ \Sigma F_y = N - W \cos 20° = 0. \end{array} \right.$$

Solving yields

$$f = W \sin 20° = (100 \text{ lb}) \sin 20° = 34.2 \text{ lb},$$
$$N = W \cos 20° = (100 \text{ lb}) \cos 20° = 94.0 \text{ lb}.$$

Calculate the maximum static friction force the surfaces will support. This value is less than the friction force necessary for equilibrium, so *the crate does slip.*

$\longrightarrow \mu_s N = (0.2)(94.0 \text{ lb}) = 18.8 \text{ lb}.$

Apply Newton's second law to determine the crate's acceleration. The magnitude of the friction force on the slipping crate is $\mu_k N$.

$$\Sigma F_x = W \sin 20° - \mu_k N = ma_x :$$

$$a_x = \frac{W \sin 20° - \mu_k N}{m},$$

The mass of the crate is

$$m = \frac{W}{g} = \frac{100 \text{ lb}}{32.2 \text{ ft/s}^2} = 3.11 \text{ slug},$$

so the acceleration is

$$a_x = \frac{(100 \text{ lb}) \sin 20° - (0.15)(94.0 \text{ lb})}{3.11 \text{ slug}} = 6.47 \text{ ft/s}^2.$$

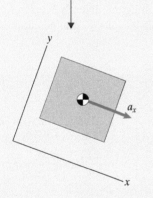

Integrate to determine the crate's velocity as a function of time. At $t = 1$ s, the crate is moving 6.47 ft/s.

$$a_x = \frac{dv_x}{dt} = 6.47 \text{ ft/s}^2,$$

$$\int_0^{v_x} dv_x = \int_0^t 6.47 \, dt,$$

$$v_x = 6.47t \text{ ft/s}.$$

Practice Problem Suppose that the inclined surface is smooth. (We say that a surface is "smooth" when it is assumed to exert negligible friction force.) How fast is the crate moving at $t = 1$ s?

Answer: 11.0 ft/s.

Active Example 14.2   Cartesian Coordinates (▶ *Related Problem 14.10*)

The 2-kg object is constrained to move in the *x–y* plane. The total force on the object is given as a function of time by $\Sigma \mathbf{F} = 6\mathbf{i} + 2t\mathbf{j}$ (N). At $t = 0$, the object's position is $\mathbf{r} = 5\mathbf{i} + 3\mathbf{j}$ (m) and its velocity is $\mathbf{v} = 12\mathbf{i} + 5\mathbf{j}$ (m/s). What is the object's position at $t = 3$ s?

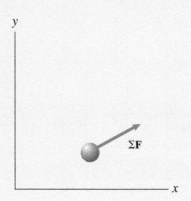

Strategy

We can use Newton's second law to determine the object's acceleration as a function of time, then integrate to determine its velocity and position as functions of time.

Solution

Use Newton's second law to determine the components of the acceleration.

$$
\begin{cases}
a_x = \dfrac{\Sigma F_x}{m} = \dfrac{6\text{ N}}{2\text{ kg}} = 3\text{ m/s}^2, \\[2mm]
a_y = \dfrac{\Sigma F_y}{m} = \dfrac{2t\text{ N}}{2\text{ kg}} = t\text{ m/s}^2.
\end{cases}
$$

Integrate to determine v_x, using the condition $v_x = 12$ m/s at $t = 0$.

$$
\begin{cases}
a_x = \dfrac{dv_x}{dt} = 3\text{ m/s}^2, \\[2mm]
\displaystyle\int_{12}^{v_x} dv_x = \int_0^t 3\,dt, \\[3mm]
v_x = 12 + 3t\text{ m/s}.
\end{cases}
$$

Integrate to determine x, using the condition $x = 5$ m at $t = 0$.

$$
\begin{cases}
v_x = \dfrac{dx}{dt} = 12 + 3t\text{ m/s}, \\[2mm]
\displaystyle\int_5^x dx = \int_0^t (12 + 3t)\,dt, \\[3mm]
x = 5 + 12t + \dfrac{3}{2}t^2\text{ m}.
\end{cases}
$$

Integrate to determine v_y, using the condition $v_y = 5$ m/s at $t = 0$.

$$\begin{cases} a_y = \dfrac{dv_y}{dt} = t \text{ m/s}^2. \\[2mm] \displaystyle\int_5^{v_y} dv_y = \int_0^t t\, dt, \\[2mm] v_y = 5 + \tfrac{1}{2}t^2 \text{ m/s}. \end{cases}$$

Integrate to determine y, using the condition $y = 3$ m at $t = 0$.

$$\begin{cases} v_y = \dfrac{dy}{dt} = 5 + \tfrac{1}{2}t^2 \text{ m/s}. \\[2mm] \displaystyle\int_3^{y} dy = \int_0^t \left(5 + \tfrac{1}{2}t^2\right) dt, \\[2mm] y = 3 + 5t + \tfrac{1}{6}t^3 \text{ m}. \end{cases}$$

Determine the position at $t = 3$ s.

$$\begin{cases} x|_{t=3\,\text{s}} = 5 + 12(3) + \tfrac{3}{2}(3)^2 = 54.5 \text{ m}, \\[2mm] y|_{t=3\,\text{s}} = 3 + 5(3) + \tfrac{1}{6}(3)^3 = 22.5 \text{ m}. \end{cases}$$

Practice Problem The 10-lb object is constrained to move in the x–y plane. The object's position is given as a function of time by $\mathbf{r} = 8t^2\mathbf{i} + t^3\mathbf{j}$ (ft). What total force acts on the object at $t = 4$ s?

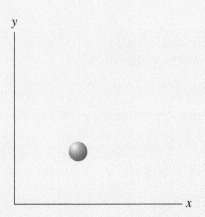

Answer: $\Sigma \mathbf{F} = 4.97\mathbf{i} + 7.45\mathbf{j}$ (lb).

| Example 14.3 | Connected Objects in Straight-Line Motion (▶ *Related Problem 14.28*) |

The two crates are released from rest. Their masses are $m_A = 40$ kg and $m_B = 30$ kg, and the coefficients of friction between crate A and the inclined surface are $\mu_s = 0.2$ and $\mu_k = 0.15$. What is the acceleration of the crates?

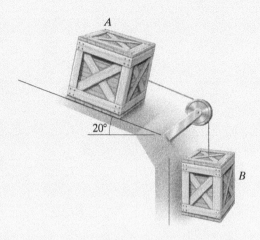

Strategy

We must first determine whether A slips. We will assume that the crates remain stationary and see whether the force of friction necessary for equilibrium exceeds the maximum friction force. If slip occurs, we can determine the resulting acceleration by drawing free-body diagrams of the crates and applying Newton's second law to them individually.

Solution

We draw the free-body diagram of crate A and introduce a coordinate system in Fig. a. If we assume that the crate does not slip, the following equilibrium equations apply:

$$\Sigma F_x = T + m_A g \sin 20° - f = 0;$$

$$\Sigma F_y = N - m_A g \cos 20° = 0.$$

In the first equation, the tension T equals the weight of crate B; therefore, the friction force necessary for equilibrium is

$$f = m_B g + m_A g \sin 20°$$

$$= (30 \text{ kg})(9.81 \text{ m/s}^2) + (40 \text{ kg})(9.81 \text{ m/s}^2) \sin 20°$$

$$= 429 \text{ N}.$$

The normal force $N = m_A g \cos 20°$, so the maximum friction force the surface will support is

$$f_{max} = \mu_s N$$

$$= (0.2)[(40 \text{ kg})(9.81 \text{ m/s}^2) \cos 20°]$$

$$= 73.7 \text{ N}.$$

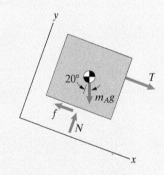

(a) Free-body diagram of crate A.

Crate A will therefore slip, and the friction force is $f = \mu_k N$. We show the crate's acceleration down the plane in Fig. b. Its acceleration perpendicular to the plane is zero (i.e., $a_y = 0$). Applying Newton's second law yields

$$\Sigma F_x = T + m_A g \sin 20° - \mu_k N = m_A a_x$$

$$\Sigma F_y = N - m_A g \cos 20° = 0.$$

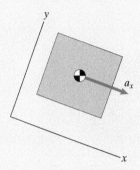

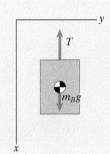

(b) The crate's acceleration.

(c) Free-body diagram of crate B.

In this case, *we do not know* the tension T, because crate B is not in equilibrium. We show the free-body diagram of crate B and its vertical acceleration in Figs. c and d. The equation of motion is

$$\Sigma F_x = m_B g - T = m_B a_x.$$

(In terms of the two coordinate systems we use, the two crates have the same acceleration a_x.) Thus, by applying Newton's second law to both crates, we have obtained three equations in terms of the unknowns T, N, and a_x. Solving for a_x, we obtain $a_x = 5.33$ m/s^2.

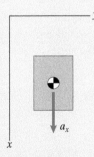

(d) Vertical acceleration of crate B.

(e) The tension is assumed to be the same on both sides of the pulley.

Critical Thinking

Notice that we assumed the tension in the cable to be the same on each side of the pulley (Fig. e). In fact, however, the tensions must be different, because a moment is necessary to cause angular acceleration of the pulley. For now, our only recourse is to assume that the pulley is light enough that the moment necessary to accelerate it is negligible. In Chapter 18 we include the analysis of the angular motion of the pulley in problems of this type and obtain more realistic solutions.

| Example 14.4 | Application to Straight-Line Motion (▶ *Related Problem 14.45*) |

The airplane touches down on the aircraft carrier with a horizontal velocity of 50 m/s relative to the carrier. The arresting gear exerts a horizontal force of magnitude $T_x = 10{,}000v$ newtons (N), where v is the plane's velocity in meters per second. The plane's mass is 6500 kg.

(a) What maximum horizontal force does the arresting gear exert on the plane?

(b) If other horizontal forces can be neglected, what distance does the plane travel before coming to rest?

Strategy

(a) Since the plane begins to decelerate when it contacts the arresting gear, the maximum force occurs at first contact when $v = 50$ m/s.

(b) The horizontal force exerted by the arresting gear equals the product of the plane's mass and its acceleration. Once we know the acceleration, we can integrate to determine the distance required for the plane to come to rest.

Solution

(a) We draw the free-body diagram of the airplane and introduce a coordinate system in Fig. a. The forces T_x and T_y are the horizontal and vertical components of force exerted by the arresting gear, and N is the vertical force on the landing

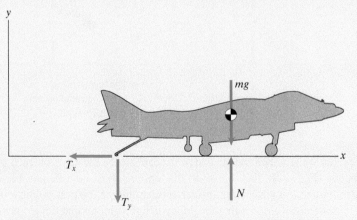

(a) Introducing a coordinate system with the x axis parallel to the horizontal force.

gear. The horizontal force on the plane is $\Sigma F_x = -T_x = -10{,}000v$ N. The magnitude of the maximum force is

$$10{,}000v = (10{,}000)(50) = 500{,}000 \text{ N},$$

or 112,400 lb.

(b) In terms of the plane's horizontal component of acceleration (Fig. b), we obtain the equation of motion

$$\Sigma F_x = ma_x:$$

$$-10{,}000v_x = ma_x.$$

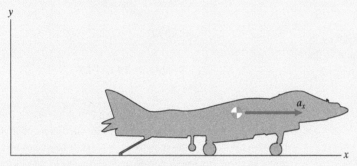

(b) The airplane's horizontal acceleration.

The airplane's acceleration is a function of its velocity. We use the chain rule to express the acceleration in terms of a derivative with respect to x:

$$ma_x = m\frac{dv_x}{dt} = m\frac{dv_x}{dx}\frac{dx}{dt} = m\frac{dv_x}{dx}v_x = -10{,}000v_x.$$

Now we separate variables and integrate, defining $x = 0$ to be the position at which the plane contacts the arresting gear:

$$\int_{50}^{0} m\, dv_x = -\int_{0}^{x} 10{,}000\, dx.$$

Evaluating the integrals and solving for x, we obtain

$$x = \frac{50m}{10{,}000} = \frac{(50)(6500)}{10{,}000} = 32.5 \text{ m}.$$

Critical Thinking

The force exerted by the arresting gear depended on the airplane's velocity, which resulted in an acceleration that depended on velocity. Our use of the chain rule to determine the velocity as a function of position when the acceleration is a function of the velocity is discussed in Section 13.3.

Problems

▶ **14.1** In Active Example 14.1, suppose that the coefficient of kinetic friction between the crate and the inclined surface is $\mu_k = 0.12$. Determine the distance the crate has moved down the inclined surface at $t = 1$ s.

14.2 The mass of the Sikorsky UH-60A helicopter is 9300 kg. It takes off vertically with its rotor exerting a constant upward thrust of 112 kN.

(a) How fast is the helicopter rising 3 s after it takes off?

(b) How high has it risen 3 s after it takes off?

    Strategy: Be sure to draw the free-body diagram of the helicopter.

14.3 The mass of the Sikorsky UH-60A helicopter is 9300 kg. It takes off vertically at $t = 0$. The pilot advances the throttle so that the upward thrust of its engine (in kN) is given as a function of time in seconds by $T = 100 + 2t^2$.

(a) How fast is the helicopter rising 3 s after it takes off?

(b) How high has it risen 3 s after it takes off?

Problems 14.2/14.3

14.4 The horizontal surface is smooth. The 30-lb box is at rest when the constant force F is applied. Two seconds later, the box is moving to the right at 20 ft/s. Determine F.

14.5 The coefficient of kinetic friction between the 30-lb box and the horizontal surface is $\mu_k = 0.1$. The box is at rest when the constant force F is applied. Two seconds later, the box is moving to the right at 20 ft/s. Determine F.

Problems 14.4/14.5

14.6 The inclined surface is smooth. The velocity of the 14-kg box is zero when it is subjected to a constant horizontal force $F = 20$ N. What is the velocity of the box two seconds later?

14.7 The coefficient of kinetic friction between the 14-kg box and the inclined surface is $\mu_k = 0.1$. The velocity of the box is zero when it is subjected to a constant horizontal force $F = 20$ N. What is the velocity of the box two seconds later?

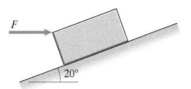

Problems 14.6/14.7

14.8 The 170-lb skier is schussing on a 25° slope. At the instant shown, he is moving at 40 ft/s. The kinetic coefficient of friction between his skis and the snow is $\mu_k = 0.08$. If he makes no attempt to check his speed, how long does it take for it to increase to 60 ft/s?

14.9 The 170-lb skier is schussing on a 25° slope. At the instant shown, he is moving at 40 ft/s. The kinetic coefficient of friction between his skis and the snow is $\mu_k = 0.08$. Aerodynamic drag exerts a resisting force on him of magnitude $0.015v^2$, where v is the magnitude of his velocity. If he makes no attempt to check his speed, how long does it take for it to increase to 60 ft/s?

Problems 14.8/14.9

▶ **14.10** The total external force on the 10-kg object is constant and equal to $\Sigma\mathbf{F} = 90\mathbf{i} - 60\mathbf{j} + 20\mathbf{k}$ (N). At time $t = 0$, its velocity is $\mathbf{v} = -14\mathbf{i} + 26\mathbf{j} + 32\mathbf{k}$ (m/s). What is its velocity at $t = 4$ s? (See Active Example 14.2.)

14.11 The total external force on the 10-kg object shown in Problem 14.10 is given as a function of time by $\Sigma\mathbf{F} = (-20t + 90)\mathbf{i} - 60\mathbf{j} + (10t + 40)\mathbf{k}$ (N). At time $t = 0$, its position is $\mathbf{r} = 40\mathbf{i} + 30\mathbf{j} - 360\mathbf{k}$ (m) and its velocity is $\mathbf{v} = -14\mathbf{i} + 26\mathbf{j} + 32\mathbf{k}$ (m/s). What is its position at $t = 4$ s?

14.12 The position of the 10-kg object is given as a function of time by $\mathbf{r} = (20t^3 - 300)\mathbf{i} + 60t^2\mathbf{j} + (6t^4 - 40t^2)\mathbf{k}$ (m). What is the total external force on the object at $t = 2$ s?

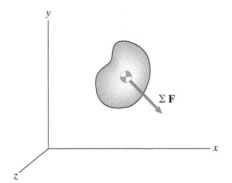

Problems 14.10–14.12

14.13 The total force exerted on the 80,000-lb launch vehicle by the thrust of its engine, its weight, and aerodynamic forces during the interval of time from $t = 2$ s to $t = 4$ s is given as a function of time by $\Sigma\mathbf{F} = (2000 - 400t^2)\mathbf{i} + (5200 + 440t)\mathbf{j} + (800 + 60t^2)\mathbf{k}$ (lb). At $t = 2$ s, its velocity is $\mathbf{v} = 12\mathbf{i} + 220\mathbf{j} - 30\mathbf{k}$ (ft/s). What is its velocity at $t = 4$ s?

Problem 14.13

14.14 At the instant shown, the horizontal component of acceleration of the 26,000-lb airplane due to the sum of the external forces acting on it is 14 ft/s². If the pilot suddenly increases the magnitude of the thrust T by 4000 lb, what is the horizontal component of the plane's acceleration immediately afterward?

Problem 14.14

14.15 At the instant shown, the rocket is traveling straight up at 100 m/s. Its mass is 90,000 kg and the thrust of its engine is 2400 kN. Aerodynamic drag exerts a resisting force (in newtons) of magnitude $0.8v^2$, where v is the magnitude of the velocity. How long does it take for the rocket's velocity to increase to 200 m/s?

Problem 14.15

14.16 A 2-kg cart containing 8 kg of water is initially stationary (Fig. P14.16a). The center of mass of the "object" consisting of the cart and water is at $x = 0$. The cart is subjected to the time-dependent force shown in Fig. P14.16b, where $F_0 = 5$ N and $t_0 = 2$ s. Assume that no water spills out of the cart and that the horizontal forces exerted on the wheels by the floor are negligible.

(a) Do you know the acceleration of the cart during the period $0 < t < t_0$?

(b) Do you know the acceleration of the center of mass of the "object" consisting of the cart and water during the period $0 < t < t_0$?

(c) What is the x coordinate of the center of mass of the "object" when $t > 2t_0$?

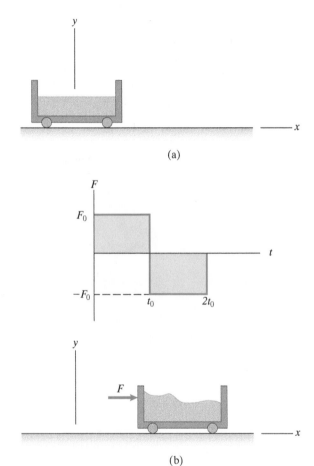

Problem 14.16

14.17 The combined weight of the motorcycle and rider is 360 lb. The coefficient of kinetic friction between the tires and the road is $\mu_k = 0.8$. The rider starts from rest, spinning the rear wheel. Neglect the horizontal force exerted on the front wheel by the road. In two seconds, the motorcycle moves 35 ft. What was the normal force between the rear wheel and the road?

Problem 14.17

14.18 The mass of the bucket B is 180 kg. From $t = 0$ to $t = 2$ s, the x and y coordinates of the center of mass of the bucket are

$$x = -0.2t^3 + 0.05t^2 + 10 \text{ m},$$
$$y = 0.1t^2 + 0.4t + 6 \text{ m}.$$

Determine the x and y components of the force exerted on the bucket by its supports at $t = 1$ s.

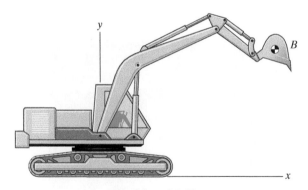

Problem 14.18

14.19 During a test flight in which a 9000-kg helicopter starts from rest at $t = 0$, the acceleration of its center of mass from $t = 0$ to $t = 10$ s is

$$\mathbf{a} = 0.6t\mathbf{i} + (1.8 - 0.36t)\mathbf{j} \ (\text{m/s}^2).$$

What is the magnitude of the total external force on the helicopter (including its weight) at $t = 6$ s?

14.20 The engineers conducting the test described in Problem 14.19 want to express the total force on the helicopter at $t = 6$ s in terms of three forces: the weight W, a component T tangent to the path, and a component L normal to the path. What are the values of W, T, and L?

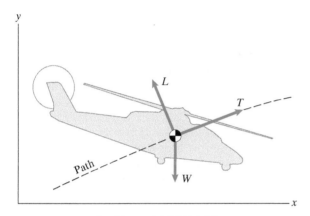

Problems 14.19/14.20

14.21 At the instant shown, the 11,000-kg airplane's velocity is $\mathbf{v} = 270\mathbf{i}$ (m/s). The forces acting on the plane are its weight, the thrust $T = 110$ kN, the lift $L = 260$ kN, and the drag $D = 34$ kN. (The x axis is parallel to the airplane's path.) Determine the magnitude of the airplane's acceleration.

14.22 At the instant shown, the 11,000-kg airplane's velocity is $\mathbf{v} = 300\mathbf{i}$ (m/s). The rate of change of the magnitude of the velocity is $dv/dt = 5$ m/s^2. The radius of curvature of the airplane's path is 4500 m, and the y axis points toward the concave side of the path. The thrust is $T = 120,000$ N. Determine the lift L and drag D.

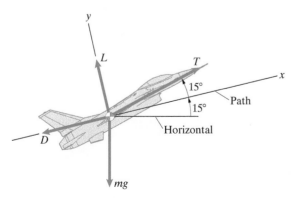

Problems 14.21/14.22

14.23 The coordinates in meters of the 360-kg sport plane's center of mass relative to an earth-fixed reference frame during an interval of time are

$$x = 20t - 1.63t^2,$$
$$y = 35t - 0.15t^3,$$

and

$$z = -20t - 1.38t^2,$$

where t is the time in seconds. The y axis points upward. The forces exerted on the plane are its weight, the thrust vector $\mathbf{T}$ exerted by its engine, the lift force vector $\mathbf{L}$, and the drag force vector $\mathbf{D}$. At $t = 4$ s, determine $\mathbf{T} + \mathbf{L} + \mathbf{D}$.

14.24 The force in newtons exerted on the 360-kg sport plane in Problem 14.23 by its engine, the lift force, and the drag force during an interval of time is

$$\mathbf{T} + \mathbf{L} + \mathbf{D} = (-1000 + 280t)\mathbf{i} + (4000 - 430t)\mathbf{j}$$
$$+ (720 + 200t)\mathbf{k},$$

where t is the time in seconds. If the coordinates of the plane's center of mass are $(0, 0, 0)$ and its velocity is $20\mathbf{i} + 35\mathbf{j} - 20\mathbf{k}$ (m/s) at $t = 0$, what are the coordinates of the center of mass at $t = 4$ s?

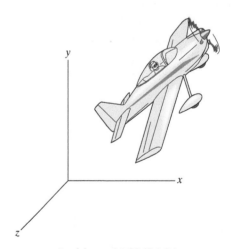

Problems 14.23/14.24

14.25 The robot manipulator is programmed so that $x = 40 + 24t^2$ mm, $y = 4t^3$ mm, and $z = 0$ during the interval of time from $t = 0$ to $t = 4$ s. The y axis points upward. What are the x and y components of the total force exerted by the jaws of the manipulator on the 2-kg widget A at $t = 3$ s?

14.26 The robot manipulator is programmed so that it is stationary at $t = 0$ and the components of the acceleration of A are $a_x = 400 - 0.8v_x$ mm/s² and $a_y = 200 - 0.4v_y$ mm/s² from $t = 0$ to $t = 2$ s, where v_x and v_y are the components of the velocity in mm/s. The y axis points upward. What are the x and y components of the total force exerted by the jaws of the manipulator on the 2-kg widget A at $t = 1$ s?

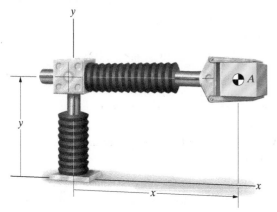

Problems 14.25/14.26

14.27 In the sport of curling, the object is to slide a "stone" weighing 44 lb onto the center of a target located 31 yards from the point of release. In terms of the coordinate system shown, the point of release is at $x = 0, y = 0$. Suppose that a shot comes to rest at $x = 31.0$ yards, $y = 1$ yard. Assume that the coefficient of kinetic friction is constant and equal to $\mu_k = 0.01$. What were the x and y components of the stone's velocity at release?

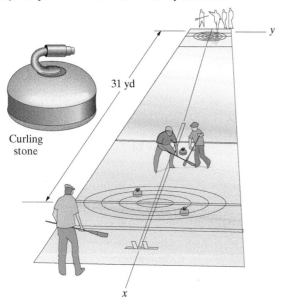

Problem 14.27

▶ **14.28** The two masses are released from rest. How fast are they moving at $t = 0.5$ s? (See Example 14.3.)

Problem 14.28

14.29 The two weights are released from rest. The horizontal surface is smooth. (a) What is the tension in the cable after the weights are released? (b) How fast are the weights moving one second after they are released?

14.30 The two weights are released from rest. The coefficient of kinetic friction between the horizontal surface and the 5-lb weight is $\mu_k = 0.18$. (a) What is the tension in the cable after the weights are released? (b) How fast are the weights moving one second after they are released?

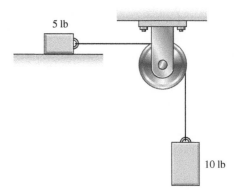

Problems 14.29/14.30

14.31 The mass of each box is 14 kg. One second after they are released from rest, they have moved 0.3 m from their initial positions. What is the coefficient of kinetic friction between the boxes and the surface?

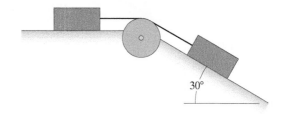

Problem 14.31

14.32 The masses $m_A = 15$ kg and $m_B = 30$ kg, and the coefficients of friction between all of the surfaces are $\mu_s = 0.4$ and $\mu_k = 0.35$. The blocks are stationary when the constant force F is applied. Determine the resulting acceleration of block B if (a) $F = 200$ N; (b) $F = 400$ N.

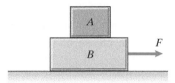

Problem 14.32

14.33 The crane's trolley at A moves to the right with constant acceleration, and the 800-kg load moves without swinging.

(a) What is the acceleration of the trolley and load?

(b) What is the sum of the tensions in the parallel cables supporting the load?

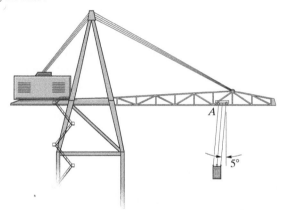

Problem 14.33

14.34 The mass of A is 30 kg and the mass of B is 5 kg. The horizontal surface is smooth. The constant force F causes the system to accelerate. The angle $\theta = 20°$ is constant. Determine F.

14.35 The mass of A is 30 kg and the mass of B is 5 kg. The coefficient of kinetic friction between A and the horizontal surface is $\mu_k = 0.2$. The constant force F causes the system to accelerate. The angle $\theta = 20°$ is constant. Determine F.

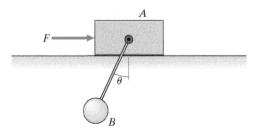

Problems 14.34/14.35

14.36 The 100-lb crate is initially stationary. The coefficients of friction between the crate and the inclined surface are $\mu_s = 0.2$ and $\mu_k = 0.16$. Determine how far the crate moves from its initial position in 2 s if the horizontal force $F = 90$ lb.

14.37 In Problem 14.36, determine how far the crate moves from its initial position in 2 s if the horizontal force $F = 30$ lb.

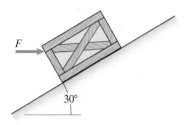

Problems 14.36/14.37

14.38 The crate has a mass of 120 kg, and the coefficients of friction between it and the sloping dock are $\mu_s = 0.6$ and $\mu_k = 0.5$.

(a) What tension must the winch exert on the cable to start the stationary crate sliding up the dock?

(b) If the tension is maintained at the value determined in part (a), what is the magnitude of the crate's velocity when it has moved 2 m up the dock?

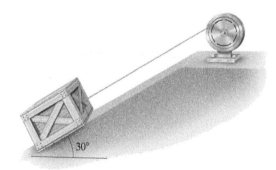

Problem 14.38

14.39 The coefficients of friction between the load A and the bed of the utility vehicle are $\mu_s = 0.4$ and $\mu_k = 0.36$. If the floor is level ($\theta = 0$), what is the largest acceleration (in m/s^2) of the vehicle for which the load will not slide on the bed?

14.40 The coefficients of friction between the load A and the bed of the utility vehicle are $\mu_s = 0.4$ and $\mu_k = 0.36$. The angle $\theta = 20°$. Determine the largest forward and rearward accelerations of the vehicle for which the load will not slide on the bed.

Problems 14.39/14.40

14.41 The package starts from rest and slides down the smooth ramp. The hydraulic device B exerts a constant 2000-N force and brings the package to rest in a distance of 100 mm from the point at which it makes contact. What is the mass of the package?

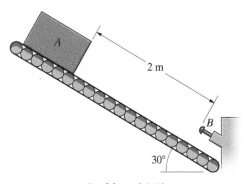

Problem 14.41

14.42 The force exerted on the 10-kg mass by the linear spring is $F = -ks$, where k is the spring constant and s is the displacement of the mass relative to its position when the spring is unstretched. The value of k is 40 N/m. The mass is in the position $s = 0$ and is given an initial velocity of 4 m/s toward the right. Determine the velocity of the mass as a function of s.

Strategy: Use the chain rule to write the acceleration as

$$\frac{dv}{dt} = \frac{dv}{ds}\frac{ds}{dt} = \frac{dv}{ds}v.$$

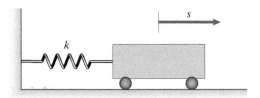

Problem 14.42

14.43 The 450-kg boat is moving at 10 m/s when its engine is shut down. The magnitude of the hydrodynamic drag force (in newtons) is $40v^2$, where v is the magnitude of the velocity in m/s. When the boat's velocity has decreased to 1 m/s, what distance has it moved from its position when the engine was shut down?

Problem 14.43

14.44 A sky diver and his parachute weigh 200 lb. He is falling vertically at 100 ft/s when his parachute opens. With the parachute open, the magnitude of the drag force (in pounds) is $0.5 \, v^2$.

(a) What is the magnitude of the sky diver's acceleration at the instant the parachute opens?

(b) What is the magnitude of his velocity when he has descended 20 ft from the point where his parachute opens?

Problem 14.44

▶ **14.45** The Panavia Tornado with a mass of 18,000 kg lands at a speed of 213 km/h. The decelerating force (in newtons) exerted on it by its thrust reversers and aerodynamic drag is $80{,}000 + 2.5v^2$, where v is the airplane's velocity in m/s. What is the length of the airplane's landing roll? (See Example 14.4.)

Problem 14.45

14.46 A 200-lb bungee jumper jumps from a bridge 130 ft above a river. The bungee cord has an unstretched length of 60 ft and has a spring constant $k = 14$ lb/ft.

(a) How far above the river is the jumper when the cord brings him to a stop?

(b) What maximum force does the cord exert on him?

Problem 14.46

14.47 A helicopter weighs 20,500 lb. It takes off vertically from sea level, and its upward velocity in ft/s is given as a function of its altitude h in feet by $v = 66 - 0.01h$.

(a) How long does it take the helicopter to climb to an altitude of 4000 ft?

(b) What is the sum of the vertical forces on the helicopter when its altitude is 2000 ft?

14.48 In a cathode-ray tube, an electron (mass $= 9.11 \times 10^{-31}$ kg) is projected at O with velocity $\mathbf{v} = (2.2 \times 10^7)\mathbf{i}$ (m/s). While the electron is between the charged plates, the electric field generated by the plates subjects it to a force $\mathbf{F} = -eE\mathbf{j}$, where the charge of the electron $e = 1.6 \times 10^{-19}$ C (coulombs) and the electric field strength $E = 15$ kN/C. External forces on the electron are negligible when it is not between the plates. Where does the electron strike the screen?

14.49 In Problem 14.48, determine where the electron strikes the screen if the electric field strength is $E = 15 \sin(\omega t)$ kN/C, where the frequency $\omega = 2 \times 10^9$ s^{-1}.

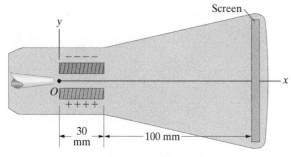

Problems 14.48/14.49

14.50 An astronaut wants to travel from a space station to a satellite S that needs repair. She departs the space station at O. A spring-loaded launching device gives her maneuvering unit an initial velocity of 1 m/s (relative to the space station) in the y direction. At that instant. the position of the satellite is $x = 70$ m, $y = 50$ m, $z = 0$, and it is drifting at 2 m/s (relative to the station) in the x direction. The astronaut intercepts the satellite by applying a constant thrust parallel to the x axis. The total mass of the astronaut and her maneuvering unit is 300 kg.

(a) How long does it take the astronaut to reach the satellite?

(b) What is the magnitude of the thrust she must apply to make the intercept?

(c) What is the astronaut's velocity *relative to the satellite* when she reaches it?

Problem 14.50

14.51 What is the acceleration of the 8-kg collar A relative to the smooth bar?

14.52 Determine the acceleration of the 8-kg collar A relative to the bar if the coefficient of kinetic friction between the collar and the bar is $\mu_k = 0.1$.

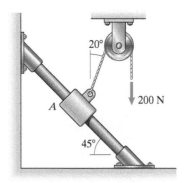

Problems 14.51/14.52

14.53 The force $F = 50$ lb. What is the magnitude of the acceleration of the 20-lb collar A along the smooth bar at the instant shown?

14.54* In Problem 14.53, determine the magnitude of the acceleration of the 20-lb collar A along the bar at the instant shown if the coefficient of static friction between the collar and the bar is $\mu_k = 0.2$.

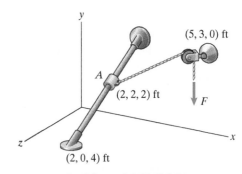

Problems 14.53/14.54

14.55 The 6-kg collar starts from rest at position A, where the coordinates of its center of mass are (400, 200, 200) mm, and slides up the smooth bar to position B, where the coordinates of its center of mass are (500, 400, 0) mm, under the action of a constant force $\mathbf{F} = -40\mathbf{i} + 70\mathbf{j} - 40\mathbf{k}$ (N). How long does the collar take to go from A to B?

14.56* In Problem 14.55, how long does the collar take to go from A to B if the coefficient of kinetic friction between the collar and the bar is $\mu_k = 0.2$?

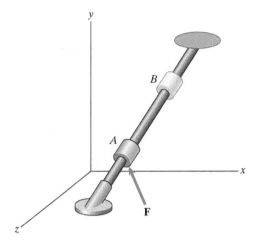

Problems 14.55/14.56

14.57 The crate is drawn across the floor by a winch that retracts the cable at a constant rate of 0.2 m/s. The crate's mass is 120 kg, and the coefficient of kinetic friction between the crate and the floor is $\mu_k = 0.24$.

(a) At the instant shown, what is the tension in the cable?

(b) Obtain a "quasi-static" solution for the tension in the cable by ignoring the crate's acceleration. Compare this solution with your result in part (a).

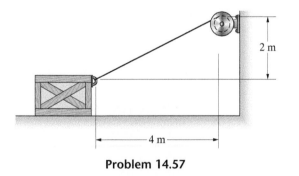

Problem 14.57

14.58 If $y = 100$ mm, $dy/dt = 600$ mm/s, and $d^2y/dt^2 = -200$ mm/s^2, what horizontal force is exerted on the 0.4-kg slider A by the smooth circular slot?

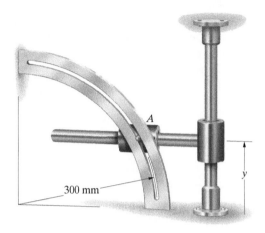

300 mm

Problem 14.58

14.59 The 1-kg collar P slides on the vertical bar and has a pin that slides in the curved slot. The vertical bar moves with constant velocity $v = 2$ m/s. The y axis points upward. What are the x and y components of the total force exerted on the collar by the vertical bar and the slotted bar when $x = 0.25$ m?

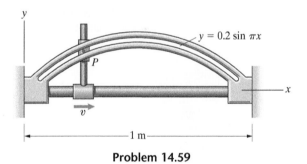

$y = 0.2 \sin \pi x$

1 m

Problem 14.59

14.60* The 1360-kg car travels along a straight road of increasing grade whose vertical profile is given by the equation shown. The magnitude of the car's velocity is a constant 100 km/h. When $x = 200$ m, what are the x and y components of the total force acting on the car (including its weight)?

Strategy: You know that the tangential component of the car's acceleration is zero. You can use this condition together with the equation for the profile of the road to determine the x and y components of the car's acceleration.

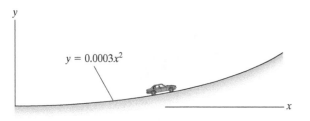

$y = 0.0003x^2$

Problem 14.60

14.61* The two 100-lb blocks are released from rest. Determine the magnitudes of their accelerations if friction at all the contacting surfaces is negligible.

Strategy: Use the fact that the components of the accelerations of the blocks perpendicular to their mutual interface must be equal.

14.62* The two 100-lb blocks are released from rest. The coefficient of kinetic friction between all contacting surfaces is $\mu_k = 0.1$. How long does it take block A to fall 1 ft?

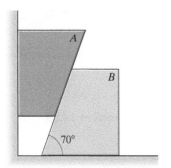

A

B

$70°$

Problems 14.61/14.62

14.63 The 3000-lb vehicle has left the ground after driving over a rise. At the instant shown, it is moving horizontally at 30 mi/h and the bottoms of its tires are 24 in above the (approximately) level ground. The earth-fixed coordinate system is placed with its origin 30 in above the ground, at the height of the vehicle's center of mass when the tires first contact the ground. (Assume that the vehicle remains horizontal.) When that occurs, the vehicle's center of mass initially continues moving downward and then rebounds upward due to the flexure of the suspension system. While the tires are in contact with the ground, the force exerted on them by the ground is $-2400\mathbf{i} - 18,000y\mathbf{j}$ (lb), where y is the vertical position of the center of mass in feet. When the vehicle rebounds, what is the vertical component of the velocity of the center of mass at the instant the wheels leave the ground? (The wheels leave the ground when the center of mass is at $y = 0$.)

24 in

30 in

x

30 in

24 in

y

Problem 14.63

14.64* A steel sphere in a tank of oil is given an initial velocity $\mathbf{v} = 2\mathbf{i}$ (m/s) at the origin of the coordinate system shown. The radius of the sphere is 15 mm. The density of the steel is 8000 kg/m³ and the density of the oil is 980 kg/m³. If V is the sphere's volume, the (upward) buoyancy force on the sphere is equal to the weight of a volume V of oil. The magnitude of the hydrodynamic drag force $\mathbf{D}$ on the sphere as it falls is $|\mathbf{D}| = 1.6|\mathbf{v}|$ N, where $|\mathbf{v}|$ is the magnitude of the sphere's velocity in m/s. What are the x and y components of the sphere's velocity at $t = 0.1$ s?

14.65* In Problem 14.64, what are the x and y coordinates of the sphere at $t = 0.1$ s?

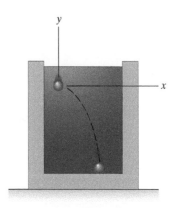

y

x

Problems 14.64/14.65

14.3 Applications—Normal and Tangential Components

When an object moves in a curved path, we can resolve the sum of the forces acting on it into normal and tangential components (Fig. 14.5a). We can also express the object's acceleration in terms of normal and tangential components (Fig. 14.5b) and write Newton's second law, $\Sigma \mathbf{F} = m\mathbf{a}$, in the form

$$\Sigma F_t \mathbf{e}_t + \Sigma F_n \mathbf{e}_n = m(a_t \mathbf{e}_t + a_n \mathbf{e}_n), \tag{14.6}$$

where

$$a_t = \frac{dv}{dt} \quad \text{and} \quad a_n = \frac{v^2}{\rho}.$$

Equating the normal and tangential components in Eq. (14.6), we obtain two scalar equations of motion:

$$\Sigma F_t = ma_t = m\frac{dv}{dt}, \qquad \Sigma F_n = ma_n = m\frac{v^2}{\rho}. \tag{14.7}$$

The sum of the forces in the tangential direction equals the product of the mass and the rate of change of the magnitude of the velocity, and the sum of the forces in the normal direction equals the product of the mass and the normal component of acceleration. If the path of the object's center of mass lies in a plane, the acceleration of the center of mass perpendicular to the plane is zero, so the sum of the forces perpendicular to the plane is zero.

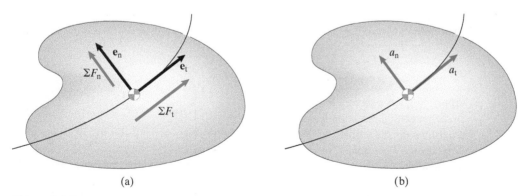

(a)   (b)

Figure 14.5
(a) Normal and tangential components of the sum of the forces on an object.
(b) Normal and tangential components of the acceleration of the center of mass of the object.

Active Example 14.5   Tangential and Normal Components (▶ *Related Problem 14.66*)

The boat, which with its passengers weighs 1200 lb, is moving at 20 ft/s in a circular path with radius $R = 40$ ft. At $t = 0$, the driver advances the throttle so that the tangential component of the total force acting on the boat increases to 100 lb and remains constant. He continues following the same circular path. At $t = 2$ s, determine the magnitude of the boat's velocity and the total force acting on the boat in the direction perpendicular to its path.

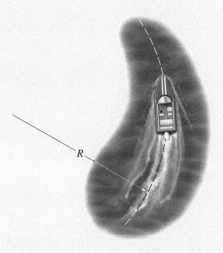

R

Strategy

We can apply Newton's second law in the tangential direction to determine the tangential component of the boat's acceleration and integrate the acceleration to obtain the velocity as a function of time. Once the velocity at $t = 2$ s has been determined, we can apply Newton's second law in the direction perpendicular to the boat's path to determine the total normal force at $t = 2$ s.

Solution

Determine the boat's mass. ⟶ $m = \dfrac{W}{g} = \dfrac{1200 \text{ lb}}{32.2 \text{ ft/s}^2} = 37.3 \text{ slug}.$

Apply Newton's second law in the tangential direction to determine the tangential component of the boat's acceleration.

$$\begin{cases} \Sigma F_t = m a_t: \\ 100 \text{ lb} = (37.3 \text{ slug}) a_t, \\ a_t = \dfrac{100 \text{ lb}}{37.3 \text{ slug}} \\ = 2.68 \text{ ft/s}^2 \end{cases}$$

<table>
<tr>
<td>

Integrate the tangential acceleration to determine the boat's velocity as a function of time.

</td>
<td>

$$a_t = \frac{dv}{dt} = 2.68 \text{ ft/s}^2:$$

$$\int_{20}^{v} dv = \int_{0}^{t} 2.68 \, dt,$$

$$v = 20 + 2.68t \text{ ft/s}.$$

</td>
</tr>
<tr>
<td>

Evaluate the velocity at $t = 2$ s.

</td>
<td>

$$v = 20 + 2.68(2)$$

$$= 25.4 \text{ ft/s}.$$

</td>
</tr>
<tr>
<td>

Determine the normal component of the boat's acceleration at $t = 2$ s.

</td>
<td>

$$a_n = \frac{v^2}{\rho} = \frac{(25.4 \text{ ft/s})^2}{40 \text{ ft}} = 16.1 \text{ ft/s}^2.$$

</td>
</tr>
<tr>
<td>

Apply Newton's second law in the normal direction to determine the normal force acting on the boat at $t = 2$ s.

</td>
<td>

$$\Sigma F_n = ma_n$$

$$= (37.3 \text{ slugs})(16.1 \text{ ft/s}^2)$$

$$= 600 \text{ lb}.$$

</td>
</tr>
</table>

Practice Problem The boat is moving at 20 ft/s in a circular path with radius $R = 40$ ft. Suppose that at $t = 0$ the driver advances the throttle so that the tangential component of the total force (in pounds) acting on the boat is given as a function of time by $\Sigma F_t = 200t$. He continues following the same circular path. At $t = 2$ s, determine the magnitude of the boat's velocity and the total force acting on the boat in the direction perpendicular to its path.

Answer: Velocity is 30.7 ft/s, normal force is 880 lb.

Active Example 14.6 | Train on a Banked Track (▶ *Related Problem 14.79*)

The train is supported by magnetic repulsion forces exerted in the direction perpendicular to the track. Motion of the train in the transverse direction is prevented by lateral supports. The 20,000-kg train is traveling at 30 m/s on a circular segment of track with radius $R = 150$ m, and the bank angle of the track is 40°. What force must the magnetic levitation system exert to support the train, and what force is exerted by the lateral supports?

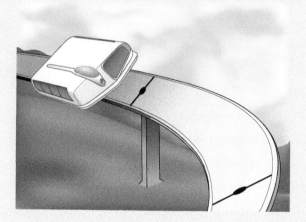

Strategy

We know the train's velocity and the radius of its circular path, so we can determine its normal component of acceleration. By expressing Newton's second law in terms of normal and tangential components, we can determine the components of force normal and transverse to the track.

Solution

View of the train from above showing the normal and tangential unit vectors. The vector $\mathbf{e}_t$ is tangential to the train's path and the vector $\mathbf{e}_n$ points toward the center of its circular path.

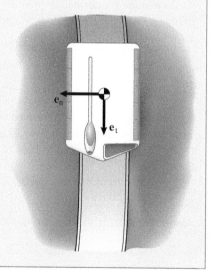

View of the front of the train. The forces acting on it are its weight, the magnetic force M normal to the track, and the force S exerted by the lateral supports.	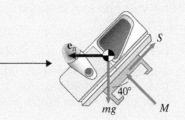

The sum of the forces in the vertical direction (perpendicular to the train's circular path) must equal zero.

$$M \cos 40° + S \sin 40° - mg = 0. \quad (1)$$

Apply Newton's second law in the $\mathbf{e}_n$ direction.

$$\begin{cases} \Sigma F_n = ma_n: \\ M \sin 40° - S \cos 40° = m\dfrac{v^2}{\rho}. \quad (2) \end{cases}$$

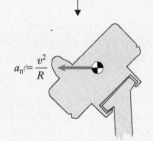

Solving Eqs. (1) and (2) with $m = 20{,}000$ kg, $g = 9.81$ m/s^2, $v = 30$ m/s, and $\rho = 150$ m yields $M = 227$ kN and $S = 34.2$ kN.

Practice Problem For what speed v of the train would the lateral force S be zero? (This is the optimum speed for the train to travel on the banked track. If you were a passenger, you would not need to exert any lateral force to remain in place in your seat.)

Answer: 35.1 m/s.

Example 14.7   Newton's Second Law in Normal and Tangential Components
(▶ *Related Problem 14.73*)

Future space stations may be designed to rotate in order to provide simulated gravity for their inhabitants. If the distance from the axis of rotation of the station to the occupied outer ring is $R = 100$ m, what rotation rate is necessary to simulate one-half of earth's gravity?

Strategy
By drawing the free-body diagram of a person and expressing Newton's second law in terms of normal and tangential components, we can relate the force exerted on the person by the floor to the angular velocity of the station. The person exerts an equal and opposite force on the floor, which is his effective weight.

Solution
We draw the free-body diagram of a person standing in the outer ring in Fig. a, where N is the force exerted on him by the floor. Relative to a nonrotating reference frame with its origin at the center of the station, the person moves in a

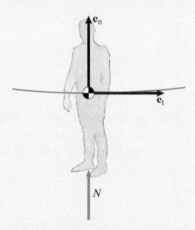

(a) Free-body diagram of a person standing in the occupied ring.

circular path of radius R. His normal and tangential components of acceleration are shown in Fig. b. Applying Eqs. (14.7), we obtain

$$\Sigma F_\mathrm{t} = 0 = m\frac{dv}{dt}$$

and

$$\Sigma F_\mathrm{n} = N = m\frac{v^2}{R}.$$

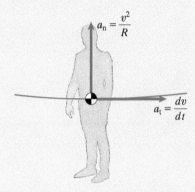

(b) The person's normal and tangential components of acceleration.

The first equation simply indicates that the magnitude of the person's velocity is constant. The second equation tells us the force N. The magnitude of his velocity is $v = R\omega$, where ω is the angular velocity of the station. If one-half of earth's gravity is simulated, $N = \frac{1}{2}mg$. Therefore

$$N = \frac{1}{2}mg = m\frac{(R\omega)^2}{R}.$$

Solving for ω, we obtain the necessary angular velocity of the station:

$$\omega = \sqrt{\frac{g}{2R}} = \sqrt{\frac{9.81 \text{ m/s}^2}{2(100 \text{ m})}} = 0.221 \text{ rad/s}.$$

This is one revolution every 28.4 s.

Critical Thinking

When you are standing in a room, the floor pushes upward on you with a force N equal to your weight. The effect of gravity on your body is indistinguishable from the effect of a force of magnitude N pushing on your feet and accelerating you upward with acceleration g in the absence of gravity. (This observation was one of Einstein's starting points in developing his general theory of relativity.) This is the basis of simulating gravity by using rotation, and it explains why we set $N = mg/2$ in this example to simulate one-half of earth's gravity.

Example 14.8 | **Motor Vehicle Dynamics** (▶ *Related Problems 14.89, 14.90*)

A civil engineer's preliminary design for a freeway off-ramp is circular with radius $R = 60$ m. If she assumes that the coefficient of static friction between tires and road is at least $\mu_s = 0.4$, what is the maximum speed at which vehicles can enter the ramp without losing traction?

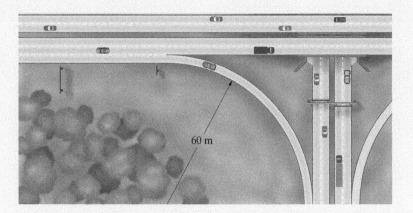

60 m

Strategy

Since a vehicle on the off-ramp moves in a circular path, it has a normal component of acceleration that depends on its velocity. The necessary normal component of force is exerted by friction between the tires and the road, and the friction force cannot be greater than the product of μ_s and the normal force. By assuming that the friction force is equal to this value, we can determine the maximum velocity for which slipping will not occur.

Solution

We view the free-body diagram of a car on the off-ramp from above the car in Fig. a and from the front of the car in Fig. b. In Fig. c, we show the car's acceleration, which is perpendicular to the circular path of the car and toward the center of the path. The sum of the forces in the $\mathbf{e}_n$ direction equals the product of the mass and the normal component of the acceleration; that is,

$$\Sigma F_n = ma_n = m\frac{v^2}{R},$$

or

$$f = m\frac{v^2}{R}.$$

The required friction force increases as v increases. The maximum friction force the surfaces will support is $f_{max} = \mu_s N = \mu_s mg$. Therefore, the maximum velocity for which slipping does not occur is

$$v = \sqrt{\mu_s g R} = \sqrt{0.4(9.81 \text{ m/s}^2)(60 \text{ m})} = 15.3 \text{ m/s},$$

or 55.2 km/h (34.3 mi/h).

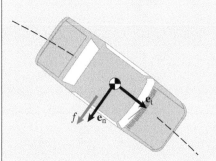

(a) Top view of the free-body diagram.

f $\mathbf{e}_n$ $\mathbf{e}_t$

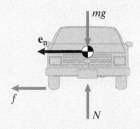

mg

$\mathbf{e}_n$

f

N

(b) Front view of the free-body diagram.

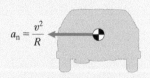

$a_n = \dfrac{v^2}{R}$

(c) The acceleration seen in the front view.

Problems

▶ **14.66** The boat in Active Example 14.5 weighs 1200 lb with its passengers. Suppose that the boat is moving at a constant speed of 20 ft/s in a circular path with radius $R = 40$ ft. Determine the tangential and normal components of force acting on the boat.

14.67 In preliminary design studies for a sun-powered car, it is estimated that the mass of the car and driver will be 100 kg and the torque produced by the engine will result in a 60-N tangential force on the car. Suppose that the car starts from rest on the track at A and is subjected to a constant 60-N tangential force. Determine the magnitude of the car's velocity and the normal component of force on the car when it reaches B.

14.68 In a test of a sun-powered car, the mass of the car and driver is 100 kg. The car starts from rest on the track at A, moving toward the right. The tangential force exerted on the car (in newtons) is given as a function of time by $\Sigma F_t = 20 + 1.2t$. Determine the magnitude of the car's velocity and the normal component of force on the car at $t = 40$ s.

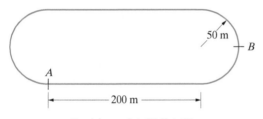

Problems 14.67/14.68

14.69 An astronaut candidate with a mass of 72 kg is tested in a centrifuge with a radius of 10 m. The centrifuge rotates in the horizontal plane. It starts from rest at time $t = 0$ and has a constant angular acceleration of 0.2 rad/s². Determine the magnitude of the horizontal force exerted on him by the centrifuge (a) at $t = 0$; (b) at $t = 10$ s.

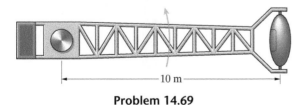

Problem 14.69

14.70 The circular disk lies *in the horizontal plane*. At the instant shown, the disk rotates with a counterclockwise angular velocity of 4 rad/s and a counterclockwise angular acceleration of 2 rad/s². The 0.5-kg slider A is supported horizontally by the smooth slot and the string attached at B. Determine the tension in the string and the magnitude of the horizontal force exerted on the slider by the slot.

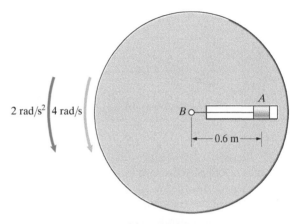

Problem 14.70

14.71 The circular disk lies *in the horizontal plane* and rotates with a constant counterclockwise angular velocity of 4 rad/s. The 0.5-kg slider A is supported horizontally by the smooth slot and the string attached at B. Determine the tension in the string and the magnitude of the horizontal force exerted on the slider by the slot.

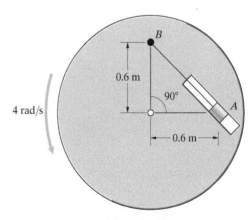

Problem 14.71

14.72 The 32,000-lb airplane is flying in the vertical plane at 420 ft/s. At the instant shown, the angle $\theta = 30°$, and the cartesian components of the plane's acceleration are $a_x = -6$ ft/s^2, $a_y = 30$ ft/s^2.

(a) What are the tangential and normal components of the total force acting on the airplane (including its weight)?

(b) What is $d\theta/dt$ in degrees per second?

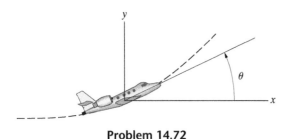

Problem 14.72

▶ **14.73** Consider a person with a mass of 72 kg who is in the space station described in Example 14.7. When he is in the occupied outer ring, his simulated weight in newtons is $\frac{1}{2}(72 \text{ kg})(9.81 \text{ m/s}^2) = 353$ N. Suppose that he climbs to a position in one of the radial tunnels that leads to the center of the station. Let r be his distance in meters from the center of the station. (a) Determine his simulated weight in his new position in terms of r. (b) What would his simulated weight be when he reaches the center of the station?

14.74 Small parts on a conveyer belt moving with constant velocity v are allowed to drop into a bin. Show that the angle θ at which the parts start sliding on the belt satisfies the equation

$$\cos \theta - \frac{1}{\mu_s} \sin \theta = \frac{v^2}{gR},$$

where μ_s is the coefficient of static friction between the parts and the belt.

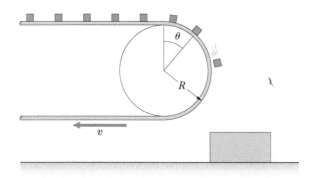

Problem 14.74

14.75 The 1-slug mass m rotates around the vertical pole in a horizontal circular path. The angle $\theta = 30°$ and the length of the string is $L = 4$ ft. What is the magnitude of the velocity of the mass?

Strategy: Notice that the vertical acceleration of the mass is zero. Draw the free-body diagram of the mass and write Newton's second law in terms of tangential and normal components.

14.76 The 1-slug mass m rotates around the vertical pole in a horizontal circular path. The length of the string is $L = 4$ ft. Determine the magnitude of the velocity of the mass and the angle θ if the tension in the string is 50 lb.

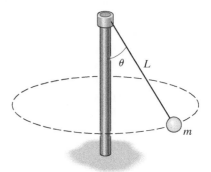

Problems 14.75/14.76

14.77 The 10-kg mass m rotates around the vertical pole in a horizontal circular path of radius $R = 1$ m. If the magnitude of the velocity of the mass is $v = 3$ m/s, what are the tensions in the strings A and B?

14.78 The 10-kg mass m rotates around the vertical pole in a horizontal circular path of radius $R = 1$ m. For what range of values of the velocity v of the mass will the mass remain in the circular path described?

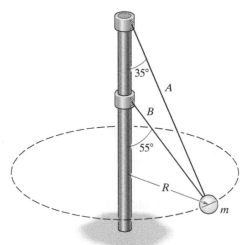

Problems 14.77/14.78

▶ **14.79** Suppose you are designing a monorail transportation system that will travel at 50 m/s, and you decide that the angle θ that the cars swing out from the vertical when they go through a turn must not be larger than 20°. If the turns in the track consist of circular arcs of constant radius R, what is the minimum allowable value of R? (See Active Example 14.6.)

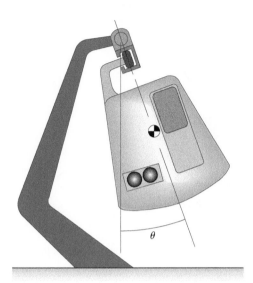

Problem 14.79

14.80 An airplane of weight $W = 200,000$ lb makes a turn at constant altitude and at constant velocity $v = 600$ ft/s. The bank angle is 15°.

(a) Determine the lift force L.

(b) What is the radius of curvature of the plane's path?

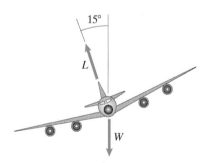

Problem 14.80

14.81 The suspended 2-kg mass m is stationary.

(a) What are the tensions in the strings A and B?

(b) If string A is cut, what is the tension in string B immediately afterward?

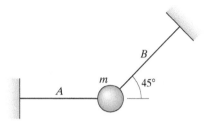

Problem 14.81

14.82 The airplane flies with constant velocity v along a circular path in the vertical plane. The radius of the airplane's circular path is 2000 m. The mass of the pilot is 72 kg.

(a) The pilot will experience "weightlessness" at the top of the circular path if the airplane exerts no net force on him at that point. Draw a free-body diagram of the pilot and use Newton's second law to determine the velocity v necessary to achieve this condition.

(b) Suppose that you don't want the force exerted on the pilot by the airplane to exceed four times his weight. If he performs this maneuver at $v = 200$ m/s, what is the minimum acceptable radius of the circular path?

Problem 14.82

14.83 The smooth circular bar rotates with constant angular velocity ω_0 about the vertical axis AB. The radius $R = 0.5$ m. The mass m remains stationary relative to the circular bar at $\beta = 40°$. Determine ω_0.

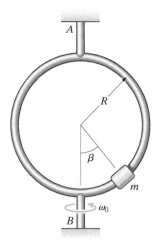

Problem 14.83

14.84 The force exerted on a charged particle by a magnetic field is

$$\mathbf{F} = q\mathbf{v} \times \mathbf{B},$$

where q and $\mathbf{v}$ are the charge and velocity vector of the particle and $\mathbf{B}$ is the magnetic field vector. A particle of mass m and positive charge q is projected at O with velocity $\mathbf{v} = v_0\mathbf{i}$ into a uniform magnetic field $\mathbf{B} = B_0\mathbf{k}$. Using normal and tangential components, show that (a) the magnitude of the particle's velocity is constant and (b) the particle's path is a circle with radius mv_0/qB_0.

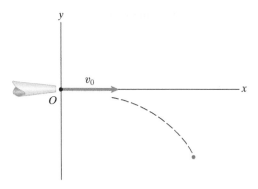

Problem 14.84

14.85 The mass m is attached to a string that is wrapped around the fixed post of radius R. At $t = 0$, the mass is given a velocity v_0 as shown. Neglect external forces on m other than the force exerted by the string. Determine the tension in the string as a function of the angle θ.

   Strategy: The velocity vector of the mass is perpendicular to the string. Express Newton's second law in terms of normal and tangential components.

14.86 The mass m is attached to a string that is wrapped around the fixed post of radius R. At $t = 0$, the mass is given a velocity v_0 as shown. Neglect external forces on m other than the force exerted by the string. Determine the angle θ as a function of time.

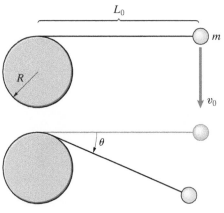

Problems 14.85/14.86

14.87 The sum of the forces in newtons exerted on the 360-kg sport plane (including its weight) during an interval of time is

$$(-1000 + 280t)\mathbf{i} + (480 - 430t)\mathbf{j} + (720 + 200t)\mathbf{k},$$

where t is the time in seconds. At $t = 0$, the velocity of the plane's center of mass relative to the earth-fixed reference frame is $20\mathbf{i} + 35\mathbf{j} - 20\mathbf{k}$ (m/s). If you resolve the sum of the forces on the plane into components tangent and normal to the plane's path at $t = 2$ s, what are the values of ΣF_t and ΣF_n?

14.88 In Problem 14.87, what is the instantaneous radius of curvature of the plane's path at $t = 2$ s? The vector components of the sum of the forces in the directions tangential and normal to the path lie in the osculating plane. Determine the components of a unit vector perpendicular to the osculating plane at $t = 2$ s.

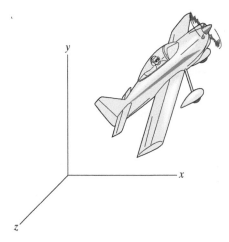

Problems 14.87/14.88

▶ **14.89** The freeway off-ramp is circular with 60-m radius (Fig. a). The off-ramp has a slope $\beta = 15°$ (Fig. b). If the coefficient of static friction between the tires of a car and the road is $\mu_s = 0.4$, what is the maximum speed at which it can enter the ramp without losing traction? (See Example 14.8.)

▶ **14.90*** The freeway off-ramp is circular with 60-m radius (Fig. a). The off-ramp has a slope β (Fig. b). If the coefficient of static friction between the tires of a car and the road is $\mu_s = 0.4$ what minimum slope β is needed so that the car could (in theory) enter the off-ramp at any speed without losing traction? (See Example 14.8.)

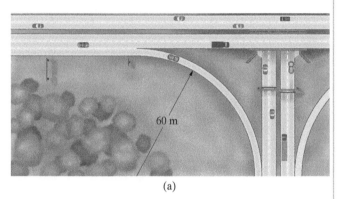

(a)

(b)

Problems 14.89/14.90

14.91 A car traveling at 30 m/s is at the top of a hill. The coefficient of kinetic friction between the tires and the road is $\mu_k = 0.8$. The instantaneous radius of curvature of the car's path is 200 m. If the driver applies the brakes and the car's wheels lock, what is the resulting deceleration of the car in the direction tangent to its path?

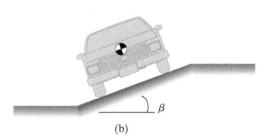

Problem 14.91

14.92 A car traveling at 30 m/s is at the bottom of a depression. The coefficient of kinetic friction between the tires and the road is $\mu_k = 0.8$. The instantaneous radius of curvature of the car's path is 200 m. If the driver applies the brakes and the car's wheel's lock, what is the resulting deceleration of the car in the direction tangential to its path? Compare your answer to that of Problem 14.91.

Problem 14.92

14.93 The combined mass of the motorcycle and rider is 160 kg. The motorcycle starts from rest at $t = 0$ and moves along a circular track with a 400-m radius. The tangential component of acceleration of the motorcycle as a function of time is $a_t = 2 + 0.2t$ m/s². The coefficient of static friction between the tires and the track is $\mu_s = 0.8$. How long after it starts does the motorcycle reach the limit of adhesion, which means that its tires are on the verge of slipping? How fast is the motorcycle moving when that occurs?

Strategy: Draw a free-body diagram showing the tangential and normal components of force acting on the motorcycle.

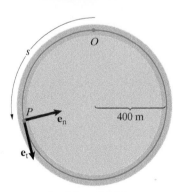

Problem 14.93

14.4 Applications—Polar and Cylindrical Coordinates

When an object moves in a planar curved path, we can describe the motion of the center of mass of the object in terms of polar coordinates. Resolving the sum of the forces parallel to the plane into polar components (Fig. 14.6a) and expressing the acceleration of the center of mass in terms of polar components (Fig. 14.6b), we can write Newton's second law, $\Sigma\mathbf{F} = m\mathbf{a}$, in the form

$$\Sigma F_r \mathbf{e}_r + \Sigma F_\theta \mathbf{e}_\theta = m(a_r \mathbf{e}_r + a_\theta \mathbf{e}_\theta), \tag{14.8}$$

where

$$a_r = \frac{d^2 r}{dt^2} - r\left(\frac{d\theta}{dt}\right)^2 = \frac{d^2 r}{dt^2} - r\omega^2$$

and

$$a_\theta = r\frac{d^2\theta}{dt^2} + 2\frac{dr}{dt}\frac{d\theta}{dt} = r\alpha + 2\frac{dr}{dt}\omega.$$

Equating the $\mathbf{e}_r$ and $\mathbf{e}_\theta$ components in Eq. (14.8), we obtain the scalar equations

$$\Sigma F_r = ma_r = m\left(\frac{d^2 r}{dt^2} - r\omega^2\right) \tag{14.9}$$

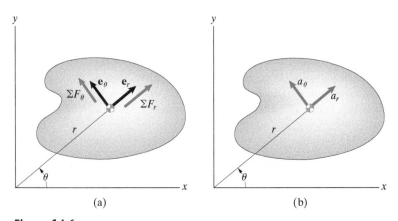

Figure 14.6
Polar components of (a) the sum of the forces and (b) the acceleration of the center of mass.

and

$$\Sigma F_\theta = ma_\theta = m\left(r\alpha + 2\frac{dr}{dt}\omega\right).$$ (14.10)

We can describe the three-dimensional motion of an object using cylindrical coordinates, in which the position of the center of mass perpendicular to the x–y plane is measured by the coordinate z and the unit vector $\mathbf{e}_z$ points in the positive z direction. We resolve the sum of the forces into radial, transverse, and z components (Fig. 14.7a) and express the acceleration of the center of mass in terms of radial, transverse, and z components (Fig. 14.7b). The three scalar equations of motion are the polar equations (14.9) and (14.10) and the equation of motion in the z direction,

$$\Sigma F_z = ma_z = m\frac{dv_z}{dt} = m\frac{d^2z}{dt^2}.$$ (14.11)

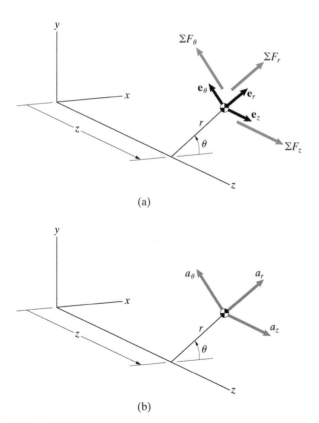

(a)

(b)

Figure 14.7
(a) Components of the sum of the forces on an object in cylindrical coordinates.
(b) Components of the acceleration of the center of mass.

Active Example 14.9 | **Polar Coordinates** (▶ *Related Problems 14.98, 14.99*)

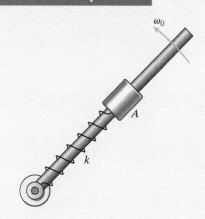

The smooth bar rotates *in the horizontal plane* with constant angular velocity ω_0. The unstretched length of the linear spring is r_0. The collar A has mass m and is released at $r = r_0$ with no radial velocity. Determine the radial velocity of the collar as a function of r.

Strategy

The only force on the collar in the radial direction is the force of the spring, which we can express in polar coordinates in terms of r. By integrating Eq. (14.9), we can determine the radial component of the velocity $v_r = dr/dt$ as a function of r.

Solution

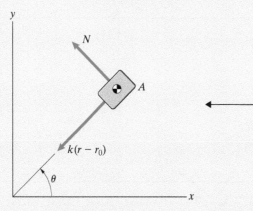

Free-body diagram of the collar A with the force exerted by the spring expressed in terms of r. The bar exerts a transverse force N on the collar.

Apply Newton's second law in the radial direction. This results in an equation for the radial component of the acceleration as a function of r.

$$\Sigma F_r = ma_r:$$

$$-k(r - r_0) = m\left(\frac{d^2r}{dt^2} - r\omega^2\right) = m\left(\frac{dv_r}{dt} - r\omega_0^2\right),$$

which we can write as

$$\frac{dv_r}{dt} = r\omega_0^2 - \frac{k}{m}(r - r_0).$$

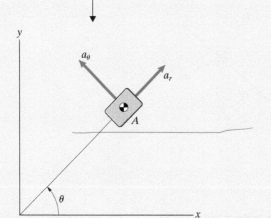

Use the chain rule to express the radial acceleration in terms of r instead of t, separate variables, and integrate.

$$\begin{cases} \dfrac{dv_r}{dt} = \dfrac{dv_r}{dr}\dfrac{dr}{dt} = \dfrac{dv_r}{dr}v_r = r\omega_0^2 - \dfrac{k}{m}(r - r_0), \\[2mm] \displaystyle\int_0^{v_r} v_r\,dv_r = \int_{r_0}^r \left[\left(\omega_0^2 - \dfrac{k}{m}\right)r + \dfrac{k}{m}r_0\right]dr, \\[2mm] \dfrac{1}{2}v_r^2 = \dfrac{1}{2}\left(\omega_0^2 - \dfrac{k}{m}\right)(r^2 - r_0^2) + \dfrac{k}{m}r_0(r - r_0). \end{cases}$$

Solve to obtain the radial velocity as a function of r.

$$v_r = \sqrt{\left(\omega_0^2 - \dfrac{k}{m}\right)(r^2 - r_0^2) + \dfrac{2k}{m}r_0(r - r_0)}.$$

Practice Problem Determine the transverse force N exerted on the collar by the bar as a function of r.

Answer: $N = 2m\omega_0\sqrt{\left(\omega_0^2 - \dfrac{k}{m}\right)(r^2 - r_0^2) + \dfrac{2k}{m}r_0(r - r_0)}.$

Problems

14.94 The center of mass of the 12-kg object moves in the x–y plane. Its polar coordinates are given as functions of time by $r = 12 - 0.4t^2$ m, $\theta = 0.02t^3$ rad. Determine the polar components of the total force acting on the object at $t = 2$ s.

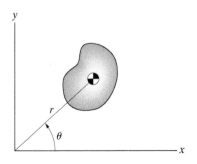

Problem 14.94

14.95 A 100-lb person walks on a large disk that rotates with constant angular velocity $\omega_0 = 0.3$ rad/s. He walks at a constant speed $v_0 = 5$ ft/s along a straight radial line painted on the disk. Determine the polar components of the horizontal force exerted on him when he is 6 ft from the center of the disk. (How are these forces exerted on him?)

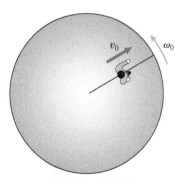

Problem 14.95

14.96 The robot is programmed so that the 0.4-kg part A describes the path

$$r = 1 - 0.5 \cos 2\pi t \text{ m},$$
$$\theta = 0.5 - 0.2 \sin 2\pi t \text{ rad}.$$

Determine the polar components of force exerted on A by the robot's jaws at $t = 2$ s.

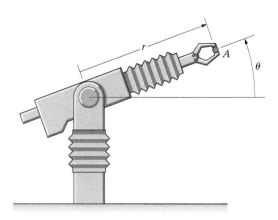

Problem 14.96

14.97 A 50-lb object P moves along the spiral path $r = (0.1)\theta$ ft, where θ is in radians. Its angular position is given as a function of time by $\theta = 2t$ rad, and $r = 0$ at $t = 0$. Determine the polar components of the total force acting on the object at $t = 4$ s.

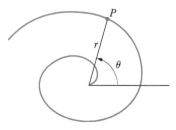

Problem 14.97

▶ **14.98** The smooth bar rotates *in the horizontal plane* with constant angular velocity $\omega_0 = 60$ rpm. If the radial velocity of the 1-kg collar A is $v_r = 10$ m/s when its radial position is $r = 1$ m, what is its radial velocity when $r = 2$ m? (See Active Example 14.9.)

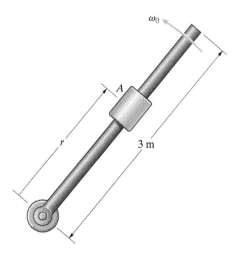

Problem 14.98

▶ **14.99** The smooth bar rotates *in the horizontal plane* with constant angular velocity $\omega_0 = 60$ rpm. The spring constant is $k = 20$ N/m and the unstretched length of the spring is 3 m. If the radial velocity of the 1-kg collar A is $v_r = 10$ m/s when its radial position is $r = 1$ m, what is its radial velocity when $r = 2$ m? (See Active Example 14.9.)

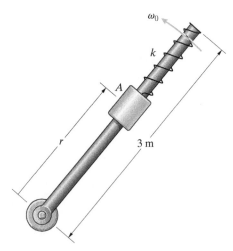

Problem 14.99

14.100 The 2-kg mass m is released from rest with the string horizontal. The length of the string is $L = 0.6$ m. By using Newton's second law in terms of polar coordinates, determine the magnitude of the velocity of the mass and the tension in the string when $\theta = 45°$.

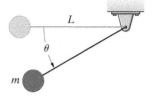

Problem 14.100

14.101 The 1-lb block A is given an initial velocity $v_0 = 14$ ft/s to the right when it is in the position $\theta = 0$, causing it to slide up the smooth circular surface. By using Newton's second law in terms of polar coordinates, determine the magnitude of the velocity of the block when $\theta = 60°$.

14.102 The 1-lb block is given an initial velocity $v_0 = 14$ ft/s to the right when it is in the position $\theta = 0$, causing it to slide up the smooth circular surface. Determine the normal force exerted on the block by the surface when $\theta = 60°$.

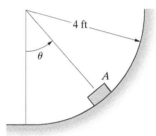

Problems 14.101/14.102

14.103 The skier passes point A going 17 m/s. From A to B, the radius of his circular path is 6 m. By using Newton's second law in terms of polar coordinates, determine the magnitude of the skier's velocity as he leaves the jump at B. Neglect tangential forces other than the tangential component of his weight.

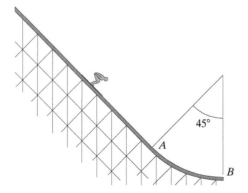

Problem 14.103

14.104* A 2-kg mass rests on a flat horizontal bar. The bar begins rotating *in the vertical plane* about O with a constant angular acceleration of 1 rad/s^2. The mass is observed to slip relative to the bar when the bar is 30° above the horizontal. What is the static coefficient of friction between the mass and the bar? Does the mass slip toward or away from O?

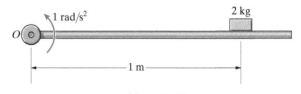

Problem 14.104

14.105* The 1/4-lb slider A is pushed along the circular bar by the slotted bar. The circular bar lies *in the horizontal plane*. The angular position of the slotted bar is $\theta = 10t^2$ rad. Determine the polar components of the total external force exerted on the slider at $t = 0.2$ s.

14.106* The 1/4-lb slider A is pushed along the circular bar by the slotted bar. The circular bar lies *in the vertical plane*. The angular position of the slotted bar is $\theta = 10t^2$ rad. Determine the polar components of the total force exerted on the slider by the circular and slotted bars at $t = 0.25$ s.

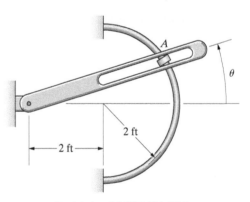

Problems 14.105/14.106

14.107* The slotted bar rotates *in the horizontal plane* with constant angular velocity ω_0. The mass m has a pin that fits in the slot of the bar. A spring holds the pin against the surface of the fixed cam. The surface of the cam is described by $r = r_0(2 - \cos\theta)$. Determine the polar components of the total external force exerted on the pin as functions of θ.

14.108* In Problem 14.107, suppose that the unstretched length of the spring is r_0. Determine the smallest value of the spring constant k for which the pin will remain on the surface of the cam.

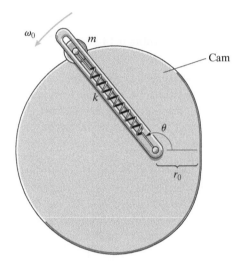

Problems 14.107/14.108

14.109 A charged particle P in a magnetic field moves along the spiral path described by $r = 1$ m, $\theta = 2z$ rad, where z is in meters. The particle moves along the path in the direction shown with constant speed $|\mathbf{v}| = 1$ km/s. The mass of the particle is 1.67×10^{-27} kg. Determine the sum of the forces on the particle in terms of cylindrical coordinates.

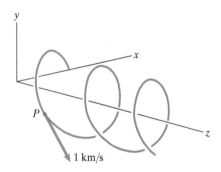

Problem 14.109

14.110 At the instant shown, the cylindrical coordinates of the 4-kg part A held by the robotic manipulator are $r = 0.6$ m, $\theta = 25°$, and $z = 0.8$ m. (The coordinate system is fixed with respect to the earth, and the y axis points upward.) A's radial position is increasing at $dr/dt = 0.2$ m/s, and $d^2r/dt^2 = -0.4$ m/s^2. The angle θ is increasing when $d\theta/dt = 1.2$ rad/s, and $d^2\theta/dt^2 = 2.8$ rad/s^2. The base of the manipulator arm is accelerating in the z direction at $d^2z/dt^2 = 2.5$ m/s^2. Determine the force vector exerted on A by the manipulator in terms of cylindrical coordinates.

14.111 Suppose that the robotic manipulator is used in a space station to investigate zero-g manufacturing techniques. During an interval of time, the manipulator is programmed so that the cylindrical coordinates of the 4-kg part A are $\theta = 0.15t^2$ rad, $r = 0.5(1 + \sin\theta)$ m, and $z = 0.8(1 + \theta)$ m. Determine the force vector exerted on A by the manipulator at $t = 2$ s in terms of cylindrical coordinates.

14.112* In Problem 14.111, draw a graph of the magnitude of the force exerted on part A by the manipulator as a function of time from $t = 0$ to $t = 5$ s, and use the graph to estimate the maximum force during that interval of time.

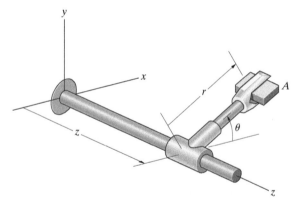

Problems 14.110–14.112

14.5 Orbital Mechanics

It is appropriate to include a discussion of orbital mechanics in our chapter on applications of Newton's second law. Newton's analytical determination of the elliptical orbits of the planets, which had been deduced from observational data by Johannes Kepler, was a triumph for Newtonian mechanics and confirmation of the inverse-square relation for gravitational acceleration.

We can use Newton's second law expressed in polar coordinates to determine the orbit of an earth satellite or a planet. Suppose that at $t = 0$ a satellite has an initial velocity v_0 at a distance r_0 from the center of the earth (Fig. 14.8a). We assume that the initial velocity is perpendicular to the line from the center of the earth to the satellite. The satellite's position during its subsequent motion is specified by its polar coordinates (r, θ), where θ is measured from the satellite's position at $t = 0$ (Fig. 14.8b). Our objective is to determine r as a function of θ.

Determination of the Orbit

If we model the earth as a homogeneous sphere, the force exerted on the satellite by gravity at a distance r from the center of the earth is mgR_E^2/r^2, where R_E is the earth's radius. (See Eq. 12.5.) From Eq. (14.9), the equation of motion in the radial direction is

$$\Sigma F_r = ma_r:$$

$$-\frac{mgR_E^2}{r^2} = m\left[\frac{d^2r}{dt^2} - r\left(\frac{d\theta}{dt}\right)^2\right].$$

From Eq. (14.10), the equation of motion in the transverse direction is

$$\Sigma F_\theta = ma_\theta:$$

$$0 = m\left(r\frac{d^2\theta}{dt^2} + 2\frac{dr}{dt}\frac{d\theta}{dt}\right).$$

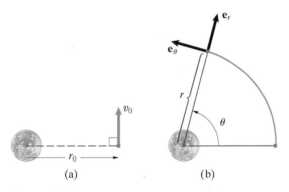

Figure 14.8
(a) Initial position and velocity of an earth satellite.
(b) Specifying the subsequent path in terms of polar coordinates.

We therefore obtain the two equations

$$\frac{d^2r}{dt^2} - r\left(\frac{d\theta}{dt}\right)^2 = -\frac{gR_E^2}{r^2} \tag{14.12}$$

and

$$r\frac{d^2\theta}{dt^2} + 2\frac{dr}{dt}\frac{d\theta}{dt} = 0. \tag{14.13}$$

We can write Eq. (14.13) in the form

$$\frac{1}{r}\frac{d}{dt}\left(r^2\frac{d\theta}{dt}\right) = 0,$$

which indicates that

$$r^2\frac{d\theta}{dt} = rv_\theta = \text{constant.} \tag{14.14}$$

At $t = 0$, the components of the velocity are $v_r = 0$ and $v_\theta = v_0$, and the radial position is $r = r_0$. We can therefore write the constant in Eq. (14.14) in terms of the initial conditions:

$$r^2\frac{d\theta}{dt} = rv_\theta = r_0v_0. \tag{14.15}$$

Using this equation to eliminate $d\theta/dt$ from Eq. (14.12), we obtain

$$\frac{d^2r}{dt^2} - \frac{r_0^2v_0^2}{r^3} = -\frac{gR_E^2}{r^2}. \tag{14.16}$$

We can solve this differential equation by introducing the change of variable

$$u = \frac{1}{r}. \tag{14.17}$$

In doing so, we will also change the independent variable from t to θ, because we want to determine r as a function of the angle θ instead of time. To express Eq. (14.16) in terms of u, we must determine d^2r/dt^2 in terms of u. Using the chain rule, we write the derivative of r with respect to time as

$$\frac{dr}{dt} = \frac{d}{dt}\left(\frac{1}{u}\right) = -\frac{1}{u^2}\frac{du}{dt} = -\frac{1}{u^2}\frac{du}{d\theta}\frac{d\theta}{dt}. \tag{14.18}$$

Notice from Eq. (14.15) that

$$\frac{d\theta}{dt} = \frac{r_0v_0}{r^2} = r_0v_0u^2. \tag{14.19}$$

Substituting this expression into Eq. (14.18), we obtain

$$\frac{dr}{dt} = -r_0 v_0 \frac{du}{d\theta}. \tag{14.20}$$

We differentiate Eq. (14.20) with respect to time and apply the chain rule again:

$$\frac{d^2 r}{dt^2} = \frac{d}{dt}\left(-r_0 v_0 \frac{du}{d\theta}\right) = -r_0 v_0 \frac{d\theta}{dt}\frac{d}{d\theta}\left(\frac{du}{d\theta}\right) = -r_0 v_0 \frac{d\theta}{dt}\frac{d^2 u}{d\theta^2}.$$

Using Eq. (14.19) to eliminate $d\theta/dt$ from this expression, we obtain the second time derivative of r in terms of u:

$$\frac{d^2 r}{dt^2} = -r_0^2 v_0^2 u^2 \frac{d^2 u}{d\theta^2}.$$

Substituting this result into Eq. (14.16) yields a linear differential equation for u as a function of θ:

$$\frac{d^2 u}{d\theta^2} + u = \frac{g R_E^2}{r_0^2 v_0^2}.$$

The general solution of this equation is

$$u = A \sin\theta + B \cos\theta + \frac{g R_E^2}{r_0^2 v_0^2}, \tag{14.21}$$

where A and B are constants. We can use the initial conditions to determine A and B. When $\theta = 0$, $u = 1/r_0$. Also, when $\theta = 0$ the radial component of velocity $v_r = dr/dt = 0$, so from Eq. (14.20) we see that $du/d\theta = 0$. From these two conditions, we obtain

$$A = 0 \quad \text{and} \quad B = \frac{1}{r_0} - \frac{g R_E^2}{r_0^2 v_0^2}.$$

Substituting these results into Eq. (14.21), we can write the resulting solution for $r = 1/u$ as

$$\frac{r}{r_0} = \frac{1 + \varepsilon}{1 + \varepsilon\cos\theta}, \tag{14.22}$$

where

$$\varepsilon = \frac{r_0 v_0^2}{g R_E^2} - 1. \tag{14.23}$$

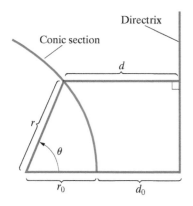

Figure 14.9
If the ratio r/d is constant, the curve describes a conic section.

Types of Orbits

The curve called a *conic section* (Fig. 14.9) has the property that the ratio of r to the perpendicular distance d to a straight line called the *directrix* is constant. This ratio, $r/d = r_0/d_0$, is called the *eccentricity* of the curve. From the figure, we see that

$$r \cos \theta + d = r_0 + d_0,$$

which we can write as

$$\frac{r}{r_0} = \frac{1 + (r_0/d_0)}{1 + (r_0/d_0) \cos \theta}.$$

Comparing this expression with Eq. (14.22), we see that *the satellite's orbit describes a conic section with eccentricity ε.* The value of the eccentricity determines the character of the orbit.

Circular Orbit   If the initial velocity v_0 is chosen so that $\varepsilon = 0$, Eq. (14.22) reduces to $r = r_0$ and the orbit is circular (Fig. 14.10). Setting $\varepsilon = 0$ in Eq. (14.23) and solving for v_0, we obtain

$$v_0 = \sqrt{\frac{gR_E^2}{r_0}}, \tag{14.24}$$

which agrees with the velocity for a circular orbit we obtained by a different method in Example 13.5.

Elliptic Orbit   If $0 < \varepsilon < 1$, the orbit is an ellipse (Fig. 14.10). The maximum radius of the ellipse occurs when $\theta = 180°$. Setting θ equal to $180°$ in Eq. (14.22), we obtain an expression for the maximum radius of the ellipse in terms of the initial radius and ε:

$$r_{\max} = r_0 \left(\frac{1 + \varepsilon}{1 - \varepsilon} \right). \tag{14.25}$$

Parabolic Orbit   Notice from Eq. (14.25) that the maximum radius of the elliptic orbit increases without limit as $\varepsilon \to 1$. When $\varepsilon = 1$, the orbit is a parabola (Fig. 14.10). The corresponding velocity v_0 is the minimum initial velocity for which the radius r increases without limit, which is the escape velocity. Setting $\varepsilon = 1$ in Eq. (14.23) and solving for v_0, we obtain

$$v_0 = \sqrt{\frac{2gR_E^2}{r_0}}.$$

This is the same value for the escape velocity we obtained in Example 13.5 for the case of an object moving in a straight path directly away from the center of the earth.

Hyperbolic Orbit   If $\varepsilon > 1$, the orbit is a hyperbola (Fig. 14.10).

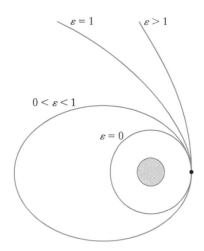

Figure 14.10
Orbits for different eccentricities.

The solution we have presented, based on the assumption that the earth is a homogeneous sphere, approximates the orbit of an earth satellite. Determining the orbit accurately requires taking into account the variations in the earth's gravitational field due to its actual mass distribution. Similarly, depending on the accuracy required, determining the orbit of a planet around the sun may require accounting for perturbations due to the gravitational attractions of the other planets.

RESULTS

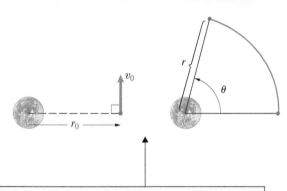

Polar equation for the orbit of an earth satellite with the initial conditions shown. The parameter

$$\varepsilon = \frac{r_0 v_0^2}{g R_E^2} - 1, \qquad (14.23)$$

where g is the acceleration due to gravity at sea level and R_E is the radius of the earth modeled as a homogeneous sphere.

$$\frac{r}{r_0} = \frac{1 + \varepsilon}{1 + \varepsilon \cos \theta}, \qquad (14.22)$$

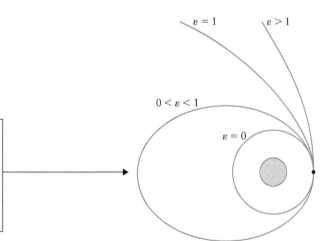

The character of the orbit is determined by the value of ε.

$\varepsilon = 0$	Circular
$0 < \varepsilon < 1$	Elliptic
$\varepsilon = 1$	Parabolic
$\varepsilon > 1$	Hyperbolic

The radial position of the satellite and its transverse component of velocity satisfy the relation $r v_\theta = $ constant.   (14.14)

Active Example 14.10 Orbit of an Earth Satellite (▶ *Related Problem 14.115*)

An earth satellite is placed into orbit with an initial velocity $v_0 = 9240$ m/s. The satellite's initial position is 6600 km from the center of the earth. Show that the resulting orbit is elliptic and determine its maximum radius. The earth's radius is 6370 km.

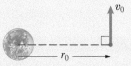

Strategy

We must calculate the value of ε from Eq. (14.23) to determine the type of orbit. We can use the polar equation for the orbit, Eq. (14.22), to obtain the maximum radius.

Solution

Calculate the value of ε. The orbit is elliptic.

$$
\begin{cases}
\varepsilon = \dfrac{r_0 v_0^2}{g R_E^2} - 1 \\[2mm]
\quad = \dfrac{(6600 \times 10^3 \text{ m})(9240 \text{ m/s})^2}{(9.81 \text{ m/s}^2)(6370 \times 10^3 \text{ m})^2} - 1 \\[2mm]
\quad = 0.416.
\end{cases}
$$

Determine the maximum radius from the polar equation for the orbit with $\theta = 180°$. The graph of the elliptic orbit is shown.

$$
\begin{cases}
r_{\max} = r_0 \left(\dfrac{1 + \varepsilon}{1 + \varepsilon \cos 180°} \right) \\[2mm]
\quad = r_0 \left(\dfrac{1 + \varepsilon}{1 - \varepsilon} \right) \\[2mm]
\quad = (6600 \text{ km}) \left(\dfrac{1 + 0.416}{1 - 0.416} \right) \\[2mm]
\quad = 16{,}000 \text{ km}.
\end{cases}
$$

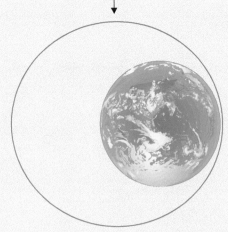

Practice Problem Determine the velocity of the satellite when it is at its maximum radius.

Answers: 3810 m/s.

Problems

Use the values $R_E = 6370$ km $= 3960$ mi for the radius of the earth.

14.113 The International Space Station is in a circular orbit 225 miles above the earth's surface.
(a) What is the magnitude of the velocity of the space station?
(b) How long does it take to complete one revolution?

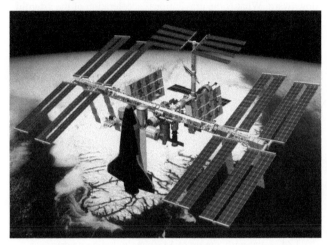

Problem 14.113

14.114 The moon is approximately 383,000 km from the earth. Assume that the moon's orbit around the earth is circular with velocity given by Eq. (14.24).
(a) What is the magnitude of the moon's velocity?
(b) How long does it take to complete one revolution around the earth?

▶ **14.115** Suppose that you place a satellite into an elliptic earth orbit with an initial radius $r_0 = 6700$ km and an initial velocity v_0 such that the maximum radius of the orbit is 13,400 km. (a) Determine v_0. (b) What is the magnitude of the satellite's velocity when it is at its maximum radius? (See Active Example 14.10.)

Problem 14.115

14.116 A satellite is given an initial velocity $v_0 = 6700$ m/s at a distance $r_0 = 2R_E$ from the center of the earth as shown in Fig. 14.8a. Draw a graph of the resulting orbit.

14.117 The time required for a satellite in a circular earth orbit to complete one revolution increases as the radius of the orbit increases. If you choose the radius properly, the satellite will complete one revolution in 24 hours. If a satellite is placed in such an orbit directly above the equator and moving from west to east, it will remain above the same point on the earth as the earth rotates beneath it. This type of orbit, conceived by Arthur C. Clarke, is called *geosynchronous*, and is used for communication and television broadcast satellites. Determine the radius of a geosynchronous orbit in km.

14.118* You can send a spacecraft from the earth to the moon in the following way: First, launch the spacecraft into a circular "parking" orbit of radius r_0 around the earth (Fig. P14.118a). Then, increase its velocity in the direction tangent to the circular orbit to a value v_0 such that it will follow an elliptic orbit whose maximum radius is equal to the radius r_M of the moon's orbit around the earth (Fig. P14.118b). The radius $r_M = 238,000$ mi. Let $r_0 = 4160$ mi. What velocity v_0 is necessary to send a spacecraft to the moon? (This description is simplified in that it disregards the effect of the moon's gravity.)

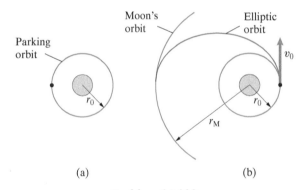

(a)   (b)

Problem 14.118

14.119* At $t = 0$, an earth satellite is a distance r_0 from the center of the earth and has an initial velocity v_0 in the direction shown. Show that the polar equation for the resulting orbit is

$$\frac{r}{r_0} = \frac{(\varepsilon + 1)\cos^2\beta}{[(\varepsilon + 1)\cos^2\beta - 1]\cos\theta - (\varepsilon + 1)\sin\beta\cos\beta\sin\theta + 1},$$

where $\varepsilon = (r_0 v_0^2 / g R_E^2) - 1$.

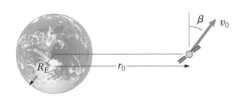

Problem 14.119

Review Problems

14.120 The Acura NSX can brake from 60 mi/h to a stop in a distance of 112 ft. The car weighs 3250 lb. (a) If you assume that the vehicle's deceleration is constant, what are its deceleration and the magnitude of the horizontal force its tires exert on the road? (b) If the car's tires are at the limit of adhesion (i.e., slip is impending), and the normal force exerted on the car by the road equals the car's weight, what is the coefficient of friction μ_s? (This analysis neglects the effects of horizontal and vertical aerodynamic forces.)

14.121 Using the coefficient of friction obtained in Problem 14.120, determine the highest constant speed at which the NSX could drive on a flat, circular track of 600-ft radius without skidding.

14.122 A "cog" engine hauls three cars of sightseers to a mountaintop in Bavaria. The mass of each car, including its passengers, is 10,000 kg, and the friction forces exerted by the wheels of the cars are negligible. Determine the forces in the couplings 1, 2, and 3 if (a) the engine is moving at constant velocity and (b) the engine is accelerating up the mountain at 1.2 m/s^2.

Problem 14.122

14.123 In a future mission, a spacecraft approaches the surface of an asteroid passing near the earth. Just before it touches down, the spacecraft is moving downward at a constant velocity relative to the surface of the asteroid and its downward thrust is 0.01 N. The computer decreases the downward thrust to 0.005 N, and an onboard laser interferometer determines that the acceleration of the spacecraft relative to the surface becomes 5×10^{-6} m/s^2 downward. What is the gravitational acceleration of the asteroid near its surface?

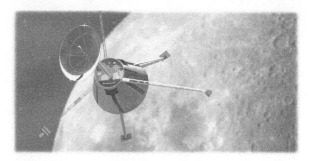

Problem 14.123

14.124 A car with a mass of 1470 kg, including its driver, is driven at 130 km/h over a slight rise in the road. At the top of the rise, the driver applies the brakes. The coefficient of static friction between the tires and the road is $\mu_s = 0.9$, and the radius of curvature of the rise is 160 m. Determine the car's deceleration at the instant the brakes are applied, and compare it with the deceleration on a level road.

Problem 14.124

14.125 The car drives at constant velocity up the straight segment of road on the left. If the car's tires continue to exert the same tangential force on the road after the car has gone over the crest of the hill and is on the straight segment of road on the right, what will be the car's acceleration?

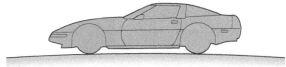

Problem 14.125

14.126 The aircraft carrier *Nimitz* weighs 91,000 tons. (A ton is 2000 lb.) Suppose that it is traveling at its top speed of approximately 30 knots (a knot is 6076 ft/h) when its engines are shut down. If the water exerts a drag force of magnitude $20,000v$ lb, where v is the carrier's velocity in feet per second, what distance does the carrier move before coming to rest?

14.127 If $m_A = 10$ kg, $m_B = 40$ kg, and the coefficient of kinetic friction between all surfaces is $\mu_k = 0.11$, what is the acceleration of B down the inclined surface?

14.128 If A weighs 20 lb, B weighs 100 lb, and the coefficient of kinetic friction between all surfaces is $\mu_k = 0.15$, what is the tension in the cord as B slides down the inclined surface?

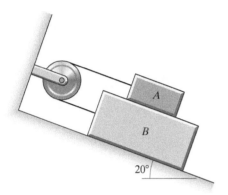

Problems 14.127/14.128

14.129 A gas gun is used to accelerate projectiles to high velocities for research on material properties. The projectile is held in place while gas is pumped into the tube to a high pressure p_0 on the left and the tube is evacuated on the right. The projectile is then released and is accelerated by the expanding gas. Assume that the pressure p of the gas is related to the volume V it occupies by $pV^\gamma = $ constant, where γ is a constant. If friction can be neglected, show that the velocity of the projectile at the position x is

$$v = \sqrt{\frac{2p_0 A x_0^\gamma}{m(\gamma - 1)} \left(\frac{1}{x_0^{\gamma-1}} - \frac{1}{x^{\gamma-1}} \right)},$$

where m is the mass of the projectile and A is the cross-sectional area of the tube.

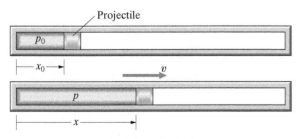

Problem 14.129

14.130 The weights of the blocks are $W_A = 120$ lb and $W_B = 20$ lb, and the surfaces are smooth. Determine the acceleration of block A and the tension in the cord.

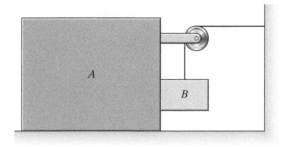

Problem 14.130

14.131 The 100-Mg space shuttle is in orbit when its engines are turned on, exerting a thrust force $\mathbf{T} = 10\mathbf{i} - 20\mathbf{j} + 10\mathbf{k}$ (kN) for 2 s. Neglect the resulting change in mass of the shuttle. At the end of the 2-s burn, fuel is still sloshing back and forth in the shuttle's tanks. What is the change in the velocity of the center of mass of the shuttle (including the fuel it contains) due to the 2-s burn?

14.132 The water skier contacts the ramp with a velocity of 25 mi/h parallel to the surface of the ramp. Neglecting friction and assuming that the tow rope exerts no force on him once he touches the ramp, estimate the horizontal length of the skier's jump from the end of the ramp.

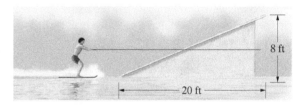

Problem 14.132

14.133 Suppose you are designing a roller-coaster track that will take the cars through a vertical loop of 40-ft radius. If you decide that, for safety, the downward force exerted on a passenger by his or her seat at the top of the loop should be at least one-half the passenger's weight, what is the minimum safe velocity of the cars at the top of the loop?

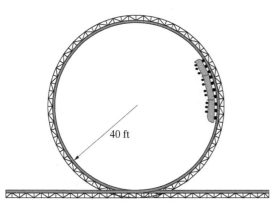

40 ft

Problem 14.133

14.134 As the smooth bar rotates *in the horizontal plane*, the string winds up on the fixed cylinder and draws the 1-kg collar A inward. The bar starts from rest at $t = 0$ in the position shown and rotates with constant angular acceleration. What is the tension in the string at $t = 1$ s?

14.135 In Problem 14.134, suppose that the coefficient of kinetic friction between the collar and the bar is $\mu_k = 0.2$. What is the tension in the string at $t = 1$ s?

6 rad/s²

400 mm

A

100 mm

Problems 14.134/14.135

14.136 If you want to design the cars of a train to tilt as the train goes around curves in order to achieve maximum passenger comfort, what is the relationship between the desired tilt angle θ, the velocity v of the train, and the instantaneous radius of curvature, ρ, of the track?

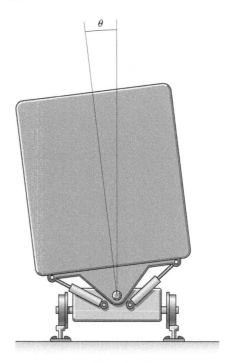

θ

Problem 14.136

14.137 To determine the coefficient of static friction between two materials, an engineer at the U.S. National Institute of Standards and Technology places a small sample of one material on a horizontal disk whose surface is made of the other material and then rotates the disk from rest with a constant angular acceleration of 0.4 rad/s². If she determines that the small sample slips on the disk after 9.903 s, what is the coefficient of friction?

200 mm

Problem 14.137

14.138* The 1-kg slider A is pushed along the curved bar by the slotted bar. The curved bar lies *in the horizontal plane*, and its profile is described by $r = 2(\theta/2\pi + 1)$ m, where θ is in radians. The angular position of the slotted bar is $\theta = 2t$ rad. Determine the polar components of the total external force exerted on the slider when $\theta = 120°$.

14.139* In Problem 14.138, suppose that the curved bar lies *in the vertical plane*. Determine the polar components of the total force exerted on A by the curved and slotted bars at $t = 0.5$ s.

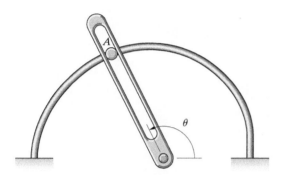

Problems 14.138/14.139

Design Project

The proposed design for an energy-absorbing bumper for a car exerts a decelerating force of magnitude $bs + cv$ on the car when it collides with a rigid obstacle, where s is the distance the car travels from the point where it contacts the obstacle and v is the car's velocity. Thus the force exerted on the car by the bumper is a function of the car's position and velocity.

(a) Suppose that at $t = 0$ the car contacts the obstacle with initial velocity v_0. Prove that the car's position is given as a function of time by

$$s = \frac{v_0}{2h}\left[e^{-(d-h)t} - e^{-(d+h)t}\right],$$

where $d = c/2m$, $h = \sqrt{d^2 - b/m}$, and m is the mass of the car. To do this, first show that this equation satisfies Newton's second law. Then confirm that it satisfies the initial conditions $s = 0$ and $v = v_0$ at $t = 0$.

(b) Investigate the effects of the car's mass, the initial velocity, and the constants b and c on the motion of the car when it strikes the obstacle. (Assume that $d^2 > b/m$.) Pay particular attention to how your choices for the constants b and c affect the maximum deceleration to which the occupants of the car would be subjected. Write a brief report presenting the results of your analysis and giving your conclusions concerning the design of energy-absorbing bumpers.

CHAPTER
15

Energy Methods

The concepts of energy and conservation of energy originated in large part from the study of classical mechanics. A simple transformation of Newton's second law results in an equation that motivates the definitions of work, kinetic energy (energy due to an object's motion), and potential energy (energy due to an object's position). This equation can greatly simplify the solution of problems involving certain forces that depend on an object's position, including gravitational forces and forces exerted by springs.

◀ A swing provides excitement by transforming the potential energy of height into the kinetic energy of motion. In this chapter we use energy methods to analyze motions of objects.

15.1 Work and Kinetic Energy

BACKGROUND

Principle of Work and Energy

We have used Newton's second law to relate the acceleration of an object's center of mass to external forces acting on it. We will now show how Newton's second law, which is a vector equation, can be transformed into a scalar equation that is extremely useful in particular circumstances. We begin with Newton's second law in the form

$$\Sigma \mathbf{F} = m \frac{d\mathbf{v}}{dt}, \tag{15.1}$$

and take the dot product of both sides with the velocity:

$$\Sigma \mathbf{F} \cdot \mathbf{v} = m \frac{d\mathbf{v}}{dt} \cdot \mathbf{v}. \tag{15.2}$$

We write the left side of this equation as

$$\Sigma \mathbf{F} \cdot \mathbf{v} = \Sigma \mathbf{F} \cdot \frac{d\mathbf{r}}{dt}$$

and write the right side as

$$m \frac{d\mathbf{v}}{dt} \cdot \mathbf{v} = \tfrac{1}{2} m \frac{d}{dt} (\mathbf{v} \cdot \mathbf{v}),$$

obtaining

$$\Sigma \mathbf{F} \cdot d\mathbf{r} = \tfrac{1}{2} m \, d(v^2), \tag{15.3}$$

where $v^2 = \mathbf{v} \cdot \mathbf{v}$ is the square of the magnitude of the velocity. The term on the left side of Eq. (15.3) is the *work* expressed in terms of the total external force on the object and an infinitesimal displacement $d\mathbf{r}$ of its center of mass. Integrating Eq. (15.3) yields

$$\int_{\mathbf{r}_1}^{\mathbf{r}_2} \Sigma \mathbf{F} \cdot d\mathbf{r} = \tfrac{1}{2} m v_2^2 - \tfrac{1}{2} m v_1^2, \tag{15.4}$$

where v_1 and v_2 are the magnitudes of the velocity of the center of mass of the object when it is at positions $\mathbf{r}_1$ and $\mathbf{r}_2$, respectively. The term $\tfrac{1}{2} m v^2$ is called the *kinetic energy* associated with the motion of the center of mass. Denoting the work done as the center of mass moves from $\mathbf{r}_1$ to $\mathbf{r}_2$ by

$$U_{12} = \int_{\mathbf{r}_1}^{\mathbf{r}_2} \Sigma \mathbf{F} \cdot d\mathbf{r}, \tag{15.5}$$

we obtain the principle of work and energy:

The work done on an object as it moves between two positions equals the change in its kinetic energy.

$$U_{12} = \tfrac{1}{2} m v_2^2 - \tfrac{1}{2} m v_1^2. \tag{15.6}$$

The dimensions of work, and therefore the dimensions of kinetic energy, are (force) × (length). In SI units, work is usually expressed in N-m or joules (J). In U.S. Customary units, work is usually expressed in ft-lb.

If the work done on an object as it moves between two positions can be evaluated, the principle of work and energy permits us to determine the change in the magnitude of the object's velocity. We can also apply this principle to a system of objects, equating the total work done by external forces to the change in the total kinetic energy of the system. But the principle must be applied with caution, because, as we demonstrate in Example 15.3, net work can be done on a system by internal forces.

Although the principle of work and energy relates a change in the position of an object to the change in its velocity, it is not convenient for obtaining other information about the motion of the object, such as the time it takes the object to move from one position to another. Furthermore, since the work is an integral with respect to position, we can usually evaluate it only when the forces doing work are known as functions of position. Despite these limitations, the principle is extremely useful for certain problems because the work can be determined very easily.

Evaluating the Work

Let us consider an object in curvilinear motion relative to an inertial reference frame (Fig. 15.1a) and specify its position by the coordinate s measured along its path from a reference point O. In terms of the tangential unit vector $\mathbf{e_t}$, the object's velocity is

$$\mathbf{v} = \frac{ds}{dt}\mathbf{e_t}.$$

Because $\mathbf{v} = d\mathbf{r}/dt$, we can multiply the velocity by dt to obtain an expression for the vector $d\mathbf{r}$ describing an infinitesimal displacement along the path (Fig. 15.1b):

$$d\mathbf{r} = \mathbf{v}\, dt = ds\, \mathbf{e_t}.$$

The work done by the external forces acting on the object as a result of the displacement $d\mathbf{r}$ is

$$\Sigma\mathbf{F} \cdot d\mathbf{r} = (\Sigma\mathbf{F} \cdot \mathbf{e_t})\, ds = \Sigma F_t ds,$$

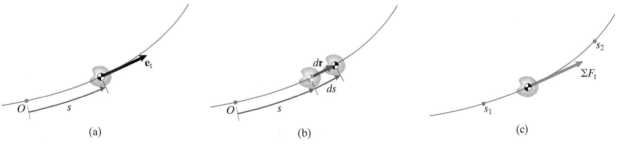

Figure 15.1
(a) The coordinate s and tangential unit vector.
(b) An infinitesimal displacement $d\mathbf{r}$.
(c) The work done from s_1 to s_2 is determined by the tangential component of the external forces.

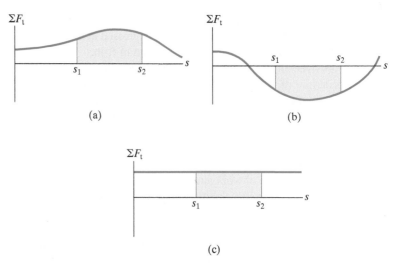

Figure 15.2
(a) The work equals the area defined by the graph of the tangential force as a function of the distance along the path.
(b) Negative work is done if the tangential force is opposite to the direction of the motion.
(c) The work done by a constant tangential force equals the product of the force and the distance.

where ΣF_t is the tangential component of the total force. Therefore, as the object moves from a position s_1 to a position s_2 (Fig. 15.1c), the work is

$$U_{12} = \int_{s_1}^{s_2} \Sigma F_t \, ds. \tag{15.7}$$

The work is equal to the integral of the tangential component of the total force with respect to distance along the path. Thus, the work done is equal to the area defined by the graph of the tangential force from s_1 to s_2 (Fig. 15.2a). *Components of force perpendicular to the path do no work.* Notice that if ΣF_t is opposite to the direction of motion over some part of the path, which means that the object is decelerating, the work is negative (Fig. 15.2b). If ΣF_t is constant between s_1 and s_2, the work is simply the product of the total tangential force and the displacement (Fig. 15.2c):

$$U_{12} = \Sigma F_t(s_2 - s_1). \qquad \text{Constant tangential force} \tag{15.8}$$

Power

Power is the rate at which work is done. The work done by the external forces acting on an object during an infinitesimal displacement $d\mathbf{r}$ is

$$\Sigma \mathbf{F} \cdot d\mathbf{r}.$$

We obtain the power P by dividing this expression by the interval of time dt during which the displacement takes place:

$$P = \Sigma \mathbf{F} \cdot \mathbf{v}. \tag{15.9}$$

This is the power transferred to or from the object, depending on whether P is positive or negative. In SI units, power is expressed in newton-meters per second, which is joules per second (J/s) or watts (W). In U.S. Customary units, power is expressed in foot-pounds per second or in the anachronistic horsepower (hp), which is 746 W or approximately 550 ft-lb/s.

Notice from Eq. (15.3) that the power equals the rate of change of the kinetic energy of the object:

$$P = \frac{d}{dt}\left(\tfrac{1}{2}mv^2\right).$$

Transferring power to and from an object causes its kinetic energy to increase and decrease, respectively. Using the preceding relation, we can write the average with respect to time of the power during an interval of time from t_1 to t_2 as

$$P_{\text{av}} = \frac{1}{t_2 - t_1}\int_{t_1}^{t_2} P\, dt = \frac{1}{t_2 - t_1}\int_{v_1^2}^{v_2^2} \tfrac{1}{2}m\, d(v^2).$$

Performing the integration, we find that the average power transferred to or from an object during an interval of time is equal to the change in its kinetic energy, or the work done, divided by the interval of time:

$$P_{\text{av}} = \frac{\tfrac{1}{2}mv_2^2 - \tfrac{1}{2}mv_1^2}{t_2 - t_1} = \frac{U_{12}}{t_2 - t_1}. \tag{15.10}$$

RESULTS

Principle of Work and Energy

The *kinetic energy* associated with the motion of the center of mass of an object of mass m is defined to be $\tfrac{1}{2}mv^2$, where v^2 is the square of the magnitude of the velocity of the center of mass.

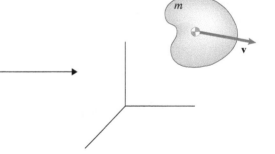

Let the *work* done by the total external force acting on an object as its center of mass moves from a position $\mathbf{r}_1$ to a position $\mathbf{r}_2$ be defined by

$$U_{12} = \int_{r_1}^{r_2} \Sigma\mathbf{F} \cdot d\mathbf{r}. \tag{15.5}$$

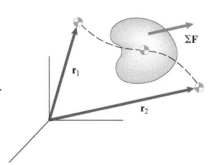

The *principle of work and energy* states that the work done on an object as it moves between two positions equals the change in its kinetic energy.

$$U_{12} = \tfrac{1}{2}mv_2^2 - \tfrac{1}{2}mv_1^2. \tag{15.6}$$

Evaluating the Work

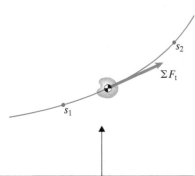

Work done as an object moves from a point s_1 on its path to a point s_2, where ΣF_t is the tangential component of the total external force on the object. *Components of force normal to the path do no work.*

$$U_{12} = \int_{s_1}^{s_2} \Sigma F_t \, ds, \tag{15.7}$$

If ΣF_t is *constant* between s_1 and s_2, the work is the product of the tangential force and the distance along the path.

$$U_{12} = \Sigma F_t \, (s_2 - s_1). \tag{15.8}$$

Power

The *power*, or the rate at which work is done on an object by the total external force acting on it, where $\mathbf{v}$ is the velocity of the center of mass.

$$P = \Sigma \mathbf{F} \cdot \mathbf{v}, \tag{15.9}$$

The average power transferred to an object during an interval of time from t_1 to t_2 is equal to the change in its kinetic energy, or the work done on it, divided by the interval of time.

$$P_{\text{av}} = \frac{\tfrac{1}{2}mv_2^2 - \tfrac{1}{2}mv_1^2}{t_2 - t_1} = \frac{U_{12}}{t_2 - t_1}. \tag{15.10}$$

| Active Example 15.1 | **Work and Energy in Straight-Line Motion** (▶ *Related Problem 15.1*) |

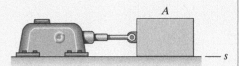

The 180-kg container *A* starts from rest in position $s = 0$. The horizontal force (in newtons) that is exerted on the container by the hydraulic piston is given as a function of the position *s* in meters by $F = 700 - 150s$. The coefficient of kinetic friction between the container and the floor is $\mu_k = 0.26$. What is the velocity of the container when it has reached the position $s = 1$ m?

Strategy
The force acting on the container is given as a function of its position, so we can use Eq. (15.7) to determine the work done on it. By applying the principle of work and energy, we can determine the change in its velocity.

Solution

Draw the free-body diagram of the container and identify the forces that do work. The force exerted by the hydraulic cylinder and the friction force are tangent to the path. The normal force *N* is needed to calculate the friction force. The container has no acceleration in the vertical direction, so $N = (180 \text{ kg})(9.81 \text{ m/s}^2) = 1770$ N.

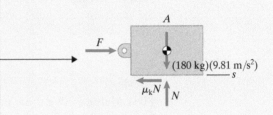

Evaluate the work done as the container moves from its initial position to $s = 1$ m.

$$U_{12} = \int_{s_1}^{s_2} \Sigma F_t \, ds$$

$$= \int_0^1 (F - \mu_k N) ds$$

$$= \int_0^1 [(700 - 150s) - (0.26)(1770)] ds$$

$$= 166 \text{ N-m}.$$

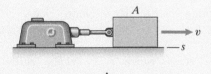

Apply the principle of work and energy to determine the container's velocity when it reaches $s = 1$ m. Solving yields $v_2 = 1.36$ m/s.

$$\begin{cases} U_{12} = \frac{1}{2}mv_2^2 - \frac{1}{2}mv_1^2 : \\ 166 \text{ N-m} = \frac{1}{2}(180 \text{ kg})v_2^2 - 0. \end{cases}$$

Practice Problem Suppose that the mass of the container *A* is 120 kg. What is its velocity when it has reached the position $s = 1$ m?

Answer: 2.31 m/s.

Example 15.2 | **Applying Work and Energy to a System** (▶ *Related Problem 15.23*)

The two crates are released from rest. Their masses are $m_A = 40$ kg and $m_B = 30$ kg, and the kinetic coefficient of friction between crate A and the inclined surface is $\mu_k = 0.15$. What is the magnitude of the velocity of the crates when they have moved 400 mm?

Strategy
We will determine the velocity in two ways.

First Method By drawing free-body diagrams of each of the crates and applying the principle of work and energy to them individually, we can obtain two equations in terms of the magnitude of the velocity and the tension in the cable.

Second Method We can draw a single free-body diagram of the two crates, the cable, and the pulley and apply the principle of work and energy to the entire system.

Solution

First Method We draw the free-body diagram of crate A in Fig. a. The forces that do work as the crate moves down the plane are the forces tangential to its path: the tension T; the tangential component of the weight, $m_A g \sin 20°$; and the friction force $\mu_k N$. Because the acceleration of the crate normal to the surface is zero, $N = m_A g \cos 20°$. The magnitude v of the velocity at which A moves parallel to the surface equals the magnitude of the velocity at which B falls (Fig. b). Using Eq. (15.7) to determine the work, we equate the work done on A as it moves from $s_1 = 0$ to $s_2 = 0.4$ m to the change in the kinetic energy of A.

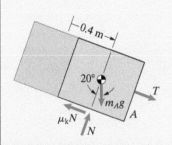

(a) Free-body diagram of A.

$$\int_{s_1}^{s_2} \Sigma F_t \, ds = \tfrac{1}{2}mv_2^2 - \tfrac{1}{2}mv_1^2:$$

$$\int_0^{0.4} \left[T + m_A g \sin 20° - \mu_k(m_A g \cos 20°) \right] ds = \tfrac{1}{2}m_A v_2^2 - 0. \quad (1)$$

The forces that do work on crate B are its weight $m_B g$ and the tension T (Fig. c). The magnitude of B's velocity is the same as that of crate A. The work done on B equals the change in its kinetic energy.

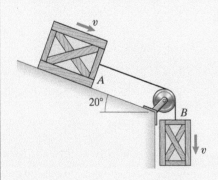

(b) The magnitude of the velocity of each crate is the same.

$$\int_{s_1}^{s_2} \Sigma F_t \, ds = \tfrac{1}{2}mv_2^2 - \tfrac{1}{2}mv_1^2:$$

$$\int_0^{0.4} (m_B g - T) \, ds = \tfrac{1}{2}m_B v_2^2 - 0. \quad (2)$$

By summing Eqs. (1) and (2), we eliminate T, obtaining

$$\int_0^{0.4} (m_A g \sin 20° - \mu_k m_A g \cos 20° + m_B g)\, ds = \tfrac{1}{2}(m_A + m_B)v_2^2:$$

$$[40 \sin 20° - (0.15)(40) \cos 20° + 30](9.81)(0.4) = \tfrac{1}{2}(40 + 30)v_2^2.$$

Solving for the velocity, we get $v_2 = 2.07$ m/s.

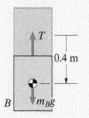

(c) Free-body diagram of B.

Second Method We draw the free-body diagram of the system consisting of the crates, cable, and pulley in Fig. d. Notice that the cable tension does not appear in this diagram. The reactions at the pin support of the pulley do no work, because the support does not move. The total work done by external forces on the system as the boxes move 400 mm is equal to the change in the total kinetic energy of the system.

$$\int_0^{0.4} [m_A g \sin 20° - \mu_k(m_A g \cos 20°)]\, ds + \int_0^{0.4} m_B g\, ds$$

$$= \tfrac{1}{2}m_A v_2^2 + \tfrac{1}{2}m_B v_2^2 - 0:$$

$$[40 \sin 20° - (0.15)(40) \cos 20° + 30](9.81)(0.4) = \tfrac{1}{2}(40 + 30)v_2^2.$$

This equation is identical to the one we obtained by applying the principle of work and energy to the individual crates.

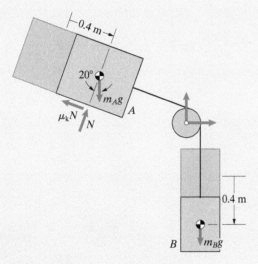

(d) Free-body diagram of the system.

Critical Thinking

You will often find it simpler to apply the principle of work and energy to an entire system instead of its separate parts. However, as we demonstrate in the next example, you need to be aware that internal forces in a system can do net work.

Example 15.3 | **Net Work by Internal Forces** (▶ *Related Problem 15.30*)

Crates A and B are released from rest. The coefficient of kinetic friction between A and B is μ_k, and friction between B and the inclined surface can be neglected. What is the velocity of the crates when they have moved a distance b?

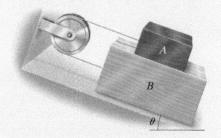

Strategy
By applying the principle of work and energy to each crate, we can obtain two equations in terms of the tension in the cable and the velocity.

Solution
We draw the free-body diagrams of the crates in Figs. a and b. The acceleration of A normal to the inclined surface is zero, so $N = m_A g \cos \theta$. The magnitudes of the velocities of A and B are equal (Fig. c). The work done on A equals the change in its kinetic energy.

$$U_{12} = \tfrac{1}{2} m_A v_2^2 - \tfrac{1}{2} m_A v_1^2:$$

$$\int_0^b (T - m_A g \sin \theta - \mu_k m_A g \cos \theta) \, ds = \tfrac{1}{2} m_A v_2^2. \qquad (1)$$

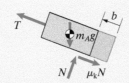

(a) Free-body diagram of A.

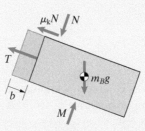

(b) Free-body diagram of B.

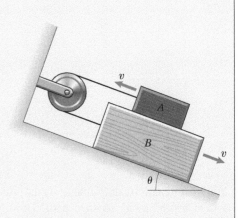

(c) The magnitude of the velocity of each crate is the same.

The work done on B equals the change in *its* kinetic energy.

$$U_{12} = \tfrac{1}{2}m_B v_2^2 - \tfrac{1}{2}m_B v_1^2:$$

$$\int_0^b (-T + m_B g \sin\theta - \mu_k m_A g \cos\theta)\, ds = \tfrac{1}{2}m_B v_2^2. \qquad (2)$$

Summing these equations to eliminate T and solving for v_2, we obtain

$$v_2 = \sqrt{2gb[(m_B - m_A)\sin\theta - 2\mu_k m_A \cos\theta]/(m_A + m_B)}.$$

Critical Thinking

If we attempt to solve this example by applying the principle of work and energy to the system consisting of the crates, the cable, and the pulley (Fig. d), we obtain an incorrect result. Equating the work done by external forces to the change in the total kinetic energy of the system, we obtain

$$\int_0^b m_B g \sin\theta\, ds - \int_0^b m_A g \sin\theta\, ds = \tfrac{1}{2}m_A v_2^2 + \tfrac{1}{2}m_B v_2^2:$$

$$(m_B g \sin\theta)b - (m_A g \sin\theta)b = \tfrac{1}{2}m_A v_2^2 + \tfrac{1}{2}m_B v_2^2.$$

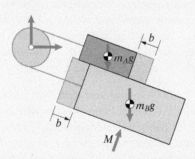

(**d**) Free-body diagram of the system.

But if we sum our work and energy equations for the individual crates—Eqs. (1) and (2)—we obtain the correct equation:

$$[(m_B g \sin\theta)b - (m_A g \sin\theta)b] + [-(2\mu_k m_A g \cos\theta)b] = \tfrac{1}{2}m_A v_2^2 + \tfrac{1}{2}m_B v_2^2.$$

| Work done by external forces | Work done by internal forces |

The internal frictional forces the crates exert on each other do net work on the system. We did not account for this work in applying the principle of work and energy to the free-body diagram of the entire system.

Problems

▶ **15.1** In Active Example 15.1, what is the velocity of the container when it has reached the position $s = 2$ m?

15.2 The mass of the Sikorsky UH-60A helicopter is 9300 kg. It takes off vertically with its rotor exerting a constant upward thrust of 112 kN. Use the principle of work and energy to determine how far it has risen when its velocity is 6 m/s.

Strategy: Be sure to draw the free-body diagram of the helicopter.

Problem 15.2

15.3 The 20-lb box is at rest on the horizontal surface when the constant force $F = 5$ lb is applied. The coefficient of kinetic friction between the box and the surface is $\mu_k = 0.2$. Determine how fast the box is moving when it has moved 2 ft from its initial position (a) by applying Newton's second law; (b) by applying the principle of work and energy.

Problem 15.3

15.4 At the instant shown, the 30-lb box is moving up the smooth inclined surface at 2 ft/s. The constant force $F = 15$ lb. How fast will the box be moving when it has moved 1 ft up the surface from its present position?

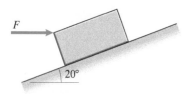

Problem 15.4

15.5 The 0.45-kg soccer ball is 1 m above the ground when it is kicked straight upward at 10 m/s. By using the principle of work and energy, determine: (a) how high above the ground the ball goes, (b) the magnitude of the ball's velocity when it falls back to a height of 1 m above the ground, (c) the magnitude of the ball's velocity immediately before it hits the ground.

15.6 Assume that the soccer ball is stationary the instant before it is kicked upward at 12 m/s. The duration of the kick is 0.02 s. What average power is transferred to the ball during the kick?

Problems 15.5/15.6

15.7 The 2000-lb drag racer starts from rest and travels a quarter-mile course. It completes the course in 4.524 seconds and crosses the finish line traveling at 325.77 mi/h. (a) How much work is done on the car as it travels the course? (b) Assume that the horizontal force exerted on the car is constant and use the principle of work and energy to determine it.

15.8 The 2000-lb drag racer starts from rest and travels a quarter-mile course. It completes the course in 4.524 seconds and crosses the finish line traveling at 325.77 mi/h. Assume that the horizontal force exerted on the car is constant. Determine (a) the maximum power and (b) the average power transferred to the car as it travels the quarter-mile course.

Problems 15.7/15.8

15.9 As the 32,000-lb airplane takes off, the tangential component of force exerted on it by its engines is $\Sigma F_t = 45,000$ lb. Neglecting other forces on the airplane, use the principle of work and energy to determine how much runway is required for its velocity to reach 200 mi/h.

15.10 As the 32,000-lb airplane takes off, the tangential component of force exerted on it by its engines is $\Sigma F_t = 45,000$ lb. Neglecting other forces on the airplane, determine (a) the maximum power and (b) the average power transferred to the airplane as its velocity increases from zero to 200 mi/h.

15.11 The 32,000-lb airplane takes off from rest in the position $s = 0$. The total tangential force exerted on it by its engines and aerodynamic drag (in pounds) is given as a function of its position s by $\Sigma F_t = 45,000 - 5.2s$. Use the principle of work and energy to determine how fast the airplane is traveling when its position is $s = 950$ ft.

Problems 15.9–15.11

15.12 The spring ($k = 20$ N/m) is unstretched when $s = 0$. The 5-kg cart is moved to the position $s = -1$ m and released from rest. What is the magnitude of its velocity when it is in the position $s = 0$?

15.13 The spring ($k = 20$ N/m) is unstretched when $s = 0$. The 5-kg cart is moved to the position $s = -1$ m and released from rest. What maximum distance down the sloped surface does the cart move relative to its initial position?

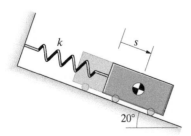

Problems 15.12/15.13

15.14 The force exerted on a car by a prototype crash barrier as the barrier crushes is $F = -(120s + 40s^3)$ lb, where s is the distance in feet from the initial contact. The effective length of the barrier is 18 ft. How fast can a 5000-lb car be moving and be brought to rest within the effective length of the barrier?

15.15 A 5000-lb car hits the crash barrier at 80 mi/h and is brought to rest in 0.11 seconds. What average power is transferred from the car during the impact?

Problems 15.14/15.15

15.16 A group of engineering students constructs a sun-powered car and tests it on a circular track with a 1000-ft radius. The car, with a weight of 460 lb including its occupant, starts from rest. The total tangential component of force on the car is

$$\Sigma F_t = 30 - 0.2s \text{ lb,}$$

where s is the distance (in ft) the car travels along the track from the position where it starts.

(a) Determine the work done on the car when it has gone a distance $s = 120$ ft.

(b) Determine the magnitude of the *total* horizontal force exerted on the car's tires by the road when it is at the position $s = 120$ ft.

15.17 At the instant shown, the 160-lb vaulter's center of mass is 8.5 ft above the ground, and the vertical component of his velocity is 4 ft/s. As his pole straightens, it exerts a vertical force on the vaulter of magnitude $180 + 2.8y^2$ lb, where y is the vertical position of his center of mass *relative to its position at the instant shown*. This force is exerted on him from $y = 0$ to $y = 4$ ft, when he releases the pole. What is the maximum height above the ground reached by the vaulter's center of mass?

Problem 15.17

15.18 The springs ($k = 25$ lb/ft) are unstretched when $s = 0$. The 50-lb weight is released from rest in the position $s = 0$.

(a) When the weight has fallen 1 ft, how much work has been done on it by each spring?

(b) What is the magnitude of the velocity of the weight when it has fallen 1 ft?

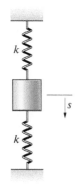

Problem 15.18

15.19 The coefficients of friction between the 160-kg crate and the ramp are $\mu_s = 0.3$ and $\mu_k = 0.28$.

(a) What tension T_0 must the winch exert to start the crate moving up the ramp?

(b) If the tension remains at the value T_0 after the crate starts sliding, what total work is done on the crate as it slides a distance $s = 3$ m up the ramp, and what is the resulting velocity of the crate?

15.20 In Problem 15.19, if the winch exerts a tension $T = T_0(1 + 0.1s)$ after the crate starts sliding, what total work is done on the crate as it slides a distance $s = 3$ m up the ramp, and what is the resulting velocity of the crate?

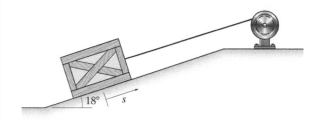

Problems 15.19/15.20

15.21 The 200-mm-diameter gas gun is evacuated on the right of the 8-kg projectile. On the left of the projectile, the tube contains gas with pressure $p_0 = 1 \times 10^5$ Pa (N/m²). The force F is slowly increased, moving the projectile 0.5 m to the left from the position shown. The force is then removed, and the projectile accelerates to the right. If you neglect friction and assume that the pressure of the gas is related to its volume by $pV = $ constant, what is the velocity of the projectile when it has returned to its original position?

15.22 In Problem 15.21, if you assume that the pressure of the gas is related to its volume by $pV = $ constant while the gas is compressed (an isothermal process) and by $pV^{1.4} = $ constant while it is expanding (an isentropic process), what is the velocity of the projectile when it has returned to its original position?

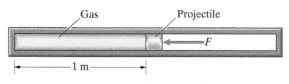

Problems 15.21/15.22

▶ **15.23** In Example 15.2, suppose that the angle between the inclined surface and the horizontal is increased from 20° to 30°. What is the magnitude of the velocity of the crates when they have moved 400 mm?

15.24 The system is released from rest. The 4-kg mass slides on the smooth horizontal surface. By using the principle of work and energy, determine the magnitude of the velocity of the masses when the 20-kg mass has fallen 1 m.

15.25 Solve Problem 15.24 if the coefficient of kinetic friction between the 4-kg mass and the horizontal surface is $\mu_k = 0.4$.

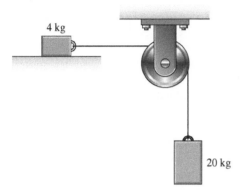

4 kg

20 kg

Problems 15.24/15.25

15.26 Each box weighs 50 lb and the inclined surfaces are smooth. The system is released from rest. Determine the magnitude of the velocities of the boxes when they have moved 1 ft.

15.27 Solve Problem 15.26 if the coefficient of kinetic friction between the boxes and the inclined surfaces is $\mu_k = 0.05$.

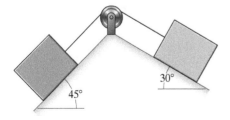

30°

45°

Problems 15.26/15.27

15.28 The masses of the three blocks are $m_A = 40$ kg, $m_B = 16$ kg, and $m_C = 12$ kg. Neglect the mass of the bar holding C in place. Friction is negligible. By applying the principle of work and energy to A and B individually, determine the magnitude of their velocity when they have moved 500 mm.

15.29 Solve Problem 15.28 by applying the principle of work and energy to the system consisting of A, B, the cable connecting them, and the pulley.

▶ **15.30** The masses of the three blocks are $m_A = 40$ kg, $m_B = 16$ kg, and $m_C = 12$ kg. The coefficient of kinetic friction between all surfaces is $\mu_k = 0.1$. Determine the magnitude of the velocity of blocks A and B when they have moved 500 mm. (See Example 15.3.)

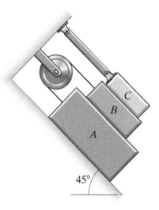

C

B

A

45°

Problems 15.28–15.30

15.2 Work Done by Particular Forces

BACKGROUND

We have seen that if the tangential component of the total external force on an object is known as a function of distance along the object's path, the principle of work and energy can be used to relate a change in the position of the object to the change in its velocity. For certain types of forces, however, not only can we determine the work without knowing the tangential component of the force as a function of distance along the path, but we don't even need to know the path. Two important examples are weight and the force exerted by a spring.

Weight

To evaluate the work done by an object's weight, we orient a cartesian coordinate system with the y axis upward and suppose that the object moves from position 1 with coordinates (x_1, y_1, z_1) to position 2 with coordinates (x_2, y_2, z_2) (Fig. 15.3a). The force exerted by the object's weight is $\mathbf{F} = -mg\mathbf{j}$. (Other forces may act on the object, but we are concerned only with the work done by its weight.) Because $\mathbf{v} = d\mathbf{r}/dt$, we can multiply the velocity, expressed in cartesian coordinates, by dt to obtain an expression for the vector $d\mathbf{r}$:

$$d\mathbf{r} = \left(\frac{dx}{dt}\mathbf{i} + \frac{dy}{dt}\mathbf{j} + \frac{dz}{dt}\mathbf{k} \right) dt = dx\,\mathbf{i} + dy\,\mathbf{j} + dz\,\mathbf{k}.$$

Taking the dot product of $\mathbf{F}$ and $d\mathbf{r}$ yields

$$\mathbf{F} \cdot d\mathbf{r} = (-mg\mathbf{j}) \cdot (dx\,\mathbf{i} + dy\,\mathbf{j} + dz\,\mathbf{k}) = -mg\,dy.$$

The work done as the object moves from position 1 to position 2 reduces to an integral with respect to y:

$$U_{12} = \int_{\mathbf{r}_1}^{\mathbf{r}_2} \mathbf{F} \cdot d\mathbf{r} = \int_{y_1}^{y_2} -mg\,dy.$$

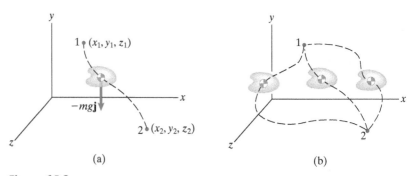

(a)   (b)

Figure 15.3
(a) An object moving between two positions.
(b) The work done by the weight is the same for any path.

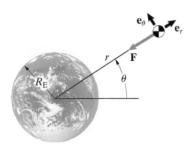

Figure 15.4
Expressing an object's weight
in polar coordinates.

Evaluating the integral, we obtain the work done by the weight of an object as
it moves between two positions:

$$U_{12} = -mg(y_2 - y_1). \tag{15.11}$$

The work is simply the product of the weight and the change in the object's
height. The work done is negative if the height increases and positive if it decreases. Notice that *the work done is independent of the path the object follows
from position 1 to position 2* (Fig. 15.3b). Thus, we don't need to know the path
to determine the work done by an object's weight—we only need to know the
relative heights of the initial and final positions.

What work is done by an object's weight if we account for its variation
with distance from the center of the earth? In terms of polar coordinates, we
can write the weight of an object at a distance r from the center of the earth as
(Fig. 15.4)

$$\mathbf{F} = -\frac{mgR_E^2}{r^2}\mathbf{e}_r.$$

Using the expression for the velocity in polar coordinates, we obtain, for the
vector $d\mathbf{r} = \mathbf{v}\, dt$,

$$d\mathbf{r} = \left(\frac{dr}{dt}\mathbf{e}_r + r\frac{d\theta}{dt}\mathbf{e}_\theta\right) dt = dr\, \mathbf{e}_r + r\, d\theta\, \mathbf{e}_\theta. \tag{15.12}$$

The dot product of $\mathbf{F}$ and $d\mathbf{r}$ is

$$\mathbf{F} \cdot d\mathbf{r} = \left(-\frac{mgR_E^2}{r^2}\mathbf{e}_r\right) \cdot (dr\, \mathbf{e}_r + r\, d\theta\, \mathbf{e}_\theta) = -\frac{mgR_E^2}{r^2}dr,$$

so the work reduces to an integral with respect to r:

$$U_{12} = \int_{\mathbf{r}_1}^{\mathbf{r}_2} \mathbf{F} \cdot d\mathbf{r} = \int_{r_1}^{r_2} -\frac{mgR_E^2}{r^2}dr.$$

Evaluating the integral, we obtain the work done by an object's weight,
accounting for the variation of the weight with height:

$$U_{12} = mgR_E^2\left(\frac{1}{r_2} - \frac{1}{r_1}\right). \tag{15.13}$$

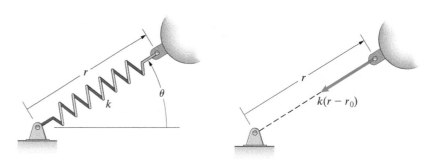

Figure 15.5
Expressing the force exerted by a linear spring in polar
coordinates.

Again, the work is independent of path from position 1 to position 2. To
evaluate it, we only need to know the object's radial distance from the center of
the earth at the two positions.

Springs

Suppose that a linear spring connects an object to a fixed support. In terms of
polar coordinates (Fig. 15.5), the force exerted on the object is

$$\mathbf{F} = -k(r - r_0)\mathbf{e}_r,$$

where k is the spring constant and r_0 is the unstretched length of the spring.
Using Eq. (15.12), we get the dot product of $\mathbf{F}$ and $d\mathbf{r}$:

$$\mathbf{F} \cdot d\mathbf{r} = [-k(r - r_0)\mathbf{e}_r] \cdot (dr\, \mathbf{e}_r + r\, d\theta\, \mathbf{e}_\theta) = -k(r - r_0)\, dr.$$

It is convenient to express the work done by a spring in terms of its *stretch*, defined by $S = r - r_0$. (Although the word *stretch* usually means an increase in
length, we use the term more generally to denote the change in length of the
spring. A negative stretch is a decrease in length.) In terms of this variable,
$\mathbf{F} \cdot d\mathbf{r} = -kS\, dS$, and the work is

$$U_{12} = \int_{\mathbf{r}_1}^{\mathbf{r}_2} \mathbf{F} \cdot d\mathbf{r} = \int_{S_1}^{S_2} -kS\, dS.$$

The work done on an object by a spring attached to a fixed support is

$$U_{12} = -\tfrac{1}{2}k(S_2^2 - S_1^2), \tag{15.14}$$

where S_1 and S_2 are the values of the stretch at the initial and final positions. We
don't need to know the object's path to determine the work done by the spring.
Remember, however, that Eq. (15.14) applies only to a linear spring. In Fig. 15.6,
we determine the work done in stretching a linear spring by calculating the area
defined by the graph of the force as a function of S.

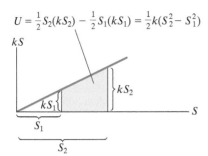

$$U = \tfrac{1}{2}S_2(kS_2) - \tfrac{1}{2}S_1(kS_1) = \tfrac{1}{2}k(S_2^2 - S_1^2)$$

Figure 15.6
Work done in stretching a linear spring
from S_1 to S_2. (If $S_2 > S_1$, the work
done *on* the spring is positive, so the
work done *by* the spring is negative.)

RESULTS

For some types of
forces, the work done
during a motion from
a position 1 to a
position 2 can be
determined easily.
Notice that *the work
is independent of the
path from 1 to 2.*

Weight
When the weight can be
regarded as constant, the work is

$$U_{12} = -mg(y_2 - y_1), \quad (15.11)$$

where the positive y axis points
upwards. *The work is the
product of the weight and the
change in height. It is negative
if the height increases and
positive if it decreases.*

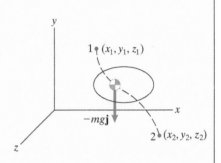

Variable Weight
when the variation of gravity with
height must be considered, the
work is

$$U_{12} = mgR_{\mathrm{E}}^2\left(\frac{1}{r_2} - \frac{1}{r_1}\right), \quad (15.13)$$

where R_{E} is the radius of the earth.

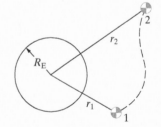

Springs
The work done on an object by a
linear spring is

$$U_{12} = -\tfrac{1}{2}k(S_2^2 - S_1^2), \quad (15.14)$$

where S_1 and S_2 are the values of
the stretch of the spring at the
initial and final positions.

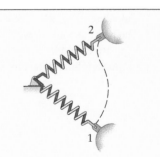

| **Active Example 15.4** | **Work Done by Weight and Springs** (▶ *Related Problem 15.49*) |

The 40-kg hammer is lifted to position 1 and released from rest. It falls and strikes a workpiece when it is in position 2. The spring constant is $k = 1500$ N/m, and the springs are unstretched when the hammer is in position 2. Neglect friction. What is the velocity of the hammer just before it strikes the workpiece?

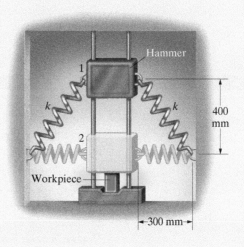

Strategy

Work is done on the hammer by its weight and by the forces exerted on it by the springs. We can apply the principle of work and energy to the motion of the hammer from position 1 to position 2 to determine the velocity at position 2.

Solution

Calculate the work done by the weight: The hammer falls downward, so the work is positive, and its magnitude is the product of the weight and the change in height.	$\begin{cases} U_{\text{weight}} = (\text{weight})(\text{change in height}) \\ \quad = [(40 \text{ kg})(9.81 \text{ m/s}^2)](0.4 \text{ m}) \\ \quad = 157 \text{ N-m}. \end{cases}$

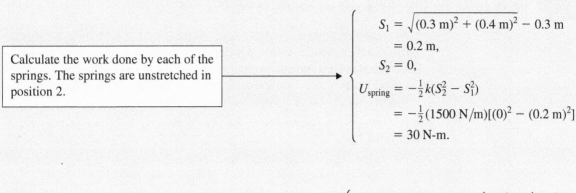

Calculate the work done by each of the springs. The springs are unstretched in position 2.

$$
\left\{
\begin{aligned}
S_1 &= \sqrt{(0.3 \text{ m})^2 + (0.4 \text{ m})^2} - 0.3 \text{ m} \\
&= 0.2 \text{ m}, \\
S_2 &= 0, \\
U_{\text{spring}} &= -\tfrac{1}{2} k(S_2^2 - S_1^2) \\
&= -\tfrac{1}{2}(1500 \text{ N/m})[(0)^2 - (0.2 \text{ m})^2] \\
&= 30 \text{ N-m}.
\end{aligned}
\right.
$$

Apply work and energy to obtain the velocity of the hammer in position 2.

$$
\left\{
\begin{aligned}
U_{\text{weight}} + 2(U_{\text{spring}}) &= \tfrac{1}{2} m v_2^2 - \tfrac{1}{2} m v_1^2 : \\
157 \text{ N-m} + 2(30 \text{ N-m}) &= \tfrac{1}{2}(40 \text{ kg})v_2^2 - 0. \\
\text{Solving, we obtain} \\
v_2 &= 3.29 \text{ m/s}.
\end{aligned}
\right.
$$

Practice Problem The 40-kg hammer is given a downward velocity of 2 m/s in position 1. It falls and strikes a workpiece when it is in position 2. The spring constant is $k = 1500$ N/m, and the springs are unstretched when the hammer is in position 1. Neglect friction. What is the velocity of the hammer just before it strikes the workpiece?

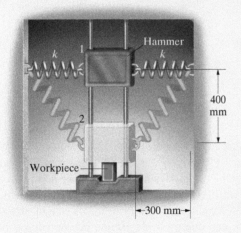

Answer: $v_2 = 2.97$ m/s.

| Example 15.5 | Work Done by Weight (▶ *Related Problem 15.31*) |

At position 1, the skier is approaching his jump at 15 m/s. When he reaches the horizontal end of the ramp at position 2, 20 m below position 1, he jumps upward, achieving a vertical component of velocity of 3 m/s. (Disregard the small change in the vertical position of his center of mass due to his jumping motion.) Neglect aerodynamic drag and the frictional forces on his skis.

(a) What is the magnitude of the skier's velocity as he leaves the ramp at position 2?

(b) At the highest point of his jump, position 3, what are the magnitude of his velocity and the height of his center of mass above position 2?

Strategy

(a) If we neglect aerodynamic and frictional forces, the only force doing work from position 1 to position 2 is the skier's weight. The normal force exerted on his skis by the ramp does no work because it is perpendicular to his path. We need to know only the change in the skier's height from position 1 to position 2 to determine the work done by his weight, so we can apply the principle of work and energy to determine his velocity at position 2 before he jumps.

(b) From the time he leaves the ramp at position 2 until he reaches position 3, the only force acting on the skier is his weight, so the horizontal component of his velocity is constant. This means that we know the magnitude of his velocity at position 3, because he is moving horizontally at that point. Therefore, we can apply the principle of work and energy to his motion from position 2 to position 3 to determine his height above position 2.

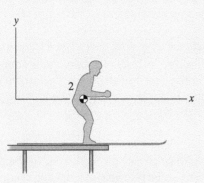

(a) The height of the skier's center of mass is measured relative to position 2.

Solution

(a) We will use Eq. (15.11) to evaluate the work done by the skier's weight, measuring the height of his center of mass relative to position 2 (Fig. a). The principle of work and energy from position 1 to position 2 is

$$U_{12} = -mg(y_2 - y_1) = \tfrac{1}{2}mv_2^2 - \tfrac{1}{2}mv_1^2:$$

$$-m(9.81)(0 - 20) = \tfrac{1}{2}mv_2^2 - \tfrac{1}{2}m(15)^2.$$

Solving for v_2, we find that the skier's horizontal velocity at position 2 before he jumps upward is 24.8 m/s. After he jumps upward, the magnitude of his velocity at position 2 is $v_2' = \sqrt{(24.8)^2 + (3)^2} = 25.0$ m/s.

(b) The magnitude of the skier's velocity at position 3 is equal to the horizontal component of his velocity at position 2: $v_3 = v_2 = 24.8$ m/s. Applying work and energy to his motion from position 2 to position 3, we obtain

$$U_{23} = -mg(y_3 - y_2) \qquad = \tfrac{1}{2}mv_3^2 - \tfrac{1}{2}m(v_2')^2:$$

$$-m(9.81)(y_3 - 0) = \tfrac{1}{2}m(24.8)^2 - \tfrac{1}{2}m(25.0)^2,$$

from which it follows that $y_3 = 0.459$ m.

Critical Thinking

Why didn't we need to include the effect of the normal force exerted on the skier by the ramp? The reason is that *it is perpendicular to his path and so does no work.* To obtain an accurate prediction of the skier's motion, we would need to account for the friction force exerted by the ramp and aerodynamic forces. Nevertheless, our approximate analysis in this example provides useful insight, showing how the work done by gravity as he descends increases his kinetic energy. Notice that the work done by gravity is determined by his change in height, not the length of his path.

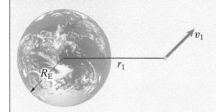

Example 15.6 **Work Done by the Earth's Gravity** (▶ *Related Problem 15.74*)

A spacecraft at a distance $r_1 = 2R_E$ from the center of the earth has a velocity of magnitude $v_1 = \sqrt{2gR_E/3}$ relative to a nonrotating reference frame with its origin at the center of the earth. Determine the magnitude of the spacecraft's velocity when it is at a distance $r_2 = 4R_E$ from the center of the earth.

Strategy
By applying Eq. (15.13) to determine the work done by the gravitational force on the spacecraft, we can use the principle of work and energy to determine the magnitude of the spacecraft's velocity.

Solution
From Eq. (15.13), the work done by gravity as the spacecraft moves from a distance r_1 from the center of the earth to a distance r_2 is

$$U_{12} = mgR_E^2\left(\frac{1}{r_2} - \frac{1}{r_1}\right).$$

Let v_2 be the magnitude of the velocity of the spacecraft when it is at a distance r_2 from the center of the earth. Applying the principle of work and energy yields

$$U_{12} = mgR_E^2\left(\frac{1}{r_2} - \frac{1}{r_1}\right) = \tfrac{1}{2}mv_2^2 - \tfrac{1}{2}mv_1^2.$$

We solve for v_2, obtaining

$$v_2 = \sqrt{v_1^2 + 2gR_E^2\left(\frac{1}{r_2} - \frac{1}{r_1}\right)}$$

$$= \sqrt{\left(\frac{2gR_E}{3}\right) + 2gR_E^2\left(\frac{1}{4R_E} - \frac{1}{2R_E}\right)}$$

$$= \sqrt{\frac{gR_E}{6}}.$$

The velocity $v_2 = v_1/2$.

Critical Thinking
Notice that we did not need to specify the direction of the spacecraft's initial velocity to determine the magnitude of its velocity at a different distance from the center of the earth. This illustrates the power of the principle of work and energy, as well as one of its limitations. Even if we know the direction of the initial velocity, the principle of work and energy tells us only the *magnitude* of the velocity at a different distance.

Problems

▶ **15.31** In Example 15.5, suppose that the skier is moving at 20 m/s when he is in position 1. Determine the horizontal component of his velocity when he reaches position 2, 20 m below position 1.

15.32 Suppose that you stand at the edge of a 200-ft cliff and throw rocks at 30 ft/s in the three directions shown. Neglecting aerodynamic drag, use the principle of work and energy to determine the magnitude of the velocity of the rock just before it hits the ground in each case.

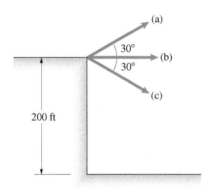

Problem 15.32

15.33 The 30-kg box is sliding down the smooth surface at 1 m/s when it is in position 1. Determine the magnitude of the box's velocity at position 2 in each case.

15.34 Solve Problem 15.33 if the coefficient of kinetic friction between the box and the inclined surface is $\mu_k = 0.2$.

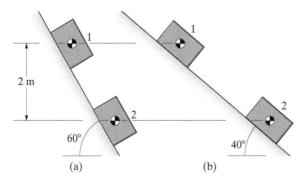

Problems 15.33/15.34

15.35 In case (a), a 5-lb ball is released from rest at position 1 and falls to position 2. In case (b), the ball is released from rest at position 1 and swings to position 2. For each case, use the principle of work and energy to determine the magnitude of the ball's velocity at position 2. [In case (b), notice that the force exerted on the ball by the string is perpendicular to the ball's path.]

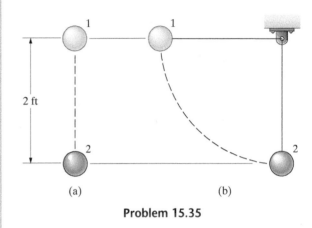

Problem 15.35

15.36 The 2-kg ball is released from rest in position 1 with the string horizontal. The length of the string is $L = 1$ m. What is the magnitude of the ball's velocity when it is in position 2?

15.37 The 2-kg ball is released from rest in position 1 with the string horizontal. The length of the string is $L = 1$ m. What is the tension in the string when the ball is in position 2?

Strategy: Draw the free-body diagram of the ball when it is in position 2 and write Newton's second law in terms of normal and tangential components.

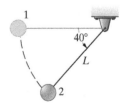

Problems 15.36/15.37

15.38 The 400-lb wrecker's ball swings at the end of a 25-ft cable. If the magnitude of the ball's velocity at position 1 is 4 ft/s, what is the magnitude of its velocity just before it hits the wall at position 2?

15.39 The 400-lb wrecker's ball swings at the end of a 25-ft cable. If the magnitude of the ball's velocity at position 1 is 4 ft/s, what is the maximum tension in the cable as the ball swings from position 1 to position 2?

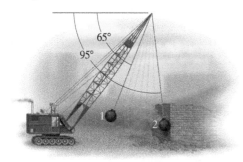

Problems 15.38/15.39

15.40 A stunt driver wants to drive a car through the circular loop of radius $R = 5$ m. Determine the minimum velocity v_0 at which the car can enter the loop and coast through without losing contact with the track. What is the car's velocity at the top of the loop?

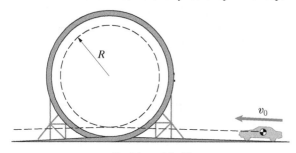

Problem 15.40

15.41 The 2-kg collar starts from rest at position 1 and slides down the smooth rigid wire. The y axis points upward. What is the magnitude of the velocity of the collar when it reaches position 2?

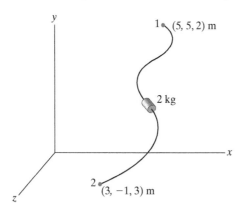

Problem 15.41

15.42 The 4-lb collar slides down the smooth rigid wire from position 1 to position 2. When it reaches position 2, the magnitude of its velocity is 24 ft/s. What was the magnitude of its velocity at position 1?

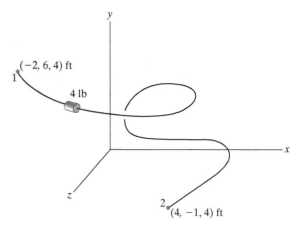

Problem 15.42

15.43 The forces acting on the 28,000-lb airplane are the thrust T and drag D, which are parallel to the airplane's path; the lift L, which is perpendicular to the path; and the weight W. The airplane climbs from an altitude of 3000 ft to an altitude of 10,000 ft. During the climb, the magnitude of its velocity decreases from 800 ft/s to 600 ft/s.

(a) What work is done on the airplane by its lift during the climb?

(b) What work is done by the thrust and drag combined?

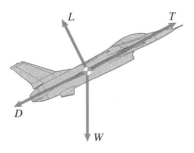

Problem 15.43

15.44 The 2400-lb car is traveling 40 mi/h at position 1. If the combined effect of the aerodynamic drag on the car and the tangential force exerted on its wheels by the road is that they exert no net tangential force on the car, what is the magnitude of the car's velocity at position 2?

15.45 The 2400-lb car is traveling 40 mi/h at position 1. If the combined effect of the aerodynamic drag on the car and the tangential force exerted on its wheels by the road is that they exert a constant 400-lb tangential force on the car in the direction of its motion, what is the magnitude of the car's velocity at position 2?

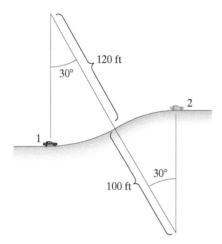

Problems 15.44/15.45

15.46 The mass of the rocket is 250 kg. Its engine has a constant thrust of 45 kN. The length of the launching ramp is 10 m. If the magnitude of the rocket's velocity when it reaches the end of the ramp is 52 m/s, how much work is done on the rocket by friction and aerodynamic drag?

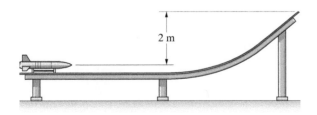

Problem 15.46

15.47 A bioengineer interested in the energy requirements of sports determines from videotape that when the athlete begins his motion to throw the 7.25-kg shot (Fig. P15.47a), the shot is stationary and 1.50 m above the ground. At the instant the athlete releases it (Fig. P15.47b), the shot is 2.10 m above the ground. The shot reaches a maximum height of 4.60 m above the ground and travels a horizontal distance of 18.66 m from the point where it was released. How much work does the athlete do on the shot from the beginning of his motion to the instant he releases it?

(a)   (b)

Problem 15.47

15.48 A small pellet of mass $m = 0.2$ kg starts from rest at position 1 and slides down the smooth surface of the cylinder to position 2, where $\theta = 30°$.

(a) What work is done on the pellet as it slides from position 1 to position 2?

(b) What is the magnitude of the pellet's velocity at position 2?

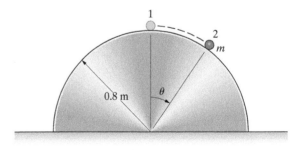

Problem 15.48

▶ **15.49** In Active Example 15.4, suppose that you want to increase the value of the spring constant k so that the velocity of the hammer just before it strikes the workpiece is 4 m/s. What is the required value of k?

15.50 Suppose that you want to design a bumper that will bring a 50-lb package moving at 10 ft/s to rest 6 in from the point of contact with the bumper. If friction is negligible, what is the necessary spring constant k?

15.51 In Problem 15.50, what spring constant is necessary if the coefficient of kinetic friction between the package and the floor is $\mu_k = 0.3$ and the package contacts the bumper moving at 10 ft/s?

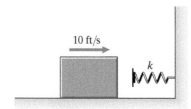

Problems 15.50/15.51

15.52 The 50-lb package starts from rest, slides down the smooth ramp, and is stopped by the spring.

(a) If you want the package to be brought to rest 6 in from the point of contact, what is the necessary spring constant k?

(b) What maximum deceleration is the package subjected to?

15.53 The 50-lb package starts from rest, slides down the ramp, and is stopped by the spring. The coefficient of static friction between the package and the ramp is $\mu_k = 0.12$. If you want the package to be brought to rest 6 in from the point of contact, what is the necessary spring constant k?

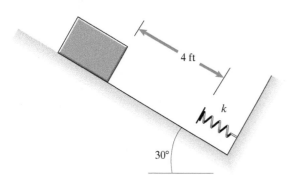

Problems 15.52/15.53

15.54 The system is released from rest with the spring un-stretched. The spring constant is $k = 200$ N/m. Determine the magnitude of the velocity of the masses when the right mass has fallen 1 m.

15.55 The system is released from rest with the spring unstretched. The spring constant is $k = 200$ N/m. What maximum downward velocity does the right mass attain as it falls?

Problems 15.54/15.55

15.56 The system is released from rest. The 4-kg mass slides on the smooth horizontal surface. The spring constant is $k = 100$ N/m, and the tension in the spring when the system is released is 50 N. By using the principle of work and energy, determine the magnitude of the velocity of the masses when the 20-kg mass has fallen 1 m.

15.57 Solve Problem 15.56 if the coefficient of kinetic friction between the 4-kg mass and the horizontal surface is $\mu_k = 0.4$.

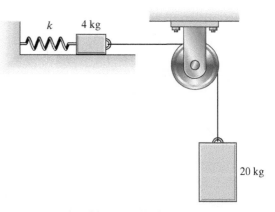

Problems 15.56/15.57

15.58 The 40-lb crate is released from rest on the smooth inclined surface with the spring unstretched. The spring constant is $k = 8$ lb/ft.

(a) How far down the inclined surface does the crate slide before it stops?

(b) What maximum velocity does the crate attain on its way down?

15.59 Solve Problem 15.58 if the coefficient of kinetic friction between the 4-kg mass and the horizontal surface is $\mu_k = 0.2$.

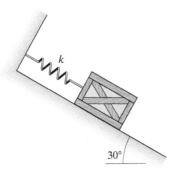

Problems 15.58/15.59

15.60 The 4-kg collar starts from rest in position 1 on the smooth bar with the spring unstretched. The spring constant is $k = 100$ N/m. How far does the collar fall relative to position 1?

15.61 In position 1 on the smooth bar, the 4-kg collar has a downward velocity of 1 m/s and the spring is unstretched. The spring constant is $k = 100$ N/m. What maximum downward velocity does the collar attain as it falls?

15.62 The 4-kg collar starts from rest in position 1 on the smooth bar. The tension in the spring in position 1 is 20 N. The spring constant is $k = 100$ N/m. How far does the collar fall relative to position 1?

Problems 15.60–15.62

15.63 The 4-kg collar is released from rest in position 1 on the smooth bar. If the spring constant is $k = 6$ kN/m and the spring is unstretched in position 2, what is the velocity of the collar when it has fallen to position 2?

15.64 The 4-kg collar is released from rest in position 1 on the smooth bar. The spring constant is $k = 4$ kN/m. The tension in the spring in position 2 is 500 N. What is the velocity of the collar when it has fallen to position 2?

15.65 The 4-kg collar starts from rest in position 1 on the smooth bar. Its velocity when it has fallen to position 2 is 4 m/s. The spring is unstretched when the collar is in position 2. What is the spring constant k?

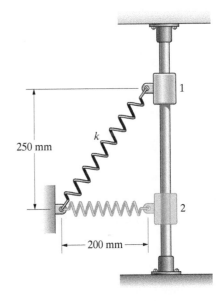

Problems 15.63–15.65

15.66 The 10-kg collar starts from rest at position 1 and slides along the smooth bar. The y axis points upward. The spring constant is $k = 100$ N/m, and the unstretched length of the spring is 2 m. What is the velocity of the collar when it reaches position 2?

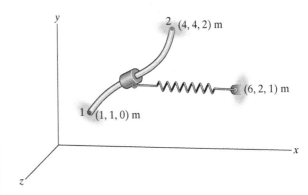

Problem 15.66

15.67 A spring-powered mortar is used to launch 10-lb packages of fireworks into the air. The package starts from rest with the spring compressed to a length of 6 in. The unstretched length of the spring is 30 in. If the spring constant is $k = 1300$ lb/ft, what is the magnitude of the velocity of the package as it leaves the mortar?

15.68 Suppose you want to design the mortar in Problem 15.67 to throw the package to a height of 150 ft above its initial position. Neglecting friction and drag, determine the necessary spring constant.

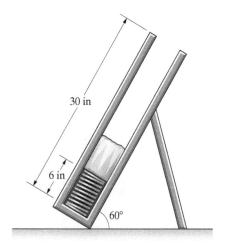

Problems 15.67/15.68

15.69 Suppose an object has a string or cable with *constant* tension T attached as shown. The force exerted on the object can be expressed in terms of polar coordinates as $\mathbf{F} = -T\mathbf{e}_r$. Show that the work done on the object as it moves along an *arbitrary* plane path from a radial position r_1 to a radial position r_2 is $U_{12} = -T(r_2 - r_1)$.

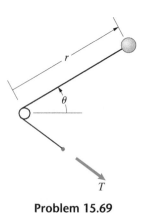

Problem 15.69

15.70 The 2-kg collar is initially at rest at position 1. A constant 100-N force is applied to the string, causing the collar to slide up the smooth vertical bar. What is the velocity of the collar when it reaches position 2? (See Problem 15.69.)

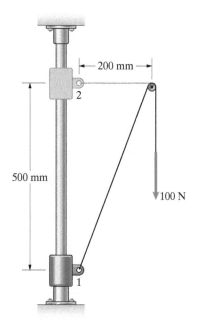

Problem 15.70

15.71 The 10-kg collar starts from rest at position 1. The tension in the string is 200 N, and the y axis points upward. If friction is negligible, what is the magnitude of the velocity of the collar when it reaches position 2? (See Problem 15.69.)

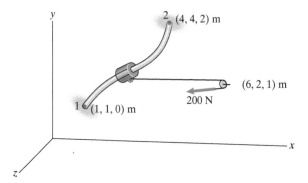

Problem 15.71

15.72 As the F/A-18 lands at 210 ft/s, the cable from A to B engages the airplane's arresting hook at C. The arresting mechanism maintains the tension in the cable at a constant value, bringing the 26,000-lb airplane to rest at a distance of 72 ft. What is the tension in the cable? (See Problem 15.69.)

15.73 If the airplane in Problem 15.72 lands at 240 ft/s, what distance does it roll before the arresting system brings it to rest?

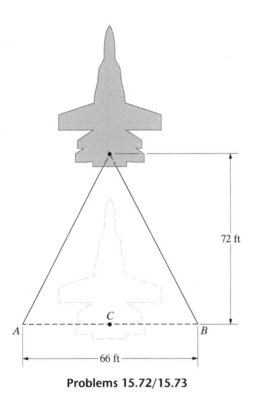

Problems 15.72/15.73

▶ **15.74** A spacecraft 320 km above the surface of the earth is moving at escape velocity $v_{esc} = 10,900$ m/s. What is its distance from the center of the earth when its velocity is 50 percent of its initial value? The radius of the earth is 6370 km. (See Example 15.6.)

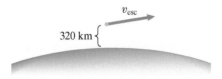

Problem 15.74

15.75 A piece of ejecta is thrown up by the impact of a meteor on the moon. When it is 1000 km above the moon's surface, the magnitude of its velocity (relative to a nonrotating reference frame with its origin at the center of the moon) is 200 m/s. What is the magnitude of its velocity just before it strikes the moon's surface? The acceleration due to gravity at the surface of the moon is 1.62 m/s². The moon's radius is 1738 km.

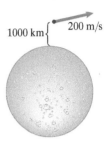

Problem 15.75

15.76 A satellite in a circular orbit of radius r around the earth has velocity $v = \sqrt{gR_E^2/r}$, where $R_E = 6370$ km is the radius of the earth. Suppose you are designing a rocket to transfer a 900-kg communication satellite from a circular parking orbit with 6700-km radius to a circular geosynchronous orbit with 42,222-km radius. How much work must the rocket do on the satellite?

15.77 The force exerted on a charged particle by a magnetic field is

$$\mathbf{F} = q\mathbf{v} \times \mathbf{B},$$

where q and $\mathbf{v}$ are the charge and velocity of the particle and $\mathbf{B}$ is the magnetic field vector. Suppose that other forces on the particle are negligible. Use the principle of work and energy to show that the magnitude of the particle's velocity is constant.

15.3 Potential Energy and Conservative Forces

BACKGROUND

Potential Energy

The work done on an object by some forces can be expressed as the change of a function of the object's position called the potential energy. When all the forces that do work on a system have this property, we can state the principle of work and energy as a conservation law: The sum of the kinetic and potential energies is constant.

When we derived the principle of work and energy in Section 15.1 by integrating Newton's second law, we were able to evaluate the integral on one side of the equation, obtaining the change in the kinetic energy:

$$U_{12} = \int_{\mathbf{r}_1}^{\mathbf{r}_2} \Sigma \mathbf{F} \cdot d\mathbf{r} = \tfrac{1}{2} m v_2^2 - \tfrac{1}{2} m v_1^2. \tag{15.15}$$

Suppose we could determine a scalar function of position V such that

$$dV = -\Sigma \mathbf{F} \cdot d\mathbf{r}. \tag{15.16}$$

Then we could also evaluate the integral defining the work:

$$U_{12} = \int_{\mathbf{r}_1}^{\mathbf{r}_2} \Sigma \mathbf{F} \cdot d\mathbf{r} = \int_{V_1}^{V_2} - dV = -(V_2 - V_1), \tag{15.17}$$

where V_1 and V_2 are the values of V at the positions $\mathbf{r}_1$ and $\mathbf{r}_2$, respectively. Substituting this expression into Eq. (15.15), we obtain the principle of work and energy in the form

$$\tfrac{1}{2} m v_1^2 + V_1 = \tfrac{1}{2} m v_2^2 + V_2. \tag{15.18}$$

If the kinetic energy increases as the object moves from position 1 to position 2, the function V must decrease, and vice versa, as if V represents a reservoir of "potential" kinetic energy. For this reason, V is called the *potential energy*.

Equation (15.18) states that the sum of the kinetic and potential energies of an object has the same value at any two points. Energy is *conserved*. However, *there is an important restriction on the use of this result.* We arrived at Eq. (15.18) by assuming that a function V, the potential energy, exists that satisfies Eq. (15.16). This is true only for a limited class of forces, which are said to be *conservative*. We discuss conservative forces in the next section. If *all* of the forces that do work on an object are conservative, Eq. (15.18) can be applied, where V is the sum of the potential energies of the forces that do work on the object. Otherwise, Eq. (15.18) cannot be used. A system is said to be conservative if all of the forces that do work on the system are conservative. The sum of the kinetic and potential energies of a conservative system is conserved.

An object may be subjected to both conservative and nonconservative forces. When that is the case, it is often convenient to introduce the potential energies of the forces that are conservative into the statement of the principle of work and energy. To allow for this option, we write Eq. (15.15) as

$$\tfrac{1}{2} m v_1^2 + V_1 + U_{12} = \tfrac{1}{2} m v_2^2 + V_2. \tag{15.19}$$

When the principle of work and energy is written in this form, the term U_{12} includes the work done by all nonconservative forces acting on the object. If a conservative force does work on the object, there is a choice. The work can be calculated and included in U_{12}, *or* the force's potential energy can be included in V. This procedure can also be applied to a system that is subjected to both conservative and nonconservative forces. The sum of the kinetic and potential energies of a system in position 1 plus the work done as the system moves from position 1 to position 2 is equal to the total sum of the kinetic and potential energies in position 2.

Conservative Forces

We can apply conservation of energy only if the forces doing work on an object or system are conservative and we know (or can determine) their potential energies. In this section, we determine the potential energies of some conservative forces and use the results to demonstrate applications of conservation of energy. But before discussing forces that are conservative, we demonstrate with a simple example that *frictional forces are not conservative*.

The work done by a conservative force as an object moves from a position 1 to a position 2 is independent of the object's path. This result follows from Eq. (15.17), which states that the work depends only on the values of the potential energy at positions 1 and 2. Equation (15.17) also implies that if the object moves along a closed path, returning to position 1, the work done by a conservative force is zero. Suppose that a book of mass m rests on a table and you push it horizontally so that it slides along a path of length L. The magnitude of the force of friction is $\mu_k mg$, and the direction of the force is opposite to that of the book's motion (Fig. 15.7). The work done is

$$U_{12} = \int_0^L -\mu_k mg \ ds = -\mu_k mg L.$$

The work is proportional to the length of the object's path and therefore is not independent of the path. As this simple example demonstrates, friction forces are not conservative.

The weight of an object and the force exerted by a spring attached to a fixed support are conservative forces. Using them as examples, we demonstrate how you can determine the potential energies of other conservative forces. We also use the potential energies of these forces in examples of the use of conservation of energy to analyze the motions of conservative systems.

Weight   To determine the potential energy associated with an object's weight, we use a cartesian coordinate system with its y axis pointing upward (Fig. 15.8). The weight is $\mathbf{F} = -mg\,\mathbf{j}$, and its dot product with the vector $d\mathbf{r}$ is

$$\mathbf{F} \cdot d\mathbf{r} = (-mg\mathbf{j}) \cdot (dx\,\mathbf{i} + dy\,\mathbf{j} + dz\,\mathbf{k}) = -mg\,dy.$$

From Eq. (15.16), the potential energy V must satisfy the relation

$$dV = -\mathbf{F} \cdot d\mathbf{r} = mg\,dy, \tag{15.20}$$

which we can write as

$$\frac{dV}{dy} = mg.$$

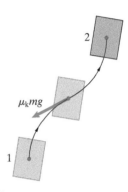

Figure 15.7
The book's path from position 1 to position 2. The force of friction points opposite to the direction of the motion.

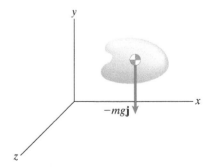

Figure 15.8
Weight of an object expressed in terms of a coordinate system with the y axis pointing upward.

Integrating this equation, we obtain

$$V = mgy + C,$$

where C, the constant of integration, is arbitrary. This expression satisfies Eq. (15.20) for any value of C. Another way of understanding why C is arbitrary is to notice in Eq. (15.18) that it is the difference in the potential energy between two positions that determines the change in the kinetic energy. We will let $C = 0$ and write the potential energy of the weight of an object as

$$V = mgy. \tag{15.21}$$

The potential energy is the product of the object's weight and height. The height can be measured from any convenient reference level, or *datum*. Since it is the difference in potential energy that determines the change in the kinetic energy, it is the difference in height that matters, not the level from which the height is measured.

The roller coaster (Fig. 15.9a) is a classic example of conservation of energy. If aerodynamic and frictional forces are neglected, the weight is the only force doing work, and the system is conservative. The potential energy of the roller coaster is proportional to the height of the track relative to a datum. In Fig. 15.9b,

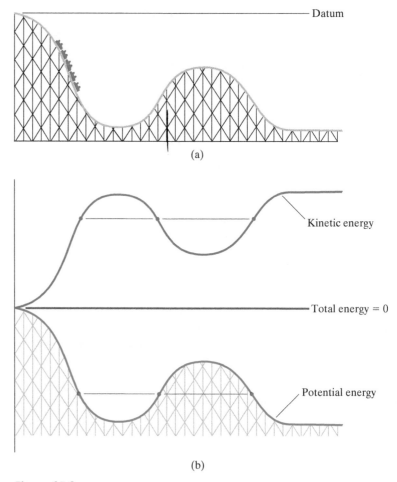

Figure 15.9
(a) Roller coaster and a reference level, or datum.
(b) The sum of the potential and kinetic energies is constant.

we assume that the roller coaster started from rest at the datum level. The sum of the kinetic and potential energies is constant, so the kinetic energy "mirrors" the potential energy. At points of the track that have equal heights, the magnitudes of the velocities are equal.

To account for the variation of weight with distance from the center of the earth, we can express the weight in polar coordinates as

$$\mathbf{F} = -\frac{mgR_{\mathrm{E}}^2}{r^2}\mathbf{e}_r,$$

where r is the distance from the center of the earth (Fig. 15.10). From Eq. (15.12), the vector $d\mathbf{r}$ in terms of polar coordinates is

$$d\mathbf{r} = dr\,\mathbf{e}_r + r\,d\theta\,\mathbf{e}_\theta. \tag{15.22}$$

The potential energy must satisfy

$$dV = -\mathbf{F}\cdot d\mathbf{r} = \frac{mgR_{\mathrm{E}}^2}{r^2}dr,$$

or

$$\frac{dV}{dr} = \frac{mgR_{\mathrm{E}}^2}{r^2}.$$

We integrate this equation and let the constant of integration be zero, obtaining the potential energy

$$V = -\frac{mgR_{\mathrm{E}}^2}{r}. \tag{15.23}$$

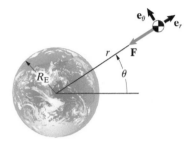

Figure 15.10
Expressing weight in terms of polar coordinates.

Compare this expression with the gravitational potential energy given by Eq. (15.21), in which the variation of the gravitational force with height is neglected. (See Problem 15.109.)

Springs In terms of polar coordinates, the force exerted on an object by a linear spring is

$$\mathbf{F} = -k(r - r_0)\mathbf{e}_r,$$

where r_0 is the unstretched length of the spring (Fig. 15.11). Using Eq. (15.22), we see that the potential energy must satisfy

$$dV = -\mathbf{F}\cdot d\mathbf{r} = k(r - r_0)\,dr.$$

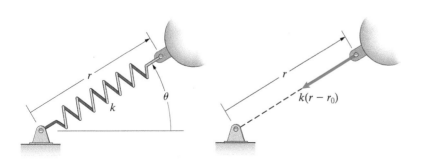

Figure 15.11
Expressing the force exerted by a linear spring in polar coordinates.

Expressed in terms of the stretch of the spring $S = r - r_0$, this equation is $dV = kS \, dS$, or

$$\frac{dV}{dS} = kS.$$

Integrating, we obtain the potential energy of a linear spring:

$$V = \tfrac{1}{2} kS^2. \tag{15.24}$$

RESULTS

Conservative Forces and Potential Energy

For a given force $\mathbf{F}$, if there is a function of position V such that

$dV = -\mathbf{F} \cdot d\mathbf{r}$,

then $\mathbf{F}$ is said to be *conservative*, and V is called the *potential energy* associated with $\mathbf{F}$.

Conservation of Energy

If all of the forces that do work on an object are conservative, the sum of the kinetic energy and the total potential energy is the same at any two positions.

$$\tfrac{1}{2} mv_1^2 + V_1 = \tfrac{1}{2} mv_2^2 + V_2. \tag{15.18}$$

When both conservative and nonconservative forces do work on an object, the principle of work and energy can be expressed in terms of the potential energy V of the conservative forces and the work U_{12} done by nonconservative forces.

$$\tfrac{1}{2} mv_1^2 + V_1 + U_{12} = \tfrac{1}{2} mv_2^2 + V_2. \tag{15.19}$$

	1. *Determine whether the forces are conservative.* Draw a free-body diagram to identify the forces that do work and confirm that they are conservative.
Applying conservation of energy typically involves three steps.	2. *Determine the potential energy.* Evaluate the potential energies of the forces that do work.
	3. *Apply conservation of energy.* Equate the sum of the kinetic and potential energies at two positions. This results in an expression relating a change in position to the change in the kinetic energy.

Potential Energies Associated with Particular Forces

Weight
When the weight can be regarded as constant, the potential energy is

$$V = mgy, \qquad (15.21)$$

where the positive y axis points upward. The potential energy is the product of the weight and the height above an arbitrary reference level, or *datum*.

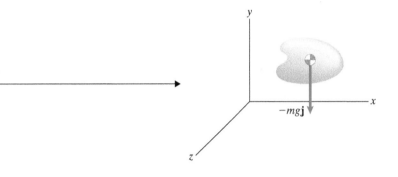

Variable Weight
When the variation of gravity with height must be considered, the potential energy is

$$V = -\frac{mgR_{\mathrm{E}}^2}{r}, \qquad (15.23)$$

where R_{E} is the radius of the earth.

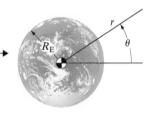

Springs
The potential energy of a linear spring is

$$V = \tfrac{1}{2} kS^2, \qquad (15.24)$$

where S is the stretch of the spring.

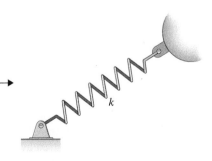

| Active Example 15.7 | Potential Energy of Weight and Springs (▶ *Related Problem 15.89*) |

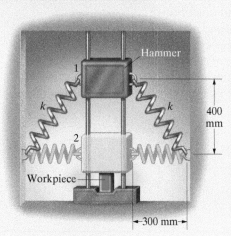

The 40-kg hammer is lifted to position 1 and released from rest. It falls and strikes a workpiece when it is in position 2. The spring constant is $k = 1500$ N/m, and the springs are unstretched when the hammer is in position 2. Neglect friction. Use conservation of energy to determine the hammer's velocity when it reaches position 2.

Strategy

We must confirm that the forces that do work on the hammer are conservative. If they are, we can determine the velocity of the hammer at position 2 by equating the sum of its kinetic and potential energies at position 1 to the sum of its kinetic and potential energies at position 2.

Solution

| From the free-body diagram of the hammer, we see that work is done only by its weight and the forces exerted by the springs. The system is conservative. |

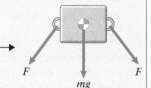

| Choose a datum for the potential energy associated with the weight of the hammer. Let the datum ($y = 0$) be position 2. |

$V_{\text{weight}} = mgy.$

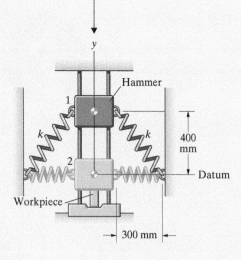

| Potential energy of one of the springs in terms of the stretch S of the spring. |

$V_{\text{spring}} = \frac{1}{2}kS^2.$

Calculate the stretch of one of the springs at positions 1 and 2.

$$\begin{cases} S_1 = \sqrt{(0.3 \text{ m})^2 + (0.4 \text{ m})^2} - 0.3 \text{ m} \\ \qquad = 0.2 \text{ m}, \\ S_2 = 0. \end{cases}$$

Apply conservation of energy to positions 1 and 2 to determine the velocity at position 2.

$$\begin{cases} (V_{\text{weight}})_1 + 2(V_{\text{spring}})_1 + \tfrac{1}{2} m v_1^2 = (V_{\text{weight}})_2 + 2(V_{\text{spring}})_2 + \tfrac{1}{2} m v_2^2: \\ \qquad mgy_1 + 2\left(\tfrac{1}{2} k S_1^2\right) + \tfrac{1}{2} m v_1^2 = mgy_2 + 2\left(\tfrac{1}{2} k S_2^2\right) + \tfrac{1}{2} m v_2^2, \\ (40 \text{ kg})\left(9.81 \text{ m/s}^2\right)(0.4 \text{ m}) + 2\left[\tfrac{1}{2}(1500 \text{ N/m})(0.2 \text{ m})^2\right] + 0 \\ \qquad\qquad\qquad\qquad\qquad\qquad = 0 + 0 + \tfrac{1}{2}(40 \text{ kg})v_2^2. \\ \text{Solving, we obtain} \\ \qquad v_2 = 3.29 \text{ m/s}. \end{cases}$$

Practice Problem The 40-kg hammer is given a downward velocity of 2 m/s in position 1. It falls and strikes a workpiece when it is in position 2. The spring constant is $k = 1500$ N/m, and the springs are unstretched when the hammer is in position 1. Neglect friction. Use conservation of energy to determine the velocity of the hammer just before it strikes the workpiece.

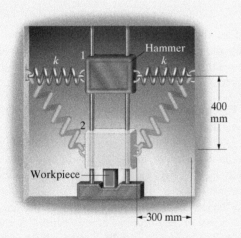

Answer: $v_2 = 2.97$ m/s.

Example 15.8   Conservation of Energy of a System (▶ *Related Problem 15.91*)

The spring ($k = 300$ N/m) is connected to the floor and to the 90-kg collar A. Collar A is at rest, supported by the spring, when the 135-kg box B is released from rest in the position shown. What are the velocities of A and B when B has fallen 1 m?

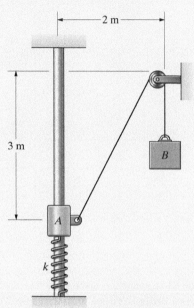

Strategy
If all of the forces that do work on the system are conservative, we can apply conservation of energy to obtain one equation in terms of the velocities of A and B when B has fallen 1 m. To complete the solution, we must also use kinematics to determine the relationship between the velocities of A and B.

Solution
Determine whether the System Is Conservative   We consider the collar A, box B, and pulley as a single system. From the free-body diagram of the system in Fig. a, we see that work is done only by the weights of the collar and box and the spring force F. The system is therefore conservative.

Determine the Potential Energy   Using the initial position of collar A as its datum, the potential energy associated with the weight of A when it has risen a distance x_A (Fig. b) is $V_A = m_A g x_A$. Using the initial position of box B as its datum, the potential energy associated with its weight when it has fallen a distance x_B is $V_B = -m_B g x_B$. (The minus sign is necessary because x_B is positive downward.)

To determine the potential energy associated with the spring force, we must account for the fact that in the initial position the spring is compressed by the weight of collar A. The spring is initially compressed a distance δ such that $m_A g = k\delta$ (Fig. c). When the collar has moved upward a distance x_A, the stretch of the spring is $S = x_A - \delta = x_A - m_A g/k$, so its potential energy is

$$V_S = \tfrac{1}{2}kS^2 = \tfrac{1}{2}k\left(x_A - \frac{m_A g}{k}\right)^2.$$

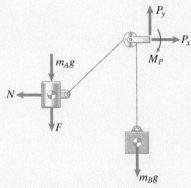

(a) Free-body diagram of the system.

The total potential energy of the system in terms of the displacements of the collar and box is

$$V = V_A + V_B + V_S$$

$$= m_A g x_A - m_B g x_B + \frac{1}{2} k \left(x_A - \frac{m_A g}{k} \right)^2.$$

Apply Conservation of Energy   The sum of the kinetic and potential energies of the system in its initial position and in the position shown in Fig. b must be equal. Denoting the total kinetic energy by T, we have

$$T_1 + V_1 = T_2 + V_2:$$

$$0 + \frac{1}{2} k \left(-\frac{m_A g}{k} \right)^2 = \frac{1}{2} m_A v_A^2 + \frac{1}{2} m_B v_B^2$$

$$+ m_A g x_A - m_B g x_B + \frac{1}{2} k \left(x_A - \frac{m_A g}{k} \right)^2. \tag{1}$$

We want to determine v_A and v_B when $x_B = 1$ m, but we have only one equation in terms of x_A, x_B, v_A, and v_B. To complete the solution, we must relate the displacement and velocity of the collar A to the displacement and velocity of the box B.

From Fig. b, the decrease in the length of the rope from A to the pulley as the collar rises must equal the distance the box falls:

$$\sqrt{(3 \text{ m})^2 + (2 \text{ m})^2} - \sqrt{(3 \text{ m} - x_A)^2 + (2 \text{ m})^2} = x_B.$$

Solving this equation for the value of x_A when $x_B = 1$ m, we obtain $x_A = 1.33$ m. By taking the derivative of this equation with respect to time, we also obtain a relation between v_A and v_B:

$$\left[\frac{3 \text{ m} - x_A}{\sqrt{(3 \text{ m} - x_A)^2 + (2 \text{ m})^2}} \right] v_A = v_B.$$

Setting $x_A = 1.33$ m, we determine from the preceding equation that

$$0.641 v_A = v_B.$$

We solve this equation together with Eq. (1) for the velocities of the collar and box when $x_A = 1.33$ m and $x_B = 1$ m, obtaining $v_A = 3.82$ m/s and $v_B = 2.45$ m/s.

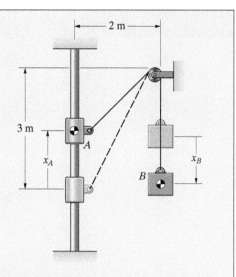

(b) Displacements of the collar and box.

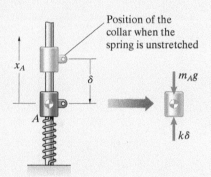

(c) Determining the initial compression of the spring.

Critical Thinking

Why didn't we have to consider the forces exerted on the collar and box by the rope? The reason is that they are internal forces when the collar, box, and pulley are regarded as a single system. This example clearly demonstrates the advantage of applying conservation of energy to an entire system whenever possible.

| Example 15.9 | Conservation of Energy of a Spacecraft (▶ *Related Problem 15.103*) |

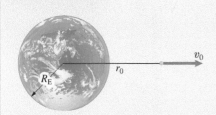

A spacecraft at a distance $r_0 = 2R_E$ from the center of the earth is moving outward with initial velocity $v_0 = \sqrt{2gR_E/3}$. Determine the velocity of the craft as a function of its distance from the center of the earth.

Strategy
The potential energy associated with the earth's gravity is given by Eq. (15.23). The initial radial position and velocity of the spacecraft are given, so we can use conservation of energy to determine its velocity as a function of its radial position.

Solution
Determine whether the System Is Conservative If work is done on the spacecraft by gravity alone, the system is conservative.

Determine the Potential Energy The potential energy associated with the weight of the spacecraft is given in terms of its distance r from the center of the earth by Eq. (15.23):

$$V = -\frac{mgR_E^2}{r}.$$

Apply Conservation of Energy Let v be the magnitude of the spacecraft's velocity at an arbitrary distance r. The sums of the potential and kinetic energies at r_0 and at r must be equal.

$$-\frac{mgR_E^2}{r_0} + \tfrac{1}{2}mv_0^2 = -\frac{mgR_E^2}{r} + \tfrac{1}{2}mv^2:$$

$$-\frac{mgR_E^2}{2R_E} + \tfrac{1}{2}m\left(\tfrac{2}{3}gR_E\right) = -\frac{mgR_E^2}{r} + \tfrac{1}{2}mv^2.$$

Solving for v, we find that the spacecraft's velocity as a function of r is

$$v = \sqrt{gR_E\left(\frac{2R_E}{r} - \frac{1}{3}\right)}.$$

Critical Thinking
The graph shows the kinetic energy, potential energy, and total energy as functions of r/R_E. The kinetic energy decreases and the potential energy increases as the spacecraft moves outward until its velocity decreases to zero at $r = 6R_E$.

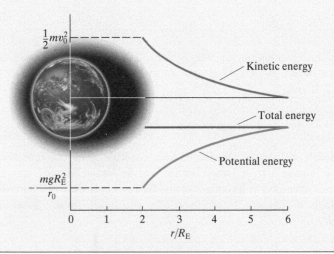

Problems

15.78 The 10-lb box is released from rest at position 1 and slides down the smooth inclined surface to position 2.

(a) If the datum is placed at the level of the floor as shown, what is the sum of the kinetic and potential energies of the box when it is in position 1?

(b) What is the sum of the kinetic and potential energies of the box when it is in position 2?

(c) Use conservation of energy to determine the magnitude of the box's velocity when it is in position 2.

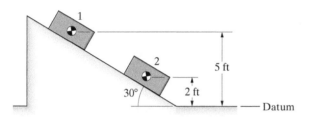

Problem 15.78

15.79 The 0.45-kg soccer ball is 1 m above the ground when it is kicked upward at 12 m/s. Use conservation of energy to determine the magnitude of the ball's velocity when it is 4 m above the ground. Obtain the answer by placing the datum (a) at the level of the ball's initial position and (b) at ground level.

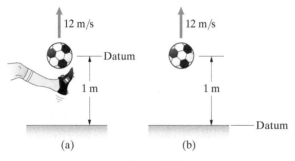

Problem 15.79

15.80 The Lunar Module used in the Apollo moon landings could make a safe landing if the magnitude of its vertical velocity at impact was no greater than 5 m/s. Use conservation of energy to determine the maximum height h at which the pilot could shut off the engine if the vertical velocity of the lander is (a) 2 m/s downward and (b) 2 m/s upward. The acceleration due to gravity at the moon's surface is 1.62 m/s^2.

Problem 15.80

15.81 The 0.4-kg collar starts from rest at position 1 and slides down the smooth rigid wire. The y axis points upward. Use conservation of energy to determine the magnitude of the velocity of the collar when it reaches point 2.

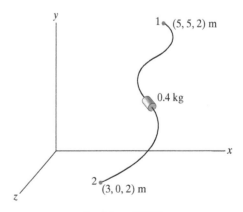

Problem 15.81

15.82 At the instant shown, the 20-kg mass is moving downward at 1.6 m/s. Let d be the downward displacement of the mass relative to its present position. Use conservation of energy to determine the magnitude of the velocity of the 20-kg mass when $d = 1$ m.

4 kg

20 kg

Problem 15.82

15.83 The mass of the ball is $m = 2$ kg, and the string's length is $L = 1$ m. The ball is released from rest in position 1 and swings to position 2, where $\theta = 40°$.

(a) Use conservation of energy to determine the magnitude of the ball's velocity at position 2.

(b) Draw graphs of the kinetic energy, the potential energy, and the total energy for values of θ from zero to 180°.

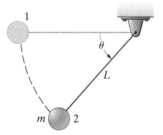

1

θ

L

m 2

Problem 15.83

15.84 The mass of the ball is $m = 2$ kg and the string's length is $L = 1$ m. The ball is released from rest in position 1. When the string is vertical, it hits the fixed peg shown.

(a) Use conservation of energy to determine the minimum angle θ necessary for the ball to swing to position 2.

(b) If the ball is released at the minimum angle θ determined in part (a), what is the tension in the string just before and just after it hits the peg?

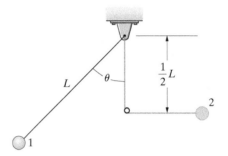

L

θ

$\frac{1}{2}L$

2

1

Problem 15.84

15.85 A small pellet of mass $m = 0.2$ kg starts from rest at position 1 and slides down the smooth surface of the cylinder to position 2. The radius $R = 0.8$ m. Use conservation of energy to determine the magnitude of the pellet's velocity at position 2 if $\theta = 45°$.

15.86 In Problem 15.85, what is the value of the angle θ at which the pellet loses contact with the surface of the cylinder?

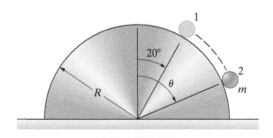

1

20°

θ

R

2

m

Problems 15.85/15.86

15.87 The bar is smooth. The 10-kg slider at A is given a downward velocity of 6.5 m/s.

(a) Use conservation of energy to determine whether the slider will reach point C. If it does, what is the magnitude of its velocity at point C?

(b) What is the magnitude of the normal force the bar exerts on the slider as it passes point B?

15.88 The bar is smooth. The 10-kg slider at A is given a downward velocity of 7.5 m/s.

(a) Use conservation of energy to determine whether the slider will reach point D. If it does, what is the magnitude of its velocity at point D?

(b) What is the magnitude of the normal force the bar exerts on the slider as it passes point B?

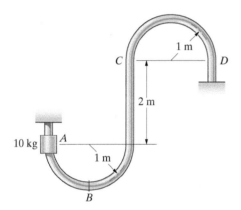

Problems 15.87/15.88

▶ **15.89** In Active Example 15.7, suppose that you want to increase the value of the spring constant k so that the velocity of the hammer just before it strikes the workpiece is 4 m/s. Use conservation of energy to determine the required value of k.

15.90 A rock climber of weight W has a rope attached a distance h below him for protection. Suppose that he falls, and assume that the rope behaves like a linear spring with unstretched length h and spring constant $k = C/h$, where C is a constant. Use conservation of energy to determine the maximum force exerted on the climber by the rope. (Notice that the maximum force is independent of h, which is a reassuring result for climbers: The maximum force resulting from a long fall is the same as that resulting from a short one.)

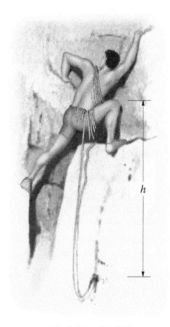

Problem 15.90

▶ **15.91** The collar A slides on the smooth horizontal bar. The spring constant $k = 40$ lb/ft. The weights are $W_A = 30$ lb and $W_B = 60$ lb. At the instant shown, the spring is unstretched and B is moving downward at 4 ft/s. Use conservation of energy to determine the velocity of B when it has moved downward 2 ft from its current position. (See Example 15.8.)

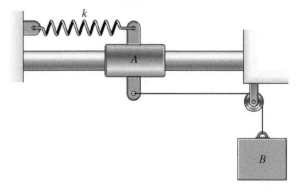

Problem 15.91

15.92 The spring constant $k = 700$ N/m. The masses $m_A = 14$ kg and $m_B = 18$ kg. The horizontal bar is smooth. At the instant shown, the spring is unstretched and the mass B is moving downward at 1 m/s. How fast is B moving when it has moved downward 0.2 m from its present position?

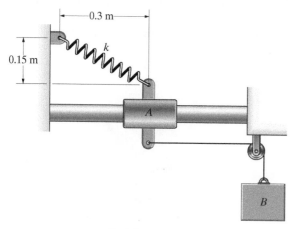

Problem 15.92

15.93 The semicircular bar is smooth. The unstretched length of the spring is 10 in. The 5-lb collar at A is given a downward velocity of 6 ft/s, and when it reaches B the magnitude of its velocity is 15 ft/s. Determine the spring constant k.

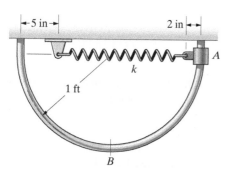

Problem 15.93

15.94 The mass $m = 1$ kg, the spring constant $k = 200$ N/m, and the unstretched length of the spring is 0.1 m. When the system is released from rest in the position shown, the spring contracts, pulling the mass to the right. Use conservation of energy to determine the magnitude of the velocity of the mass when the string and the spring are parallel.

15.95 In Problem 15.94, what is the tension in the string when the string and spring are parallel?

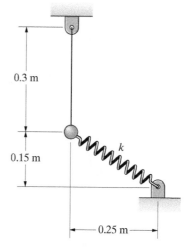

Problems 15.94/15.95

15.96 The force exerted on an object by a *nonlinear* spring is

$$\mathbf{F} = -[k(r - r_0) + q(r - r_0)^3]\mathbf{e}_r,$$

where k and q are constants and r_0 is the unstretched length of the spring. Determine the potential energy of the spring in terms of its stretch $S = r - r_0$.

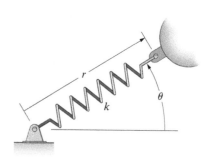

Problem 15.96

15.97 The 20-kg cylinder is released at the position shown and falls onto the linear spring ($k = 3000$ N/m). Use conservation of energy to determine how far down the cylinder moves after contacting the spring.

15.98 The 20-kg cylinder is released at the position shown and falls onto the *nonlinear* spring. In terms of the stretch S of the spring, its potential energy is $V = \frac{1}{2}kS^2 + \frac{1}{4}qS^4$, where $k = 3000$ N/m and $q = 4000$ N/m^3. What is the velocity of the cylinder when the spring has been compressed 0.5 m?

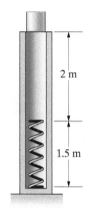

2 m

1.5 m

Problems 15.97/15.98

15.99 The string exerts a force of constant magnitude T on the object. Use polar coordinates to show that the potential energy associated with this force is $V = Tr$.

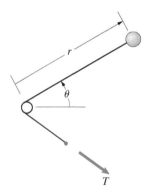

r

θ

T

Problem 15.99

15.100 The system is at rest in the position shown, with the 12-lb collar A resting on the spring ($k = 20$ lb/ft), when a constant 30-lb force is applied to the cable. What is the velocity of the collar when it has risen 1 ft? (See Problem 15.99.)

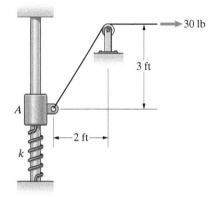

30 lb

3 ft

A

—2 ft—

k

Problem 15.100

15.101 A 1-kg disk slides on a smooth horizontal table and is attached to a string that passes through a hole in the table. A constant force $T = 10$ N is exerted on the string. At the instant shown, $r = 1$ m and the velocity of the disk in terms of polar coordinates is $\mathbf{v} = 6\mathbf{e}_\theta$ (m/s). Use conservation of energy to determine the magnitude of the velocity of the disk when $r = 2$ m. (See Problem 15.99.)

15.102 A 1-kg disk slides on a smooth horizontal table and is attached to a string that passes through a hole in the table. A constant force $T = 10$ N is exerted on the string. At the instant shown, $r = 1$ m and the velocity of the disk in terms of polar coordinates is $\mathbf{v} = 8\mathbf{e}_\theta$ (m/s). Because this is central-force motion, the product of the radial position r and the transverse component of velocity v_θ is constant. Use this fact and conservation of energy to determine the velocity of the disk in terms of polar coordinates when $r = 2$ m.

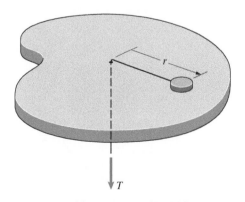

r

T

Problems 15.101/15.102

▶ **15.103** A satellite initially is inserted into orbit at a distance $r_0 = 8800$ km from the center of the earth. When it is at a distance $r = 18,000$ km from the center of the earth, the magnitude of its velocity is $v = 7000$ m/s. Use conservation of energy to determine its initial velocity v_0. The radius of the earth is 6370 km. (See Example 15.9.)

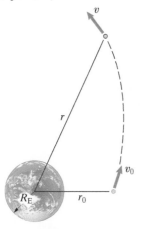

Problem 15.103

15.104 Astronomers detect an asteroid 100,000 km from the earth moving at 2 km/s relative to the center of the earth. Suppose the asteroid strikes the earth. Use conservation of energy to determine the magnitude of its velocity as it enters the atmosphere. (You can neglect the thickness of the atmosphere in comparison to the earth's 6370-km radius.)

15.105 A satellite is in the elliptic earth orbit shown. Its velocity in terms of polar coordinates when it is at the perigee A is $\mathbf{v} = 8640\mathbf{e}_\theta$ (m/s). Determine the velocity of the satellite in terms of polar coordinates when it is at point B.

15.106 Use conservation of energy to determine the magnitude of the velocity of the satellite in Problem 15.105 at the apogee C. Using your result, confirm numerically that the velocities at perigee and apogee satisfy the relation $r_A v_A = r_C v_C$.

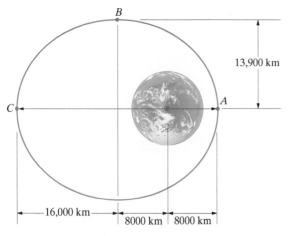

Problems 15.105/15.106

15.107 The *Voyager* and *Galileo* spacecraft observed volcanic plumes, believed to consist of condensed sulfur or sulfur dioxide gas, above the surface of the Jovian satellite Io. The plume observed above a volcano named Prometheus was estimated to extend 50 km above the surface. The acceleration due to gravity at the surface is 1.80 m/s^2. Using conservation of energy and neglecting the variation of gravity with height, determine the velocity at which a solid particle would have to be ejected to reach 50 km above Io's surface.

15.108 Solve Problem 15.107 using conservation of energy and accounting for the variation of gravity with height. The radius of Io is 1815 km.

Problems 15.107/15.108

15.109* What is the relationship between Eq. (15.21), which is the gravitational potential energy neglecting the variation of the gravitational force with height, and Eq. (15.23), which accounts for the variation? Express the distance from the center of the earth as $r = R_E + y$, where R_E is the earth's radius and y is the height above the surface, so that Eq. (15.23) can be written as

$$V = -\frac{mgR_E}{1 + \dfrac{y}{R_E}}.$$

By expanding this equation as a Taylor series in terms of y/R_E and assuming that $y/R_E \ll 1$, show that you obtain a potential energy equivalent to Eq. (15.21).

15.4 Relationships between Force and Potential Energy

Here we consider two questions: (1) Given a potential energy, how can we determine the corresponding force? (2) Given a force, how can we determine whether it is conservative? That is, how can we tell whether an associated potential energy exists?

The potential energy V of a force $\mathbf{F}$ is a function of position that satisfies the relation

$$dV = -\mathbf{F} \cdot d\mathbf{r}. \tag{15.25}$$

Let us express V in terms of a cartesian coordinate system:

$$V = V(x, y, z).$$

The differential of V is

$$dV = \frac{\partial V}{\partial x} dx + \frac{\partial V}{\partial y} dy + \frac{\partial V}{\partial z} dz. \tag{15.26}$$

Expressing $\mathbf{F}$ and $d\mathbf{r}$ in terms of cartesian components and taking their dot product yields

$$\mathbf{F} \cdot d\mathbf{r} = (F_x \mathbf{i} + F_y \mathbf{j} + F_z \mathbf{k}) \cdot (dx\mathbf{i} + dy\mathbf{j} + dz\mathbf{k})$$
$$= F_x\, dx + F_y\, dy + F_z\, dz.$$

Substituting this expression and Eq. (15.26) into Eq. (15.25), we obtain

$$\frac{\partial V}{\partial x} dx + \frac{\partial V}{\partial y} dy + \frac{\partial V}{\partial z} dz = -(F_x\, dx + F_y\, dy + F_z\, dz),$$

which implies that

$$F_x = -\frac{\partial V}{\partial x}, \qquad F_y = -\frac{\partial V}{\partial y}, \quad \text{and} \quad F_z = -\frac{\partial V}{\partial z}. \tag{15.27}$$

Given a potential energy V expressed in cartesian coordinates, we can use Eqs. (15.27) to determine the corresponding force. The force

$$\mathbf{F} = -\left(\frac{\partial V}{\partial x}\mathbf{i} + \frac{\partial V}{\partial y}\mathbf{j} + \frac{\partial V}{\partial z}\mathbf{k} \right) = -\nabla V, \tag{15.28}$$

where ∇V is the *gradient* of V. By using expressions for the gradient in terms of other coordinate systems, we can determine the force $\mathbf{F}$ when we know the potential energy in terms of those coordinate systems. For example, in terms of cylindrical coordinates,

$$\mathbf{F} = -\left(\frac{\partial V}{\partial r}\mathbf{e}_r + \frac{1}{r}\frac{\partial V}{\partial \theta}\mathbf{e}_\theta + \frac{\partial V}{\partial z}\mathbf{e}_z \right). \tag{15.29}$$

If a force $\mathbf{F}$ is conservative, its *curl* $\nabla \times \mathbf{F}$ is zero. The expression for the curl of $\mathbf{F}$ in cartesian coordinates is

$$\nabla \times \mathbf{F} = \begin{vmatrix} \mathbf{i} & \mathbf{j} & \mathbf{k} \\ \dfrac{\partial}{\partial x} & \dfrac{\partial}{\partial y} & \dfrac{\partial}{\partial z} \\ F_x & F_y & F_z \end{vmatrix}. \qquad (15.30)$$

Substituting Eqs. (15.27) into this expression confirms that $\nabla \times \mathbf{F} = \mathbf{0}$ when $\mathbf{F}$ is conservative. The converse is also true. A force $\mathbf{F}$ is conservative if its curl is zero. We can use this condition to determine whether a given force is conservative. In terms of cylindrical coordinates, the curl of $\mathbf{F}$ is

$$\nabla \times \mathbf{F} = \frac{1}{r} \begin{vmatrix} \mathbf{e}_r & r\mathbf{e}_\theta & \mathbf{e}_z \\ \dfrac{\partial}{\partial r} & \dfrac{\partial}{\partial \theta} & \dfrac{\partial}{\partial z} \\ F_r & rF_\theta & F_z \end{vmatrix}. \qquad (15.31)$$

RESULTS

$$dV = -\mathbf{F} \cdot d\mathbf{r}. \qquad (15.25)$$

Definition of the potential energy V associated with a conservative force $\mathbf{F}$.

A conservative force $\mathbf{F}$ can be determined from its its potential energy V.

Cartesian Coordinates

$$\mathbf{F} = -\left(\frac{\partial V}{\partial x}\mathbf{i} + \frac{\partial V}{\partial y}\mathbf{j} + \frac{\partial V}{\partial z}\mathbf{k} \right). \qquad (15.28)$$

Cylindrical Coordinates

$$\mathbf{F} = -\left(\frac{\partial V}{\partial r}\mathbf{e}_r + \frac{1}{r}\frac{\partial V}{\partial \theta}\mathbf{e}_\theta + \frac{\partial V}{\partial z}\mathbf{e}_z \right). \qquad (15.29)$$

A force $\mathbf{F}$ is conservative if and only if its *curl* $\nabla \times \mathbf{F}$ is zero.

Cartesian Coordinates

$$\nabla \times \mathbf{F} = \begin{vmatrix} \mathbf{i} & \mathbf{j} & \mathbf{k} \\ \dfrac{\partial}{\partial x} & \dfrac{\partial}{\partial y} & \dfrac{\partial}{\partial z} \\ F_x & F_y & F_z \end{vmatrix}. \qquad (15.30)$$

Cylindrical Coordinates

$$\nabla \times \mathbf{F} = \frac{1}{r} \begin{vmatrix} \mathbf{e}_r & r\mathbf{e}_\theta & \mathbf{e}_z \\ \dfrac{\partial}{\partial r} & \dfrac{\partial}{\partial \theta} & \dfrac{\partial}{\partial z} \\ F_r & rF_\theta & F_z \end{vmatrix}. \qquad (15.31)$$

Active Example 15.10   Determining the Force from a Potential Energy
(▶ *Related Problems 15.112, 15.113*)

The potential energy associated with the weight of an object of mass m at a distance r from the center of the earth is (in cylindrical coordinates)

$$V = -\frac{mgR_E^2}{r},$$

where R_E is the radius of the earth. Use this expression to determine the force exerted on the object by its weight.

Strategy
The potential energy is expressed in cylindrical coordinates, so we can obtain the force from Eq. (15.29).

Solution

Evaluate the partial derivatives in Eq. (15.29). $\longrightarrow$

$$\begin{cases} \dfrac{\partial V}{\partial r} = \dfrac{mgR_E^2}{r^2}, \\[2mm] \dfrac{\partial V}{\partial \theta} = 0, \\[2mm] \dfrac{\partial V}{\partial z} = 0. \end{cases}$$

Determine the force from Eq. (15.29). $\longrightarrow$

$$\mathbf{F} = -\frac{mgR_E^2}{r^2}\mathbf{e}_r.$$

Practice Problem Determine whether the force $\mathbf{F}$ obtained in this example is conservative.

Answer: Yes

Problems

15.110 The potential energy associated with a force $\mathbf{F}$ acting on an object is $V = x^2 + y^3$ N-m, where x and y are in meters.

(a) Determine $\mathbf{F}$.

(b) Suppose that the object moves from position 1 to position 2 along path A, and then moves from position 1 to position 2 along path B. Determine the work done by $\mathbf{F}$ along each path.

15.111 An object is subjected to the force $\mathbf{F} = y\mathbf{i} - x\mathbf{j}$ (N), where x and y are in meters.

(a) Show that $\mathbf{F}$ is *not* conservative.

(b) Suppose the object moves from point 1 to point 2 along the paths A and B shown in Problem 15.110. Determine the work done by $\mathbf{F}$ along each path.

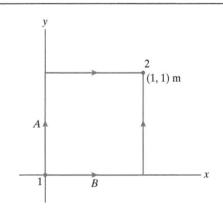

Problems 15.110/15.111

▶ **15.112** In terms of polar coordinates, the potential energy associated with the force **F** exerted on an object by a *nonlinear* spring is

$$V = \frac{1}{2}k(r - r_0)^2 + \frac{1}{4}q(r - r_0)^4,$$

where k and q are constants and r_0 is the unstretched length of the spring. Determine **F** in terms of polar coordinates. (See Active Example 15.10.)

▶ **15.113** In terms of polar coordinates, the force exerted on an object by a *nonlinear* spring is

$$\mathbf{F} = -[k(r - r_0) + q(r - r_0)^3]\mathbf{e}_r,$$

where k and q are constants and r_0 is the unstretched length of the spring. Use Eq. (15.31) to show that **F** is conservative. (See Active Example 15.10.)

15.114 The potential energy associated with a force **F** acting on an object is $V = -r \sin \theta + r^2 \cos^2 \theta$ ft-lb, where r is in feet.

(a) Determine **F**.

(b) If the object moves from point 1 to point 2 along the circular path, how much work is done by **F**?

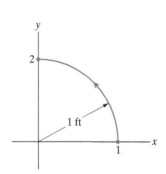

Problem 15.114

15.115 In terms of polar coordinates, the force exerted on an object of mass m by the gravity of a hypothetical two-dimensional planet is $\mathbf{F} = -(mg_T R_T/r)\mathbf{e}_r$, where g_T is the acceleration due to gravity at the surface, R_T is the radius of the planet, and r is the distance of the object from the center of the planet.

(a) Determine the potential energy associated with this gravitational force.

(b) If the object is given a velocity v_0 at a distance r_0, what is its velocity v as a function of r?

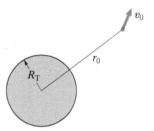

Problem 15.115

15.116 By substituting Eqs. (15.27) into Eq. (15.30), confirm that $\nabla \times \mathbf{F} = \mathbf{0}$ if **F** is conservative.

15.117 Determine which of the following forces are conservative:

(a) $\mathbf{F} = (3x^2 - 2xy)\mathbf{i} - x^2\mathbf{j}$;

(b) $\mathbf{F} = (x - xy^2)\mathbf{i} + x^2y\mathbf{j}$;

(c) $\mathbf{F} = (2xy^2 + y^3)\mathbf{i} + (2x^2y - 3xy^2)\mathbf{j}$.

Review Problems

15.118 The driver of a 3000-lb car moving at 40 mi/h applies an increasing force on the brake pedal. The magnitude of the resulting frictional force exerted on the car by the road is $f = 250 + 6s$ lb, where s is the car's horizontal position (in feet) relative to its position when the brakes were applied. Assuming that the car's tires do not slip; determine the distance required for the car to stop (a) by using Newton's second law and (b) by using the principle of work and energy.

15.119 Suppose that the car in Problem 15.118 is on wet pavement and the coefficients of friction between the tires and the road are $\mu_s = 0.4$ and $\mu_k = 0.35$. Determine the distance required for the car to stop.

Problems 15.118/15.119

15.120 An astronaut in a small rocket vehicle (combined mass = 450 kg) is hovering 100 m above the surface of the moon when he discovers that he is nearly out of fuel and can exert the thrust necessary to cause the vehicle to hover for only 5 more seconds. He quickly considers two strategies for getting to the surface: (a) Fall 20 m, turn on the thrust for 5 s, and then fall the rest of the way; (b) fall 40 m, turn on the thrust for 5 s, and then fall the rest of the way. Which strategy gives him the best chance of surviving? How much work is done by the engine's thrust in each case? ($g_{moon} = 1.62$ m/s^2.)

15.121 The coefficients of friction between the 20-kg crate and the inclined surface are $\mu_s = 0.24$ and $\mu_k = 0.22$. If the crate starts from rest and the horizontal force $F = 200$ N, what is the magnitude of the velocity of the crate when it has moved 2 m?

15.122 The coefficients of friction between the 20-kg crate and the inclined surface are $\mu_s = 0.24$ and $\mu_k = 0.22$. If the crate starts from rest and the horizontal force $F = 40$ N, what is the magnitude of the velocity of the crate when it has moved 2 m?

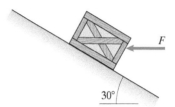

Problems 15.121/15.122

15.123 The Union Pacific Big Boy locomotive weighs 1.19 million lb, and the tractive effort (tangential force) of its drive wheels is 135,000 lb. If you neglect other tangential forces, what distance is required for the train to accelerate from zero to 60 mi/h?

15.124 In Problem 15.123, suppose that the acceleration of the locomotive as it accelerates from zero to 60 mi/h is $(F_0/m)(1 - v/88)$, where $F_0 = 135,000$ lb, m is the mass of the locomotive, and v is its velocity in feet per second.

(a) How much work is done in accelerating the train to 60 mi/h?
(b) Determine the locomotive's velocity as a function of time.

Problems 15.123/15.124

15.125 A car traveling 65 mi/h hits the crash barrier described in Problem 15.14. Determine the maximum deceleration to which the passengers are subjected if the car weighs (a) 2500 lb and (b) 5000 lb.

15.126 In a preliminary design for a mail-sorting machine, parcels moving at 2 ft/s slide down a smooth ramp and are brought to rest by a linear spring. What should the spring constant be if you don't want a 10-lb parcel to be subjected to a maximum deceleration greater than 10 g's?

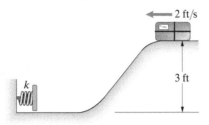

Problem 15.126

15.127 When the 1-kg collar is in position 1, the tension in the spring is 50 N, and the unstretched length of the spring is 260 mm. If the collar is pulled to position 2 and released from rest, what is its velocity when it returns to position 1?

15.128 When the 1-kg collar is in position 1, the tension in the spring is 100 N, and when the collar is in position 2, the tension in the spring is 400 N.

(a) What is the spring constant k?

(b) If the collar is given a velocity of 15 m/s at position 1, what is the magnitude of its velocity just before it reaches position 2?

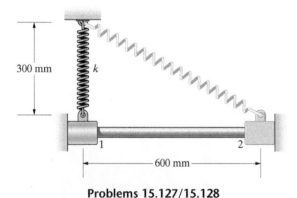

Problems 15.127/15.128

15.129 The 30-lb weight is released from rest with the two springs ($k_A = 30$ lb/ft, $k_B = 15$ lb/ft) unstretched.

(a) How far does the weight fall before rebounding?

(b) What maximum velocity does it attain?

Problem 15.129

15.130 The piston and the load it supports are accelerated upward by the gas in the cylinder. The total weight of the piston and load is 1000 lb. The cylinder wall exerts a constant 50-lb frictional force on the piston as it rises. The net force exerted on the piston by pressure is $(p_2 - p_{atm})A$, where p is the pressure of the gas, $p_{atm} = 2117$ lb/ft^2 is atmospheric pressure, and $A = 1$ ft^2 is the cross-sectional area of the piston. Assume that the product of p and the volume of the cylinder is constant. When $s = 1$ ft, the piston is stationary and $p = 5000$ lb/ft^2. What is the velocity of the piston when $s = 2$ ft?

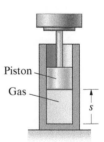

Problem 15.130

15.131 When a 22,000-kg rocket's engine burns out at an altitude of 2 km, the velocity of the rocket is 3 km/s and it is traveling at an angle of 60° relative to the horizontal. Neglect the variation in the gravitational force with altitude.

(a) If you neglect aerodynamic forces, what is the magnitude of the velocity of the rocket when it reaches an altitude of 6 km?

(b) If the actual velocity of the rocket when it reaches an altitude of 6 km is 2.8 km/s, how much work is done by aerodynamic forces as the rocket moves from 2 km to 6 km altitude?

15.132 The 12-kg collar A is at rest in the position shown at $t = 0$ and is subjected to the tangential force $F = 24 - 12t^2$ N for 1.5 s. Neglecting friction, what maximum height h does the collar reach?

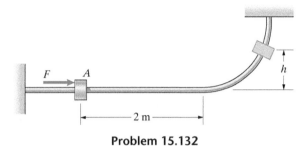

Problem 15.132

15.133 Suppose that, in designing a loop for a roller coaster's track, you establish as a safety criterion that at the top of the loop the normal force exerted on a passenger by the roller coaster should equal 10 percent of the passenger's weight. (That is, the passenger's "effective weight" pressing him down into his seat is 10 percent of his actual weight.) The roller coaster is moving at 62 ft/s when it enters the loop. What is the necessary instantaneous radius of curvature ρ of the track at the top of the loop?

Problem 15.133

15.134 A 180-lb student runs at 15 ft/s, grabs a rope, and swings out over a lake. He releases the rope when his velocity is zero.
(a) What is the angle θ when he releases the rope?
(b) What is the tension in the rope just before he releases it?
(c) What is the maximum tension in the rope?

15.135 If the student in Problem 15.134 releases the rope when $\theta = 25°$, what maximum height does he reach relative to his position when he grabs the rope?

Problems 15.134/15.135

15.136 A boy takes a running start and jumps on his sled at position 1. He leaves the ground at position 2 and lands in deep snow at a distance $b = 25$ ft. How fast was he going at position 1?

15.137 In Problem 15.136, if the boy starts at position 1 going 15 ft/s, what distance b does he travel through the air?

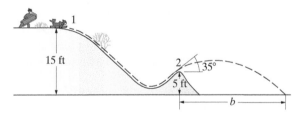

Problems 15.136/15.137

15.138 The 1-kg collar A is attached to the linear spring ($k = 500$ N/m) by a string. The collar starts from rest in the position shown, and the initial tension in the string is 100 N. What distance does the collar slide up the smooth bar?

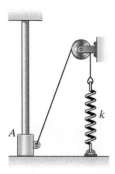

Problem 15.138

15.139 The masses $m_A = 40$ kg and $m_B = 60$ kg. The collar A slides on the smooth horizontal bar. The system is released from rest. Use conservation of energy to determine the velocity of the collar A when it has moved 0.5 m to the right.

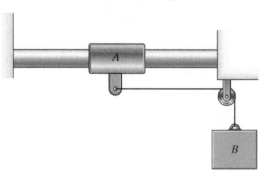

Problem 15.139

15.140 The spring constant is $k = 850$ N/m, $m_A = 40$ kg, and $m_B = 60$ kg. The collar A slides on the smooth horizontal bar. The system is released from rest in the position shown with the spring unstretched. Use conservation of energy to determine the velocity of the collar A when it has moved 0.5 m to the right.

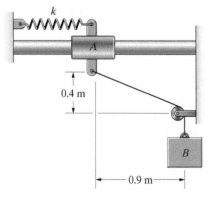

Problem 15.140

15.141 The y axis is vertical and the curved bar is smooth. If the magnitude of the velocity of the 4-lb slider is 6 ft/s at position 1, what is the magnitude of its velocity when it reaches position 2?

15.142 In Problem 15.141, determine the magnitude of the velocity of the slider when it reaches position 2 if it is subjected to the additional force $\mathbf{F} = 3x\mathbf{i} - 2\mathbf{j}$ (lb) during its motion.

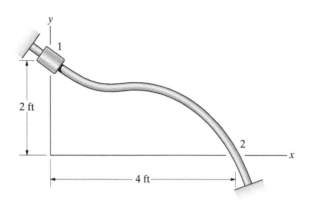

Problems 15.141/15.142

15.143 Suppose that an object of mass m is beneath the surface of the earth. In terms of a polar coordinate system with its origin at the earth's center, the gravitational force on the object is $-(mgr/R_E)\mathbf{e}_r$, where R_E is the radius of the earth. Show that the potential energy associated with the gravitational force is $V = mgr^2/2R_E$.

15.144 It has been pointed out that if tunnels could be drilled straight through the earth between points on the surface, trains could travel between those points using gravitational force for acceleration and deceleration. (The effects of friction and aerodynamic drag could be minimized by evacuating the tunnels and using magnetically levitated trains.) Suppose that such a train travels from the North Pole to a point on the equator. Disregard the earth's rotation. Determine the magnitude of the velocity of the train (a) when it arrives at the equator and (b) when it is halfway from the North Pole to the equator. The radius of the earth is $R_E = 3960$ mi. (See Problem 15.143.)

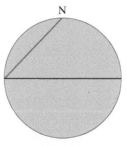

Problem 15.144

15.145 In Problem 15.123, what is the maximum power transferred to the locomotive during its acceleration?

15.146 Just before it lifts off, a 10,500-kg airplane is traveling at 60 ft/s. The total horizontal force exerted by the plane's engines is 189 kN, and the plane is accelerating at 15 m/s^2.

(a) How much power is being transferred to the plane by its engines?

(b) What is the total power being transferred to the plane?

Problem 15.146

15.147 The "Paris Gun" used by Germany in World War I had a range of 120 km, a 37.5-m barrel, and a muzzle velocity of 1550 m/s and fired a 120-kg shell.

(a) If you assume the shell's acceleration to be constant, what maximum power was transferred to the shell as it traveled along the barrel?

(b) What average power was transferred to the shell?

Problem 15.147

Design Project

Determine the specifications (unstretched length and spring constant k) for the elastic cord to be used at a bungee-jumping facility. Participants are to jump from a platform 150 ft above the ground. When they rebound, they must avoid an obstacle that extends 15 ft below the point at which they jumped. In determining the specifications for the cord, establish reasonable safety limits for the minimum distances by which participants must avoid the ground and obstacle. Account for the fact that participants will have different weights. If necessary, specify a maximum allowable weight for participants. Write a brief report presenting your analyses and making a design recommendation for the specifications of the cord.

APPENDIX

A

Review of Mathematics

A.1 Algebra

Quadratic Equations

The solutions of the quadratic equation

$$ax^2 + bx + c = 0$$

are

$$x = \frac{-b \pm \sqrt{b^2 - 4ac}}{2a}.$$

Natural Logarithms

The natural logarithm of a positive real number x is denoted by $\ln x$. It is defined to be the number such that

$$e^{\ln x} = x,$$

where $e = 2.7182\ldots$ is the base of natural logarithms.

Logarithms have the following properties:

$$\ln(xy) = \ln x + \ln y,$$

$$\ln(x/y) = \ln x - \ln y,$$

$$\ln y^x = x \ln y.$$

A.2 Trigonometry

The trigonometric functions for a right triangle are

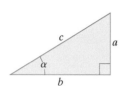

$$\sin \alpha = \frac{1}{\csc \alpha} = \frac{a}{c}, \qquad \cos \alpha = \frac{1}{\sec \alpha} = \frac{b}{c}, \qquad \tan \alpha = \frac{1}{\cot \alpha} = \frac{a}{b}.$$

The sine and cosine satisfy the relation

$$\sin^2 \alpha + \cos^2 \alpha = 1,$$

and the sine and cosine of the sum and difference of two angles satisfy

$$\sin(\alpha + \beta) = \sin \alpha \cos \beta + \cos \alpha \sin \beta,$$

$$\sin(\alpha - \beta) = \sin \alpha \cos \beta - \cos \alpha \sin \beta,$$

$$\cos(\alpha + \beta) = \cos \alpha \cos \beta - \sin \alpha \sin \beta,$$

$$\cos(\alpha - \beta) = \cos \alpha \cos \beta + \sin \alpha \sin \beta.$$

The **law of cosines** for an arbitrary triangle is

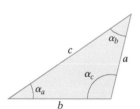

$$c^2 = a^2 + b^2 - 2ab \cos \alpha_c,$$

and the **law of sines** is

$$\frac{\sin \alpha_a}{a} = \frac{\sin \alpha_b}{b} = \frac{\sin \alpha_c}{c}.$$

A.3 Derivatives

$$\frac{d}{dx} x^n = nx^{n-1} \qquad\qquad \frac{d}{dx} \sin x = \cos x \qquad\qquad \frac{d}{dx} \sinh x = \cosh x$$

$$\frac{d}{dx} e^x = e^x \qquad\qquad \frac{d}{dx} \cos x = -\sin x \qquad\qquad \frac{d}{dx} \cosh x = \sinh x$$

$$\frac{d}{dx} \ln x = \frac{1}{x} \qquad\qquad \frac{d}{dx} \tan x = \frac{1}{\cos^2 x} \qquad\qquad \frac{d}{dx} \tanh x = \frac{1}{\cosh^2 x}$$

A.4 Integrals

$$\int x^n \, dx = \frac{x^{n+1}}{n+1} \qquad (n \neq -1)$$

$$\int \frac{dx}{(1 + a^2 x^2)^{1/2}} = \frac{1}{a} \ln\left[x + \left(\frac{1}{a^2} + x^2 \right)^{1/2} \right]$$

$$\int x^{-1} \, dx = \ln x$$

$$\int \frac{dx}{(1 - a^2 x^2)^{1/2}} = \frac{1}{a} \arcsin ax \quad \text{or} \quad -\frac{1}{a} \arccos ax$$

$$\int \frac{dx}{a - bx^2} = \frac{1}{(ab)^{1/2}} \arctan \frac{(ab)^{1/2} x}{a}$$

$$\int \sin x \, dx = -\cos x$$

$$\int \frac{dx}{a - bx^2} = \frac{1}{2(ab)^{1/2}} \ln \frac{a + x(ab)^{1/2}}{a - x(ab)^{1/2}}$$

$$\int \cos x \, dx = \sin x$$

$$\int \frac{x \, dx}{a - bx^2} = -\frac{1}{2b} \ln(a - bx^2)$$

$$\int \sin^2 x \, dx = -\frac{1}{2} \sin x \cos x + \frac{1}{2} x$$

$$\int (a + bx)^{1/2} \, dx = \frac{2}{3b} (a + bx)^{3/2}$$

$$\int \cos^2 x \, dx = \frac{1}{2} \sin x \cos x + \frac{1}{2} x$$

$$\int x(a + bx)^{1/2} \, dx = -\frac{2(2a - 3bx)(a + bx)^{3/2}}{15b^2}$$

$$\int \sin^3 x \, dx = -\frac{1}{3} \cos x (\sin^2 x + 2)$$

$$\int (1 + a^2 x^2)^{1/2} \, dx = \frac{1}{2} \left\{ x(1 + a^2 x^2)^{1/2} \right.$$

$$\int \cos^3 x \, dx = \frac{1}{3} \sin x (\cos^2 x + 2)$$

$$+ \frac{1}{a} \ln\left[x + \left(\frac{1}{a^2} + x^2 \right)^{1/2} \right] \right\}$$

$$\int \cos^4 x \, dx = \frac{3}{8} x + \frac{1}{4} \sin 2x + \frac{1}{32} \sin 4x$$

$$\int x(1 + a^2 x^2)^{1/2} \, dx = \frac{a}{3} \left(\frac{1}{a^2} + x^2 \right)^{3/2}$$

$$\int \sin^n x \cos x \, dx = \frac{(\sin x)^{n+1}}{n+1} \qquad (n \neq -1)$$

$$\int x^2 (1 + a^2 x^2)^{1/2} \, dx = \frac{1}{4} ax \left(\frac{1}{a^2} + x^2 \right)^{3/2}$$

$$\int \sinh x \, dx = \cosh x$$

$$-\frac{1}{8a^2} x(1 + a^2 x^2)^{1/2} - \frac{1}{8a^3} \ln\left[x + \left(\frac{1}{a^2} + x^2 \right)^{1/2} \right]$$

$$\int \cosh x \, dx = \sinh x$$

$$\int (1 - a^2 x^2)^{1/2} \, dx = \frac{1}{2} \left[x(1 - a^2 x^2)^{1/2} + \frac{1}{a} \arcsin ax \right]$$

$$\int \tanh x \, dx = \ln \cosh x$$

$$\int x(1 - a^2 x^2)^{1/2} \, dx = -\frac{a}{3} \left(\frac{1}{a^2} - x^2 \right)^{3/2}$$

$$\int e^{ax} \, dx = \frac{e^{ax}}{a}$$

$$\int x^2 (a^2 - x^2)^{1/2} \, dx = -\frac{1}{4} x(a^2 - x^2)^{3/2}$$

$$\int xe^{ax} \, dx = \frac{e^{ax}}{a^2} (ax - 1)$$

$$+ \frac{1}{8} a^2 \left[x(a^2 - x^2)^{1/2} + a^2 \arcsin \frac{x}{a} \right]$$

A.5 Taylor Series

The Taylor series of a function $f(x)$ is

$$f(a + x) = f(a) + f'(a)x + \frac{1}{2!}f''(a)x^2 + \frac{1}{3!}f'''(a)x^3 + \cdots,$$

where the primes indicate derivatives.

Some useful Taylor series are

$$e^x = 1 + x + \frac{x^2}{2!} + \frac{x^3}{3!} + \cdots,$$

$$\sin(a + x) = \sin a + (\cos a)x - \frac{1}{2}(\sin a)x^2 - \frac{1}{6}(\cos a)x^3 + \cdots,$$

$$\cos(a + x) = \cos a - (\sin a)x - \frac{1}{2}(\cos a)x^2 + \frac{1}{6}(\sin a)x^3 + \cdots,$$

$$\tan(a + x) = \tan a + \left(\frac{1}{\cos^2 a}\right)x + \left(\frac{\sin a}{\cos^3 a}\right)x^2$$

$$+ \left(\frac{\sin^2 a}{\cos^4 a} + \frac{1}{3 \cos^2 a}\right)x^3 + \cdots.$$

A.6 Vector Analysis

Cartesian Coordinates

The gradient of a scalar field ψ is

$$\nabla\psi = \frac{\partial\psi}{\partial x}\mathbf{i} + \frac{\partial\psi}{\partial y}\mathbf{j} + \frac{\partial\psi}{\partial z}\mathbf{k}.$$

The divergence and curl of a vector field $\mathbf{v} = v_x\mathbf{i} + v_y\mathbf{j} + v_z\mathbf{k}$ are

$$\nabla \cdot \mathbf{v} = \frac{\partial v_x}{\partial x} + \frac{\partial v_y}{\partial y} + \frac{\partial v_z}{\partial z},$$

$$\nabla \times \mathbf{v} = \begin{vmatrix} \mathbf{i} & \mathbf{j} & \mathbf{k} \\ \dfrac{\partial}{\partial x} & \dfrac{\partial}{\partial y} & \dfrac{\partial}{\partial z} \\ v_x & v_y & v_z \end{vmatrix}.$$

Cylindrical Coordinates

The gradient of a scalar field ψ is

$$\nabla\psi = \frac{\partial\psi}{\partial r}\mathbf{e}_r + \frac{1}{r}\frac{\partial\psi}{\partial\theta}\mathbf{e}_\theta + \frac{\partial\psi}{\partial z}\mathbf{e}_z.$$

The divergence and curl of a vector field $\mathbf{v} = v_r\mathbf{e}_r + v_\theta\mathbf{e}_\theta + v_z\mathbf{e}_z$ are

$$\nabla \cdot \mathbf{v} = \frac{\partial v_r}{\partial r} + \frac{v_r}{r} + \frac{1}{r}\frac{\partial v_\theta}{\partial\theta} + \frac{\partial v_z}{\partial z},$$

$$\nabla \times \mathbf{v} = \frac{1}{r}\begin{vmatrix} \mathbf{e}_r & r\mathbf{e}_\theta & \mathbf{e}_z \\ \dfrac{\partial}{\partial r} & \dfrac{\partial}{\partial\theta} & \dfrac{\partial}{\partial z} \\ v_r & rv_\theta & v_z \end{vmatrix}.$$

APPENDIX

B

Properties of Areas and Lines

B.1 Areas

The coordinates of the centroid of the area A are

$$\overline{x} = \frac{\int_A x \, dA}{\int_A dA}, \qquad \overline{y} = \frac{\int_A y \, dA}{\int_A dA}.$$

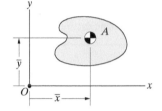

The moment of inertia about the x axis I_x, the moment of inertia about the y axis I_y, and the product of inertia I_{xy} are

$$I_x = \int_A y^2 \, dA, \qquad I_y = \int_A x^2 \, dA, \qquad I_{xy} = \int_A xy \, dA.$$

The polar moment of inertia about O is

$$J_O = \int_A r^2 \, dA = \int_A (x^2 + y^2) \, dA = I_x + I_y.$$

Area $= bh$

$$I_x = \frac{1}{3}bh^3, \qquad I_y = \frac{1}{3}hb^3, \qquad I_{xy} = \frac{1}{4}b^2h^2$$

$$I_{x'} = \frac{1}{12}bh^3, \qquad I_{y'} = \frac{1}{12}hb^3, \qquad I_{x'y'} = 0$$

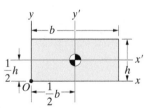

Rectangular area

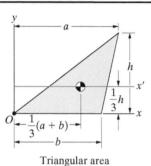

Triangular area

$$\text{Area} = \frac{1}{2}bh$$

$$I_x = \frac{1}{12}bh^3, \qquad I_y = \frac{1}{4}hb^3, \qquad I_{xy} = \frac{1}{8}b^2h^2$$

$$I_{x'} = \frac{1}{36}bh^3, \qquad I_{y'} = \frac{1}{36}hb^3, \qquad I_{x'y'} = \frac{1}{72}b^2h^2$$

Triangular area

$$\text{Area} = \frac{1}{2}bh \qquad I_x = \frac{1}{12}bh^3, \qquad I_{x'} = \frac{1}{36}bh^3$$

Circular area

$$\text{Area} = \pi R^2 \qquad I_{x'} = I_{y'} = \frac{1}{4}\pi R^4, \qquad I_{x'y'} = 0$$

Semicircular area

$$\text{Area} = \frac{1}{2}\pi R^2 \qquad I_x = I_y = \frac{1}{8}\pi R^4, \qquad I_{xy} = 0$$

$$I_{x'} = \frac{1}{8}\pi R^4, \qquad I_{y'} = \left(\frac{\pi}{8} - \frac{8}{9\pi}\right)R^4, \qquad I_{x'y'} = 0$$

$$\text{Area} = \frac{1}{4}\pi R^2 \qquad I_x = I_y = \frac{1}{16}\pi R^4, \qquad I_{xy} = \frac{1}{8}R^4$$

$$I_{x'} = I_{y'} = \left(\frac{\pi}{16} - \frac{4}{9\pi}\right)R^4, \qquad I_{x'y'} = \left(\frac{1}{8} - \frac{4}{9\pi}\right)R^4$$

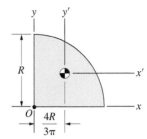

Quarter-circular area

$$\text{Area} = \alpha R^2$$

$$I_x = \frac{1}{4}R^4\left(\alpha - \frac{1}{2}\sin 2\alpha\right), \qquad I_y = \frac{1}{4}R^4\left(\alpha + \frac{1}{2}\sin 2\alpha\right),$$

$$I_{xy} = 0$$

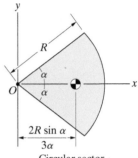

Circular sector

$$\text{Area} = \frac{1}{4}\pi ab$$

$$I_x = \frac{1}{16}\pi ab^3, \qquad I_y = \frac{1}{16}\pi a^3 b, \qquad I_{xy} = \frac{1}{8}a^2 b^2$$

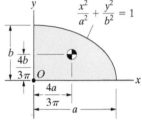

Quarter-elliptical area

$$\text{Area} = \frac{cb^{n+1}}{n+1}$$

$$I_x = \frac{c^3 b^{3n+1}}{9n+3}, \qquad I_y = \frac{cb^{n+3}}{n+3}, \qquad I_{xy} = \frac{c^2 b^{2n+2}}{4n+4}$$

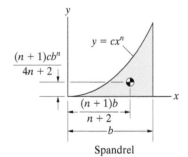

Spandrel

B.2 Lines

The coordinates of the centroid of the line L are

$$\bar{x} = \frac{\int_L x \, dL}{\int_L dL}, \qquad \bar{y} = \frac{\int_L y \, dL}{\int_L dL}, \qquad \bar{z} = \frac{\int_L z \, dL}{\int_L dL}.$$

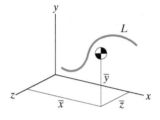

Length $= \pi R$

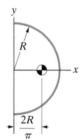

Semicircular arc

Length $= \frac{1}{2}\pi R$

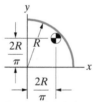

Quarter-circular arc

Length $= 2\alpha R$

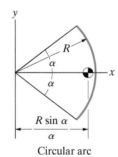

Circular arc

APPENDIX

C

Properties of Volumes and Homogeneous Objects

The moments and products of inertia of the object in terms of the xyz coordinate system are,

$$I_{x \text{ axis}} = I_{xx} = \int_m (y^2 + z^2)\, dm,$$

$$I_{y \text{ axis}} = I_{yy} = \int_m (x^2 + z^2)\, dm,$$

$$I_{z \text{ axis}} = I_{zz} = \int_m (x^2 + y^2)\, dm,$$

$$I_{xy} = \int_m xy\, dm, \quad I_{yz} = \int_m yz\, dm,$$

$$I_{zx} = \int_m zx\, dm.$$

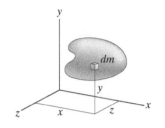

$$I_{x \text{ axis}} = 0, \qquad I_{y \text{ axis}} = I_{z \text{ axis}} = \frac{1}{3}ml^2,$$

$$I_{xy} = I_{yz} = I_{zx} = 0.$$

$$I_{x' \text{ axis}} = 0, \qquad I_{y' \text{ axis}} = I_{z' \text{ axis}} = \frac{1}{12}ml^2,$$

$$I_{x'y'} = I_{y'z'} = I_{z'x'} = 0.$$

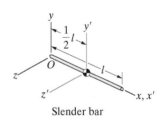

Slender bar

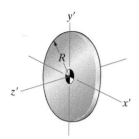

$$I_{x' \text{ axis}} = I_{y' \text{ axis}} = \frac{1}{4}mR^2, \qquad I_{z' \text{ axis}} = \frac{1}{2}mR^2,$$

$$I_{x'y'} = I_{y'z'} = I_{z'x'} = 0.$$

Thin circular plate

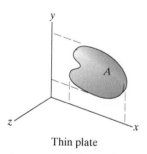

$$I_{x \text{ axis}} = \frac{1}{3}mh^2, \qquad I_{y \text{ axis}} = \frac{1}{3}mb^2, \qquad I_{z \text{ axis}} = \frac{1}{3}m(b^2 + h^2),$$

$$I_{xy} = \frac{1}{4}mbh, \qquad I_{yz} = I_{zx} = 0.$$

$$I_{x' \text{ axis}} = \frac{1}{12}mh^2, \qquad I_{y' \text{ axis}} = \frac{1}{12}mb^2, \qquad I_{z' \text{ axis}} = \frac{1}{12}m(b^2 + h^2),$$

$$I_{x'y'} = I_{y'z'} = I_{z'x'} = 0.$$

Thin rectangular plate

$$I_{x \text{ axis}} = \frac{m}{A}I_x, \qquad I_{y \text{ axis}} = \frac{m}{A}I_y, \qquad I_{z \text{ axis}} = I_{x \text{ axis}} + I_{y \text{ axis}},$$

$$I_{xy} = \frac{m}{A}I_{xy}^A, \qquad I_{yz} = I_{zx} = 0.$$

(The terms I_x, I_y, and I_{xy}^A are the moments and product of inertia of the plate's cross-sectional area A).

Thin plate

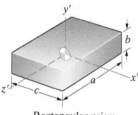

Volume $= abc$

$$I_{x' \text{ axis}} = \frac{1}{12}m(a^2 + b^2), \qquad I_{y' \text{ axis}} = \frac{1}{12}m(a^2 + c^2),$$

$$I_{z' \text{ axis}} = \frac{1}{12}m(b^2 + c^2), \qquad I_{x'y'} = I_{y'z'} = I_{z'x'} = 0.$$

Rectangular prism

Volume $= \pi R^2 l$

$$I_{x \text{ axis}} = I_{y \text{ axis}} = m\left(\frac{1}{3}l^2 + \frac{1}{4}R^2\right), \qquad I_{z \text{ axis}} = \frac{1}{2}mR^2,$$

$$I_{xy} = I_{yz} = I_{zx} = 0.$$

$$I_{x' \text{ axis}} = I_{y' \text{ axis}} = m\left(\frac{1}{12}l^2 + \frac{1}{4}R^2\right), \qquad I_{z' \text{ axis}} = \frac{1}{2}mR^2,$$

$$I_{x'y'} = I_{y'z'} = I_{z'x'} = 0.$$

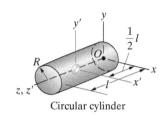

Circular cylinder

Volume $= \frac{1}{3}\pi R^2 h$

$$I_{x \text{ axis}} = I_{y \text{ axis}} = m\left(\frac{3}{5}h^2 + \frac{3}{20}R^2\right), \qquad I_{z \text{ axis}} = \frac{3}{10}mR^2,$$

$$I_{xy} = I_{yz} = I_{zx} = 0.$$

$$I_{x' \text{ axis}} = I_{y' \text{ axis}} = m\left(\frac{3}{80}h^2 + \frac{3}{20}R^2\right), \qquad I_{z' \text{ axis}} = \frac{3}{10}mR^2,$$

$$I_{x'y'} = I_{y'z'} = I_{z'x'} = 0.$$

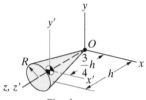

Circular cone

Volume $= \frac{4}{3}\pi R^3$

$$I_{x' \text{ axis}} = I_{y' \text{ axis}} = I_{z' \text{ axis}} = \frac{2}{5}mR^2,$$

$$I_{x'y'} = I_{y'z'} = I_{z'x'} = 0.$$

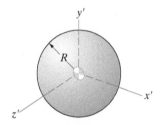

Sphere

Volume $= \frac{2}{3}\pi R^3$

$$I_{x \text{ axis}} = I_{y \text{ axis}} = I_{z \text{ axis}} = \frac{2}{5}mR^2$$

$$I_{x' \text{ axis}} = I_{y' \text{ axis}} = \frac{83}{320}mR^2, \qquad I_{z' \text{ axis}} = \frac{2}{5}mR^2$$

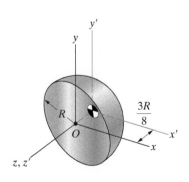

Hemisphere

APPENDIX
D

Spherical Coordinates

This appendix summarizes the equations of kinematics and vector calculus in spherical coordinates.

The position vector, velocity, and acceleration are

$$\mathbf{r} = r\mathbf{e}_r,$$

$$\mathbf{v} = \frac{dr}{dt}\mathbf{e}_r + r\frac{d\phi}{dt}\mathbf{e}_\phi + r\frac{d\theta}{dt}\sin\phi\,\mathbf{e}_\theta,$$

$$\mathbf{a} = \left[\frac{d^2r}{dt^2} - r\left(\frac{d\phi}{dt}\right)^2 - r\left(\frac{d\theta}{dt}\right)^2\sin^2\phi\right]\mathbf{e}_r$$

$$+ \left[r\frac{d^2\phi}{dt^2} + 2\frac{dr}{dt}\frac{d\phi}{dt} - r\left(\frac{d\theta}{dt}\right)^2\sin\phi\cos\phi\right]\mathbf{e}_\phi$$

$$+ \left[r\frac{d^2\theta}{dt^2}\sin\phi + 2\frac{dr}{dt}\frac{d\theta}{dt}\sin\phi + 2r\frac{d\phi}{dt}\frac{d\theta}{dt}\cos\phi\right]\mathbf{e}_\theta.$$

The gradient of a scalar field ψ is

$$\nabla\psi = \frac{\partial\psi}{\partial r}\mathbf{e}_r + \frac{1}{r}\frac{\partial\psi}{\partial\phi}\mathbf{e}_\phi + \frac{1}{r\sin\phi}\frac{\partial\psi}{\partial\theta}\mathbf{e}_\theta.$$

The divergence and curl of a vector field $\mathbf{v} = v_r\mathbf{e}_r + v_\theta\mathbf{e}_\theta + v_\phi\mathbf{e}_\phi$ are

$$\nabla\cdot\mathbf{v} = \frac{1}{r^2}\frac{\partial}{\partial r}(r^2 v_r) + \frac{1}{r\sin\phi}\frac{\partial}{\partial\phi}(v_\phi\sin\phi) + \frac{1}{r\sin\phi}\frac{\partial v_\theta}{\partial\theta},$$

$$\nabla\times\mathbf{v} = \frac{1}{r^2\sin\phi}\begin{vmatrix} \mathbf{e}_r & r\mathbf{e}_\phi & r\sin\phi\,\mathbf{e}_\theta \\ \dfrac{\partial}{\partial r} & \dfrac{\partial}{\partial\phi} & \dfrac{\partial}{\partial\theta} \\ v_r & rv_\phi & r\sin\phi v_\theta \end{vmatrix}.$$

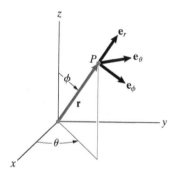

APPENDIX

E

D'Alembert's Principle

This appendix describes an alternative approach for obtaining the equations of planar motion for a rigid body. By writing Newton's second law as

$$\Sigma \mathbf{F} + (-m\mathbf{a}) = \mathbf{0}, \qquad (E.1)$$

we can regard it as an "equilibrium" equation stating that the sum of the forces, including an *inertial force* $-m\mathbf{a}$, equals zero (Fig. E.1). To state the equation of angular motion in an equivalent way, we use Eq. (18.19), which relates the total moment about a fixed point O to the acceleration of the center of mass and the angular acceleration in general planar motion:

$$\Sigma M_O = (\mathbf{r} \times m\mathbf{a}) \cdot \mathbf{k} + I\alpha.$$

We write this equation as

$$\Sigma M_O + [\mathbf{r} \times (-m\mathbf{a})] \cdot \mathbf{k} + (-I\alpha) = 0. \qquad (E.2)$$

The term $[\mathbf{r} \times (-m\mathbf{a})] \cdot \mathbf{k}$ is the moment about O due to the inertial force $-m\mathbf{a}$. We can therefore regard this equation as an "equilibrium" equation stating that the sum of the moments about any fixed point, including the moment due to the inertial force $-m\mathbf{a}$ acting at the center of mass and an *inertial couple* $-I\alpha$, equals zero.

Stated in this way, the equations of motion for a rigid body are analogous to the equations for static equilibrium: The sum of the forces equals zero and the sum of the moments about any fixed point equals zero when we properly account for inertial forces and couples. This is called *D'Alembert's principle*.

If we define ΣM_O and α to be positive in the counterclockwise direction, the unit vector $\mathbf{k}$ in Eq. (E.2) points out of the page and the term $[\mathbf{r} \times (-m\mathbf{a})] \cdot \mathbf{k}$ is the counterclockwise moment due to the inertial force. This vector operation determines the moment, or we can evaluate it by using the fact that its magnitude is the product of the magnitude of the inertial force and the perpendicular distance from point O to the line of action of the force (Fig. E.2 a). The moment is positive if it is counterclockwise, as in Fig. E.2a, and negative if it is clockwise. Notice that the sense of the inertial couple is opposite to that of the angular acceleration (Fig. E.2b).

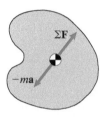

Figure E.1
The sum of the external forces and the inertial force is zero.

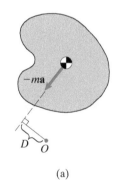

(a)

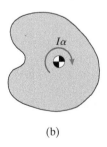

(b)

Figure E.2
(a) The magnitude of the moment due to the inertial force is $|-m\mathbf{a}|D$.
(b) A clockwise inertial couple results from a counterclockwise angular acceleration.

609

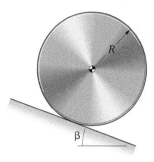

Figure E.3
Disk rolling on an inclined surface.

As an example, consider a disk of mass m and moment of inertia I that is rolling on an inclined surface (Fig. E.3). We can use D'Alembert's principle to determine the disk's angular acceleration and the forces exerted on it by the surface. The angular acceleration of the disk and the acceleration of its center are shown in Fig. E.4a. In Figure E.4b, we draw the free-body diagram of the disk showing its weight, the normal and friction forces exerted by the surface, *and the inertial force and couple.* Equation (E.1) is

$$\Sigma \mathbf{F} + (-m\mathbf{a}) = 0:$$

$$(mg \sin \beta - f)\mathbf{i} + (N - mg \cos \beta)\mathbf{j} - ma_x\mathbf{i} = 0.$$

From this vector equation, we obtain the equations

$$mg \sin \beta - f - ma_x = 0,$$

$$N - mg \cos \beta = 0. \tag{E.3}$$

We now apply Eq. (E.2). By evaluating moments about the point where the disk is in contact with the surface, we can eliminate f and N from the resulting equation:

$$\Sigma M_O + [\mathbf{r} \times (-m\mathbf{a})] \cdot \mathbf{k} + (-I\alpha) = 0:$$

$$-R(mg \sin \beta) + R(ma_x) - I\alpha = 0. \tag{E.4}$$

The acceleration of the center of the rolling disk is related to the counterclockwise angular acceleration by $a_x = -R\alpha$. Substituting this relation into Eq. (E.4) and solving for the angular acceleration, we obtain

$$\alpha = -\frac{mgR \sin \beta}{mR^2 + I}.$$

From this result, we also know a_x and can therefore solve Eqs. (E.3) for the normal and friction forces, obtaining

$$N = mg \cos \beta, \qquad f = \frac{mgI \sin \beta}{mR^2 + I}.$$

In Eq. (E.4) we evaluated the moment due to the inertial force by simply multiplying the magnitude of the force and the perpendicular distance from O to its line of action, but we could have evaluated it with the vector expression:

$$[\mathbf{r} \times (-m\mathbf{a})] \cdot \mathbf{k} = [(R\mathbf{j}) \times (-ma_x\mathbf{i})] \cdot \mathbf{k} = R(ma_x).$$

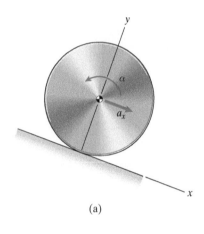

(a)

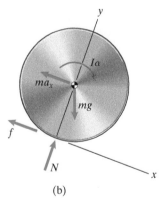

(b)

Figure E.4
(a) Acceleration of the center of the disk and its angular acceleration.
(b) Free-body diagram including the inertial force and couple.

Solutions to Practice Problems

Active Example 12.1

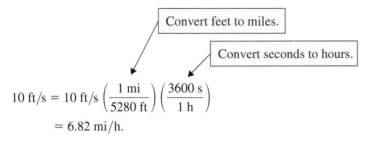

Convert feet to miles.

Convert seconds to hours.

$$10 \text{ ft/s} = 10 \text{ ft/s} \left(\frac{1 \text{ mi}}{5280 \text{ ft}} \right) \left(\frac{3600 \text{ s}}{1 \text{ h}} \right)$$

$$= 6.82 \text{ mi/h.}$$

Active Example 12.4

Use Eq. (12.6) to calculate the weight in newtons. $\longrightarrow$ $W = mg = (0.397 \text{ kg}) (9.81 \text{ m/s}^2) = 3.89 \text{ N.}$

Active Example 13.1

Integrate the acceleration to determine the velocity as a function of time. A is an integration constant. $\longrightarrow$

$$\begin{cases} a = \dfrac{dv}{dt} = 2t, \\ v = t^2 + A. \end{cases}$$

Integrate the velocity to determine the position as a function of time. B is an integration constant. $\longrightarrow$

$$\begin{cases} v = \dfrac{ds}{dt} = t^2 + A, \\ s = \dfrac{1}{3}t^3 + At + B. \end{cases}$$

Use the known conditions at $t = 3$ s to determine A and B, obtaining $A = 5$ and $B = 6$. $\longrightarrow$

$$\begin{cases} s|_{t=3\text{ s}} = 30 = \dfrac{1}{3}(3)^3 + A(3) + B, \\ v|_{t=3\text{ s}} = 14 = (3)^2 + A. \end{cases}$$

Beginning with the x component of the position, differentiate to determine the x components of the velocity and acceleration as functions of time. $\longrightarrow$

$$\begin{cases} x = 8t^2 \text{ ft,} \\ v_x = \dfrac{dx}{dt} = 16t \text{ ft/s,} \\ a_x = \dfrac{dv_x}{dt} = 16 \text{ ft/s}^2. \end{cases}$$

Active Example 13.4

First apply the chain rule to express the acceleration in terms of velocity and position instead of velocity and time.

$$\frac{dv}{dt} = \frac{dv}{ds}\frac{ds}{dt} = \frac{dv}{ds}v = -0.004v^2.$$

Separate variables.

$$\frac{dv}{v} = -0.004\,ds.$$

Integrate, defining $s = 0$ to be the position at which the velocity is 80 m/s. Here v is the velocity at position s.

$$\begin{cases} \displaystyle\int_{80}^{v}\frac{dv}{v} = -0.004\int_{0}^{s}ds, \\[2mm] \left[\ln v\right]_{80}^{v} = -0.004\left[s\right]_{0}^{s}, \\[2mm] \ln v - \ln 80 = -0.004(s - 0). \end{cases}$$

Solve for s in terms of the velocity. From this equation we find that the distance required for the velocity to decrease to 10 m/s is 520 m.

$$s = 250\ln\left(\frac{80}{v}\right).$$

Active Example 13.6

Integrate the x component of the velocity to determine the x component of the position as a function of time.	$\begin{cases} v_x = \dfrac{dx}{dt} = 0.3t^2, \\[2mm] \displaystyle\int_0^x dx = 0.3\int_0^t t^2\, dt, \\[2mm] x = 0.1t^3. \end{cases}$

Evaluate the x component of the position at $t = 6$ s.	$x\big|_{t=6\,\text{s}} = 0.1(6)^3 = 21.6$ m.

Integrate the y component of the velocity to determine the y component of the position as a function of time.	$\begin{cases} v_y = \dfrac{dy}{dt} = 1.8t - 0.18t^2, \\[2mm] \displaystyle\int_0^y dy = \int_0^t (1.8t - 0.18t^2)\, dt, \\[2mm] y = 0.9t^2 - 0.06t^3. \end{cases}$

Evaluate the y component of the position at $t = 6$ s.	$y\big|_{t=6\,\text{s}} = 0.9(6)^2 - 0.06(6)^3 = 19.4 \text{ m/s}^2.$

Express the position vector at $t = 6$ s in terms of its components.	$\mathbf{r}\big|_{t=6\,\text{s}} = 21.6\mathbf{i} + 19.4\mathbf{j}$ (m).

Position of the helicopter as a function of time.	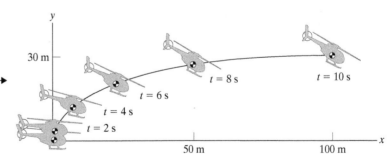

Active Example 13.8

Use the chain rule to express the angular acceleration in terms of the angular velocity and the angle instead of the angular velocity and the time, then separate variables.

$$\begin{cases} \alpha = \dfrac{d\omega}{dt} = \dfrac{d\omega}{d\theta}\dfrac{d\theta}{dt} = \dfrac{d\omega}{d\theta}\,\omega = -0.02\omega, \\ d\omega = -0.02\,d\theta. \end{cases}$$

Integrate, defining $\theta = 0$ to be the angle at which the angular velocity is 10,000 rpm $= 10{,}000\,\pi/30$ rad/s.

$$\begin{cases} \displaystyle\int_{10{,}000\,\pi/30}^{1000\,\pi/30} d\omega = -0.02\int_0^\theta d\theta, \\[2mm] \big[\omega\big]_{10{,}000\,\pi/30}^{1000\,\pi/30} = -0.02\big[\theta\big]_0^\theta, \\[2mm] \dfrac{1000\,\pi}{30} - \dfrac{10{,}000\,\pi}{30} = -0.02\theta. \end{cases}$$

Solve for θ.

$\theta = 15{,}000\,\pi$ rad $= 7500$ revolutions.

Active Example 13.9

Calculate the tangential component of the acceleration at $t = 10$ s.

$$\begin{cases} a_t = 2 + 0.2(10) \\ = 4 \text{ m/s}^2. \end{cases}$$

Calculate the normal component of the acceleration at $t = 10$ s.

$$\begin{cases} a_n = \dfrac{v^2}{\rho} \\[2mm] = \dfrac{(30 \text{ m/s})^2}{400 \text{ m}} \\[2mm] = 2.25 \text{ m/s}^2. \end{cases}$$

Express the acceleration at $t = 10$ s as a vector in terms of normal and tangential components.

$$\begin{cases} \mathbf{a} = a_t\mathbf{e}_t + a_n\mathbf{e}_n. \\ = 4\mathbf{e}_t + 2.25\mathbf{e}_n \text{ (m/s}^2). \end{cases}$$

Active Example 13.13

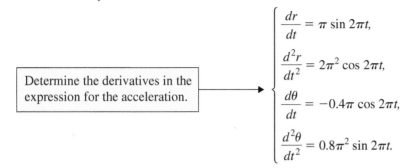

Determine the derivatives in the expression for the acceleration.

$$\begin{cases} \dfrac{dr}{dt} = \pi \sin 2\pi t, \\[2mm] \dfrac{d^2r}{dt^2} = 2\pi^2 \cos 2\pi t, \\[2mm] \dfrac{d\theta}{dt} = -0.4\pi \cos 2\pi t, \\[2mm] \dfrac{d^2\theta}{dt^2} = 0.8\pi^2 \sin 2\pi t. \end{cases}$$

Determine the components of the acceleration as functions of time.

$$\begin{cases} a_r = \dfrac{d^2r}{dt^2} - r\left(\dfrac{d\theta}{dt}\right)^2 \\[2mm] \quad = 2\pi^2 \cos 2\pi t - (1 - 0.5\cos 2\pi t)(-0.4\pi \cos 2\pi t)^2, \\[2mm] a_\theta = r\dfrac{d^2\theta}{dt^2} + 2\dfrac{dr}{dt}\dfrac{d\theta}{dt} \\[2mm] \quad = (1 - 0.5\cos 2\pi t)(0.8\pi^2 \sin 2\pi t) \\[2mm] \quad\quad + 2(\pi \sin 2\pi t)(-0.4\pi \cos 2\pi t). \end{cases}$$

Evaluate the acceleration at $t = 0.8$ s.

$\mathbf{a} = 5.97\mathbf{e}_r - 4.03\mathbf{e}_\theta \ (\text{m/s}^2).$

Active Example 13.16

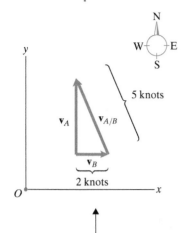

The ship's velocity relative to
the earth is equal to the water's
velocity relative to the earth plus
the ship's velocity relative to the
water.

$$\mathbf{v}_A = \mathbf{v}_B + \mathbf{v}_{A/B}$$

Determine the magnitude of the
velocity $\mathbf{v}_A$ relative to the earth.

$$|\mathbf{v}_A| = \sqrt{(5\text{ knots})^2 - (2\text{ knots})^2} = 4.58\text{ knots}.$$

The components of the ship's velocity
relative to the water indicate that the
helmsman must point the ship at
arctan $(2/4.58) = 23.6°$ west of north
to travel north relative to the earth.

$$\mathbf{v}_{A/B} = -2\mathbf{i} + 4.58\mathbf{j}\text{ (knots)}.$$

Active Example 14.1

Apply Newton's second law to determine the crate's acceleration when there is no friction force.	$\begin{cases} \Sigma F_x = W \sin 20° = ma_x: \\ \\ a_x = \dfrac{mg \sin 20°}{m} = (32.2) \sin 20° = 11.0 \text{ m/s}^2. \end{cases}$

Integrate to determine the crate's velocity as a function of time. At $t = 1$ s, the crate is moving 11.0 ft/s.	$\begin{cases} a_x = \dfrac{dv_x}{dt} = 11.0 \text{ ft/s}^2, \\ \\ \displaystyle\int_0^{v_x} dv_x = \int_0^t 11.0 \, dt, \\ \\ v_x = 11.0t \text{ ft/s}. \end{cases}$

Active Example 14.2

Beginning with the x component of the position, differentiate to determine the x components of the velocity and acceleration as functions of time.	$\begin{cases} x = 8t^2 \text{ ft,} \\ \\ v_x = \dfrac{dx}{dt} = 16t \text{ ft/s,} \\ \\ a_x = \dfrac{dv_x}{dt} = 16 \text{ ft/s}^2. \end{cases}$

Beginning with the y component of the position, differentiate to determine the y components of the velocity and acceleration as functions of time.	$\begin{cases} y = t^3 \text{ ft,} \\ \\ v_y = \dfrac{dy}{dt} = 3t^2 \text{ ft/s,} \\ \\ a_y = \dfrac{dv_y}{dt} = 6t \text{ ft/s}^2. \end{cases}$

Determine the object's mass.	$m = \dfrac{W}{g} = \dfrac{10 \text{ lb}}{32.2 \text{ ft/s}^2} = 0.311 \text{ slug.}$

Use Newton's second law to determine the components of the total force.	$\begin{cases} \Sigma F_x = ma_x\vert_{t=4\,s} \\ \qquad = (0.311 \text{ slug})(16 \text{ ft/s}^2) \\ \qquad = 4.97 \text{ lb,} \\ \\ \Sigma F_y = ma_y\vert_{t=4\,s} \\ \qquad = (0.311 \text{ slug})\left[(6)(4) \text{ ft/s}^2\right] \\ \qquad = 7.45 \text{ lb.} \end{cases}$

Active Example 14.5

Apply Newton's second law in the tangential direction to determine the tangential component of the boat's acceleration as a function of time.	$\sum F_t = ma_t:$ $200t \text{ lb} = (37.3 \text{ slug})a_t,$ $a_t = \dfrac{200t \text{ lb}}{37.3 \text{ slug}}$ $= 5.37t \text{ ft/s}^2.$

Integrate the tangential acceleration to determine the boat's velocity as a function of time.	$a_t = \dfrac{dv}{dt} = 5.37t \text{ ft/s}^2:$ $\displaystyle\int_{20}^{v} dv = \int_{0}^{t} 5.37t \, dt,$ $v = 20 + 2.68t^2 \text{ ft/s}.$

Evaluate the velocity at $t = 2$ s.	$v = 20 + 2.68(2)^2$ $= 30.7 \text{ ft/s}.$

Determine the normal component of the boat's acceleration at $t = 2$ s.	$a_n = \dfrac{v^2}{\rho} = \dfrac{(30.7 \text{ ft/s})^2}{40 \text{ ft}} = 23.6 \text{ ft/s}^2.$

Apply Newton's second law in the normal direction to determine the normal force acting on the boat a $t = 2$ s.	$\sum F_n = ma_n$ $= (37.3 \text{ slug})(23.6 \text{ ft/s}^2)$ $= 880 \text{ lb}.$

Active Example 14.6

The sum of the forces in the vertical direction (perpendicular to the train's circular path) must equal zero.	$M \cos 40° + S \sin 40° - mg = 0.$ (1)

Apply Newton's second law in the e_n direction.	$\sum F_n = ma_n:$ $M \sin 40° - S \cos 40° = m\dfrac{v^2}{\rho}.$ (2)

Solving Eqs. (1) and (2) with $m = 20,000$ kg, $g = 9.81$ m/s^2, $\rho = 150$ m, and $S = 0$ yields $M = 256$ kN and $v = 35.1$ m/s.

Active Example 14.9

Apply Newton's second law in the transverse direction. Notice that $\alpha = d\omega/dt = 0$.

$$\Sigma F_\theta = ma_\theta:$$

$$N = m\left(r\alpha + 2\frac{dr}{dt}\omega\right) = 2m\omega_0 v_r.$$

Substitute the expression for v_r as a function of r obtained in the example to determine N as a function of r.

$$N = 2m\omega_0 \sqrt{\left(\omega_0^2 - \frac{k}{m}\right)(r^2 - r_0^2) + \frac{2k}{m}r_0(r - r_0)}.$$

Active Example 14.10

When an earth satellite in elliptic orbit is at the position of minimum radius, called its *perigee*, and when it is at the position of maximum radius, called its *apogee*, it has only a transverse component of velocity. Therefore the velocities at perigee and apogee satisfy Eq. (14.14). Let v_a be the velocity at apogee.

$$r_0 v_0 = r_{\max} v_a,$$

$$v_a = \frac{r_0}{r_{\max}} v_0$$

$$= \frac{6600 \text{ km}}{16{,}000 \text{ km}}(9240 \text{ m/s})$$

$$= 3810 \text{ m/s}.$$

Active Example 15.1

In this case the normal force $N = (120 \text{ kg})(9.81 \text{ m/s}^2) = 1180$ N.

Evaluate the work done as the container moves from its initial position to $s = 1$ m.

$$U_{12} = \int_{s_1}^{s_2} \Sigma F_t \, ds$$

$$= \int_0^1 (F - \mu_k N) ds$$

$$= \int_0^1 [(700 - 150s) - (0.26)(1180)] ds$$

$$= 319 \text{ N-m}.$$

Apply the principle of work and energy to determine the container's velocity when it reaches $s = 1$ m. Solving yields $v_2 = 2.31$ m/s.

$$U_{12} = \frac{1}{2}mv_2^2 - \frac{1}{2}mv_1^2:$$

$$319 \text{ N-m} = \frac{1}{2}(120 \text{ kg})v_2^2 - 0.$$

Active Example 15.4

Calculate the work done by the weight:
The hammer falls downward, so the work is positive, and its magnitude is the product of the weight and the change in height.

$$
\begin{cases}
U_{\text{weight}} = (\text{weight})(\text{change in height}) \\
\qquad = [(40 \text{ kg})(9.81 \text{ m/s}^2)](0.4 \text{ m}) \\
\qquad = 157 \text{ N-m}.
\end{cases}
$$

Calculate the work done by each of the springs. The springs are unstretched in position 1.

$$
\begin{cases}
S_1 = 0, \\
S_2 = \sqrt{(0.3 \text{ m})^2 + (0.4 \text{ m})^2} - 0.3 \text{ m} \\
\qquad = 0.2 \text{ m}, \\
U_{\text{spring}} = -\tfrac{1}{2}k(S_2^2 - S_1^2) \\
\qquad = -\tfrac{1}{2}(1500 \text{ N/m})[(0.2 \text{ m})^2 - (0)^2] \\
\qquad = -30 \text{ N-m}.
\end{cases}
$$

Apply work and energy to obtain the velocity of the hammer in position 2.

$$
\begin{cases}
U_{\text{weight}} + 2(U_{\text{spring}}) = \tfrac{1}{2}mv_2^2 - \tfrac{1}{2}mv_1^2 : \\[4pt]
157 \text{ N-m} + 2(-30 \text{ N-m}) = \tfrac{1}{2}(40 \text{ kg})v_2^2 - \tfrac{1}{2}(40 \text{ kg})(2 \text{ m/s})^2. \\[4pt]
\text{Solving, we obtain} \\
v_2 = 2.97 \text{ m/s}.
\end{cases}
$$

Active Example 15.7

Choose a datum for the potential energy associated with the weight of the hammer. Let the datum ($y = 0$) be position 2.

$\longrightarrow$ $V_{\text{weight}} = mgy.$

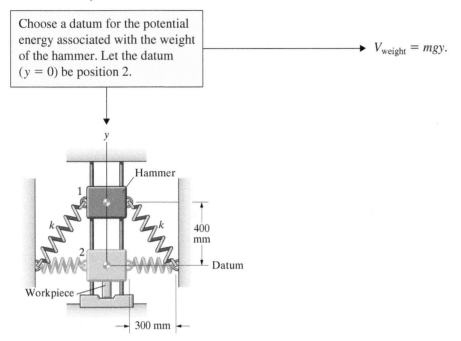

Potential energy of one of the springs in terms of the stretch S of the spring.

$\longrightarrow$ $V_{\text{spring}} = \frac{1}{2}kS^2.$

Calculate the stretch of one of the springs at positions 1 and 2.

$\longrightarrow$
$$
\begin{cases}
S_1 = 0, \\
S_2 = \sqrt{(0.3 \text{ m})^2 + (0.4 \text{ m})^2} - 0.3 \text{ m} \\
\quad = 0.2 \text{ m},
\end{cases}
$$

Apply conservation of energy to positions 1 and 2 to determine the velocity at position 2.

$\longrightarrow$
$$
\begin{cases}
(V_{\text{weight}})_1 + 2(V_{\text{spring}})_1 + \frac{1}{2}mv_1^2 = (V_{\text{weight}})_2 + 2(V_{\text{spring}})_2 + \frac{1}{2}mv_2^2: \\[4pt]
mgy_1 + 2\left(\frac{1}{2}kS_1^2\right) + \frac{1}{2}mv_1^2 = mgy_2 + 2\left(\frac{1}{2}kS_2^2\right) + \frac{1}{2}mv_2^2, \\[8pt]
(40 \text{ kg})(9.81 \text{ m/s}^2)(0.4 \text{ m}) + 0 + \frac{1}{2}(40 \text{ kg})\,(2 \text{ m/s})^2 \\[4pt]
\quad = 0 + 2\left[\frac{1}{2}(1500 \text{ N/m})(0.2 \text{ m})^2\right] + \frac{1}{2}mv_2^2. \\[4pt]
\text{Solving, we obtain} \\
\quad v_2 = 2.97 \text{ m/s}.
\end{cases}
$$

Active Example 15.10

The definition of a conservative force is that a potential energy exists, so the fact that the force was obtained from its potential energy guarantees that it is conservative. Alternatively, we can confirm that the force is conservative by showing that its curl is zero:

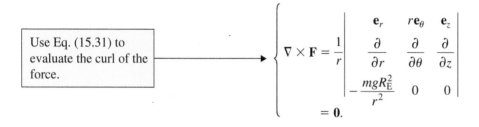

$$\nabla \times \mathbf{F} = \frac{1}{r} \begin{vmatrix} \mathbf{e}_r & r\mathbf{e}_\theta & \mathbf{e}_z \\ \dfrac{\partial}{\partial r} & \dfrac{\partial}{\partial \theta} & \dfrac{\partial}{\partial z} \\ -\dfrac{mgR_E^2}{r^2} & 0 & 0 \end{vmatrix}$$

$$= \mathbf{0}.$$

Use Eq. (15.31) to evaluate the curl of the force.

Answers to Even-Numbered Problems

Chapter 12

12.2 (a) $e = 2.7183$; (b) $e^2 = 7.3891$; (c) $e^2 = 7.3892$.

12.4 $17.8 \ m^2$.

12.6 The 1-in wrench fits the 25-mm nut.

12.8 (a) 267 mi/h; (b) 392 ft/s.

12.10 310 N-m.

12.12 $g = 32.2 \ ft/s^2$.

12.14 (a) $0.0208 \ m^2$; (b) $32.2 \ in^2$.

12.16 2.07×10^6 Pa.

12.18 27.4 lb/ft.

12.20 (a) kg-m/s; (b) 2.70 slug-ft/s.

12.22 (a) 0.397 kg; (b) 0.643 N.

12.24 (a) 4.60×10^{19} slug; (b) 6.71×10^{20} kg.

12.26 163 lb.

12.28 32.1 km.

12.30 345,000 km.

Chapter 13

13.2 $v = 0$, $a = -4 \ in/s^2$.

13.4 (a) $v = 13.0$ m/s, $a = 1.28 \ m/s^2$;
(b) $v = 14.7$ m/s at $t = 6.67$ s.

13.6 (a) $v = 28$ m/s at $t = 4$ s; (b) $a = 0$.

13.8 (a) $v = -1.78$ m/s, $a = -11.2 \ m/s^2$;
(b) 2.51 m/s; (c) Zero.

13.10 (a) 0.628 m/s; (b) $3.95 \ m/s^2$.

13.12 $s = 77$ m, $v = 66$ m/s.

13.14 $s = 100$ m, $v = 80$ m/s.

13.16 $4.33 \ m/s^2$.

13.18 2.47 s, 2430 m/s.

13.20 $a = -6.66 \ m/s^2$.

13.22 $s = 505$ ft.

13.24 $s = 1070$ m, $a = -24 \ m/s^2$.

13.26 825 ft.

13.28 3630 ft.

13.30 No. 66.7 ft/s (45.5 mi/h).

13.32 51.9 solar years.

13.34 (a) 45.5 s; (b) 3390 m.

13.36 10 s.

13.38 $v = 6.73$ ft/s, $a = -8.64 \ ft/s^2$.

13.40 20 s.

13.42 $v = 3.33$ m/s.

13.44 $v = 2.80$ in/s.

13.46 11.2 km.

13.48 3240 ft.

13.50 2300 m.

13.52 42.5 m/s.

13.54 $v = 3.42$ ft/s.

13.56 $c = 38,900$.

13.58 $v = -2(1 - s^2)^{1/2}$ m/s.

13.60 (a) 1.29 ft; (b) 4.55 ft/s.

13.62 $v_0 = 35,900$ ft/s $= 24,500$ mi/hr.

13.66 1266 s or 21.1 min.

13.68 $\mathbf{r} = 266.0\mathbf{i} + 75.3\mathbf{j} - 36.7\mathbf{k}$ (m).

13.70 (a) $R = 35.3$ m; (b) $R = 40.8$ m; (c) $R = 35.3$ m.

13.72 98.3 ft/s.

13.74 19.0 m.

13.76 $31.2 < v_0 < 34.2$ ft/s.

13.78 (a) Yes; (b) No.

13.80 82.5 m.

13.82 $|\mathbf{v}| = 38.0$ ft/s, $t = 1.67$ s.

13.84 17.2 m.

13.86 $\mathbf{v} = 0.602\mathbf{i} - 4.66\mathbf{j}$ (m/s).

13.90 $\mathbf{a} = -0.099\mathbf{i} + 0.414\mathbf{j}$ (m/s^2).

13.94 (a) Positive; (b) 7.27×10^{-5} rad/s, earth rotates $15°$.

13.96 430 s.

13.98 14.6 s.

13.100 (a) $\omega = 1.70$ rad/s; (b) $\theta = 1$ rad $(57.3°)$.

13.102 $d\mathbf{e}/dt = -8.81\mathbf{i} + 13.4\mathbf{j}$.

13.104 $\mathbf{v} = 12.5\mathbf{e_t}$ (m/s), $\mathbf{a} = 3\mathbf{e_t} + 0.391\mathbf{e_n}$ (m/s^2).

13.106 (a) 1730 rpm; (b) $3.01 \ rad/s^2$.

13.108 $1060 \ m/s^2$ (108 g's).

13.110 (a) $\mathbf{v} = 16\mathbf{e_t}$ (m/s), $\mathbf{a} = 16\mathbf{e_t} + 64\mathbf{e_n}$ (m/s^2);
(b) $s = 8$ m.

13.112 (a) $\mathbf{v}_B = 87.3 \ \mathbf{e_t}$ (ft/s); (b) $\mathbf{v}_B = -61.7\mathbf{i} - 61.7\mathbf{j}$ (ft/s).

13.114 $v = R\sqrt{g/R_E}$.

13.116 $\mathbf{v} = 18.3\mathbf{e_t}$ (m/s), $\mathbf{a} = 0.6\mathbf{e_t} + 6.68\mathbf{e_n}$ (m/s^2).

13.118 $\mathbf{v} = 12.05\mathbf{e_t}$ (m/s), $\mathbf{a} = 0.121\mathbf{e_t} + 2.905\mathbf{e_n}$ (m/s^2).

13.120 (a) $|\mathbf{a}| = 45.0 \ ft/s^2$; (b) $|\mathbf{a}| = 59.9 \ ft/s^2$.

13.122 $\mathbf{v} = 6.46\mathbf{e_t}$ (m/s).

13.124 (a) $\mathbf{v} = 15.2\mathbf{e_t}$ (m/s), $\mathbf{a} = -1.63\mathbf{e_t} + 9.67\mathbf{e_n}$ (m/s^2);
(b) $\rho = 24.0$ m.

13.126 218 m.

13.128 $\mathbf{a} = 3.59\mathbf{e_t} + 1.72\mathbf{e_n}$ (m/s^2).

13.130 $a_n = g/\sqrt{1 + (gt/v_0)^2}$.

13.132 $dy/dt = 0.260$ m/s, $d^2y/dt^2 = -0.150 \ m/s^2$.

13.134 (a) $\rho = 16.7$ ft; (b) $a_n = 77.3 \ ft/s^2$.

13.138 $\mathbf{v} = -0.971\mathbf{e}_r - 1.76\mathbf{e}_\theta$ (m/s).

13.140 $\mathbf{a}_A = 0.331\mathbf{e}_r + 0.480\mathbf{e}_\theta$ (m/s^2).

13.142 (a) $\mathbf{v}_A = 3.75\mathbf{e}_r + 1.40\mathbf{e}_\theta$ (ft/s);
(b) $d\theta/dt = 0.468$ rad/s.

13.144 (a) $\mathbf{v} = 0.32\mathbf{e}_r + 2.03\mathbf{e}_\theta$ (m/s);
(b) $\mathbf{v} = 0.32\mathbf{i} + 2.03\mathbf{j}$ (m/s).

13.146 $\mathbf{a}_A = -58.0\mathbf{e}_r - 27.0\mathbf{e}_\theta$ (m/s^2).

13.148 $\mathbf{a}_A = -1.09\mathbf{e}_r$ (m/s^2).

13.152 $\mathbf{v}_C = 13.2\mathbf{e}_r + 18\mathbf{e}_\theta$ (m/s).

13.154 $\mathbf{a} = \mathbf{0}$, $\alpha = -0.631 \ rad/s^2$.

13.156 (a) $\mathbf{a} = -3.52\mathbf{e}_r + 4.06\mathbf{e}_\theta$ (m/s^2);
(b) $\mathbf{a} = -0.38\mathbf{i} - 5.36\mathbf{j}$ (m/s^2).

13.158 (a) $\mathbf{a} = -225\mathbf{e}_r - 173\mathbf{e}_\theta$ (ft/s^2);
(b) $\mathbf{a} = -108\mathbf{i} - 263\mathbf{j}$ (ft/s^2).

13.160 $\mathbf{v} = 1047\mathbf{e}_\theta + 587\mathbf{e}_z$ (ft/s),
$\mathbf{a} = -219{,}000\mathbf{e}_r$ (ft/s^2).

13.162 (a), (b) $\mathbf{v}_{A/B} = -3.66\mathbf{i} + 3.66\mathbf{j}$ (m/s).

13.164 $\mathbf{a}_{A/B} = 200\mathbf{i} + 200\mathbf{j}$ (ft/s^2).

13.166 $\mathbf{a}_{A/B} = 5\mathbf{i} - 2\mathbf{j}$ (ft/s^2).

13.168 9.93° east of north, 42.0 min.

13.170 2.34 m/s, 342 s.

13.172 (a) 7.10 m; (b) 2.22 s; (c) 11.8 m/s.

13.174 $v = 42.3$ m/s.

13.176 13.1 s.

13.178 68.6 ft/s.

13.180 $|\mathbf{v}| = 2.19$ m/s, $|\mathbf{a}| = 5.58$ m/s^2.

13.182 $\mathbf{a} = -2.75\mathbf{e}_r - 4.86\mathbf{e}_\theta$ (m/s^2).

13.184 (a) $\mathbf{v} = -2.13\mathbf{e}_r + 6.64\mathbf{e}_\theta$ (m/s);
(b) $\mathbf{v} = -5.90\mathbf{i} + 3.71\mathbf{j}$ (m/s).

Chapter 14

14.2 (a) 6.70 m/s; (b) 10.0 m.

14.4 $F = 9.91$ lb.

14.6 4.03 m/s down the inclined surface.

14.8 1.77 s.

14.10

14.12 $\Sigma\mathbf{F} = 2.40\mathbf{i} + 1.20\mathbf{j} + 2.08\mathbf{k}$ (kN).

14.14 18.8 ft/s^2.

14.16 (a) No; (b) Yes, $a_x = 0.5$ m/s^2; (c) $x = 2$ m.

14.18 $F_x = -198$ N, $F_y = 1800$ N.

14.20 $W = 88.3$ kN, $T = 61.7$ kN, $L = 66.9$ kN.

14.22 $L = 293.2$ kN, $D = 33.0$ kN.

14.24 $(66, 138, -58)$ m.

14.26 $F_x = 0.359$ N, $F_y = 19.888$ N.

14.28 2.10 m/s.

14.30 (a) 3.93 lb; (b) 19.5 ft/s.

14.32 (a) 1.01 m/s^2; (b) 6.47 m/s^2.

14.34 $F = 125$ N.

14.36 4.43 ft up the surface.

14.38 (a) 1200 N; (b) 1.84 m/s.

14.40 0.332 m/s^2 forward, 7.04 m/s^2 rearward.

14.42 $v = \pm 2\sqrt{4 - s^2}$ m/s.

14.44 (a) 773 ft/s^2 $(24\ g)$; (b) 28.0 ft/s.

14.46 (a) 11.9 ft; (b) 813 lb.

14.48 $y = -18.8$ mm.

14.50 (a) 50 s; (b) 40.8 N; (c) $4.8\mathbf{i} + \mathbf{j}$ (m/s).

14.52 2.06 m/s^2 up the bar.

14.54 $|\mathbf{a}_A| = 7.89$ ft/s^2.

14.56 $t = 0.600$ s.

14.58 $F_x = -0.544$ N.

14.60 $F_x = -73.4$ N, $F_y = 612$ N.

14.62 0.284 s.

14.64 $v_x = 0.486$ m/s, $v_y = -0.461$ m/s.

14.66 $\Sigma F_t = 0$, $\Sigma F_n = 373$ lb.

14.68 $v = 17.6$ m/s, $\Sigma F_n = 620$ N.

14.70 Tension is 4.8 N, force is 0.6 N.

14.72 (a) $\Sigma F_t = 9740$ lb, $\Sigma F_n = 28{,}800$ lb;
(b) $d\theta/dt = 3.95°$/s.

14.76 $\theta = 49.9°$, $|\mathbf{v}| = 10.8$ ft/s.

14.78 $2.62 \le v \le 3.74$ m/s.

14.80 (a) 207,000 lb; (b) 41,700 ft.

14.82 (a) $v = 140$ m/s; (b) $\rho = 815$ m.

14.86 $\theta = L_0/R - \sqrt{(L_0/R)^2 - (2v_0/R)t}$.

14.88 $\rho = 697$ m, $\mathbf{e} = 0.916\mathbf{i} - 0.308\mathbf{j} + 0.256\mathbf{k}$.

14.90 $\beta = 68.2°$

14.92 11.4 m/s^2.

14.94 $\Sigma F_r = -16.8$ N, $\Sigma F_\theta = 20.7$ N.

14.96 $9.46\mathbf{e}_r + 3.44\mathbf{e}_\theta$ (N).

14.98 $v_r = 14.8$ m/s.

14.100 $|\mathbf{v}| = 2.89$ m/s, $T = 41.6$ N.

14.102 $N = 1.02$ lb.

14.104 $\mu_s = 0.406$. The mass slips toward O.

14.106 $-1.48\mathbf{e}_r - 0.20\mathbf{e}_\theta$ (lb).

14.108 $k = 2m\omega_0^2$.

14.110 $11.5\mathbf{e}_r + 44.2\mathbf{e}_\theta + 10\mathbf{e}_z$ (N).

14.112 $|\Sigma\mathbf{F}| = 8.36$ N at $t = 4.39$ s.

14.114 (a) $|\mathbf{v}| = 1020$ m/s; (b) $t = 2.36 \times 10^6$ s (27.3 days).

14.116

14.118 $v_0 = 35{,}500$ ft/s.

14.120 (a) 34.6 ft/s^2, 3490 lb; (b) $\mu_s = 1.07$.

14.122 (a) $F_1 = 63$ kN, $F_2 = 126$ kN, $F_3 = 189$ kN.
(b) $F_1 = 75$ kN, $F_2 = 150$ kN, $F_3 = 225$ kN.

14.124 Deceleration is 1.49 m/s^2, compared with 8.83 m/s^2 on a level road.

14.126 14,300 ft (2.71 mi).

14.128 10.5 lb.

14.130 $a_A = 4.02$ ft/s^2, $T = 17.5$ lb.

14.132 29.7 ft.

14.134 9.30 N.

14.136 $\tan\alpha = v^2/\rho g$.

14.138 $\Sigma\mathbf{F} = -10.7\mathbf{e}_r + 2.55\mathbf{e}_\theta$ (N).

Chapter 15

15.2 8.06 m.

15.4 3.50 ft/s.

15.6 $P_{ave} = 1.62$ kW (kilowatts).

15.8 (a) 2.57×10^6 ft-lb/s (4670 hp).
(b) 1.57×10^6 ft-lb/s (2850 hp).

15.10 (a) 1.32×10^7 ft-lb/s (24,000 hp).
(b) 6.60×10^6 ft-lb/s (12,000 hp).

15.12 3.27 m/s.

15.14 117 ft/s (80.0 mi/h).

15.16 (a) 2160 ft-lb; (b) 7.39 lb.

15.18 (a) -12.5 ft-lb; (b) 5.67 ft/s.

15.20 Work $= 509$ N-m, $v = 2.52$ m/s.

15.22 $v = 21.8$ m/s.

15.24 4.04 m/s.

15.26 2.58 ft/s.

15.28 $v = 1.72$ m/s.

15.30

15.32 (a), (b), (c) 117 ft/s.

15.34 (a) 5.98 m/s;
(b) 5.56 m/s.

15.36 3.55 m/s.

15.38 12.7 ft/s.

15.40 $v_0 = 15.66$ m/s, $v_{top} = 7.00$ m/s.

15.42 11.2 ft/s.

15.44 39.3 ft/s or 26.8 mi/hr.

15.46 -107 kN-m.

15.48 (a) $U_{12} = 0.210$ N-m; (b) $v_2 = 1.45$ m/s.

15.50 621 lb/ft.

15.52 (a) $k = 900$ lb/ft; (b) 274 ft/s^2.

15.54 2.18 m/s.

15.56 2.83 m/s.

15.58 (a) 5 ft; (b) 6.34 ft/s.

15.60 0.785 m.

15.62 0.385 m.

15.64 $v_2 = 7.03$ m/s.

15.66 5.77 m/s.

15.68 $k = 997$ lb/ft.

15.70 4.90 m/s.

15.72 193,000 lb.

15.74 26,600 km.

15.76 2.25×10^{10} N-m.

15.78 (a) 50 ft-lb; (b) 50 ft-lb; (c) 13.9 ft/s.

15.80 (a), (b) 6.48 m.

15.82 3.95 m/s.

15.84 (a) $\alpha = 60°$;
(b) Before, 39.2 N; after, 58.9 N.

15.86 $\theta = 51.2°$.

15.88 (a) No; (b) 857 N.

15.90 $W[1 + \sqrt{1 + 4C/W}]$.

15.92 1.56 m/s.

15.94 1.99 m/s.

15.96 $V = \frac{1}{2}kS^2 + \frac{1}{4}qS^4$.

15.98 $v = 2.30$ m/s.

15.100 $v = 8.45$ ft/s.

15.102 $\mathbf{v} = 5.29\mathbf{e}_r + 4\mathbf{e}_\theta$ (m/s).

15.104 $v = 11.0$ km/s.

15.106 2880 m/s.

15.108 $v = 419$ m/s.

15.110 (a) $\mathbf{F} = -2x\mathbf{i} - 3y^2\mathbf{j}$ (N);
(b) -2 N-m along each path.

15.112 $\mathbf{F} = -[k(r - r_0) + q(r - r_0)^3]\mathbf{e}_r$.

15.114 (a) $\mathbf{F} = (\sin\theta - 2r\cos^2\theta)\mathbf{e}_r$
$+ (\cos\theta + 2r - \sin\theta\cos\theta)\mathbf{e}_\theta$.
(b) The work is 2 ft-lb for any path from 1 to 2.

15.118 (a), (b) 193 ft.

15.120 He should choose (b).
Impact velocity is 11.8 m/s, work is -251 kN-m.
In (a), impact velocity is 13.9 m/s, work is -119 kN-m.

15.122 $v = 2.08$ m/s.

15.124 (a) 14.3×10^7 ft-lb; (b) $v = 88[1 - e^{-(F_0/88m)t}]$.

15.126 $k = 163$ lb/ft.

15.128 (a) $k = 809$ N/m; (b) $v_2 = 6.29$ m/s.

15.130 4.39 ft/s.

15.132 $h = 0.179$ m.

15.134 (a) $\theta = 27.9°$; (b) 159 lb; (c) 222 lb.

15.136 $v_1 = 4.73$ ft/s.

15.138 1.02 m.

15.140 2.00 m/s.

15.142 24.8 ft/s.

15.144 (a) $v = 0$;
(b) $v = \sqrt{gR_E/2} = 18,300$ ft/s or 12,500 mi/hr.

15.146 (a) 11.3 MW (megawatts); (b) 9.45 MW

Index